CHILDREN'S CORE COLLECTION

TWENTY-SECOND EDITION

CORE COLLECTION SERIES

**FORMERLY
STANDARD CATALOG SERIES**

MARIA HUGGER, GENERAL EDITOR

**CHILDREN'S CORE COLLECTION
MIDDLE AND JUNIOR HIGH CORE COLLECTION
SENIOR HIGH CORE COLLECTION
NONFICTION CORE COLLECTION
FICTION CORE COLLECTION
GRAPHIC NOVEL CORE COLLECTION**

CHILDREN'S
CORE COLLECTION

TWENTY-SECOND EDITION

Volume 2

Fiction and SC
Author, Title, and Subject Index

EDITED BY

JULIE CORSARO

KENDAL SPIRES

AND

GABRIELA TOTH

H. W. Wilson

A Division of EBSCO Information Services

Ipswich, Massachusetts

2015

GREY HOUSE PUBLISHING

Set: 978-1-61925-705-4
Volume 1: 978-1-68217-074-8
Volume 2: 978-1-68217-075-5

Abridged Dewey Decimal Classification and Relative Index, Edition 15 is © 2004-2012 OCLC Online Computer Library Center, Inc. Used with Permission. DDC, Dewey, Dewey Decimal Classification, and WebDewey are registered trademarks of OCLC.

Children's Core Collection, 2015, published by Grey House Publishing, Inc., Amenia, NY, under exclusive license from EBSCO Infomation Systems, Inc.

A catalog record for this title is available from the Library of Congress.

CONTENTS

CONTENTS

Fic FICTION

50 Cent (Musician), 1975-
Playground; with Aura Moser. Razorbill 2011 314p
$17.99
Grades: 5 6 7 8   **Fic**
1. Bullies -- Fiction
ISBN 978-1-59514-434-8; 1-59514-434-X
Thirteen-year-old Butterball doesn't have much going
for him. He's teased about his weight. He hates the Long
Island suburb his mom moved them to so she could go to
nursing school and start her life over. He wishes he still
lived with his dad in New York City where there's always
something happening, even if his dad doesn't have much
time for him. Still, that's not why he beat up Maurice on
the playground.
"Readers who were ever confused about having a gay
parent, or being overweight, or going through a parental
breakup, or just wanting to fit in and be accepted by their
peers, will relate to Butterball. 50 Cents's debut young adult
novel is a quick read that will be great for discussions on a
variety of important and timely topics." VOYA

Abbott, Tony, 1952-
Firegirl. Little, Brown 2006 145p $15.99; pa $5.99
Grades: 5 6 7 8   **Fic**
1. School stories 2. Burns and scalds -- Fiction
ISBN 978-0-316-01171-6; 0-316-01171-1; 978-0-316-
01170-9 pa; 0-316-01170-3 pa
LC 2005-07964
A middle school boy's life is changed when Jessica, a
girl disfigured by burns, starts attending his Catholic school
while receiving treatment at a local hospital.
"Through realistic settings and dialogue, and believable
characters, readers will be able to relate to the social dynamics of these adolescents who are trying to handle a difficult
situation." SLJ

The **forbidden** stone; by Tony Abbott. Katherine Tegen Books, an imprint of HarperCollinsPublishers 2014
432 p. (The Copernicus legacy) (hardback) $16.99
Grades: 4 5 6 7   **Fic**
1. Antiquities -- Fiction 2. Secret societies -- Fiction
3. Voyages and travels -- Fiction 4. Adventure and
adventurers -- Fiction
ISBN 006219447X; 9780062194473
LC 2013038560
"Four precocious preteens and a distracted astrophysi-
cist travel to Europe to unravel a mystery that has already
claimed several lives...Filled with riddles and ciphers,
this first of 12 installments will keep readers intellectually
stimulated as well as entertained. The stepbrothers' bond, a
budding crush and a mystery that plays off of real historical
figures and facts make this more than a pedestrian whodunit.
With engaging characters, a globe-trotting plot and dangerous villains, it is hard to find something not to like. Equal
parts edge-of-your-seat suspense and heartfelt coming-of-
age." (Kirkus)

Kringle; illustrated by Greg Call. Scholastic Press
2005 324p il $14.99
Grades: 5 6 7 8   **Fic**
1. Fantasy fiction 2. Orphans -- Fiction 3. Santa Claus

-- Fiction
ISBN 0-439-74942-5
LC 2005-12697
In the fifth century A.D., as order retreats from Britain
with the departing Roman Army, orphaned, twelve-year-old
Kringle determines to rescue his beloved guardian from the
evil goblins who terrorize the countryside by kidnapping and
enslaving humans and, in the process, with the help of elves
and others along the way, discovers his true destiny.
"The enticing premise, appealing young hero, and nonstop action will appeal to many fantasy lovers." Booklist

The **serpent's** curse; Tony Abbott, Bill Perkins; [edited
by] Claudia Gabel. HarperCollins 2014 496 p. illustrations
(The copernicus legacy) (hardcover) $16.99
Grades: 4 5 6 7   **Fic**
1. Curses -- Fiction 2. Relics -- Fiction 3. Kidnapping
-- Fiction 4. Adventure and adventurers 5. Adventure
stories 6. Antiquities -- Fiction 7. Secret societies --
Fiction 8. Voyages and travels -- Fiction
ISBN 0062194461; 9780062194466
LC 2014937634
Sequel to: The Forbidden Stone (2014)
This book, by Tony Abbott, is "a globe-trotting adven-
ture packed with more riddles, puzzles, and secret histories.
The hunt for Copernicus's first relic sent Wade, Darrell, Lily,
and Becca to the far reaches of the world and put them in se-
rious danger. But they never imagined Sara Kaplan - Darrell
and Wade's mother - would be kidnapped by the conniving
Galina Krause. Now they must race the evil Teutonic Order
to find the Serpens relic and rescue Sara before it's too late."
(Publisher's note)
"Still reeling from their last adventure in The Forbidden
Stone (HarperCollins, 2014) which ended only hours before,
Wade, Darrell, Becca, and Lily are nearly killed by Galina
and the evil Order...Readers learn a bit more about each of
the four young heroes in this second installment, but those
wishing for more character development will want to read
the novellas. Fans of the series will eagerly await the next
entry."

Wade and the scorpion's claw; by Tony Abbott. Kath-
erine Tegen Books/HarperCollins 2014 224 p. illustrations
(The Copernicus archives) (paperback) $3.99
Grades: 4 5 6 7   **Fic**
1. Adventure fiction 2. Relics -- Fiction 3. Antiquities
-- Fiction 4. Secret societies -- Fiction 5. Voyages
and travels -- Fiction 6. Adventure and adventurers --
Fiction
ISBN 0062314726; 9780062314727
LC 2014010026
"'Wade and the Scorpion's Claw' picks up right where
'The Copernicus Legacy: The Forbidden Stone' left off, with
the Kaplan family seeking the next Copernicus relic. Now
Wade, the curious, analytical, yet starry-eyed member of
the group, leads the chase for another relic through the busy
streets of San Francisco while on the run from one of Galina
Krause's most treacherous henchmen." (Publisher's note)
"This first in a string of novellas is intended to link each
of the six full-length novels in the Copernicus Legacy series.
... This fast-paced adventure features vivid settings, difficult brainteasers and likable characters." Kirkus

Abdel-Fattah, Randa

★ **Where** the streets had a name; Randa Abdel-Fattah. Scholastic Press 2010 313p (reinforced binding) $17.99

Grades: 5 6 7 8   **Fic**

1. Jerusalem -- Fiction 2. Voyages and travels -- Fiction 3. Jewish-Arab relations -- Fiction 4. Israel -- Fiction 5. Muslims -- Fiction 6. West Bank -- Fiction 7. Family life -- Fiction 8. Palestinian Arabs -- Fiction

ISBN 0545172926; 9780545172929; 978-0-545-17292-9; 0-545-17292-6

LC 2009043122

This book tells the story of 13-year-old Hayaat, who "lives behind the Israeli-built Separation Wall in the West Bank City of Bethlehem. When her beloved grandmother falls ill . . . [she] decides to make her way to Jerusalem to fill an empty hummus jar with soil from the land of her grandmother's ancestral home. She is certain that this will mend her heart. Unfortunately, although Jerusalem is merely minutes away, curfews, checkpoints, and an identity card that doesn't allow her to cross the border mean that Hayaat and her soccer-loving, troublemaker friend Samy face a perilous journey." (School Lib J) "At the many checkpoints, the friends encounter soldiers, both brutal and kind, and also an Israeli peacenik couple who helps the kids get past the towering barriers." (Booklist)

"Hayaat chronicles this life-altering journey in the first-person, present tense, giving readers an intimate glimpse into the life of her warm, eccentric Muslim family, who survive despite the volatile political environment. A refreshing and hopeful teen perspective on the Israeli-Palestinian dilemma." Kirkus

Abdul-Jabbar, Kareem, 1947-

Sasquatch in the paint; by Kareem Abdul-Jabbar and Raymond Obstfeld. Disney-Hyperion Books 2013 272 p. (hardback) $16.99

Grades: 4 5 6 7   **Fic**

1. Clubs -- Fiction 2. Basketball -- Fiction 3. School sports -- Fiction 4. Schools -- Fiction 5. Science clubs -- Fiction 6. Middle schools -- Fiction 7. African Americans -- Fiction 8. Mystery and detective stories 9. Jews -- United States -- Fiction 10. Interpersonal relations -- Fiction

ISBN 142317870X; 9781423178705

LC 2013007147

In this book by Kareem Abdul-Jabbar and Raymond Obstfeld "Theo Rollins' . . . new height is making everyone expect more from him. Coach Mandrake wants to transform him from . . . science geek into star basketball player, even though Theo has little experience. Training is starting to hurt his science club's chances of winning the "Aca-lympics," the school's trivia competition. Theo . . . [is] accused of stealing. Can he find the real thief before he is kicked off the basketball and science club teams?' (Publisher's note)

Stealing the game; Kareem Abdul-Jabbar and Raymond Obstfeld. Disney-Hyperion Books 2015 304 p. (Streetball crew) hc $16.99

Grades: 4 5 6 7   **Fic**

1. Brothers -- Fiction 2. Basketball -- Fiction 3. Schools -- Fiction 4. Middle schools -- Fiction 5. African Americans -- Fiction 6. Mystery and detective stories 7. Robbers and outlaws -- Fiction 8. Criminal investigation -- Fiction

ISBN 9781423178712; 1423178718

LC 2013046413

"Jax asks Chris to recruit his best middle school teammates for a pick-up basketball game. Chris doesn't think much of it until the wrong team wins and Jax goes ballistic. It turns out that Jax bet on the game, hoping to earn enough money to repay a debt. While Chris tries to walk a thin tightrope between helping his brother and staying out of trouble, his friend Theo [tries] to learn what Jax has been up to." (Publisher's note)

"The shifting structure of the story and a clever series of blind alleys keep readers on tenterhooks. A deft, understated sports thriller with a solid moral compass." Kirkus

Abela, Deborah

The **ghosts** of Gribblesea Pier. Farrar Straus Giroux 2011 232p $16.99

Grades: 4 5 6   **Fic**

1. Ghost stories 2. Circus -- Fiction 3. Family life -- Fiction 4. Great Britain -- Fiction 5. Swindlers and swindling -- Fiction 6. Eccentrics and eccentricities -- Fiction

ISBN 978-0-374-36239-3; 0-374-36239-4

LC 2010022517

Aurelie Bonhoffen, who has grown up in the circus, discovers a remarkable family secret on her twelfth birthday that may help in dealing with a sinister man who wants to take over her family's pier.

This is a "charmer of a ghostly adventure tale. . . . This fast-paced, engaging, and charming story has echoes of Jeanne Birdsall's 'Penderwicks' . . . and some Dickensian elements, but in the end this is just a finely executed story of family and friendship and the ties that bind a community." SLJ

Abouet, Marguerite

Akissi; feline invasion. by Marguerite Abouet; illustrated by Mathieu Sapin. Flying Eye Books 2013 48 p. ill. (hbk.) $14.95

Grades: 2 3 4 5   **Fic**

1. Siblings 2. Conduct of life

ISBN 190926301X; 9781909263017

This book, by Marguerite Abouet, presents "African vignettes aimed at a younger audience. All seven episodes feature young Akissi and her brother Fofana or her friends getting into trouble for less-than-exemplary . . . behavior. In 'Good Mums,' . . . she borrows a neighbor's baby and tenderly feeds it a stew concocted from discarded scraps found in the market. 'Home Cinema' has her playing lookout while Fofana sells spots in front of the television set to neighborhood children." (Kirkus Reviews)

Abraham, Susan Gonzales

Cecilia's year; by Susan Gonzales Abraham & Denise Gonzales Abraham. Cinco Puntos Press 2004 210p il $16.95; pa $11.95

Grades: 4 5 6 7   **Fic**

1. Poverty -- Fiction 2. Sex role -- Fiction 3. New Mexico -- Fiction 4. Hispanic Americans -- Fiction

ISBN 978-0-938317-87-6; 0-938317-87-3; 978-1-933693-02-6 pa; 1-933693-02-9 pa

LC 2004-13374

Nearly fourteen and poor, Ceclia Gonzales wants desperately to go to high school and become a teacher until her mother's old-fashioned ideas about a woman's place threaten her dreams

"The cultural details are vivid and integrated into the story, providing a rich context and a snapshot of an entire community. . . . This fictionalized biography succeeds on several levels." SLJ

Another title about Cecilia is:
Surprising Cecilia (2005)

Acampora, Paul
Rachel Spinelli punched me in the face. Roaring Brook Press 2011 168p $15.99
Grades: 5 6 7 8   **Fic**
1. Moving -- Fiction 2. Friendship -- Fiction 3. Connecticut -- Fiction 4. Family life -- Fiction 5. Single parent family -- Fiction
ISBN 978-1-59643-548-3; 1-59643-548-8
    LC 2010027436
When fourteen-year-old Zachary and his father move to Falls, Connecticut, he spends a summer falling in love, coming to terms with his mother's absence, and forming eclectic friendships.

"Realistic dialogue and poignantly amusing situations . . . all come together to gently flesh out a few months in the lives of people readers will savor getting to know. . . . An outstanding, humane coming-of-age tale of loss, yearning and forgiveness." Kirkus

Achebe, Chinua
How the leopard got his claws; [by] Chinua Achebe and John Iroaganachi; illustrated by Mary Grandpre. Candlewick Press 2011 il $16.99
Grades: 4 5 6   **Fic**
1. Allegories 2. Jungles -- Fiction 3. Leopards -- Fiction
ISBN 978-0-7636-4805-3; 0-7636-4805-1
    LC 2010040344
Recounts how the leopard got his claws and teeth and why he rules the forest with terror.

"First published in the 1970s, this political fable still makes provocative reading. Grand Pré's new Lion King-style illustrations both capture the tale's intensity and provide a needed contemporary look. . . . The stately prose will make a profound impression on readers, as will the large, dimly lit closeups of snarling jaws and strong animal bodies." Booklist

Ada, Alma Flor, 1938-
Dancing home; [by] Alma Flor Ada and Gabriel M. Zubizarreta. Atheneum Books for Young Readers 2011 147p $14.99
Grades: 3 4 5 6   **Fic**
1. Cousins -- Fiction 2. California -- Fiction 3. Family life -- Fiction 4. Mexican Americans -- Fiction 5. Father-daughter relationship -- Fiction
ISBN 978-1-4169-0088-7; 1-4169-0088-8
    LC 2010013229
When Margie's cousin Lupe comes from Mexico to live in California with Margie's family, Lupe must adapt to America, while Margie, who thought it would be fun to have her cousin there, finds that she is embarrassed by her in school and jealous of her at home.

"This story will assist readers in embracing their own heritage and developing an appreciation for their classmates' backgrounds. It's an enjoyable offering (and a great read-aloud) that will capture readers' attention." SLJ

Adams, Richard
★ **Watership** Down; Scribner classics ed.; Scribner 1996 429p $30; pa $15
Grades: 6 7 8 9 10   **Fic**
1. Allegories 2. Rabbits -- Fiction
ISBN 0-684-83605-X; 0-7432-7770-8 pa
First published 1972 in the United Kingdom; first United States edition 1974 by Macmillan

"Faced with the annihilation of its warren, a small group of male rabbits sets out across the English downs in search of a new home. Internal struggles for power surface in this intricately woven, realistically told adult adventure when the protagonists must coordinate tactics in order to defeat an enemy rabbit fortress. It is clear that the author has done research on rabbit behavior, for this tale is truly authentic." Shapiro Fic for Youth. 3d edition

Adderson, Caroline
Jasper John Dooley; Not in Love. by Caroline Adderson; illustrated by Ben Clanton. Kids Can Pr 2014 132 p.
Grades: 1 2 3   **Fic**
1. Crushes -- Fiction 2. Love 3. Trampolines and trampolining -- Fiction 4. Humorous stories 5. Schools -- Fiction 6. Only child -- Fiction
ISBN 1554538033; 9781554538034
In this book, by Caroline Adderson, "Jasper struggles to deal with the excessive attentions of his classmate Isabel, who just won't leave him alone. . . . After school, she invites him over for a playdate! When Jasper complains to his parents that he's too sick to go to her house. . . . However, once he arrives, Jasper is thrilled to discover Isabel has a trampoline. . . . Can Jasper find a way to keep using her trampoline and get her to stop being in love with him?" (Publisher's note)

"All Jasper wants to do is play knights and dragons, but his friend Isabel insists on playing babies and planning their wedding. Yuck! At least she has a cool trampoline in her backyard. Like the previous two installments, this third book features short chapters, ample white space, and periodic black-and-white illustrations." SLJ

Jasper John Dooley; You're in Trouble. by Caroline Adderson; illustrated by Ben Clanton. Kids Can Press 2015 122 p. illustrations (Jasper John Dooley) $15.95
Grades: 1 2 3 4   **Fic**
1. Caffeine -- Fiction 2. Bad behavior -- Fiction
ISBN 1554538084; 9781554538089
"Jasper John Dooley realizes a can of Torpedo High Energy Drink has rolled out of the vending machine instead of the bottle of apple juice he selected. . . . Jasper finds the allure of the ice-cold can irresistible. He just has to take a sip. . . And before Jasper knows what hit him, the overabundance of caffeine and sugar in the energy drink has fueled all kinds of misbehavior." (Publisher's note)

"Jasper is as charming as ever, and his ever-so-slightly naughty behavior is funny and relatable to the early elementary school audience." SLJ

Adler, David A.

★ **Cam** Jansen and the mystery of the stolen diamonds; illustrated by Susanna Natti. Viking 1980 58p il hardcover o.p. $13.99

Grades: 2 3 4   **Fic**

1. Mystery fiction
ISBN 0-670-20039-5; 0-14-034670-8 pa
LC 79-20695

Cam Jansen, a fifth-grader with a photographic memory, and her friend Eric help solve the mystery of the stolen diamonds

This is a "fast-action uncomplicated adventure . . . [with] a touch of humor, a breezy writing style, and some very enjoyable pen-and-ink drawings." Booklist

Other titles about Cam Jansen are:
Cam Jansen and the barking treasure mystery (1999)
Cam Jansen and the birthday mystery (2000)
Cam Jansen and the catnapping mystery (1998)
Cam Jansen and the chocolate fudge mystery (1993)
Cam Jansen and the first day of school mystery (2002)
Cam Jansen and the ghostly mystery (1996)
Cam Jansen and the mystery at the haunted house (1992)
Cam Jansen and the mystery at the monkey house (1985)
Cam Jansen and the mystery of Flight 54 (1989)
Cam Jansen and the mystery of the Babe Ruth baseball (1982)
Cam Jansen and the mystery of the carnival prize (1984)
Cam Jansen and the mystery of the circus clown (1983)
Cam Jansen and the mystery of the dinosaur bones (1981)
Cam Jansen and the mystery of the gold coins (1982)
Cam Jansen and the mystery of the monster movie (1984)
Cam Jansen and the mystery of the stolen corn popper (1986)
Cam Jansen and the mystery of the television dog (1981)
Cam Jansen and the mystery of the UFO (1980)
Cam Jansen and the scary snake mystery (1997)
Cam Jansen and the school play mystery (2001)
Cam Jansen and the Secret Service mystery (2006)
Cam Jansen and the snowy day mystery (2004)
Cam Jansen and the Sports Day mysteries (2009)
Cam Jansen and the summer camp mysteries (2007)
Cam Jansen and the tennis trophy mystery (2003)
Cam Jansen and the Triceratops Pops mystery (1995)
Cam Jansen and the Valentine baby mystery (2005)
Cam Jansen and the wedding cake mystery (2011)

Agell, Charlotte

The **accidental** adventures of India McAllister. Henry Holt 2010 151p il $16.99

Grades: 3 4 5   **Fic**

1. Maine -- Fiction 2. Divorce -- Fiction 3. Friendship -- Fiction 4. Homosexuality -- Fiction 5. Chinese Americans -- Fiction
ISBN 978-0-8050-8902-8; 0-8050-8902-0
LC 2009-18907

India, an unusual nine-and-a-half-year-old living in small-town Maine, has a series of adventures which bring her closer to her artist-mother, strengthen her friendship with a neighbor boy, and help her to accept the man for whom her father moved away.

"The word "adventures" could mislead some readers, but those looking for a realistic new character to love won't

be disappointed in nine-year-old India McCallister, who could step right out of the lifestyles section of any contemporary newspaper...An adventure for India is an early-morning walk with her dog; her worst day is when her best (boy) friend walks home from school with her archenemy. Sketchy line drawings, accompanied by India's commentary, provide appealing additional diary-like detail. A delightful addition to the middle-grade canon." PW

Aiken, Joan

The **wolves** of Willoughby Chase; illustrated by Pat Marriott. Delacorte Press 2000 181p il hardcover o.p. pa $6.99

Grades: 5 6 7 8   **Fic**

1. Great Britain -- Fiction
ISBN 0-385-32790-0; 0-440-49603-9 pa

First published 1962 in the United Kingdom; first United States edition 1963 by Doubleday

"Plot, characterization, and background blend perfectly into an amazing whole. . . . Highly recommended." SLJ

Other titles in this series are:
Black hearts in Battersea (1964)
Cold Shoulder Road (1996)
The cuckoo tree (1971)
Dangerous games (1999)
Is underground (1993)
Midwinter nightingale (2003)
Nightbirds on Nantucket (1966)
The stolen lake (1981)
The witch of Clatteringshaws (2005)

Ain, Beth

Starring Jules (in drama-rama) Beth Ain; illustrated by Anne Keenan Higgins. Scholastic Press 2013 176 p. (Starring Jules) (alk. paper) $14.99

Grades: 2 3 4 5   **Fic**

1. Child actors 2. Acting -- Fiction 3. Schools -- Fiction 4. Auditions -- Fiction 5. Friendship -- Fiction 6. Best friends -- Fiction 7. New York (N.Y.) -- Fiction 8. Elementary schools -- Fiction
ISBN 0545443547; 9780545443548
LC 2012041838

This is the second of Beth Ain's Jules Bloom books. Here, "Jules has been asked to audition for a TV show about a New York City family; she would be the youngest of three siblings. . . . Jules skitters from problem to problem like a city cab, balancing her audition with another project: cheering up her new friend Elinor, who is from London. Things are busy at school, too: Her ex-best friend Charlotte continues to steal the limelight there, receiving the plum role in the end-of-the-year play." (Kirkus Reviews)

Albarn, Jessica

The **boy** in the oak; [text & illustrations by] Jessica Albarn. Simply Read Books 2010 un il $17.95

Grades: 4 5 6 7   **Fic**

1. Fantasy fiction 2. Magic -- Fiction 3. Trees -- Fiction 4. Fairies -- Fiction
ISBN 978-1-897476-52-9; 1-897476-52-3

"A spare, lightly haunting narrative tells a fairy-tale-like story of a lonely boy whose play in the woods was 'insensitive and cruel. He trampled the flowers. He tore limbs off trees and carved his initials into their trunks.' A group of fairies . . . trap him inside an ancient 'Druidic Oak,' where the boy watches the seasons pass until a young girl arrives. . . . Pages of prose alternate with wordless spreads featuring spindly artwork and semitranslucent sheets imprinted with close-up photos of nature textures. . . . The book draws the most lasting power from its harmonious layers of imagery and sophisticated bookmaking." Booklist

Alber, Merryl

And the tide comes in; exploring a Georgia salt marsh. by Merryl Alber; illustrated by Joyce Mihran Turley. Taylor Trade Pub. 2012 32 p. ill. (hardcover) $15.95

Grades: 1 2 3   **Fic**

     1. Marshes 2. Picture books for children 3. Ecology

     ISBN 0981770053; 9780981770055

In this children's picture book, a "child in Georgia takes her Colorado cousin on daily visits to a nearby salt marsh. Ginger discovers the cyclical nature of this habitat as she observes and asks about this ecosystem. Alongside the description of the activities of the two girls is an explanation of an aspect of the marsh. Representational animals such as fiddler crabs, blue crabs, and shrimp and the importance of a marsh to their survival are described." (School Library Journal)

Alcott, Louisa May

Little women; illustrated by Scott McKowen. Sterling Pub. 2004 525p il $9.95

Grades: 5 6 7 8   **Fic**

     1. Sisters -- Fiction 2. Family life -- Fiction 3. New England -- Fiction

     ISBN 978-1-4027-1458-0; 1-4027-1458-0

                                  LC 2004-15669

     First published 1868

Chronicles the joys and sorrows of the four March sisters as they grow into young women in mid-nineteenth-century New England.

     Other titles about members of the March family are:

     Eight cousins (1875)

     Jo's boys (1886)

     Little men (1871)

     Rose in bloom (1876)

Alexander, Kwame

The **crossover**; by Kwame Alexander. Houghton Mifflin Harcourt 2014 240 p. hc $16.99

Grades: 7 8 9 10 11 12   **Fic**

     1. Rap music 2. Brothers -- Fiction 3. Basketball -- Fiction 4. Novels in verse 5. Twins -- Fiction 6. Fathers and sons -- Fiction 7. African Americans -- Fiction

     ISBN 0544107713; 9780544107717

                                  LC 2013013810

     Newbery Medal (2015)

     Coretta Scott King Author Award Honor Book (2015)

     In this novel, by Kwame Alexander, "12-year old Josh Bell . . . and his twin brother Jordan are awesome on the court. But Josh has more than basketball in his blood, he's got mad beats, too, that tell his family's story in verse. . . . Josh and Jordan must come to grips with growing up on and off the court to realize breaking the rules comes at a terrible price, as their story's . . . climax proves a game-changer for the entire family." (Publisher's note)

     "Twins Josh and Jordan are junior high basketball stars, thanks in large part to the coaching of their dad, a former professional baller who was forced to quit playing for health

reasons, and the firm, but loving support of their assistant-principal mom...Despite his immaturity, Josh is a likable, funny, and authentic character. Underscoring the sports and the fraternal tension is a portrait of a family that truly loves and supports one another. Alexander has crafted a story that vibrates with energy and heart and begs to be read aloud. A slam dunk." SLJ

Alexander, Lloyd

     ★ The **book** of three; rev ed.; Holt & Co. 1999 190p (Chronicles of Prydain) $19.95; pa $6.99

Grades: 5 6 7 8   **Fic**

     1. Fantasy fiction

     ISBN 978-0-8050-6132-1; 0-8050-6132-0; 978-0-8050-8048-3 pa; 0-8050-8048-1 pa

                                  LC 98-40901

     First published 1964

     "Related in a simple, direct style, this fast-paced tale of high adventure has a well-balanced blend of fantasy, realism, and humor." SLJ

     Other titles about the mythical land of Prydain are:

     The black cauldron (1965)

     The castle of Llyr (1966)

     The foundling and other tales of Prydain (1999)

     The high king (1968)

     Taran Wanderer (1967)

The **golden** dream of Carlo Chuchio. Henry Holt & Co. 2007 306p il $16.95

Grades: 5 6 7 8 9   **Fic**

     1. Fantasy fiction 2. Middle East -- Fiction 3. Buried treasure -- Fiction 4. Voyages and travels -- Fiction

     ISBN 978-0-8050-8333-0; 0-8050-8333-2

                                  LC 2006-49710

     Naive and bumbling Carlo, his shady camel-puller Baksheesh, and Shira, a girl determined to return home, follow a treasure map through the deserts and cities of the infamous Golden Road, as mysterious strangers try in vain to point them toward real treasures

     This "is an exuberant and compassionate tale of adventure." Publ Wkly

The **remarkable** journey of Prince Jen. Dutton Children's Bks. 1991 273p hardcover o.p. pa $6.99

Grades: 5 6 7 8   **Fic**

     1. Adventure fiction 2. China -- Fiction

     ISBN 0-14-240225-7 pa

                                  LC 91-13720

     Bearing six unusual gifts, young Prince Jen in Tang Dynasty China embarks on a perilous quest and emerges triumphantly into manhood

     "Alexander satisfies the taste for excitement, but his vivid characters and the food for thought he offers will nourish long after the last page is turned." SLJ

Alexander, William

Ambassador; William Alexander. Margaret K. McElderry Books 2014 240 p. (hardcover) $16.99

Grades: 5 6 7 8   **Fic**

     1. Science fiction 2. Human-alien encounters -- Fiction 3. Ambassadors -- Fiction 4. Illegal aliens -- Fiction 5. Mexican Americans -- Fiction

     ISBN 1442497645; 9781442497641; 9781442497658

                                  LC 2013037333

In this middle grade book by William Alexander, "Gabe Fuentes is reading under the covers one summer night when he is interrupted by a creature who looks like a purple sock puppet. The sock puppet introduces himself as the Envoy and asks if Gabe wants to be Earth's ambassador to the galaxy. What sane eleven-year-old could refuse?" (Publisher's note)

"A shape-shifting creature called 'the Envoy' informs eleven-year-old Gabe that it has appointed him Earth's ambassador to 'everyone else.' Gabe travels across space (while he's asleep) to the Embassy. When he wakes up back home, he discovers his father is to be deported to Mexico the next day--and one of the other ambassadors is trying to kill Gabe. A meaty and entertaining novel." Horn Book

Allison, Jennifer

★ **Gilda** Joyce, psychic investigator. Sleuth/Dutton 2005 321p pa $6.99; $13.99

Grades: 5 6 7 8   **Fic**
1. Mystery fiction 2. Cousins -- Fiction
ISBN 0-14-240698-8 pa; 0-525-47375-0; 978-0-14-240698-4 pa; 978-0-525-47375-6
LC 2004-10834

During the summer before ninth grade, intrepid Gilda Joyce invites herself to the San Francisco mansion of distant cousin Lester Splinter and his thirteen-year-old daughter, where she uses her purported psychic abilities and detective skills to solve the mystery of the mansion's boarded-up tower.

"Allison pulls off something special here. She not only offers a credible mystery . . . but also . . . provides particularly strong characterizations." Booklist

Other titles about Gilda Joyce are:
Gilda Joyce: the Ladies of the Lake (2006)
Gilda Joyce: the ghost sonata (2007)
Gilda Joyce: the dead drop (2009)
Gilda Joyce: the bones of the holy (2011)

Gilda Joyce, psychic investigator: the bones of the holy. Dutton Children's Books 2011 286p $16.99

Grades: 5 6 7 8   **Fic**
1. Ghost stories 2. Mystery fiction 3. Florida -- Fiction 4. Remarriage -- Fiction
ISBN 978-0-525-42212-9; 0-525-42212-9
LC 2010038069

Psychic investigator Gilda Joyce is appalled that her mother plans to remarry, but while they are in St. Augustine, Florida, making wedding arrangements Gilda discovers that the city is full of ghosts and mysteries, including one involving her stepfather-to-be.

"Gilda fans will rally to her latest caper, while newcomers should revel in her ghostly escapades in old St. Augustine." Kirkus

Almond, David, 1951-
The **boy** who climbed into the moon; illustrated by Polly Dunbar. Candlewick Press 2010 117p il $15.99

Grades: 3 4 5   **Fic**
1. Adventure fiction 2. Moon -- Fiction 3. Great Britain -- Fiction
ISBN 978-0-7636-4217-4; 0-7636-4217-7
LC 2009-11158

Helped by a very long ladder, some unusual acquaintances, two rather worried parents, and a great deal of community spirit, a young English boy makes an astonishing

discovery when he embarks on a mission to prove that the moon is nothing but a big hole in the sky

"Almond employs all manners of amusements . . . while never losing sight of some refreshing realities: Paul's parents are a real presence, and the city feels appropriately dense. . . . Dunbar's full-color illustrations . . . nimbly dodge the prose." Booklist

The **Boy** who swam with piranhas; David Almond, illustrated by Oliver Jeffers. Candlewick Press 2013 256 p. $15.99

Grades: 4 5 6 7   **Fic**
1. Orphans -- Fiction 2. Carnivals -- Fiction 3. Runaway children -- Fiction
ISBN 0763661694; 9780763661694
LC 2012947721

Heaven Eyes. Delacorte Press 2001 233p hardcover o.p. pa $5.50

Grades: 5 6 7 8   **Fic**
1. Adventure fiction 2. Orphans 3. Orphans -- Fiction 4. Adventure and adventurers
ISBN 0-385-32770-6; 0-440-22910-3 pa
LC 00-31798

First published 2000 in the United Kingdom

Having escaped from their orphanage on a raft, Erin, January, and Mouse float down into another world of abandoned warehouses and factories, meeting a strange old man and an even stranger girl with webbed fingers and toes named Heaven Eyes. "Intermediate, middle school." (Horn Book)

"The ambiguous and surreal setting and the lyricism of the metaphor-laden prose make this a compelling and original novel." SLJ

Mouse bird snake wolf; David Almond, illustrated by David McKean. Candlewick Press 2013 80 p. (reinforced) $17.99

Grades: 4 5 6 7   **Fic**
1. Animals -- Juvenile fiction 2. Fantasy fiction -- Juvenile fiction
ISBN 0763659126; 9780763659127
LC 2012950556

In this book, "Harry, Sue, and Little Ben live in a world whose lazy gods have made creatures like whales and camels but have given up their work, leaving blank spaces . . . . The children discover that they can create animals themselves, using sticks, leaves, and clay; Little Ben makes a mouse; Sue, a bird; and Harry, a snake. But Harry and Sue aren't satisfied. They create a terrifying wolf that turns on them and eats them, and Little Ben must summon the courage to save them." (Publishers Weekly)

My dad's a birdman; illustrated by Polly Dunbar. Candlewick Press 2008 115p il $15.99

Grades: 4 5 6   **Fic**
1. Flight -- Fiction 2. Fathers -- Fiction
ISBN 978-0-7636-3667-8; 0-7636-3667-3

In a rainy town in the north of England, there are strange goings-on. Dad is building a pair of wings, eating flies, and feathering his nest. Lizzie is missing her Mom and looking after Dad by letting him follow his newfound whimsy. What's behind it all? It's the great human bird competition.

"Handsomely produced, the book is printed in varying size typefaces and enhanced by Dunbar's pencil, watercolor, and collage illustrations interspersed throughout the text. Casual yet evocative, they perfectly interpret Almond's broadly sketched characters. A fine read-aloud." SLJ

★ **My** name is Mina. Delacorte Press 2011 300p $15.99; lib bdg $18.99

Grades: 5 6 7 8   Fic

1. Authorship -- Fiction

ISBN 978-0-385-74073-9; 0-385-74073-5; 978-0-375-98964-3 lib bdg; 0-375-98964-1 lib bdg; 978-0-375-98965-0 e-book

LC 2010040143

"This intimate prequel to Skellig is built around Mina McKee, the curious and brilliant home-schooled child who eventually befriends that book's protagonist, Michael. Mina, a budding writer, reveals her love of words in her journal; most of the book unfolds in a handwritten-looking font, with Mina's more emphatic entries exploding onto the pages in massive display type. Her lyrical, nonlinear prose records her reflections on her past, existential musings . . . and self-directed writing exercises. . . . Almond gives readers a vivid picture of the joyfully freeform workings of Mina's mind and her mixed emotions about being an isolated child. Her gradual emergence from the protective shell of home is beautifully portrayed. . . . This novel will inspire children to let their imaginations soar." Publ Wkly

★ **Skellig**; 10th anniversary ed.; Delacorte Press 2009 182p $16.99; pa $6.99

Grades: 5 6 7 8 9 10   Fic

1. Fantasy fiction

ISBN 978-0-385-32653-7; 0-385-32653-X; 978-0-440-41602-9 pa; 0-440-41602-7 pa

First published 1998 in the United Kingdom; first United States edition 1999

Michael L. Printz Award honor book

Unhappy about his baby sister's illness and the chaos of moving into a dilapidated old house, Michael retreats to the garage and finds a mysterious stranger who is something like a bird and something like an angel.

"The plot is beautifully paced and the characters are drawn with a graceful, careful hand. . . . A lovingly done, thought-provoking novel." SLJ

Slog's dad; illustrated by Dave McKean. Candlewick Press 2011 52p il $15.99

Grades: 5 6 7 8   Fic

1. Death -- Fiction 2. Future life -- Fiction 3. Great Britain -- Fiction 4. Father-son relationship -- Fiction

ISBN 978-0-7636-4940-1; 0-7636-4940-6

LC 2010-38700

When Slog's father died he promised to return for one last visit in the spring, but when Slog spots a scruffy man on a bench outside the butcher shop and identifies him as his father, his best friend Davie is skeptical.

"This grief-strafed wonder tale is brilliantly matched by some of McKean's most moving artwork yet. Text pages, featuring a voice steeped on Northern English flavor, are counterpoised against wordless illustration sequences that move readers from heaven to earth and back again, beginning with a celestial descent from the sky to a park bench

by a man trailing clouds of watercolor glory." Bull Cent Child Books

Alvarez, Julia

★ **How** Tia Lola came to visit/stay. Knopf 2001 147p $15.95; pa $5.50

Grades: 4 5 6 7   Fic

1. Aunts -- Fiction 2. Divorce -- Fiction 3. Vermont -- Fiction 4. Dominican Americans -- Fiction

ISBN 0-375-80215-0; 0-440-41870-4 pa

LC 00-62932

Although ten-year-old Miguel is at first embarrassed by his colorful aunt, Tia Lola, when she comes to Vermont from the Dominican Republic to stay with his mother, his sister, and him after his parents' divorce, he learns to love her.

"Readers will enjoy the funny situations, identify with the developing relationships and conflicting feelings of the characters, and will get a spicy taste of Caribbean culture in the bargain." SLJ

Other titles about Tia Lola are:

How Tia Lola learned to teach (2010)

How Tia Lola saved the summer (2011)

How Tia Lola ended up starting over (2011)

★ **Return** to sender. Alfred A. Knopf 2009 325p $16.99; lib bdg $19.99

Grades: 4 5 6 7   Fic

1. Vermont -- Fiction 2. Farm life -- Fiction 3. Friendship -- Fiction 4. Migrant labor -- Fiction 5. Illegal aliens -- Fiction

ISBN 978-0-375-85838-3; 0-375-85838-5; 978-0-375-95838-0 lib bdg; 0-375-95838-X lib bdg

LC 2008-23520

Awarded the Belpre Author Medal (2010)

After his family hires migrant Mexican workers to help save their Vermont farm from foreclosure, eleven-year-old Tyler befriends the oldest daughter, but when he discovers they may not be in the country legally, he realizes that real friendship knows no borders.

"Readers will be moved by small moments. . . . A tender, well-constructed book." Publ Wkly

Amato, Mary

Edgar Allan's official crime investigation notebook. Holiday House 2010 140p

Grades: 3 4 5   Fic

1. School stories 2. Mystery fiction 3. Poetry -- Fiction 4. Teachers -- Fiction 5. Lost and found possessions -- Fiction

ISBN 0-8234-2271-2; 978-0-8234-2271-5

LC 2010-11604

When someone takes a pet goldfish, then other items from Ms. Herschel's classroom, each time leaving a clue in the form of a poem, student Edgar Allan competes with a classmate to be the first to solve the mystery. "Grades three to five." (Bull Cent Child Books)

"While there is enough of a mystery plot here to satisfy genre fans, this is ulitmately a story about friendship, and Amato is particularly adept at developing strong characterizations of a diverse group of kids without delving into stereotypes." Bull Cent Child Books

Snarf attack, underfoodle, and the secret of life; the Riot brothers tell all. by Mary Amato; illustrated by Ethan

CHILDREN'S CORE COLLECTION
TWENTY-SECOND EDITION

Long. Holiday House 2004 151p il (The Riot Brothers) $16.95; pa $6.95

Grades: 2 3 4 **Fic**

1. School stories 2. Brothers -- Fiction

ISBN 0-8234-1750-6; 0-8234-2062-0 pa

Orville and Wilbur Riot have no shortage of daily adventures. Sometimes they are undercover detectives. Other times they challenge each other to see who can get the most underwear on his head in exactly thirty seconds.

"Young readers will appreciate the Riot brothers' attempts to make something exciting happen every day. Long's playful cartoon illustrations extend the fun." Booklist

Anaya, Rudolfo A.

The **first** tortilla; a bilingual story. [by] Rudolfo Anaya; illustrated by Amy Cordova; translated into Spanish by Enrique R. Lamadrid. University of New Mexico 2007 un il $16.95

Grades: 2 3 4 **Fic**

1. Mexico -- Fiction 2. Bilingual books -- English-Spanish

ISBN 978-0-8263-4214-0

Guided by a blue hummingbird, Jade brings an offering to the Mountain Spirit who lives near her village in Mexico, and asks if he will send rain to end the drought that threatens the people.

"Anaya has retold a Mexican legend and made it his own with his spiritual prose. . . . Córdova's rich acrylic paintings lend a traditional feel to the setting while maintaining the tale's mystical elements. A beautifully written and illustrated title." SLJ

Andersen, Hans Christian

The **little** match girl; illustrated by Rachel Isadora. Putnam 1987 30p il $16.99

Grades: 3 4 5 **Fic**

ISBN 0-399-21336-8

LC 85-30082

The wares of the poor little match girl illuminate her cold world, bringing some beauty to her brief, tragic life

"Isadora follows Andersen's lead, neither sensationalizing nor apologizing for the tale's potentially sentimental plot. . . . A moving, original picture-book interpretation of the classic tale." Booklist

The **princess** and the pea; illustrated by Dorothée Duntze. North-South Bks. 1985 un il $16.95; pa $7.95

Grades: K 1 2 3 **Fic**

1. Fairy tales

ISBN 1-55858-034-4; 1-55858-381-5 pa

LC 85-7199

A young girl feels a pea through twenty mattresses and twenty featherbeds and proves she is a real princess

"This classic Andersen fairy tale is presented in simple text and with elaborate illustrations. . . . Duntze appears to set the story during the Renaissance, and her illustrations are precise, intricate and detailed." SLJ

Anderson, Jodi Lynn

May Bird among the stars; book two. [by] Jodi Lynn Anderson. 1st ed.; Atheneum Books for Young Readers 2006 260p $16.95

Grades: 5 6 7 8 **Fic**

1. Fantasy fiction

ISBN 978-0-689-86924-2; 0-689-86924-X

LC 2005028832

Sequel to May Bird and The Ever After (2005)

Still trapped in The Ever After, ten-year-old May Bird struggles to decide whether to save the world of her ghostly friends from the evil Bo Cleevil or to return to her West Virginia home.

"Anderson has clearly had a great deal of fun creating a world not so different from our own where spirits go after death, and readers will love her humorous jabs at popular culture." SLJ

Followed by May Bird, warrior princess (2007)

May Bird, warrior princess; book three. [by] Jodi Lynn Anderson. Atheneum Books for Young Readers 2007 244p $16.99

Grades: 5 6 7 8 **Fic**

1. Fantasy fiction

ISBN 0-689-86925-8; 978-0-689-86925-9

LC 2007002944

Three years after her return from the Ever After, May Bird, now thirteen, draws her scattered friends—Pumpkin, Fabbio, Beatrice, and Lucius—out of hiding to take a final stand against Evil Bo Cleevil, as May herself makes ready to live up to the prophecy that placed the fate of the Ever After, and her own world, in her hands.

"The novel . . . will not disappoint fans. A reading of the previous two titles is recommended." SLJ

Anderson, John David

Minion; John David Anderson. Walden Pond Press, an imprint of HarperCollins 2014 288 p. (hardback) $16.99

Grades: 4 5 6 7 **Fic**

1. Adoption -- Fiction 2. Criminals -- Fiction 3. Superheroes -- Fiction 4. Good and evil -- Fiction 5. Supervillains -- Fiction

ISBN 006213311X; 9780062133113

LC 2013043188

In this book, by John David Anderson, "Michael Morn might be a villain, but he's really not a bad guy. When you live in New Liberty, known across the country as the City without a Super, there are only two kinds of people, after all: those who turn to crime and those who suffer. Michael and his adoptive father spend their days building boxes—special devices with mysterious abilities. . . . But then a Super comes to town, and Michael's world is thrown into disarray." (Publisher's note)

"The author of Sidekicked (2013) continues to scuff up the line between heroism and villainy. Spirited from the orphanage when he was nine, Michael Marion Magdalene Morn (named by the nuns) has spent four years in hiding with kind but closemouthed Professor Edson—an eccentric inventor of small black boxes capable of all sorts of shady exploit...Michael's musing that "sometimes it's just hard to know what's right and what's best and why there even has to be a difference" provides both a specific theme for this outing and an overall one for all of the author's thought-provoking work to date." (Booklist)

★ **Sidekicked**; John David Anderson. Walden Pond Press, an imprint of HarperCollinsPublishers 2013 384 p. (hardback) $16.99

Grades: 4 5 6 7 **Fic**
1. Adolescence -- Fiction 2. Superheroes -- Fiction 3. Humorous stories 4. Ability -- Fiction 5. Schools -- Fiction 6. Identity -- Fiction 7. Middle schools -- Fiction 8. Self-confidence -- Fiction

ISBN 0062133144; 9780062133144

LC 2012025495

In this book, "the main character is a sidekick named Andrew Bean. Like the best superheroes, he's down on his luck, always forgetting his utility belt when he needs it. Andrew is part of a school environmental club, H.E.R.O., that . . . doubles as a training program for sidekicks (motto: 'WE KEEP THE TRASH OFF THE STREETS'). Andrew's mentor is the Titan, an aging hero who'd rather go out drinking than fight crime." (Kirkus Reviews)

Anderson, Laurie Halse, 1961-
★ **Chains**; seeds of America. Simon & Schuster Books for Young Readers 2008 316p $17.99
Grades: 6 7 8 9 10 **Fic**
1. Spies -- Fiction 2. Slavery -- Fiction 3. New York (N.Y.) -- Fiction 4. African Americans -- Fiction
ISBN 1-4169-0585-5; 1-4169-0586-3 pa; 978-1-4169-0585-1; 978-1-4169-0586-8 pa

LC 2007-52139

After being sold to a cruel couple in New York City, a slave named Isabel spies for the rebels during the Revolutionary War. "Grades seven to ten." (Bull Cent Child Books)

"This gripping novel offers readers a startlingly provocative view of the Revolutionary War. . . . [Anderson's] solidly researched exploration of British and Patriot treatment of slaves during a war for freedom is nuanced and evenhanded, presented in service of a fast-moving, emotionally involving plot." Publ Wkly

Followed by: Forge (2010)

Fever, 1793. Simon & Schuster Bks. for Young Readers 2000 251p $17.99; pa $6.99
Grades: 5 6 7 8 9 **Fic**
1. Epidemics -- Fiction 2. Yellow fever -- Fiction 3. Philadelphia (Pa.) -- Fiction
ISBN 978-0-689-83858-3; 0-689-83858-1; 978-0-689-84891-9 pa; 0-689-84891-9 pa

LC 00-32238

ALA YALSA Margaret A. Edwards Award (2009)

In 1793 Philadelphia, sixteen-year-old Matilda Cook, separated from her sick mother, learns about perseverance and self-reliance when she is forced to cope with the horrors of a yellow fever epidemic. "Age ten and up." (N Y Times Book Rev)

"A vivid work, rich with well-drawn and believable characters. Unexpected events pepper the top-flight novel that combines accurate historical detail with a spellbinding story line." Voice Youth Advocates

★ **Forge**. Atheneum Books for Young Readers 2010 297p (Seeds of America) $16.99
Grades: 6 7 8 9 10 **Fic**
1. Slavery -- Fiction 2. Soldiers -- Fiction 3. Pennsylvania -- Fiction 4. African Americans -- Fiction 5. United States -- History -- 1775-1783, Revolution -- Fiction
ISBN 978-1-4169-6144-4; 1-4169-6144-5

LC 2010-15971

Sequel to: Chains (2008)

Separated from his friend Isabel after their daring escape from slavery, fifteen-year-old Curzon serves as a free man in the Continental Army at Valley Forge until he and Isabel are thrown together again, as slaves once more.

"Weaving a huge amount of historical detail seamlessly into the story, Anderson creates a vivid setting, believable characters both good and despicable and a clear portrayal of the moral ambiguity of the Revolutionary age. Not only can this sequel stand alone, for many readers it will be one of the best novels they have ever read." Kirkus

Anderson, M. T., 1968-
The **chamber** in the sky. Scholastic Press 2012 282 p. (hardcover) $17.99
Grades: 5 6 7 8 **Fic**
1. American satire 2. Fantasy fiction 3. Human-alien encounters -- Fiction
ISBN 0545334934; 9780545334938

This novel, by National Book Award and Printz Honor winner M. T. Anderson, is book four of "The Norumbegan Quartet" series. "Brian and Gregory have . . . . gone to investigate intergalactic suburban sprawl that was infringing on the Vermont forests, and landed in the empire of New Norumbega inside the huge body of an alien. They've escaped certain death . . . and wreaked small amounts of havoc of their own. And finally, they're going to make sense of all their travels and adventures." (Publisher's note)

The **Game** of Sunken Places; [by] M. T. Anderson. Scholastic Press 2004 260p (The Norumbegan quartet) $16.95; pa $5.99
Grades: 5 6 7 8 **Fic**
1. Games -- Fiction 2. Vermont -- Fiction
ISBN 0-439-41660-4; 0-439-41661-2 pa

LC 2003-20055

When two boys stay with an eccentric relative at his mansion in rural Vermont, they discover an old-fashioned board game that draws them into a mysterious adventure.

"Deliciously scary, often funny, and crowned by a pair of deeply satisfying surprises, this tour de force leaves one marveling at Anderson's ability to slip between genres as fluidly as his middle-grade heroes straddle worlds." Booklist

Other titles in this series are:
The suburb beyond the stars (2010)
The empire of gut and bone (2011)

He laughed with his other mouths; M.T. Anderson; illustrations by Kurt Cyrus. First edition Beach Lane Books 2014 304 p. illustrations (Pals in peril) (hardcover) $17.99
Grades: 4 5 6 7 **Fic**
1. Adventure fiction 2. Outer space -- Fiction 3. Humorous stories 4. Extraterrestrial beings -- Fiction 5. Adventure and adventurers -- Fiction
ISBN 1442451106; 9781442451100; 9781442451117

LC 2013034710

"In this action-packed conclusion to the celebrated Pals in Peril series, Jasper Dash soars to unprecedented heights--as in, intergalactic, out-of-this-world dimensions--in order to locate the father he's never known." (Publisher's note)

"The novel doesn't transcend the wacky sci-fi of old that inspired it but rather embraces it and dissects it, celebrating it and exploring why so many people fell in love with these silly worlds and gee-whiz heroes in the first place." Kirkus

★ **Whales** on stilts; illustrations by Kurt Cyrus. Harcourt 2005 188p il (Pals in peril) $15; pa $5.95

Grades: 4 5 6 7   Fic

1. Science fiction

ISBN 0-15-205340-9; 0-15-205394-8 pa

LC 2004-17754

Racing against the clock, shy middle-school student Lily and her best friends, Katie and Jasper, must foil the plot of her father's conniving boss to conquer the world using an army of whales.

"A story written with the author's tongue shoved firmly into his cheek. . . . It's full of witty pokes at other series novels and Jasper's nutty inventions." SLJ

Other titles in this series are:

The clue of the linoleum lederhosen (2006)

Jasper Dash and the Flame-pits of Delaware (2009)

Agent Q., or the smell of danger! (2010)

Zombie mommy (2011)

Zombie mommy; illustrations by Kurt Cyrus. Beach Lane Books 2011 220p il (Pals in peril) $16.99

Grades: 4 5 6 7   Fic

1. Adventure fiction 2. Zombies -- Fiction 3. Children's literature -- Works -- Grades two through six

ISBN 978-1-4169-8641-6; 1-4169-8641-3

LC 2010047668

In this entry in the Pals in Peril series, "Lily's mom has become possessed by a menacing zombie who wants to take over the world! (Or, at least, the world of stage and screen.) Thank goodness Lily's friends Katie, Jasper, and foxy Blue-Hen-State monk Drgnan Pghlik are around—accompanied by Jasper's Astounding High-Pressure Holy Water Extruder Gun, of course—to help save the day." (Publisher's note) "Intermediate, middle school." (Horn Book)

"Ridiculous in all the best ways." Kirkus

Angleberger, Tom

Fake mustache; or, how Jodie O'Rodeo and her wonder horse (and some nerdy guy) saved the U.S. Presidential election from a mad genius criminal mastermind. Tom Angleberger; illustrated by Jen Wang. Amulet Books 2012 196 p. ill. (hardback) $13.95

Grades: 2 3 4 5 6   Fic

1. Humorous stories 2. Disguise -- Fiction 3. Criminals -- Fiction 4. Hypnotism -- Fiction 5. Mustaches -- Fiction

ISBN 1419701940; 9781419701948

LC 2012000556

Edgar Award: Best Juvenile Shortlist (2013)

In this book, "[w]hen twelve-year-old Lenny . . . lends his best friend, Casper, ten dollars to purchase . . . [a] fake mustache at a local gag shop, he has no idea he's just become an accomplice in Casper's plot for world domination. In the days following, a mysterious man with some impressive facial hair . . . steamrolls his way into the governor's seat, takes over the . . . nation's leading manufacturer of voting booths and launches a presidential campaign," (Bulletin of the Center for Children's Books)

Princess Labelmaker to the rescue! an Origami Yoda book. by Tom Angleberger. Harry N. Abrams Inc. 2014 208 p. $13.95

Grades: 4 5 6 7   Fic

1. School stories 2. Star Wars films 3. Origami -- Fiction 4. Schools -- Fiction 5. Finger puppets -- Fiction 6. Interpersonal relations -- Fiction 7. Eccentrics and eccentricities -- Fiction

ISBN 1419710524; 9781419710520

LC 2013047291

In this book, part of the Origami Yoda series, by Tom Angleberger, "At McQuarrie Middle School, the war against the FunTime Menace--aka test prep--wages on. . . . To defeat the Dark Standardized Testing Forces they're going to need an even bigger, even more surprising ally: Principal Rabbski. But with great forces--aka the school board--pushing her from above, will the gang's former enemy don a finger puppet and join the Rebellion--or will her transformation to Empress Rabbski, Dark Lord of the Sith, be complete?" (Publisher's note)

"The FunTime Menace (a deadly boring test prep program) is still wreaking havoc at McQuarrie Middle School in the sixth book in the series. The only way to abolish Fun-Time is to get Principal Rabbski on the side of the Rebellion, but the Origami Rebel Alliance will have to risk everything to win her over. Angleberger continues to develop authentic and engaging voices in these "case files."" Horn Book

Other titles include:

The surprise attack of Jabba the Puppett

Darth Paper strikes back

The strange case of Origami Yoda

Emperor Pickletine rides the bus

The secret of the Fortune Wookiee

Horton Halfpott; or, The fiendish mystery of Smugwick Manor, or, The loosening of M'Lady Luggertuck's corset. Tom Angleberger with illustrations by the author. Amulet Books 2011 206p il $14.95

Grades: 4 5 6 7   Fic

1. Mystery fiction 2. Social classes -- Fiction 3. Household employees -- Fiction 4. Eccentrics and eccentricities -- Fiction 5. Great Britain -- History -- 19th century -- Fiction

ISBN 978-0-8109-9715-8; 0-8109-9715-0

LC 2010-38096

Horton, an upstanding kitchen boy in a castle in nineteenth-century England, becomes embroiled in a mystery surrounding a series of thefts. "Grades four to six." (Bull Cent Child Books)

"Readers will enjoy Angleberger's . . . penchant for the absurd as well as his many droll asides. . . . The ending satisfies, and with Angleberger's many eclectic characters, his wild-and-witty storytelling, and a lighthearted but perplexing mystery . . . readers are in for a treat." Publ Wkly

Angus, Jennifer

In search of Goliathus hercules; by Jennifer Angus. Albert Whitman 2012 350 p. (hardcover) $17.99

Grades: 3 4 5 6 7   Fic

1. Fantasy fiction 2. Insects -- Fiction 3. Human-animal communication -- Fiction 4. Metamorphosis

-- Fiction

ISBN 0807529907; 9780807529904

LC 2011037135

In this novel, by Jennifer Angus, "Henri Bell, . . . in 1890 . . . strikes up a conversation with a friendly fly on the windowsill and discovers he possesses the astounding ability to speak with insects. Thus commences an epic journey for Henri as he manages a flea circus, commands an army of beetles, and ultimately sets out to British Malaya to find the mythical giant insect known as Goliathus Hercules." (Publisher's note)

Appelt, Kathi

★ **Keeper**; illustrations by August Hall. Atheneum Books for Young Readers 2010 399p il $16.99

Grades: 5 6 7 8 **Fic**

1. Ocean -- Fiction 2. Sailing -- Fiction 3. Mermaids and mermen -- Fiction 4. Mother-daughter relationship -- Fiction

ISBN 978-1-4169-5060-8; 1-4169-5060-5

LC 2010000795

On the night of the blue moon when mermaids are said to gather on a sandbar in the Gulf of Mexico, ten-year-old Keeper sets out in a small boat, with her dog BD and a seagull named Captain, determined to find her mother, a mermaid, as Keeper has always believed, who left long ago to return to the sea.

"Deftly spinning together mermaid lore, local legend and natural history, this stunning tale proves 'every landscape has its magical beings,' and the most unlikely ones can form a perfect family. Hall's black-and-white illustrations lend perspective and immediacy. Beautiful and evocative—an absolute 'keeper.' " Kirkus

★ The **true** blue scouts of Sugarman Swamp; by Kathi Appelt. 1st ed. Atheneum Books for Young Readers 2013 336 p. (hardcover) $16.99

Grades: 5 6 7 8 **Fic**

1. Swamps -- Fiction 2. Raccoons -- Fiction 3. Humorous stories 4. Swamp animals -- Fiction 5. Land developers -- Fiction 6. Scouting (Youth activity) -- Fiction

ISBN 1442421053; 9781442421059; 9781442481213

LC 2012023723

This book is "told from the perspectives of animals and humans. . . .The main concern of Bingo and Jeremiah, two raccoon Swamp Scouts, is the approaching brood of feral hogs, which could destroy the precious canebrake sugar used to make fried pies at the local Paradise Pies cafe. Meanwhile, 12-year-old Chap Brayburn, the cafe proprietor's son, is worried about rich, horrible Sonny Boy Beaucoup, who wants to turn the swamp into the 'Gator World Wrestling Arena and Theme Park.'" (Publishers Weekly)

★ The **underneath**; illustrated by David Small. Atheneum Books for Young Readers 2008 313p il $16.99; pa $7.99

Grades: 3 4 5 6 **Fic**

1. Cats -- Fiction 2. Dogs -- Fiction

ISBN 978-1-4169-5058-5; 1-4169-5058-3; 978-1-4169-5059-2 pa; 1-4169-5059-1 pa

LC 2007031969

A Newbery Medal honor book, 2009

An abandoned "calico cat, about to have kittens, hears the lonely howl of [Ranger], a chained-up hound deep in the backwaters of the bayou. . . . Ranger urges the cat to hide underneath the porch, to raise her kittens there because Gar-Face, the man living inside the house, will surely use them as alligator bait should he find them." (Publisher's note) "Intemediate." (Horn Book)

"Well realized in Small's excellent full-page drawings, this fine book is most of all distinguished by the originality of the story and the fresh beauty of its author's voice." Horn Book

Applegate, Katherine

Home of the brave. Feiwel & Friends 2007 249p $16.95

Grades: 5 6 7 8 **Fic**

1. Novels in verse 2. Cattle -- Fiction 3. Africans -- Fiction 4. Refugees -- Fiction 5. Minnesota -- Fiction 6. Immigrants -- Fiction

ISBN 0-312-36765-1; 978-0-312-36765-7

LC 2006-32053

Kek, an African refugee, is confronted by many strange things at the Minneapolis home of his aunt and cousin, as well as in his fifth grade classroom, and longs for his missing mother, but finds comfort in the company of a cow and her owner.

"This beautiful story of hope and resilience is written in free verse." Voice Youth Advocates

★ The **one** and only Ivan; illustrated by Patricia Castelao. Harper 2012 il $16.99

Grades: 3 4 5 6 **Fic**

1. Gorillas -- Fiction 2. Elephants -- Fiction 3. Animal welfare -- Fiction

ISBN 978-0-06-199225-4; 0-06-199225-9

LC 2011010034

John Newbery Medal (2013)

When Ivan, a gorilla who has lived for years in a down-and-out circus-themed mall, meets Ruby, a baby elephant that has been added to the mall, he decides that he must find her a better life.

"Ivan narrates his tale in short, image-rich sentences and acute, sometimes humorous, observations that are all the more heartbreaking for their simple delivery. . . . Spot art captures poignant moments throughout. Utterly believable, this bittersweet story, complete with an author's note identifying the real Ivan, will inspire a new generation of advocates." Kirkus

Arbuthnott, Gill

The **Keepers'** tattoo. Chicken House 2010 425p $17.99

Grades: 6 7 8 9 **Fic**

1. Fantasy fiction 2. Dreams -- Fiction 3. Uncles -- Fiction 4. Tattooing -- Fiction 5. Identity (Psychology) -- Fiction

ISBN 978-0-545-17166-3; 0-545-17166-0

LC 2009-26327

Months before her fifteenth birthday, Nyssa learns that she is a special member of a legendary clan, the Keepers of Knowledge, as she and her uncle try to escape from Alaric, the White Wolf, who wants to use lines tattooed on her to destroy the rest of her people.

Arbuthnott "writes with restraint and thoughtfulness, never condescending to her readers. Nyssa is a convincing mixture of ignorance, courage, and resourcefulness." Publ Wkly

Armstrong, Alan

Looking for Marco Polo; illustrated by Tim Jessell. Random House 2009 286p $16.99

Grades: 4 5 6 7   **Fic**

1. Travelers 2. Travel writers 3. Venice (Italy) -- Fiction 4. Missing persons -- Fiction

ISBN 978-0-375-83321-2; 0-375-83321-8

When they lose touch with his father's Gobi Desert expedition, eleven-year-old Mark accompanies his mother to Venice, Italy, and there, while waiting for news of his father, learns about the legendary Marco Polo and his adventures in the Far East.

"Armstrong ably conjures up the atmosphere of damp, foggy Venice in late December while blowing some dust off of the accounts of Marco Polo's travels with his lively storytelling. . . . Whether or not readers know the specifics of Marco Polo's voyages, they will enjoy this entertaining blend of contemporary and historical adventure." Booklist

Racing the moon; by Alan Armstrong; illustrated by Tim Jessell. Random House 2012 214 p. (hc: alk. paper) $16.99

Grades: 5 6 7 8   **Fic**

1. Adventure fiction 2. Historical fiction 3. Siblings -- Fiction 4. Aeronautics -- Fiction 5. Space flight -- Fiction 6. Brothers and sisters -- Fiction 7. Rockets (Aeronautics) -- Fiction 8. Adventure and adventurers -- Fiction

ISBN 037585889X; 9780375858895; 9780375858901; 9780375893094

LC 2012016261

In this children's book by Alan Armstrong "Twelve-year-old Alex hangs out with her reckless 17-year-old brother Chuck, who's always getting them in trouble. . . . Alex wants to be another Amelia Earhart [and][m]eeting her new neighbor, Captain Ebbs, Alex finds a mentor. . . . She arranges for Alex to meet pioneer rocket scientist Wernher von Braun, organizes a sailing trip to a Chesapeake Bay island near a rocket launch and provides needed direction for the risk-taking duo." (Kirkus)

Raleigh's page; illustrated by Tim Jessell. Random House 2007 328p il $16.99; lib bdg $19.99

Grades: 4 5 6 7   **Fic**

1. Poets 2. Authors 3. Explorers 4. Historians 5. Adventure fiction 6. Courtiers 7. Travel writers 8. Virginia -- Fiction 9. Native Americans -- Fiction 10. Great Britain -- History -- 1485-1603, Tudors -- Fiction

ISBN 978-0-375-83319-9; 978-0-375-93319-6 lib bdg

LC 2006-08434

In the late 16th century, fifteen-year-old Andrew leaves school in England and must prove himself as a page to Sir Walter Raleigh before embarking for Virginia, where he helps to establish relations with the Indians.

Armstrong "weaves a richly detailed historical narrative. . . . Historical figures such as Raleigh, Thomas Harriot, and Manteo mix with fictional characters in an adventure that

makes for compelling reading. Illustrated with expressive pencil drawings." Booklist

★ Whittington; illustrated by S. D. Schindler. Random House 2005 191p il $14.95; lib bdg $16.99; pa $6.50

Grades: 4 5 6   **Fic**

1. Cats -- Fiction 2. Domestic animals -- Fiction

ISBN 0-375-82864-8; 0-375-92864-2 lib bdg; 0-375-82865-6 pa

LC 2004-05789

A Newbery Medal honor book, 2006

"A battered cat who calls himself Whittington takes up residence in a shabby barn already inhabited by a variety of scruffy livestock, owned by Bernie. . . . Bernie offers refuge not only to his animals but also to his parentless grandchildren, Abby and Ben, who carry burdens of their own. The children [can] communicate . . . with the animals, so Abby and Ben join the audience when Whittington the cat retells the story of Dick Whittington and his cat." (Bull Cent Child Books) "Intermediate, middle school." (Horn Book)

"The story works beautifully, both as historical fiction about medieval street life and commerce and as a witty, engaging tale of barnyard camaraderie and survival." Booklist

Armstrong, William Howard

★ Sounder; [by] William H. Armstrong; illustrations by James Barkley. Harper & Row 1969 116p il $15.99; pa $5.99

Grades: 5 6 7 8   **Fic**

1. Dogs -- Fiction 2. Family life -- Fiction 3. African Americans -- Fiction

ISBN 0-06-020143-6; 0-06-440020-4 pa

Awarded the Newbery Medal, 1970

"Set in the South in the era of sharecropping and segregation, this succinctly told tale poignantly describes the courage of a father who steals a ham in order to feed his undernourished family; the determination of the eldest son, who searches for his father despite the apathy of prison authorities; and the devotion of a coon dog named Sounder." Shapiro. Fic for Youth. 3d edition

Arnold, Elana K.

The question of miracles; by Elana K. Arnold. Houghton Mifflin Harcourt 2015 240 p. (hardback) $16.99

Grades: 4 5 6 7   **Fic**

1. Miracles -- Fiction 2. Friendship -- Fiction 3. Grief -- Fiction 4. Corvallis (Or.) -- Fiction 5. Moving, Household -- Fiction

ISBN 0544334647; 9780544334649

LC 2014000738

In this novel by Elana K. Arnold "Iris is starting sixth grade in a new school in Oregon-new house, new people, new life. Her parents want to distract her from the recent death of her best friend in California. . . . She turns away from potential friends, seeking instead someone she can barely tolerate--so that she must only endure minimal interaction. His name is Boris, and while he is obviously an outcast, Iris prefers to be on the outskirts." (School Library Journal)

"Sixth-grader Iris hates her new home in rainy Corvallis, Oregon. The move from Southern California was ostensibly because of her mother's new job...She asks the questions that many children would ask in this circumstance, and the book puts a smart circle of caring adults to help her find answers. But it is her realistic relationship with the matter-of-fact Boris, a most unlikely miracle, that will catch readers and help pull them toward seeking answers of their own for the story's very large questions." Booklist

Arnosky, Jim

The **pirates** of Crocodile Swamp. G. P. Putnam's Sons 2009 230p il $15.99

Grades: 3 4 5 6   **Fic**

1. Adventure fiction 2. Florida -- Fiction 3. Brothers -- Fiction 4. Wetlands -- Fiction 5. Runaway children -- Fiction

ISBN 978-0-399-25068-2; 0-399-25068-9

Kidnapped by their father, two boys escape into the mangrove swamps of Key Largo, Florida, where they learn to live on their own among the wildlife.

This "is an exciting story, with plenty of Arnosky's trademark insight into the delights and dangers of the natural (and human) world. The prose is direct and gripping, the characterization strong, and the story includes just enough of the author's illustrations to enrich the fast-moving tale." SLJ

Arnston, Steven

★ The **Wikkeling**; illustrated by Daniela Jaglenka Terrazzini. Running Press Kids 2011 256p il $18

Grades: 4 5 6   **Fic**

1. Science fiction

ISBN 978-0-7624-3903-4; 0-7624-3903-3

"In Henrietta's world, every part of life is monitored and regulated by computers. House cats are considered wild and dangerous animals. Old houses and old books can make children sick. The girl's orderly and safe life is disrupted the day she discovers a secret attic above her bedroom. . . . Soon after this discovery, she starts seeing the Wikkeling, a menacing yellow creature that gives children headaches with the touch of a finger. . . . Arntson has created a detailed and fascinating dystopian world that seems eerily similar to our own, and Terrazzini's illustrations strike just the right note." SLJ

Aronson, Sarah

Beyond lucky. Dial Books for Young Readers 2011 250p $16.99

Grades: 4 5 6 7   **Fic**

1. Mystery fiction 2. Chance -- Fiction 3. Soccer -- Fiction 4. Brothers -- Fiction 5. Jews -- United States -- Fiction

ISBN 978-0-8037-3520-0; 0-8037-3520-0

         LC 2010-28800

Twelve-year-old Ari Fish is sure that the rare trading card he found has changed his luck and that of his soccer team, but after the card is stolen he comes to know that we make our own luck, and that heroes can be fallible.

"Aronson skillfully dodges the predictability of sports-themed books by creating multilayered characters and an intriguing whodunit. . . . Aronson . . . includes a lot of fun on-field action, but the off-field story is just as interesting. . . . Aronson's graceful storytelling will keep even nonsoccer buffs turning pages." Publ Wkly

Asch, Frank

Star jumper; journal of a cardboard genius. Kids Can Press 2006 128p $14.95; pa $5.95

Grades: 3 4 5   **Fic**

1. Brothers -- Fiction 2. Inventors -- Fiction 3. Space vehicles -- Fiction

ISBN 978-1-55337-886-0; 1-55337-886-5; 978-1-55337-887-7 pa; 1-55337-887-3 pa

"Using his astounding scientific ability . . . Alex designs the Star Jumper. This advanced cardboard spacecraft will take him across the galaxy to a brother-free planet—if only he can keep the first grader out of the way until liftoff. The first-person narration is lively and realistic." SLJ

Other titles about Alex and his brother are:

Gravity buster (2007)

Time twister (2008)

Ashley, Bernard

Ronnie's war. Frances Lincoln Children's Books 2011 190p $16.95

Grades: 3 4 5   **Fic**

1. London (England) -- Fiction 2. World War, 1939-1945 -- Fiction 3. Mother-son relationship -- Fiction

ISBN 978-1-84780-162-3; 1-84780-162-5

Eleven-year-old Ronnie and his mother struggle through hardships and joys caused by World War II in England.

"Ashley makes a clear, straightforward narrative that accommodates a surprising amount of information about England during the war, and he does it with a strong story lucid and true enough to engage younger readers. . . . A moving snapshot of a time that still resonates." Kirkus

Atinuke (Author)

★ **Anna** Hibiscus; illustrated by Lauren Tobia. Kane/Miller 2010 109p il

Grades: 1 2 3 4   **Fic**

1. Africa -- Fiction 2. Family life -- Fiction

ISBN 1-935279-73-4 pa; 978-1-935279-73-0 pa

"Linked short stories star Anna Hibiscus, who lives in a large house in a compound in 'amazing Africa' with baby brothers Double and Triple, parents and extended family. . . . The family goes on vacation, an auntie visits from America, Anna learns what it is to do hard work and she gets an invitation to visit her Canadian grandmother. . . . These stories celebrate the extended family and the combination of traditional ways with conveniences of the modern world; they contrast Anna's relatively privileged life with that of others in her country. . . . Tobia's sketches, pen-and-ink with a gray wash, will help early readers visualize the family, unfamiliar customs and clothing and Anna's community." Kirkus

Other titles about Anna Hibiscus are:

Hooray for Anna Hibiscus! (2011)

Good luck, Anna Hibiscus! (2011)

Have fun, Anna Hibiscus! (2011)

Anna Hibiscus' song; [illustrated by] Lauren Tobia. Kane/Miller 2011 un il $15.99

Grades: PreK K   **Fic**

1. Africa -- Fiction 2. Happiness -- Fiction 3. Family life -- Fiction

ISBN 978-1-61067-040-1; 1-61067-040-X

"In amazing Africa, Anna Hibiscus discovers her own special way to show her happiness after trying out what other family members do. . . . Tobia illustrated the Anna Hibiscus chapter books with gray scale drawings, but here she presents Anna in full color. . . . Young readers and listeners will surely embrace her as enthusiastically as chapter-book readers already have." Kirkus Reviews

The **no.** 1 car spotter; illustrated by Warwick Johnson Cadwell. Kane/Miller 2011 il pa $5.99

Grades: 1 2 3   **Fic**
1. Africa -- Fiction 2. Travel -- Fiction 3. Automobiles -- Fiction
ISBN 978-1-61067-051-7; 1-61067-051-5

"Oluwalase Babatunde Benson, otherwise known as No. 1, is not only the best car-spotter in his African village, his electric ideas improve village life." Kirkus Reviews

"Stylized black-and-white illustrations have the energy to match No. 1. . . . A welcome addition to the very small selection of books—particularly early chapter books—about modern Africa." Horn Book

Atkinson, E. J.
★ **I,** Emma Freke; [by] Elizabeth Atkinson. Carolrhoda Books 2010 234p $16.95

Grades: 4 5 6 7   **Fic**
1. Wisconsin -- Fiction 2. Family life -- Fiction 3. Massachusetts -- Fiction 4. Family reunions -- Fiction 5. Single parent family -- Fiction 6. Eccentrics and eccentricities -- Fiction
ISBN 978-0-7613-5604-2; 0-7613-5604-5

LC 2009-38923

Growing up near Boston with her free-spirited mother and old-world grandfather, twelve-year-old Emma has always felt out of place but when she attends the family reunion her father's family holds annually in Wisconsin, she is in for some surprises.

"This rich story of self-acceptance offers readers much to think about. . . . The first-person narrative moves along briskly, with believable dialogue and plenty of humor." Booklist

Atwater, Richard Tupper
★ **Mr.** Popper's penguins; [by] Richard and Florence Atwater; illustrated by Robert Lawson. Little, Brown 1988 138p il $18.99; pa $6.99

Grades: 3 4 5   **Fic**
1. Penguins -- Fiction
ISBN 0-316-05842-4; 0-316-05843-2 pa
Reissue first published in 1938
A Newbery Medal honor book, 1939

When Mr. Popper, a mild little painter and decorator with a taste for books and movies on polar explorations, was presented with a penguin, he named it Captain Cook. From that moment on life was changed for the Popper family

"To the depiction of the penguins in all conceivable moods Robert Lawson [the] artist has brought not only his skill but his individual humor, and his portrayal of the wistful Mr. Popper is memorable." N Y Times Book Rev

Auch, Mary Jane
A **dog** on his own. Holiday House 2008 153p $16.95; pa $6.95

Grades: 3 4 5   **Fic**
1. Dogs -- Fiction
ISBN 978-0-8234-2088-9; 0-8234-2088-4; 978-0-8234-2243-2 pa; 0-8234-2243-7 pa

LC 2008-15963

After a daring escape from the animal shelter, Pearl, Peppy, and K-10—so named because he is one step above all the other canines—explore the outside world while moving from one adventure to another.

"This is a compelling, affectionate story of opening not just one's home, but also one's heart." Booklist

I was a third grade science project; illustrated by Herm Auch. Holiday House 1998 96p il $16.95; pa $5.50

Grades: 2 3 4   **Fic**
1. School stories 2. Hypnotism -- Fiction
ISBN 0-8234-1357-8; 0-440-41606-X

LC 97-41996

While trying to hypnotize his dog for the third grade science fair, Brian accidentally makes his best friend Josh think he's a cat

"Auch's wisecracking third-graders and superb comic timing will have readers rolling on the floor." Booklist
Other titles about Brian are:
I was a third grade bodyguard (2003)
I was a third grade spy (2001)

Journey to nowhere. Holt & Co. 1997 202p hardcover o.p. pa $4.99

Grades: 4 5 6 7   **Fic**
1. New York (State) -- Fiction 2. Frontier and pioneer life -- Fiction
ISBN 0-440-41491-1 pa

LC 96-42249

This is the first title in the Genesee trilogy. In 1815, while traveling by covered wagon to settle in the wilderness of western New York, eleven-year-old Mem experiences a flood and separation from her family

"A well-written, realistic, and thoroughly researched novel." Booklist
Other titles in the Genesee trilogy are
Frozen summer (1998)
The road to home (2000)

One-handed catch; [by] MJ Auch. Henry Holt and Co. 2006 248p $16.95; pa $6.99

Grades: 4 5 6   **Fic**
1. Family life -- Fiction 2. People with disabilities -- Fiction
ISBN 978-0-8050-7900-5; 0-8050-7900-9; 978-0-312-53575-9 pa; 0-312-53575-9 pa

LC 2006-00370

After losing his hand in an accident in his father's butcher shop in 1946, sixth-grader Norman uses hard work and humor to learn to live with his disability and to succeed at baseball, art, and other activities.

"Loosely based on childhood experiences of the author's husband, this story offers both inspiration and useful information, deftly wrapped in an engaging narrative." Booklist

Wing nut; [by] MJ Auch. Henry Holt & Co. 2005 231p $16.95

Grades: 4 5 6   **Fic**
1. Birds -- Fiction 2. Moving -- Fiction 3. Old age -- Fiction
ISBN 0-8050-7531-3

LC 2004-54046

When twelve-year-old Grady and his mother relocate yet again, they find work taking care of an elderly man, who teaches Grady about cars, birds, and what it means to have a home

"Auch's story . . . is engaging. . . . What will attract readers . . . is the author's careful integration of bird lore and the unusual challenges of creating and maintaining a purple martin colony." Booklist

Auxier, Jonathan

★ The **Night** Gardener; by Jonathan Auxier. Amulet Books 2014 368 p. (hardback) $16.95

Grades: 4 5 6 7 **Fic**

1. Ghost stories 2. Young adult literature 3. Horror stories 4. Ghosts -- Fiction 5. Orphans -- Fiction 6. Dwellings -- Fiction 7. Storytelling -- Fiction 8. Household employees -- Fiction 9. Blessing and cursing -- Fiction 10. Brothers and sisters -- Fiction

ISBN 141971144X; 9781419711442

LC 2013047655

School Library Journal (April 1, 2014); Kirkus (March 1, 2014)

"'The Night Gardener' follows two abandoned Irish siblings who travel to work as servants at a creepy, crumbling English manor house. But the house and its family are not quite what they seem. Soon the children are confronted by a mysterious spectre and an ancient curse that threatens their very lives." (Publisher's note)

"Molly's whimsical tales illustrate life's essential lessons even as they entertain. As the characters face the unhealthy pull of the tree's allurements, they grow and change, revealing unexpected personality traits. Storytelling as a force to cope with life's challenges is subtly expressed and adds complexity to the fast-paced plot." SLJ reviews

Peter Nimble and his fantastic eyes; a story. Amulet Books 2011 381p il $16.95

Grades: 4 5 6 7 **Fic**

1. Eye -- Fiction 2. Blind -- Fiction 3. Magic -- Fiction 4. Orphans -- Fiction 5. Thieves -- Fiction

ISBN 978-1-4197-0025-5; 1-4197-0025-1

LC 2010048692

Raised to be a thief, blind orphan Peter Nimble, age ten, steals from a mysterious stranger three pairs of magical eyes, that lead him to a hidden island where he must decide to become a hero or resume his life of crime.

"The fast-paced, episodic story, accompanied by Auxier's occasional pen-and-ink drawings, is inventive, unpredictable, and—like its hero—nimble." Publ Wkly

Avi

A **beginning,** a muddle, and an end; the right way to write writing. with illustrations by Tricia Tusa. Harcourt 2008 164p il $14.95

Grades: 3 4 5 **Fic**

1. Ants -- Fiction 2. Snails -- Fiction 3. Animals -- Fiction 4. Authorship -- Fiction

ISBN 978-0-15-205555-4; 0-15-205555-X

LC 2007-16580

Avon the snail decides to become a writer with the help of his friend Edward the ant, which leads them into a series of adventures involving close encounters with an anteater, a crow, a tree frog, and a hungry fish.

"Clever prose provides thought-provoking scenes full of wit and charm, and well-placed sketches add insightful visuals into the mood of the characters." SLJ

The **Book** Without Words; a fable of medieval magic. Hyperion Books for Children 2005 203p hardcover o.p. pa $5.99

Grades: 5 6 7 8 **Fic**

1. Magic -- Fiction 2. Middle Ages -- Fiction 3. Supernatural -- Fiction 4. Great Britain -- History -- 0-1066 -- Fiction

ISBN 0-7868-0829-2; 0-7868-1659-7 pa

"At the dawning of the Middle Ages, Thorston, an old alchemist, works feverishly to create gold and to dose himself with a concoction that will enable him to live forever. The key to his success lies in a mysterious book with blank pages that can only be read by desperate, green-eyed people. . . . Avi's compelling language creates a dreary foreboding. . . . Clearly this is a story with a message, a true fable. Thoughtful readers will devour its absorbing plot and humorous elements, and learn a 'useful truth' along the way." SLJ

Catch you later, traitor; a novel. by Avi. Algonquin Young Readers 2015 304 p. hbk $16.95

Grades: 4 5 6 7 **Fic**

1. Mystery fiction 2. Communism -- Fiction 3. Families -- Fiction 4. Brooklyn (New York, N.Y.) -- History -- 20th century -- Fiction

ISBN 1616203595; 9781616203597

LC 2014031983

This novel by Avi is set in 1951 Brooklyn, New York. "Pete Collison is a regular kid who loves Sam Spade detective books and radio crime dramas, but when an FBI agent shows up at Pete's doorstep accusing his father of being a Communist, Pete finds himself caught in a real-life mystery. Could there really be Commies in Pete's family? As Pete follows the quickly accumulating clues, he begins to wonder if the truth could put his family's livelihood--and even their freedom--at risk." (Publisher's note)

"Avi's tale of one Brooklyn family living in a time of intolerance effectively explores the natures of suspicion, loyalty, and freedom, following a young protagonist who comes to learn the importance of freedom of speech and 'staying true to your own thoughts.'" Horn Book

Includes bibliographical references

★ **City** of orphans; with illustrations by Greg Ruth. Atheneum Books for Young Readers 2011 350p il $16.99

Grades: 5 6 7 8 **Fic**

1. Mystery fiction 2. Gangs -- Fiction 3. Immigrants -- Fiction 4. Family life -- Fiction 5. New York (N.Y.) -- Fiction 6. Homeless persons -- Fiction 7. Waldorf-Astoria Hotel (New York, N.Y.) -- Fiction.

ISBN 978-1-4169-7102-3; 1-4169-7102-5

LC 2010049229

In 1893 New York, thirteen-year-old Maks, a newsboy, teams up with Willa, a homeless girl, to clear his older sister, Emma, from charges that she stole from the brand new Waldorf Hotel, where she works. Includes historical notes.

"Avi's vivid recreation of the sights and sounds of that time and place is spot on, masterfully weaving accurate historical details with Maks' experiences." Kirkus

Includes bibliographical references

★ **Crispin**: the cross of lead. Hyperion Bks. for Children 2002 $15.99; pa $6.99

Grades: 5 6 7 8 **Fic**

1. Orphans -- Fiction 2. Middle Ages -- Fiction 3. Great Britain -- History -- 1154-1399, Plantagenets -- Fiction

ISBN 0-7868-0828-4; 0-7868-1658-9 pa

LC 2001-51829

Awarded the Newbery Medal, 2001

Falsely accused of theft and murder, an orphaned peasant boy in fourteenth-century England flees his village and meets a larger-than-life juggler who holds a dangerous secret

This "book is a page-turner from beginning to end. . . . A meticulously crafted story, full of adventure, mystery, and action." SLJ

Other titles in this series are:

Crispin at the edge of the world (2006)

Crispin: the end of time (2010)

The **end** of the beginning; being the adventures of a small snail (and an even smaller ant) with illustrations by Tricia Tusa. Harcourt 2004 143p il $14.95; pa $6.95

Grades: 3 4 5 **Fic**

1. Ants -- Fiction 2. Snails -- Fiction

ISBN 0-15-204968-1; 0-15-205532-0 pa

LC 2004-2696

Avon the snail and Edward, a take-charge ant, set off together on a journey to an undetermined destination in search of unspecified adventures.

"Whimsical pen-and-ink sketches add much to this wise little book. It's perfect for reading and discussing." SLJ

Another title about Avon the snail and Edward the ant is:

A beginning, a muddle, and an end (2008)

Ereth's birthday; illustrated by Brian Floca. HarperCollins Pubs. 2000 180p il (Dimwood Forest tales) pa $5.99

Grades: 3 4 5 **Fic**

1. Foxes -- Fiction 2. Animals -- Fiction 3. Porcupines -- Fiction

ISBN 0-380-97734-6; 0-380-80490-5 pa

LC 99-46481

Feeling neglected on his birthday, Ereth, the cantankerous old porcupine, sets out looking for his favorite treat and instead finds himself acting as "mother" to three young fox kits.

"Avi delivers another crackling good read, one shot through with memorable descriptions . . . and crisp, credible dialogue." Publ Wkly

The **fighting** ground. Lippincott 1984 157p hardcover o.p. lib bdg $16.89; pa $5.99; rpt $5.99

Grades: 5 6 7 8 **Fic**

1. United States -- History -- 1775-1783, Revolution -- Fiction

ISBN 0-397-32073-6; 0-397-32074-4 lib bdg; 0-06-440185-5 pa; 9780064401852 rpt

LC 82-47719

"It's April 1776, and the fighting ground is both the farm country of Pennsylvania and the heart of a boy which is 'wonderful ripe for war.' Twenty-four hours transform Jonathan from a cocky 13-year-old, eager to take on the British, into a young man who now knows the horror, the pathos, the ambiguities of war." Voice Youth Advocates

Iron thunder; the battle between the Monitor and the Merrimac, a civil war novel. Hyperion 2007 205p il $15.99; pa $5.99

Grades: 4 5 6 **Fic**

1. Ships -- Fiction 2. Brooklyn (New York, N.Y.) -- Fiction 3. United States -- History -- 1861-1865, Civil War -- Fiction

ISBN 978-1-4231-0446-9; 1-4231-0446-3; 978-1-4231-0518-3 pa; 1-4231-0518-4 pa

"This fascinating adventure taken from U.S. history begins in Brooklyn in 1862, when Tom Carroll, 13, is hired at the Iron Works in Greenpoint for a secret project, derisively known around the borough as Ericsson's Folly. John Ericsson, a Swedish inventor, is trying to build an ironclad ship that can battle the Merrimac, a Confederate ship being outfitted with metal plates in Virginia. . . . Illustrated with period engravings, this is gripping historical fiction from a keenly imagined perspective." Publ Wkly

Midnight magic. Scholastic Press 1999 249p hardcover o.p. pa $5.99

Grades: 5 6 7 8 **Fic**

1. Italy -- Fiction 2. Magicians -- Fiction 3. Renaissance -- Fiction

ISBN 0-590-36035-3; 0-439-24219-3 pa

LC 98-50192

In Italy in 1491, Mangus the magician and his apprentice are summoned to the castle of Duke Claudio to determine if his daughter is indeed being haunted by a ghost.

An "entertaining tale of mystery and intrigue." SLJ

Another title about Mangus and Fabrizio is:

Murder at midnight (2009)

★ **Sophia's** war; a tale of the Revolution. Avi. Beach Lane Books 2012 302 p. (hardcover) $16.99

Grades: 5 6 7 8 **Fic**

1. Traitors -- Fiction 2. Women spies -- Fiction 3. United States -- History -- 1775-1783, Revolution -- Fiction 4. Spies -- Fiction 5. United States -- History -- Revolution, 1775-1783 -- Fiction 6. New York (N.Y.) -- History -- Revolution, 1775-1783 -- Fiction 7. United States -- History -- Revolution, 1775-1783 -- Prisoners and prisons -- Fiction

ISBN 1442414413; 9781442414419; 9781442414426; 9781442414433

LC 2012007962

In this novel by Avi "Sophia Calderwood witnesses the execution of Nathan Hale in New York City, which is newly occupied by the British army . . . in 1776. . . . Recruited as a spy, . . . she becomes aware that someone in the American army might be switching sides, and she uncovers a plot that will grievously damage the Americans if it succeeds. But the identity of the would-be traitor is so shocking that no one believes her, and so Sophia decides to stop the treacherous plot herself." (Publisher's note)

Includes bibliographical references

Traitor's gate. Atheneum Books for Young Readers 2007 351p $17.99

Grades: 5 6 7 8 **Fic**

1. Spies -- Fiction 2. Poverty -- Fiction 3. Family life -- Fiction 4. London (England) -- Fiction

ISBN 0-689-85335-1

When his father is arrested as a debtor in 1849 London, fourteen-year-old John Huffman must take on unexpected responsibilities, from asking a distant relative for help to determining why people are spying on him and his family.

"With plenty of period detail, this action-packed narrative of twists, turns, and treachery is another winner from a master craftsman." SLJ

★ The **true** confessions of Charlotte Doyle; decorations by Ruth E. Murray. Orchard Bks. 1990 215p $16.95; pa $5.99; rpt $16.99

Grades: 5 6 7 **Fic**

1. Sea stories

ISBN 0-531-05893-X; 0-380-72885-0 pa; 9780545477116 rpt

LC 90-30624

A Newbery Medal honor book, 1991

"Charlotte Doyle, thirteen, returning from school in England to join her family in Rhode Island, is deposited on a seedy ship with a ruthless, mad captain and a mutinous crew. Refusing to heed warnings about Captain Jaggery's brutality, Charlotte seeks his guidance and approval only to become his victim." (SLJ)

The author has "fashioned an intriguing, suspenseful, carefully crafted tale, with nonstop action on the high seas." Booklist

Axelrod, Amy

Your friend in fashion, Abby Shapiro. Holiday House 2011 261p il $17.95

Grades: 4 5 6 **Fic**

1. Editors 2. Socialites 3. Letters -- Fiction 4. Spouses of presidents 5. Family life -- Fiction 6. Massachusetts -- Fiction 7. Fashion designers -- Fiction 8. Jews -- United States -- Fiction

ISBN 978-0-8234-2340-8; 0-8234-2340-9

LC 2010-24185

Beginning in 1959, Abby, nearly eleven, writes a series of letters to Jackie Kennedy, each with sketches of outfits she has designed, as she faces family problems, concerns about neighbors, and her own desperate desire for both her first bra and a Barbie doll.

"Abby is an especially memorable protagonist, but all [Axelrod's] characters vibrate with life. . . . Funny, lively, sensitive—a real winner." Kirkus

Babbitt, Natalie

The **eyes** of the Amaryllis. Farrar, Straus & Giroux 1977 127p hardcover o.p. pa $6.99

Grades: 5 6 7 8 **Fic**

1. Sea stories 2. Grandmothers -- Fiction

ISBN 0-312-37008-3 pa

LC 77-11862

"The book succeeds as a well-wrought narrative in which a complex philosophic theme is developed through the balanced, subtle use of symbol and imagery. It is a rare story." Horn Book

"The sea holds countless mysteries and gives up very few secrets; when she does, it is truly a remarkable event, an event that eleven-year-old Geneva Reade experiences when she visits her grandmother who lives in a house by the water's edge. Sent for to tend her Gran through a broken leg, Jenny is put to work, at once, combing the beach for a sign from her grandfather, a captain lost at sea with his ship and crew thirty years ago." Child Book Rev Serv

Jack Plank tells tales. Scholastic 128p il $15.95

Grades: 3 4 5 6 **Fic**

1. Pirates -- Fiction 2. Storytelling -- Fiction

ISBN 978-0-5450-0496-1; 0-5450-0496-9

Jack Plank, a former pirate, tells stories at the boarding house where he lives explaining why he is not well suited to jobs such as farmer, baker, and fisherman.

"Written in a straightforward manner with touches of wry wit, Jack's stories unfold with the economy and assurance that readers expect of Babbitt." Booklist

Kneeknock Rise; story and pictures by Natalie Babbitt. Farrar, Straus & Giroux 1970 117p il hardcover o.p. pa $6.99

Grades: 4 5 6 **Fic**

1. Allegories 2. Superstition -- Fiction

ISBN 0-312-37009-1 pa

A Newbery Medal honor book, 1971

"An enchanting tale imbued with a folk flavor, enlivened with piquant imagery and satiric wit." Booklist

"Did you ever meet a Megrimum? There is one in KneeKnock Rise, and on stormy nights the villagers of Instep tremble in delicious delight as its howls echo over the Mammoth Mountains. Egan learns a lesson when he climbs to meet and conquer the Megrimum." Best Sellers

The **moon** over High Street; Natalie Babbitt. Scholastic 2012 148 p. (alk. paper) $15.95

Grades: 3 4 5 6 7 **Fic**

1. Family -- Fiction 2. Friendship -- Fiction 3. Decision making -- Fiction 4. Adopted children -- Fiction

ISBN 054537636X; 9780545376365

LC 2011926886

This children's novel by Natalie Babbitt "presents 12-year-old Joe. . . . Orphaned shortly after his birth, Joe, who loves the moon, has been raised by his Gran, but after she breaks a hip, he's sent to spend some of the summer with his father's cousin. . . . In nearly idyllic Midville, . . . he inadvertently comes to the attention of the very wealthy factory owner Mr. Boulderwall . . . who decides that he will adopt Joe and raise him to take over his company." (Kirkus)

The **search** for delicious. Farrar, Straus & Giroux 1969 167p il hardcover o.p. pa $6.99

Grades: 5 6 7 8 **Fic**

1. Fantasy fiction

ISBN 0-374-36534-2; 0-312-36982-4 pa

The Prime Minister is compiling a dictionary and when no one at court can agree on the meaning of delicious, the King sends his twelve-year-old messenger to poll the country

"The theme, foolish arguments can lead to great conflict, may not be clear to all children who will enjoy this fantasy." Best Sellers

★ **Tuck** everlasting. Farrar, Straus & Giroux 1975 139p $16; pa $6.99

Grades: 5 6 7 8   **Fic**

1. Fantasy fiction

ISBN 0-374-37848-7; 0-312-36981-6 pa

The Tuck family is confronted with an agonizing situation when they discover that a ten-year-old girl and a malicious stranger now share their secret about a spring whose water prevents one from ever growing any older

"The story is macabre and moral, exciting and excellently written." N Y Times Book Rev

Baccalario, Pierdomenico

The **long-lost map**; [text by Pierdomenico Baccalario; original cover and illustrations by Iacopo Bruno; graphics by Iacopo Bruno and Laura Zuccotti; translation by Leah Janeczko] Scholastic 2006 261p il (Ulysses Moore) $12.99

Grades: 4 5 6   **Fic**

1. Mystery fiction 2. Adventure fiction 3. Twins -- Fiction

ISBN 0-439-77439-X

LC 2005032129

Eleven-year-old twins Jason and Julia, along with their friend Rick, find themselves in ancient Egypt in search of an important map after going through a magical door in their old English mansion.

"The characters are clearly delineated, but adventure is prime here. The illustrations (including handsome pencil drawings) at the beginnings of chapters have a three-dimensional quality in keeping with the book's pretense that readers are looking at the recovered manuscripts of the mysterious Ulysses Moore." Booklist

Bacigalupi, Paolo

Zombie baseball beatdown; by Paolo Bacigalupi. Little, Brown and Co. 2013 304 p. $17

Grades: 5 6 7 8   **Fic**

1. Horror fiction 2. Zombies -- Fiction 3. Packinghouses -- Fiction 4. Hispanic Americans -- Fiction 5. East Indian Americans -- Fiction 6. Racially mixed people -- Fiction

ISBN 0316220787; 9780316220781

LC 2012041463

In this book, middle school friends "Rabi, Miguel, and Joe literally smell trouble wafting from their small town's meatpacking plant, where they find cows living in filthy conditions and behaving oddly. Then the boys' baseball coach turns up moaning 'Brainsssss!' and tries to bite Rabi. When the children discover that meat from the sick cows is being packaged and sent to local supermarkets, they are on their own to prevent a zombie cow apocalypse because no one believes their story." (School Library Journal)

Bacon, Lee

The **nameless** hero; Lee Bacon. Delacorte Press, an imprint of Random House Children's Books, a division of Random House, Inc 2013 304 p. (Joshua Dread) (hardback) $16.99

Grades: 4 5 6 7   **Fic**

1. Fame -- Fiction 2. Camps -- Fiction 3. Friendship

-- Fiction 4. Superheroes -- Fiction 5. Supervillains -- Fiction

ISBN 0385741863; 9780375990281; 9780385741866

LC 2013003310

This is the second book in Lee Bacon's Joshua Dread series. Here, "Joshua Dread, secretly superpowered sixth grader (whose parents are the Dread Duo) is looking forward to a quiet summer with his normal best buddy, Milton, and their superstrong friend, Sophie. Their plans are thwarted when Joshua and Sophie receive invitations to Gyfted & Talented, a summer camp for superpowered teens. . . . Milton forges an invite." Their first mission goes horribly wrong, and things get weird. (Kirkus Reviews)

Baggott, Julianna

The **Prince** of Fenway Park. HarperCollinsPublishers 2009 322p $16.99; lib bdg $17.89

Grades: 4 5 6 7   **Fic**

1. Orphans -- Fiction 2. Baseball -- Fiction 3. Supernatural -- Fiction 4. Father-son relationship -- Fiction 5. Fenway Park (Boston, Mass.) -- Fiction 6. Boston Red Sox (Baseball team) -- Fiction

ISBN 978-0-06-087242-7; 0-06-087242-X; 978-0-06-087243-4 lib bdg; 0-06-087243-8 lib bdg

LC 2008-19666

In the fall of 2004, twelve-year-old Oscar Egg is sent to live with his father in a strange netherworld under Boston's Fenway Park, where he joins the fairies, pooka, banshee, and other beings that are trapped there, waiting for someone to break the eighty-six-year-old curse that has prevented the Boston Red Sox from winning a World Series

"Both whimsical and provocative (the 'N' word crops up in some historical references), this story will engage readers who like clever tales, and also those who enjoy chewing over controversial themes." SLJ

Baker, Deirdre F.

Becca at sea. Groundwood 2007 165p $16.95

Grades: 4 5 6   **Fic**

1. Islands -- Fiction 2. Family life -- Fiction 3. Grandmothers -- Fiction 4. British Columbia -- Fiction

ISBN 978-0-88899-737-1

After Becca's mom becomes pregnant, Becca visits her grandmother at her rustic cabin by the sea alone, and although she dreads it at first, she finds adventures and friendship and returns to the island again and again.

"Each episode enriches the portrait of Becca's memorable extended family with delightfully preposterous, yet insightful detail. . . . This funny, endearing book should find a wide audience." Horn Book

Baker, Matthew

If you find this; by Matthew Baker. Little, Brown & Co. 2015 368 p. illustrations (hardcover) $17

Grades: 4 5 6 7   **Fic**

1. Old age -- Fiction 2. Heirlooms -- Fiction 3. Friendship -- Fiction 4. Grandfathers -- Fiction 5. Lost and found possessions -- Fiction

ISBN 0316240087; 9780316240086

LC 2013044749

In this book, by Matthew Baker, "Nicholas is a math and music genius with no friends and a huge problem: His father has lost his job, and they'll have to sell their house, which holds the only memory Nicholas has of his younger brother.

Just in time, Nicholas's senile grandfather arrives, filled with tales of priceless treasure he has hidden somewhere in town--but where?" (Publisher's note)

"The vivid setting, complex characters, and original writing style result in a story with lasting impact. Reminiscent of Louis Sachar's Holes (1998), this is a rich, captivating tale about family and redemption that redefines the meaning of treasure." Booklist

Baker-Smith, Grahame

Farther; Grahame Baker-Smith. Templar Publishing 2010 32 p. (reinforced) $17.99

Grades: K 1 2   **Fic**
1. Flight -- Fiction 2. Picture books for children 3. Father-son relationship -- Fiction 4. Flight -- Pictorial works 5. Ambition -- Pictorial works 6. Fathers and sons -- Pictorial works

ISBN 0763663700; 9780763663704
                                                           LC 2011431018

In this Kate Greenaway Medal children's picture book, by Grahame Baker-Smith, "a boy lovingly remembers . . . [how] his father worked ceaselessly to fashion a flying machine. . . . That dream is never to be realized, as the day comes when the father dons a uniform and leaves for a great war, never to return. Years later, the son, now grown, resumes work on the machine, succeeds and then shares the vision with his own son." (Kirkus Reviews)

Balliett, Blue

★ **Chasing** Vermeer; illustrated by Brett Helquist. Scholastic Press 2004 254p il $16.95

Grades: 5 6 7 8   **Fic**
1. Artists 2. Painters 3. Mystery fiction 4. Art -- Fiction

ISBN 0-439-37294-1
                                                           LC 2002-152106

When seemingly unrelated and strange events start to happen and a precious Vermeer painting disappears, eleven-year-olds Petra and Calder combine their talents to solve an international art scandal.

Balliett's purpose "seems to be to get children to think—about relationships, connections, coincidences, and the subtle language of artwork. . . . [This is] a book that offers children something new upon each reading. . . . Helquist . . . outdoes himself here, providing an interactive mystery in his pictures." Booklist

Other titles about Petra and Calder are:
The Wright 3 (2006)
The Calder game (2008)

The **Danger** Box. Scholastic Press 2010 306p $16.99

Grades: 5 6 7 8   **Fic**
1. Naturalists 2. Travel writers 3. Diaries -- Fiction 4. Writers on science 5. Antiques -- Fiction 6. Michigan -- Fiction 7. Family life -- Fiction 8. Grandparents -- Fiction

ISBN 978-0-439-85209-8; 0-439-85209-9
                                                           LC 2010-16622

In small-town Michigan, twelve-year-old Zoomy and his new friend Lorrol investigate the journal found inside a mysterious box and find family secrets and a more valuable treasure, while a dangerous stranger watches and waits.

"This highly satisfying story will enlighten readers even as it inspires them to think about their own danger boxes." SLJ

Hold fast; by Blue Balliett. Scholastic Press 2013 288 p. (jacketed hardcover) $17.99

Grades: 3 4 5 6   **Fic**
1. Theft -- Fiction 2. Mystery fiction 3. Smuggling -- Fiction 4. Kidnapping -- Fiction 5. Chicago (Ill.) -- Fiction 6. Missing persons -- Fiction 7. Homeless persons -- Fiction 8. Mystery and detective stories 9. Fathers and daughters -- Fiction

ISBN 0545299888; 9780545299886
                                                           LC 2012041035

This book focuses on "the Pearl family: Dash, Summer, 11-year-old Early, and the little Jubie. Do they have a lot? Well, yes, they have Dash's love of words, their devotion to each other, and their dream: to have a home. Trying to help that dream along, Dash, a page at the Chicago Public Library, makes extra money inventorying a private collection of old books. One . . . day, Dash disappears, and the family must move to a shelter after an odd robbery sees their . . . apartment destroyed." (Booklist)

"The four Pearls live in a one-room apartment in South Side Chicago, rejoicing in their love for reading and celebrating words and poetic rhythms while keeping their eye on the dream of a house of their own...This is an engaging mystery in which books are both the problem and the solution, and the author shows that the fight to hold fast to your dreams rewards those who persevere. Excellent." SLJ

Pieces and players; Blue Balliett; [edited by] David Levithan. Scholastic Press 2015 320 p. illustrations $17.99

Grades: 5 6 7 8   **Fic**
1. Mystery fiction 2. Art thefts -- Fiction 3. Art museums -- Fiction

ISBN 054529990X; 9780545299909
                                                           LC 2014947736

In this children's book, by Blue Balliett, "thirteen extremely valuable pieces of art have been stolen from one of the most secretive museums in the world. A Vermeer has vanished. A Manet is missing. And nobody has any idea where they and the other eleven artworks might be . . . or who might have stolen them. . . . Calder, Petra, and Tommy are no strangers to heists and puzzles. Now they've been matched with two new sleuths -- Zoomy . . . and Early." (Publisher's note)

"This time it's a small family museum and 13 missing pieces of art providing the mystery that brings back characters met in previous titles. Tommy, Petra, and Calder are joined by Early Pearl and Zoomy Chamberlain. With all five kids led by their teacher Mrs. Hussey, each of the detective's special skills add to their understanding and help them arrive at the solution. Fans of the previous books will be delighted as these characters continue with their familiar predilections such as Calder's pentominoes clacking in his pockets. . . . Fun and engaging; a fitting addition for readers addicted to these art mysteries." SLJ

Banerjee, Anjali

★ **Looking** for Bapu. Wendy Lamb Books 2006 162p hardcover o.p. pa $6.50

Grades: 4 5 6 7   **Fic**
1. Hindus -- Fiction 2. Bereavement -- Fiction 3.

Grandfathers -- Fiction 4. East Indians -- United States -- Fiction

ISBN 978-0-385-74657-1; 0-385-90894-6; 978-0-553-49425-9 pa; 0-553-49425-2 pa

LC 2006-02021

When his beloved grandfather dies, eight-year-old Anu feels that his spirit is near and will stop at nothing to bring him back, including trying to become a Hindu holy man.

"With episodes that ring true to a boy's perspective, Banerjee's novel provides discussable issues and multicultural insights as well as humor and emotion. An excellent read aloud." Booklist

Seaglass summer. Wendy Lamb Books 2010 163p il $15.99; lib bdg $18.99

Grades: 4 5 6   **Fic**

1. Uncles -- Fiction 2. Veterinarians -- Fiction 3. Washington (State) -- Fiction 4. East Indian Americans -- Fiction

ISBN 978-0-385-73567-4; 0-385-73567-7; 978-0-385-90555-8 lib bdg; 0-385-90555-6 lib bdg

LC 2009-25468

"Eleven-year-old Poppy wants to be a veterinarian like her uncle Sanjay. So while her parents are in India visiting relatives, she spends several weeks with him on Nisqually Island, Washington, helping out at his Furry Friends Animal Clinic. Episodic chapters focus on the people and animals that Poppy meets, [and] her efforts to do a good job. . . . There are many moving events here. . . . Sometimes amusing, sometimes gross, and always true to itself, this should find a wide readership. Pencil illustrations enliven the chapter headings." Booklist

Banks, Angelica

Finding Serendipity; Angelica Banks; illustrations by Stevie Lewis. Henry Holt & Co. 2015 281 p. illustrations (hardcover) $16.99

Grades: 4 5 6   **Fic**

1. Magic -- Fiction 2. Adventure fiction 3. Books and reading -- Fiction 4. Authors -- Fiction 5. Authorship -- Fiction 6. Adventure and adventurers -- Fiction

ISBN 162779154X; 9781627791540

LC 2014037083

In this book, "when Tuesday McGillicuddy goes to check on her author mother's progress, Serendipity has disappeared, with only a mysterious box containing the words 'The End' offering a clue to her whereabouts. Tuesday types her own story in hopes that it will bring her to her mother at The End, and her words take on the form of silver thread, encircling Tuesday and her loyal dog, Baxterr, and pulling them out the window into the night." (Bulletin of the Center for Children's Books)

"Spunky characters; spot-on pacing, providing perfectly timed plot revelations; and fully imagined worlds make this a charming winner for curling up with a good book or classroom read-alouds." Booklist

Banks, Kate

Dillon Dillon. Foster Bks. 2002 150p hardcover o.p. pa $5.95

Grades: 4 5 6 7   **Fic**

1. Loons -- Fiction 2. Adoption -- Fiction 3. Family

life -- Fiction 4. New Hampshire -- Fiction

ISBN 0-374-31786-0; 0-374-41715-6 pa

LC 2001-33207

During the summer that he turns ten years old, Dillon Dillon learns the surprising story behind his name and develops a relationship with three loons, living on the lake near his family's New Hampshire cabin, that help him make sense of his life

This "succeeds as an emotionally intricate, quietly well-observed, symbolically charged novel." Horn Book

Banks, Lynne Reid

The **Indian** in the cupboard; illustrated by Brock Cole. Doubleday 1980 181p il $16.95; pa $6.99

Grades: 5 6 7 8   **Fic**

1. Fantasy fiction

ISBN 0-385-17051-3; 0-375-84753-7 pa

LC 79-6533

A nine-year-old boy receives a plastic Indian, a cupboard, and a little key for his birthday and finds himself involved in adventure when the Indian comes to life in the cupboard and befriends him

Other titles in this series are:

The key to the Indian (1998)

The mystery of the cupboard (1993)

The return of the Indian (1986)

The secret of the Indian (1989)

Bar-el, Dan

Audrey (cow) an oral account of a most daring escape, based more or less on a true story. Dan Bar-el. Tundra Books of Northern New York 2014 240 p. illustrations (hardcover) $19.99

Grades: 4 5 6   **Fic**

1. Farms -- Fiction 2. Cattle -- Fiction 3. cows -- fiction 4. animals -- fiction 5. escapes -- fiction

ISBN 1770496025; 9781770496026

LC 2013953683

In this children's book, by Dan Bar-El, "Audrey is a cow with poetry in her blood, who yearns for the greener pastures beyond Bittersweet Farms. But when Roy the horse tells this bovine dreamer that she is headed for Abbot's War, the slaughter house, Audrey knows that she must leave her home and friends sooner than she ever imagined. With the help of a whole crew of animals and humans alike, Audrey attempts to escape the farm she lives on--and certain death." (Publisher's note)

"Move aside Wilbur and Babe. There's a new farmyard hero in town, and she has no desire to end up hamburger. Audrey isn't like the other cows. They might accept their lot as 'food cows,' but she has other ideas. After her mother is taken away to a slaughterhouse, the feisty Charolais concocts an elaborate escape for herself using the expertise and help of her barnyard friends. However, the escape itself proves to be only half the battle, and Audrey's experiences in the wild forest with its unpredictable denizens put both brains and moxie to the test. In a multiple-perspective, documentary-like format, each animal tells its part of the story with terrific humor and personality. . . . the many voices make the book an ideal read-aloud for a classroom and ideal fodder for reader s' theater. . . . Part Great Escape, part Hatchet, part Charlotte's Web, all wonderful." Kirkus

Barden, Stephanie

★ **Cinderella** Smith; illustrations by Diane Goode. Harper 2011 148p il

Grades: 3 4 5   **Fic**

1. School stories 2. Friendship -- Fiction 3. Family life -- Fiction 4. Stepsisters -- Fiction 5. Tap dancing -- Fiction 6. Seattle (Wash.) -- Fiction

ISBN 0-06-196423-9; 978-0-06-196423-7

LC 2010015980

Cast off by her old friends, Cinderella agrees to help a new student deal with the stepsisters she will soon have, and meantime, a former friend tries to prevent Cinderella from dancing the lead in their tap recital.

"Line illustrations by the gifted Goode enhance the lightheartedness and fun of the story. . . . The awkwardness Cinderella feels with her former friends is palpable yet not overly serious, and her inclusive enjoyment of life is contagious. The resolution to the stepsister problem is especially satisfying." Booklist

The **super** secret mystery; by Stephanie Barden; illustrations by Diane Goode. Harpercollins Childrens Books 2013 144 p. (Cinderella Smith) (hardcover bdgs) $16.99

Grades: 3 4 5   **Fic**

1. Report writing 2. Mystery fiction 3. Libraries -- Fiction 4. Schools -- Fiction 5. Endangered species -- Fiction 6. Mystery and detective stories

ISBN 0062004433; 9780062004437

LC 2012050667

In this book by Stephanie Barden, "third in the Cinderella Smith chapter-book series, Cinderella is excited to write a report on an endangered species. She can't wait to investigate this important environmental issue. But every book she needs to do her research has disappeared from the library! That won't stop Cinderella. She won't be stopped by the mean-girl bullies and will follow every clue until she solves the mystery." (Publisher's note)

Barker, M. P.

A **difficult** boy. Holiday House 2008 298p $16.95; pa $7.95

Grades: 5 6 7 8   **Fic**

1. Massachusetts -- Fiction 2. Contract labor -- Fiction 3. Irish Americans -- Fiction 4. Swindlers and swindling -- Fiction

ISBN 978-0-8234-2086-5; 0-8234-2086-8; 978-0-8234-2244-9 pa; 0-8234-2244-5 pa

LC 2007-37059

In Farmington, Massachusetts, in 1839, nine-year-old Ethan experiences hardships as an indentured servant of the wealthy Lyman family alongside Daniel, a boy scorned simply for being Irish, and the boys bond as they try to right a terrible wrong.

"A memorable tale of friendship and a fascinating glimpse into mid-19th-century Massachusetts." SLJ

Mending horses; by M.P. Barker. Holiday House 2014 309 p. (hardcover) $17.95

Grades: 5 6 7 8   **Fic**

1. Orphans -- Fiction 2. Prejudices -- Fiction 3. Child abuse -- Fiction 4. Irish Americans -- Fiction 5. Peddlars -- Fiction 6. Sex role -- Fiction 7. New England -- History -- 1775-1865 -- Fiction

ISBN 0823429482; 9780823429486

LC 2013019208

In this book, by M.P. Barker, "Daniel Linnehan is an indentured servant no more. He has his papers, his beloved horse, Ivy, and a new direction in life. But an Irish teenager, wearing fine clothes and riding an even finer horse, is asking for trouble. After a terrible misunderstanding leaves Daniel beaten, the peddler Jonathan Stocking takes Daniel under his wing. But Billy, another Irish youngster traveling with Mr. Stocking, is not thrilled that the two must work together." (Publishe'rs note)

"In 1830s New England, Irish immigrant Daniel, formerly indentured as a servant, gains his freedom only to be accused of stealing his former master's horse, a rumor that quickly escalates to include mass murder and leads to his near lynching...Readers who discovered the joy and agony of historical fiction in L. A. Meyer's Bloody Jack (2002) will find this vivid account every bit as compelling." Booklist

Barnett, Mac

★ The **case** of the case of mistaken identity; illustrations by Adam Rex. Simon & Schuster Books for Young Readers 2009 179p il (The Brixton Brothers) $14.99

Grades: 4 5 6   **Fic**

1. Mystery fiction 2. Police -- Fiction 3. Quilts -- Fiction 4. Librarians -- Fiction 5. Books and reading -- Fiction

ISBN 978-1-4169-7815-2; 1-4169-7815-1

LC 2008-43305

When twelve-year-old Steve Brixton, a fan of Bailey Brothers detective novels, is mistaken for a real detective, he must elude librarians, police, and the mysterious Mr. E as he seeks a missing quilt containing coded information.

The book provides "action and adventure but adds a level of humor that will sometimes have readers laughing out loud. Similarly, Rex's illustrations have a mid-twentieth-century look, and in an accomplished, deadpan manner, offer one of the book's funniest moments." Booklist

Other titles in this series are:

The ghostwriter secret (2010)

It happened on a train (2011)

The **terrible** two; by Mac Barnett & Jory John; illustrated by Kevin Cornell. Harry N. Abrams 2015 224 p. illustrations (The terrible two) (hardback) $13.95

Grades: 4 5 6 7 8   **Fic**

1. School stories 2. Practical jokes 3. Humorous stories 4. Tricks -- Fiction 5. Schools -- Fiction 6. Practical jokes -- Fiction 7. Moving, Household -- Fiction

ISBN 1419714910; 9781419714917

LC 2014027503

In this book by Mac Barnett and Jory John "Miles Murphy is not happy to be moving. In his old school, everyone knew him as the town's best prankster, but Miles quickly discovers that Yawnee Valley already has a prankster, and a great one. If Miles is going to take the title from this mystery kid, he is going to have to raise his game. It's prankster against prankster in an epic war of trickery, until the two finally decide to join forces and pull off the biggest prank ever seen." (Publisher's note)

"Two rival pranksters headline this boisterous series opener set in Yawnee Valley, "the cow capital of the United States, this side of the Mississippi, excluding a couple of towns that cheat."... Eventually, Miles finally forms a partnership with his unlikely nemesis to create a "secret society founded on mutual admiration and the joy of pranking." Cornell's (The Chicken Squad) b&w cartoons layer on the laughs, especially when portraying the megalomaniacal Principal Barkin, and Barnett and John's deadpan writing lets Yawnee Valley's absurdity shine." PW

Barnhill, Kelly Regan

★ The **mostly** true story of Jack; by Kelly Barnhill. Little, Brown 2011 323p il $16.99

Grades: 5 6 7 8 **Fic**

1. Iowa -- Fiction 2. Magic -- Fiction 3. Friendship -- Fiction 4. Family life -- Fiction

ISBN 978-0-316-05670-0; 0-316-05670-7

LC 2010044934

Jack is practically invisible at home, but when his parents send him to Hazelwood, Iowa, to spend a summer with his odd aunt and uncle, he suddenly makes friends, is beaten up by the town bully, and is plotted against by the richest man in town.

"A truly splendid amalgamation of mystery, magic and creeping horror will spellbind the middle-grade set. . . . The mystery deepens with each chapter, revealing exactly the right amount with each step. Answers are doled out so meticulously that readers will be continually intrigued rather than frustrated. The result is the ultime page-turner." Kirkus

★ The **witch's** boy; Kelly Barnhill. Algonquin Young Readers 2014 384 p. $16.95

Grades: 5 6 7 8 **Fic**

1. Fantasy 2. Magic -- Fiction 3. Twins -- Fiction 4. Witches -- Fiction 5. Brothers -- Fiction 6. Friendship -- Fiction 7. Robbers and outlaws -- Fiction

ISBN 9781616203511

LC 2014014704

In this juvenile fantasy novel, by Kelly Regan Barnhill, "when Ned and his identical twin brother tumble from their raft into a raging river, only Ned survives. Villagers are convinced the wrong boy lived. But when a Bandit King comes to steal the magic Ned's mother, a witch, is meant to protect, it's Ned who safeguards the magic and summons the strength to protect his family and community." (Publisher's note)

"The story of Ned, the witch's boy, and Aine, the Bandit King's daughter, begins when Ned survives a drowning accident that kills his twin brother. Ned's mother, known as Sister Witch, binds dead Tam's soul to the living Ned. She does this to save Ned, who is ill from his experience, but the dire magic damages him in the process...The writing is beautiful and lyrical, but keeps pace with an action-packed story. Powerful themes of grief, redemption, forgiveness, sacrifice, and generosity are all present. Recommend this title to those who like retellings and strong, narrative fantasy." (VOYA)

Barnholdt, Lauren

Girl meets ghost; by Lauren Barnholdt. Aladdin 2013 224 p. (alk. paper) $15.99

Grades: 4 5 6 7 **Fic**

1. Ghost stories 2. School stories 3. Mystery fiction 4. Dead -- Fiction 5. Ghosts -- Fiction 6. Schools -- Fiction 7. Middle schools -- Fiction 8. Psychic ability -- Fiction 9. Mystery and detective stories

ISBN 1442442468; 9781442442467

LC 2012032234

In this children's story, by Lauren Barnholt, "a tween girl becomes a reluctant medium. . . . There's an old saying that 'dead men tell no tales'--but that saying is definitely not true. Just ask twelve-year-old Kendall Williams, who can't get dead people to stop talking to her. . . . It's pretty frustrating being able to hear and see people that no one else can. . . . But Kendall is going to have to learn how to deal, because the only way to quiet the dead is to help them." (Publisher's note)

Barrett, Tracy

The **100**-year-old secret. Henry Holt and Co. 2008 157p (The Sherlock files) $15.95

Grades: 4 5 6 7 **Fic**

1. Mystery fiction 2. Siblings -- Fiction 3. Great Britain -- Fiction

ISBN 978-0-8050-8340-8; 0-8050-8340-5

LC 2007034004

Xena and Xander Holmes, an American brother and sister living in London for a year, discover that Sherlock Holmes was their great-great-great grandfather when they are inducted into the Society for the Preservation of Famous Detectives and given his unsolved casebook, from which they attempt to solve the case of a famous missing painting

"The main characters are observant, bright, and gifted with powers of deduction." SLJ

Other titles in this series are:
The beast of Blackslope (2009)
The case that time forgot (2010)
The missing heir (2011)

Barrie, J. M.

Peter Pan and Wendy; illustrated by Robert Ingpen; foreword by David Barrie. Centenary edition; Sterling 2010 216p il $19.95

Grades: 3 4 5 6 **Fic**

1. Fairy tales

ISBN 978-1-4027-2868-6; 1-4027-2868-9

First published 1911 by Scribner with title: Peter and Wendy; a reissue of the 2004 edition published by Orchard Books

The adventures of the three Darling children in Neverland with Peter Pan, the boy who would not grow up.

This "edition is notable for its painterly illustrations, which reflect touches of Sendak, Wyeth, the pre-Raphaelites, and others. The overall effect of the art is impressionistic, and the book itself is handsome." Horn Book Guide

Barron, T. A.

★ The **lost** years of Merlin. Philomel Bks. 1996 326p $19.99; pa $7.99

Grades: 5 6 7 8 **Fic**

1. Fantasy fiction 2. Merlin (Legendary character) -- Fiction

ISBN 978-0-399-23018-1; 978-0-441-00668-7 pa

LC 96-33920

"A boy, hurled on the rocks by the sea, regains consciousness unable to remember anything—not his parents, not his own name. He is sure that the secretive Branwen is not his mother, despite her claims, and that Emrys is not his real name. The two soon find themselves feared because of Branwen's healing abilities and Emrys' growing powers. . . . Barron has created not only a magical land populated by remarkable beings but also a completely magical tale, filled with ancient Celtic and Druidic lore, that will enchant readers." Booklist

Other titles in this series are:
The seven songs of Merlin (1997)
The fires of Merlin (1998)
The mirror of Merlin (1999)
The wings of Merlin (2000)
The book of magic (2011)

Barrow, Randi G.

Saving Zasha; by Randi Barrow. Scholastic Press 2011 229p $16.99

Grades: 4 5 6 7   **Fic**

1. Dogs -- Fiction 2. Russia -- Fiction 3. Journalists -- Fiction 4. Single parent family -- Fiction 5. World War, 1939-1945 -- Fiction

ISBN 978-0-545-20632-7; 0-545-20632-4

LC 2010-16899

In 1945 Russia, those who own German shepherds are considered traitors, but thirteen-year-old Mikhail and his family are determined to keep the dog a dying man brought them, while his classmate Katia strives to learn his secret.

"Mikhail's sense of humor, concern for his family, and love of Zasha are all readily apparent in his narration, which smoothly incorporates background information for readers unfamiliar with 20th-century Russian life and history. . . . Barrow's novel is quick reading yet weighty, and captures the prejudices and aftereffects of war." Publ Wkly

Barrows, Annie

★ **Ivy** + Bean; written by Annie Barrows; illustrated by Sophie Blackall. Chronicle Books 2006 113p il $14.95; pa $5.99

Grades: 1 2 3   **Fic**

1. Friendship -- Fiction

ISBN 978-0-8118-4903-6; 0-8118-4903-1; 978-0-8118-4909-8 pa; 0-8118-4909-0 pa

LC 2005023944

When seven-year-old Bean plays a mean trick on her sister, she finds unexpected support for her antics from Ivy, the new neighbor, who is less boring than Bean first suspected.

"The deliciousness here is in the details, with both girls drawn distinctly and with flair. . . . Even with all the text's strong points, what takes the book to a higher level is Blackall's artwork, which captures the girls' spirit." Booklist

Other titles about Ivy and Bean are:
Ivy + Bean and the ghost that had to go (2006)
Ivy + Bean break the fossil record (2007)
Ivy + Bean take care of the babysitter (2008)
Ivy + Bean: bound to be bad (2009)
Ivy + Bean: doomed to dance (2009)
Ivy + Bean: what's the big idea? (2010)

The **magic** half. Bloomsbury Children's Books 2008 211p $15.95; pa $6.99

Grades: 3 4 5   **Fic**

1. Twins -- Fiction 2. Sisters -- Fiction

ISBN 978-1-59990-132-9; 1-59990-132-3; 978-1-59990-358-3 pa; 1-59990-358-X pa

LC 2007-23551

Eleven-year-old Miri Gill feels left out in her family, which has two sets of twins and her, until she travels back in time to 1935 and discovers Molly, her own lost twin, and brings her back to the present day.

"Readers will savor the author's lively observations . . . while the heroine's adaptability and independent thinking endow her with the appeal of a Ramona Quimby or a Clementine." Publ Wkly

Barry, Dave

Peter & the shadow thieves; by Dave Barry and Ridley Pearson; illustrations by Greg Call. Disney Editions/Hyperion Books for Children 2006 556p il $18.99

Grades: 5 6 7   **Fic**

1. Fairy tales 2. Adventure fiction

ISBN 0-7868-3787-X

LC 2005-56033

Sequel to Peter and the starcatchers (2004)

Realizing that Molly and the other Starcatchers are in danger when the sinister being Lord Ombra visits the island and seems to control people through their shadows, Peter and Tinker Bell travel to England to help save the stardust. "Age ten and up." (N Y Times Book Rev)

This "is filled with enough rollicking, death-defying adventure to satisfy anyone." SLJ

Followed by Peter and the secret of Rundoon (2007)

Peter and the secret of Rundoon; by Dave Barry and Ridley Pearson; illustrations by Greg Call. Disney Editions/Hyperion Books for Children 2007 482p il $18.99

Grades: 5 6 7   **Fic**

1. Fairy tales 2. Adventure fiction

ISBN 0-7868-3788-8; 978-0-7868-3788-5

LC 2007006306

Sequel to Peter and the shadow thieves (2006)

Fearing that the sinister Lord Ombra was not destroyed, Peter and Molly travel to the land of Rundoon, which is ruled by the evil King Zarboff.

"This is a fun, intense, and totally worthwhile adventure." SLJ

Followed by Peter and the Sword of Mercy (2009)

Peter and the starcatchers; by Dave Barry and Ridley Pearson; illustrations by Greg Call. Hyperion 2004 451p il $17.99; pa $7.99

Grades: 5 6 7   **Fic**

1. Fairy tales 2. Adventure fiction 3. Pirates -- Fiction

ISBN 0-7868-5445-6; 0-7868-4907-X pa

LC 2004-55275

Soon after Peter, an orphan, sets sail from England on the ship Never Land, he befriends Molly, a young Starcatcher, whose mission is to guard a trunk of magical stardust from a greedy pirate and the native inhabitants of a remote island. "Age ten and up." (N Y Times Book Rev)

"The authors plait multiple story lines together in short, fast-moving chapters. . . . Capitalizing on familiar material, this adventure is carefully crafted to set the stage for Peter's later exploits. This smoothly written page-turner just might send readers back to the original." SLJ

Peter and the Sword of Mercy; by Dave Barry and Ridley Pearson; illustrations by Greg Call. Disney/Hyperion Books 2009 515p il $18.99

Grades: 5 6 7   **Fic**

1. Fairy tales 2. Adventure fiction

ISBN 978-1-4231-2134-3; 1-4231-2134-1

Sequel to: Peter and the secret of Rundoon (2007)

CHILDREN'S CORE COLLECTION
TWENTY-SECOND EDITION

James, one of Peter's original Lost Boys, is now working for Scotland Yard and suspects that the heir to England's throne, Prince Albert Edward, is under the influence of shadow creatures who are after starstuff hidden in an underground vault which has only one key: the Sword of Mercy.

"This adventure is fast and intense, and readers will feel compelled to find out what happens next." VOYA

Followed by: The bridge to Never Land (2011)

Barshaw, Ruth McNally

Ellie McDoodle: have pen, will travel; written and illustrated by Ruth McNally Barshaw. Bloomsbury Children's Books 2007 170p il $11.95; pa $5.99

Grades: 2 3 4 5   **Fic**

1. Camping -- Fiction 2. Cousins -- Fiction

ISBN 978-1-58234-745-5; 1-58234-745-X; 978-1-59990-276-0 pa; 1-59990-276-1 pa

LC 2006-28424

Eleven-year-old Ellie McDoodle illustrates her sketchbook with chronicles of her adventures and mishaps while camping with her cousins, aunt, and uncle.

"The engaging text reflects a contemporary preadolescent sensibility and is chock-full of clean, distinguished line drawings on each spread." SLJ

Other titles about Ellie McDoodle are:

Ellie McDoodle: new kid in school (2008)

Ellie McDoodle: best friends fur-ever (2010)

Bartoletti, Susan Campbell

★ The **boy** who dared. Scholastic Press 2008 202p $16.99

Grades: 5 6 7 8   **Fic**

1. Courage -- Fiction 2. Underground leaders 3. National socialism -- Fiction 4. Germany -- History -- 1933-1945 -- Fiction

ISBN 978-0-439-68013-4; 0-439-68013-1

LC 2007014166

In October, 1942, seventeen-year-old Helmuth Hübener, imprisoned for distributing anti-Nazi leaflets, recalls his past life and how he came to dedicate himself to bringing the truth about Hitler and the war to the German people.

Bartoletti "does and excellent job of conveying the political climate surrounding Hitler's ascent to power, seamlessly integrating a complex range of socioeconomic conditions into her absorbing drama." Publ Wkly

Base, Graeme

Enigma; a magical mystery. [by] Graeme Base. Abrams Books for Young Readers 2008 36p il $19.95

Grades: 3 4 5   **Fic**

1. Picture puzzles 2. Stories in rhyme 3. Badgers -- Fiction 4. Ciphers -- Fiction 5. Rabbits -- Fiction 6. Magicians -- Fiction 7. Grandfathers -- Fiction

ISBN 978-0-8109-7245-2; 0-8109-7245-X

LC 2007042397

When Bertie the badger visits his grandfather at a retirement home for magicians, he learns that his grandfather's rabbit, Enigma, has disappeared along with everyone's magical things, and the reader is invited to help break a code to find the items hidden throughout the book. Includes a built-in decoder.

"Readers could simply hunt for the missing objects, which Base conceals within elaborately detailed paintings, but then they would miss out on the tricky fun of mastering

several codes also embedded in the book. ... A set of bonus challenges will keep kids (and older siblings) poring closely over the pages for weeks, enthralled." Publ Wkly

Baskin, Nora Raleigh, 1961-

★ **Anything** but typical. Simon & Schuster Books for Young Readers 2009 195p il $15.99

Grades: 4 5 6 7   **Fic**

1. School stories 2. Autism -- Fiction 3. Authorship -- Fiction 4. Family life -- Fiction 5. Young adult literature -- Works

ISBN 1416963782; 9781416963783

LC 2008-20994

ALA Schneider Family Book Award Honor Book (2010)

Jason, a twelve-year-old who wants to become a writer, relates what life is like as he tries to make sense of his world. "Grades six to nine." (Bull Cent Child Books)

"This is an enormously difficult subject, but Baskin, without dramatics or sentimentality, makes it universal." Booklist

Runt; Nora Raleigh Baskin. Simon & Schuster Books for Young Readers 2013 208 p. (hardback) $15.99

Grades: 5 6 7 8   **Fic**

1. School stories 2. Female friendship 3. Dogs -- Fiction 4. Schools -- Fiction 5. Bullying -- Fiction 6. Popularity -- Fiction 7. Middle schools -- Fiction 8. Online social networks -- Fiction

ISBN 1442458070; 9781442458079; 9781442458086

LC 2012049461

This book shows "the day-to-day torments of students in a sixth-grade class. In a series of brief vignettes, [Nora Raleigh Baskin] moves between classmates including 'Smelly-Girl' Elizabeth, who can't shake the lingering scent (or shed hair) of her mother's dog-sitting business; Elizabeth's nemesis, Maggie, who . . . hasn't been able to repair her fallout with her artistically talented former best friend Freida; and Stewart and Matthew, two athletes whose rivalry leads to a fight." (Publishers Weekly)

The **truth** about my Bat Mitzvah. Simon & Schuster Books for Young Readers 2008 138p $15.99; pa $5.99

Grades: 5 6 7 8   **Fic**

1. Jews -- Fiction 2. Bat mitzvah -- Fiction 3. Grandmothers -- Fiction

ISBN 978-1-4169-3558-2; 1-4169-3558-4; 978-1-4169-7469-7 pa; 1-4169-7469-5 pa

LC 2007-01248

After her beloved grandmother, Nana, dies, non-religious twelve-year-old Caroline becomes curious about her mother's Jewish ancestry.

"Readers will identify with Caroline and her preoccupations. . . . This quick read will be a hit with preteens contemplating their own identities." Booklist

Bateman, Colin

Running with the Reservoir Pups; [by] Colin Bateman. Delacorte Press 2005 263p (Eddie & the gang with no name) hardcover o.p. lib bdg $17.99

Grades: 5 6 7 8   **Fic**

1. Gangs -- Fiction 2. Divorce -- Fiction 3. Northern Ireland -- Fiction

ISBN 0-385-73244-9; 0-385-90268-9 lib bdg

LC 2004-43912

First published 2003 in the United Kingdom

When his parents divorce and his mother moves with him to Belfast, Northern Ireland, twelve-year-old Eddie contends with the Reservoir Pups, a gang of children who rule his neighborhood.

This "author's hilarious, dark Northern Irish wit, penchant for action-packed mayhem, sense of irony, and snappy dialogue are all evident in this [book]." SLJ

Another title about Eddie is:

Bring me the head of Oliver Plunkett (2005)

Bateson, Catherine

Being Bee. Holiday House 2007 126p il $16.95; pa $7.95

Grades: 4 5 6   Fic

1. Australia -- Fiction 2. Family life -- Fiction 3. Guinea pigs -- Fiction 4. Father-daughter relationship -- Fiction

ISBN 978-0-8234-2104-6; 0-8234-2104-X; 978-0-8234-2208-1 pa; 0-8234-2208-9 pa

LC 2006-101561

Bee faces friction at home and at school when her widowed father begins seriously dating Jazzi, who seems to take over the house and their lives, but as shared secrets and common interests finally begin to draw them together, Jazzi accidentally makes a terrible mistake.

"Bee's emotions are perspectives are honest and clearly presented. . . . She is a likable, believable character." SLJ

Magenta McPhee. Holiday House 2010 170p $16.95

Grades: 4 5 6 7   Fic

1. Australia -- Fiction 2. Authorship -- Fiction 3. Single parent family -- Fiction 4. Dating (Social customs) -- Fiction 5. Father-daughter relationship -- Fiction

ISBN 978-0-8234-2253-1; 0-8234-2253-4

LC 2009-10854

First published 2009 in Australia

Thinking her father needs a new interest in his life after he is laid-off of work, teenaged Magenta, who envisions herself as a future fantasy author, decides to dabble in matchmaking which brings unexpected results.

"With a personality as colorful as her name, Bateson's . . . eponymous heroine has a narrative voice that is smart, wry, and down-to-earth. . . . This [is a] real and ultimately reassuring story." Publ Wkly

Baucom, Ian

Through the skylight; a Venice tale. Ian Baucom. 1st ed. Atheneum Books for Young Readers 2013 400 p. ill. (hardcover) $17.99

Grades: 5 6 7 8   Fic

1. Fantasy fiction 2. Time travel -- Fiction 3. Venice (Italy) -- Fiction 4. Italy -- Fiction 5. Magic -- Fiction 6. Americans -- Italy -- Fiction 7. Mystery and detective stories 8. Brothers and sisters -- Fiction

ISBN 1416917772; 9781416917779

LC 2012010642

In this juvenile novel, by Ian Baucom, illustrated by Justin Gerard, "when Jared, Shireen, and Miranda are each given one glittering gift from an old Venetian shopkeeper, they never fathom the powers they are now able to unleash. . . . For in another time, centuries earlier, another trio . . . have been kidnapped and, along with hundreds of other children,

will be sold into child slavery. Unless, that is, they can find some way to save them all." (Publisher's note)

"Frequent black-and-white illustrations support the narrative. Baucom's familiarity with the setting and use of Italian words heighten the atmosphere. . . . The mix of protagonists' genders, historical details, and interesting magic creates a story with broad appeal and a message about the power of words. . . ." SLJ

Bauer, A. C. E.

★ **Come** Fall. Random House 2010 231p $15.99; lib bdg $18.99

Grades: 4 5 6 7   Fic

1. School stories 2. Crows -- Fiction 3. Fairies -- Fiction 4. Friendship -- Fiction 5. Foster home care -- Fiction

ISBN 978-0-375-85825-3; 0-375-85825-3; 978-0-375-95855-7 lib bdg; 0-375-95855-X lib bdg

LC 2009-32419

Drawn together by a mentoring program and an unusual crow, middle school misfits Salman, Lu, and Blos form a strong friendship despite teasing by fellow students and the maneuverings of fairies Oberon, Titania, and Puck.

"Weaving in magic, dreams, doubles, contrasts, and other elements from the original play, Bauer spins an enticing variant." Booklist

★ **No** castles here. Random House 2007 270p $15.99; lib bdg $18.99

Grades: 4 5 6 7   Fic

1. Magic -- Fiction 2. New Jersey -- Fiction 3. Choirs (Music) -- Fiction 4. Books and reading -- Fiction 5. City and town life -- Fiction

ISBN 978-0-375-83921-4; 978-0-375-93921-1 lib bdg

LC 2006023601

Eleven-year-old Augie Boretski dreams of escaping his rundown Camden, New Jersey, neighborhood, but things start to turn around with help from a Big Brother, a music teacher, and a mysterious bookstore owner, so when his school is in trouble, he pulls the community together to save it

This is a "heartwarming novel." Booklist

Bauer, Joan

Almost home; by Joan Bauer. Viking 2012 264 p. (hardcover) $16.99

Grades: 5 6 7 8   Fic

1. Pets -- Fiction 2. Homeless persons -- Fiction 3. Mother-daughter relationship -- Fiction 4. Mothers and daughters -- Fiction

ISBN 0670012890; 9780670012893

LC 2011050483

In this book by Joan Bauer, "when twelve-year-old Sugar's grandfather dies and her gambling father takes off yet again, Sugar and her mother . . . head to Chicago for a fresh start, only to discover that fresh starts aren't so easy to come by for the homeless. . . .With the help of a rescue dog . . . a foster family . . . and her own grace and good humor, Sugar comes to understand that while she can't control the hand life deals her, she can control how she responds." (Publisher's note)

Close to famous. Viking 2011 250p $16.99

Grades: 5 6 7 8 **Fic**
1. Baking -- Fiction 2. Literacy -- Fiction 3. Country life -- Fiction 4. West Virginia -- Fiction 5. Single parent family -- Fiction
ISBN 0-670-01282-3; 978-0-670-01282-4
LC 2010030022
Twelve-year-old Foster McFee and her mother escape from her mother's abusive boyfriend and end up in the small town of Culpepper, West Virginia, where they use their strengths and challenge themselves to build a new life, with the help of the friends they make there.

"Bauer skillfully brings readers to the heart of Culpepper with rich depictions of contemporary small town and its residents and rhythms." Publ Wkly

Bauer, Marion Dane, 1938-
A **bear** named Trouble. Clarion Books 2005 120p $15
Grades: 3 4 5 6 **Fic**
1. Zoos -- Fiction 2. Bears -- Fiction 3. Alaska -- Fiction
ISBN 0-618-51738-3
LC 2004-21259
In Anchorage, Alaska, two lonely boys make a connection—a brown bear injured just after his mother sends him out on his own, and a human whose father is a new keeper at the Alaska Zoo and whose mother and sister are still in Minnesota.

"With a strong plot, well-developed characters, and an engaging writing format, this book is a great choice for young readers." SLJ

★ The **blue** ghost; illustrated by Suling Wang. Random House 2005 85p il $11.95; lib bdg $13.99; pa $3.99
Grades: 2 3 4 **Fic**
1. Ghost stories
ISBN 0-375-83179-7; 0-375-93179-1 lib bdg; 0-375-83339-0 pa
At her grandmother's log cabin, nine-year-old Liz is led to make contact with children she believes may be her ancestors.

"This gentle ghost story, written in simple prose, blends mild suspense with a look at how the past connects to and influences the present. Mystery fans will enjoy the spooky premise, and Wang's softly rendered black-and-white drawings increase the ghostly atmosphere." Booklist

Other titles in this series are:
The green ghost (2008)
The red ghost (2008)
The golden ghost (2011)

Little dog, lost; Marion Dane Bauer; with illustrations by Jennifer Bell. Atheneum Books for Young Readers 2012 197p. ill. (hardcover) $14.99
Grades: 4 5 6 7 **Fic**
1. Dogs -- Fiction 2. Picture books for children 3. Interpersonal relations -- Fiction 4. Novels in verse 5. Parks -- Fiction 6. Loneliness -- Fiction 7. City and town life -- Fiction
ISBN 1442434236; 9781442434233; 9781442434257
LC 2011034024
This book tells the tale of "three needy creatures." Buddy the dog is "re-homed with a clueless though kind woman" after her family moves; Mark "feels his life is empty without the dog he desperately needs but his mother won't permit";

and "Charles Larue, the aging caretaker of a nearby mansion . . . spends his lonely days waiting for something—anything—to bring meaning to his life." The story is written in "[l]ong, thin lines of free-verse text." Additionally, "black-and-white illustrations" are included. (Kirkus)

★ **On** my honor. Clarion Bks. 1986 90p $15
Grades: 4 5 6 7 **Fic**
1. Accidents -- Fiction
ISBN 0-89919-439-7
LC 86-2679
A Newbery Medal honor book, 1987
When his best friend drowns while they are both swimming in a treacherous river that they had promised never to go near, Joel is devastated and terrified at having to tell both sets of parents the terrible consequences of their disobedience

"Bauer's association of Joel's guilt with the smell of the polluted river on his skin is particularly noteworthy. Its miasma almost rises off the pages. Descriptions are vivid, characterization and dialogue natural, and the style taut but unforced. A powerful, moving book." SLJ

Bauer, Michael Gerard
Just a dog; Michael Gerard Bauer. Scholastic Press 2012 144 p. (hc) $15.99
Grades: 4 5 6 **Fic**
1. Family life 2. Dogs -- Fiction 3. Dalmatians -- Fiction
ISBN 0545374529; 9780545374521; 9780545374538
LC 2012014425
This children's book, by Michael Gerard Bauer, is about a family's pet dog. "Sometimes a dog isn't just a dog--sometimes he's the glue the holds a whole family together. Mr. Mosely is a special dog. . . . He's special because he seems to know exactly what everyone in Corey's family needs, even when they don't know themselves. This is the story of Mr. Mosely, from his puppyhood to the last time he curls up on the back porch." (Publisher's note)

Baum, L. Frank
The **Wizard** of Oz; illustrated by Charles Santore; with an introduction by Michael Patrick Hearn. Sterling 2009 96p il $16.95
Grades: 3 4 5 **Fic**
1. Fantasy fiction
ISBN 978-1-4027-6625-1; 1-4027-6625-4
LC 2008046862
A reissue of the edition first published 1991 by Random House
After a cyclone transports her to the land of Oz, Dorothy must seek out the great Wizard in order to return to Kansas

"This edition has been skillfully condensed for those not ready for the longer original work. Santore's many paintings, including spot art and full- and double-page spreads, add a successful dose of drama to the classic fantasy." Horn Book Guide

★ The **wonderful** Wizard of Oz; with pictures by W. W. Denslow. 100th anniversary ed.; HarperCollins Publishers 2000 267p $24.99
Grades: 3 4 5 6 **Fic**
1. Fantasy fiction
ISBN 0-06-029323-3
LC 2001-265945

First published 1900

After a cyclone transports her to the land of Oz, Dorothy must seek out the great wizard in order to return to Kansas.

"For those who want the look and feel of the 1900 publication, this fills the bill. It's a very handsome facsimile, printed on high-quality paper and containing all of W. W. Denslow's 24 original colorplates and 130 two-color drawings." Booklist

Bawden, Nina

Granny the Pag. Clarion Bks. 1996 184p $16

Grades: 4 5 6 7   **Fic**

1. Grandmothers -- Fiction 2. Parent-child relationship -- Fiction

ISBN 0-395-77604-X

LC 95-38191

First published 1995 in the United Kingdom

Originally abandoned by her actor parents who later attempt to gain custody, Cat wages a spirited campaign to decide her own fate and remain with her grandmother

"Bawden has created some enormously appealing characters in this funny and very touching novel." SLJ

Beard, Darleen Bailey

Annie Glover is not a tree lover; pictures by Heather Maione. Farrar Straus Giroux 2009 120p il $15.99

Grades: 3 4 5   **Fic**

1. Trees -- Fiction 2. Grandmothers -- Fiction 3. Environmental protection -- Fiction

ISBN 978-0-374-30351-8; 0-374-30351-7

LC 2008043418

When her grandmother chains herself to the tree across from the school to save it from being cut down, fourth-grader Annie wants to die of humiliation, but when she dicovers the town's history, her attitude changes.

"Light fun, with a save-the-planet message, Beard's fast-paced plot accompanied by Maione's comic illustrations will have plenty of fans, including reluctant readers." SLJ

Operation Clean Sweep; [by] Darleen Bailey Beard. Farrar Straus Giroux 2004 151p $16

Grades: 3 4 5 6   **Fic**

1. Oregon -- Fiction 2. Elections -- Fiction 3. Women -- Suffrage -- Fiction

ISBN 0-374-38034-1

LC 2003-49430

In 1916, just four years after getting the right to vote, the women of Umatilla, Oregon band together to throw the mayor and other city officials out of office, replacing them with women

"Beard's story, based on real events, features believable characters, strong local color, and a plot that gently makes its point without offending anyone." Booklist

Bearn, Emily

★ **Tumtum** & Nutmeg: adventures beyond Nutmouse Hall. Little, Brown Books for Young Readers 2009 504p $16.99

Grades: 4 5 6   **Fic**

1. Mice -- Fiction 2. Siblings -- Fiction

ISBN 978-0-316-02703-8; 0-316-02703-0

LC 2008-45294

Wealthy, married mice Tumtum and Nutmeg find adventure when they secretly try to help two human siblings

who live in a tumbledown cottage with their absent-minded inventor father.

"The stories are filled with descriptions of good food, cheering fires and warm beds. Price's black-and-white line drawings have a scratchy, comic air that brings a welcome edge to the gentle storytelling. . . . The sympathetic characters, enchanting setting and quickly paced plots will hold readers' interest." Publ Wkly

Another title in this series is:

Tumtum & Nutmeg: The Rose Cottage tales (2010)

Tumtum & Nutmeg: the Rose Cottage tales. Little, Brown 2010 398p $16.99

Grades: 4 5 6   **Fic**

1. Mice -- Fiction 2. Seashore -- Fiction 3. Siblings -- Fiction 4. Birthdays -- Fiction 5. Christmas -- Fiction

ISBN 0-316-08599-5; 978-0-316-08599-1

LC 2010032962

Wealthy, married mice Tumtum and Nutmeg have a series of adventures as they try to help the impoverished human children, Arthur and Lucy Mildew, to have a good Christmas, enjoy a seaside holiday, and celebrate Arthur's birthday.

This book includes "three rousing adventures. . . . Even when [Tumtun & Nutmeg's] world gets exciting, though, it's still a cozy read." Kirkus

Beaty, Andrea

Attack of the fluffy bunnies; illustrated by Dan Santat. Amulet Books 2010 184p il $12.95

Grades: 3 4 5   **Fic**

1. Camps -- Fiction 2. Twins -- Fiction 3. Siblings -- Fiction 4. Extraterrestrial beings -- Fiction

ISBN 978-0-8109-8416-5; 0-8109-8416-4

At Camp Whatsitooya, twins Joules and Kevin and new friend Nelson face off against large, rabbitlike creatures from the Mallow Galaxy who thrive on sugar, but are not above hypnotizing and eating human campers.

"Beaty's tale of high silliness is sure to please, and it's dotted with Santat's mini-comics and spot illustrations, which move the story along. If at times the reach for a larff is a bit of a stretch, it's all in fun. The hint at a possible sequel will have humorous-adventure lovers asking." Kirkus

Cicada summer. Amulet Books 2008 167p $15.95

Grades: 4 5 6 7   **Fic**

1. Illinois -- Fiction 2. Siblings -- Fiction 3. Bereavement -- Fiction

ISBN 978-0-8109-9472-0; 0-8109-9472-0

LC 2007-22266

Twelve-year-old Lily mourns her brother, and has not spoken since the accident she feels she could of prevented but the summer Tinny comes to town she is the only one who realizes Lily's secret.

"This is compelling fiction that will be a hit with young readers. . . . Rich and thought-provoking and yet . . . accessible." Horn Book

Dorko the magnificent; by Andrea Beaty. Amulet Books 2013 213 p. (hardcover) $16.95

Grades: 3 4 5 6   **Fic**

1. Magicians -- Fiction 2. Grandmothers -- Fiction 3. Humorous stories 4. Family life -- Fiction 5. Magic

tricks -- Fiction
ISBN 1419706381; 9781419706387

LC 2012045674

In this book by Andrea Beaty "Robbie loves magic and
he's good at it—sort of. When Grandma Melvyn moves in
and takes over his room, Robbie discovers that she was once
an internationally renowned magician and learns about the
heartache that turned her into a bitter woman. Against all
odds, Robbie and Grandma Melvyn form an uneasy alliance
to show the world—or at least the kids of Hobson Elementary School—that he is a true magician." (Publisher's note)

Becker, Bonny

Holbrook; a lizard's tale. by Bonny Becker; illustrated
by Abby Carter. Clarion Books 2006 150p il $15

Grades: 3 4 5   **Fic**
   1. Artists -- Fiction 2. Lizards -- Fiction 3. City and
town life -- Fiction
   ISBN 978-0-618-71458-2; 0-618-71458-8

LC 2006-03962

Holbrook the lizard has an artist's soul, but when his
paintings are ridiculed by the owls, geckoes, and other creatures in his desert town, he decides to seek his fortune in the
big city, unaware of the dangers of urban life.

   "The story moves along quickly, enlivened by dramatic
situations, dry wit, and dynamic full-page illustrations. An
enjoyable romp." Booklist

The **magical** Ms. Plum; illustrated by Amy Portnoy.
Alfred A. Knopf 2009 104p il $12.99; lib bdg $15.99

Grades: 2 3 4   **Fic**
   1. School stories 2. Magic -- Fiction 3. Teachers --
Fiction
   ISBN 978-0-375-85637-2; 0-375-85637-4; 978-0-375-
95637-9 lib bdg; 0-375-95637-9 lib bdg

LC 2008-42682

The students in Ms Plum's third grade class soon learn
that there is something very special about their teacher and
her classroom's mysterious supply closet.

   "Readers will relate to the youngsters' problems and
enjoy their magical resolutions. Illustrated with delightful
black-and-white drawings and filled with clever and short
vignettes, this fast-paced story is a good choice for struggling readers." SLJ

Behrens, Andy

The **fast** and the furriest. Alfred A. Knopf 2010 247p
$15.99; lib bdg $18.99

Grades: 4 5 6 7   **Fic**
   1. Dogs -- Fiction 2. Obesity -- Fiction 3. Football
-- Fiction
   ISBN 978-0-375-85922-9; 0-375-85922-5; 978-0-375-
95922-6 lib bdg; 0-375-95922-X lib bdg

LC 2009018365

   The overweight and unathletic son of a famous former
football star discovers that his equally fat and lazy dog is
unexpectedly—and obsessively—interested in competing in
dog agility contests.

   "Behrens's engaging style will appeal to children. Students will relate to likable Kevin's self-deprecating humor,
and Cromwell's perseverance gives anyone with an unreal-
ized dream a glimmer of hope." SLJ

Beil, Michael

The **Red** Blazer Girls: the mistaken masterpiece. Alfred A. Knopf 2011 309p $16.99; lib bdg $19.99

Grades: 5 6 7 8   **Fic**
   1. School stories 2. Mystery fiction 3. Puzzles --
Fiction 4. Art thefts -- Fiction
   ISBN 978-0-375-86740-8; 0-375-86740-6; 978-0-375-
96740-5 lib bdg; 0-375-96740-0 lib bdg

LC 2010030006

Sophie and her friends, who call themselves The Red
Blazer Girls, embark on solving a case involving mistaken identities, switched paintings, and some priceless
family heirlooms.

   "Sophie narrates with humor and self-effacing aplomb.
Visual evidence inserted in the text invites reader participation." Kirkus

Beil, Michael D.

★ The **Red** Blazer Girls: the ring of Rocamadour. Alfred A. Knopf 2009 299p $15.99; lib bdg $18.99

Grades: 5 6 7 8   **Fic**
   1. School stories 2. Mystery fiction 3. Puzzles --
Fiction 4. Friendship -- Fiction
   ISBN 978-0-375-84814-8; 0-375-84814-2; 978-0-375-
94814-5 lib bdg; 0-375-94814-7 lib bdg

LC 2008-25254

Catholic-schooled seventh-graders Sophie, Margaret,
Rebecca, and Leigh Ann help an elderly neighbor solve
a puzzle her father left for her estranged daughter twenty
years ago.

   "The dialogue is fast and funny, the clues are often solv-
able." Booklist

   Other titles about the Red Blazer Girls are:
   The Red Blazer Girls: the vanishing violin (2010)
   The Red Blazer Girls: the mistaken masterpiece (2011)

Bell, Cathleen Davitt

Little blog on the prairie. Bloomsbury 2010 276p
$16.99

Grades: 6 7 8   **Fic**
   1. Camps -- Fiction 2. Weblogs -- Fiction 3. Wyoming
-- Fiction 4. Frontier and pioneer life -- Fiction
   ISBN 978-1-59990-286-9; 1-59990-286-9

LC 2009-46897

Thirteen-year-old Genevieve's summer at a frontier family history camp in Laramie, Wyoming, with her parents and
brother is filled with surprises, which she reports to friends
back home on the cell phone she sneaked in, and which they
turn into a blog.

   This is a "a lively journey with empathetic characters."
Publ Wkly

Bell, Krista

If the shoe fits; [illustrated by] Craig Smith. Charlesbridge 2008 60p il $14.95; pa $5.95

Grades: 2 3 4   **Fic**
   1. Dance -- Fiction
   ISBN 978-1-58089-338-1; 1-58089-338-4; 978-1-
58089-339-8 pa; 1-58089-339-2 pa

LC 2007027022

First published 2006 in Australia

Cassie wants to be a dancer when she grows up but is
afraid to dance in front of anyone outside her family, until

the day of her first jazz performance arrives and her mother and a new friend help her to gain confidence.

"The text tells a believable story in a straightforward way, and readers will empathize with the characters. Scribbly pencil drawings reflect Cassie's inner turmoil." Horn Book Guide

Bellairs, John

The **house** with a clock in its walls; pictures by Edward Gorey. Dial Bks. for Young Readers 1973 179p il pa $5.99

Grades: 5 6 7 8   **Fic**

1. Witchcraft -- Fiction

ISBN 0-14-240257-5

In 1948, Lewis, a ten-year-old orphan, goes to New Zebedee, Michigan with his warlock Uncle Jonathan, who lives in a big mysterious house and practices white magic. Together with their neighbor, Mrs. Zimmerman, a witch, they search to find a clock that is programmed to end the world and has been hidden in the walls of the house by the evil Isaac Izard

"Bellairs's story and Edward Gorey's pictures are satisfyingly frightening." Publ Wkly

Other titles about Lewis are:

The doom of the haunted opera (1995)

The figure in the shadows (1975)

The ghost in the mirror (1993)

The letter, the witch, and the ring (1976)

The vengeance of the witch-finder (1993)

Berk, Josh

Strike three, you're dead; Josh Berk. Knopf Books for Young Readers 2013 256 p. (hardback) $16.99

Grades: 3 4 5 6 7   **Fic**

1. Mystery fiction 2. Baseball -- Fiction 3. Friendship -- Fiction 4. Murder -- Fiction 5. Best friends -- Fiction 6. Philadelphia Phillies (Baseball team) -- Fiction

ISBN 0375870083; 9780375870088; 9780375970085; 9780375987366

LC 2012023892

Edgar Award Finalist: Best Juvenile (2014)

In this mystery, by Josh Berk, twelve-year-old "Lenny, with the help of his buddies Mike and Other Mike, enters and wins a contest to guest-announce a Philadelphia Phillies game. When the hot rookie pitcher drops dead, the kids suspect that it's more than a previously undetected heart condition. They join another local sports fan and begin investigating the crime . . . while meeting their hero, flashy catcher Ramon Famosa, and other players in the process." (Publishers Weekly)

"Baseball aficionados will appreciate all the trivia Berk works into the story, with references to famous players and Phillies history scattered throughout. The wisecracking interplay between the boys is a strong point, though the solution to the mystery is really never in doubt." Pub Wkly

Berkeley, Jon

The **hidden** boy. Katherine Tegen Books 2010 262p (Bell Hoot fables) $16.99

Grades: 3 4 5 6   **Fic**

1. Adventure fiction 2. Siblings -- Fiction 3. Missing children -- Fiction

ISBN 978-0-06-168758-7; 0-06-168758-8; 978-0-06-168759-4 lib bdg; 0-06-168759-6 lib bdg

LC 2009-12272

When Bea and her family are transported aboard an underwater bus to a strange land, her younger brother Theo is lost during the voyage, and somehow it falls to Bea to find out what has become of him.

"Berkeley's arch writing and his characters' hilarious, pathos-inspiring temperments and abilities make this magical stew both compelling and delightful." Booklist

Berlin, Eric

The **potato** chip puzzles; Eric Berlin; [drawings by Katrina Damkoehler] G.P. Putnam's Sons 2009 244p il $16.99; pa $7.99

Grades: 4 5 6 7   **Fic**

1. Mystery fiction 2. Puzzles -- Fiction 3. Contests -- Fiction

ISBN 978-0-399-25198-6; 0-399-25198-7; 978-0-14-241637-2 pa; 0-14-241637-1 pa

LC 2008-33698

Sequel to: The puzzling world of Winston Breen (2007)

Winston and his friends enter an all-day puzzle contest to win fifty-thousand dollars for their school, but they must also figure out who is trying to keep them from winning. Puzzles for the reader to solve are included throughout the text.

"The pace is suspenseful but allows for pauses for problem-solving. The joy for both contestants and readers of this brain-teasing mystery will be in the process." Kirkus

★ The **puzzling** world of Winston Breen; the secret in the box. Putnam 2007 215p il $16.99; pa $7.99

Grades: 4 5 6 7   **Fic**

1. Mystery fiction 2. Puzzles -- Fiction 3. Siblings -- Fiction

ISBN 978-0-399-24693-7; 0-399-24693-2; 978-0-14-241388-3 pa; 0-14-241388-7 pa

LC 2006-20531

Puzzle-crazy, twelve-year-old Winston and his ten-year-old sister Katie find themselves involved in a dangerous mystery involving a hidden ring. Puzzles for the reader to solve are included throughout the text

"A delightfully clever mystery. . . . There is plenty of suspense to engage readers." SLJ

Followed by: The potato chip puzzles (2009)

Berner, Rotraut Susanne

Hound and hare; translated by Shelley Tanaka. Groundwood Books 2011 75p il $18.99

Grades: K 1 2   **Fic**

1. Dogs -- Fiction 2. Rabbits -- Fiction

ISBN 978-0-88899-987-0; 0-88899-987-9

"The illustrations are done in colored pencil and ink, each creature and picture frame defined by soft blue lines. Hounds and hares emerge as regular Hatfields and McCoys and overtly harass each other with wickedly humorous, singsong taunts. Although classmates Harley Hare and Hugo Hound share interests, they've absorbed their families' prejudices and shun each other. . . . The happily-ever-after ending delivers a satisfying resolution to a story about tolerance that successfully uses humor and engaging artwork to avoid didacticism." Kirkus

Betancourt, Jeanne

Ava Tree and the wishes three. Feiwel and Friends 2009 130p il $14.99

Grades: 2 3 4   **Fic**

1. Wishes -- Fiction 2. Orphans -- Fiction 3. Parties -- Fiction 4. Siblings -- Fiction 5. Birthdays -- Fiction

ISBN 978-0-312-37760-1; 0-312-37760-6

LC 2008015265

"Waking up on her eighth birthday, Ava tears up thinking about her parents, who died in a car accident. . . . She now lives with her 22-year-old brother, Jack. . . . Struggling to clean her pet rabbit's litter box, Ava wishes it 'would use the toilet like a person' and when it suddenly does, Ava and Jack wonder if it could be a birthday gift from their mother, who had been a magician. Ava's 'wishing power' seems to continue, though some of her wishes—that her parents weren't dead—go unanswered. . . . Kids will embrace this bighearted novel and its thoughtful, resilient narrator." Publ Wkly

Bianco, Margery Williams

★ The velveteen rabbit; or, How toys become real. by Margery Williams; with illustrations by William Nicholson. Doubleday 1991 33p il $13.95

Grades: 2 3 4   **Fic**

1. Fairy tales 2. Toys -- Fiction 3. Rabbits -- Fiction

ISBN 0-385-07725-4

LC 90-25339

First published 1922 by Doran

By the time the velveteen rabbit is dirty, worn out, and about to be burned, he has almost given up hope of ever finding the magic called Real.

"Quiet, graceful illustrations accentuate the classic tale's nostalgic tone." Publ Wkly

Billingsley, Franny

The Folk Keeper. Atheneum Bks. for Young Readers 1999 162p hardcover o.p. pa $4.99; pa $5.99

Grades: 5 6 7 8   **Fic**

1. Fantasy fiction

ISBN 0-689-82876-4; 0-689-84461-1 pa; 9780689844614 pa

LC 98-48778

Boston Globe Horn Book Winner (2000)

Orphaned Corinna disguises herself as a boy to pose as a Folk Keeper, one who keeps the supernatural Folk underground at bay. She discovers her heritage as a seal maiden when she is summoned to become the Folk Keeper for a wealthy family in their manor by the sea. "Ages ten to fourteen." (N Y Times Book Rev)

"The intricate plot, vibrant characters, dangerous intrigue, and fantastical elements combine into a truly remarkable novel steeped in atmosphere." Horn Book

Binding, Tim

★ Sylvie and the songman; with illustrations by Angela Barrett. Random House 2009 339p il $15.99; lib bdg $18.99

Grades: 5 6 7 8   **Fic**

1. Fantasy fiction

ISBN 978-0-385-75157-5; 0-385-75159-1; 978-0-385-75159-9 lib bdg; 0-385-75159-1 lib bdg

"Sylvie's composer father . . . goes missing and that's the first odd thing that interrupts her happy routine. Next, the animals seem to have lost their voices. The third is the arrival of the eerie, malevolent Woodpecker Man. . . . The dense narrative is packed with surreal imagery. . . . It's a testament to Binding's assured writing that the abstractions become visceral thrills, like a dream you just can't shake. . . . An unforgettable tale." Booklist

Birdsall, Jeanne

★ The Penderwicks; a summer tale of four sisters, two rabbits, and a very interesting boy. Knopf 2005 262p (The Penderwicks) $15.95; lib bdg $17.77; pa $6.99

Grades: 3 4 5 6   **Fic**

1. Sisters -- Fiction 2. Single parent family -- Fiction

ISBN 0-375-83143-6; 0-375-93143-0 lib bdg; 0-440-42047-4 pa

LC 2004-20364

"Four sisters—Rosalind, Skye, Jane, and Batty—spend a few weeks with their father and dog at a cottage on the grounds of a stately home in the Berkshires, where they complicate the lives of a handsome gardener, a lonely boy, and the boy's officious mother. . . . Grades four to seven." (Bull Cent Child Books)

"This comforting family story . . . [offers] . . . four marvelously appealing sisters, true childhood behavior . . . , and a writing style that will draw readers close." Booklist

The Penderwicks at Point Mouette. Alfred A. Knopf 2011 295p (The Penderwicks) $16.99

Grades: 4 5 6 7   **Fic**

1. Maine -- Fiction 2. Summer -- Fiction 3. Vacations -- Fiction 4. Family life -- Fiction

ISBN 978-0-375-85851-2; 0-375-85851-2

This is the third book about the Penderwick family, who appeared previously in The Penderwicks (2005) and The Penderwicks on Gardam Street (2008). "When summer comes around, it's off to the beach for Rosalind . . . and off to Maine with Aunt Claire for the rest of the Penderwick girls, as well as their old friend, Jeffrey. That leaves Skye as OAP (oldest available Penderwick). . . . Things look good as they settle into their cozy cottage. . . . But can Skye hold it together long enough to figure out Rosalind's directions about not letting Batty explode? Will Jane's Love Survey come to a tragic conclusion after she meets the alluring Dominic? . . . And will Jeffrey be able to keep peace between the girls?" (Publisher's note) "Intermediate." (Horn Book)

"Balancing the novel's comedy is an affecting, neatly crafted subplot that builds up to the emotionally charged revelation involving Jeffrey. From start to finish, this is a summer holiday to savor." Publ Wkly

The Penderwicks in spring; Jeanne Birdsall. Knopf Books for Young Readers 2015 352 p. (The Penderwicks) (hardback) $16.99; (lib. bdg.) $19.99

Grades: 4 5 6 7   **Fic**

1. Birthdays -- Fiction 2. Family life -- Fiction 3. Massachusetts -- Fiction 4. Money-making projects for children -- Fiction 5. Singing -- Fiction 6. Surprise -- Fiction 7. Moneymaking projects -- Fiction 8. Single-parent families -- Fiction 9. Family life -- Massachusetts -- Fiction

ISBN 0375870776; 9780375870774; 9780375970771

LC 2014023537

Sequel to: The Penderwicks at Point Mouette (2011)

In this book, by Jeanne Birdsall, "springtime is finally arriving on Gardam Street, and there are surprises in store for each member of the family. Some surprises are just wonderful, like neighbor Nick Geiger coming home from war. And some are ridiculous, like Batty's new dog-walking business. Batty is saving up her dog-walking money for an extra-special surprise for her family, which she plans to present on her upcoming birthday." (Publisher's note)

"[T]he compelling story line examines the guilt that Batty feels over both the death of her mother and her inability to keep the family dog, Hound, alive--and it does so in touching ways. Batty is the narrator most of the time, but younger Ben takes over on occasion, and 2-year-old Lydia is an eccentric presence." Booklist

The **Penderwicks** on Gardam Street; [illustrations by David Frankland] Alfred A. Knopf 2008 307p il $15.99; lib bdg $18.99

Grades: 3 4 5 6 7   **Fic**
1. Sisters -- Fiction 2. Family life -- Fiction 3. Massachusetts -- Fiction 4. Dating (Social customs) -- Fiction
ISBN 978-0-3758-4090-6; 978-0-375-94090-3 lib bdg
         LC 2007-49232

Sequel to: The Penderwicks (2005)

The four Penderwick sisters are faced with the unimaginable prospect of their widowed father dating, and they hatch a plot to stop him.

"Laugh-out-loud moments abound and the humor comes naturally from the characters and situations. . . . This is a book to cherish." SLJ

Birdseye, Tom
Storm Mountain. Holiday House 2010 135p $16.95

Grades: 4 5 6 7   **Fic**
1. Adventure fiction 2. Cousins -- Fiction 3. Blizzards -- Fiction 4. Mountaineering -- Fiction 5. Washington (State) -- Fiction 6. Wilderness survival -- Fiction
ISBN 978-0-8234-2130-5; 0-8234-2130-9
         LC 2010005768

Two thirteen-year-old cousins Cat and Ty are trapped in a blizzard on the same treacherous mountain in the Cascades that claimed the lives of their world-famous, mountain-climber, twin fathers exactly two years earlier.

"Birdseye's prose, full of careening action, melodrama and overwrought similes, reflects Ty's bulldozing personality. Add believable characters, the author's mountain-climbing expertise and a tear-jerking conclusion, and there's plenty here for young adventure enthusiasts." Kirkus

Birney, Betty G.
The **seven** wonders of Sassafras Springs; written by Betty Birney; illustrated by Matt Phelan. Atheneum Books for Young Readers 2005 210p il $16.95; pa $6.99

Grades: 3 4 5 6   **Fic**
1. Family life -- Fiction 2. Country life -- Fiction
ISBN 0-689-87136-8; 1-4169-3489-8 pa
         LC 2004-11399

Eben McAllister searches his small town to see if he can find anything comparable to the real Seven Wonders of the World

"Black-and-white sketches enhance the text and its folksy character. Perfect for reading aloud." SLJ

Summer according to Humphrey. G.P. Putnam's Sons 2010 167p $14.99

Grades: 2 3 4   **Fic**
1. Camps -- Fiction 2. Hamsters -- Fiction
ISBN 978-0-399-24732-3; 0-399-24732-7
         LC 2009008532

When summer arrives, Humphrey, the pet hamster of Longfellow School's Room 26, is surprised and pleased to learn that he will be going to Camp Happy Hollow.

The **world** according to Humphrey. G. P. Putnam's Sons 2004 124p $14.99; pa $5.99

Grades: 2 3 4   **Fic**
1. School stories 2. Hamsters -- Fiction
ISBN 978-0-399-24198-7; 0-399-24198-1; 978-0-14-240352-5 pa; 0-14-240352-0 pa
         LC 2003-5974

Humphrey, pet hamster at Longfellow School, learns that he has an important role to play in helping his classmates and teacher.

The "lively, first-person narrative, filled with witty commentary on human and hamster behavior, makes for an engaging, entertaining read." Booklist

Other titles about Humphrey are:
Friendship according to Humphrey (2005)
Trouble according to Humphrey (2007)
Surprises according to Humphrey (2008)
Adventure according to Humphrey (2009)
Summer according to Humphrey (2010)

Björk, Christina
★ **Linnea** in Monet's garden; text, Christina Björk; drawings, Lena Anderson. Sourcebooks Jabberwocky 2012 46 p. il $16.99

Grades: 2 3 4 5   **Fic**
1. Artists 2. Painters 3. Paris (France) -- Fiction 4. Art 5. Gardens 6. Painters -- France -- Biography
ISBN 9781402277290; 1402277296
         LC 8745163

Original Swedish edition, 1985

Linnea, a young Swedish garden enthusiast, and her elderly neighbor, Mr. Bloom, "travel to Paris, visit Monet's home in Giverny, picnic in the artist's garden, and admire the waterlilies and the Japanese bridge which he often painted. In Paris, the two companions stop at a museum to see Impressionist paintings, view the sunlight over the Seine, and chatter about the life and times of the artist. The book ends with a page of information about things to do and see in Paris." (SLJ)

"This twenty-fifth anniversary edition (in a revised format) introduces a new generation of readers to artist Claude Monet and the Impressionism movement through art- and flower-lover Linnea's exuberant description of a trip to Paris. The book's engaging mix of photographs, watercolor illustrations, and reproductions of Monet's paintings pull readers into the story, which smoothly incorporates facts and information." Horn Book

Black, Holly, 1971-
★ **Doll** bones; Holly Black. 1st ed. Margaret K. McElderry Books 2013 256 p. (hardcover) $16.99

Grades: 5 6 7 8   **Fic**
1. Ghost stories 2. Dolls -- Fiction 3. Adventure fiction 4. Ghosts -- Fiction 5. Friendship -- Fiction 6. Family problems -- Fiction 7. Adventure and adventurers --

Fiction
ISBN 1416963987; 9781416963981; 9781442474871
LC 2012018299
Newberry Honor Book (2104)

In this book, by Holly Black, illustrated by Eliza Wheeler, "a doll that may be haunted leads three friends on a thrilling adventure. . . . Zach, Poppy, and Alice have been . . . playing one continuous, ever-changing game. . . . Ruling over all is the Great Queen, . . . cursing those who displease her. . . . Zach and Alice and Poppy set off on one last adventure to lay the Queen's ghost to rest. But nothing goes according to plan, and . . . creepy things begin to happen." (Publisher's note)

"Veteran Black packs both heft and depth into a deceptively simple (and convincingly uncanny) narrative. . . . A few rich metaphors . . . are woven throughout the story, as every encounter redraws the blurry lines between childishness and maturity, truth and lies, secrecy and honesty, magic and madness. Spooky, melancholy, elegiac and ultimately hopeful; a small gem." Kirkus

The **iron** trial; Holly Black, Cassandra Clare. First edition Scholastic Press 2014 304 p. illustrations (Magisterium) (hardcover) $17.99
Grades: 4 5 6 7 8   Fic
1. Fantasy fiction 2. Magic -- Fiction
ISBN 0545522250; 9780545522250
LC 2014937300

In this fantasy novel by Holly Black and Cassandra Clare, part of the Magisterium series, "most kids would do anything to pass the Iron Trial. Not Callum Hunt. He wants to fail. All his life, Call has been warned by his father to stay away from magic. If he succeeds at the Iron Trial and is admitted into the Magisterium, he is sure it can only mean bad things for him." (Publisher's note)

"The third-person narration, filtered through Callum's delightfully insecure-and-overcompensating-with-snarky-bravado perspective, carries a tone that will likely have readers chortling in recognition. A promising beginning to a complex exploration of good and evil, as well as friendship's loyalty." Kirkus

Black, Peter Jay
Urban outlaws; Peter Jay Black. Bloomsbury USA Childrens 2014 288 p. illustration (hardback) $16.99
Grades: 5 6 7 8   Fic
1. Science fiction 2. Ability -- Fiction 3. Orphans -- Fiction 4. Criminals -- Fiction 5. Adventure and adventurers 6. Computers -- Fiction 7. Adventure and adventurers -- Fiction
ISBN 1619634007; 9781619634008
LC 2014005604

In this middle-grades book, by Peter Jay Black, "deep beneath the city live five extraordinary kids: world-famous hacker Jack, gadget geek Charlie, free runner Slink, communications chief Obi, and decoy expert Wren. Orphans bonded over their shared sense of justice, the kids have formed the Urban Outlaws, a group dedicated to outsmarting criminals and handing out their stolen money through Random Acts of Kindness (R.A.K.s)." (Publisher's note)

"Five orphans—Jack, Charlie, Wren, Obi, and Slink—have made a home for themselves in a WWII bunker under the London subway. They are skilled in various ways—technological savvy, surveillance, and physical prowess in

particular—and work together as the Urban Outlaws, using their knowledge to play Robin Hood against local criminals and sharing the benefits of their activities with those less fortunate than themselves...The characters are warm and well developed and will appeal to reluctant readers across middle school. This new series will be an excellent choice for younger fans of Alex Rider." Booklist

Blackwood, Gary
Curiosity; by Gary Blackwood. Dial Books for Young Readers, an imprint of Penguin Group (USA) Inc. 2014 320 p. (hardcover) $16.99
Grades: 5 6 7 8   Fic
1. Chess -- Fiction 2. Robots -- Fiction 3. Historical fiction 4. Poverty -- Fiction 5. Apprentices -- Fiction 6. Philadelphia (Pa.) -- History -- 19th century -- Fiction
ISBN 0803739249; 9780803739246
LC 2013013438

This novel, by Gary Blackwood, begins in "Philadelphia, PA, 1835. Rufus, a twelve-year-old chess prodigy, is recruited by a shady showman named Maelzel to secretly operate a mechanical chess player called the Turk. . . . But Rufus's job working the automaton must be kept secret, and he fears he may never be able to escape his unscrupulous master. And what has happened to the previous operators of the Turk, who seem to disappear as soon as Maelzel no longer needs them?" (Publisher's note)

"In 1835, Rufus, twelve-year-old hunchback and chess prodigy, is taken in by Johann Maelzel, owner of the Turk, a chess-playing automaton. They can't seem to escape the mysterious Woman in Black, or the attention of Edgar Allan Poe, who aims to expose their operation for the fraud it is. Blackwood excels in writing historical fiction that is as informative as it is entertaining." Horn Book

Blackwood, Gary L.
Second sight; [by] Gary Blackwood. Dutton 2005 279p hardcover o.p. pa $6.99
Grades: 5 6 7 8   Fic
1. Lawyers 2. Presidents 3. State legislators 4. Members of Congress 5. Clairvoyance -- Fiction 6. Washington (D.C.) -- Fiction 7. United States -- History -- 1861-1865, Civil War -- Fiction
ISBN 0-525-47481-1; 0-14-240747-X pa

In Washington, D.C., during the last days of the Civil War, a teenage boy who performs in a mind reading act befriends a clairvoyant girl whose frightening visions foreshadow an assassination plot.

"This is a well-researched, engrossing story grounded in historical detail." SLJ

★ The **Shakespeare** stealer; [by] Gary Blackwood. Dutton Children's Bks. 1998 216p $15.99; pa $5.99
Grades: 5 6 7 8   Fic
1. Poets 2. Authors 3. Dramatists 4. Orphans -- Fiction 5. Theater -- Fiction 6. Great Britain -- History -- 1485-1603, Tudors -- Fiction
ISBN 0-525-45863-8; 0-14-130595-9 pa
LC 97-42987

A young orphan boy is ordered by his master to infiltrate Shakespeare's acting troupe in order to steal the script of "Hamlet," but he discovers instead the meaning of friendship and loyalty

"Wry humor, cliffhanger chapter endings, and a plucky protagonist make this a fitting introduction to Shakespeare's world." Horn Book

Other titles in this series are:

Shakespeare's scribe (2000)
Shakespeare's spy (2003)

Blackwood, Sage

★ **Jinx**; Sage Blackwood. Harper 2013 368 p. (Jinx) (trade bdg.) $16.99

Grades: 4 5 6 7   **Fic**

1. Fantasy fiction 2. Magic -- Fiction 3. Voyages and travels -- Fiction 4. Fantasy
ISBN 0062129902; 9780062129901

LC 2012005249

This fantasy book is set "in the Urwald, an enormous, sentient forest where humans exist on sufferance . . . . After Jinx's brutal stepfather decides to abandon him in the forest, the boy is saved by a crusty, morally ambiguous wizard named Simon, who takes him in as a servant, eventually teaching him some magic. Years later, a 12-year-old Jinx and two new friends set off to find another wizard, the monstrous Bonemaster, in hopes he can help them overcome their respective magical troubles." (Publishers Weekly)

"...Rounding out the exciting story are terrifying dangers, delightful bouts of wordplay, and vivid settings that will appeal to readers' imaginations, senses of humor, and desire for fair play. A literary cut above Eoin Colfer's Artemis Fowl books but with no less tension or bravado, this exciting, thought-provoking debut will leave readers eager for follow-up adventures." Booklist

Jinx's fire; Sage Blackwood. Katherine Tegen Books, an imprint of HarperCollinsPublishers 2015 400 p. map (hardback) $16.99

Grades: 4 5 6 7   **Fic**

1. Fantasy fiction 2. Wizards -- Fiction 3. Forests and forestry -- Fiction 4. Fantasy 5. Magic -- Fiction 6. Orphans -- Fiction
ISBN 0062129961; 9780062129963

LC 2014022688

Sequel to: Jinx's magic

In this novel by Sage Blackwood, "the young wizard Jinx concludes his suspenseful and dryly humorous adventures in the magical forest of the Urwald with this third installment in the series. . . . The forest is under attack and its magic is fading. Can Jinx summon enough of his magic . . . to rescue Simon, defeat the Bonemaster, unite the Urwald, and fight off the invaders?" (Publisher's note)

"In this concluding volume of Blackwood's critically acclaimed series, Jinx is nearly 15, and he finally rescues his mentor, Simon, from the fate the evil Bonemaster wrought in Jinx's Magic (2014). . . . Series fans will be elated to have another outing with the sweetly sardonic hero, whose conscience is almost as troublesome as his grasp of spells. Fans of Cornelia Funke should add this to their stacks." Booklist

Jinx's magic; Sage Blackwood. Katherine Tegen Books 2014 400 p. (hardcover) $16.99

Grades: 4 5 6 7   **Fic**

1. Fantasy 2. Magic -- Fiction 3. Wizards -- Fiction 4. Orphans -- Fiction 5. Forests and forestry -- Fiction
ISBN 9780062129932; 0062129937

LC 2013010171

Sequel to: Jinx

"Jinx knows he can do magic. But he doesn't know why he's being stalked by a werewolf with a notebook, why the trees are starting to take back the only safe paths through the Urwald, or why the elves think Jinx and the evil Bonemaster are somehow connected." (Publisher's note)

"The plot is a little convoluted, wrapping up loose ends from the first volume and setting up elements for the next before finally establishing its own internal tension, but the unique setting, smart pace, likable characters, and sprightly voice hold the narrative together." Horn Book

Blakemore, Megan Frazer

The **spy** catchers of Maple Hill; by Megan Frazer Blakemore. Bloomsbury 2014 320 p. (hardback) $16.99

Grades: 4 5 6 7   **Fic**

1. Mystery fiction 2. Vermont -- Fiction 3. Country life -- Fiction 4. Spies -- Fiction 5. Cold War -- Fiction 6. Friendship -- Fiction 7. City and town life -- Vermont -- Fiction 8. Vermont -- History -- 20th century -- Fiction
ISBN 1619633485; 9781619633483

LC 2013039857

In this children's novel by Megan Frazer Blakemore, "Hazel Kaplansky is a firm believer in the pursuit of knowledge and truth--and she also happens to love a good mystery. When suspicions swirl that a Russian spy has infiltrated her small town of Maple Hill, Vermont, amidst the fervor of Cold War era McCarthyism, Hazel knows it's up to her to find a suspect starting with Mr. Jones, the quietly suspicious grave digger." (Publisher's note)

"The book does a wonderful job of displaying the way in which the fear inherent in the McCarthy era turned neighbor against neighbor. While the heart of the story lies within the issues of trust and truth, the writing is never preachy, using Hazel's innate humor to deflect moments that veer close to saccarine or preachy. A strong work of historical fiction for mystery fans." SLJ Reviews

The **Water** Castle; by Megan Frazer Blakemore. Walker 2013 352 p. (hardback) $16.99

Grades: 3 4 5 6 7   **Fic**

1. Magic -- Fiction 2. Castles 3. Family secrets -- Fiction 4. Maine -- Fiction 5. Families -- Fiction 6. Dwellings -- Fiction 7. Moving, Household -- Fiction 8. Discoveries in science -- Fiction
ISBN 0802728391; 9780802728395

LC 2012016442

In this novel by Megan Frazer Blakemore "Ephraim Appledore-Smith is an ordinary boy, and up until his father's stroke he lived an ordinary life. But all that changes when his family moves to the Water Castle. . . . Mallory Green's family has always been the caretakers of the Water Castle. . . . She has been raised to protect the legendary Fountain of Youth, hidden on the estate grounds. When Ephraim learns of the Fountain, he's sure finding it can cure his dad." (Publisher's note)

Block, Francesca Lia

★ **House** of dolls; illustrated by Barbara McClintock. Harper 2010 61p il $15.99

Grades: 3 4 5 6   **Fic**

1. Fantasy fiction 2. Dolls -- Fiction
ISBN 978-0-06-113094-6; 0-06-113094-X

"Young Madison is growing tired of her dollhouse and its residents. . . . Increasingly abandoned by her mother, Madison begins exercising a capacious cruelty [to the dolls]. . . . The reality/unreality of any of this is a tightrope Block toes with precision. . . . What at first seems to be about the perennial war between familial generations is expanded into a message about the global forces of pride and avarice that plunge innocents into devastation. This is powerful, haunting, and—just when you don't think it's possible—inspiring too." Booklist

Blom, Jen K.
Possum summer. Holiday House 2011 155p $17.95
Grades: 3 4 5   **Fic**
1. Dogs -- Fiction 2. Oklahoma -- Fiction 3. Opossums -- Fiction 4. Ranch life -- Fiction 5. Father-daughter relationship -- Fiction
ISBN 978-0-8234-2331-6; 0-8234-2331-X
                                              LC 2010023476
While her father is away at war, eleven-year-old Princess ignores his warning that pet ownership leads to pain when she raises an orphaned possum on their Oklahoma ranch, then tries to send it back to the wild.
"Animal-loving readers will sympathize with P throughout this well-paced coming-of-age story." Horn Book Guide

Blos, Joan W.
★ A **gathering** of days: a New England girl's journal, 1830-32; a novel. Scribner 1979 144p $16.95; pa $4.99
Grades: 6 7 8 9   **Fic**
1. New Hampshire -- Fiction
ISBN 0-684-16340-3; 0-689-71419-X pa
                                              LC 79-16898
Awarded the Newbery Medal, 1980
The journal of a 14-year-old girl, kept the last year she lived on the family farm, records daily events in her small New Hampshire town, her father's remarriage, and the death of her best friend
"The 'simple' life on the farm is not facilely idealized, the larger issues of the day are felt . . . but it is the small moments between parent and child, friend and friend that are at the fore, and the core, of this low-key, intense, and reflective book." SLJ

Letters from the corrugated castle; a novel of gold rush California, 1850-1852. Atheneum Books for Young Readers 2007 310p $17.99; pa $5.99
Grades: 5 6 7 8   **Fic**
1. California -- Fiction 2. Mexican Americans -- Fiction 3. Gold mines and mining -- Fiction 4. Frontier and pioneer life -- Fiction 5. Mother-daughter relationship -- Fiction
ISBN 978-0-689-87077-4; 0-689-87077-9; 978-0-689-87078-1 pa; 0-689-87078-7 pa
                                              LC 2007-02673
A series of letters and newspaper articles reveals life in California in the 1850s, especially for thirteen-year-old Eldora, who was raised in Massachusetts as an orphan only to meet her influential mother in San Francisco, and Luke, who hopes to find a fortune in gold.
"It is Blos' sturdy characters, whose experiences reveal the complexity of human relationships and wisdom about 'the salt and the sweet of life,' who will make this last." Booklist

Blume, Judy
Are you there God?, it's me, Margaret; rev format ed.; Atheneum 2001 149p pbk. $8.99
Grades: 4 5 6 7   **Fic**
1. Religion -- Fiction 2. Coming of age -- Fiction 3. Puberty -- Fiction
ISBN 9780385739863; 0-689-84158-2; 9781481413978
A reissue of the title first published 1970 by Bradbury Press
A "story about the emotional, physical, and spiritual ups and downs experienced by 12-year-old Margaret, child of a Jewish-Protestant union." Natl Counc of Teach of Engl. Adventuring with Books. 2d edition
Faced with the difficulties of growing up and choosing a religion, a twelve-year-old girl talks over her problems with her own private God.

Freckle juice; illustrated by Sonia O. Lisker. Four Winds Press 1971 40p il lib bdg $17.95
Grades: 2 3 4   **Fic**
1. Freckles -- Fiction 2. School stories 3. Self-perception -- Fiction 4. Humorous stories
ISBN 0-02-711690-5; 9781481411035
"Spontaneous humor, sure to appeal to the youngest reader." Horn Book
"A gullible second-grader pays 50¢ for a recipe to grow freckles." Best Books for Child

Otherwise known as Sheila the Great. Dutton Children's Books 2002 138p $16.99; pa $5.99
Grades: 4 5 6   **Fic**
1. Fear -- Fiction 2. Vacations -- Fiction
ISBN 978-0-525-46928-5; 0-525-46928-1; 978-0-14-240879-7 pa; 0-14-240879-4 pa
A reissue of the title first published 1972
A summer in Tarrytown, N.Y., is a lot of fun for ten-year-old Sheila even though her friends make her face up to some self-truths she doesn't want to admit.
"An unusual and merry treatment of the fears of a young girl. . . . This is a truly appealing book in which the author makes her points without a single preachy word." Publ Wkly

Soupy Saturdays with The Pain and The Great One; illustrations by James Stevenson. Delacorte Press 2007 108p il $12.99; lib bdg $16.99
Grades: 1 2 3   **Fic**
1. Siblings -- Fiction
ISBN 978-0-385-73305-2; 0-385-73305-4; 978-0-385-90324-0 lib bdg; 0-385-90324-3 lib bdg
                                              LC 2006-26892
"Third-grader Abigail calls her little brother 'The Pain' because he causes so much trouble. Jake is in first grade and calls his older sister 'The Great One' because she thinks so highly of herself. The book . . . . is a series of vignettes in which the children continually clash and then reconcile. . . . The stories are sweet and accurately depict the growing pains of childhood. Stevenson's black-and-white ink illustrations are entertaining." SLJ
Other titles about the The Pain and The Great One are:
Cool zone with The Pain and The Great One (2008)
Going, going, gone! with The Pain and The Great One (2008)

Friend or fiend? with The Pain and The Great One (2009)

★ **Tales** of a fourth grade nothing. Dutton Children's Books 2002 120p $15.99; pa $5.99

Grades: 3 4 5 6 **Fic**

1. Brothers -- Fiction 2. Family life -- Fiction

ISBN 0-525-46931-1; 0-14-240881-6 pa

A reissue of the title first published 1972

This story describes the trials and tribulations of nine-year-old Peter Hatcher who is saddled with a pesky two-year-old brother named Fudge who is constantly creating trouble, messing things up, and monopolizing their parents' attention. Things come to a climax when Fudge gets at Peter's pet turtle

"The episode structure makes the book a good choice for reading aloud." Saturday Rev

Other titles about Peter and Fudge are:

Double Fudge (2002)

Fudge-a-mania (1990)

Superfudge (1980)

Blume, Lesley M. M.

Cornelia and the audacious escapades of the Somerset sisters. Knopf 2006 264p $15.95; pa $5.99

Grades: 4 5 6 **Fic**

1. Sisters -- Fiction 2. Friendship -- Fiction 3. Storytelling -- Fiction

ISBN 0-375-83523-7; 0-440-42110-1 pa

LC 2005-18295

Cornelia, eleven-years-old and lonely, learns about language and life from an elderly new neighbor who has many stories to share about the fabulous adventures she and her sisters had while traveling around the world

This "is a fabulous read that will enchant its audience with the magic to be found in everyday life." SLJ

The **rising** star of Rusty Nail; [by] Lesley M.M. Blume. Alfred A. Knopf 2007 270p $15.99; lib bdg $18.99; pa $6.50

Grades: 4 5 6 **Fic**

1. Pianists -- Fiction 2. Minnesota -- Fiction 3. Musicians -- Fiction 4. Russian Americans -- Fiction

ISBN 978-0-375-83524-7; 978-0-375-93524-4 lib bdg; 978-0-440-42111-5 pa

LC 2006024252

In the small town of Rusty Nail, Minnesota, in the early 1950s, musically talented ten-year-old Franny wants to take advanced piano lessons from newcomer Olga Malenkov, a famous Russian musician suspected of being a communist spy by gossipy members of the community

"Blume has skillfully combined humor, history, and music to create an enjoyable novel that builds to a surprising crescendo." SLJ

Blundell, Judy

A **city** tossed and broken; the diary of Minnie Bonner. Judy Blundell. Scholastic Inc. 2013 224 p. (paper over board) $12.99

Grades: 4 5 6 7 **Fic**

1. Historical fiction 2. Household employees -- Fiction 3. San Francisco (Calif.) -- History -- Fiction 4. Diaries -- Fiction 5. Earthquakes -- Fiction 6. Household employees -- Fiction 7. Family life -- California --

Fiction

ISBN 0545310229; 9780545310222

LC 2012014742

This novel, by Judy Blundell, presents the diary of the girl Minnie Bonner during the San Francisco, California earthquake of 1906 as part of the "Dear America" series. A "wealthy gentleman . . . offers Minnie a chance to work as a lady's maid. . . . But when a powerful earthquake strikes, Minnie finds herself the sole survivor among them. . . . Minnie has turned into an heiress overnight . . . and she is soon wrapped up in a deception that leads her down a dangerous path." (Publisher's note)

"The author deftly incorporates true events, circumstances and key historical figures into the rapidly unfolding fictional plot... Exciting, suspenseful, absorbing and informative." Kirkus

Bode, N. E.

The **slippery** map; by N.E. Bode; illustrated by Brandon Dorman. HarperCollinsPublishers 2007 273p il $16.99; lib bdg $17.89

Grades: 4 5 6 **Fic**

1. Adventure fiction 2. Parents -- Fiction 3. Convents -- Fiction 4. Imagination -- Fiction 5. Baltimore (Md.) -- Fiction

ISBN 978-0-06-079108-7; 0-06-079108-X; 978-0-06-079109-4 lib bdg; 0-06-079109-8 lib bdg

LC 2007010900

Oyster R. Motel, a lonely boy raised as a foundling in a Baltimore nunnery, travels through a portal to the imaginary world of his parents, where he heroically confronts the villainous Dark Mouth

The author "effortlessly renders an expansive, entertainingly quirky cast of creatures benign and malevolent. Her snappy prose makes the case for the story's explicit messages about the value of unbridled imagination." Publ Wkly

Bodeen, S. A.

Shipwreck Island; by S. A. Bodeen. Feiwel & Friends 2014 192 p. hc $16.99

Grades: 5 6 7 8 **Fic**

1. Islands -- Fiction 2. Shipwrecks -- Fiction 3. Family life -- Fiction 4. Stepmothers -- Fiction

ISBN 9781250027771; 1250027772

In this book, by S. A. Bodeen, "Sarah is not happy that her dad has married again, forcing her to deal with a new stepmom and two new brothers. To help them bond, Sarah's dad and stepmom decide to take everyone on a vacation to Tahiti, rent a yacht, and cruise to their own private island. They sail right into a terrible storm, the captain is swept overboard, and the yacht runs aground on a deserted island.." (Library Media Connection)

"These very human protagonists respond in believable ways to their new family situation while encountering freakish animals, bizarrely dangerous weather, and a creepy, empty house." SLJ

Boelts, Maribeth

Happy like soccer; illustrated by Lauren Castillo. 1st ed. Candlewick Press 2012 32 p. col. ill. (reinforced trade) $15.99

Grades: 2 3 4 **Fic**

1. Soccer teams 2. Soccer -- Fiction 3. Family life -- Fiction 4. Aunts -- Fiction 5. Social classes -- Fiction

6. Problem solving -- Fiction
ISBN 0763646164; 9780763646165

LC 2011018624

In this children's book by Maribeth Boelts, "Sierra struggles with conflicting emotions about her new soccer team. Traveling out of the city, Sierra now plays on . . . fields unlike the one near the apartment where she lives with her aunt, which is exciting. However, being on this new team has some drawbacks. . . . Sierra is sad to be the only player without family members to cheer for her during games. Yet, with a little ingenuity, Sierra discovers a solution to her dilemma." (Kirkus Reviews)

★ The **PS** brothers. Harcourt 2010 137p $15
Grades: 3 4 5   **Fic**
1. Dogs -- Fiction 2. Uncles -- Fiction 3. Bullies -- Fiction 4. Money-making projects for children -- Fiction
ISBN 978-0-547-34249-8; 0-547-34249-7

LC 2009-49975

Sixth-graders Russell and Shawn, poor and picked on, work together scooping dog droppings to earn money for a Rottweiler puppy to protect them from bullies, but when they learn the puppies' owner is running an illegal dog-fighting ring, they are torn about how to respond.

This is "a genuinely touching look at a boy who doesn't believe that there's anybody of consequence on his side. . . . There is humor in Russell and Shawn's business, but the kids are admirably industrious as well; the ethical quandary they encounter . . . is one that will hit kids right in their dog-loving and impoverished guts." Bull Cent Child Books

Boie, Kirsten
The **princess** plot; translated by David Henry Wilson. Scholastic 2009 378p $17.99
Grades: 5 6 7 8   **Fic**
1. Princesses -- Fiction 2. Conspiracies -- Fiction
ISBN 978-0-545-03220-9; 0-545-03220-2

LC 2008-24403

Original German edition, 2005

Believing that she is on a film set after auditioning and winning the role of a princess, fourteen-year-old Jenna becomes the unsuspecting pawn in a royal conspiracy

"This novel takes simple, straightforward writing and layers it with kidnappings, political intrigue, and an abundance of secret plots. Readers will enjoy leisurely uncovering the mystery of Jenna's heritage, right along with Jenna herself." Booklist

Another title about Jenna is:
The princess trap (2010)

The **princess** trap; translated by David Henry Wilson. Chicken House/Scholastic 2010 405p $17.99
Grades: 5 6 7 8   **Fic**
1. School stories 2. Princesses -- Fiction
ISBN 978-0-545-22261-7; 0-545-22261-3

LC 2010010072

Sequel to: The princess plot (2009)
Original German edition, 2007

Palace rules, boarding school, and paparazzi have Jenna, princess of the newly unified kingdom of Scandia, longing for her former anonymity, but when she runs away she finds herself in grave danger—and in a position to prevent the outbreak of civil war.

Bolden, Tonya
★ **Finding** family. Bloomsbury 2010 181p il $15.99
Grades: 4 5 6 7   **Fic**
1. Aunts -- Fiction 2. Family life -- Fiction 3. Grandfathers -- Fiction 4. West Virginia -- Fiction 5. African Americans -- Fiction
ISBN 978-1-59990-318-7; 1-59990-318-0

LC 2010-00535

Raised in Charleston, West Virginia, at the turn of the twentieth century by her grandfather and aunt on off-putting tales of family members she has never met, twelve-year-old Delana is shocked when, after Aunt Tilley dies, she learns the truth about her parents and some of her other relatives.

"This richly lyrical and historically persuasive coming-of-age story explores the ties that bind, break and renew an affuent African-American family. . . . Period photographic portraits from Bolden's personal collection illustrate the book. Each carefully posed subject is a fascinating enigma." Kirkus

Boles, Philana Marie
Little divas. Amistad 2006 164p $15.99; lib bdg $16.89; pa $5.99
Grades: 5 6 7 8   **Fic**
1. Cousins -- Fiction 2. Divorce -- Fiction 3. African Americans -- Fiction 4. Father-daughter relationship -- Fiction
ISBN 0-06-073299-7; 0-06-073300-4 lib bdg; 0-06-073301-2 pa

The summer before seventh grade, Cassidy Carter must come to terms with living with her father, practically a stranger, as well as her relationships with her cousins, all amidst the overall confusion of adolescence.

"Boles portrays this variable age well, and readers will feel for Cassidy's trials." SLJ

Boling, Katharine
January 1905. Harcourt 2004 170p $16; pa $5.95
Grades: 4 5 6 7   **Fic**
1. Twins -- Fiction 2. Sisters -- Fiction 3. Child labor -- Fiction
ISBN 0-15-205119-8; 0-15-205121-X pa

LC 2003-24470

In a 1905 mill town, eleven-year-old twin sisters, Pauline, who goes to work with the rest of the family, and Arlene, whose crippled foot keeps her home doing the cooking, cleaning, and washing, are convinced that the other sister has an easier life until a series of incidents helps them see each other in a new light.

"This vivid account will draw readers into the period." Horn Book Guide

Bond, Michael
★ A **bear** called Paddington; with drawings by Peggy Fortnum. Houghton Mifflin 1998 128p il $15; pa $4.95
Grades: 2 3 4 5   **Fic**
1. Bears -- Fiction 2. Great Britain -- Fiction
ISBN 0-395-92951-2; 0-618-15071-4 pa

First published 1958 in the United Kingdom; first United States edition 1960

"Mr. and Mrs. Brown first met Paddington on a railway platform in London. Noticing the sign on his neck reading 'Please look after this bear. Thank you,' they decided to do just that. From there on home was never the same though the Brown children were delighted." Publ Wkly

Other titles about Paddington Bear are:
More about Paddington
Paddington abroad
Paddington at large
Paddington at work
Paddington goes to town
Paddington here and now
Paddington helps out
Paddington marches on
Paddington on screen
Paddington on stage
Paddington on top
Paddington takes the air
Paddington takes the test
Paddington takes to TV
Paddington treasury

Bond, Nancy

A **string** in the harp. Atheneum Pubs. 1976 370p il $19.95; pa $6.99

Grades: 6 7 8 9   **Fic**

1. Fantasy fiction 2. Wales -- Fiction

ISBN 0-689-50036-X; 1-4169-2771-9 pa

LC 75-28181

A Newbery Medal honor book, 1977

"Present-day realism and the fantasy world of sixth-century Taliesin meet in an absorbing novel set in Wales. The story centers around the Morgans—Jen, Peter, Becky, and their father—their adjustment to another country, their mother's death, and especially, Peter's bitter despair, which threatens them all." LC. Child Books, 1976

Bond, Victoria

Zora and me; the song of Ivory. [by] Victoria Bond and T. R. Simon. Candlewick Press 2010 170p $16.99; pa $6.99

Grades: 4 5 6 7   **Fic**

1. Authors 2. Novelists 3. Dramatists 4. Memoirists 5. Folklorists 6. Short story writers 7. Race relations -- Fiction 8. African Americans -- Fiction

ISBN 978-0-7636-4300-3; 0-7636-4300-9; 978-0-7636-5814-4 pa; 0-7636-5814-6 pa

LC 2009-47410

Coretta Scott King/John Steptoe New Talent Award (Author), 2011

This is a fictionalized account of Zora Neale Hurston's childhood with her best friend Carrie, in Eatonville, Florida. Annotated bibliography. "Grades four to seven." (Bull Cent Child Books)

"The brilliance of this novel is its rendering of African-American child life during the Jim Crow era as a time of wonder and imagination, while also attending to its harsh realities. Absolutely outstanding." Kirkus

Bondoux, Anne-Laure

★ A **time** of miracles. Delacorte Press 2010 180p map $17.99; lib bdg $20.99

Grades: 5 6 7 8   **Fic**

1. War stories 2. Europe -- Fiction 3. Refugees --

Fiction
ISBN 978-0-385-73922-1; 0-385-73922-2; 978-0-385-90777-4 lib bdg; 0-385-90777-X lib bdg

LC 2010008539

Mildred L. Batchelder Award, 2011

"Raised by a woman in the Republic of Georgia who claims that his critically-injured mother begged her to save him when he was just a baby, 7-year-old Blaise is forced to flee with his adoptive mother and embark on a revelatory five-year journey by foot through Europe following the collapse of the Soviet Union." (Publisher's note)

"This beautifully written novel about a young refugee boy, Koumail, and his guardian, Gloria, who, in the mid-1990s, leave their war-torn home in the Caucasus and head for France, is full of harsh yet tender moments. As Koumail grows older, the mystery of his origins and of Gloria's past deepen. Bondoux evokes their journey in prose that is both exquisitely poetic and unsparing." Horn Book

Boniface, William

The **hero** revealed; [by] William Boniface; illustrations by Stephen Gilpin. HarperCollins Pub. 2006 294p il (The extraordinary adventures of Ordinary Boy) $15.99; lib bdg $16.89; pa $6.99

Grades: 4 5 6 7   **Fic**

1. Superheroes -- Fiction

ISBN 978-0-06-077464-6; 0-06-077464-9; 978-0-06-077465-3 lib bdg; 0-06-077465-7 lib bdg; 978-0-06-077466-0 pa; 0-06-077466-5 pa

LC 2005018676

Ordinary Boy, the only resident of Superopolis without a superpower, uncovers and foils a sinister plot to destroy the town

"This first book in a new series is great fun. . . . Boniface wields a cynical, but definitely kid-friendly, sense of humor, and Gilpin's illustrations are sharp and witty." SLJ

Other titles in this series are:
The return of Meteor Boy? (2007)
The great powers outage (2008)

Booraem, Ellen

★ **Small** persons with wings. Dial Books for Young Readers 2011 302p $16.99

Grades: 4 5 6 7   **Fic**

1. Fantasy fiction 2. Magic -- Fiction 3. Fairies -- Fiction 4. Grandfathers -- Fiction 5. Lost and found possessions -- Fiction

ISBN 978-0-8037-3471-5; 0-8037-3471-9

LC 2010008400

When Mellie Turpin's grandfather dies and leaves her family his run-down inn and bar, she learns that for generations her family members have been fairy guardians. "Grades five to eight." (Bull Cent Child Books)

"In a fairy story that's wistful, humorous, and clever, Booraem . . . suggests that the real world—with its disappointments and failings—is still better than living with illusions. . . . The theme of making progress, rather than ignoring problems, is a strong one, gently presented." Publ Wkly

Texting the underworld; by Ellen Booraem. Dial Books for Young Readers 2013 319 p. (hardcover) $16.99

Grades: 5 6 7 8   **Fic**

1. School stories 2. Fantasy fiction 3. Death -- Fiction 4. Humorous stories 5. Schools -- Fiction 6. Banshees

-- Fiction 7. Future life -- Fiction 8. Supernatural --
Fiction 9. Middle schools -- Fiction
ISBN 0803737041; 9780803737044

LC 2012032488

In this book by Ellen Booraem, "Conor O'Neill is a
smart but timid seventh-grader. . . . When a banshee straight
out of his Irish-born grandfather's stories appears in Conor's
room, he's terrified that someone he loves is going to die
soon. The banshee, Ashling, is new at her job, and . . . she's
curious about the present day, [so] she masquerades as a new
student at Conor's school." (Publishers Weekly)

Borden, Louise

Across the blue Pacific; a World War II story. illustrated by Robert Andrew Parker. Houghton Mifflin 2006
un il $17
Grades: 2 3 4 5   **Fic**
1. World War, 1939-1945 -- Fiction
ISBN 0-618-33922-1

LC 2004-9206

A woman reminisces about her neighbor's son who was
the object of a letter writing campaign by some fourth-graders when he went away to war in 1943.

"Beautifully written in an understated tone, the story offers a believable picture of life during the war. . . . Restrained
yet expressive, the artwork conveys moods and mindsets as
well as a strong sense of the time and place." Booklist

The **greatest** skating race; a World War II story from
the Netherlands. illustrated by Niki Daly. Margaret K.
McElderry Books 2004 44p il $18.95
Grades: 2 3 4 5   **Fic**
1. Ice skating -- Fiction 2. Netherlands -- Fiction 3.
World War, 1939-1945 -- Fiction
ISBN 0-689-84502-2

LC 2002-12040

During World War II in the Netherlands, a ten-year-old
boy's dream of skating in a famous race allows him to help
two children escape to Belgium by ice skating past German
soldiers and other enemies.

"Told with immediacy and suspense. . . . The gorgeously
detailed watercolor illustrations capture a sense of the time.
The subdued, winter hues of brown and smoky gray are
those often found in the oil paintings of Dutch and Flemish
masters and match the quiet tone of the text." SLJ

The **last** day of school; written by Louise Borden; illustrated by Adam Gustavson. Margaret K. McElderry Books
2005 un il $15.95
Grades: 2 3 4   **Fic**
1. School stories 2. Gifts -- Fiction
ISBN 0-689-86869-3

LC 2003025124

Matthew Perez, the official timekeeper of Mrs. Mallory's third-grade class, has a special goodbye gift for her

"Varied sizes of colorful oil illustrations accompany the
tale of Matts patient delivery of the perfect gift. True to a
childs remembrance of final school days, each page recalls
memorable moments for students and teachers." SLJ

The **lost**-and-found tooth; [by] Louise Borden; illustrated by Adam Gustavson. Margaret K. McElderry Books
2008 un il $16.99

Grades: K 1 2   **Fic**
1. School stories 2. Teeth -- Fiction 3. Lost and found
possessions -- Fiction
ISBN 978-1-4169-1814-1; 1-4169-1814-0

LC 2006028761

A special calendar hangs in Mr. Reilly's second grade
classroom, and Lucy Webb impatiently awaits the day when
she can add her name for losing a tooth, but when her time
arrives something unexpected happens

"The low-key story is nicely illustrated with watercolors
and is well suited to either independent reading or classroom
sharing." Booklist

Bosch, Pseudonymous

The **name** of this book is secret; by Pseudonymous
Bosch; illustrations by Gilbert Ford. Little, Brown & Co.
2007 360p il $16.99; pa $5.99
Grades: 4 5 6   **Fic**
1. Adventure fiction 2. Immortality -- Fiction
ISBN 978-0-316-11366-3; 0-316-11366-2; 978-0-316-
11369-4 pa; 0-316-11369-7 pa

LC 2007021909

Two eleven-year-old misfits try to solve the mystery of a
dead magician and stop the evil Dr. L and Ms. Mauvais, who
are searching for the secret of immortality

This "is equal parts supernatural whodunit, suspense-
filled adventure and evocative coming-of-age tale."
Publ Wkly
Other titles in this series are:
If you're reading this, it's too late (2008)
This book is not good for you (2009)
This isn't what it looks like (2010)

Bouwman, H. M.

The **remarkable** and very true story of Lucy and Snow-
cap; [by] H.M. Bouwman. Marshall Cavendish 2008 270p
$16.99
Grades: 5 6 7 8   **Fic**
1. Adventure fiction 2. Magic -- Fiction 3. Infants
-- Fiction 4. Islands -- Fiction
ISBN 978-0-7614-5441-0; 0-7614-5441-1

LC 2008003180

In 1788, thirteen years after English convicts are shipwrecked on the magical islands of Tathenland, two twelve-
year-old girls, one a native Colay, the other the child-gover-
nor of the English, set out on a journey to stop the treachery
from which both peoples are suffering

"The page-turning adventure fronts for a subtle moral
tale about loyalty, perseverance, and the power of finding
one's own particular gifts. . . . . The combination of historical and fantasy elements gives Lucy and Snowcap's quest
folkloric as well as dramatic appeal." Bull Cent Child Books

Boyne, John

The **Terrible** Thing That Happened to Barnaby Brocket; John Boyne; illustrated by Oliver Jeffers. Knopf Books
for Young Readers 2013 288 p. ill. $16.99
Grades: 2 3 4 5   **Fic**
1. Runaway children 2. Adventure fiction
ISBN 0307977625; 9780307977625; 9780307977632

LC 2012277133

In this novel, by John Boyne and illustrated by Oliver
Jeffers, "Barnaby Brocket is an ordinary 8-year-old boy in
most ways, but he was born different in one important way:

he floats. Unlike everyone else, Barnaby does not obey the law of gravity.... And when the unthinkable happens, Barnaby finds himself on a journey that takes him all over the world. From Brazil to New York, ... and ... meets all sorts of different people--and discovers who he really is along the way." (Publisher's note)

Bradford, Chris

Young samurai: the way of the sword. Disney-Hyperion Books 2010 422p $16.99

Grades: 4 5 6 7   **Fic**

1. Adventure fiction 2. Japan -- Fiction 3. Ninja -- Fiction 4. Orphans -- Fiction 5. Samurai -- Fiction 6. Martial arts -- Fiction

ISBN 978-1-4231-2025-4; 1-4231-2025-6

LC 2009008309

Sequel to: Young samurai: the way of the warrior (2009)

In 1611 Japan, English orphan Jack Fletcher continues his difficult training at Niten Ichi Ryu Samurai School, while also trying to get back the rutter, his father's navigational logbook, that an evil ninja wants to possess.

"With straightforward prose, [Bradford] has managed to pen lively and exciting fight sequences and is slowly beginning to develop a keen edge to his cast of characters, laying significant groundwork for future installments." Booklist

★ **Young** samurai: the way of the warrior. Hyperion Books for Children 2009 359p $16.99

Grades: 4 5 6 7   **Fic**

1. Adventure fiction 2. Japan -- Fiction 3. Samurai -- Fiction 4. Martial arts -- Fiction

ISBN 978-1-4231-1871-8; 1-4231-1871-5

LC 2008-46180

First published 2008 in the United Kingdom

Orphaned by a ninja pirate attack off the coast of Japan in 1611, twelve-year-old English lad Jack Fletcher is determined to prove himself, despite the bullying of fellow students, when the legendary sword master who rescued him begins training him as a samurai warrior.

"Jack's story alone makes for a page-turner, but coupling it with intriguing bits of Japanese history and culture, Bradford produces an adventure novel to rank among the genre's best." Publ Wkly

Includes bibliographical references

Followed by: Young samurai: the way of the sword (2010)

Bradley, Kimberly Brubaker

★ **Jefferson's** sons; a founding father's secret children. Dial Books for Young Readers 2011 368p $17.99

Grades: 5 6 7 8   **Fic**

1. Slaves 2. Architects 3. Presidents 4. Vice-presidents 5. Essayists 6. Mistresses 7. Slavery -- Fiction 8. Virginia -- Fiction 9. African Americans -- Fiction

ISBN 978-0-8037-3499-9; 0-8037-3499-9

LC 2010049650

"The characters spring to life. ... [This is a] fascinating story of an American family that represents so many of the contradictions of our history. The afterword is as fascinating as the novel." Kirkus

The **war** that saved my life; by Kimberly Brubaker Bradley. Dial Books for Young Readers, an imprint of Penguin Group (USA) Inc. 2015 320 p. (hardcover) $16.99

Grades: 4 5 6 7   **Fic**

1. Brothers and sisters -- Fiction 2. People with disabilities -- Fiction 3. Great Britain -- History -- 20th century -- Fiction 4. World War, 1939-1945 -- Evacuation of civilians -- Fiction 5. Great Britain -- History -- George VI, 1936-1952 -- Fiction

ISBN 0803740816; 9780803740815

LC 2014002168

In this book, by Kimberly Brubaker Bradley, "[n]ine-year-old Ada has never left her one-room apartment. Her mother is too humiliated by Ada's twisted foot to let her outside. So when her little brother Jamie is shipped out of London to escape the war, Ada doesn't waste a minute - she sneaks out to join him. So begins a new adventure of Ada, and for Susan Smith, the woman who is forced to take the two kids in." (Publisher's note)

"When word starts to spread about Germans bombing London, Ada's mother decides to send her little brother, Jamie, to the country. Not 11-year-old Ada, though—she was born with a crippling clubfoot, and her cruel mother treats her like a slave...The home-front realities of WWII, as well as Ada's realistic anger and fear, come to life in Bradley's affecting and austerely told story, and readers will cheer for steadfast Ada as she triumphs over despair." Booklist

Brandeis, Gayle

My life with the Lincolns. Holt & Co. 2010 248p $16.99

Grades: 4 5 6 7   **Fic**

1. Family life -- Fiction 2. Race relations -- Fiction 3. African Americans -- Fiction

ISBN 978-0-8050-9013-0; 0-8050-9013-4

LC 2009-24151

"Twelve-year-old Mina Edelman is convinced that her family members are the Lincolns reincarnate, and she has many coincidences to back her up. ... The strong theme of social justice creates a unifying thread in this informative, clear, personal, and passionate novel." Booklist

Branford, Anna

★ **Violet** Mackerel's natural habitat; by Anna Branford and illustrated by Elanna Allen. Atheneum Books for Young Readers 2013 112 p. (hardcover: alk. paper) $15.99

Grades: 1 2 3   **Fic**

1. Ladybugs -- Fiction 2. Family life -- Fiction 3. Habitat (Ecology) -- Fiction

ISBN 1442435941; 9781442435940; 9781442435957; 9781442435964

LC 2012015000

In this book, by Anna Branford, "Violet is the smallest in her family, and has a special affinity for Small Things everywhere. So when she finds a tiny ladybug in the garden, she expects she knows how it feels. Violet wants to help the ladybug, so she names her Small Gloria, puts her in a jar, and feeds her. Violet wakes up to a horrible surprise. But thankfully, even as Violet learns a hard lesson about natural habitats, she realizes how nice it is to share her own habitat with a big sister." (Publisher's note)

Violet Mackerel's personal space; Anna Branford; illustrated by Elanna Allen. Atheneum Books for Young Readers 2013 128 p. (Violet Mackerel) (pbk.) $5.99

Grades: 2 3 4   **Fic**

1. Moving -- Fiction 2. Weddings -- Fiction 3.

Remarriage -- Fiction 4. Family life -- Fiction 5. Moving, Household -- Fiction

ISBN 1442435925; 9781442435919; 9781442435926

LC 2012025783

In this children's book, by Anna Branford, "Violet Mackerel believes that wherever you leave something small, a tiny part of you gets to stay too - like how the little piece of green sea glass under the mattress at the beach house means that a little piece of Violet gets to stay on summer holiday. Violet's theory is put to the test when Mama and Vincent announce some very special news: They are going to get married. And they are all going to move." (Publisher's note)

"Mama and her boyfriend, Vincent, are getting married. Planning for the wedding is fun, but looking for a new house is divisive...With its gentle wisdom and sincerity, this series has made a space for itself among early chapter books, and hopefully there are more Violet Mackerel books to come."

Other titles in the series include:

Violet Mackerel's Brilliant Plot (2012)
Violet Mackerel's Natural Habitat (2013)
Violet Mackerel's Pocket Protest (2014)
Violet Mackerel's Possible Friend (2014)
Violet Mackerel's Remarkable Recovery (2011)

Branford, Henrietta

Fire, bed, & bone. Candlewick Press 1998 122p hardcover o.p. pa $5.99

Grades: 5 6 7 8   **Fic**

1. Dogs -- Fiction 2. Middle Ages -- Fiction 3. Great Britain -- History -- 1154-1399, Plantagenets -- Fiction

ISBN 0-7636-0338-4; 0-7636-2992-8 pa

LC 97-17491

In 1381 in England, a hunting dog recounts what happens to his beloved master Rufus and his family when they are arrested on suspicion of being part of the peasants' rebellion led by Wat Tyler and the preacher John Ball

"The dog's observant eye, sympathetic personality, and courageous acts hook the reader into what is both irresistible adventure and educational historical fiction." Booklist

Bransford, Nathan

Jacob Wonderbar and the cosmic space kapow. Dial Books for Young Readers 2011 281p il $14.99

Grades: 4 5 6   **Fic**

1. Adventure fiction 2. Fathers -- Fiction 3. Teachers -- Fiction

ISBN 978-0-8037-3537-8; 0-8037-3537-5

LC 2010-38152

When sixth-grade classroom terror Jacob Wonderbar and his friends Sarah and Dexter find a spaceship crashed in the woods near their suburban neighborhood, their discovery leads them to a series of adventures including space travel, substitute teachers, kidnapping, and more.

"Readers will appreciate Bransford's unique view of the universe. . . . Jacob's ongoing search for his father . . . promises to keep this series moving through at least two forthcoming sequels." Booklist

Brauner, Barbara

The **magic** mistake; Barbara Brauner and James Iver Mattson; illustrated by Abigail Halpin. Disney-Hyperion Books 2014 256 p. illustrations (Oh my godmother) (hardback) $16.99

Grades: 4 5 6 7   **Fic**

1. School stories 2. Humorous fiction 3. Fractured fairy tales 4. Magic -- Fiction 5. Schools -- Fiction 6. Middle schools -- Fiction 7. Fairy godmothers -- Fiction

ISBN 142316475X; 9781423164753

LC 2013029798

"Twelve year old Lacey Unger-Ware . . . is invited to attend the Godmother Academy. . . . But this is an offer Lacey can't refuse. . . . Lacey will be cursed forever if she doesn't complete the magical test. Now Lacey must find the true love for one special lady and arrange the perfect wedding before time runs out." (Publisher's note)

"The real draw here is Lacey, whose relatively normal life just happens to be touched with unexpected magic. She is the type of character that readers will cheer for and could see as their own best friend as well." Booklist

Brawer, Michael

Archie takes flight; by Wendy Mass and Michael Brawer; illustrated by Elise Gravel. Little, Brown & Co. 2014 112 p. V1 illustrations (hardcover) $15

Grades: 2 3 4   **Fic**

1. Science fiction 2. Outer space -- Fiction 3. Extraterrestrial beings -- Fiction 4. Father-son relationship -- Fiction 5. Fathers and sons -- Fiction 6. Interplanetary voyages -- Fiction 7. Adventure and adventurers -- Fiction

ISBN 0316243191; 9780316243193

LC 2013021622

In this book, the first in a series by Wendy Mass and Michael Brawer, "Archie Morningstar is finally old enough to join his dad on the midnight taxi shift for 'Take Your Kid to Work Day.' When they blast out of orbit, it quickly becomes clear that his dad has an unusual job and that his vehicle is no ordinary taxi. Archie is now privy to the secret family business: driving aliens around the galaxy in a high-tech space vehicle." (School Library Journal)

"Archie Morningstar has been waiting for 'eight years, eight months, and eight days' to ride along with his taxicab-driving father. But when the night finally arrives, the experience proves to be out of this world. Archie had been looking forward to seeing more of the city, but his father is no ordinary cabbie. He drives a space taxi, with fares all over the known universe. Archie serves as his father's co-pilot for the night, helping him navigate wormholes, avoid asteroid fields and work the taxi's thrusters. . . . Zany adventures, a wacky plot and plenty of slapstick humor make this a quick, enjoyable read. Simple illustrations and a trio of scientific definitions add to the narrative. A solid start to a new chapter-book series." Kirkus

Water planet rescue; by Wendy Mass and Michael Brawer; illustrations by Elise Gravel. Little, Brown & Co. 2014 128 p. illustrations (Space taxi) (hardcover) $15

Grades: 2 3 4   **Fic**

1. Interplanetary voyages -- Fiction 2. Father-son relationship -- Fiction 3. Fathers and sons -- Fiction 4. Adventure and adventurers -- Fiction

ISBN 031624323X; 9780316243230

LC 2013044221

In this children's book, by Wendy Mass and Michael Brawer, "Archie Morningstar's dad drives a taxi through outer space! And with the help of a talking cat named Pockets, Archie and his dad help fight crime across the universe.

In the second book in this series, Archie, his dad, and Pockets fly to a planet in peril: someone is stealing the water from this underwater world!" (Publisher's note)

"The second installment of the Space Taxi series find eight-year-old Archie Morningstar, navigator of his father's space taxi and newly appointed deputy of the Intergalactic Security Force, setting out on a mission to the watery planet Nautilus...This rollicking adventure, full of goofy antics and subtle lessons in acceptance, is complemented by simple line drawings and concludes with a trio of fun space facts "to impress your friends and teachers." Booklist

Breathed, Berke
Flawed dogs; the shocking raid on Westminster. written and illustrated by Berkeley Breathed. Philomel Books 2009 216p il $16.99

Grades: 4 5 6   **Fic**
1. Dogs -- Fiction
ISBN 978-0-399-25218-1; 0-399-25218-5
     LC 2009-2638

After being framed by a jealous poodle, a dachshund is left for dead, but comes back with a group of mutts from the National Last Ditch Dog Depository to disrupt the prestigious Westminster Kennel Club dog show and exact revenge on Cassius the poodle.

"Dramatically lit and featuring comically exaggerated characters (human and canine alike), Berkeley's b&w artwork augments the story's drama and humor. A moving tale about the beauty of imperfections and the capacity for love." Publ Wkly

Bredsdorff, Bodil
The **Crow**-girl; translated from the Danish by Faith Ingwersen. Farrar Straus Giroux 2004 155p map (The children of Crow Cove) $16

Grades: 4 5 6   **Fic**
1. Denmark -- Fiction 2. Orphans -- Fiction 3. Grandmothers -- Fiction
ISBN 0-374-31247-8
     LC 2003-49310

Original Danish editon, 1993

After the death of her grandmother, a young orphaned girl leaves her house by the cove and begins a journey which leads her to people and experiences that exemplify the wisdom her grandmother had shared with her

"Touching on universal themes, this quiet adventure story has the depth and flavor of a tale from long ago and far away." SLJ

Other titles in this series are:
Eidi (2009)
Tink (2011)

★ **Eidi**; translated from the Danish by Kathryn Mahaffy. Farrar Straus Giroux 2009 138p (The children of Crow Cove series) $16.99

Grades: 4 5 6   **Fic**
1. Denmark -- Fiction 2. Orphans -- Fiction
ISBN 978-0-374-31267-1; 0-374-31267-2
     LC 2008-26052

Sequel to: The Crow-girl (2004)
Batchelder Award honor book (2010)

Eidi leaves her mother and stepfather in Crow Cove to live in a nearby village, where she meets the much younger

Tink and rescues him from the abusive man he has been living with

"This unassuming yet compelling story is notable for the simplicity and power of the storytelling, the clarity of description and characterization, and the humanity of the ideas at the novel's heart." Booklist

Followed by: Tink (2011)

Brewster, Hugh
Carnation, Lily, Lily, Rose; the story of a painting. by Hugh Brewster; with paintings by John Singer Sargent. Kids Can Press 2007 48p il $17.95

Grades: 3 4 5   **Fic**
1. Artists 2. Painters 3. Artists -- Fiction
ISBN 978-1-55453-137-0; 1-55453-137-3

This volume "introduces a true episode from nineteenth-century art history, delivering facts about John Singer Sargent and his luminous masterwork, Carnation, Lily, Lily, Rose, through the imagined words of a child present during its creation. . . . Widely accessible are the profuse visuals, including some of Sargent's sketchbook doodles and real photos of the featured family." Booklist

Brezenoff, Steve
The **burglar** who bit the Big Apple; illustrated by C. B. Canga. Stone Arch Books 2010 81p il (Field trip mysteries) lib bdg $23.99; pa $5.95

Grades: 2 3 4   **Fic**
1. School stories 2. Mystery fiction 3. New York (N.Y.) -- Fiction
ISBN 978-1-4342-2139-1 lib bdg; 1-4342-2139-3 lib bdg; 978-1-4342-2771-3 pa; 1-4342-2771-5 pa

"Cat, Sam, Egg, and Gum are sixth-grade pals with a penchant for solving mysteries. . . . In [this book], they arrive in New York City just as a lunch box has been lifted from the Ralph Kramden statue in the Port Authority Bus Terminal. Later there is more vandalism at the Museum of Natural History and the Bronx Zoo, setting these kids on the trail of a suspicious girl who just happens to know their itinerary. . . . [This] compact chapter [book] offers leading characters of both genders, some full-page, full-color illustrations, a 'detective's dictionary' (aka glossary), a useful model of a school report on the featured city, and evidence-based discussion questions. [This title is an] excellent [introduction] to the mystery genre; the graphics and short chapters make [it] accessible to struggling or reluctant readers." SLJ

The **painting** that wasn't there; illustrated by C.B. Canga. Stone Arch Books 2010 $17.99

Grades: 3 4 5 6   **Fic**
1. School stories 2. Mystery fiction
ISBN 9781434216083
     LC 2009002572

"This title...marries the always high-interest topic of an art heist with a breezy, straightforward story just right for reluctant readers." Booklist

"James ""Gum"" Shoo's art class heads to the museum. They've been learning about forged art, but they never expected to find a fake in the gallery! Only Gum and his gumshoe friends will be able to solve this museum caper." (Publisher's note)

The **zombie** who visited New Orleans; illustrated by C. B. Canga. Stone Arch Books 2010 80p il (Field trip mysteries) lib bdg $23.99; pa $5.95

Grades: 2 3 4   **Fic**

1. School stories 2. Mystery fiction 3. Zombies -- Fiction 4. New Orleans (La.) -- Fiction

ISBN 978-1-4342-2141-4 lib bdg; 1-4342-2141-5 lib bdg; 978-1-4342-2773-7 pa; 1-4342-2773-1 pa

LC 2010022580

"Cat, Sam, Egg, and Gum are sixth-grade pals with a penchant for solving mysteries. . . . In New Orleans, the friends witness acts of voodoo at every tourist attraction and wonder if certain people might be zombies in disguise. . . . [This] compact chapter [book] offers leading characters of both genders, some full-page, full-color illustrations, a 'detective's dictionary' (aka glossary), a useful model of a school report on the featured city, and evidence-based discussion questions. [This title is an] excellent [introduction] to the mystery genre; the graphics and short chapters make [it] accessible to struggling or reluctant readers." SLJ

Brink, Carol Ryrie

★ **Caddie** Woodlawn; illustrated by Trina Schart Hyman. Macmillan 1973 275p il $17.95; pa $6.99

Grades: 4 5 6   **Fic**

1. Wisconsin -- Fiction 2. Frontier and pioneer life -- Fiction

ISBN 0-02-713670-1; 1-4169-4028-6 pa

A newly illustrated edition of the title first published 1935

Awarded the Newbery Medal, 1936

Caddie Woodlawn was eleven in 1864. Because she was frail, she had been allowed to grow up a tomboy. Her capacity for adventure was practically limitless, and there was plenty of adventure on the Wisconsin frontier in those days. The story covers one year of life on the pioneer farm, closing with the news that Mr. Woodlawn had inherited an estate in England, and the unanimous decision of the family to stay in Wisconsin. Based upon the reminiscences of the author's grandmother

The typeface "is eminently clear and readable, and the illustrations in black and white . . . are attractive and expressive." Wis Libr Bull

Britt, Fanny

Jane, the fox & me; [written by] Fanny Britt; [illustrated by] Isabelle Arsenault; translated by Christine Morelli and Susan Ouriou. Pgw 2013 101 p. $19.95

Grades: 5 6 7 8 9   **Fic**

1. Teenage girls -- Fiction 2. Alienation (Social psychology) -- Fiction

ISBN 1554983606; 9781554983605

Written by Fanny Britt, illustrated by Isabelle Arsentault, and translated by Christine Morelli and Susan Ouriou, this "graphic novel reveals the casual brutality of which children are capable, but also assures readers that redemption can be found through connecting with another, whether the other is a friend, a fictional character or even, amazingly, a fox." (Publisher's note) It "centers on Hélène, ostracized by her former friends and now a loner at school." (Horn Book Magazine)

"Britt's well-constructed narrative is achieved sensitively through Arsenault's impressionistic artwork. . . . An elegant and accessible approach to an important topic." Booklist

Brittain, Bill

The **wish** giver; three tales of Coven Tree; drawings by Andrew Glass. Harper & Row 1983 181p il $16.89; pa $5.99

Grades: 5 6 7 8   **Fic**

1. Magic -- Fiction 2. Wishes -- Fiction

ISBN 0-06-020687-X; 0-06-440168-5 pa

LC 82-48264

A Newbery Medal honor book, 1984

"Captivating, fresh, and infused with homespun humor." Horn Book

"Witchy and devilish things happen in Coven Tree, New England, and their chronicler is Stew Meat, proprietor of the Coven Tree store. . . . Stew relates the King Midas luck that came to three young people, each of whom had a wish fulfilled, and each of whom rued that fulfillment." SLJ

Other titles about Coven Tree are:

Dr. Dredd's wagon of wonders (1987)

Professor Popkin's prodigious polish (1990)

Broach, Elise

Masterpiece; illustrated by Kelly Murphy. Henry Holt & Co. 2008 292p il $16.95

Grades: 4 5 6 7   **Fic**

1. Mystery fiction 2. Artists -- Fiction 3. Beetles -- Fiction 4. New York (N.Y.) -- Fiction

ISBN 978-0-8050-8270-8; 0-8050-8270-0

After Marvin, a beetle, makes a miniature drawing as an eleventh birthday gift for James, a human with whom he shares a house, the two new friends work together to help recover a Durer drawing stolen from the Metropolitan Museum of Art.

Broach "packs this fast-moving story with perennially seductive themes: hidden lives and secret friendships, miniature worlds lost to disbelievers. . . . Loosely implying rather than imitating the Old Masters they reference, the finely hatched drawings depict the settings realistically and the characters, especially the beetles, with joyful comic license." Publ Wkly

The **miniature** world of Marvin & James; Elise Broach; illustrated by Kelly Murphy. Henry Holt and Co. 2014 112 p. illustrations (The masterpiece adventures) (hardback) $15.99

Grades: 1 2 3   **Fic**

1. Beetles -- Fiction 2. Insects -- Fiction 3. Vacations -- Poetry 4. Friendship -- Fiction 5. Human-animal relationships -- Fiction

ISBN 0805091904; 9780805091908

LC 2013036081

In this book, by Elise Broach and illustrated by Kelly Murphy, "James is going on vacation for a week. His best friend, Marvin the beetle, has to stay at home. Without James to keep him company, Marvin has to play with his annoying cousin, Elaine. Marvin and Elaine quickly find themselves getting into all sorts of trouble, even getting trapped inside a pencil sharpener! Marvin misses James and starts to worry about their friendship." (Publisher's note)

"A new early chapter book series follows the friendship of beetle Marvin and human James (Masterpiece) for a younger audience. The sentences are shorter and the illustrations more prominent, but the amiable tone and relatable characters are the same. New readers will be rewarded by this page-turning adventure, written throughout with emo-

tional authenticity and ending with a satisfying conclusion."
Horn Book

The miniature world of Marvin and James

★ **Missing** on Superstition Mountain; [illustrated by Antonio Javier Caparo] Henry Holt 2011 262p il $15.99
Grades: 3 4 5 **Fic**
1. Mystery fiction 2. Arizona -- Fiction 3. Brothers -- Fiction 4. Mountains -- Fiction
ISBN 978-0-8050-9047-5; 0-8050-9047-9
LC 2010-49007

When brothers Simon, Henry, and Jack move with their parents to Arizona, they are irresistably drawn to explore the aptly named Superstition Mountain, in spite of warnings that it is not safe.

"Caparo's skillful grayscale illustrations add a spooky element: three skulls mark each new chapter, and images like a black cat sitting on a crooked gravestone inspire chills. Classic horror and thriller elements combine with modern touches in Broach's page-turner." Publ Wkly

Revenge of Superstition Mountain; Elise Broach; illustrated by Aleksey and Olga Ivanov. Christy Ottaviano Books 2014 294 p. illustrations (hardback) $16.99
Grades: 3 4 5 **Fic**
1. Mystery fiction 2. Arizona -- Fiction 3. Brothers -- Fiction 4. Mountains -- Fiction 5. Mystery and detective stories 6. Superstition Mountains (Ariz.) -- Fiction
ISBN 0805089098; 9780805089097; 9781250056863
LC 2014005283

In this book, by Elise Broach, illustrated by Aleksey and Olga Ivanov, "the Barker brothers and their good friend Delilah secretly climb up to Superstition Mountain one last time. There are still mysteries to solve-is the creepy librarian really the ghost of Julia Thomas from a century before? What was their uncle Hank's role in discovering the gold mine? . . . And, most of all, who is trying to kill them?" (Publisher's note)

"The Barker brothers and Delilah are back on Superstition Mountain for one last secret climb, determined to solve its mysteries and get back into the gold mine that was covered by the avalanche in book two. A satisfying end to a fun and creepy series." SLJ

Other titles in the series include:
Missing on Superstition Mountain (2011)
Treasure on Superstition Mountain (2012)

Shakespeare's secret; [by] Elise Broach. Henry Holt 2005 250p il $16.95; pa $5.99
Grades: 5 6 7 8 **Fic**
1. Mystery fiction
ISBN 0-8050-7387-6; 0-312-37132-2 pa
LC 2004-54020

Named after a character in a Shakespeare play, misfit sixth-grader Hero becomes interested in exploring this unusual connection because of a valuable diamond supposedly hidden in her new house, an intriguing neighbor, and the unexpected attention of the most popular boy in school.

"The mystery alone will engage readers. . . . The main characters are all well developed, and the dialogue is both realistic and well planned." SLJ

Brodien-Jones, Christine
The **glass** puzzle; Christine Brodien-Jones. Delacorte Press 2013 336 p. (hc) $16.99
Grades: 4 5 6 7 **Fic**
1. Horror fiction 2. Fantasy fiction 3. Wales -- Fiction 4. Cousins -- Fiction 5. Time travel -- Fiction 6. Supernatural -- Fiction 7. Tenby (Wales) -- Fiction 8. Adventure and adventurers -- Fiction 9. Wales -- History -- 1063-1284 -- Fiction
ISBN 0385742975; 9780307979933; 9780375990878; 9780385742979; 9780385742986
LC 2012015999

In this book, Zoé Badger and her cousin find an antique glass puzzle and unwittingly release Scravens—evil creatures with a craterous third eye and massive wings—into Tenby. The cousins, in turn, are magically transported to Wythernsea, an island long submerged underwater, whence the Scravens come. There they learn that Scravens are taking over the bodies of Tenby inhabitants—as well as terrorizing Wythernsea—and that they must save both towns from the creatures." (Kirkus Reviews)

Bromley, Anne C.
The **lunch** thief; [by] Anne C. Bromley; illustrated by Robert Casilla. Tilbury House Publishers 2010 un il
Grades: 4 5 6 **Fic**
1. School stories 2. Theft -- Fiction 3. Homeless persons -- Fiction
ISBN 0-88448-311-8; 978-0-88448-311-3
LC 2008045822

Rafael is angry that a new student is stealing lunches, but he takes time to learn what the real problem is before acting.

"Full-color illustrations realistically portray the cast of characters and the boys' multicultural school. With a few well-placed remarks by Rafael's hardworking mother and no preachy overtones, this entirely credible story of how a thoughtful boy elects to 'light one candle' in response to the larger problem of homelessness and hunger would make an excellent touchstone for class discussion." SLJ

Brooks, Bruce
Everywhere. Harper & Row 1990 70p lib bdg $16.89
Grades: 4 5 6 7 **Fic**
1. Death -- Fiction 2. Grandfathers -- Fiction
ISBN 0-06-020729-9
LC 90-4073

Afraid that his beloved grandfather will die after suffering a heart attack, a nine-year-old boy agrees to join ten-year-old Dooley in performing a mysterious ritual called soul switching

"Echoes of the great Southern writers with their themes of loneliness and faith can be heard in this masterly novella. . . . Brooks's precise use of language is a tour de force." Horn Book

Brown, Susan Taylor
Hugging the rock; [by] Susan Taylor Brown; [cover illustration by Michael Morgenstern] Tricycle Press 2006 170p $14.95; pa $6.95
Grades: 5 6 7 8 **Fic**
1. Divorce -- Fiction 2. Father-daughter relationship --

Fiction 3. Mother-daughter relationship -- Fiction
ISBN 978-1-58246-180-9; 1-58246-180-5; 978-1-58246-236-3 pa; 1-58246-236-4 pa

LC 2006005738

Through a series of poems, Rachel expresses her feelings about her parents' divorce, living without her mother, and her changing attitude towards her father

"This is a poignant character study of a dysfunctional family. . . . Written in straightforward language, the text clearly reveals Rachel's emotions, describing moments both painful and reassuring." SLJ

Brown, Tami Lewis

The **map** of me. Farrar Straus Giroux 2011 152p $16.99

Grades: 4 5 6   **Fic**
1. Sisters -- Fiction 2. Kentucky -- Fiction 3. Family life -- Fiction 4. Automobile travel -- Fiction
ISBN 978-0-374-35655-2; 0-374-35655-6

LC 2010029261

Twelve-year-old Margie finds her sister, Peep, intolerable since the youngster skipped from third grade to sixth, but when their mother leaves home, Margie packs Peep into their father's car and starts driving across Kentucky to find her.

This novel "combines pathos and humor for an emotionally resonant story." Publ Wkly

Bruchac, Joseph, 1942-

The **arrow** over the door; pictures by James Watling. Dial Bks. for Young Readers 1998 89p il hardcover o.p. pa $4.99

Grades: 4 5 6   **Fic**
1. Native Americans -- Fiction 2. Society of Friends -- Fiction 3. United States -- History -- 1775-1783, Revolution -- Fiction
ISBN 0-8037-2078-5; 0-14-130571-1 pa

LC 96-36701

"Bruchac's elegant and powerful writing fills in much of the fascinating detail of this serendipitous wartime friendship. . . . Watling's rugged, textured pen-and-ink drawings provide an atmospheric backdrop." Publ Wkly

Bearwalker; [by] Joseph Bruchac; illustrations by Sally Wern Comport. HarperCollinsPublishers 2007 208p il $15.99; lib bdg $16.89; pa $5.99

Grades: 5 6 7 8   **Fic**
1. Bears -- Fiction 2. Camping -- Fiction 3. Mohawk Indians -- Fiction 4. Adirondack Mountains (N.Y.) -- Fiction
ISBN 978-0-06-112309-2; 0-06-112309-9; 978-0-06-112311-5 lib bdg; 0-06-112311-0 lib bdg; 978-0-06-112315-3 pa; 0-06-112315-3 pa

LC 2006-30420

Although the littlest student in his class, thirteen-year-old Baron Braun calls upon the strength and wisdom of his Mohawk ancestors to face both man and beast when he tries to get help for his classmates, who are being terrorized during a school field trip in the Adirondacks.

"This exciting horror story, illustrated with b/w drawings, is based on Native American folklore." Kliatt

★ The **dark** pond; illustrations by Sally Wern Comport. HarperCollins 2004 142p il hardcover o.p. pa $6.99

Grades: 5 6 7 8   **Fic**
1. Ponds -- Fiction 2. Monsters -- Fiction 3. Shawnee Indians -- Fiction
ISBN 0-06-052995-4; 0-06-052998-9 pa

LC 2003-22212

After he feels a mysterious pull drawing him toward a dark, shadowy pond in the woods, Armie looks to old Native American tales for guidance about the dangerous monster lurking in the water

"Effectively illustrated by Comport, this eerie story skillfully entwines Native American lore, suspense, and the realization that people and things are not always what they seem to be on the surface. . . . A perfect choice for reluctant readers." SLJ

Dragon castle. Dial Books for Young Readers 2011 346p $16.99

Grades: 4 5 6 7   **Fic**
1. Fairy tales 2. Dragons -- Fiction 3. Princes -- Fiction 4. Kings and rulers -- Fiction
ISBN 978-0-8037-3376-3; 0-8037-3376-3

LC 2010028798

Young prince Rashko, aided by wise old Georgi, must channel the power of his ancestor, Pavol the great, and harness a magical dragon to face the evil Baron Temny after the foolish King and Queen go missing.

Bruchac "spins a good-natured and humorous fairy tale. . . . With its subtle focus on peaceful resistance and use of classic folk-tale elements, this story exudes a gentle sense of fun." Publ Wkly

Night wings; illustrations by Sally Wern Comport. HarperCollins 2009 194p $15.99; lib bdg $16.89

Grades: 5 6 7 8   **Fic**
1. Monsters -- Fiction 2. New Hampshire -- Fiction 3. Abnaki Indians -- Fiction
ISBN 978-0-06-112318-4; 0-06-112318-8; 978-0-06-112319-1 lib bdg; 0-06-112319-6 lib bdg

LC 2008032096

After being taken captive by a band of treasure seekers, thirteen-year-old Paul and his Abenaki grandfather must face a legendary Native American monster at the top of Mount Washington.

"The intriguing Native lore, the realistic teen narrative, and cliffhanger sentences that build suspense at the end of each chapter are signature Bruchac and will captivate readers." SLJ

★ **Skeleton** man. HarperCollins Pubs. 2001 114p il $15.99; pa $4.99

Grades: 4 5 6 7   **Fic**
1. Kidnapping -- Fiction 2. Mohawk Indians -- Fiction
ISBN 0-06-029075-7; 0-06-440888-4 pa

LC 00-54345

After her parents disappear and she is turned over to the care of a strange "great-uncle," Molly must rely on her dreams about an old Mohawk story for her safety and maybe even for her life

"The mix of traditional and contemporary cultural references adds to the story's haunting appeal, and the quick pace and suspense . . . will likely hold the interest of young readers." Publ Wkly

Another title about Skeleton man is:

The return of Skeleton man (2006)

Squanto's journey; the story of the first Thanksgiving. Joseph Bruchac; illustrated by Greg Shed. Silver Whistle 2000 32 p. col. ill. (paperback) $6.99; (prebind) $15.99; (reinforced) $17

Grades: 2 3 4 5   **Fic**

1. Pilgrims (New England colonists) -- Fiction 2. Wampanoag Indians -- Fiction 3. Indians of North America -- Massachusetts -- Fiction

ISBN 9780152060442; 9781442073890; 0152018174; 9780152018177

LC 99012012

This illustrated children's book, by Joseph Bruchac, illustrated by Greg Shed, tells the story of the 17th century Native American Squanto. "In 1620 an English ship called the Mayflower landed on the shores inhabited by the Pokanoket people, and it was Squanto who welcomed the newcomers and taught them how to survive in the rugged land they called Plymouth." (Publisher's note)

Bruel, Nick

Bad Kitty; Drawn to Trouble. Nick Bruel. Roaring Brook Press 2013 128 p. (hardcover) $13.99

Grades: 2 3 4   **Fic**

1. Cartooning 2. Cats -- Fiction 3. Humorous stories 4. Authorship -- Fiction 5. Illustration of books -- Fiction

ISBN 1596436719; 9781596436718

LC 2013001633

In this book by Nick Bruel, "Kitty encounters what may be her most formidable foe yet: her creator! Kitty soon learns that feline manipulation works both ways--especially when you're at the wrong end of your author's pencil. Along the way, Nick shows kids how a book is created, despite the frequent interruptions." (Publisher's note)

"Bad Kitty makes her tenth appearance in this humorous (and partly nonfiction!) introduction to writing stories. Bruel teaches readers how to draw Bad Kitty and write stories of their own by introducing key story components (plot, conflict, character, etc.) and demonstrating them with good old Bad Kitty, who proves an unwilling model...Fun Facts and a glossary are included to help readers grasp the fundamentals of composition. Bruel's sky's-the-limit attitude will encourage boys and girls to use their imaginations and get writing." (Booklist)

Bad Kitty gets a bath. Roaring Brook Press 2008 125p il $12.95

Grades: 2 3 4   **Fic**

1. Cats -- Fiction 2. Baths -- Fiction

ISBN 978-1-59643-341-0; 1-59643-341-8

LC 2008-20296

Takes a humorous look at the normal way cats bathe, why it is inappropriate for humans to bathe that way, and the challenges of trying to give a cat a real bath with soap and water. Includes fun facts, glossary, and other information.

This "pairs Bruel's witty asides and spastic, tongue-in-cheek commentaries with more high-energy cartoon illustrations. . . . Young and reluctant readers will get plenty of laughs from this comic and informative chapter book." Booklist

Bad kitty meets the baby. Roaring Brook Press 2011 143p il $13.99

Grades: 2 3 4   **Fic**

1. Cats -- Fiction 2. Infants -- Fiction 3. Adoption -- Fiction

ISBN 978-1-59643-597-1; 1-59643-597-6

LC 2010035699

Bad kitty is not pleased when a baby joins her family. Includes fun facts and tips for training a cat to perform tricks.

Bruel "offers his trademark spastic black-and-white illustrations in full-bleed and spots with plenty of baby and cat sounds in dialogue bubbles (translated into English where necessary). . . . Further proof that Bad Kitty can be good . . . especially in the eyes of her many fans." Kirkus

Bad Kitty vs. Uncle Murray; the uproar at the front door. Roaring Brook Press 2010 157p il $13.99

Grades: 2 3 4   **Fic**

1. Cats -- Fiction

ISBN 978-1-59643-596-4; 1-59643-596-8

Uncle Murray "is here to 'pet sit' Bad Kitty and Poor Puppy. The feline is not happy with this arrangement and gives Uncle Murray a horrible time. . . . Different fonts and huge scrawling words appear throughout, and the black-and-white cartoons on every page often show Bad Kitty and Murray with exaggerated gestures. The style gives the book a fast pace and adds to the comedic atmosphere." SLJ

Happy birthday Bad Kitty. Roaring Brook Press 2009 159p il $13.99

Grades: 2 3 4   **Fic**

1. Cats -- Fiction 2. Birthdays -- Fiction

ISBN 978-1-59643-342-7; 1-59643-342-6

"Bad Kitty's day starts off with a special alphabetical "Birthday Breakfast" that includes Aardvark Bagels, Clam Doughnuts and Eel Fritters. Each chapter focuses on a different part of the day's festivities. . . . The story becomes a whodunit when Bad Kitty's presents vanish and the prime suspect ends up being the lovable slow-wit, Puppy. . . . Bruel has fun with the format, using footnotes, different font sizes, comedic/informative interludes about cat behavior. . . . As usual, it's Bad Kitty's unapologetic, curmudgeon nature that delivers the laugh-out-loud funny." SLJ

Buckley, Michael

The **fairy-tale** detectives; pictures by Peter Ferguson. Amulet Books 2005 284p il (The sisters Grimm) $15.95

Grades: 4 5 6   **Fic**

1. Fairy tales 2. Orphans -- Fiction 3. Sisters -- Fiction 4. Monsters -- Fiction 5. Grandmothers -- Fiction

ISBN 0-8109-5925-9

LC 2005011784

"After the mysterious disappearance of their parents, Sabrina and Daphne Grimm spend a year and a half as victims of New York's foster care system until a woman claiming to be their long-dead grandmother comes to claim them. . . . Granny reveals to the girls that they are descendants of the Brothers Grimm, and the fairy tales that the brothers wrote are actually a history of the magical people known as 'Everafters.' . . . Sabrina and Daphne are intrepid heroines, and the modern interpretations of familiar fairy-tale characters are often truly hilarious." Voice Youth Advocates

Other titles in this series are:

The usual suspects (2005)
The problem child (2006)
Once upon a crime (2007)

Magic and other misdemeanors (2007)
Tales from the hood (2008)
The Everafter War (2009)
The inside story (2010)

Burg, Ann E.
Serafina's promise; by Ann E. Burg. Scholastic Press 2013 304 p. (alk. paper) $16.99
Grades: 5 6 7 8   **Fic**
1. Girls -- Fiction 2. Floods -- Fiction 3. Haiti -- Social conditions 4. Novels in verse 5. Haiti -- Fiction 6. Earthquakes -- Fiction 7. Brothers and sisters -- Fiction 8. Family life -- Haiti -- Fiction 9. Port-au-Prince (Haiti) -- Fiction
ISBN 0545535646; 9780545535649
LC 2012045609
Parents' Choice: Gold Medal Fiction (2013)
In this book, by Ann E. Burg, "Serafina is an 11-year-old Haitian struggling to keep her dream of becoming a doctor alive. Living in a desolate mountain village, Serafina toils at her daily chores while planning to attend school . Serafina has a warm family . . . who all come to support her vision. Then a flood washes away the family home, and the roaring stampede of an earthquake devastates the city of Port-au-Prince, where Serafina's father works." (Publisher's note)

Burnett, Frances Hodgson
A **little** princess; illustrated by Tasha Tudor. Harper-Collins 1999 245p il (Illustrated junior library) $17.99; pa $6.99
Grades: 4 5 6   **Fic**
1. School stories 2. Great Britain -- Fiction
ISBN 978-0-3973-0693-0; 0-3973-06938; 978-0-06-440187-6 pa; 0-06-440187-1 pa
First American edition published 1892 by Scribner in shorter form with title: Sara Crewe
The story of Sara Crewe, a girl who is sent from India to a boarding school in London, left in poverty by her father's death, and rescued by a mysterious benefactor
"The story is inevitably adorned with sentimental curlicues but the reader will hardly notice them since the story itself is such a satisfying one. Tasha Tudor's gentle, appropriate illustrations make this a lovely edition." Publ Wkly

The **secret** garden; illustrated by Inga Moore. Candlewick Press 2008 278p il $21.99
Grades: 3 4 5 6   **Fic**
1. Gardens -- Fiction 2. Orphans -- Fiction 3. Great Britain -- Fiction
ISBN 0-7636-3161-2; 978-0-7636-3161-1
LC 2006051838
First published 1911
A ten-year-old orphan comes to live in a lonely house on the Yorkshire moors where she discovers an invalid cousin and the mysteries of a locked garden.
"Burnett's tale . . . is presented in an elegant, oversize volume and handsomely illustrated with Moore's detailed ink and watercolor paintings. Cleanly laid-out text pages are balanced by artwork ranging from delicate spot images to full-page renderings." SLJ

Burns, Khephra
Mansa Musa; the lion of Mali. illustrated by Leo & Diane Dillon. Harcourt 2001 un il $18

Grades: 4 5 6 7   **Fic**
1. Kings 2. Mali -- Fiction
ISBN 0-15-200375-4
LC 97-50559
A fictional account of the nomadic wanderings of the boy who grew up to become Mali's great fourteenth-century leader, Mansa Musa
This is "part coming-of-age tale, part cautionary tale, and part fairy tale. . . . Burn's story moves in a languid magical atmosphere beautifully supported by the Dillons' jewel-like illustrations and stylized text ornaments, which, together with parchment-colored pages, give the impression of an illuminated manuscript." Horn Book

Butler, Dori Hillestad
The **case** of the lost boy; pictures by Jeremy Tugeau. Albert Whitman 2010 123p il (The Buddy files) $14.99
Grades: 1 2 3   **Fic**
1. Mystery fiction 2. Dogs -- Fiction 3. Missing children -- Fiction
ISBN 978-0-8075-0910-4; 0-8075-0910-8
LC 2009-23763
While searching for his mysteriously lost human family, King the dog detective is adoped by another family, who names him Buddy.
"The type is large, the text is easy, and the occasional black-and-white illustrations complement the text well. The clues are unique and true to the fact that a dog is telling the story." SLJ
Other titles in this series are:
The case of the mixed up mutts (2010)
The case of the fire alarm (2010)
The case of the missing family (2010)
The case of the library monster (2011)

The **truth** about Truman School; by Dori Hillestad Butler. Albert Whitman 2008 170p $15.95; pa $7.99
Grades: 5 6 7 8   **Fic**
1. School stories 2. Bullies -- Fiction 3. Journalism -- Fiction 4. Newspapers -- Fiction
ISBN 978-0-8075-8095-0; 0-8075-8095-3; 978-0-8075-8096-7 pa; 0-8075-8096-1 pa
LC 2007-29977
Tired of being told what to write by the school newspaper's advisor, Zibby and her friend Amr start an underground newspaper online where everyone is free to post anything, but things spiral out of control when a cyberbully starts using the site to harrass one popular girl.
"The story moves at a good pace and the timely subject of cyberbullying will be relevant to readers. The language is accessible and the students' voices ring true." SLJ

Butterworth, Oliver
★ The **enormous** egg; illustrated by Louis Darling. Little, Brown 1956 187p il hardcover o.p. pa $6.99
Grades: 4 5 6 7   **Fic**
1. Dinosaurs -- Fiction
ISBN 0-316-11920-2 pa
This story is "great fun. . . . And if you have any trouble visualizing a Triceratops moving placidly through the twentieth-century world you need only turn to Louis Darling's illustrations to believe." NY Times Book Rev
"Up in Freedom, New Hampshire, one of the Twitchell's hens laid a remarkable egg. . . . Six weeks later when a live

dinosaur hatched from the egg, the hen was dazed and upset, the Twitchells dumbfounded, and the scientific world went crazy. Twelve-year-old Nate who had taken care of the egg and made a pet out of the triceratops tells of the hullabaloo." Booklist

Buyea, Rob

★ **Because** of Mr. Terupt. Delacorte Press 2010 269p $16.99; lib bdg $19.99

Grades: 4 5 6   **Fic**

1. School stories 2. Teachers -- Fiction 3. Connecticut -- Fiction 4. Family life -- Fiction

ISBN 0-385-73882-X; 0-385-90749-4 lib bdg; 978-0-385-73882-8; 978-0-385-90749-1 lib bdg

LC 2010-03414

Seven fifth-graders at Snow Hill School in Connecticut relate how their lives are changed for the better by "rookie teacher" Mr. Terupt. "Grades four to six." (Bull Cent Child Books)

"Introducing characters and conflicts that will be familiar to any middle-school student, this powerful and emotional story is likely to spur discussion." Publ Wkly

Mr. Terupt falls again; Rob Buyea. Delacorte Press 2012 356 p. (hc) $16.99

Grades: 4 5 6   **Fic**

1. Love stories 2. School stories 3. Teacher-student relationship -- Fiction 4. Summer -- Fiction 5. Classrooms -- Fiction

ISBN 0385742053; 9780375989100; 9780375990380; 9780385742054

LC 2012010897

This book is a follow-up to Rob Buyea's "Because of Mr. Terupt." Here, "looping with his students into sixth grade, Mr. Terupt continues to surprise them with challenging projects and perfect reading suggestions." For the seven students who narrate the story, "family worries go along with lingering questions about the health of their teacher. Sixth-grade relationships and a grown-up romance" are also explored. (Kirkus)

Byars, Betsy Cromer

The **dark** stairs; a Herculeah Jones mystery. by Betsy Byars. Viking 1994 130p hardcover o.p. pa $5.99

Grades: 4 5 6   **Fic**

1. Mystery fiction

ISBN 0-670-85487-5; 0-14-240592-2 pa

LC 94-14012

The intrepid Herculeah Jones helps her mother, a private investigator, solve a puzzling and frightening case

"There is plenty to laugh at in this book, including classic chapter headings guaranteed to cause shivers for the uninitiated; practiced mystery readers may feel that they are in on a bit of a joke and appreciate the hint of parody. This is a page-turner that is sure to entice the most reluctant readers." SLJ

Other titles about Herculeah Jones are:

Tarot says beware (1995)
Dead letter (1996)
Death's door (1997)
Disappearing acts (1998)
The black tower (2006)
King of murder (2006)

The **keeper** of the doves; by Betsy Byars. Viking 2002 121p $14.99; pa $5.99

Grades: 4 5 6 7   **Fic**

1. Sisters -- Fiction 2. Kentucky -- Fiction 3. Family life -- Fiction

ISBN 0-670-03576-9; 0-14-240063-7 pa

LC 2002-9283

In the late 1800s in Kentucky, Amie McBee and her four sisters both fear and torment the reclusive and seemingly sinister Mr. Tominski, but their father continues to provide for his needs

"This is Byars at her best—witty, appealing, thought-provoking." Horn Book

Little Horse; [by] Betsy Byars; illustrated by David McPhail. Holt & Co. 2001 45p il $15.95

Grades: 1 2 3   **Fic**

1. Horses -- Fiction

ISBN 0-8050-6413-3

LC 00-40983

Little Horse falls into the stream and is swept away into a dangerous adventure and a new life

"Byars deftly combines crisp action with a lyrically evoked setting. Language is simple, but not simplistic; uncommon terms are clearly defined in the text and the soft black-and-white art." Horn Book Guide

Another title about Little Horse is:

Little Horse on his own (2004)

★ The **pinballs**; [by] Betsy Byars. Harper & Row 1977 136p lib bdg $16.89; pa $5.99

Grades: 5 6 7 8   **Fic**

1. Friendship -- Fiction 2. Foster home care -- Fiction

ISBN 0-06-020918-6 lib bdg; 0-06-440198-7 pa

"A deceptively simple, eloquent story, its pain and acrimony constantly mitigated by the author's light, offhand style and by Carlie's wryly comic view of life." Horn Book

The **SOS** file; [by] Betsy Byars, Betsy Duffey, Laurie Myers; illustrated by Arthur Howard. Henry Holt 2004 71p il $15.95

Grades: 3 4 5   **Fic**

1. School stories

ISBN 0-8050-6888-0

LC 2003-18240

The students in Mr. Magro's class submit stories for the SOS file about their biggest emergencies, and then they read them aloud for extra credit

"Some tales are poignant, others are humorous; all are as credible as the characters sketched. . . . Lighthearted sketches enhance characterization. . . . [An] engaging, plausible, and highly readable collection of anecdotes." SLJ

★ **Tornado**; by Betsy Byars; illustrations by Doron Ben-Ami. HarperCollins Pubs. 1996 49p il lib bdg $15.89; pa $4.99

Grades: 2 3 4   **Fic**

1. Dogs -- Fiction 2. Tornadoes -- Fiction

ISBN 0-06-026452-7 lib bdg; 0-06-442063-9 pa

LC 95-41584

As they wait out a tornado in their storm cellar, a family listens to their farmhand tell stories about the dog that was blown into his life by another tornado when he was a boy

"The handsome illustrations by Doron Ben-Ami give the volume a more distinguished, less juvenile look than the typical chapter book and convey the story's drama, warmth, and occasional humor. Parents and teachers will find this an excellent book to read aloud, and dog lovers of any age will find it irresistible." Booklist

Cabot, Meg

Allie Finkle's rules for girls: book two; The new girl; [by] Meg Cabot. 1st ed.; Scholastic Press 2008 222p $15.99

Grades: 3 4 5   **Fic**

1. School stories 2. Moving -- Fiction 3. Bullies -- Fiction 4. Friendship -- Fiction 5. Family life -- Fiction 6. Grandmothers -- Fiction

ISBN 978-0-545-04049-5; 0-545-04049-3

LC 2007050719

Guided by her rules, nine-year-old Allie works to get past being just the new girl at school, eagerly awaits the arrival of her kitten, and faces turmoil when her grandmother visits while the family is still settling into their new home.

Part of the series "Allie Finkle's rules for girls".

Moving day. Scholastic Press 2008 228p (Allie Finkle's rules for girls) $15.99; pa $5.99

Grades: 3 4 5   **Fic**

1. School stories 2. Moving -- Fiction 3. Friendship -- Fiction 4. Family life -- Fiction

ISBN 978-0-545-03947-5; 0-545-03947-9; 978-0-545-04041-9 pa; 0-545-04041-8 pa

LC 2007-27836

Nine-year-old Allie Finkle has rules for everything and is even writing her own rule book, but her world is turned upside-down when she learns that her family is moving across town, which will mean a new house, school, best friend, and plenty of new rules.

Cabot's "trademark frank humor makes for compulsive reading—as always. . . . Allie is funny, believable and plucky . . . but most of all, and most interestingly, Allie is ambivalent." Publ Wkly

Other titles in this series are:

The new girl (2008)

Best friends and drama queens (2009)

Stage fright (2009)

Glitter girls and the great fake out (2010)

Blast from the past (2010)

Cadenhead, Mackenzie

Sally's bones; illustrated by T. S. Spookytooth. Sourcebook Jabberwocky 2011 il pa $6.99

Grades: 4 5 6   **Fic**

1. Mystery fiction 2. Dogs -- Fiction 3. Skeleton -- Fiction

ISBN 978-1-4022-5943-2; 1-4022-5943-3

2 Months, 28 Days, 9 Hours, and 12 minutes earlier Sally Simplesmith's life changed forever. She came face-to-face with death a delightful, dearly departed little dog she lovingly calls Bones. But when the cadaverous canine is accused of a crime he didn't commit, Sally decides to solve the case herself!

"Writing a novel that tackles tough issues like grief and loss while maintaining a measure of levity is no easy feat, but that is exactly what Cadenhead accomplishes here. . . .

Spooky without being scary, dark without being morbid, this is a winning tale about loyalty in the face of loss." Booklist

Calkhoven, Laurie

Daniel at the Siege of Boston, 1776. Dutton Children's Books 2010 195p (Boys of wartime) $16.99

Grades: 4 5 6 7   **Fic**

1. Spies -- Fiction 2. Patriotism -- Fiction 3. Family life -- Fiction 4. Boston (Mass.) -- Fiction 5. United States -- History -- 1775-1783, Revolution -- Fiction

ISBN 978-0-525-42144-3; 0-525-42144-0

LC 2009012125

In 1776 Boston, twelve-year-old Daniel Prescott enjoys assuming his father's role in taking care of his mother and sister, as well as his work as a spy and messenger for the American revolutionaries, but the pleasure ends when he witnesses the horrors of war firsthand, and learns that a trusted patriot is actually a British spy.

"This historical novel weaves actual people, places, and events of the Siege of Boston into an engaging fictional narrative." Booklist

Michael at the invasion of France, 1943; by Laurie Calkhoven. Dial Books for Young Readers 2012 231 p. (hardcover) $16.99

Grades: 4 5 6 7   **Fic**

1. Children and war -- Fiction 2. Holocaust, 1939-1945 -- Fiction 3. France -- History -- 1940-1945, German occupation -- Fiction 4. World War, 1939-1945 -- Underground movements -- France -- Fiction 5. France -- History -- German occupation, 1940-1945 -- Fiction

ISBN 0803737246; 9780803737242

LC 2011021634

In this young adult novel, a "young Parisian joins the French Resistance in this Boys of Wartime series entry. . . . Michael joins a friend in distributing taunting leaflets. His involvement in Resistance activities soon escalates into helping captured British and American airmen make their way to Spain. At first he acts only as a courier of forged identity documents, but later he helps first to slip a Jewish neighbor's child out of the city, then hides an ailing American. . . . Meanwhile, he serves as a witness to . . . wartime life under the Nazis, while seeing friends, neighbors and his own older brother taken away and ultimately earning sufficient self-esteem to lose his dependence on his father's regard." (Kirkus

Includes bibliographical references

Will at the Battle of Gettysburg, 1863. Dutton Children's Books 2011 230p (Boys of wartime) $16.99

Grades: 4 5 6 7   **Fic**

1. Gettysburg (Pa.), Battle of, 1863 -- Fiction 2. United States -- History -- 1861-1865, Civil War -- Fiction

ISBN 978-0-525-42145-0; 0-525-42145-9

LC 2010013307

In 1863, twelve-year-old Will, who longs to be a drummer in the Union army, is stuck in his sleepy hometown of Gettysburg, Pennsylvania, but when the Union and Confederate armies meet right there in his town, he and his family are caught up in the fight. Includes historical notes, glossary, and a timeline of events.

"This solid piece of fiction will appeal to history buffs and reluctant readers alike." SLJ

Includes glossary and bibliographical references

Cameron, Ann

Colibri. Farrar, Straus & Giroux 2003 227p $17; pa $5.99

Grades: 5 6 7 8   **Fic**

1. Mayas -- Fiction 2. Kidnapping -- Fiction

ISBN 0-374-31519-1; 0-440-42052-0 pa

LC 2002-192542

Kidnapped when she was very young by an unscrupulous man who has forced her to lie and beg to get money, a twelve-year-old Mayan girl endures an abusive life, always wishing she could return to the parents she can hardly remember

"The taut, chilling suspense and search for riches will keep readers flying through the pages. But it's Cameron's beautiful language and Rosa's larger identity quest that make this novel extraordinary." Booklist

Gloria's way; pictures by Lis Toft. Farrar, Straus & Giroux 2000 96p il hardcover o.p. pa $4.99

Grades: 2 3 4   **Fic**

1. Friendship -- Fiction 2. Family life -- Fiction 3. African Americans -- Fiction

ISBN 0-374-32670-3; 0-14-230023-3 pa

LC 99-12104

This companion volume to the series featuring Julian and Huey centers on their friend Gloria. Gloria shares special times with her mother and father and with her friends

"Lis Toft's shaded pencil drawings portray these African American characters and their predicaments with warmth and humor." Booklist

Another title about Gloria is:

Gloria rising (2002)

★ Spunky tells all; pictures by Lauren Castillo. Farrar Straus Giroux 2011 105p il $15.99

Grades: 2 3 4   **Fic**

1. Cats -- Fiction 2. Dogs -- Fiction

ISBN 978-0-374-38000-7; 0-374-38000-7

LC 2010019815

Called a troublemaker by his human family, a reflective dog defends himself and then relates the family's adoption of an aristocratic but incompetent cat, who gives him a life purpose and and new way of looking at his world.

"Readers ready for chapter books will delight in seeing the world through Spunky's eyes and powerful nose." Kirkus

★ The stories Julian tells; illustrated by Ann Strugnell. Pantheon Bks. 1981 71p il hardcover o.p. pa $4.99

Grades: 2 3 4   **Fic**

1. Family life -- Fiction 2. African Americans -- Fiction

ISBN 0-394-82892-5 pa

LC 80-18023

"Strugnell's delightful drawings depict Julian, his little brother Huey and their parents as black, but they could be members of any family with a stern but loving and understanding father." Publ Wkly

Other titles about Julian and his family are:

Julian, dream doctor (1990)

Julian, secret agent (1988)

Julian's glorious summer (1987)

More stories Huey tells (1997)

More stories Julian tells (1986)

The stories Huey tells (1995)

Cameron, Anne

The lightning catcher; by Anne Cameron. Greenwillow Books, an imprint of HarperCollinsPublishers 2013 432 p. (trade ed.) $16.99

Grades: 4 5 6   **Fic**

1. Storms -- Fiction 2. Fantasy fiction 3. Weather -- Fiction 4. Adventure and adventurers -- Fiction

ISBN 9780062112767; 0062112767

LC 2012042848

The young adult fantasy book, "The Lightning Catcher," is the first in a four-book series by Anne Cameron. Here, 11-year-old Angus McFangus, a "trainee at the Perilous Exploratorium for Violent Weather and Vicious Storms on the Isle of Imbur, tries to find his missing parents and prevent the unleashing of an eternal storm." The adventure story features themes including world domination. (Kirkus Reviews)

Cammuso, Frank

The Misadventures of Salem Hyde; Spelling Trouble. Harry N Abrams Inc 2013 96 p.

Grades: 2 3 4   **Fic**

1. Occult fiction 2. School stories

ISBN 1419708031; 9781419708039

This is the first book in Frank Cammuso's Salem Hyde series. Here, "Salem Hyde just wants a friend. After a misguided attempt to use her magic lands her in the principal's office, Salem's family decides she needs an animal companion. One well-placed call later, she meets knowledgeable and talkative feline Percival J. Whamsford III, otherwise known as Whammy. Whammy isn't just a chatty kitty; he is a Magical Animal Companion and will help Salem learn how to use her magic properly." (Kirkus Reviews)

Carbone, Elisa Lynn

Blood on the river; James Town 1607. [by] Elisa Carbone. Viking 2006 237p $16.99; pa $6.99

Grades: 5 6 7 8   **Fic**

1. Powhatan Indians -- Fiction 2. Jamestown (Va.) -- History -- Fiction 3. United States -- History -- 1600-1775, Colonial period -- Fiction

ISBN 0-670-06060-7; 0-14-240932-4 pa

LC 2005023646

Traveling to the New World in 1606 as the page to Captain John Smith, twelve-year-old orphan Samuel Collier settles in the new colony of James Town, where he must quickly learn to distinguish between friend and foe.

"A strong, visceral story of the hardship and peril settlers faced, as well as the brutal realities of colonial conquest." Booklist

Storm warriors; [by] Elisa Carbone. Knopf 2001 168p hardcover o.p. pa $6.50

Grades: 4 5 6 7   **Fic**

1. North Carolina -- Fiction 2. African Americans -- Fiction 3. United States -- Life-Saving Service -- Fiction

ISBN 0-375-80664-4; 0-440-41879-8 pa

LC 00-59924

In 1895, after his mother's death, twelve-year-old Nathan moves with his father and grandfather to Pea Island off the coast of North Carolina, where he hopes to join the all-black crew at the nearby lifesaving station, despite his father's objections

"This thoughtfully crafted first-person narrative combines historical figures with created characters in the best traditions of the historical novel." Horn Book Guide

Carey, Benedict

Poison most vial; a mystery. by Benedict Carey. Amulet Books 2012 215 p. (hardcover) $16.95

Grades: 5 6 7 8   Fic

1. Mystery fiction 2. Forensic sciences -- Fiction 3. Murder -- Fiction 4. Neighbors -- Fiction 5. Mystery and detective stories 6. Fathers and daughters -- Fiction

ISBN 1419700316; 9781419700316

LC 2011038222

In this novel by Benedict Carey "Ruby's janitor father becomes the prime suspect in a murder . . . [of] [f]orensics expert Dr. Ramachandran . . . [and] the eighth grader decides it's up to her to clear his name. . . . [She] enlists the aid of her large, Jamaican buddy, Rex, and reclusive, retired toxicologist Clara Whitmore, who lives in Ruby's building. What with hacking into computers, evading gangs and like spy-jinx, the mystery demands a lot of brain work." (Kirkus)

Carlson, Natalie Savage

The **family** under the bridge; pictures by Garth Williams. Harper & Row 1958 99p il lib bdg $16.89; pa $5.99

Grades: 3 4 5   Fic

1. Tramps -- Fiction 2. Christmas -- Fiction 3. Paris (France) -- Fiction

ISBN 0-06-020991-7 lib bdg; 0-06-440250-9 pa

A Newbery Medal honor book, 1959

"Garth Williams' illustrations are perfect for this thoroughly delightful story of humor and sentiment." Libr J

"Old Armand, a Parisian hobo, enjoyed his solitary, carefree life. . . . Then came a day just before Christmas when Armand, who wanted nothing to do with children because they spelled homes, responsibility, and regular work, found that three homeless children and their working mother had claimed his shelter under the bridge. How the hobo's heart and life become more and more deeply entangled with the little family and their quest for a home is told." Booklist

Carman, Patrick

The **field** of wacky inventions; Patrick Carman. Scholastic Press 2013 224 p. (jacketed hardcover) $16.99

Grades: 3 4 5 6   Fic

1. Fantasy fiction 2. Voyages and travels 3. Adventure stories 4. Puzzles -- Fiction 5. Hotels, motels, etc. -- Fiction

ISBN 054525521X; 9780545255219

LC 2013006690

This is the final book in Patrick Carman's hotel trilogy. "With their parents away on their honeymoon and Merganzer D. Whippet looking after them, stepbrothers Leo and Remi are poised for adventure. . . . The boys have just spent a week or so knocking about learning its secrets. They have missed a rather big one though, which becomes evident when the entire top floor lifts off of the building. They travel a vast, mysterious distance." (Children's Literature)

Floors. Scholastic Press 2011 261p $16.99

Grades: 3 4 5 6   Fic

1. Puzzles -- Fiction 2. Hotels and motels -- Fiction 3.

Eccentrics and eccentricities -- Fiction

ISBN 978-0-545-25519-6; 0-545-25519-8

LC 2011032516

Ten-year-old Leo's future and the fate of the extraordinary Whippet Hotel, where his father is the maintenance man, are at stake when a series of cryptic boxes leads Leo to hidden floors, strange puzzles, and unexpected alliances.

"The author is a fine storyteller; he rides the mystery right up to the edge invests his characters with quirks that aren't merely cute but essential to the person's identity." Kirkus

Carmichael, Clay

★ **Wild** things; [written and illustrated by Clay Carmichael] Front Street 2009 248p il $18.95

Grades: 5 6 7 8   Fic

1. Cats -- Fiction 2. Uncles -- Fiction 3. Artists -- Fiction 4. Orphans -- Fiction 5. Family life -- Fiction

ISBN 978-1-59078-627-7; 1-59078-627-0

LC 2007-49911

Stubborn, self-reliant, eleven-year-old Zoe, recently orphaned, moves to the country to live with her prickly half-uncle, a famous doctor and sculptor, and together they learn about trust and the strength of family

"Carmichael gives a familiar plot a fresh new life in this touching story with a finely crafted sense of place." Booklist

Carris, Joan Davenport

Welcome to the Bed & Biscuit; [by] Joan Carris; illustrated by Noah Jones. Candlewick Press 2006 116p il $15.99; pa $5.99

Grades: 2 3 4   Fic

1. Animals -- Fiction 2. Veterinarians -- Fiction

ISBN 0-7636-2151-X; 0-7636-4621-0 pa

LC 2004062857

The family animals at the Bed & Biscuit begin to feel slighted when Dr. Bender returns from a fire with something that occupies the time usually reserved for them.

"This is a small, remarkably sweet beginning chapter book with more than its fair share of amusing illustrations and gentle humor." SLJ

Another title about the Bed & Biscuit is:

Wild times at the Bed & Biscuit (2009)

Wild times at the Bed & Biscuit; [by] Joan Carris; illustrated by Noah Z. Jones. Candlewick Press 2009 124p il $15.99; pa $5.99

Grades: 2 3 4   Fic

1. Animals -- Fiction 2. Veterinarians -- Fiction

ISBN 978-0-7636-3705-7; 0-7636-3705-X; 978-0-7636-5294-4 pa; 0-7636-5294-6 pa

LC 2008-938398

Ever since Grampa Bender opened his doors (and veterinary skills) to a despondent Canada goose, a cranky muskrat, and two tiny but rebellious fox kits, his animal boarding house has been turned upside down.

This "would make a great read-aloud for the primary grades and is sure to be a hit with competent easy-chapter-book readers." SLJ

Carroll, Lewis, 1832-1898

Alice's adventures in Wonderland; illustrated by Alison Jay. Dial Books for Young Readers 2006 203p il $25.99

Grades: 4 5 6 7   **Fic**

1. Fantasy fiction

ISBN 0-8037-2940-5

Alice falls down a rabbit hole and discovers a world of nonsensical and amusing characters.

"Heavy white pages and spacious book design showcase Jay's distinctive paintings. Combining elegance with innocence, the artwork features rounded forms of people, trees, and animals that are each a little apart from the others, isolated in a splendid but strange dream world. . . . The paintings glow with color under the crackle-glaze textured varnish." Booklist

Lewis Carroll's Alice in Wonderland; illustrated by Rodney Matthews. Candlewick Press 2009 95p il $24.99
Grades: 4 5 6 7   **Fic**

1. Fantasy fiction

ISBN 978-0-7636-4568-7; 0-7636-4568-0

On a hot summer day, a little girl sitting by her sister on the bank, having nothing to do, begins to let her imagination grow. Her curiosity and hatred of logic cause her to dream of a nonsensical world filled with amusing characters

Matthews' illustrations "have an imagination-stretching, otherworldly veneer. . . . The cartoon artwork portrays Alice with a somewhat angular face and straight blond hair. The depictions of the other characters are fresh and creative. . . . The small-size type, which may demand more accomplished or patient readers, and the sophisticated visual tone make this volume appropriate for older Alice fans." SLJ

Carroll, Michael Owen, 1966-

Hunter; a Super human clash. Michael Carroll. Philomel Books, an imprint of Penguin Group (USA) 2014 360 p. hbk $16.99
Grades: 5 6 7 8 9   **Fic**

1. Superheroes -- Fiction 2. Supervillains -- Fiction

ISBN 0399163670; 9780399163678

LC 2013024006

"The defeat of the near-invincible villain Krodin has left a void in the superhuman hierarchy, a void that two opposing factors are trying to fill. The powerful telepath Max Dalton believes that the human race must be controlled and shepherded to a safe future, while his rival Casey Duval believes that strength can only be achieved through conflict." (Publisher's note)

"After parting ways with the superhumans, Lance relies on his persuasive skills to make his way in the world and evade mind-controlling Max Dalton. This fourth book follows Lance's journey over the years, from working in a traveling circus to running his own global organization. Series followers will appreciate con-man Lance's character development and the implications of the story's surprising conclusion." Horn Book

Other titles in this series are:

Super Human (2010)

The Ascension (2011)

Stronger (2012)

Super human; Michael Carroll. Philomel Books 2010 325 p. ill. (hardcover) $16.99; (paperback) $8.99

Grades: 5 6 7 8 9   **Fic**

1. Superheroes -- Fiction 2. Good and evil -- Fiction

ISBN 9780399252976; 9780142419052; 0142419052; 0399252975

LC 2009-29965

A group of teenage superheroes tackle a powerful warrior who has been brought back from 4,000 years in the past to enslave the modern world. "Grades eight to ten." (Bull Cent Child Books)

The "exuberant prose is just right for setting, story, and characters alike-this is basically a novel-length superhero comic, sans illustrations, and should easily appeal to fans of the X-Men, Justice League, etc." Publ Wkly

"There is enough fighting in this book to appeal to middle school boys, and the telekinetic Roz, with a controlling superhero big brother, will appeal to girls. This title is a fast read with tension, suspense, and likeable characters." Libr Media Connect

Followed by: The ascension: a super human clash (2011)

Casanova, Mary

The **klipfish** code; by Mary Casanova. Houghton Mifflin Company 2007 227p map $16
Grades: 4 5 6 7   **Fic**

1. Norway -- Fiction 2. Family life -- Fiction 3. World War, 1939-1945 -- Norway -- Fiction 4. World War, 1939-1945 -- Underground movements -- Fiction

ISBN 978-0-618-88393-6; 0-618-88393-2

LC 2007012752

Sent with her younger brother to Godøy Island to live with her aunt and grandfather after Germans bomb Norway in 1940, ten-year-old Merit longs to join her parents in the Resistance and when her aunt, a teacher, is taken away two years later, she resents even more the Nazis' presence and her grandfather's refusal to oppose them.

"Casanova spins an adventure-filled and harrowing story." SLJ

Includes glossary and bibliographical references

Cassidy, Cathy

Dizzy; a novel. by Cathy Cassidy. Viking 2004 247p hardcover o.p. pa $6.99
Grades: 5 6 7 8   **Fic**

1. Great Britain -- Fiction 2. Mother-daughter relationship -- Fiction

ISBN 0-670-05936-6; 0-14-240474-8 pa

LC 2004-1642

After an eight-year absence, Dizzy's "New Age traveler" mother suddenly shows up on her twelfth birthday and whisks her away to a series of festivals throughout Scotland in her rattletrap van.

"The eclectic characters and their lifestyle are presented as captivating yet questionable in the girl's first-person narrative, and the well-developed plot fosters concern for Dizzy from the beginning. A unique, satisfying story." SLJ

Indigo Blue. Viking 2005 215p hardcover o.p. pa $6.99
Grades: 5 6 7 8   **Fic**

1. Moving -- Fiction 2. Abused women -- Fiction 3. Great Britain -- Fiction

ISBN 0-670-05927-7; 0-14-240703-8 pa

Eleven-year-old Indigo, her mother, and her toddler sister have to move out of their apartment because of troubles with Mum's boyfriend, while Indie is also having best friend problems at school, leaving her stressed, confused, and lonely.

"This British story of domestic abuse is firmly child-centered, and Indigo's confusion and fear . . . are sensitively portrayed. . . . The hopeful ending rings true." Booklist

Catalanotto, Peter

No more pumpkins; [by] Peter Catalanotto and Pamela Schembri. Henry Holt 2007 62p (2nd-grade friends) $15.95

Grades: 1 2 3   **Fic**
1. School stories 2. Pumpkin -- Fiction 3. Friendship -- Fiction

ISBN 978-0-8050-7839-8; 0-8050-7839-8
LC 2006035464

Second-grader Emily is tired of pumpkins being at the center of every lesson in school, but she is not prepared when a jealous friend damages the jacko-lantern portrait Emily made for Open House

"The black-and-white illustrations are well done and expressive. Fans of Barbara Park's 'Junie B. Jones' series and Patricia Reilly Giff's 'Polk Street School' books . . . will enjoy this beginning chapter book." SLJ

Other titles in this series are:
The secret lunch special (2006)
The Veteran's Day visitor (2008)

Catanese, P. W.

Dragon games. Aladdin 2010 373p il (The books of Umber) $16.99

Grades: 5 6 7 8   **Fic**
1. Fantasy fiction 2. Adventure fiction

ISBN 1-4169-7521-7; 978-1-4169-7521-2
LC 2009018743

Sequel to: Happenstance found (2009)

This is a sequel to Happenstance Found (2009). Having learned more about his mysterious past, Happenstance accompanies Lord Umber on a journey that could affect the future of Kuraharen. "Grades seven to ten." (Bull Cent Child Books)

"The fast-paced and high-energy action of this video-game-like quest will please fantasy adventure fans." Kirkus

Happenstance found. Aladdin 2009 342p il (The books of Umber) $16.99

Grades: 5 6 7 8   **Fic**
1. Fantasy fiction 2. Adventure fiction 3. Magic -- Fiction

ISBN 978-1-4169-7519-9; 1-4169-7519-5
LC 2008-45966

A boy awakens, blindfolded, with no memory of even his name, but soon meets Lord Umber, an adventurer and inventor, who calls him Happenstance and tells him that he has a very important destiny—and a powerful enemy.

"Catanese packs a lot into the book: rich characterizations, . . . well-choreographed action sequences and genuinely surprising twists at the end." Publ Wkly

Followed by: Dragon games (2010)

Catmull, Katherine

Summer and Bird; by Katherine Catmull. Dutton Children's Books 2012 344 p. (hardback) $16.99

Grades: 5 6 7 8   **Fic**
1. Fairy tales 2. Fantasy fiction 3. Fantasy 4. Birds -- Fiction 5. Sisters -- Fiction 6. Puppeteers -- Fiction 7. Adventure and adventurers -- Fiction

ISBN 0525953469; 9780525953463
LC 2012015587

This children's book, by Katherine Catmull, is "an enchanting--and twisted--tale of two sisters' quest to find their parents. When their parents disappear in the middle of the night, young sisters Summer and Bird set off on a quest to find them. A cryptic picture message from their mother leads them to a familiar gate in the woods, but comfortable sights quickly give way to a new world entirely--Down--one inhabited by talking birds and the evil Puppeteer queen." (Publisher's note)

Cavanaugh, Nancy J.

★ **This** journal belongs to Ratchet; by Nancy J. Cavanaugh. Sourcebooks Jabberwocky 2013 320 p. (hardcover) $12.99

Grades: 4 5 6 7   **Fic**
1. Diaries -- Fiction 2. Home schooling -- Fiction 3. Father-daughter relationship -- Fiction 4. Self-acceptance -- Fiction 5. Fathers and daughters -- Fiction 6. Environmental protection -- Fiction

ISBN 1402281064; 9781402281068
LC 2012041339

This juvenile novel, by Nancy Cavanaugh, begins on "the first day of school for all the kids in the neighborhood. But not for me. I'm homeschooled. . . . The best I've got is this notebook. I'm supposed to use it for my writing assignments, but my dad never checks. Here's what I'm really going to use it for: Ratchet's Top Secret Plan . . . turn my old, recycled, freakish, friendless, motherless life into something shiny and new." (Publisher's note)

"At first it seems artificial, with observations that are too on-the-nose. But as the novel's unexpectedly multifaceted plot comes together, it becomes increasingly compelling, suspenseful and moving. Triumphant enough to make readers cheer; touching enough to make them cry." Kirkus

Cazet, Denys

Minnie and Moo, hooves of fire; by Denys Cazet. Creston Books 2014 208 p. (hardcover) $15.95

Grades: 2 3 4 5   **Fic**
1. Humorous fiction 2. Farm life -- Fiction 3. Fund raising -- Fiction 4. Talent shows -- Fiction 5. Cows -- Fiction 6. Humorous stories 7. Domestic animals -- Fiction

ISBN 1939547083; 9781939547088
LC 2013038846

In this children's book, by Denys Cazet, "it's a perfect day for the First Annual Hoot, Holler, and Moo Talent Festival. . . . Mr. and Mrs. Farmer are away on vacation, Minnie and Moo are dressed in their togas, Elvis has his bagpipe, the hyenas their jokes, the fox his magic tricks, the sheep a protest poem, and the cash box is stuffed with money from ticket sales. A perfect day. Wait a minute . . . Where is the cash box?" (Publisher's note)

"When the farmer and his wife take a vacation, cows Minnie and Moo seize the opportunity to put on a show. There's no shortage of local talent and wannabe stars...The second entry in the chapter book series is a good bet for kids who discovered the characters when they began reading and are ready for longer books. With amusing dialogue, expressive black-and-white drawings, and a chapter called "Race of the Port-A-Potties," fans won't be disappointed." Booklist

Hooves of fire

Other titles include:

Minnie & Moo and the Seven Wonders of the World (2003)

Cerra, Kerry O'Malley

Just a drop of water; Kerry O'Malley Cerra. Skyhorse Publishing, Inc. 2014 320 p. (hardback) $14.95

Grades: 5 6 7 8 9   **Fic**

1. School stories 2. Friendship -- Fiction 3. September 11 terrorist attacks, 2001 -- Fiction 4. Muslims -- Fiction 5. Best friends -- Fiction 6. Arab Americans -- Fiction 7. Family life -- Florida -- Fiction 8. September 11 Terrorist Attacks, 2001 -- Fiction

ISBN 1629146137; 9781629146133

                    LC 2014015987

In this novel by Kerry O'Malley Cerra's "historical novel takes place in . . . the days leading up to and after September 11, 2001. Jake Green struggles with the knowledge that one of the hijackers was living in his town prior to the attacks. His best friend and neighbor, Sam Medina, an Arab Muslim, is targeted by boys in their class. [When] Sam's father is taken into FBI custody after the discovery that he serviced the hijacker at the bank he worked . . . Jake soon finds himself at odds with his immediate family." (School Library Journal)

"The tragedy of 9/11 forces a 13-year-old Florida boy who has always lived with a comfortable, straightforward code of conduct to explore the issues of loyalty, patriotism and fair play... Cerra does a good job of re-creating the combination of fear, confusion, patriotism, prejudice and community spirit the attack engendered, and readers should identify with Jake's plight. A perceptive exploration of an event its audience already sees as history." Kirkus

Cervantes, Angela

Gaby, Lost and Found. Scholastic Inc. 2013 224 p. $16.99

Grades: 5 6 7   **Fic**

1. Bullies -- Juvenile fiction 2. Immigrants -- Juvenile fiction

ISBN 0545489458; 9780545489454

In this book, Gaby's mother is deported to Honduras, "Though she lives with her dad, Gaby basically parents herself with the help of her friend Alma's family. Her physical and emotional needs are barely met at home. Gaby's world brightens when her class begins a long-term volunteer project at the Furry Friends animal shelter. Like her mom, Gaby is an animal lover, and she develops her writing talent by crafting adoption profiles for the cats and dogs." (Kirkus Reviews)

Cervantes, Jennifer

Tortilla sun. Chronicle Books 2010 224p $16.99

Grades: 5 6 7 8   **Fic**

1. New Mexico -- Fiction 2. Grandmothers -- Fiction 3. Father-daughter relationship -- Fiction

ISBN 978-0-8118-7015-3; 0-8118-7015-4

While spending a summer in New Mexico with her grandmother, twelve-year-old Izzy makes new friends, learns to cook, and for the first time hears stories about her father, who died before she was born.

"Cervantes evokes the beauty of the setting and develops a memorable cast of characters, brought to life through Izzy's heartfelt narration. A beautiful and engaging debut novel." Kirkus

Chabon, Michael

Summerland. Hyperion Bks. for Children 2002 500p hardcover o.p. pa $8.95

Grades: 5 6 7 8   **Fic**

1. Fantasy fiction 2. Magic -- Fiction 3. Baseball -- Fiction

ISBN 0-7868-0877-2; 0-7868-1615-5 pa

                    LC 2002-27497

Ethan Feld, the worst baseball player in the history of the game, finds himself recruited by a 100-year-old scout to help a band of fairies triumph over an ancient enemy

"Much of the prose is beautifully descriptive as Chabon navigates vividly imagined other worlds and offers up some timeless themes." Horn Book

Chari, Sheela

Vanished. Disney/Hyperion Books 2011 240p $16.99

Grades: 5 6 7 8   **Fic**

1. Mystery fiction 2. East Indian Americans -- Fiction 3. Lost and found possessions -- Fiction

ISBN 978-1-4231-3163-2; 1-4231-3163-0

                    LC 2010019660

Eleven-year-old Neela must solve the mystery when her beautiful, but cursed, veena, a classical Indian musical instrument, goes missing.

"Well-paced and with moments of family humor . . . the novel offers a strong cast of characters and richly-described settings; both the legend and the contemporary come alive for readers. . . . Chari . . . strikes the right note with this engaging, intricate story that spans generations and two countries." Kirkus

Includes bibliographical references

Chatterton, Martin

The **Brain** finds a leg. Peachtree Publishers 2009 212p $16.95

Grades: 4 5 6   **Fic**

1. School stories 2. Mystery fiction 3. Animals -- Fiction 4. Australia -- Fiction 5. Intellect -- Fiction 6. Inventions -- Fiction

ISBN 978-1-56145-503-4; 1-56145-503-2

                    LC 2009-00304

First published 2007 in Australia

In Farrago Bay, Australia, thirteen-year-old Sheldon is recruited by a new student, Theo Brain, to help investigate a murder, which is tied not only to bizzare animal behavior but also to a diabolical plot to alter human intelligence.

"Several deaths in the story war against the comedy but the laughs win. Readers shouldn't expect anything remotely realistic and instead surrender themselves to the industrial-strength zaniness." Kirkus

Another title about The Brain is:

The Brain full of holes (2010)

The **Brain** full of holes. Peachtree 2010 250p $16.95

Grades: 4 5 6   **Fic**

1. Mystery fiction 2. Inventions -- Fiction 3.

Switzerland -- Fiction

ISBN 978-1-56145-527-0; 1-56145-527-X

"Kid detective The Brain and his Watson are called in on a missing-person case. Their search takes them to Switzerland, home of the new super-particle accelerator, but their real adventure occurs in an alternate universe filled with zaniness. Chatterton explores speculations about physics throughout in amusing ways. . . . Those who like laughs along with a sf-influenced mystery will enjoy this." Booklist

Cheaney, J. B.

My friend, the enemy. Knopf 2005 266p hardcover o.p. pa $6.50

Grades: 5 6 7 8   **Fic**

1. Friendship -- Fiction 2. Japanese Americans -- Fiction 3. World War, 1939-1945 -- Fiction

ISBN 0-375-81432-9; 0-440-42102-0 pa

LC 2004-26927

During World War II, a twelve-year-old girl becomes friends with a young Japanese-American boy she discovers being sheltered and hidden by her neighbor.

"Written in first person, this novel offers quiet but finely tuned portrayal of the stresses that changed life on the home front and one child's attempts to cope with it all." Booklist

Chen, Pauline

Peiling and the chicken-fried Christmas; [by] Pauline Chen. Bloomsbury Children's Books 2007 133p $15.95

Grades: 4 5 6   **Fic**

1. Christmas -- Fiction 2. Taiwanese Americans -- Fiction

ISBN 978-1-59990-122-0; 1-59990-122-6

LC 2006102095

Fifth-grader Peiling Wang wants to celebrate "a real American Christmas," much to the displeasure of her traditional, Taiwanese-born father

"Peiling makes an appealingly levelheaded protagonist, and . . . [Chen] doesn't miss much in this often-amusing picture of the Wang family working at fitting its new and old cultures together." Booklist

Cheng, Andrea

Brushing Mom's hair; illustrations by Nicole Wong. Wordsong 2009 59p il $17.95

Grades: 4 5 6 7 8   **Fic**

1. Novels in verse 2. Sick -- Fiction 3. Cancer -- Fiction 4. Mother-daughter relationship -- Fiction

ISBN 978-1-59078-599-7; 1-59078-599-1

LC 2009021965

A fourteen-year-old girl, whose mother's breast cancer diagnosis and treatment have affected every aspect of their lives, finds release in ballet and art classes.

"With one or two words on each line, the poems are a fast read, but the chatty voice packs in emotion. . . . Wong's small black-and-white pencil drawings on every page extend the poetry through the characters' body language." Booklist

Honeysuckle house. Front Street 2004 136p $16.95; pa $10.95

Grades: 3 4 5   **Fic**

1. Friendship -- Fiction 2. Immigrants -- Fiction 3. Chinese Americans -- Fiction

ISBN 1-886910-99-5; 1-59078-632-7 pa

An all-American girl with Chinese ancestors and a new immigrant from China find little in common when they meet in their fourth grade classroom, but they are both missing their best friends and soon discover other connections

"Told in first person in alternating chapters, the narratives balance well between large issues . . . and more intimate ones. . . . With a smoothly drawn and interesting plot, strong characters, and graceful writing, the story has more immediacy than much realistic contemporary fiction." SLJ

The **lace** dowry. Front Street 2005 113p $16.95

Grades: 4 5 6 7   **Fic**

1. Hungary -- Fiction 2. Sex role -- Fiction 3. Friendship -- Fiction

ISBN 1-932425-20-9

LC 2004-21186

In Hungary in 1933, a twelve-year-old from Budapest befriends the Halas village family of lacemakers hired to stitch her dowry.

"Cheng tells a familiar story of children discovering empathy across class and cultural divides, enriching the theme with a vivid historical setting and Juli's strong narration, which is written in spare language and a believable voice." Booklist

Only one year; illustrations by Nicole Wong. Lee & Low Books 2010 97p il $16.95

Grades: 2 3 4   **Fic**

1. Siblings -- Fiction 2. Family life -- Fiction 3. Chinese Americans -- Fiction

ISBN 978-1-60060-252-8; 1-60060-252-5

LC 201044

"Although she sometimes finds him troublesome, fourth-grader Sharon can't bear the idea that her two-year-old brother, Di Di, will spend a whole school year with relatives in China while she and her first-grade sister, Mary, go to school and her parents work. . . . Supportive black-and-white illustrations and a glossary/pronunciation guide for the occasional Chinese words and phrases complete the appealing package of this gentle family story." Booklist

Shanghai messenger; illustrated by Ed Young. Lee & Low 2005 un il $18.95

Grades: 3 4 5 6   **Fic**

1. Novels in verse 2. China -- Fiction 3. Chinese Americans -- Fiction

ISBN 1-58430-238-0

LC 2004-4025934

A free-verse novel about eleven-year-old Xiao Mei's visit with her extended family in China, where the Chinese-American girl finds many differences but also the similarities that bind a family together.

"Cheng does an admirable job of capturing this experience from the perspective of a child, and each free-verse chapter is brief but satisfying. . . . Young's illustrations delicately intertwine with the text, gently supporting each vignette. This is a superb book." SLJ

Where do you stay? Boyds Mills Press 2011 134p $17.95

Grades: 4 5 6 7   **Fic**

1. Aunts -- Fiction 2. Cousins -- Fiction 3. Pianists -- Fiction 4. Bereavement -- Fiction 5. Homeless persons

-- Fiction
ISBN 1-59078-707-2; 978-1-59078-707-6

Jerome is staying with his Aunt Geneva and her family, now that his mother has passed away. Aunt Geneva tries to make Jerome feel welcome, but his cousins are not happy about the new "member" of their family. Though Jerome has a place to stay, he doesn't feel he has a home, until he meets Mr. Willie, who lives in a ramshackle carriage house.

"In short chapters of lyrical prose, Cheng . . . provides a moving tribute to a multigenerational community's ability to sustain and recreate itself in times of change through resilience, hard work, and a commitment to beauty and kindness." Publ Wkly

Where the steps were. Front Street 2008 143p il $16.95
Grades: 3 4 5 6   **Fic**
1. School stories 2. Novels in verse 3. Teachers -- Fiction 4. Friendship -- Fiction
ISBN 978-1-932425-88-8; 1-932425-88-8
LC 2007-18787

Verse from the perspectives of five students in Miss D.'s third grade class details the children's last year together before their inner city school is to be torn down

This is "a spare, eloquent novel in verse illustrated in [the author's] own bold block prints." Publ Wkly

The **year** of the baby; by Andrea Cheng; illustrated by Patrice Barton. Houghton Mifflin Harcourt 2013 176 p. $15.99
Grades: 2 3 4 5   **Fic**
1. Adopted children -- Fiction 2. Science projects -- Fiction 3. Chinese Americans -- Fiction 4. Interracial adoption -- Fiction 5. Babies -- Fiction 6. Adoption -- Fiction 7. Friendship -- Fiction 8. Best friends -- Fiction
ISBN 0547910673; 9780547910673
LC 2012018679

Sequel to: Year of the book

In this children's book, by Andrea Cheng, "Anna and her best friends Laura and Camille return in an engaging new story. Anna's family has adopted a new baby from China, but her new sister is not thriving and refuses to eat When Anna and her friends are assigned a science experiment in school, they decide to use the assignment as a way to help Baby Kaylee." (Library Media Connection)

"In this follow-up to The Year of the Book (2012), the focus of 11-year-old narrator Anna shifts to the new girl in the house, adopted a few months ago from China...Cheng's tying up of story threads is as tidy as Barton's spot illustrations. To top it off, young cooks get a recipe for bao zi buns. " Booklist

The **year** of the book; by Andrea Cheng; illustrated by Abigail Halpin. Houghton Mifflin 2012 146 p. $15.99
Grades: 2 3 4 5   **Fic**
1. School stories 2. Friendship -- Fiction 3. Chinese Americans -- Fiction 4. Best friends -- Fiction
ISBN 0547684630; 9780547684635
LC 2011036331

Sequel: Year of the baby

In this children's book, by Andrea Cheng, "narrator Anna Wang . . . always has her head stuck in a book. Nine-year-old

Anna reads for all the right reasons, . . . but she also uses reading as a shield against social exclusion . . . and her own lack of confidence. . . . At school, Anna's friend from last year . . . now hangs out with the popular girls. . . . Sometimes a book helps illuminate Anna's own life, . . . sometimes a book is part of the external plot." (Horn Book Magazine)

"A slim but solid novel about friends and family issues, Cheng's latest follows an Asian American girl through most of fourth grade. At the start, Anna Wang finds companionship in books, partly because last year's best friend, Laura, has become less friendly... Cheng also describes Anna's challenges in learning Chinese—she is resistant at first, since her American-born dad has done fine without knowing the language. Halpin's illustrations offer sweet scenes and images of Anna's life, including her growing interest in Chinese characters." Booklist

The **year** of the fortune cookie; by Andrea Cheng; illustrations by Patrice Barton. Houghton Mifflin Harcourt 2014 176 p. (hardback) $15.99
Grades: 2 3 4 5   **Fic**
1. Middle schools -- Fiction 2. Chinese Americans -- Fiction 3. China -- Fiction 4. Adoption -- Fiction 5. Identity -- Fiction
ISBN 0544105192; 9780544105195
LC 2013024155

Sequel to: Year of the baby

In this children's book by Andrea Cheng, illustrated by Patrice Barton, "Eleven-year-old Anna heads off to sixth grade, leaving the comfort and familiarity of elementary school behind and entering the larger, more complex world of middle school. Surrounded by classmates who have their roots all in America, Anna begins to feel out of place and wonders where she really belongs." (Publisher's note)

"In this pitch-perfect sequel, Anna juggles the usual "starting middle school" trials in addition to trying to fit into both her Chinese and American cultures, spurred by her trip to China with her former teacher. Anna's new friend Andee helps her with this big step by sending her fortune cookies with personalized notes. Barton's winning illustrations continue to delight." SLJ

Cheshire, Simon
The **curse** of the ancient mask and other case files; pictures by R. W. Alley. Roaring Book Press 2009 169p il (Saxby Smart, private detective) $13.95
Grades: 3 4 5   **Fic**
1. Mystery fiction 2. Lost and found possessions -- Fiction
ISBN 978-1-59643-474-5; 1-59643-474-0

First published 2007 in the United Kingdom

"Saxby Doyle Christie Chandler Ellin Allan Smart wants to be a detective as good as the greats. . . . In the first of three 'case files,' . . . Saxby . . . discovers that [an ancient] mask's real curse is a case of competitive sabotage. [In the] second case file . . . Saxby uncovers the secret behind the appearance of purple goo on his classmates' projects. In the third mystery, Saxby sets out to find the thief of a valuable coat clasp. . . . The stories are liberally illustrated with Alley's homey sketches plus representations of Saxby's notebooks. While each short mystery is involving, the distinguishing aspect of this series opener is Saxby's enthusiastic invitations to readers to participate in the sleuthing." Kirkus

Other titles in this series are:

The treasure of Dead Man's Lane and other case files (2010)

The pirate's blood and other case files (2011)

Chick, Bryan

The **secret** zoo. Greenwillow Books 2010 295p $16.99

Grades: 4 5 6   **Fic**

1. Fantasy fiction 2. Mystery fiction 3. Zoos -- Fiction 4. Animals -- Fiction 5. Siblings -- Fiction

ISBN 978-0-06-198750-2; 0-06-198750-6

First published 2007 by Second Wish Press

Noah and his friends follow a trail of mysterious clues to uncover a secret behind the walls of the Clarksville City Zoo—a secret that must be protected at all costs.

"Chick debuts with an action-packed and breathless story about teamwork. . . . The story should appeal both to animal-lovers and a broader audience. While many threads are resolved, Chick lays the groundwork for later books." Publ Wkly

Other titles in this series are:

The secret zoo: secrets and shadows (2011)

The secret zoo: riddles and danger (2011)

Child, Lauren

Clarice Bean spells trouble; [by] Lauren Child. Candlewick Press 2005 189p il $15.99; pa $5.99

Grades: 3 4 5   **Fic**

1. Authorship -- Fiction 2. Friendship -- Fiction

ISBN 0-7636-2813-1; 0-7636-2903-0 pa

Clarice Bean, aspiring actress and author, unsuccessfully tries to avoid getting into trouble as she attempts to help a friend in need by following the rules of the fictional spy, Ruby Redfort.

This is written "with fresh, childlike turns of phrase and a hyperawareness of words. . . . With a sprinkling of small, childlike line drawings, a few other illustrations, and some creative typography, this entertaining chapter book will please readers." Booklist

Other titles about Clarice Bean are:

Clarice Bean, don't look now (2007)

Utterly me, Clarice Bean (2003)

Choldenko, Gennifer

Al Capone does my homework; by Gennifer Choldenko. Dial Books for Young Readers 2013 224 p. (Al Capone Trilogy) (hardcover) $17.99

Grades: 5 6 7 8   **Fic**

1. Mystery fiction 2. Historical fiction 3. Fires -- Fiction 4. Autism -- Fiction 5. Brothers and sisters -- Fiction 6. Swindlers and swindling -- Fiction 7. Alcatraz Island (Calif.) -- History -- 20th century -- Fiction 8. United States Penitentiary, Alcatraz Island, California -- Fiction

ISBN 0803734727; 9780803734722

LC 2012039138

Sequel to: Al Capone shines my shoes

This book, set on Alcatraz Island in the 1930s, is the third in Gennifer Choldenko's Al Capone trilogy. Moose lives with his parents and autistic sister on the island. "When Moose's dad gets promoted to Associate Warden, . . . it's a big deal. But the cons have a point system for targeting prison employees, and his dad is now in serious danger. After a fire starts in the Flanagan's apartment. Natalie is blamed,

and Moose bands with the other kids to track down the possible arsonist." (Publisher's note)

Includes bibliographical references

★ **Al** Capone does my shirts. G.P. Putnam's Sons 2004 225p il $15.99; pa $6.99

Grades: 5 6 7 8   **Fic**

1. Autism -- Fiction 2. Siblings -- Fiction 3. Alcatraz Island (Calif.) -- Fiction

ISBN 0-399-23861-1; 0-14-240370-9 pa

LC 2002-31766

A Newbery Medal honor book, 2005

A twelve-year-old boy named Moose moves to Alcatraz Island in 1935 when guards' families were housed there, and has to contend with his extraordinary new environment in addition to life with his autistic sister.

"With its unique setting and well-developed characters, this warm, engaging coming-of-age story has plenty of appeal, and Choldenko offers some fascinating historical background on Alcatraz Island in an afterword." Booklist

Followed by: Al Capone shines my shoes (2009)

Al Capone shines my shoes. Dial Books for Young Readers 2009 274p $16.99

Grades: 5 6 7 8   **Fic**

1. Autism -- Fiction 2. Siblings -- Fiction 3. Alcatraz Island (Calif.) -- Fiction

ISBN 978-0-8037-3460-9; 0-8037-3460-3

LC 2009-04157

Sequel to: Al Capone does my shirts (2004)

Moose Flanagan, who lives on Alcatraz along with his family and the families of the other prison guards, is frightened when he discovers that noted gangster Al Capone, a prisoner there, wants a favor in return for the help that he secretly gave Moose.

"Effortless period dialogue, fully developed secondary characters and a perfectly paced plot combine to create a solid-gold sequel that will not disappoint." Kirkus

Includes bibliographical references

No passengers beyond this point. Dial Books for Young Readers 2011 244p $16.99

Grades: 5 6 7 8   **Fic**

1. Fantasy fiction 2. Siblings -- Fiction 3. Space and time -- Fiction

ISBN 978-0-8037-3534-7; 0-8037-3534-0

LC 2009-51661

With their house in foreclosure, sisters India and Mouse and brother Finn are sent to stay with an uncle in Colorado until their mother can join them, but when the plane lands, the children are welcomed by cheering crowds to a strange place where each of them has a perfect house and a clock that is ticking down the time.

"Choldenko keeps the plot moving rapidly and constantly shifts the point of view, with each chapter narrated by one of the three siblings, so that both readers and characters feel discombobulated—everything is both concrete yet dreamlike. . . . No one can write a hormonal teenage girl at war with her family like Choldenko, but in the end the family relationships and the determination each sibling has to protect the others is what saves them all." Horn Book

Notes from a liar and her dog. Putnam 2001 216p hardcover o.p. pa $5.99

Grades: 5 6 7 8 **Fic**
1. Family life -- Fiction 2. Truthfulness and falsehood -- Fiction
ISBN 0-399-23591-4; 0-14-250068-2 pa

LC 00-55354

Eleven-year-old Ant, stuck in a family that she does not like, copes by pretending that her "real" parents are coming to rescue her, by loving her dog Pistachio, by volunteering at the zoo, and by bending the truth and telling lies

"Choldenko's writing is snappy and tender, depicting both Ant's bravado and her isolation with sympathy." Bull Cent Child Books

Christopher, John

The **White** Mountains; 35th anniversary ed; Simon & Schuster Bks. for Young Readers 2003 164p hardcover o.p. pa $5.99

Grades: 5 6 7 8 **Fic**
1. Science fiction
ISBN 0-689-85504-4; 0-689-85672-5 pa

LC 2002-70808

A reissue of the title first published 1967 by Macmillan

Young Will Parker and his companions make a perilous journey toward an outpost of freedom where they hope to escape from the ruling Tripods, who capture mature human beings and make them docile, obedient servants

This "remarkable story . . . belongs to the school of science-fiction which puts philosophy before technology and is not afraid of telling an exciting story." Times Lit Suppl

Other titles about the Tripods are:
The city of gold and lead (2003 c1967)
The pool of fire (2003 c1968)
When the Tripods came (2003 c1988)

Christopher, Lucy

Flyaway; Lucy Christopher. Chicken House 2011 314p $16.99

Grades: 5 6 7 8 **Fic**
1. Sick -- Fiction 2. Swans -- Fiction 3. Hospitals -- Fiction 4. Wildlife conservation -- Fiction 5. Family life -- Fiction 6. Father-daughter relationship -- Fiction
ISBN 0545317711; 9780545317719

LC 2010051425

In this young adult novel, "when newly constructed power lines ruin the annual return of the whooping swans Isla and her father rise early to witness, the death of several of the wild creatures and her father's sudden and severe illness both confound Isla and emphasize her loneliness. At the hospital where her father awaits a heart operation, Harry, waiting there for a bone-marrow transplant, befriends Isla and points out the young swan he can see from his bed. . . . News broadcasts . . . about deadly outbreaks of bird flu contrast with the small unfolding of Isla's widowed grandfather's stiff grief as he helps her construct an art project--a harness and wings from an ancient stuffed swan--and innocent romance flutters between Isla and Harry even as the young swan regains flight and her father begins to recover." (Kirkus)

Christopher offers "readers a quiet but compelling story with several well-realized, idiosyncratic characters. She skillfully develops the novel's varied elements and weaves them into a unified narrative. . . . This sensitive novel will resonate with many readers." Booklist

Clark, Clara Gillow

Secrets of Greymoor. Candlewick Press 2009 166p $15.99

Grades: 4 5 6 7 **Fic**
1. School stories 2. Wealth -- Fiction 3. Grandmothers -- Fiction 4. New York (State) -- Fiction
ISBN 978-0-7636-3249-6; 0-7636-3249-X

LC 2008019063

As her grandmother's financial situation worsens, Hattie is forced to attend a "common school," in late nineteenth-century Kingston, New York, where she stands up to a show-off, shares embellished stories about life as a rich girl, and tries to recover her family's wealth.

"Even readers new to Hattie's story will cheer. . . . [This is an] accessible first-person narrative." Booklist

Clayton, Emma

The **roar**. Chicken House/Scholastic Inc. 2009 481p $17.99

Grades: 5 6 7 8 **Fic**
1. Science fiction 2. Twins -- Fiction
ISBN 978-0-439-92593-8; 0-439-92593-2

LC 2008-8311

"Mika and Ellie live in a future behind a wall: Solid concrete topped with high-voltage razor wire and guarded by a battalion of Ghengis Borgs, it was built to keep out the animals, because animals carry the plague. At least that's what Ellie, who was kidnapped as a child, has always been taught. But when she comes to suspect the truth behind her captivity, she's ready to risk exposure to the elements and answer the call of the wild." (Publisher's note) "Grades six to nine." (Bull Cent Child Books)

"This is an unusually gripping adventure that targets a younger audience than most young adult sci-fi." Bull Cent Child Books

Cleary, Beverly

Beezus and Ramona; illustrated by Louis Darling. Avon Books 1990 159p il pa $5.99

Grades: 3 4 5 **Fic**
1. Sisters -- Fiction
ISBN 0-380-70918-X

A reissue of the title first published 1955

Beezus' biggest problem is her 4-year-old sister Ramona. Even though Beezus knows sisters are supposed to love each other, with a sister like Ramona, it seems impossible.

★ **Dear** Mr. Henshaw; illustrated by Paul O. Zelinsky. Morrow 1983 133p il $15.99; lib bdg $16.89; pa $5.99

Grades: 4 5 6 7 **Fic**
1. School stories 2. Divorce -- Fiction 3. Parent-child relationship -- Fiction
ISBN 0-688-02405-X; 0-688-02406-8 lib bdg; 0-380-70958-9 pa

LC 83-5372

Awarded the Newbery Medal, 1984

"Leigh Botts lives with his recently divorced mother and writes to his favorite author, Boyd Henshaw. When Henshaw answers his letters and encourages him to keep a journal, he does so, and in the process solves the mystery of who is stealing food from his lunchbox, tries to write a novel, and in the end, writes a prize-winning short story about an experience with his father. . . . Grades four to seven." (SLJ)

"Leigh Botts started writing letters to his favorite author, Boyd Henshaw, in the second grade. Now, Leigh is in the sixth grade, in a new school, and his parents are recently divorced. This year he writes many letters to Mr. Henshaw, and also keeps a journal. Through these the reader learns how Leigh adjusts to new situations, and of his triumphs." Child Book Rev Serv

Followed by: Strider (1991)

Henry Huggins; illustrated by Louis Darling. Harper-Collins Pubs. 2000 155p il $15.99; pa $5.99

Grades: 3 4 5   **Fic**

1. School stories 2. Family life -- Fiction

ISBN 0-688-21385-5; 0-380-70912-0 pa

LC 00-27567

A reissue of the title first published 1950 by Morrow

"Henry Huggins is a typical small boy who, quite innocently, gets himself into all sorts of predicaments—often with the very apt thought, 'Won't Mom be surprised.' There is not a dull moment but some hilariously funny ones in the telling of Henry's adventures at home and at school." Booklist

Other titles about Henry Huggins are:

Henry and Beezus (1952)

Henry and Ribsy (1954)

Henry and the clubhouse (1962)

Henry and the paper route (1957)

Ribsy (1964)

The **mouse** and the motorcycle; illustrated by Louis Darling. Morrow 1965 158p il $16; pa $5.99

Grades: 3 4 5   **Fic**

1. Mice -- Fiction

ISBN 0-688-21698-6; 0-380-70924-4 pa

"The author shows much insight into the thoughts of children. She carries the reader into an imaginative world that contains many realistic emotions." Wis Libr Bull

Other titles about Ralph are:

Ralph S. Mouse (1982)

Runaway Ralph (1970)

★ **Muggie** Maggie; illustrated by Kay Life. Morrow Junior Bks. 1990 70p il $15.99; pa $5.99

Grades: 2 3 4   **Fic**

1. School stories 2. Handwriting -- Fiction

ISBN 0-688-08553-9; 0-380-71087-0 pa

LC 89-38959

Maggie resists learning cursive writing in the third grade, until she discovers that knowing how to read and write cursive promises to open up an entirely new world of knowledge for her

"This deceptively simple story is accessible to primary-grade readers able to read longhand, as some of the text is in script. . . . Everything in this book rings true, and Cleary has created a likable, funny heroine about whom readers will want to know more." SLJ

Ralph S. Mouse; illustrated by Paul O. Zelinsky. Harper Trophy 2000 160p il pa $5.99

Grades: 3 4 5   **Fic**

1. Mice -- Fiction

ISBN 0-380-70957-0

LC 2001278658

A reissue of the title first published 1982

Presents the further adventures of a motorcycle-riding mouse who goes to school and becomes the instigator of an investigation of rodents and the peacemaker for two lonely boys.

★ **Ramona** the pest; illustrated by Louis Darling. Morrow 1968 192p il $16.99; pa $5.99

Grades: 3 4 5   **Fic**

1. School stories 2. Kindergarten -- Fiction

ISBN 0-688-21721-4; 0-380-70954-6 pa

"Ramona Quimby comes into her own. Beezus keeps telling her to stop acting like a pest, but Ramona is five now, and she is convinced that she is 'not' a pest; she feels very mature, having entered kindergarten, and she immediately becomes enamoured of her teacher. Ramona's insistence on having just the right kind of boots, her matter-of-fact interest in how Mike Mulligan got to a bathroom, her determination to kiss one of the boys in her class, and her refusal to go back to kindergarten because Miss Binney didn't love her any more—all of these incidents or situations are completely believable and are told in a light, humorous, zesty style." Bull Cent Child Books

Other titles about Ramona are:

Beezus and Ramona (1955)

Ramona and her father (1977)

Ramona and her mother (1979)

Ramona, forever (1984)

Ramona Quimby, age 8 (1981)

Ramona the brave (1975)

Ramona's world (1999)

Runaway Ralph; illustrated by Louis Darling. Harper-Trophy 2000 175p il pa $5.99

Grades: 3 4 5   **Fic**

1. Mice -- Fiction 2. Camps -- Fiction

ISBN 0-380-70953-8

LC 2001278668

A reissue of the title first published 1970

Ralph the mouse runs away looking for freedom but winds up a prisoner at a summer camp.

Socks; illustrated by Beatrice Darwin. Morrow 1973 156p il $16.99; pa $5.99

Grades: 3 4 5   **Fic**

1. Cats -- Fiction 2. Infants -- Fiction

ISBN 0-688-20067-2; 0-380-70926-0 pa

"Not being child-centered, this may have a smaller audience than earlier Cleary books, but it is written with the same easy grace, the same felicitous humor and sharply observant eye." Bull Cent Child Books

Strider; illustrated by Paul O. Zelinsky. Morrow Junior Bks. 1991 179p il hardcover o.p. lib bdg $16.89; pa $5.99

Grades: 4 5 6 7 **Fic**
1. Dogs -- Fiction 2. Divorce -- Fiction
ISBN 0-688-09900-9; 0-688-09901-7 lib bdg; 0-380-71236-9 pa

LC 90-6608

Sequel to Dear Mr. Henshaw

In a series of diary entries, Leigh tells how he comes to terms with his parents' divorce, acquires joint custody of an abandoned dog, and joins the track team at school

"The development of the narrative is vintage Beverly Cleary, an inimitable blend of comic and poignant moments." Horn Book

Clements, Andrew, 1949-

About average; Andrew Clements; illustrations by Mark Elliott. Simon & Schuster 2012 120 p. (hardback) $16.99
Grades: 3 4 5 6 **Fic**
1. Natural disasters -- Fiction 2. Personal appearance -- Fiction 3. School stories -- Juvenile fiction 4. Heroes -- Fiction 5. Ability -- Fiction 6. Schools -- Fiction 7. Tornadoes -- Fiction 8. Individuality -- Fiction
ISBN 1416997245; 9781416997245; 9781416997269

LC 2012015106

In author Andrew Clements's book, protagonist "Jordan Johnston is average. Not short, not tall. Not plump, not slim. Not blond, not brunette. Not gifted, not flunking out. Even her shoe size is average. She's ordinary for her school, for her town, for even the whole wide world, it seems. . . . Jordan feels doomed to a life of wallowing in the vast, soggy middle. So she makes a goal: By the end of the year, she will discover her great talent." (Publisher's note)

★ **Extra** credit; illustrations by Mark Elliott. Atheneum Books for Young Readers 2009 183p il $16.99
Grades: 4 5 6 **Fic**
1. Letters -- Fiction 2. Illinois -- Fiction 3. Afghanistan -- Fiction 4. Family life -- Fiction
ISBN 978-1-4169-4929-9; 1-4169-4929-1

LC 2008-42877

"Unless [Abby] wants to repeat the sixth grade, she'll have to meet some specific conditions, including taking on an extra-credit project: find a pen pal in a foreign country. Simple enough (even for a girl who hates homework). Abby's first letter arrives at a small school in Afghanistan, and Sadeed Bayat is chosen to be her pen pal.... Well, kind of. He is the best writer, but he is also a boy, and in his village it is not appropriate for a boy to correspond with a girl. So his younger sister dictates and signs the letter. Until Sadeed decides what his sister is telling Abby isn't what he'd like Abby to know." (Publisher's note) "Grades four to seven." (Bull Cent Child Books)

Clements "successfully bridges two cultures in this timely and insightful dual-perspective story." Publ Wkly

Fear itself; illustrated by Adam Stower. Atheneum Books for Young Readers 2010 204p il (Benjamin Pratt & the Keepers of the School) $14.99; pa $5.99
Grades: 4 5 6 **Fic**
1. School stories 2. Mystery fiction 3. Riddles -- Fiction
ISBN 978-1-4169-3887-3; 1-4169-3887-7; 978-1-4169-3908-5 pa; 1-4169-3908-3 pa

LC 2010015876

As the new Keepers of the School, sixth-graders Ben and Jill must decipher a handful of clues written as maritime riddles to save their school from demolition by a greedy company.

"Expressive pen-and-ink illustrations add detail and excitement to the adventure, including the clues and coins found. Solid writing, likable characters, danger, a seaside setting, and now treasure will make readers eager for the third installment." SLJ

★ **Frindle**; [by] Andrew Clements; pictures of Brian Selznick. Simon & Schuster Books for Young Readers 2006 105p il $15.95
Grades: 4 5 6 **Fic**
1. School stories
ISBN 978-0-689-80669-8; 0-689-80669-8

A reissue of the title first published 1996

When he decides to turn his fifth grade teacher's love of the dictionary around on her, clever Nick Allen invents a new word and begins a chain of events that quickly moves beyond his control.

"Sure to be popular with a wide range of readers, this will make a great read-aloud as well." Booklist

Lost and found; illustrations by Mark Elliott. Atheneum Books for Young Readers 2008 161p il $16.99
Grades: 4 5 6 **Fic**
1. School stories 2. Ohio -- Fiction 3. Twins -- Fiction 4. Moving -- Fiction 5. Brothers -- Fiction
ISBN 978-1-4169-0985-9; 1-4169-0985-0

LC 2008-07018

Twelve-year-old identical twins Jay and Ray have long resented that everyone treats them as one person, and so they hatch a plot to take advantage of a clerical error at their new school and pretend they are just one

"This slim story has all the elements readers have come to expect from Clements . . . a school setting, likable secondary characters, supportive adults and a challenge to the audience to see things from a different perspective." Publ Wkly

Lunch money; illustrations by Brian Selznick. Simon & Schuster Books for Young Readers 2005 222p il $15.95; pa $5.99
Grades: 4 5 6 **Fic**
1. School stories 2. Cartoons and comics -- Fiction 3. Money-making projects for children -- Fiction
ISBN 0-689-86683-6; 0-689-86685-2 pa

LC 2005-00061

Twelve-year-old Greg, who has always been good at moneymaking projects, is surprised to find himself teaming up with his lifelong rival, Maura, to create a series of comic books to sell at school.

"The characters are rich with interesting quirks and motivations. . . . Along with providing a fast-paced and humorous story line, the author examines concepts of true wealth, teamwork, community mindedness, and the value of creative expression. Selznick's pencil sketches add comic touches throughout." SLJ

★ **No** talking; illustrations by Mark Elliott. Simon & Schuster Books for Young Readers 2007 146p il $15.99; pa $5.99

Grades: 3 4 5 6 **Fic**
1. School stories
ISBN 1-4169-0983-4; 1-4169-0984-2 pa; 978-1-
4169-0983-5; 978-1-4169-0984-2 pa
LC 2006-31883

The noisy fifth grade boys of Laketon Elementary School challenge the equally loud fifth grade girls to a "no talking" contest. "Ages eight to twelve." (N Y Times Book Rev)

"This is an interesting and thought-provoking book. . . . The plot quickly draws readers in and keeps them turning pages. . . . The black-and-white pencil drawings add immediacy to the story." SLJ

The **report** card. Simon & Schuster Books for Young Readers 2004 173p
Grades: 4 5 6 **Fic**
1. School stories
ISBN 0689845154; 0689845243
LC 2003-7384

Fifth-grader Nora Rowley has always hidden the fact that she is a genius from everyone because all she wants is to be normal, but when she comes up with a plan to prove that grades are not important, things begin to get out of control. "Ages eight to twelve." (N Y Times Book Rev)

"Clements has . . . built a solid story around a controversial issue for which there is no easy answer, and to his credit, he never tries to offer one. . . . A novel sure to generate strong feelings and discussion." Booklist

Room one; a mystery or two. illustrations by Chris Blair. Simon & Schuster Books for Young Readers 2006 162p il $15.95; pa $5.99
Grades: 3 4 5 **Fic**
1. School stories 2. Mystery fiction 3. Nebraska -- Fiction 4. Homeless persons -- Fiction
ISBN 0-689-86686-9; 0-689-86687-9 pa

Ted Hammond, the only sixth grader in his small Nebraska town's one-room schoolhouse, searches for clues to the disappearance of a homeless family.

"There is a good balance of seriousness and humor with brisk, realistic dialogue and observations. Small black-and-white illustrations emphasize key points in the plot. Clements's usual excellent sense of character is evident." SLJ

Troublemaker; Andrew Clements; illustrated by Mark Elliott. Atheneum Books for Young Readers 2011 p. cm. $16.99
Grades: 4 5 6 7 **Fic**
1. Schools -- Fiction 2. Behavior -- Fiction 3. Brothers -- Fiction
ISBN 978-1-4169-4930-5; 1-4169-4930-5; 1416949305; 9781416949305
LC 2010045018

When his older brother gets in serious trouble, sixth-grader Clay decides to change his own mischief-making ways, but he cannot seem to shake his reputation as a troublemaker.

"Clements here enters into provocative territory and pulls it off like the pro he is. Kids will easily relate to Clay, and the secondary characters come alive as well." Kirkus

We the children; illustrated by Adam Stower. Atheneum Books for Young Readers 2010 142p il (Benjamin Pratt and the Keepers of the School) $14.99
Grades: 4 5 6 **Fic**
1. School stories 2. Mystery fiction 3. Adventure fiction 4. Massachusetts -- Fiction
ISBN 978-1-4169-3886-6; 1-4169-3886-9
LC 2009-36428

"Sixth-grader Ben Pratt is thrust into a mystery-adventure when his school's janitor shoves a gold coin in his hand, passing on the responsibility to save Oakes School from developers. Captain Oakes gave the school to the community back in 1783; its original building overlooks the Massachusetts town's harbor. But the land has been sold, and buildings will be razed to make way for a theme park. . . . Clements ably sets up his planned six-volume series with topical problems, convincing, likable characters and intriguing extra details." Kirkus

Another title in this series is Fear itself (2010)

Clifton, Lutricia
Freaky Fast Frankie Joe; Lutricia Clifton. Holiday House 2012 248 p. (hardcover) $16.95
Grades: 4 5 6 **Fic**
1. Boys -- Fiction 2. Family -- Fiction 3. Brothers -- Fiction 4. Illinois -- Fiction 5. Stepfamilies -- Fiction 6. Mothers and sons -- Fiction 7. Delivery of goods -- Fiction 8. Family life -- Illinois -- Fiction 9. Community life -- Illinois -- Fiction
ISBN 0823423670; 9780823423675
LC 2011019976

This is the story of Frankie Joe. While "his mom is in jail, Frankie Joe tries to adjust to living with his newly surfaced father, FJ, his stepmother and 'the four legitimate Huckaby sons.' The brothers tease Frankie Joe because, academically, he is 'freaky slow,' which is at odds with how fast he is when he runs or bikes. . . . Frankie Joe . . . launches Frankie Joe's Freaky Fast Delivery Service. With his income, he plans his escape back home from Illinois to Texas. But with each day Frankie Joe becomes more integrated into—and essential to—the town and the family, starting with his friendship with another town oddball, elderly Miss Peachcott. She tells Frankie Joe his family history." (Kirkus)

Coatsworth, Elizabeth Jane
The **cat** who went to heaven; [by] Elizabeth Coatsworth; illustrated by Lynd Ward. Macmillan 1958 62p il $17.95; pa $4.99
Grades: 4 5 6 7 **Fic**
1. Cats -- Fiction 2. Japan -- Fiction
ISBN 0-02-719710-7; 1-4169-4973-9 pa
LC 58-10917

First published 1930. The 1958 edition is a reprint with new illustrations of the book which won the Newbery Medal award in 1931

"Into this lovely and imaginative story the author has put something of the serenity and beauty of the East and of the gentleness of a religion that has a place even for the humblest of living creatures." N Y Times Book Rev

Cody, Matthew
Powerless. Alfred A. Knopf 2009 279p $15.99; lib bdg $18.99

Grades: 5 6 7 8 **Fic**

1. School stories 2. Moving -- Fiction 3. Bullies -- Fiction 4. Family life -- Fiction 5. Superheroes -- Fiction 6. Pennsylvania -- Fiction 7. Supernatural -- Fiction

ISBN 978-0-375-85595-5; 0-375-85595-5; 978-0-375-95595-2 lib bdg; 0-375-95595-X lib bdg

LC 2008-40885

Soon after moving to Noble's Green, Pennsylvania, twelve-year-old Daniel learns that his new friends have super powers that they will lose when they turn thirteen, unless he can use his brain power to protect them.

"This first novel has an intriguing premise, appealing characters, and a straightforward narrative arc with plenty of action as well as some serious moments." Booklist

Super; Matthew Cody. Alfred A. Knopf 2012 298 p. (Sequel to Powerless) (trade) $16.99; (lib. bdg.) $19.99

Grades: 5 6 7 8 **Fic**

1. Adventure fiction 2. Superheroes -- Fiction 3. Pennsylvania -- Fiction 4. Supernatural -- Fiction 5. Supervillains -- Fiction

ISBN 0375968946; 9780375868948; 9780375899799; 9780375968945

LC 2012008220

In this children's novel, by Matthew Cody, "Daniel Corrigan is as regular as can be, especially when compared to the Supers: kids in his new hometown with actual powers like flight and super strength. But . . . . only he was able to stop the Shroud, a supervillian bent on stealing his new-found friends' powers. . . . . Now Daniel himself is starting to display powers, while . . . . his friends are losing theirs. . . . Daniel worries there may be something . . . sinister at work." (Publisher's note)

Cohagan, Carolyn

The **lost** children. Aladdin 2010 313p $16.99

Grades: 4 5 6 **Fic**

1. Friendship -- Fiction 2. Time travel -- Fiction 3. Voyages and travels -- Fiction

ISBN 978-1-4169-8616-4; 1-4169-8616-2

LC 2009-16608

When twelve-year-old Josephine falls through a wormhole in her garden shed into another time and place, she realizes the troubles she has at home are minor compared to what she has to tackle now in the world where she has landed.

"The main characters are well developed, particularly the spunky and plain-spoken Ida, the laconic but loyal Fargus, and Josephine." Booklist

Cohen, Barbara

Thank you, Jackie Robinson; drawings by Richard Cuffari. Lothrop, Lee & Shepard Bks. 1974 125p il hardcover o.p. pa $4.99

Grades: 4 5 6 **Fic**

1. Baseball -- Fiction 2. Friendship -- Fiction 3. African Americans -- Fiction

ISBN 0-688-15293-7 pa

"Cohen's characters have unusual depth and her story succeeds as a warm, understanding consideration of friendship and, finally, death." Booklist

Cohn, Rachel

Two steps forward. Simon & Schuster for Young Readers 2006 227p $15.95

Grades: 5 6 7 8 **Fic**

1. Family life -- Fiction 2. Stepfamilies -- Fiction 3. Los Angeles (Calif.) -- Fiction

ISBN 0-689-86614-3

Sequel to The steps (2003)

Fourteen-year-old Annabel's extended family gathers in Los Angeles for several weeks over the summer where she must contend with step and half sisters and brothers and her own mother's failing second marriage.

"With the four blended families converging, tensions and humor run high. Chapters are told from alternating viewpoints. . . . This blended narrative offers a lighthearted glimpse into weighty matters." SLJ

Cole, Henry

★ A **nest** for Celeste; a story about art, inspiration, and the meaning of home. [written and illustrated by] Henry Cole. Katherine Tegen Books 2010 342p il $16.99; lib bdg $17.89

Grades: 4 5 6 **Fic**

1. Artists 2. Painters 3. Illustrators 4. Ornithologists 5. Home -- Fiction 6. Mice -- Fiction 7. Artists -- Fiction 8. Writers on science 9. New Orleans (La.) -- Fiction

ISBN 978-0-06-170410-9; 0-06-170410-5; 978-0-06-170411-6 lib bdg; 0-06-170411-3 lib bdg

LC 2009-11813

Celeste, a mouse longing for a real home, becomes a source of inspiration to teenaged Joseph, assistant to the artist and naturalist John James Audubon, at a New Orleans, Louisiana, plantation in 1821

"Evocative illustrations, compelling characters, and thoughtful reflections on the nature of home combine to powerful effect." Publ Wkly

Colfer, Eoin, 1965-

Airman; [by] Eoin Colfer. Hyperion Books for Children 2008 412p $17.99; pa $7.99

Grades: 5 6 7 8 9 **Fic**

1. Adventure fiction 2. Ireland -- Fiction 3. Airplanes -- Fiction 4. Inventors -- Fiction 5. Prisoners -- Fiction

ISBN 978-1-4231-0750-7; 1-4231-0750-0; 978-1-4231-0751-4 pa; 1-4231-0751-9 pa

LC 2007-38415

In the late nineteenth century, when Conor Broekhart discovers a conspiracy to overthrow the king, he is branded a traitor, imprisoned, and forced to mine for diamonds under brutal conditions while he plans a daring escape from Little Saltee prison by way of a flying machine that he must design, build, and, hardest of all, trust to carry him to safety.

This is "polished, sophisticated storytelling. . . . A tour de force." Publ Wkly

★ **Artemis** Fowl. Hyperion Bks. for Children 2001 277p $16.95; pa $7.99

Grades: 5 6 7 8 **Fic**

1. Fantasy fiction 2. Fairies -- Fiction

ISBN 0-7868-0801-2; 1-4231-2452-9 pa

LC 2001-16632

When a twelve-year-old evil genius tries to restore his family fortune by capturing a fairy and demanding a ransom in gold, the fairies fight back with magic, technology, and a particularly nasty troll

"Colfer's antihero, techno fantasy is cleverly written and filled to the brim with action, suspense, and humor." SLJ

Other titles in this series are:

Artemis Fowl: the Arctic incident (2002)

Artemis Fowl: the Eternity code (2003)

Artemis Fowl: the Opal deception (2005)

Artemis Fowl: the lost colony (2006)

Artemis Fowl: the time paradox (2008)

Artemis Fowl: the Atlantis complex (2010)

Artemis Fowl; The last guardian. Eoin Colfer. 1st U.S. ed. Disney Hyperion Books 2012 328 p. (hardcover) $18.99

Grades: 4 5 6 7 8 9   Fic

1. Fantasy fiction 2. Magic -- Fiction 3. Fairies -- Fiction 4. Spirits -- Fiction 5. Genius -- Fiction 6. Space and time -- Fiction

ISBN 1423161610; 9781423161615

LC 2012009997

Odyssey Honor Audiobook (2013)

This book by Eoin Colfer is the eighth installment of the Artemis Fowl series. "This time his arch rival has reanimated dead fairy warriors who were buried in the grounds of Fowl Manor. . . . The warriors don't seem to realize that the battle they were fighting when they died is long over. Artemis has until sunrise to get the spirits to vacate his brothers and go back into the earth where they belong." (Publisher's note)

The **hangman's** revolution; Eoin Colfer. Hyperion 2014 384 p. (W.A.R.P.) (hardback) $17.99

Grades: 5 6 7 8   Fic

1. Science fiction 2. Assassins -- Fiction 3. Time travel -- Fiction 4. London (England) -- Fiction 5. Great Britain -- History -- Fiction

ISBN 9781423161639; 1423161637

LC 2014001938

Sequel to: The Reluctant Assassin (2013)

In this book, "young FBI agent Chevie Savano arrives back in modern-day London after a time-trip to the Victorian age, to find the present very different from the one she left. Europe is being run by a Fascist movement known as the Boxites. . . . Chevie's memories come back to her in fragments, and just as she is learning about the WARP program from Professor Charles Smart, inventor of the time machine, he is killed by secret service police." (Publisher's note)

"Returning from her jaunt to Victorian London in The Reluctant Assassin, Chevie Savano finds that fellow time-traveler Colonel Box must have succeeded in his conquest, since she's now a cadet in the repressive Boxite Empire's military academy. Going back to the past, Chevie reunites with magician and good friend Riley to change history in this funny, high-octane adventure with thought-provoking time-travel insights." Horn Book

The **reluctant** assassin; Eoin Colfer. Hyperion Book CH 2013 352 p. (W.A.R.P.) (hardcover) $17.99

Grades: 5 6 7 8   Fic

1. Alternative histories -- Fiction 2. Science fiction 3. Assassins -- Fiction 4. Time travel -- Fiction 5. London (England) -- History -- 19th century -- Fiction 6. Great

Britain -- History -- Victoria, 1837-1901 -- Fiction

ISBN 1423161629; 9781423161622

LC 2012048160

This is the first book in the time-travel W.A.R.R. series from Eoin Colfer. "After a bungled mission, [FBI agent] Chevie has been sent to London where she is 'babysitting a metal capsule,' which she learns is one end of a wormhole to the year 1898, when [young assassin] Riley (and a corpse) materialize, direct from the Victorian era." (Publishers Weekly)

Collar, Orpheus

★ The **Red** Pyramid; Rick Riordan. Hyperion 2010 516 p. (Kane chronicles) (hardback) $17.99

Grades: 4 5 6 7   Fic

1. Fantasy fiction 2. Brothers and sisters -- Fiction 3. Egypt -- Fiction 4. Siblings -- Fiction 5. Secret societies -- Fiction 6. Gods and goddesses -- Fiction 7. Voyages and travels -- Fiction

ISBN 1423113381; 9781423113386

LC 2010549563

This is the first installment of the Kane chronicles. "Since their mother's death, Carter and Sadie have become near strangers. While Sadie has lived with her grandparents in London, her brother has traveled the world with their father, the brilliant Egyptologist, Dr. Julius Kane. . . . [Dr. Kane] unleashes the Egyptian god Set, who banished him to oblivion and forces the children to flee for their lives." (Publisher's note)

"The first-person narrative shifts between Carter and Sadie, giving the novel an intriguing dual perspective made more complex by their biracial heritage and the tension between the siblings. . . . This fantasy adventure delivers . . . young protagonists with previously unsuspected magical powers, a riveting story marked by headlong adventure, a complex background rooted in ancient mythology, and wry, witty twenty-first-century narration." Booklist

Collier, James Lincoln

★ **My** brother Sam is dead; by James Lincoln Collier and Christopher Collier. Four Winds Press 1985 216p $17.95

Grades: 6 7 8 9   Fic

1. United States -- History -- 1775-1783, Revolution -- Fiction

ISBN 0-02-722980-7

LC 84-28787

A reissue of the title first published 1974

A Newbery Medal honor book, 1975

"In 1775 the Meeker family lived in Redding, Connecticut, a Tory community. Sam, the eldest son, allied himself with the Patriots. The youngest son, Tim, watched a rift in the family grow because of his brother's decision. Before the war was over the Meeker family had suffered at the hands of both the British and the Patriots." Shapiro. Fic for Youth. 3d edition

War comes to Willy Freeman; [by] James Lincoln Collier, Christopher Collier. Delacorte Press 1983 178p hardcover o.p. pa $5.99

Grades: 6 7 8 9   Fic

1. Slavery -- Fiction 2. African Americans -- Fiction 3. United States -- History -- 1775-1783, Revolution --

Fiction
ISBN 0-440-49504-0 pa
LC 82-70317

This deals with events prior to those in Jump ship to freedom, and involves members of the same family. "Willy is thirteen when she begins her story, which takes place during the last two years of the Revolutionary War; her father, a free man, has been killed fighting against the British, her mother has disappeared. Willy makes her danger-fraught way to Fraunces Tavern in New York, her uncle, Jack Arabus, having told her that Mr. Fraunces may be able to help her. She works at the tavern until the war is over, goes to the Arabus home to find her mother dying, and participates in the trial (historically accurate save for the fictional addition of Willy) in which her uncle sues for his freedom and wins." Bull Cent Child Books

Collins, Pat Lowery
Daughter of winter. Candlewick Press 2010 272p $16.99
Grades: 4 5 6 7   **Fic**
1. Winter -- Fiction 2. Massachusetts -- Fiction 3. Wampanoag Indians -- Fiction 4. Wilderness survival -- Fiction
ISBN 978-0-7636-4500-7; 0-7636-4500-1
LC 2009049099

In the mid-nineteenth-century shipbuilding town of Essex, Massachusetts, twelve-year-old Addie learns a startling secret about her past when she escapes servitude by running away to live in the snowy woods and meets an elderly Wampanoag woman.

"Collins' sense of place, incorporation of cultural and historical details, and the richly evoked winter setting make for a vividly imagined novel. An engaging survival story intertwined with a search for identity." Booklist

Collins, Suzanne
★ **Gregor** the Overlander. Scholastic Press 2003 311p (Underland chronicles) $16.95; pa $5.99
Grades: 4 5 6 7   **Fic**
1. Fantasy fiction
ISBN 0-439-43536-6; 0-439-67813-7 pa
LC 2002-155865

When eleven-year-old Gregor and his two-year-old sister are pulled into a strange underground world, they trigger an epic battle involving men, bats, rats, cockroaches, and spiders while on a quest foretold by ancient prophecy

"Collins creates a fascinating, vivid, highly original world and a superb story to go along with it." Booklist

Other titles in this series are:
Gregor and the prophecy of Bane (2004)
Gregor and the curse of the warmbloods (2005)
Gregor and the marks of secret (2006)
Gregor and the code of claw (2007)

Collodi, Carlo
★ The **adventures** of Pinocchio; [by] Carlo Collodi; illustrated by Roberto Innocenti; designed by Rita Marshall. Creative Editions 2005 191p il $24.95
Grades: 3 4 5 6   **Fic**
1. Fairy tales 2. Puppets and puppet plays -- Fiction
ISBN 1-56846-190-9
LC 2003-62740

A wooden puppet full of tricks and mischief, with a talent for getting into and out of trouble, wants more than anything else to become a real boy

Innocenti's illustrations have a "19th-century European setting, and the careful composition, use of perspective, and dark earth tones are an apt visual expression of this complex moral tale." SLJ

★ **Pinocchio**; illustrated by Quentin Greban; translated by Claude Sartirano and Juanita Havill. North-South Books 2010 80p il $19.95
Grades: 3 4 5 6   **Fic**
1. Fantasy fiction 2. Puppets and puppet plays -- Fiction
ISBN 978-0-7358-2324-2; 0-7358-2324-3

A wooden puppet full of tricks and mischief, with a talent for getting into and out of trouble, wants more than anything else to become a real boy.

"This edition of the Italian classic Pinocchio strikes a good balance between nineteenth-century writing conventions and modern readers' tastes. Translated and somewhat abridged, the text offers a story that is true to the original in spirit and detail. . . . Gréban . . . creates distinctive illustrations with notable clarity of line, drama of composition, and subtlety of watercolor washes. Even libraries with several editions of Pinocchio should consider adding this one, for the clarity and grace of its writing as well as the luminous beauty of its illustrations." Booklist

Columbus, Chris, 1958-
Battle of the beasts; Chris Columbus, Ned Vizzini, Greg Call; [edited by] Alessandra Balzer. Balzer + Bray 2014 480 p. (House of secrets) (hardcover) $17.99
Grades: 5 6 7 8   **Fic**
1. Fantasy fiction 2. Adventure fiction 3. Witches -- Fiction 4. Brothers and sisters -- Fiction
ISBN 0062192493; 9780062192493
LC 2013956357

This book, by Chris Columbus and Ned Vizzini, is the sequel to "House of Secrets." "Since the siblings' last adventure, life in the Walker household is much improved the family is rich and the Wind Witch is banished. But no Walker will be safe until she is found, and summoning her to San Francisco brings all the danger that comes with her and puts the Walkers in the crosshairs of a mysterious journey through Denver Kristoff's books." (Publisher's note)

"An exorcism is just the beginning; the siblings also battle gladiators in ancient Rome, outwit cyborg Nazis, and face Yeti-like monsters in a Tibetan monastery in another imaginative, fast-paced adventure that is sure to please fans. Vizzini's older readers will miss his elegant and often eloquent, wry tone. Here's hoping another writer steps in to finish the planned trilogy." Booklist

House of secrets; Chris Columbus; Ned Vizzini. 1st ed. Balzer + Bray 2013 496 p. (hardcover) $17.99
Grades: 5 6 7 8   **Fic**
1. Haunted houses -- Fiction 2. Fantasy fiction 3. Adventure fiction 4. Fantasy 5. Dwellings -- Fiction 6. Supernatural -- Fiction 7. Books and reading -- Fiction 8. Brothers and sisters -- Fiction
ISBN 0062192469; 9780062192462
LC 2012051815

In this juvenile fantasy story, by Chris Columbus and Ned Vizzini, three siblings "relocate to an old Victorian house that used to be the home of occult novelist Denver Kristoff. . . . By the time the Walkers realize that one of their neighbors has sinister plans for them, they're banished to a primeval forest way off the grid. . . . Bloodthirsty medieval warriors patrol the woods around them, supernatural pirates roam the neighboring seas, and a power-hungry queen rules the land." (Publisher's note)

Coman, Carolyn

★ The **Memory** Bank; [by] Carolyn Coman & Rob Shepperson. Arthur A. Levine Books 2010 263p il $16.99
Grades: 3 4 5 6 **Fic**
1. Dreams -- Fiction 2. Memory -- Fiction 3. Sisters -- Fiction 4. Sabotage -- Fiction 5. Banks and banking -- Fiction
ISBN 978-0-545-21066-9; 0-545-21066-6

When Hope learns that, while her memory account is seriously low, she is a champion dreamer, she stays at the World Wide Memory Bank trying to locate her sister Honey, whom their parents abandoned and told Hope to forget.

"Energetic Quentin Blake-like pencil illustrations tell the tale of Hope's beloved Honey as she falls in with a rebel lot of lost children who threaten to overthrow the WWMB. Brilliantly crafted, thoroughly enjoyable and, though so very like Dahl, unique as a fascinating new way to ponder dreams and memories." Kirkus

Sneaking suspicions; [by] Carolyn Coman; drawings by Rob Shepperson. 1st ed.; Front Street 2007 245p il $16.95
Grades: 3 4 5 6 **Fic**
1. Siblings -- Fiction 2. Family life -- Fiction 3. Everglades (Fla.) -- Fiction 4. Swindlers and swindling -- Fiction
ISBN 978-1-59078-491-4; 1-59078-491-X
LC 2006101610

Sequel to The big house (2004)

Ivy and Ray accompany their parents on a trip to the Florida Everglades in order to find their only living relative, a distant cousin who, according to their great-grandfather's memoirs, absconded with a valuable, if unspecified, item.

"The children are believable characters. . . . Shepperson's black-and-white illustrations sprinkled liberally throughout masterfully capture the emotions of the Fitts family." SLJ

Comerford, Lynda B.

Rissa Bartholomew's declaration of independence. Scholastic Press 2009 250p $16.99
Grades: 4 5 6 7 **Fic**
1. School stories 2. Illinois -- Fiction 3. Friendship -- Fiction
ISBN 978-0-545-05058-6; 0-545-05058-8
LC 2008-26618

Having told off all of her old friends at her eleventh birthday party, Rissa starts middle school determined to make new friends while being herself, not simply being part of a herd.

"Rissa's troubles are ones that many middle-schoolers will identify with: new schools, shifting allegiances, new feelings, and changing bodies. First-time novelist Comerford gives her readers an appealing heroine who, despite her flaws and quirks, finds herself along the way." Booklist

Compestine, Ying Chang

Crouching tiger; illustrated by Yan Nascimbene. Candlewick Press 2011 il $16.99
Grades: 2 3 4 **Fic**
1. Grandfathers -- Fiction 2. Martial arts -- Fiction 3. Chinese Americans -- Fiction 4. Racially mixed people -- Fiction 5. Chinese -- United States -- Fiction
ISBN 978-0-7636-4642-4; 0-7636-4642-3
LC 2010048133

When Ming Da's Chinese grandpa comes to visit, he overcomes his initial embarrassment at his grandfather's traditions and begins to appreciate him.

"Compestine creates a simple portrait of a familiar cultural bridge, conveying Vinson's awe, shyness and embarrassment about his serious grandfather. Nascimbene captures both the compact energy of the small boy and the graceful, composed grace of the adult. His contained, quiet style with warm colors nicely matches the low-key narrative. . . . A celebration of family and Chinese New Year along with a simple introduction to Wudang martial arts, especially tai chi-and to the idea that strength can be gentle." Kirkus

Conford, Ellen

Annabel the actress starring in Gorilla my dreams; illustrated by Renée Williams-Andriani. Simon & Schuster Bks. for Young Readers 1999 64p il hardcover o.p. pa $3.99
Grades: 2 3 4 **Fic**
1. Actors -- Fiction 2. Parties -- Fiction
ISBN 0-689-81404-6; 0-689-83883-2 pa
LC 97-39449

Though a little disappointed that her first acting part is to be a gorilla at a birthday party, Annabel determines to really get into the role

"The vocabulary is appropriate for those graduating from easy-readers, but the language is never stilted. Amusing pen-and-ink illustrations appear on almost every page." SLJ

Other titles about Annabel are:
Annabel the actress starring in Hound of the Barkervilles (2002)
Annabel the actress, starring in Camping it up (2004)
Annabel the actress, starring in Just a little extra (2000)

★ A **case** for Jenny Archer; illustrated by Diane Palmisciano. Little, Brown 1988 61p il (Springboard books) hardcover o.p. pa $4.99
Grades: 2 3 4 **Fic**
1. Mystery fiction
ISBN 0-316-01486-9 pa
LC 88-14169

After reading three mysteries in a row, Jenny becomes convinced that the neighbors across the street are up to no good and decides to investigate

"This lots-of-fun advanced easy reader contains eight chapters, all about three pages long, with large, clear print, and lots of white space. . . . The children here are lively, the adults funny, wise, and supportive." SLJ

Other titles about Jenny Archer are:
Can do, Jenny Archer (1991)
Get the picture, Jenny Archer (1994)
Jenny Archer, author (1989)
Jenny Archer to the rescue (1990)
A job for Jenny Archer (1988)

Nibble, nibble, Jenny Archer (1993)
What's cooking, Jenny Archer (1989)

Conkling, Winifred
Sylvia and Aki. Tricycle Press 2011 151p $16.99; lib bdg $19.99
Grades: 3 4 5 6   **Fic**
1. Farm life -- Fiction 2. Race relations -- Fiction 3. Mexican Americans -- Fiction 4. Segregation in education -- Fiction 5. Poston Relocation Center (Ariz.) -- Fiction 6. Japanese Americans -- Evacuation and relocation, 1942-1945 -- Fiction
ISBN 978-1-58246-337-7; 1-58246-337-9; 978-1-58246-397-1 lib bdg; 1-58246-397-2 lib bdg
LC 2010024182
At the start of World War II, Japanese-American third-grader Aki and her family are sent to an internment camp in Poston, Arizona, while Mexican-American third-grader Sylvia's family leases their Orange County, California, farm and begins a fight to stop school segregation.
"Told in alternating chapters from the girls' points of view, this story about institutional racism will enlighten readers to events in recent history. From the court case of Mendez v. Westminster to the conditions at Poston, readers will be moved by this novel based on true events." SLJ

Conly, Jane Leslie
Crazy lady! HarperCollins Pubs. 1993 180p lib bdg $18.89; pa $5.99
Grades: 5 6 7 8   **Fic**
1. Death -- Fiction 2. Alcoholism -- Fiction 3. Prejudices -- Fiction 4. Mentally disabled people -- Fiction
ISBN 0-06-021360-4 lib bdg; 0-06-440571-0 pa
LC 92-18348
A Newbery Medal honor book, 1994
As he tries to come to terms with his mother's death, Vernon finds solace in his growing relationship with the neighborhood outcasts, an alcoholic and her mentally disabled son
The narration "is fast and blunt, and the conversations are lively and true." Bull Cent Child Books

★ Murder afloat. Hyperion Books for Children 2010 164p $17.99
Grades: 5 6 7 8   **Fic**
1. Adventure fiction 2. Kidnapping -- Fiction 3. Seafaring life -- Fiction
ISBN 978-1-4231-0416-2; 1-4231-0416-1
Benjamin Franklin Orville is caught up in a scuffle, kidnapped with a group of immigrants and forced to work aboard the Ella Dawn—one of the most ill-reputed oystering vessels in Baltimore.
"With compelling characters and details of the little-known process of oystering woven throughout, Conly's tale touches on the hardships of many German immigrants to the U.S., whose desperate plights offer parallels to contemporary immigration issues. Short chapters and suspenseful plot twists will keep readers turning the pages in this engaging historical adventure." Booklist

Connor, Leslie
★ Crunch. Katherine Tegen Books 2010 330p $16.99; lib bdg $17.89

Grades: 5 6 7 8   **Fic**
1. Bicycles -- Fiction 2. Siblings -- Fiction 3. Family life -- Fiction 4. New England -- Fiction 5. Energy conservation -- Fiction 6. Business enterprises -- Fiction
ISBN 978-0-06-169229-1; 0-06-169229-8; 978-0-06-169233-8 lib bdg; 0-06-169233-6 lib bdg
LC 2009-24339
This novel concerns "the trials and tribulations of 14-year-old Dewey Mariss and his family. His parents are away from home, unable to return because of a gasoline shortage. Running their small family business, the Bike Barn, with his younger brother and helping older sister Lil look after the five-year-old twins keeps Dewey plenty busy. . . . Characters are colorful but believable, dialogue crisp and amusing. The New England setting is attractively realized, and the underlying energy crisis treated seriously but not sensationally." Kirkus

★ Waiting for normal. Katherine Tegen Books 2008 290p $16.99; lib bdg $17.89
Grades: 5 6 7 8   **Fic**
1. Mothers -- Fiction 2. Family life -- Fiction 3. New York (State) -- Fiction
ISBN 978-0-06-089088-9; 0-06-089088-6; 978-0-06-089089-6 lib bdg; 0-06-089089-4 lib bdg
LC 2007-06881
Twelve-year-old Addie tries to cope with her mother's erratic behavior and being separated from her beloved stepfather and half-sisters when she and her mother go to live in a small trailer by the railroad tracks on the outskirts of Schenectady, New York.
"Connor . . . treats the subject of child neglect with honesty and grace in this poignant story. . . . Characters as persuasively optimistic as Addie are rare, and readers will gravitate to her." Publ Wkly

Conrad, Pam
★ My Daniel. Harper & Row 1989 137p pa $5.99
Grades: 5 6 7 8   **Fic**
1. Nebraska -- Fiction
ISBN 0-06-440309-2 pa
LC 88-19850
"Rendering scenes from both the past and the present with equal skill, Conrad is at the peak of her storytelling powers." Publ Wkly
"When she's 80 years old, Julia Summerwaithe decides to visit her grandchildren, Ellie and Stevie, in New York City, for the first time. She has something important to show them; in the Natural History Museum is the dinosaur she and her brother discovered on their farm in Nebraska when they were young. But even more important to Julia than seeing the dinosaur is sharing her memories of the discovery and excavation with her grandchildren." SLJ

Cook, Kacy
Nuts. Marshall Cavendish 2010 155p $16.99
Grades: 4 5 6   **Fic**
1. Ohio -- Fiction 2. Pets -- Fiction 3. Squirrels -- Fiction 4. Family life -- Fiction
ISBN 978-0-7614-5652-0; 0-7614-5652-X
LC 2009-04354
When eleven-year-old Nell finds a tiny baby squirrel on the ground in her yard, she begs her parents to let her raise

it as a pet, even after the research she does shows that this is not a good idea.

"Cook does a nice job of taking a seemingly innocent plot and almost sneaking in (a little like pureed vegetables) much weightier themes of love, honesty and death. . . . The straightforward, upbeat prose consistently engages readers, and her characters are dead on. There's more here than meets the eye." Kirkus

Coombs, Kate

The **runaway** dragon. Farrar, Straus and Giroux 2009 292p $16.99

Grades: 5 6 7 8   **Fic**

1. Fairy tales 2. Dragons -- Fiction 3. Princesses -- Fiction

ISBN 978-0-374-36361-1; 0-374-36361-7

LC 2008034362

Sequel to: The runaway princess (2006)

When her beloved dragon Laddy runs away from the castle, Princess Meg and some of her friends embark on a quest to find him and bring him home.

"Funny, lighthearted. . . . Enchanted forests, rampant transmogrification, evil sorceresses and giants are all fine fodder for Coombs's inventive twists on traditional fairy tales." Kirkus

The **runaway** princess. Farrar, Straus and Giroux 2006 279p $17

Grades: 5 6 7 8   **Fic**

1. Fairy tales 2. Dragons -- Fiction 3. Princesses -- Fiction

ISBN 0-374-35546-0

LC 2005-51225

Fifteen-year-old Princess Meg uses magic and her wits to rescue a baby dragon and escape the unwanted attentions of princes hoping to gain her hand in marriage through a contest arranged by her father, the king.

"This witty, humorous tale will be popular with fantasy buffs who enjoy takeoffs on fairy tales." Booklist

Another title about Princess Meg is:

The runaway dragon (2009)

Cooper, Ilene

Lucy on the ball; illustrated by David Merrell. Random House 2011 102p il (Absolutely Lucy) lib bdg $12.99; pa $4.99

Grades: 2 3 4   **Fic**

1. Dogs -- Fiction 2. Soccer -- Fiction

ISBN 978-0-375-95559-4 lib bdg; 0-375-95559-3 lib bdg; 978-0-375-85559-7 pa; 0-375-85559-9 pa; 978-0-375-89820-4 e-book

LC 2010005183

Lucy the beagle does not mind her humans very well until third-grader Bobby joins a soccer team. Lucy becomes the mascot, and the coach gives Lucy obedience training.

Lucy on the loose; illustrated by Amanda Harvey. Golden Books 2000 76p il (Absolutely Lucy) hardcover o.p. pa $4.99

Grades: 2 3 4   **Fic**

1. Cats -- Fiction 2. Dogs -- Fiction 3. Shyness -- Fiction 4. Lost and found possessions -- Fiction

ISBN 0-307-46508-X; 0-307-26508-0 pa

LC 00021432

When his beagle Lucy runs off chasing a big orange cat, Bobby must overcome his shyness in order to find them again.

Cooper, Susan, 1935-

★ The **Boggart**. Margaret K. McElderry Bks. 1993 196p hardcover o.p. pa $5.99

Grades: 4 5 6 7   **Fic**

1. Canada -- Fiction 2. Scotland -- Fiction 3. Supernatural -- Fiction

ISBN 0-689-50576-0; 0-689-86930-4 pa

LC 92-15527

After visiting the castle in Scotland which her family has inherited and returning home to Canada, twelve-year-old Emily finds that she has accidentally brought back with her a boggart, an invisible and mischievous spirit with a fondness for practical jokes

"Using both electronics and theater as metaphors for magic, Cooper has extended the world of high fantasy into contemporary children's lives through scenes superimposing the ordinary and the extraordinary." Bull Cent Child Books

Another title about the Boggart is:

The Boggart and the monster (1997)

The **Boggart** and the monster. Margaret K. McElderry Bks. 1997 185p $17.99; pa $5.99 **Fic**

1. Supernatural -- Fiction

ISBN 0-689-81330-9; 0-689-86931-2 pa

LC 96-42389

The Boggart, the invisible and mischievous spirit living in the Scottish Castle Keep, sets out to help save Nessie the Loch Ness Monster, one of its few remaining cousins

"Cooper adroitly incorporates ancient lore into a contemporary setting while producing an imaginative and compelling tale." Publ Wkly

★ **Ghost** Hawk; by Susan Cooper. 1st ed. Margaret K. McElderry Books 2013 328 p. map (hardcover) $16.99

Grades: 5 6 7 8   **Fic**

1. Friendship -- Fiction 2. Native Americans -- North America 3. Native Americans -- Relations with early settlers 4. Ghosts -- Fiction 5. Survival -- Fiction 6. Coming of age -- Fiction 7. Wampanoag Indians -- Fiction 8. Massachusetts -- History -- New Plymouth, 1620-1691 -- Fiction

ISBN 1442481412; 9781442481411; 9781442481435

LC 2012039892

Parents' Choice: Gold Medal Fiction (2013)

This novel is "a story of adventure and friendship between a young Native American and a colonial New England settler. Little Hawk is sent into the woods alone [and] if [he] survives three moons by himself, he will be a man. John Wakely is only ten when his father dies. . . . John sees how quickly the relationships between settlers and natives are deteriorating. His friendship with Little Hawk will put both boys in grave danger." (Publisher's note)

★ The **grey** king; illustrated by Michael Heslop. Atheneum Pubs. 1975 208p il $19.99; pa $8.99

Grades: 5 6 7 8   **Fic**

1. Fantasy fiction 2. Wales -- Fiction 3. Good and evil -- Fiction

ISBN 0-689-50029-7; 1-4169-4967-4 pa

Awarded the Newbery Medal, 1976

"So well-crafted that it stands as an entity in itself, the novel ... is nevertheless strengthened by its relationship to the preceding volumes—as the individual legends within the Arthurian cycles take on deeper significance in the context of the whole. A spellbinding tour de force." Horn Book

★ **King** of shadows. Margaret K. McElderry Bks. 1999 186p $16; pa $4.99; pa $6.99

Grades: 5 6 7 8   Fic

1. Poets 2. Authors 3. Dramatists 4. Actors -- Fiction 5. Globe Theatre (London, England) -- Fiction
ISBN 0-689-82817-9; 0-689-84445-X pa; 9780689844454 pa

LC 98-51127

Boston Globe Horn Book Honor Book (2000)

"Nat Field is thrilled when theater director Richard Babbage chooses him to become a player in the Company of Boys, an American summer drama troupe that will appear in Shakespeare's A Midsummer Night's Dream at the new replica of the Globe Theater in London. Shortly after his arrival in England, though, Nat feels ill and falls into a troubled sleep. To the doctor's astonishment, he seems to be suffering from the effects of the bubonic plague. He awakens in 1599 as another Nat Field, a child actor from St. Paul's School who is about to go to the Globe to rehearse A Midsummer Night's Dream in the role of Puck." (Booklist) "Grades six to nine." (Bull Cent Child Books)

"Cleverly explicating old and new acting and performance techniques, Susan Cooper entertains her contemporary readers while giving them a first-rate theatrical education." N Y Times Book Rev

The **magician's** boy; illustrated by Serena Riglietti. Margaret K. McElderry Bks. 2005 100p il $15.95; pa $7.95

Grades: 2 3 4   Fic

1. Fairy tales 2. Magicians -- Fiction
ISBN 0-689-87622-X; 1-4169-1555-9 pa

A boy who works for a magician meets familiar fairy tale characters when he is transported to the Land of Story in search of a missing puppet

"Fanciful and mildly amusing, the dreamlike story flows along smoothly through a strange yet vaguely familiar wonderland. Riglietti contributes a series of expressive, stylized illustrations." Booklist

★ **Over** sea, under stone; illustrated by Margery Gill. Harcourt Brace Jovanovich 1966 252p il $19; pa $5.99

Grades: 5 6 7 8   Fic

1. Fantasy fiction 2. Good and evil -- Fiction 3. Great Britain -- Fiction
ISBN 0-15-259034-X; 0-689-84035-7 pa

First published 1965 in the United Kingdom

Three children on a holiday in Cornwall find an ancient manuscript which sends them on a dangerous quest for a grail that would reveal the true story of King Arthur and that entraps them in the eternal battle between the forces of the Light and the forces of the Dark.

"The air of mysticism and the allegorical quality of the continual contest between good and evil add much value to a fine plot, setting, and characterization." Horn Book

Other titles in this series are:

The dark is rising (1973)

Greenwitch (1974)

The grey king (1975)

Silver on the tree (1977)

Victory. Margaret K. McElderry Books 2006 196p il $16.95; pa $6.99

Grades: 5 6 7 8   Fic

1. Admirals 2. Sea stories 3. Great Britain -- Fiction
ISBN 1-4169-1477-3; 1-4169-1478-1 pa

LC 2005-16747

Alternating chapters follow the mysterious connection between a homesick English girl living in present-day America and an eleven-year-old boy serving in the British Royal Navy in 1803, aboard the H.M.S. Victory, commanded by Admiral Horatio Nelson.

"Seamlessly weaving details of period seamanship into the narrative, Cooper offers a vivid historical tale within the framework of a compelling modern story." Booklist

Corbett, Sue

Free baseball; [by] Sue Corbett. Dutton Children's Books 2006 152p $15.99; pa $5.99

Grades: 5 6 7 8   Fic

1. Florida -- Fiction 2. Baseball -- Fiction 3. Cuban Americans -- Fiction
ISBN 0-525-47120-0; 0-14-241080-2 pa

LC 2005004792

Angry with his mother for having too little time for him, eleven-year-old Felix takes advantage of an opportunity to become bat boy for a minor league baseball team, hoping to someday be like his father, a famous Cuban outfielder. Includes glossaries of baseball terms and Spanish words and phrases

"An engaging, well-written story with a satisfying ending." SLJ

Cornwell, Nicki

Christophe's story; [by] Nicki Cornwell; illustrated by Karin Littlewood. Frances Lincoln Children's 2007 74p il $14.95; pa $7.95

Grades: 2 3 4   Fic

1. School stories 2. Rwanda -- Fiction 3. Refugees -- Fiction 4. Immigrants -- Fiction
ISBN 978-1-84507-765-5; 1-84507-765-2; 978-1-84507-521-7 pa; 1-84507-521-8 pa

Coping with a new country, a new school and a new language, Christophe wants to tell everyone why he had to leave Rwanda.

"The book succeeds, giving insight into the refugee experience and a glimpse of the horrors in Rwanda that will not overwhelm young readers." Booklist

Correa, Shan

Gaff; written by Shan Correa. Peachtree 2010 212p $15.95

Grades: 4 5 6 7   Fic

1. Hawaii -- Fiction 2. Roosters -- Fiction 3. Animal welfare -- Fiction
ISBN 978-1-56145-526-3; 1-56145-526-1

In Hawaii, thirteen-year-old Paul Silva is determined to find a way to get his family out of the illegal cockfighting business.

"Correa's debut evokes the lush melange of sights, sounds and smells in 13-year-old Paulie's multicultural neighborhood in Hawaii. . . . Also woven into this ethical debate, rooted in economics and traditions, is Hawaiian pidgin English, which may challenge even experienced readers. . . . A fascinating look at the United States most mainlanders have never seen." Kirkus

Cotler, Steve

Cheesie Mack is cool in a duel; Steve Cotler; illustrated by Adam McCauley. Random House 2012 229 p. (hardcover library binding) $18.99

Grades: 4 5 6   **Fic**

1. Camps -- Fiction 2. Siblings -- Fiction 3. Interpersonal relations -- Fiction 4. Maine -- Fiction 5. Contests -- Fiction

ISBN 9780375864384; 9780375895715;
9780375964381

LC 2011016921

This book is the second in the Cheesie Mack series. "Ronald 'Cheesie' Mack and his best friend Georgie secured the funds to go to summer camp on Bufflehead Lake in Maine. Days later, the duo climbs aboard a bus and head off to Camp Windward. Unfortunately Cheesie's older sister, June . . . will be none too far away at Camp Leeward. . . . T late registration results in both boys being stuck in a cabin with the older guys including Kevin, [June's] boyfriend. When Kevin gives Cheesie a hard time once too often, Cheesie suggests a Cool Duel. Each night the boys in the cabin will vote on who did the coolest thing; in a week, the loser will have to embarrass himself in front of the whole camp by bowing to the winner. Can Cheesie prevail and still have fun at the camp he worked so hard to attend?" (Kirkus Reviews)

Cheesie Mack is not a genius or anything; illustrated by Adam McCauley. Random House 2011 229p il $15.99; lib bdg $18.99

Grades: 4 5 6   **Fic**

1. Mystery fiction 2. Summer -- Fiction 3. Friendship -- Fiction

ISBN 978-0-375-86437-7; 0-375-86437-7; 978-0-375-96437-4 lib bdg; 0-375-96437-1 lib bdg; 978-0-375-89570-8 e-book

LC 2009-33329

Ronald, aka Cheesie, Mack and his best friend Georgie find opportunies for summertime mischief "when Georgie finds a nearly century-old letter containing a worn penny and a locket, a mystery that eventually leads the pals to the Haunted Toad, a local rundown mansion. . . . Cheesie's . . . easygoing, accessible voice will certainly appeal to middle-grade readers. . . . The action . . . is all fun and games. . . . A light-hearted and fast-moving read for kids looking for middle-school shenanigans." Bull Cent Child Books

Cheesie Mack is running like crazy! by Steve Cotler; illustrated by Douglas Holgate. 1st ed. Random House Inc. 2013 256 p. ill. (hardcover) $15.99; (library) $18.99; (ebook) $47.97; (paperback) $6.99

Grades: 4 5 6   **Fic**

1. Schools -- Fiction 2. Elections -- Fiction 3. Friendship -- Fiction 4. Best friends -- Fiction 5. Middle schools -- Fiction 6. Track and field -- Fiction

7. Brothers and sisters -- Fiction

ISBN 0307977145; 9780307977137; 9780307977144; 9780307977151; 9780307977168

LC 2012017978

In this book by Steve Colter, "Cheesie and his best friend, Georgie, are off to the middle school, where there will be lots of new kids and new teachers. Cheesie has a terrific idea--what better way to meet all the new kids than to run for class president? Plus, if he wins, it'll drive his evil older sister nuts! Then Cheesie gets bad news. One of his friends from his old school is also running for president." (Publisher's note

Cottrell Boyce, Frank

★ Cosmic. Walden Pond Press 2010 311p $16.99; lib bdg $17.89

Grades: 4 5 6 7   **Fic**

1. Size -- Fiction 2. Outer space -- Exploration -- Fiction

ISBN 978-0-06-183683-1; 0-06-183683-4; 978-0-06-183686-2 lib bdg; 0-06-183686-9 lib bdg

LC 2008277816

Boyce "knows how to tell a compellingly good story. But in his latest extravagantly imaginative and marvelously good-natured novel he has also written one that is bound to win readers' hearts." Booklist

"Liam has always felt a bit like he's stuck between two worlds. This is primarily because he's a twelve-year-old kid who looks like he's about thirty. . . . Liam cons his way onto the first spaceship to take civilians into space, a special flight for a group of kids and an adult chaperone, and he is going as the adult chaperone." Publisher's note

★ The unforgotten coat; photographs by Carl Hunter and Clare Heney. Candlewick Press 2011 112p il $15.99

Grades: 3 4 5 6   **Fic**

1. Mongols -- Fiction 2. Brothers -- Fiction 3. Refugees -- Fiction 4. Friendship -- Fiction 5. Immigrants -- Fiction 6. Great Britain -- Fiction

ISBN 978-0-7636-5729-1; 0-7636-5729-8

LC 2010048224

"Funny, sad, haunting and original, Cottrell Boyce's story leaves important elements unexpressed. . . . To complete the narrative, readers must actively participate. They'll find myriad paths to follow—immigration, demons, social networking, the mystery of cultural difference and the nature of enchantment. A tricky, magical delight." Kirkus

This is "a tight, powerful story—brimming with humor, mystery, and pathos—about illegal immigration and the price it exacts on children." Publ Wkly

Couloumbis, Audrey

★ Getting near to baby. Putnam 1999 211p $17.99; pa $5.99

Grades: 5 6 7 8   **Fic**

1. Aunts -- Fiction 2. Death -- Fiction 3. Sisters -- Fiction

ISBN 0-399-23389-X; 0-698-11892-8 pa

LC 99-18191

A Newbery Medal honor book, 2000

Although thirteen-year-old Willa Jo and her Aunt Patty seem to be constantly at odds, staying with her and Uncle Hob helps Willa Jo and her younger sister come to terms with the death of their family's baby

"Couloumbis's writing is strong; she captures wonderfully the Southern voices of her characters and conveys with great depth powerful emotions. . . . A compelling novel." SLJ

Jake. Random House 2010 162p $15.99; lib bdg $18.99

Grades: 3 4 5   **Fic**
1. Accidents -- Fiction 2. Christmas -- Fiction 3. Hospitals -- Fiction 4. Grandfathers -- Fiction 5. Baltimore (Md.) -- Fiction

ISBN 978-0-375-85630-3; 0-375-85630-7; 978-0-375-95630-0 lib bdg; 0-375-95630-1 lib bdg

LC 2009-29383
When ten-year-old Jake's widowed mother breaks her leg just before Christmas while her sister and best friend are both away, a grandfather Jake barely remembers must come to Baltimore, Maryland, to help a neighbor take care of him.

"Never message heavy, the drama about the meaning of family will touch readers." Booklist

★ **Lexie**; illustrated by Julia Denos. Random House 2011 199p il $15.99; lib bdg $18.99

Grades: 3 4 5 6   **Fic**
1. Beaches -- Fiction 2. Divorce -- Fiction 3. Vacations -- Fiction 4. Remarriage -- Fiction 5. Father-daughter relationship -- Fiction

ISBN 978-0-375-85632-7; 0-375-85632-3; 978-0-375-95632-4 lib bdg; 0-375-95632-8 lib bdg

LC 2010-20751
When ten-year-old Lexie goes with her father to the beach for a week, she is surprised to find that he has invited his girlfriend and her two sons to join them for the entire week.

"Couloumbis demonstrates her skill at writing with quiet understanding and unstudied polish for younger readers. Her ability to walk through complicated emotional dynamics in kid-accessible language . . . is impressive." Bull Cent Child Books

Maude March on the run! or, Trouble is her middle name. Random House 2007 309p $15.99; lib bdg $17.99

Grades: 4 5 6 7   **Fic**
1. Adventure fiction 2. Orphans -- Fiction 3. Frontier and pioneer life -- Fiction

ISBN 978-0-375-83246-8; 978-0-375-93246-5 lib bdg; 978-0-375-83248-2 pa

LC 2005036133
Due to a misunderstanding over her involvement in a botched robbery, Maude, with younger sister Sallie, hides out at the home of an uncle, but when she is discovered and arrested, the orphaned sisters flee, trying to clear Maude's name.

"The excitement of the Wild West comes to life in this action-packed sequel to The Misadventures of Maude March." SLJ

★ The **misadventures** of Maude March; or, Trouble rides a fast horse. [by] Audrey Couloumbis. Random House 2005 295p hardcover o.p. lib bdg $17.99; pa $7.50

Grades: 4 5 6 7   **Fic**
1. Adventure fiction 2. Orphans -- Fiction 3. Frontier

and pioneer life -- Fiction

ISBN 0-375-83245-9; 0-375-93245-3 lib bdg; 0-375-83247-5 pa

LC 2004-16464
After the death of the stern aunt who raised them since they were orphaned, eleven-year-old Sallie and her fifteen-year-old sister escape their self-serving guardians and begin an adventure resembling those in the dime novels Sallie loves to read. "Grades six to ten." (Bull Cent Child Books)

"Sallie's narration is delightful, with understatements that are laugh-out-loud hilarious. . . . Hard to put down, and a fun read-aloud." SLJ

★ **War** games; a novel based on a true story. [by] Audrey Couloumbis & Akila Couloumbis. Random House Children's Books 2009 232p $16.99; lib bdg $19.99

Grades: 5 6 7 8   **Fic**
1. Greece -- Fiction 2. Cousins -- Fiction 3. Brothers -- Fiction 4. World War, 1939-1945 -- Underground movements -- Fiction

ISBN 978-0-375-85628-0; 0-375-85628-5; 978-0-375-95628-7 lib bdg; 0-375-95628-X lib bdg

LC 2008-46784
"For 12-year-old Petros, World War II feels unreal and far away. . . . But when the Germans invade Greece, the war suddenly comes impossibly close. Overnight, neighbors become enemies. People begin to keep secrets (Petros's family most of all). And for the first time, Petros has the chance to show Zola that he's not just a little brother but that he can truly be counted on." (Publisher's note) "Grades six to nine." (Bull Cent Child Books)

"The climactic violence is believable, and the resolution—though it takes place offstage—is deeply satisfying. Memorable." SLJ

Coville, Bruce

Amber Brown is tickled pink; written by Bruce Coville and Elizabeth Levy; illustrated by Tony Ross. G.P. Putnam's Sons 2013 154 p. (hardcover) $14.99

Grades: 2 3 4 5   **Fic**
1. Children of divorced parents -- Fiction 2. Weddings -- Fiction 3. Remarriage -- Fiction

ISBN 0399256563; 9780399256561

LC 2011039493
In this book by Bruce Coville and Elizabeth Levy, "Amber can't wait to be Best Child when her mom and Max get married, but planning a wedding comes with lots of headaches. Amber can't find the right dress, her dad keeps making mean cracks about Max, and Mom and Max have very different ideas about how much this wedding should cost. Her mother even suggests they go to city hall and skip the party altogether!" (Publisher's note)

Jennifer Murdley's toad; a magic shop book. illustrated by Gary A. Lippincott. Harcourt 2002 159p il $17; pa $5.95

Grades: 4 5 6   **Fic**
1. Fantasy fiction 2. Toads -- Fiction

ISBN 0-15-204613-5; 0-15-206246-7 pa

LC 2002-24107
A reissue of the title first published 1992
When an ordinary-looking fifth grader purchases a talking toad, she embarks on a series of extraordinary adventures

"This light, fast-paced fantasy has touches of humor (at times low comedy), an implicit moral, and a hint that Jennifer may be in for more adventures." Booklist

★ **Jeremy** Thatcher, dragon hatcher; a magic shop book. illustrated by Gary A. Lippincott. Harcourt 2002 151p il $17; pa $5.95

Grades: 4 5 6   **Fic**

1. Fantasy fiction 2. Dragons -- Fiction
ISBN 0-15-204614-3; 0-15-206252-1 pa

LC 2002-68714

A reissue of the title first published 1991

Small for his age but artistically talented, twelve-year-old Jeremy Thatcher unknowingly buys a dragon's egg

This is "right on target. Not only is the story involving but the reader can really get a feeling for Jeremy as a person. Coville's technique of combining the real world with a fantasy one works well in this story." Voice Youth Advocates

Juliet Dove, Queen of Love; a magic shop book. Harcourt 2003 190p il $17; pa $5.95

Grades: 4 5 6   **Fic**

1. Magic -- Fiction 2. Classical mythology -- Fiction
ISBN 0-15-204561-9; 0-15-205217-8 pa

LC 2003-11846

A shy twelve-year-old girl must solve a puzzle involving characters from Greek mythology to free herself from a spell which makes her irresistible to boys

"Although humorous, the story has surprising depth. . . . Coville capably interweaves mythological characters with realistic modern ones, keeping readers truly absorbed." SLJ

The **skull** of truth; a magic shop book. illustrated by Gary A. Lippincott. Harcourt 2002 194p il $17

Grades: 4 5 6   **Fic**

1. Fantasy fiction 2. Truthfulness and falsehood -- Fiction
ISBN 0-15-204612-7

LC 2002-24244

A reissue of the title first published 1997

Charlie, a sixth-grader with a compulsion to tell lies, acquires a mysterious skull that forces its owner to tell only the truth, causing some awkward moments before he understands its power

"Coville has structured the story very carefully, with a great deal of sensitivity to children's thought processes and emotions. The mood shifts from scary to funny to serious are fused with understandable language and sentence structures." SLJ

Thor's wedding day; by Thialfi, the goat boy. as told to and translated by Bruce Coville; illustrations by Matthew Cogswell. Harcourt 2005 137p il $15; pa $5.95

Grades: 4 5 6 7   **Fic**

1. Giants -- Fiction 2. Norse mythology -- Fiction
ISBN 0-15-201455-1; 0-15-205872-9 pa

LC 2004-29580

Thialfi, the Norse thunder god's goat boy, tells how he inadvertently helped the giant Thrym to steal Thor's magic hammer, the lengths to which Thor must go to retrieve it, and his own assistance along the way.

"Coville takes a Norse poem called the Thrymskvitha and turns it into a delightful prose romp. . . . Throughout,

he injects a modern sensibility while keeping the feel of the original myth." Booklist

Cowing, Sue

You will call me Drog. Carolrhoda Books 2011 281p $16.95

Grades: 4 5 6 7   **Fic**

1. Aikido -- Fiction 2. Divorce -- Fiction 3. Illinois -- Fiction 4. Supernatural -- Fiction 5. Puppets and puppet plays -- Fiction
ISBN 978-0-7613-6076-6; 0-7613-6076-X

LC 2010050891

Unless eleven-year-old Parker can find a way to remove the sinister puppet that refuses to leave his hand, he will wind up in military school or worse but first he must stand up for himself to his best friend Wren, his mother, and his nearly-absent father.

"There is nothing else out there quite like this, and Cowing shifts fluidly from sensitive drama to startling violence to high comedy. . . . A unique look at speaking your mind." Booklist

Cowley, Joy

Snake and Lizard; [written by] Joy Cowley; [illustrated by] Gavin Bishop. Kane Miller Pub. 2008 85p il $14.95

Grades: 2 3 4   **Fic**

1. Snakes -- Fiction 2. Lizards -- Fiction 3. Friendship -- Fiction
ISBN 978-1-933605-83-8; 1-933605-83-9

"Snake and Lizard were born to squabble. . . . Each argument begins in misunderstanding and ends in companionable accord; yet their disagreements spring so obviously from their natures, and their repartee is so comical—snappy, ludicrous yet logical—that the salutary message is absorbed with delight. . . . Bishop's art (apparently pen-and-ink, with cheery watercolor added) enlivens almost every spread of this attractive small volume, capturing each interaction with wit and affection." Horn Book

Cox, Judy

Butterfly buddies; illustrated by Blanche Sims. Holiday House 2001 86p il $15.95

Grades: 2 3 4   **Fic**

1. School stories 2. Friendship -- Fiction 3. Butterflies -- Fiction
ISBN 0-8234-1654-2

LC 2001-16720

Third grader Robin has a series of mishaps and learns the value of honesty as she tries to become best friends with Zoey, her partner for a class project on raising butterflies. Includes butterfly care tips

"Written in simple, highly descriptive language that brings settings and characters alive, and sprinkled with lively drawings, this warmhearted friendship story is a good choice for readers transitioning to chapter books." Booklist

Nora and the Texas terror; illustrated by Amanda Haley. Holiday House 2010 87p il $15.95

Grades: 2 3 4   **Fic**

1. School stories 2. Oregon -- Fiction 3. Cousins -- Fiction 4. Family life -- Fiction
ISBN 978-0-8234-2283-8; 0-8234-2283-6

LC 2010-14329

When Nora's uncle loses his job and house in Texas, he and his family come to stay with Nora's family in Portland, Oregon, and Nora must try very hard to adjust to her cousin Ellie, who is loud, stubborn, and a tease.

"This is an entertaining and original early chapter book; the dynamic between Nora and Ellie is realistically portrayed, and the simple plot is well developed. . . . Monochromatic line-and-watercolor illustrations . . . add further entertainment value." Bull Cent Child Books

Puppy power; illustrated by Steve Björkman. Holiday House 2008 91p il $15.95; pa $6.95
Grades: 2 3 4   **Fic**
  1. School stories 2. Dogs -- Fiction
  ISBN 978-0-8234-2073-5; 0-8234-2073-6; 978-0-8234-2210-4 pa; 0-8234-2210-0 pa
               LC 2007-28395
Boisterous third-grader Fran has trouble controlling herself, but learning how to train her gigantic Newfoundland puppy helps her gain enough self-control to win the part of princess in the class play. Includes instructions on puppy training.

This is an "entertaining novel full of believable kids with recognizable problems. . . . With a brisk plot, short chapters, and frequent pen-and-ink illustrations, this story is a choice selection." Booklist

Ukulele Hayley; by Judy Cox; illustrated by Amanda Haley. Holiday House 2013 82 p. (hardcover) $16.95
Grades: 2 3 4   **Fic**
  1. Music -- Fiction 2. Schools -- Fiction 3. Ukulele -- Fiction
  ISBN 082342863X; 9780823428632
               LC 2012045825
In this book, by Judy Cox, "Hayley has finally found her talent: playing ukulele like her great-great aunt Ruby, who traveled all over with her band, the Ragtime Rascals. She's so enthusiastic that she gets a ukulele band started at school with the new music teacher. Just as the band is getting popular, horrible news comes: the music program and the teacher are being cut." (Publisher's note)

"This cheerful story about a third grader who finds her talent, and then uses it to organize a band (and save the school's music program), will appeal to independent readers who like everyday, undemanding school stories with a peppy heroine. The happy ending ties everything up in a neat bow. Black-and-white wash illustrations break up the chapters. Ukelele-playing tips are appended." (Horn Book)

Coy, John
  Eyes on the goal. Feiwel and Friends 2010 164p (4 for 4) $16.99
Grades: 3 4 5 6   **Fic**
  1. Soccer -- Fiction 2. Friendship -- Fiction
  ISBN 978-0-312-37330-6; 0-312-37330-9
This "finds the quartet of Jackson, Gig, Isaac, and Diego readying for a trip to soccer camp, even though except for Diego, they're more taken by sports that don't bafflingly forbid the use of hands. Like before, Coy includes some issues for character depth, from Gig's father being sent to Afghanistan to Jackson maybe having to move in with his mom's new boyfriend, but these take a firm backseat to the action on

the field, which Coy describes with straightforward, articulate prose. Light, enjoyable reading." Booklist

  Love of the game. Feiwel and Friends 2011 182p $16.99
Grades: 4 5 6 7   **Fic**
  1. School stories 2. Football -- Fiction 3. Family life -- Fiction
  ISBN 978-0-312-37331-3; 0-312-37331-7
               LC 2010050897
Sixth-grader Jackson has a rough start in middle school, with bullies on the bus, few classes with his friends, and changes at home but some good teachers, meeting a girl, joining a club, and playing football soon turn things around.

"Realistic characters, believable dialogue and a genuine feel for the rhythms and issues of middle-schoolers make this a satisfying addition to a solid middle-grade set." Kirkus

  Top of the order. Feiwel and Friends 2009 182p $16.99
Grades: 3 4 5 6   **Fic**
  1. School stories 2. Divorce -- Fiction 3. Baseball -- Fiction 4. Sex role -- Fiction 5. Friendship -- Fiction 6. Family life -- Fiction
  ISBN 978-0-312-37329-0; 0-312-37329-5
               LC 2008-28551
Ten-year-old Jackson lives for baseball, but becomes distracted by the approach of middle school, his mother's latest boyfriend, and the presence of a girl—his good friend's sister—on his team.

"Coy effortlessly captures the voices of boys on the verge of adolescence. Jackson and his friends are fully developed. . . . Gripping play-by-play and a fast-moving plot will appeal to sports enthusiasts and reluctant readers." SLJ

  Another title about Jackson is:
  Eyes on the goal (2010)

Creech, Sharon
  ★ **Absolutely** normal chaos. HarperCollins Pubs. 1995 230p $16.99; pa $5.99
Grades: 5 6 7 8   **Fic**
  1. Family life -- Fiction
  ISBN 0-06-026989-8; 0-06-440632-6 pa
               LC 95-22448
  First published 1990 in the United Kingdom
"Those in search of a light, humorous read will find it; those in search of something a little deeper will also be rewarded." SLJ

"Mary Lou Finney's summer journal describes family life in a high-spirited household in Ohio that includes five children." N Y Times Book Rev

  ★ **Bloomability**. HarperCollins Pubs. 1998 273p hardcover o.p. pa $5.99
Grades: 5 6 7 8   **Fic**
  1. School stories 2. Switzerland -- Fiction
  ISBN 0-06-026993-6; 0-06-440823-X pa
               LC 98-14601
When her aunt and uncle take her from New Mexico to Lugano, Switzerland, to attend an international school, thirteen-year-old Dinnie discovers her world expanding

"As if fresh, smart characters in a picturesque setting weren't engaging enough, Creech also poses an array of knotty questions, both personal and philosophical. . . . A story to stimulate both head and heart." Booklist

Chasing Redbird. HarperCollins Pubs. 1997 261p hardcover o.p. pa $5.99
Grades: 5 6 7 8   **Fic**
1. Kentucky -- Fiction 2. Family life -- Fiction
ISBN 0-06-026987-1; 0-06-440696-2 pa
LC 96-44128

Thirteen-year-old Zinnia Taylor uncovers family secrets and self truths while clearing a mysterious settler trail that begins on her family's farm in Kentucky

"With frequent flashbacks, the narrative makes clear the complexities of the story, while the unsolved puzzles lead the reader on to the end. The writing is laced with figurative language and folksy comments that intensify both atmosphere and emotion." Horn Book Guide

Granny Torrelli makes soup; drawings by Chris Raschka. HarperCollins Pubs. 2003 141p il $15.99; lib bdg $16.89; pa $5.99
Grades: 4 5 6   **Fic**
1. Grandmothers -- Fiction
ISBN 0-06-029290-3; 0-06-029291-1 lib bdg; 0-06-440960-0 pa
LC 2002-152662

With the help of her wise old grandmother, twelve-year-old Rosie manages to work out some problems in her relationship with her best friend, Bailey, the boy next door who is blind

"This gets high marks for its unique voice (make that voices) and for the way the subtleties that are woven into the story." Booklist

The **great** unexpected; Sharon Creech; edited by Alyson Day. HarperCollins 2012 240 p. (lib. bdg.) $17.89
Grades: 4 5 6 7   **Fic**
1. Ireland -- Fiction 2. Orphans -- Fiction 3. Friendship -- Fiction
ISBN 0061892335; 9780061892325; 9780061892332
LC 2012942431

In this book by Sharon Creech, "best friends and orphans Naomi Deane and Lizzie Scatterding are surprised when a strange boy falls out of a tree in their little town of Blackbird Tree, USA. His name is Finn, and Naomi falls immediately under his spell. . . . Meanwhile, in Ireland, an old woman and her companion talk of murder and revenge." (Horn Book Magazine)

Hate that cat. Joanna Cotler Books 2008 153p $15.99; lib bdg $16.89
Grades: 4 5 6 7   **Fic**
1. School stories 2. Novels in verse 3. Poetry -- Fiction
ISBN 978-0-06-143092-3; 978-0-06-143093-0 lib bdg
LC 2007044182

Jack is studying poetry again in school, and he continues to write poems reflecting his understanding of famous poems and how they relate to his life.

"Creech employs sensitivity and spare verse to carve an indelible portrait of a boy who discovers the power of self-expression." Booklist

★ **Love** that dog. HarperCollins Pubs. 2001 86p $15.99; lib bdg $14.89; pa $5.99
Grades: 4 5 6 7   **Fic**
1. School stories 2. Poetry 3. Poetry -- Fiction
ISBN 0-06-029287-3; 0-06-029289-X lib bdg; 0-06-440959-7 pa
LC 00-54233

"Jack thinks that boys don't write poetry. . . . The trouble is that his teacher, Ms. Stretchberry, keeps insisting that he read more and more poetry. Worse, she keeps insisting that he write poems, as well! . . . This book comes to us in the form of journal entries in Jack's own freeverse." (Christ Sci Monit) "Ages eight to twelve." (N Y Times Book Rev)

"Creech has created a poignant, funny picture of a child's encounter with the power of poetry. . . . This book is a tiny treasure." SLJ

Another title about Jack is:
Hate that cat (2008)

★ **Ruby** Holler. HarperCollins Pubs. 2002 310p hardcover o.p. pa $5.99
Grades: 4 5 6 7   **Fic**
1. Twins -- Fiction 2. Orphans -- Fiction 3. Country life -- Fiction
ISBN 0-06-027732-7; 0-06-056015-0 pa
LC 00-66371

Thirteen-year-old fraternal twins Dallas and Florida have grown up in a terrible orphanage but their lives change forever when an eccentric but sweet older couple invites them each on an adventure, beginning in an almost magical place called Ruby Holler

"This poignant story evokes a feeling as welcoming as fresh-baked bread. . . . The novel celebrates the healing effects of love and compassion." Publ Wkly

The **unfinished** angel. Joanna Cotler Books 2009 164p
Grades: 4 5 6   **Fic**
1. Angels -- Fiction 2. Orphans -- Fiction 3. Villages -- Fiction 4. Switzerland -- Fiction
ISBN 0-06-143095-1; 0-06-143096-X lib bdg; 0-06-143097-8 pa; 978-0-06-143095-4; 978-0-06-143096-1 lib bdg; 978-0-06-143097-8 pa
LC 2009-02796

In a tiny village in the Swiss Alps, an angel meets an American girl named Zola who has come with her father to open a school, and together Zola and the angel rescue a group of homeless orphans. "Ages eight to twelve." (Publisher's note)

"Some books are absolute magic, and this is one of them. . . . Creech's protagonist is hugely likable. . . . Creech's offering deserves to be read out loud and more than once to truly enjoy the angel's hilarious malapropisms and outright invented words, and to appreciate the book's tender, comical celebration of the human spirit." SLJ

★ **Walk** two moons. HarperCollins Pubs. 1994 280p $16.99; lib bdg $17.89; pa $6.99
Grades: 6 7 8 9   **Fic**
1. Death -- Fiction 2. Friendship -- Fiction 3. Family

life -- Fiction 4. Grandparents -- Fiction
ISBN 0-06-023334-6; 0-06-023337-0 lib bdg; 0-06-440517-6 pa

LC 93-31277

Awarded the Newbery Medal, 1995

After her mother leaves home suddenly, thirteen-year-old Sal and her grandparents take a car trip retracing her mother's route. Along the way, Sal recounts the story of her friend Phoebe, whose mother also left

"An engaging story of love and loss, told with humor and suspense. . . . A richly layered novel about real and metaphorical journeys." SLJ

Cronin, Doreen

The **legend** of Diamon Lil; a J.J. Tully mystery. Doreen Cronin, Kevin Cornell; [edited by] Alessandra Balzer. Balzer + Bray 2012 125 p. (lib. bdg.) $15.89

Grades: 2 3 4   **Fic**

1. Mystery fiction 2. Children's stories 3. Dogs -- Fiction 4. Humorous stories 5. Chickens -- Fiction 6. Mystery and detective stories

ISBN 0061985783; 9780061779961; 9780061985782

LC 2011945710

"'The Legend of Diamond Lil,' second book in the illustrated J.J. Tully mystery series, is perfect for elementary-school kids who love adventure and animals. . . . In this sequel to the chapter book 'The Trouble with Chickens,' all search-and-rescue dog J.J. Tully wants is to enjoy his retirement. But mama chick Moosh and chicks Dirt and Sugar are acting strange." (Publisher's note)

"The eye-catching illustrations do a great job of drawing readers' attention to important story details. Children who like a little bit of everything mixed into their reading, particularly mystery, adventure, and animals, will enjoy this book." - SLJ

The **trouble** with chickens; a J. J. Tully mystery. illustrated by Kevin Cornell. Balzer + Bray 2011 119p il $14.99; lib bdg $15.89

Grades: 2 3 4   **Fic**

1. Mystery fiction 2. Dogs -- Fiction 3. Chickens -- Fiction

ISBN 978-0-06-121532-2; 0-06-121532-5; 978-0-06-121533-9 lib bdg; 0-06-121533-3 lib bdg

LC 2009-31213

A hard-bitten former search-and-rescue dog helps solve a complicated missing chicken case.

"Fast-paced and funny, with interesting vocabulary and a well-constructed plot, this is terrific fare for readers who are ready to move beyond picture books, but are intimidated by longer works. Cornell's pencil drawings have a mix of energy and humor that adds to the fun." Publ Wkly

Crossan, Sarah

★ The **Weight** of Water; by Sarah Crossan. Bloomsbury USA 2013 224 p. $16.99

Grades: 5 6 7 8   **Fic**

1. Novels in verse 2. England -- Fiction 3. Swimming -- Fiction 4. Race relations -- Fiction 5. Coventry (England) -- Fiction 6. Immigrants -- England -- Fiction 7. Mothers and daughters -- Fiction

ISBN 1599909677; 9781599909677

LC 2012038645

In this book, "12-year-old Kasienka moves with Mama from Gdansk, Poland, to Coventry, England, to find Tata, her father. The adjustment is difficult. At school, Kasienka is ostracized. At home, she questions why they are searching for a man who ran from them. When Kasienka complains, Mama questions her love. Kasienka feels powerful only when she swims at the pool—something Tata taught her to do. That is also where William, a schoolmate, first notices her." (Kirkus Reviews)

Crowley, James

Starfish; illustrations by Jim Madsen. Disney/Hyperion Books 2010 310p il $16.99

Grades: 4 5 6 7   **Fic**

1. Adventure fiction 2. Montana -- Fiction 3. Siblings -- Fiction 4. Siksika Indians -- Fiction 5. Runaway children -- Fiction

ISBN 978-1-4231-2588-4; 1-4231-2588-6

In the early part of the 1900s, Beatrice and Lionel, two Blackfeet Indian children, escape from the Chalk Bluff Indian Boarding School in Montana to find their grandfather, and must elude their pursuers and make a life for themselves in the wilderness.

"This is a fast-paced and interesting novel that will maintain reader interest. Readers will be drawn into the plight of Native Americans trying to survive brutal conditions." Libr Media Connect

Crum, Shutta

★ **Thomas** and the dragon queen; pictures by Lee Wildish. Alfred A. Knopf 2010 267p il $15.99; lib bdg $18.99

Grades: 3 4 5   **Fic**

1. Fairy tales 2. Dragons -- Fiction 3. Princesses -- Fiction 4. Knights and knighthood -- Fiction

ISBN 978-0-375-85703-4; 0-375-85703-6; 978-0-375-95703-1 lib bdg; 0-375-95703-0 lib bdg

LC 2009-53821

When the princess is kidnapped by a dragon queen, thirteen-year-old Thomas, a new—and very small—squire-in-training boldly sets out on a quest to rescue her.

"The many likable characters . . . serve the story well. . . . Black-and-white illustrations capture the tone of the storytelling. . . . This good-hearted chapter book delivers an adventure that many young readers will enjoy." Booklist

Cuevas, Michelle

The **masterwork** of a painting elephant; pictures by Ed Young. Frances Foster Books/Farrar Straus Giroux 2011 136p il $15.99

Grades: 3 4 5 6   **Fic**

1. Love -- Fiction 2. Artists -- Fiction 3. Orphans -- Fiction 4. Elephants -- Fiction 5. Voyages and travels -- Fiction

ISBN 978-0-374-34854-0; 0-374-34854-5

LC 2010033108

Pigeon Jones, abandoned as a baby, is found and raised by Birch, a white, former circus elephant who paints beautiful pictures, and through their travels and adventures they discover the meanings of love and family.

"Pigeon's first-person voice traces the story's meanderings with a natural poetry, while Young's spare ink drawings ground the procedings, conveying remarkable emotional weight in a few gestures. The unlikely combination of zany story arc, resonant illustrations, and graceful telling come together in a memorable and original offering." Booklist

Cuffe-Perez, Mary

Skylar; a story. illustrated by Renata Liwska. Philomel Books 2008 138p il $14.99

Grades: 3 4 5   Fic

1. Geese -- Fiction 2. Birds -- Migration -- Fiction

ISBN 978-0-399-24543-5; 0-399-24543-X

LC 2007-20437

Skylar, who claims he was once wild, leads four pond geese in their first attempt at migration when an injured heron asks their help in reaching Lost Pond, where the annual Before the Migration Convention is about to be held.

"Nature imagery and extensive information on the migratory habits of Canada geese infuse a text, punctuated by occasional soft, black-and-white full-page illustrations. . . . The pace quickens when the geese talk with each other, their near constant bickering adding a dose of humor." Booklist

Cullen, Lynn

Dear Mr. Washington; by Lynn Cullen; pictures by Nancy Carpenter. Dial Books for Young Readers 2013 32 p. color illustrations (hardcover) $16.99

Grades: K 1 2 3 4   Fic

1. Portraits -- Fiction 2. Letters -- Fiction 3. Behavior -- Fiction 4. Etiquette -- Fiction 5. Brothers and sisters -- Fiction

ISBN 0803730381; 9780803730380

LC 2012001098

In this children's book by Lynn Cullen, illustrated by Nancy Carpenter, "Charlotte, James, and baby John have promised to be on their very best behavior for when George Washington comes to have his portrait painted by their father, Gilbert Stuart. But, it seems like every time George Washington comes to visit, Charlotte has to write another apology letter, even when they try to follow George Washington's Rules of Good Behavior." (Publisher's note)

"When President George Washington visits the home of the prominent painter Gilbert Stuart to have his portrait painted, Stuart's children, Charlotte, James, and baby John, try really hard to be good. But, try as they will, it's one disaster after another...The artwork, created using a combination of pen on paper, acrylic paint on canvas, and digital media, is hilarious and bright, with clever attention to detail. A fabulous addition to picture book collections." SLJ

Curry, Jane Louise

The Black Canary. Margaret K. McElderry Books 2005 279p $16.95

Grades: 5 6 7 8   Fic

1. Generals 2. Courtiers 3. Conspirators 4. Royal favorites 5. Singers -- Fiction 6. London (England) -- Fiction 7. Racially mixed people -- Fiction 8. Great Britain -- History -- 1485-1603, Tudors -- Fiction

ISBN 0-689-86478-7

LC 2003-26150

As the child of two musicians, twelve-year-old James has no interest in music until he discovers a portal to seventeenth-century London in his uncle's basement, and finds himself in a situation where his beautiful voice and the fact that he is biracial might serve him well.

"A genuinely good story that conveys a sense of darkness and mystery in the textured backdrop of a storied time and place." Booklist

Curtis, Christopher Paul, 1953-

★ Bud, not Buddy. Delacorte Press 1999 245p $16.95; pa $6.50

Grades: 4 5 6 7   Fic

1. Orphans -- Fiction 2. African Americans -- Fiction 3. Great Depression, 1929-1939 -- Fiction

ISBN 0-385-32306-9; 0-440-41328-1 pa

LC 99-10614

Coretta Scott King Award for text
Awarded the Newbery Medal, 2000

Ten-year-old Bud, a motherless boy living in Flint, Michigan, during the Great Depression, escapes a bad foster home and sets out in search of the man he believes to be his father—the renowned bandleader, H. E. Calloway of Grand Rapids

"Curtis says in a afterword that some of the characters are based on real people, including his own grandfathers, so it's not surprising that the rich blend of tall tale, slapstick, sorrow, and sweetness has the wry, teasing warmth of family folklore." Booklist

★ Elijah of Buxton. Scholastic 2007 341p $16.99; pa $7.99

Grades: 5 6 7 8   Fic

1. Canada -- Fiction 2. Slavery -- Fiction

ISBN 0-439-02344-0; 978-0-439-02344-3; 0-439-02345-9 pa; 978-0-439-02345-0 pa

LC 2007-05181

A Newbery Medal honor book, 2008

In 1859, eleven-year-old Elijah Freeman, the first freeborn child in Buxton, Canada, which is a haven for slaves fleeing the American south, uses his wits and skills to try to bring to justice the lying preacher who has stolen money that was to be used to buy a family's freedom.

"Many readers drawn to the book by humor will find themselves at times on the edges of their seats in suspense and, at other moments, moved to tears." Booklist

The madman of Piney Woods; Christopher Paul Curtis. Scholastic Press 2014 384 p. $16.99 Fic

1. Adventure fiction 2. n 3. Freedmen -- Fiction 4. Veterans -- Fiction 5. Immigrants -- Fiction 6. Irish -- Canada -- Fiction 7. Blacks -- Canada -- Fiction 8. Canada -- History -- 1867-1914 -- Fiction 9. Post-traumatic stress disorder -- Fiction 10. Chatham (Ont.) -- History -- 20th century -- Fiction 11. North Buxton (Ont.) -- History -- 20th century -- Fiction

ISBN 0545156645; 9780545156646; 9780545156653; 9780545633765

LC 2014003493

"Benji and Red couldn't be more different. They aren't friends. They don't even live in the same town. But their fates are entwined. A chance meeting leads the boys to discover that they have more in common than meets the eye. Both of them have encountered a strange presence in the forest, watching them, tracking them. Could the Madman of Piney Woods be real?" (Publisher's note)

The mighty Miss Malone; Christopher Paul Curtis. Wendy Lamb Books 2012 307 p.

Grades: 4 5 6   **Fic**
1. Girls -- Fiction 2. African Americans -- Fiction 3. Great Depression, 1929-1939 -- Fiction 4. Poverty -- Fiction 5. Family life -- Fiction 6. Depressions -- 1929 -- Fiction 7. Gary (Ind.) -- History -- 20th century -- Fiction 8. Flint (Mich.) -- History -- 20th century -- Fiction
ISBN 9780375897368; 9780385734912; 9780385904872; 9780440422143
                      LC 2011036317
This book tells the story of "Deza Malone, who shares dishwashing duties with Bud Caldwell during his brief stay at a Hooverville in Flint, Mich. . . . It's 1936 in Gary, Ind., and the Great Depression has put 12-year-old Deza's father out of work. After a near-death experience trying to catch fish for dinner, Roscoe Malone leaves for Flint, hoping he'll find work. But Deza's mother loses her job shortly after, putting all the Malones out on the street. . . . [Author Christopher Paul] Curtis threads . . . bits of African-American history throughout the narrative, using the Joe Louis-Max Schmeling fight to expose the racism prevalent even among people like the librarian who tells Deza that Louis is 'such a credit to your race.'" (Publishers Weekly)

★ The **Watsons** go to Birmingham--1963; a novel. Delacorte Press 1995 210p $16.95; pa $6.50
Grades: 4 5 6 7   **Fic**
1. Prejudices -- Fiction 2. Family life -- Fiction 3. African Americans -- Fiction
ISBN 0-385-32175-9; 0-440-41412-1 pa
                      LC 95-7091
A Newbery Medal honor book, 1996
The ordinary interactions and everyday routines of the Watsons, an African American family living in Flint, Michigan, are drastically changed after they go to visit Grandma in Alabama in the summer of 1963
"Curtis's ability to switch from fun and funky to pinpoint-accurate psychological imagery works unusually well. . . . Ribald humor, sly sibling digs, and a totally believable child's view of the world will make this book an instant hit." SLJ

Cushman, Karen
★ **Alchemy** and Meggy Swann. Clarion Books 2010 167p $16
Grades: 5 6 7 8   **Fic**
1. Alchemy -- Fiction 2. Poverty -- Fiction 3. People with disabilities -- Fiction 4. London (England) -- Fiction 5. Father-daughter relationship -- Fiction
ISBN 978-0-547-23184-6; 0-547-23184-9
                      LC 2009-16387
In 1573, the crippled, scorned, and destitute Meggy Swann goes to London, where she meets her father, an impoverished alchemist, and eventually discovers that although her legs are bent and weak, she has many other strengths.
"Writing with admirable economy and a lively ability to recreate the past believably, Cushman creates a memorable portrayal of a troubled, rather mulish girl who begins to use her strong will in positive ways." Booklist

The **ballad** of Lucy Whipple. Clarion Bks. 1996 195p $15; $16.00
Grades: 5 6 7 8   **Fic**
1. Family life -- Fiction 2. Frontier and pioneer life

-- Fiction 3. California -- Gold discoveries -- Fiction
ISBN 0-395-72806-1; 9780395728062
                      LC 95-45257
"Twelve-year-old Lucy is taken by her mother from their comfortable 19th-century home in Massachusetts to the rough-and-tumble California goldfields. Lucy's younger siblings don't object to this new life, but Lucy dislikes the dirt, hard work, and lack of civilization—especially reading material. When not helping Mama run Mr. Scatter's boarding house for miners, Lucy spends her time complaining or scheming a return to her beloved Massachusetts. Despite the losses she suffers in the makeshift town of Lucky Diggins, Lucy makes some surprising discoveries about herself and what she's gained in the West." (Christ Sci Monit) "Grades five to eight." (Booklist)
"Cushman's heroine is a delightful character, and the historical setting is authentically portrayed." SLJ

★ **Catherine,** called Birdy. Clarion Bks. 1994 169p $16
Grades: 6 7 8 9   **Fic**
1. Middle Ages -- Fiction 2. Great Britain -- Fiction
ISBN 0-395-68186-3
                      LC 93-23333
A Newbery Medal honor book, 1995
The fourteen-year-old daughter of an English country knight keeps a journal in which she records the events of her life, particularly her longing for adventures beyond the usual role of women and her efforts to avoid being married off
"In the process of telling the routines of her young life, Birdy lays before readers a feast of details about medieval England. . . . Superb historical fiction." SLJ

Matilda Bone. Clarion Bks. 2000 167p $15; pa $5.99
Grades: 5 6 7 8   **Fic**
1. Physicians -- Fiction 2. Middle Ages -- Fiction 3. Great Britain -- Fiction
ISBN 0-395-88156-0; 0-440-41822-4 pa
                      LC 00-24032
Fourteen-year-old Matilda, an apprentice bonesetter and practitioner of medicine in a village in medieval England, tries to reconcile the various aspects of her life, both spiritual and practical
"A fascinating glimpse into the colorful life and times of the 14th century. . . . Cushman's character descriptions are spare, with each word carefully chosen to paint wonderful pictures." SLJ
Includes bibliographical references

★ The **midwife's** apprentice. Clarion Bks. 1995 122p $12; pa $5.99
Grades: 6 7 8 9   **Fic**
1. Midwives -- Fiction 2. Middle Ages -- Fiction 3. Great Britain -- Fiction
ISBN 0-395-69229-6; 0-06-440630-X pa
                      LC 94-13792
Awarded the Newbery Medal, 1996
In medieval England, a nameless, homeless girl is taken in by a sharp-tempered midwife, and in spite of obstacles and hardship, eventually gains the three things she most wants: a full belly, a contented heart, and a place in this world
"Earthy humor, the foibles of humans both high and low, and a fascinating mix of superstition and genuinely help-

ful herbal remedies attached to childbirth make this a truly delightful introduction to a world seldom seen in children's literature." SLJ

Rodzina. Clarion Bks. 2003 215p $16; pa $6.50
Grades: 5 6 7 8   **Fic**
1. Orphans -- Fiction 2. Polish Americans -- Fiction
ISBN 0-618-13351-8; 0-440-41993-X pa
LC 2002-15976

A twelve-year-old Polish American girl is boarded onto an orphan train in Chicago with fears about traveling to the West and a life of unpaid slavery

"The story features engaging characters, a vivid setting, and a prickly but endearing heroine. . . . Rodzina's musings and observations provide poignancy, humor, and a keen sense of the human and topographical landscape." SLJ

Includes bibliographical references

★ **Will** Sparrow's road; Karen Cushman. Clarion Books 2012 216 p. (hardback) $16.99
Grades: 5 6 7 8   **Fic**
1. Historical fiction 2. Runaway children -- Fiction 3. Swindlers and swindling -- Fiction 4. Runaways -- Fiction 5. Freak shows -- Fiction 6. Conduct of life -- Fiction 7. Great Britain -- History -- Elizabeth, 1558-1603 -- Fiction
ISBN 0547739621; 9780547739625
LC 2011045898

In this book by Karen Cushman, set in Elizabethan England, "Will Sparrow, liar and thief, becomes a runaway. On the road, he encounters a series of con artists . . . and learns that others are more adept than he at lying and thieving. Then he reluctantly joins a traveling troupe of 'oddities,' including a dwarf and a cat-faced girl. . . . At last Will is forced to understand that appearances are misleading and that he has been his own worst deceiver." (Publisher's note)

Includes bibliographical references.

Cutler, Jane
Rats! pictures by Tracey Campbell Pearson. Farrar, Straus & Giroux 1996 114p il hardcover o.p. pa $5.95
Grades: 3 4 5   **Fic**
1. Brothers -- Fiction 2. Family life -- Fiction
ISBN 0-374-36181-9; 0-374-46203-8 pa
LC 95-22953

Fourth-grader Jason and his younger brother Edward shop for school clothes, get ready for Halloween, acquire a couple of pet rats, and deal with not-birthday presents from Aunt Bea

"The brothers, alternately squabbling and supporting each other, are convincing in this lighthearted episodic novel." Horn Book Guide

Other titles about Jason and Edward are:
'Gator aid (1999)
Leap, frog (2002)
No dogs allowed (1992)

D'Adamo, Francesco
Iqbal; a novel. written by Francesco D'Adamo; translated by Ann Leonori. Atheneum Bks. for Young Readers 2003 120p $15.95; pa $4.99
Grades: 5 6 7 8   **Fic**
1. Murder victims 2. Factory workers 3. Pakistan -- Fiction 4. Child labor -- Fiction 5. Children's rights

advocates
ISBN 0-689-85445-5; 1-4169-0329-1 pa
LC 2002-153498

Original Italian edition, 2001

A fictionalized account of the Pakistani child who escaped from bondage in a carpet factory and went on to help liberate other children like him before being gunned down at the age of thirteen

"The situation and setting are made clear in this novel. Readers cannot help but be moved by the plight of these youngsters. . . . This readable book will certainly add breadth to most collections." SLJ

D'Lacey, Chris
Gauge; illustrated by Adam Stower. Orchard Books 105p il (The dragons of Wayward Crescent) $9.99
Grades: 2 3 4   **Fic**
1. Fantasy fiction 2. Dragons -- Fiction 3. Great Britain -- Fiction 4. Clocks and watches -- Fiction
ISBN 978-0-545-16831-1; 0-545-16831-7

When the town council decides to demolish the old library clock and replace it with a fancy modern one, Lucy and her mother try to save the historic timepiece—with the help of a dragon.

Gruffen; illustrated by Adam Stower. Orchard Books 2009 104p il (The dragons of Wayward Crescent) $9.99
Grades: 2 3 4   **Fic**
1. Fantasy fiction 2. Dragons -- Fiction 3. Great Britain -- Fiction
ISBN 978-0-545-16815-1; 0-545-16815-5
LC 2009011824

Lucy thinks there is a monster lurking outside her bedroom window, so her mother makes a dragon out of clay to protect her while she sleeps.

"This is a cozy and safe tale with bits of humor sprinkled throughout. Line drawings add visual interest; their cartoon style also enforces the light, upbeat mood." SLJ

Another title in this series is:
Gauge (2009)

Dahl, Michael
Guardian of Earth; written by Michael Dahl; illustrated by Dan Schoening. Stone Arch Books 2011 48p il (DC super heroes: Green Lantern) lib bdg $25.32; pa $5.95
Grades: 2 3 4   **Fic**
1. Superheroes -- Fiction 2. Extraterrestrial beings -- Fiction
ISBN 978-1-4342-2611-2 lib bdg; 1-4342-2611-5 lib bdg; 978-1-4342-3081-2 pa; 1-4342-3081-3 pa
LC 2010025600

Ace pilot Hal Jordan has a too-close-for-comfort encounter with a UFO. His jet takes a nosedive, but a gigantic green hand appears, grabs the aircraft, and prevents the crash. Hal's alien rescuer offers him an amazing green ring of untold power and announces that the human pilot is now the new Guardian of Earth.

This "chapter-book [adaptation] of [a] popular comic [superhero has] great, full-page illustrations and . . . onomatopoeia. . . . [The cover is a] 3-D [hologram] that will attract kids. . . . [This is] action-packed." SLJ

Includes glossary and bibliographical references

The **man** behind the mask; written by Michael Dahl; illustrated by Dan Schoening; Batman created by Bob Kane. Stone Arch Books 2010 48p il (DC super heroes. Batman) lib bdg $25.32; pa $5.95

Grades: 3 4 5 **Fic**

1. Batman (Fictional character) 2. Superheroes -- Fiction

ISBN 978-1-4342-1563-5 lib bdg; 1-4342-1563-6 lib bdg; 978-1-4342-1730-1 pa; 1-4342-1730-2 pa

LC 2009006303

This "full-color chapter [book is] fast moving and entertaining. . . . The story serves as a nice starting point for readers unfamiliar with the character. . . . The retro comic-book illustrations . . . appear every few pages, adding a vibrant visual element to the proceedings. Sound effects are displayed in large, expressive fonts and colors, capturing the feel of comics." SLJ

Dahl, Roald

The **BFG**; pictures by Quentin Blake. Farrar, Straus & Giroux 1982 219p il $18

Grades: 4 5 6 **Fic**

1. Giants -- Fiction 2. Orphans -- Fiction

ISBN 0-374-30469-6

LC 82-15548

Kidsnatched from her orphanage by a BFG (Big Friendly Giant), who spends his life blowing happy dreams to children, Sophie concocts with him a plan to save the world from nine other man-gobbling cannybull giants

This "is a book not all adults will like, but most kids will. . . . Highly unusual, often hilarious, and occasionally vulgar, even grisly." Booklist

★ **Charlie** and the chocolate factory; illustrated by Quentin Blake. rev ed.; Knopf 2001 162p il $15.95; lib bdg $17.99

Grades: 4 5 6 7 **Fic**

1. Conduct of life -- Fiction

ISBN 0-375-81526-0; 0-375-91526-5 lib bdg

LC 2001-29461

A newly illustrated edition of the title first published 1964

Each of five children lucky enough to discover an entry ticket into Mr. Willy Wonka's mysterious chocolate factory takes advantage of the situation in his own way

"Blake's energetic black-and-white illustrations enliven and update Dahl's cautionary rags-to-riches story. . . . The slapdash effect of the whimsical drawings matches Wonka's hyperactive speech and the generally frenetic narrative." Horn Book Guide

The **enormous** crocodile; illustrated by Quentin Blake. Knopf 2000 un il hardcover o.p. pa $7.99

Grades: 2 3 4 **Fic**

1. Animals -- Fiction 2. Crocodiles -- Fiction

ISBN 0-14-241453-0 pa

A reissue of the title first published 1978

"Mr. Dahl's gift for sonorous and inventive language carries the story along merrily . . . and Quentin Blake's squidgy jungle and scaly villain, colorful crowds and righteous elephant couldn't be improved upon." N Y Times Book Rev

★ **James** and the giant peach; a children's story. illustrated by Lane Smith. Knopf 1996 126p il $16; lib bdg $17.99

Grades: 4 5 6 **Fic**

1. Fantasy fiction

ISBN 0-679-88090-9; 0-679-98090-3 lib bdg

LC 91-33489

A newly illustrated edition of the title first published 1961

After the death of his parents, little James is forced to live with Aunt Sponge and Aunt Spike, two cruel old harpies. A magic potion causes the growing of a giant-sized peach on a puny peach tree. James sneaks inside the peach and finds a new world of insects. With his new family, James heads for many adventures

"A 'juicy' fantasy, 'dripping' with humor and imagination." Commonweal

The **magic** finger; illustrated by Quentin Blake. Viking 1995 62p il hardcover o.p. pa $5.99

Grades: 2 3 4 **Fic**

1. Magic -- Fiction 2. Hunting -- Fiction

ISBN 0-670-85252-X; 0-14-241385-2 pa

LC 92-31443

A newly illustrated edition of the title first published 1966 by Harper & Row

Angered by a neighboring family's sport hunting, an eight-year-old girl turns her magic finger on them

This is an "original and intriguing fantasy." Booklist

Matilda; illustrations by Quentin Blake. Viking Kestrel 1988 240p il $16.99; pa $6.99

Grades: 4 5 6 **Fic**

1. School stories

ISBN 0-670-82439-9; 0-14-241037-3 pa

LC 88-40312

Odyssey Honor Recording (2014)

"Dahl has written another fun and funny book with a child's perspective on an adult world. As usual, Blake's comical sketches are the perfect complement to the satirical humor." SLJ

"Matilda knows how to be extremely and creatively naughty—lining her father's hat with super glue, putting her mother's hair bleach in her father's hair tonic bottle, for example. This streak of imaginative wickedness not only allows her to make a loyal friend, Lavender, but also to wreak revenge on her unloving parents, defeat the fiendish headmistress, Miss Turnbull, and return her victimized teacher, the enchanting Miss Honey, to her rightful place in the world." N Y Times Book Rev

Dakin, Glenn

The **Society** of Dread. Egmont USA 2010 318p (Candle Man) $15.99

Grades: 5 6 7 8 **Fic**

1. Adventure fiction 2. Superheroes -- Fiction

ISBN 978-1-60684-019-1; 1-60684-019-3

LC 2010023104

Sequel to: The Society of Unrelenting Vigilance (2009)

Now head of the Society of Good Works, teenaged Theo must reluctantly use his mysterious ability to melt evil when he ventures underground to face villains of old.

"This appealing contemporary fantasy has a fast-paced plot and enough inventive monsters and villains to captivate even the most reluctant readers." SLJ

The **Society** of Unrelenting Vigilance; [illustrations by Greg Swearingen] Egmont 2009 300p il (Candle Man) $15.99; lib bdg $18.99

Grades: 4 5 6 7   **Fic**

1. Adventure fiction 2. Superheroes -- Fiction
ISBN 978-1-60684-015-3; 1-60684-015-0; 978-1-60684-047-4 lib bdg; 1-60684-047-9 lib bdg

LC 2009-14035

Thirteen-year-old Theo, who has lived in seclusion his entire life, discovers he is the descendant of the Candle Man, a Victorian vigilante with the ability to melt criminals with a single touch.

This is a "lighthearted, action-driven adventure. . . . With the help of a cast of appealing characters, the nonstop action rolls to a satisfying conclusion." SLJ

Followed by: The Society of Dread (2010)

Dale, Anna

Magical mischief. Bloomsbury Children's Books 2011 300p $16.99; pa $7.99

Grades: 4 5 6   **Fic**

1. Magic -- Fiction 2. Booksellers and bookselling -- Fiction
ISBN 1-59990-629-5; 1-59990-630-9 pa; 978-1-59990-629-4; 978-1-59990-630-0 pa

LC 2010035627

Mr. Hardbattle, aided by his friends Miss Quint and resourceful thirteen-year-old Arthur, seeks a new place for all of the magic that has gone out of control and taken over his bookshop and home.

"Many charming details create their own sort of magic in this unusual story. . . . This chapter book should appeal to young readers who like their fantasy on the cozy side." Booklist

Daley, Michael J.

Space station rat; by Michael J. Daley. Holiday House 2005 181p $15.95; pa $6.99

Grades: 4 5 6   **Fic**

1. Science fiction 2. Rats -- Fiction 3. Space stations -- Fiction
ISBN 0-8234-1866-9; 0-8234-2151-1 pa

LC 2004-40534

A lavender rat that has escaped from a laboratory, and Jeff, a lonely boy whose parents are scientists, meet on an orbiting space station, communicate by email, and ultimately find themselves in need of each other's help and friendship

"The point of view shifts between Jeff and Rat. . . . The developing interspecies communication raises interesting questions about the nature of intelligence and individuality. A thoughtful and satisfying adventure." SLJ

Another title about Jeff and Rat is:
Rat trap (2008)

Daly, Niki

★ **Bettina** Valentino and the Picasso Club. Farrar, Straus and Giroux 2009 103p il $16

Grades: 4 5 6   **Fic**

1. School stories 2. Art -- Fiction 3. Teachers -- Fiction
ISBN 978-0-374-30753-0; 0-374-30753-9

LC 2008-03827

A controversial new teacher at Bayside Preparatory School introduces the exciting world of art to aspiring artist Bettina Valentino and her fifth-grade classmates, encouraging them to see everyday life in a different way.

"If the story's execution wasn't delightful enough (it is), Daly provides wonderful ink-and-wash drawings . . . that up the amusing ante. Not only are the cast's eccentricities on display, but Daly sometimes draws on the styles of famous artists." Booklist

Daneshvari, Gitty

Class is not dismissed! [illustrations by Carrie Gifford] Little, Brown and Company 2010 307p il $16.99

Grades: 4 5 6   **Fic**

1. School stories 2. Phobias -- Fiction
ISBN 978-0-316-03328-2; 0-316-03328-6

LC 2010006889

Sequel to: School of Fear (2009)

Thirteen-year-olds Madeleine, Theo, and Lulu, fourteen-year-old Garrison, and ten-year-old new "contestant" Hyacinth, must face their phobias and join forces to learn who is stealing wigs and pageant trophies from the School of Fear.

"Filled with an eclectic, and often eccentric, cast of characters, this sequel uses the wry humor and outrageous situations that characterized the first book and makes for an entertaining read." SLJ

School of Fear; illustrated by Carrie Gifford. Little, Brown Books for Young Readers 2009 339p il $15.99

Grades: 4 5 6   **Fic**

1. School stories 2. Phobias -- Fiction
ISBN 978-0-316-03326-8; 0-316-03326-X

LC 2008051309

Twelve-year-olds Madeleine, Theo, and Lulu, and thirteen-year-old Garrison, are sent to a remote Massachusetts school to overcome their phobias, but tragedy strikes and the quartet must work together—with no adult assistance—to face their fears.

This is "tautly paced, spine-tingling and quite funny." Publ Wkly

Followed by: Class is not dismissed! (2010)

Danneberg, Julie

Family reminders; illustrated by John Shelley. Charlesbridge 2009 105p il $14.95

Grades: 3 4 5   **Fic**

1. Colorado -- Fiction 2. Family life -- Fiction 3. Frontier and pioneer life -- Fiction
ISBN 978-1-58089-320-6; 1-58089-320-1

In 1890s Cripple Creek, Colorado, when young Mary McHugh's father loses his leg in a mining accident, she tries to help, both by earning money and by encouraging her father to go back to carving wooden figurines and playing piano.

"Shelley's India ink and pen illustrations add to the historical feel of this gentle, yet gripping story. This is a heartwarming novel about overcoming hardship." SLJ

Danziger, Paula

★ **Amber** Brown is not a crayon; illustrated by Tony Ross. Putnam 1994 80p il $15.99; pa $4.99

Grades: 2 3 4   **Fic**

1. School stories 2. Moving -- Fiction 3. Friendship -- Fiction
ISBN 0-399-22509-9; 0-14-240619-8 pa

LC 92-34678

The year she is in the third grade is a sad time for Amber because her best friend Justin is getting ready to move to a distant state

"Ross's black-and-white sketches throughout add humor and keep the pages turning swiftly. Danziger reaches out to a younger audience in this funny, touching slice of third-grade life, told in the voice of a feisty, lovable heroine." SLJ

Other titles about Amber Brown are:

Amber Brown goes fourth (1995)

Amber Brown is feeling blue (1998)

Amber Brown is green with envy (2003)

Amber Brown sees red (1997)

Amber Brown wants extra credit (1996)

Forever Amber Brown (1996)

I, Amber Brown (1999)

You can't eat your chicken pox, Amber Brown (1995)

Davies, Jacqueline

The **bell** bandit; by Jacqueline Davies. Houghton Mifflin 2012 174 p. ill. (The lemonade war series) $15.99
Grades: 3 4 5   **Fic**
1. Grandmothers -- Fiction 2. Mystery and detective stories 3. Brothers and sisters -- Fiction
ISBN 0547567375; 9780547567372
LC 2011039906

"When siblings Jessie and Evan (The Lemonade War, 2007, and The Lemonade Crime, 2011) accompany their mother on the time-honored midwinter holiday visit to their grandmother's home in the mountains, the changes are alarming. Fire damage to the house and Grandma's inability to recognize Evan are as disquieting as the disappearance of the iron bell, hung long ago by their grandmother on Lowell Hill and traditionally rung at the New Year." (Kirkus)

"Difficult issues are dealt with, including Maxwell's apparent autism-spectrum disorder and Grandma's dementia. Jessie's drawings are scattered throughout the book, adding both clarity and amusement. Though this is the third book of the Lemonade Wars series, it stands well on its own, and is a fine choice for young fans of mysteries or family stories." Library Review

Candy smash; by Jacqueline Davies. Houghton Mifflin Harcourt 2013 240 p. illustrations (The lemonade war series) $15.99
Grades: 3 4 5   **Fic**
1. School stories 2. Secrets -- Fiction 3. Love -- Fiction 4. Poetry -- Fiction 5. Schools -- Fiction 6. Brothers and sisters -- Fiction
ISBN 0544022084; 9780544022089
LC 2012033305

"As Valentine's Day approaches, Evan suffers through hearts-and-flowers crafts in school while wrestling with his secret crush on a classmate and discovering that he loves reading and writing poetry. Meanwhile, his precocious younger sister, Jessie (an aspiring journalist and also a classmate, having skipped a grade), prepares to reveal all in the latest edition of her newspaper." (Booklist)

"The Lemonade War series' fourth book captures the nuances of elementary-school drama and sibling dynamics. School-newspaper excerpts, poetry terms, and famous poems are appended." Horn Book

The **lemonade** crime. Houghton Mifflin Harcourt 2011 152p $15.99

Grades: 3 4 5   **Fic**
1. School stories 2. Trials -- Fiction 3. Siblings -- Fiction
ISBN 978-0-547-27967-1; 0-547-27967-1
LC 2010015231

Sequel to: The lemonade war (2007)

When money disappears from fourth-grader Evan's pocket and everyone thinks that his annoying classmate Scott stole it, Evan's younger sister stages a trial involving the entire class, trying to prove what happened.

"The realistic depiction of the children's emotions and ways of expressing them will resonate with readers. Great for discussion, this involving and, at times, riveting chapter book has something to say and a deceptively simple way of saying it." Booklist

The **lemonade** war. Houghton Mifflin Company 2007 173p $16; pa $6.99
Grades: 3 4 5   **Fic**
1. Siblings -- Fiction 2. Money-making projects for children -- Fiction
ISBN 978-0-618-75043-6; 0-618-75043-6; 978-0-547-23765-7 pa; 0-547-23765-0 pa
LC 2006026076

Evan and his younger sister, Jesse, react very differently to the news that they will be in the same class for fourth grade and as the end of summer approaches, they battle it out through lemonade stands, each trying to be the first to earn 100 dollars. Includes mathematical calculations and tips for running a successful lemonade stand.

The author "does a good job of showing the siblings' strengths, flaws, and points of view in this engaging chapter book." Booklist

Followed by: The lemonade crime (2011)

The **magic** trap; Book 5. by Jacqueline Davies. Houghton Mifflin Harcourt 2014 272 p. illustrations (The lemonade war series) (hardback) $15.99
Grades: 3 4 5   **Fic**
1. Children's stories 2. Magic tricks -- Fiction 3. Fathers -- Fiction 4. Brothers and sisters -- Fiction
ISBN 0544052897; 9780544052895
LC 2013024154

In this children's story by Jacqueline Davies, part of The Lemonade War Series, "Jessie and Evan Treski have waged a lemonade war, sought justice in a class trial, unmasked a bell thief, and stood at opposite ends over . . . secrets. Now they are creating a magic show--a professional magic show, in their own backyard! They practice, they study, and they practice some more. And who shows up? Their father, who has done such a good job of disappearing over the past few years." (Publisher's note)

"One of the pleasures of reading the Lemonade War series...is watching the gradual development of the two main characters and the subtle shifts in their relationship, never more apparent than in this story....Readers intrigued by the magic theme will also appreciate the appended instructions for a card trick. The series' many fans won't want to miss this one." Booklist

Davies, Katie

The **great** dog disaster; Katie Davies; illustrated by Hannah Shaw. Beach Lane Books 2013 208 p. (hardback) $12.99

Grades: 3 4 5 6 7   **Fic**
1. Dogs -- Fiction 2. Pets -- Fiction 3. Dogs -- Fiction 4. Humorous stories 5. England -- Fiction 6. Newfoundland dog -- Fiction 7. Brothers and sisters -- Fiction 8. Family life -- England -- Fiction
ISBN 1442445173; 9781442445178; 9781442445185; 9781442445192
                                          LC 2012041868
This book is the final book in the Great Critter Capers series by Katie Davies. Here, Suzanne is "thrilled to inherit Aunt Deidra's Beatrice, an ancient, smelly, incontinent Newfoundland who remains stubbornly inert until" Suzanne and her friend Anna realize: "Beatrice is depressed! To boost her spirits, the girls bathe her in Suzanne's baby brother's bath." But "a huge vet bill with the promise of more to come has Suzanne's parents murmuring that Beatrice would be better off elsewhere." (Kirkus Reviews)

The **great** hamster massacre; illustrated by Hannah Shaw. Beach Lane 2011 177p il (Great critter capers) $12.99
Grades: 2 3 4   **Fic**
1. Mystery fiction 2. Hamsters -- Fiction 3. Friendship -- Fiction
ISBN 978-1-4424-2062-5; 1-4424-2062-6
                                          LC 2011-02046
Best friends and next-door neighbors Anna and Suzanne try to solve the mystery of the death of Anna's two pet hamsters.
"Inspired use of simple words, straightforward syntax and effective repetition make this a top pick for slow or reluctant readers. . . . Under the plot's frothy surface lie serious depths. . . . An auspicious debut." Kirkus
"Another title about Anna and Suzanne is:
The great rabbit rescue (2011)

The **great** rabbit rescue; illustrated by Hannah Shaw. Beach Lane Books 2012 il (Great critter capers) $12.99
Grades: 2 3 4   **Fic**
1. Sick -- Fiction 2. Rabbits -- Fiction 3. Friendship -- Fiction
ISBN 978-1-4424-2064-9; 1-4424-2064-2
                                          LC 2011008326
When Joe goes to live with his father across town and must leave behind his beloved pet rabbit, his friends Anna and Suzanne try to take care of it for him, but when the rabbit becomes ill and then Joe follows suit, the girls are certain that both will die unless they are reunited.
This "showcases Davies' laconic style and deadpan humor, so well-matched to the chapter-book format. Neatly complementing the text, Shaw's sly, witty illustrations, pie charts and graphics are a treat." Kirkus

Davies, Nicola, 1958-
The **Lion** who stole my arm; Nicola Davies, illustrated by Annabel Wright. Candlewick Press 2014 96 p. illustrations $14.99
Grades: 2 3 4 5   **Fic**
1. Lions -- Fiction 2. Courage -- Fiction 3. Revenge -- Fiction 4. Wildlife conservation -- Fiction
ISBN 0763666203; 9780763666200
                                          LC 2013943082
This book, by Nicola Davies, is an "illustrated novel for young readers that proves you don't need two arms to be

strong. Pedru has always wanted to be a great hunter like his father, but after a lion takes his arm, he worries that he'll always be the crippled boy instead. Pedru longs to kill the lion that mauled him and strengthens himself to be ready for the hunt. But when the opportunity arises, will Pedru have the strength to turn his back on revenge?" (Publisher's note)
"The terrifying title should attract readers with strong stomachs. Pedru, son of the best local hunter, lives in a village in East Africa. His senses are attuned to the local animals, but one night, while checking his snares at dusk, a lion attacks him. Pedru courageously fights, but he loses his right arm. His life is entirely changed by this event, as the boy meets scientists who are studying lions. He and his father become involved in this project, and his father is later hired when a tourist lodge that allows the lions to be seen but not hunted is built nearby. Pedru goes to college and becomes a scientist himself. The pen-and-wash illustrations provide details on the people, animals and village life in this part of Africa. An afterword gives information about lion-conservation projects and how they protect people while allowing the large cats to live. . . . Though on the purposive side, the tale both provides adventure and fills a cultural niche for chapter-book readers ." Kirkus.

The **Promise**; Nicola Davies, illustrated by Laura Carlin. Candlewick Press 2014 40 p. $16.99
Grades: K 1 2 3 4   **Fic**
1. Girls -- Fiction 2. Life change events -- Fiction 3. Acorns -- Fiction 4. Promises -- Fiction
ISBN 0763666335; 9780763666330
                                          LC 2013934311
In this children's book by Nicola Davies, illustrated by Laura Carlin, "on a mean street in a mean, broken city, a young girl tries to snatch an old woman's bag. But the frail old woman, holding on with the strength of heroes, says the thief can't have it without giving something in return: the promise. It is the beginning of a journey that will change the thieving girl's life--and a chance to change the world, for good." (Publisher's note)
"A girl, with no name and of no particular age, describes a place as gritty as its people are hard: When I was young, I lived in a city that was mean and hard and ugly. She lives by stealing, and one day, she wrestles with an old woman for her bag, which the lady finally lets go of, with a condition: If you promise to plant them...Bright hues and plenty of greenery enliven the pages and lift the spirits. Lots to look at, think about, and discuss here." Booklist

Davis, Aubrey
A **hen** for Izzy Pippik. Kids Can 2012 32 p.
Grades: K 1 2   **Fic**
1. Folklore 2. Poverty -- Fiction 3. Cooperation -- Fiction 4. Picture books for children 5. Chickens -- Juvenile fiction
ISBN 9781554532438
This picture book depicts the adventures of a girl named Shaina, who "discovers an unusual hen . . . and strives to find its rightful owner -- a man called Izzy Pippik. Despite Shaina's insistence that he take back the hen, Pippik allows the hen, Yevka, and her flock of chicks to remain in their poor town. . . . Author Aubrey Davis has drawn upon Talmudic and Islamic folklore." (Kirkus Reviews)

Davis, Tony

Roland Wright: brand-new page; illustrated by Gregory Rogers. Delacorte Press 2010 133p il $12.99

Grades: 2 3 4 **Fic**

1. Castles -- Fiction 2. Middle Ages -- Fiction 3. Knights and knighthood -- Fiction

ISBN 978-0-385-73802-6; 0-385-73802-1

Sequel to: Roland Wright, future knight (2009)

First published 2008 in Australia

In 1409, aspiring knight Roland Wright joins the royal household at Twofold Castle as a new page, but his plan to impress King John and his knights quickly backfires.

"Goofy cartoon illustrations keep the mood light. . . . A solid choice for children who are ready to make the leap to chapter books." SLJ

Roland Wright: future knight. Delacorte Press 2009 129p il $12.99; lib bdg $15.99

Grades: 2 3 4 **Fic**

1. Middle Ages -- Fiction 2. Knights and knighthood -- Fiction

ISBN 978-0-385-73800-2; 0-385-73800-5; 978-0-385-90706-4 lib bdg; 0-385-90706-0 lib bdg

LC 2008053074

First published 2007 in the United Kingdom

In 1409, skinny, clumsy Roland, the ten-year-old son of a blacksmith, pursues his dream of becoming a knight.

"This engaging book, the first in a series, has accurate details about the Middle Ages and a feisty, persevering hero. . . . Rogers's charming pen-and-ink illustrations enhance the story and may also make it more appealing to reluctant readers." SLJ

Another title about Roland Wright is:

Roland Wright: brand-new page (2010)

De Angeli, Marguerite Lofft

The **door** in the wall; by Marguerite de Angeli. Doubleday 1989 120p il hardcover o.p. pa $4.99

Grades: 4 5 6 **Fic**

1. Middle Ages -- Fiction 2. Great Britain -- Fiction 3. Children with physical disabilities -- Fiction

ISBN 0-385-07283-X; 0-440-22779-8 pa

First published 1949

Awarded the Newbery Medal, 1950

Robin, a crippled boy in fourteenth-century England, proves his courage and earns recognition from the King

"An enthralling and inspiring tale of triumph over handicap. Unusually beautiful illustrations, full of authentic detail, combine with the text to make life in England during the Middle Ages come alive." N Y Times Book Rev

Thee, Hannah! written and illustrated by Marguerite de Angeli. Herald Press 2000 99p il pa $15.99

Grades: 3 4 5 **Fic**

1. Philadelphia (Pa.) -- Fiction 2. Society of Friends -- Fiction

ISBN 0-8361-9106-4

LC 99-52422

A reissue of the title first published 1940 by Doubleday

Nine-year-old Hannah, a Quaker living in Philadelphia just before the Civil War, longs to have some fashionable dresses like other girls but comes to appreciate her heritage and its plain dressing when her family saves the life of a runaway slave

"Hannah and the other children are very real and, in addition to the [author's] lovely pictures that follow the story, the street cries of old Philadelphia are effectively introduced and illustrated at the beginning of each chapter." Libr J

De Goldi, Kate

The **ACB** with Honora Lee; by Kate De Goldi; drawings by Gregory O'Brien. Longacre 2012 124 p. ill. (chiefly col.) (hardcover) $17.99

Grades: 4 5 6 7 **Fic**

1. Patience 2. Alphabet -- Fiction 3. Grandparent-grandchild relationship 4. Rest homes -- Fiction 5. Grandparent and child -- Fiction

ISBN 1770497226; 9781869799892; 9781770497221

LC 2012515235

In this juvenile book, by Kate De Goldi, illustrated by Gregory O'Brien, "Perry's mother and father are busy people . . . they're impatient, they're tired, they get cross easily. And they think that only children, like Perry, should be kept busy. . . . Perry . . . discovers her Gran has an unconventional interest in the alphabet, so Perry decides to make an alphabet book. . . . Soon everyone is interested in Perry's book project." (Publisher's note)

"Nine-year-old Perry, an only child, spends Thursday afternoons with her grandmother, Honora Lee, who lives at the Santa Lucia nursing home and suffers from dementia. With Honora Lee's help, Perry writes and illustrates an alphabet book about the residents. Fans of middle grade novels with quirky female protagonists will enjoy this story and its stylish color illustrations, which suit the mood of the text." Horn Book

De Guzman, Michael

Henrietta Hornbuckle's circus of life. Farrar, Straus and Giroux 2010 152p $16.99

Grades: 4 5 6 **Fic**

1. Death -- Fiction 2. Circus -- Fiction 3. Clowns -- Fiction 4. Bereavement -- Fiction 5. Family life -- Fiction

ISBN 978-0-374-33513-7; 0-374-33513-3

LC 2009-13602

Twelve-year-old Henrietta Hornbuckle and her parents perform as clowns in a tiny, ramshackle traveling circus until a family tragedy jeopardizes Henrietta's whole offbeat world

"The writing is worthy of a tall tale, but the details are all realistic. A simple and satisfying story with a likable, unusual star." Booklist

De Lint, Charles, 1951-

Seven wild sisters; A Modern Fairy Tale. written by Charles de Lint; illustrated by Charles Vess. Little, Brown and Co. 2013 272 p. color illustrations $18

Grades: 4 5 6 **Fic**

1. Magic -- Fiction 2. Fairies -- Fiction 3. Sisters -- Fiction 4. Kidnapping -- Fiction 5. Adventure and adventurers -- Fiction

ISBN 0316053562; 9780316053563

LC 2012045328

This book, by Charles de Lint, is a "companion novel to 'The Cats of Tanglewood Forest.' . . . When it comes to fairies, Sarah Jane Dillard must be careful what she wishes for. . . . When Sarah Jane discovers a tiny man wounded by a cluster of miniature poison arrows, she brings him to the reclusive Aunt Lillian for help. But the two quickly find themselves ensnared in a longtime war between rival fairy clans, and Sarah Jane's six sisters have been kidnapped to use as ransom." (Publisher's note)

"Beautiful bookmaking, lovely storytelling and wondrous illustrations make for a splendid sequel-of-sorts to The Cats of Tanglewood Forest (2013). The little girl of the earlier tale is now 'Aunt' Lillian, a woman in her 80s who lives alone and who fascinates young Sarah Jane Dillard, the middle of seven red-haired sisters. . . . The language is as pretty on the page as it is in the speaking, with rich echoes of fantasy tropes. The story and the art are reworked from a limited edition of some time ago, described by Vess in an artist's note. There is a promise of more stories at the ever-so-satisfying end, which comes with the tiniest hint of romance past and future—readers will be enchanted." Kirkus

The **tangled** tale of a circle of cats; written by Charles de Lint; illustrated by Charles Vess. Little, Brown 2013 304 p. $17.99

Grades: 4 5 6   **Fic**
1. Fantasy fiction 2. Cats -- Fiction 3. Magic -- Fiction 4. Trees -- Fiction 5. Orphans -- Fiction 6. Snakebites -- Fiction
ISBN 0316053570; 9780316053570
LC 2011042982

In this children's story, by Charles de Lint, illustrated by Charles Vess, "Lillian Kindred spends her days exploring the Tanglewood Forest, a magical, rolling wilderness. . . . Until the day the cats of the forest save her life by transforming her into a kitten. Now Lillian must set out on a perilous adventure that will lead her through untamed lands of fabled creatures--from Old Mother Possum to the fearsome Bear People--to find a way to make things right." (Publisher's note)

De Quidt, Jeremy

The **toymaker**; with illustrations by Gary Blythe. David Fickling Books 2010 356p il $16.99; lib bdg $19.99
Grades: 5 6 7 8   **Fic**
1. Adventure fiction 2. Toys -- Fiction
ISBN 978-0-385-75180-3; 0-385-75180-X; 978-0-385-75181-0 lib bdg; 0-385-75181-8 lib bdg

"Mathias . . . upon the death of his conjurer grandfather, is spirited away from the decrepit carnival they called home. His unknown new guardian appears to be after the secret contained on an inherited piece of paper, which is now in Mathias' possession. . . . Moving briskly across an atmospheric Germanic setting, the characters are chased by howling wolves, a dangerous dwarf, and unforgiving cold in a bloody, mysterious, and darkly thrilling quest." Booklist

Deedy, Carmen Agra

★ The **Cheshire** Cheese cat; a Dickens of a tale. Peachtree Publishers 2011 228p il $16.95
Grades: 5 6 7 8   **Fic**
1. Cats -- Fiction 2. Mice -- Fiction 3. London (England) -- Fiction 4. Great Britain -- History -- 19th century -- Fiction
ISBN 978-1-56145-595-9; 1-56145-595-4
LC 2010052275

"The vagaries of tavern life in 19th-century London come alive in this delightful tale. . . . The fast-moving plot is a masterwork of intricate detail that will keep readers enthralled, and the characters are well-rounded and believable.

Language is a highlight of the novel; words both elegant and colorful fill the pages. . . . Combined with Moser's precise pencil sketches of personality-filled characters, the book is a success in every way." SLJ

The **yellow** star; the legend of King Christian X of Denmark. illustrated by Henri Sørensen. Peachtree Pubs. 2000 un il $16.95
Grades: 3 4 5   **Fic**
1. Kings 2. Denmark -- Fiction 3. Holocaust, 1933-1945 -- Fiction 4. World War, 1939-1945 -- Fiction
ISBN 1-56145-208-4
LC 00-20602

Retells the story of King Christian X and the Danish resistance to the Nazis during World War II

"Deedy's language is simple and rhythmic. . . . This is an interesting and thought-provoking piece of work." SLJ

DeFelice, Cynthia C.

Bringing Ezra back. Farrar, Straus & Giroux 2006 147p $16
Grades: 4 5 6 7   **Fic**
1. Voyages and travels -- Fiction 2. Frontier and pioneer life -- Fiction
ISBN 0-374-39939-5
LC 2005-49763

In the mid-1800s, twelve-year-old Nathan journeys from his farm on the Ohio frontier to Western Pennsylvania to rescue a friend held captive by the owners of a freak show.

"Told in Nathan's voice, this adventure treats readers to a double-dip cliff-hanging plot and heart-searing maturation." SLJ

Sequel to Weasel (1990)

Fort; Cynthia DeFelice. Farrar, Straus & Giroux 2015 208 p. (hardback) $16.99
Grades: 4 5 6 7   **Fic**
1. Summer -- Fiction 2. Bullies -- Fiction 3. Friendship -- Fiction 4. Bullying -- Fiction 5. Great-aunts -- Fiction 6. Best friends -- Fiction 7. Great-uncles -- Fiction
ISBN 0374324271; 9780374324278
LC 2014040167

"When older boys tear apart the fort where they have been enjoying a wonderful summer, Wyatt and Augie team up with another bullied kid to exact revenge, with unexpected consequences. By the best-selling author of Wild Life." (Publisher's Note)

"Wyatt and Augie's friendship is strong despite the fact that they only see each other in the summer. This particular summer, Wyatt's eleventh, is told as a flashback in the "What I Did on My Summer Vacation" essay that he has no intention of showing to a teacher... Stuffed full of clever pranks and summertime nostalgia, this is a story of kindness and adventure, and a rare breed in the middle-grade canon that doesn't rely on cheap humor to hold attention. A boisterous and poignant coming-of-age tale." Booklist

The **ghost** and Mrs. Hobbs; [by] Cynthia DeFelice. Farrar, Straus & Giroux 2001 180p $16; pa $5.99
Grades: 4 5 6   **Fic**
1. Ghost stories
ISBN 0-374-38046-5; 0-06-001172-6 pa
LC 00-52827

Hindered by a fight with her friend Dub and a series of mysterious fires, eleven-year-old Allie investigates the fire seventeen years earlier which claimed the lives of the husband and infant son of a school cafeteria worker, as well as the handsome young man whose ghost asks Allie for help

"This is a diverting and suspenseful ghost story offering a likable protagonist and a thrilling romantic spark." Horn Book

The **ghost** of Cutler Creek; [by] Cynthia DeFelice. 1st ed; Farrar, Straus and Giroux 2004 181p $16; pa $5.95
Grades: 4 5 6   **Fic**
1. Ghost stories 2. Mystery fiction 3. Dogs -- Fiction
ISBN 0-374-38058-9; 0-374-40004-0 pa
                                            LC 2003-49051
When Allie is contacted by the ghost of a dog, she and Dub investigate the surly new boy at school and his father, who may be running a puppy mill, to see if they are involved.

"DeFelice has created a suspenseful tale that will leave readers rapidly turning pages." SLJ

★ The **ghost** of Fossil Glen; by Cynthia DeFelice. Farrar, Straus & Giroux 1998 167p (Ghost Mysteries) $16; pa $7.99
Grades: 4 5 6   **Fic**
1. Ghost stories
ISBN 0-374-31787-9; 9780312602130 pa
                                            LC 97-33230
"Strange events begin when a calm, unknown voice prevents Allie from panicking and falling from a dangerous cliff while fossil hunting. Then, an old journal mysteriously appears in her mailbox. Allie often feels a presence nearby and dreams of a girl falling from the cliff. She then discovers the grave marker of an 11-year-old girl who was missing and presumed dead in 1994. Because of her reputation for telling stories, Allie cannot convince anyone to believe her except her longtime friend and fellow fossil hunter, Dub. Driven to pursue the mystery, Allie finds an old diary that provides her with facts about the girl's death. Foolishly, she reveals what she knows and endangers her own life. . . . Grades four to six." (SLJ)

"Sixth-grader Allie Nichols encounters the ghost of Lucy Stiles and becomes involved with Lucy's unsolved death, eventually finding proof that Lucy was murdered." Horn Book Guide

The **ghost** of Poplar Point; [by] Cynthia DeFelice. 1st ed.; Farrar, Straus and Giroux 2007 183p $16
Grades: 4 5 6 7   **Fic**
1. Ghost stories 2. Seneca Indians -- Fiction 3. New York (State) -- Fiction
ISBN 0-374-32540-5; 978-0-374-32540-4
                                            LC 2006047329
Prompted by the ghost of a young Seneca Indian girl, twelve-year-old Allie and her friend Dub are determined, despite the opposition of an unscrupulous property developer, that the historical pageant celebrating the founding of their town tells the truth about the fate of the Seneca people who lived there during the Revolutionary War.

"This engaging book moves along quickly to a satisfying conclusion." Booklist

The **missing** manatee; [by] Cynthia DeFelice. Farrar, Straus and Giroux 2005 181p $16; pa $6.95
Grades: 5 6 7 8   **Fic**
1. Mystery fiction 2. Fishing -- Fiction 3. Florida -- Fiction
ISBN 0-374-31257-5; 0-374-40020-2 pa
                                            LC 2004-50633
While coping with his parents' separation, eleven-year-old Skeet spends most of Spring Break in his skiff on a Florida river, where he finds a manatee shot to death and begins looking for the killer

"DeFelice offers a realistic adventure story that is fast paced and full of drama. . . . The characters are multifaceted and well developed, and the story should prompt readers to think about cause and effect." SLJ

★ **Signal**. Farrar, Straus and Giroux 2009 151p $16.99
Grades: 5 6 7 8   **Fic**
1. Moving -- Fiction 2. Friendship -- Fiction 3. Loneliness -- Fiction 4. Child abuse -- Fiction 5. Country life -- Fiction
ISBN 978-0-374-39915-3; 0-374-39915-8
                                            LC 2008-09278
After moving with his emotionally distant father to the Finger Lakes region of upstate New York, twelve-year-old Owen faces a lonely summer until he meets an abused girl who may be a space alien.

"Well-drawn secondary characters create a threatening backdrop to the developing mystery, while Owen's poignant relationship with his work-driven father elicits sympathy. The tension builds on several fronts to a gripping climax and satisfying conclusion. Owen's likable voice, the plot's quick pace and the science fiction overtones make this a winner." Publ Wkly

Weasel; [by] Cynthia DeFelice. Avon Books 1990 119p pa $4.99
Grades: 4 5 6 7   **Fic**
1. Ohio -- Fiction 2. Frontier and pioneer life -- Fiction
ISBN 978-0-380-71358-5 pa; 0-380-71358-6 pa
First published 1990 by Macmillan
Alone in the frontier wilderness in the winter of 1839 while his father is recovering from an injury, eleven-year-old Nathan runs afoul of the renegade killer known as the weasel and makes a surprising discovery about the concept of revenge

"A masterfully told, riveting tale sure to inspire strong discussion about moral choices." SLJ

Wild life; by Cynthia DeFelice. Farrar, Straus and Giroux 2011 177p $16.99
Grades: 4 5 6   **Fic**
1. Dogs -- Fiction 2. Hunting -- Fiction 3. Grandparents -- Fiction 4. North Dakota -- Fiction 5. Runaway children -- Fiction 6. Wilderness survival -- Fiction
ISBN 978-0-374-38001-4; 0-374-38001-5
When twelve-year-old Eric's parents are deployed to Iraq, he goes to live with grandparents he hardly knows in small-town North Dakota, but his grandfather's hostility and the threat of losing the dog he has rescued are too much and Eric runs away.

"Themes of accepting change and learning to let go are woven into this winning tale of boy and dog." SLJ

DeGross, Monalisa

Donavan's double trouble; [by] Monalisa DeGross; illustrated by Amy Bates. Amistad 2008 180p il $15.99; lib bdg $17.89

Grades: 2 3 4   **Fic**

1. School stories 2. Uncles -- Fiction 3. Amputees -- Fiction 4. African Americans -- Fiction

ISBN 978-0-06-077293-2; 978-0-06-077294-9 lib bdg

LC 2007011244

Fourth-grader Donavan is sensitive about the problems he has understanding math, and then when his favorite uncle, a former high school basketball star, returns from National Guard duty an amputee, Donavan's problems get even worse as he struggles to accept this "new" Uncle Vic.

"The fast, funny dialogue between friends and the warm family relationships will draw readers to the realistic story." Booklist

Another title about Donavan is:

Donavan's word jar (1994)

DeJong, Meindert

The **wheel** on the school; pictures by Maurice Sendak. Harper & Row 1954 298p il $18.95; pa $6.95

Grades: 4 5 6   **Fic**

1. School stories 2. Storks -- Fiction 3. Netherlands -- Fiction

ISBN 0-06-021585-2; 0-06-021586-0 lib bdg; 0-06-440021-2 pa

Awarded the Newbery Medal, 1955

"This author goes deeply into the heart of childhood and has written a moving story, filled with suspense and distinguished for the quality of its writing." Child Books Too Good To Miss

DeKeyser, Stacy

The **Brixen** Witch; Stacy DeKeyser. Margaret K. McElderry Books 2012 208 p. (hardcover) $15.99

Grades: 4 5 6 7 8   **Fic**

1. Horror fiction 2. Occult fiction 3. Witches -- Fiction 4. Rats -- Fiction 5. Magic -- Fiction 6. Witchcraft -- Fiction 7. Community life -- Fiction

ISBN 9781442433281; 9781442433304

LC 2011033680

In this book, "12-year-old Rudi Bauer thinks he's found a treasure, [but] no good can come from taking something that belongs to the Brixen Witch. His sleep is plagued by nightmares, but when they stop there's no relief--the village is infested with rats. . . . As his Oma points out, young Rudi, the one child left behind after the children disappear and the one who precipitated the crisis, is the one to make things right." (Kirkus Reviews)

DeLaCroix, Alice

The **best** horse ever; illustrated by Ronald Himler. Holiday House 2010 74p il $15.95

Grades: 3 4 5   **Fic**

1. Horses -- Fiction 2. Friendship -- Fiction

ISBN 978-0-8234-2254-8; 0-8234-2254-2

LC 2009-25542

"Abby gets her heart's desire: her parents purchase Griffin, the gentle horse she has grown to love during her riding lessons. But when her best friend, Devon, can't get past her fear of the horse to share Abby's excitement, they quarrel. . . . Although girls who love horses are the obvious audience,

other readers will also enjoy this appealing chapter book with its simple plot and subtly drawn characters. . . .. Himler contributes shaded pencil drawings that capture the actions and emotions of the characters." Booklist

Delaney, Joseph, 1945-

The **ghost** prison; Joseph Delaney. Sourcebooks Fire 2013 112 p. (hc: alk. paper) $12.99

Grades: 4 5 6 7 8   **Fic**

1. Horror fiction 2. Prisons -- Fiction 3. Horror stories 4. Ghosts -- Fiction 5. Orphans -- Fiction 6. Supernatural -- Fiction

ISBN 1402293186; 9781402293184

LC 2013017898

This novella is set in the same universe as Joseph Delaney's Last Apprentice series. The story "is narrated by orphan Billy Calder, who is apprehensive about the new job he has landed: helping guard an infamously haunted prison on the night shift. The ghosts and dangers turn out to be all too real, as Billy learns about the prison's bloody history and has a life-altering encounter one night while on the job." (Publishers Weekly)

★ **Revenge** of the witch; illustrations by Patrick Arrasmith. Greenwillow Bks. 2005 344p il (The last apprentice) $14.99; lib bdg $15.89; pa $7.99

Grades: 5 6 7 8   **Fic**

1. Witches -- Fiction 2. Supernatural -- Fiction

ISBN 0-06-076618-2; 0-06-076619-0 lib bdg; 0-06-076620-4 pa

LC 2004-54003

Young Tom, the seventh son of a seventh son, starts work as an apprentice for the village spook, whose job is to protect ordinary folk from "ghouls, boggarts, and all manner of wicked beasties"

"Delaney grabs readers by the throat and gives them a good shake in a smartly crafted story. . . . This is a gristly thriller. . . . Yet the twisted horror is amply buffered by an exquisitely normal young hero, matter-of-fact prose, and a workaday normalcy." Booklist

Other titles in this series are:

Curse of the bane (2006)

Night of the soul-stealer (2007)

Attack of the fiend (2008)

Wrath of the Bloodeye (2008)

Clash of the demons (2009)

Rise of the huntress (2010)

Rage of the fallen (2011)

The **Spook's** Bestiary; illustrated by Julek Heller. Greenwillow Books 2011 222p il (The last apprentice) $16.99

Grades: 5 6 7 8   **Fic**

1. Horror fiction 2. Apprentices -- Fiction 3. Supernatural -- Fiction

ISBN 978-0-06-208114-8; 0-06-208114-4

LC 2010049856

Ready to be presented to the last apprentice, Tom Ward, the spook's notebook contains instructions for vanquishing boggarts, witches, the unquiet dead, and other dark creatures and spirits.

"Heller's creepy drawings fill the pages and, like the whole book, they should delight fans of the series." SLJ

Wrath of the Bloodeye; [by] Joseph Delaney; illustrations by Patrick Arrasmith. 1st ed.; Greenwillow Books 2008 511p il (The last apprentice) $17.99; lib bdg $18.89; pa $7.99

Grades: 5 6 7 8   **Fic**

1. Witches -- Fiction 2. Apprentices -- Fiction 3. Supernatural -- Fiction

ISBN 978-0-06-134459-6; 0-06-134459-1; 978-0-06-134460-2 lib bdg; 0-06-134460-5 lib bdg; 978-0-06-134461-9 pa; 0-06-134461-3 pa

LC 2008017920

The continuing adventures of Tom, the seventh son of a seventh son and apprentice to the local Spook, who faces danger and death daily in his job protecting the region from evil.

DeMatteis, J. M.

Imaginalis. Katherine Tegen Books 2010 248p $16.99

Grades: 5 6 7 8   **Fic**

1. Fantasy fiction 2. Magic -- Fiction 3. Imagination -- Fiction 4. Books and reading -- Fiction

ISBN 978-0-06-173286-7; 0-06-173286-9

Devastated that her favorite fantasy book series will not be completed, twelve-year-old Mehera discovers that only her belief, imagination, and courage will save the land of Imaginalis and its inhabitants from being lost forever.

This is "a sure-footed fantasy. . . . The well-drawn characters, abundant action and humor, and hopeful message about the power of reading and belief keep it afloat." Publ Wkly

Derby, Sally

Kyle's island. Charlesbridge 2010 191p $16.95

Grades: 5 6 7 8   **Fic**

1. Lakes -- Fiction 2. Islands -- Fiction 3. Michigan -- Fiction 4. Siblings -- Fiction 5. Family life -- Fiction

ISBN 978-1-58089-316-9; 1-58089-316-3

LC 2009-17581

Kile, almost thirteen, spends much of the summer yearning to explore a nearby island, striving to be a good brother, fishing with an elderly neighbor, and fuming at his parents over their separation that is forcing his mother to sell the family's cabin on a Michigan lake.

"Derby writes a subtle coming-of-age novel that is engaging from start to finish. Kyle's character is so well developed that many readers will be able to understand the realistic emotions and situations taking place." Libr Media Connect

Deriso, Christine Hurley

The **Right**-Under Club; [by] Christine Hurley Deriso. Delacorte Press 2007 195p $15.99; lib bdg $18.99

Grades: 5 6 7 8   **Fic**

1. Friendship -- Fiction 2. Stepfamilies -- Fiction

ISBN 978-0-385-73334-2; 978-0-385-90351-6 lib bdg

LC 2006019768

Over the summer, five middle school girls form a club based on the fact that they all feel neglected and misunderstood by their blended families

"In this timely novel, Deriso introduces solid characters. . . . The changing voices are easy to navigate and lend charm to the narrative." SLJ

Diamand, Emily

Flood and fire. Chicken House/Scholastic 2011 351p il (Raiders' ransom) $17.99

Grades: 4 5 6 7   **Fic**

1. Science fiction 2. Adventure fiction 3. Cats -- Fiction 4. Robots -- Fiction 5. Computers -- Fiction 6. Terrorism -- Fiction 7. Great Britain -- Fiction

ISBN 978-0-545-24268-4; 0-545-24268-1

LC 2010023544

Sequel to: Raiders' ransom (2009)

In 22nd-century Cambridge, England, thirteen-year-old Lilly Melkun must try to stop the strange, uncontrollable robots that were activated when a sinister-looking chip in her hand-held computer triggered a false anti-terrorist alert.

"The rare combination of action at breakneck speed and significant, believable character development makes this just about impossible to put down." Kirkus

★ **Raiders'** ransom. Chicken House/Scholastic 2009 334p map $17.99

Grades: 4 5 6 7   **Fic**

1. Science fiction 2. Adventure fiction 3. Pirates -- Fiction 4. Kidnapping -- Fiction 5. Great Britain -- Fiction 6. Environmental degradation -- Fiction

ISBN 978-0-545-14297-7; 0-545-14297-0

LC 2008-43692

It's the 22nd century and, because of climate change, much of England is underwater. Poor Lilly is out fishing with her trusty sea-cat when greedy raiders pillage the town—and kidnap the prime minister's daughter. Her village blamed, Lilly decides to find the girl.

This is a "captivating story. . . . A well-drawn world, plot twists galore and spunky characters make this one a true page-turner." Kirkus

Folllowed by: Flood and fire (2011)

DiCamillo, Kate

★ **Because** of Winn-Dixie. Candlewick Press 2000 182p $15.99; pa $6.99

Grades: 4 5 6 7   **Fic**

1. Dogs -- Fiction 2. Florida -- Fiction

ISBN 978-0-7636-0776-0; 0-7636-0776-2; 978-0-7636-4432-1 pa; 0-7636-4432-3 pa

LC 99-34260

A Newbery honor book, 2001

Ten-year-old India Opal Buloni describes her first summer in the town of Naomi, Florida, and all the good things that happen to her because of her big ugly dog Winn-Dixie

"This well-crafted, realistic, and heartwarming story will be read and reread as a new favorite deserving a long-term place on library shelves." SLJ

★ **Bink** & Gollie; [by] Kate DiCamillo and Alison McGhee; illustrated by Tony Fucile. Candlewick Press 2010 81p il $15.99

Grades: 1 2 3   **Fic**

1. Friendship -- Fiction

ISBN 0-7636-3266-X; 978-0-7636-3266-3

LC 2009-49100

Two roller-skating best friends share adventures involving bright socks, a trek to the Andes, and an unlikely companion. "Ages six to eight." (N Y Times Book Rev)

"In the first tale, Bink's outrageous socks offend Gollie's sartorial eye, but the two compromise for friendship's sake.

The second story sends Gollie on an imagined climb up the Andes, shutting Bink out of the house until she arrives at the door with a sandwich. . . . In the final episode, Gollie is jealous of Bink's new pet fish until Bink reassures her that no one can take her place. All three stories . . . offer delightful portrayals of two headstrong characters who, despite their differences and idiosyncratic quirks, know the importance of true friendship. The delightful digitalized cartoon illustrations . . . reinforce the humor of the text." SLJ

Another title about Bink & Gollie is:
Two for one (2012)

Bink and Gollie; best friends forever. Kate DiCamillo, Alison McGheeq, Tony Fucile. Candlewick Press 2013 96 p. (Bink and Gollie) (reinforced) $15.99
Grades: 1 2 3 4   **Fic**
1. Girls -- Fiction 2. Friendship -- Fiction
ISBN 0763634972; 9780763634971
                                        LC 2012942669
In this children's story, by Kate DiCamillo and Alison McGhee, illustrated by Tony Fucile, "Gollie is quite sure she has royal blood in her veins, but can Bink survive her friend's queenly airs . . . ? Bink wonders what it would be like to be as tall as her friend, but how far will she stretch her luck to find out? And when Bink and Gollie long to get their picture into a book of record holders, where will they find the kudos they seek?" (Publisher's note)

★ **Flora** and Ulysses; The Illuminated Adventures. by Kate DiCamillo; illustrated by K. G. Campbell. Candlewick Press 2013 240 p. ill. (reinforced) $17.99
Grades: 5 6 7 8   **Fic**
1. Fantasy fiction 2. Adventure fiction 3. Girls Fiction 4. Squirrels -- Fiction 5. Superheroes
ISBN 076366040X; 9780763660406
                                        LC 2012947748
Parents' Choice Awards: Gold Medal Fiction (2013)
Newberry Medal (2014)
In this book by Newbury Medalist Kate DiCamillo, "bitter about her parents' divorce. Flora Buckman has withdrawn into her favorite comic book The Amazing Incandesto! and memorized the advisories in its ongoing bonus feature, Terrible Things Can Happen to You! She puts those life-saving tips into action when a squirrel is swallowed whole by a neighbor's new vacuum cleaner. . . . Flora resuscitates the squirrel," who now has superpowers. (Publishers Weekly)

★ **Leroy** Ninker saddles up; tales from Deckawoo Drive, volume one. Kate DiCamillo. Candlewick Press 2014 96 p. (Tales from Deckawoo Drive) $12.99
Grades: 1 2 3 4   **Fic**
1. Love stories 2. Cowboys -- Fiction 3. Horses -- Fiction
ISBN 0763663395; 9780763663391
                                        LC 2013953473
In this children's book by Kate DiCamillo, illustrated by Chris Van Dusen and part of the Tales from Deckawoo Drive series, "Leroy Ninker has a hat, a lasso, and boots. What he doesn't have is a horse--until he meets Maybelline, that is, and then it's love at first sight. Maybelline loves spaghetti and sweet nothings, and she loves Leroy, too. But when Leroy forgets the third and final rule of caring for Maybelline, disaster ensues." (Publisher's note)

"Reformed robber and would-be cowboy Leroy Ninker (last seen in the Mercy Watson books) lassos his own series...DiCamillo's use of inventive and colorful language and Van Dusen's stylized gouache illustrations make this story click. Give this to graduates of the earlier series looking for a bit more of a challenge." Booklist

★ The **magician's** elephant; illustrated by Yoko Tanaka. Candlewick Press 2009 201p il $16.99
Grades: 4 5 6 7   **Fic**
1. Adventure fiction 2. Orphans -- Fiction 3. Siblings -- Fiction 4. Elephants -- Fiction 5. Missing children -- Fiction
ISBN 978-0-7636-4410-9; 0-7636-4410-2
                                        LC 2009-07359
When ten-year-old orphan Peter Augustus Duchene encounters a fortune teller in the marketplace one day and she tells him that his sister, who is presumed dead, is in fact alive, he embarks on a remarkable series of adventures as he desperately tries to find her.

"The profound and deeply affecting emotions at work in the story are bouyed up by the tale's succinct, lyrical text; gentle touches of humor; and uplifting message." Booklist

★ **Mercy** Watson to the rescue; illustrated by Chris Van Dusen. Candlewick Press 2005 68p il $12.99
Grades: K 1 2 3   **Fic**
1. Pigs -- Fiction
ISBN 0-7636-2270-2
                                        LC 2004-51896
After Mercy the pig snuggles to sleep with the Watsons, all three awaken with the bed teetering on the edge of a big hole in the floor.

"Appropriate as both a picture book and a beginning reader, this joyful story combines familiar elements . . . with a raucous telling that lets readers in on the joke. . . . The gouache illustrations are polished to a sheen and have plenty of heft." Booklist

Other titles about Mercy Watson are:
Mercy Watson fights crime (2006)
Mercy Watson goes for a ride (2006)
Mercy Watson: princess in disguise (2007)
Mercy Watson thinks like a pig (2008)
Mercy Watson: something wonky this way comes (2009)

★ The **miraculous** journey of Edward Tulane; illustrated by Bagram Ibatoulline. Candlewick Press 2006 198p il $18.99; pa $6.99
Grades: 3 4 5 6   **Fic**
1. Toys -- Fiction 2. Rabbits -- Fiction
ISBN 0-7636-2589-2; 0-7636-4367-X pa
                                        LC 2004-56129
Edward Tulane, a coldhearted and proud toy rabbit, loves only himself until he is separated from the little girl who adores him and travels across the country, acquiring new owners and listening to their hopes, dreams, and histories.

"This achingly beautiful story shows a true master of writing at her very best. . . . Ibatoulline's lovely sepia-toned gouache illustrations and beautifully rendered color plates are exquisite." SLJ

★ The **tale** of Despereaux; being the story of a mouse, a princess, some soup, and a spool of thread. illustrated by Timothy Basil Ering. Candlewick Press 2003 267p il $17.99; pa $7.99

Grades: 3 4 5 6   **Fic**

1. Fairy tales 2. Mice -- Fiction

ISBN 0-7636-1722-9; 0-7636-2529-9 pa

LC 2002-34760

Awarded the Newbery Medal, 2004

The adventures of Despereaux Tilling, a small mouse of unusual talents, the princess that he loves, the servant girl who longs to be a princess, and a devious rat determined to bring them all to ruin

"Forgiveness, light, love, and soup. These essential ingredients combine into a tale that is as soul stirring as it is delicious. . . . Ering's soft pencil illustrations reflect the story's charm." Booklist

Two for one; by Kate DiCamillo & Alison McGhee; illustrated by Tony Fucile. 1st ed. Candlewick Press 2012 75 p. ill. (some col.) (Bink & Gollie) (reinforced) $15.99; (prebind) $15.99; (paperback) $6.99

Grades: 2 3 4   **Fic**

1. Humorous fiction 2. Fairs -- Fiction 3. Friendship -- Fiction

ISBN 0763633615; 9780763633615; 9781451740134; 9780763664459

LC 2011046625

This children's story by Kate DiCamillo and Alison McGhee, illustrated by Tony Fucile, continues the Theodor Seuss Geisel Award-winning "Bink and Gollie" series. "The state fair is in town, and now Bink and Gollie . . . must use teamwork and their gray matter while navigating its many wonders. . . . As the undaunted duo steps into the mysterious tent of fortune-teller Madame Prunely, one prediction is crystal clear: this unlikely pair will always be the closest of pals." (Publisher's note)

Dickens, Charles

★ A **Christmas** carol; [by] Charles Dickens; [illustrated by] Brett Helquist; [abridged by Josh Greenhut] HarperCollins 2009 un il $17.99; lib bdg $18.89

Grades: 3 4 5 6   **Fic**

1. Ghost stories 2. Christmas -- Fiction 3. Great Britain -- History -- 19th century -- Fiction

ISBN 978-0-06-165099-4; 0-06-165099-4; 978-0-06-165100-7 lib bdg; 0-06-165100-1 lib bdg

LC 2008044031

A miser learns the true meaning of Christmas when three ghostly visitors review his past and foretell his future.

"Sacrificing none of Dickens's rich language; this retelling reads beautifully. The artist uses watercolor, pencil, and pastel to create cinematic artwork that contains amusing details; additionally, there are a number of pen-and-ink vignettes that help set the scenes. A winning combination of sparkling prose and exciting art." SLJ

Dionne, Erin

Ollie and the science of treasure hunting; a 14 day mystery. by Erin Dionne. Dial Books for Young Readers, an imprint of Penguin Group (USA) Inc. 2014 288 p. (hardcover) $16.99

Grades: 5 6 7 8   **Fic**

1. Mystery fiction 2. Camps -- Fiction 3. Adventure fiction 4. Buried treasure -- Fiction 5. Mystery and detective stories 6. Vietnamese Americans -- Fiction

7. Racially mixed people -- Fiction 8. Boston Harbor Islands (Mass.) -- Fiction

ISBN 9780803738720; 0803738722

LC 2013031211

"While at Wilderness camp on the Boston Harbor Islands, Ollie must navigate new friends, new enemies, and a high-stakes game of tag, so the last thing he needs is a mystery. But then Ollie meets Grey, an elusive girl with knowledge of the island's secrets, including the legend of a lost pirate treasure, which may not be a legend after all." (Publisher's note)

"A cast of likable campers, each with his or her own quirks --midnight swimmer, sensitive to sun, cartography genius--drive this fast-paced adventure led by a camp ranger with a gambling problem. Nothing should surprise readers in this thoroughly satisfying tale of friendship, intrigue, and Boston Harbor Island topography." Booklist

Includes bibliographical references

Companion to:

Moxie and the Art of Rule Breaking (2013)

DiSalvo, DyAnne

The **sloppy** copy slipup; [by] DyAnne DiSalvo. Holiday House 2006 103p il $16.95; pa $6.95

Grades: 2 3 4   **Fic**

1. School stories 2. Authorship -- Fiction

ISBN 0-8234-1947-9; 0-8234-2189-9 pa

Fourth-grader Brian Higman worries about how his teacher Miss Fromme—nicknamed The General—will react when he fails to hand in a writing assignment, but he ends up being able to tell his story, after all

"DiSalvo combines spot-on humor, vivid classroom scenes, and tension that builds from the first page, and Brian's story . . . will keep children eagerly engaged." Booklist

DiTerlizzi, Tony

The **battle** for WondLa; Tony DiTerlizzi; with illustrations by the author. 1st edition Simon & Schuster Books for Young Readers 2014 480 p. col. ill., col. map (The search for WondLa) (hardcover) $17.99

Grades: 2 3 4 5   **Fic**

1. Fantasy fiction 2. Extraterrestrial beings -- Fiction 3. War -- Fiction 4. Science fiction 5. Human-alien encounters -- Fiction

ISBN 1416983147; 9781416983149

LC 2013035219

"All hope for a peaceful coexistence between humankind and aliens seems lost in the third installment of the WondLa trilogy. Eva Nine has gone into hiding for fear of luring the wicked Loroc to her companions. However, news of the city Solas being captured by the human leader, Cadmus Pryde, forces Eva into action once again." (Publisher's note)

"Of particular interest is Eva's development into a young woman of unwavering compassion and courage, even in the face of betrayal, loss, and injury. DiTerlizzi's beautiful illustrations are worth the price of admission, as usual, and they do much to help the reader distinguish among the plethora of strange creatures." Booklist

A **hero** for WondLa; by Tony DiTerlizzi; with illustrations by the author. Simon & Schuster Books for Young Readers 2012 445 p. (hardcover) $17.99

Grades: 5 6 7 8   **Fic**

1. Science fiction 2. Rescue work -- Fiction 3. Life on

other planets -- Fiction 4. Identity -- Fiction 5. Human-alien encounters -- Fiction

ISBN 1416983120; 9781416983125; 9781442450844

LC 2011037031

Author Tony DiTerlizzi tells a science fiction story. "Eva Nine had never seen another human, but after a human boy named Hailey rescues her along with her companions, she couldn't be happier. Eva thinks she has everything she's ever dreamed of, especially when Hailey brings her and her friends to the colony of New Attica, where humans of all shapes and sizes live in apparent peace and harmony. But all is not idyllic in New Attica, and Eva Nine soon realizes that something sinister is going on . . . [that] could mean the end of everything and everyone on planet Orbona." (Publisher's note)

Kenny & the dragon; [by] Tony DiTerlizzi. Simon & Schuster Books for Young Readers 2008 151p $15.99

Grades: 4 5 6 7 **Fic**

1. Dragons -- Fiction 2. Rabbits -- Fiction 3. Knights and knighthood -- Fiction

ISBN 978-1-4169-3977-1; 1-4169-3977-6

LC 2008-7309

Book-loving Kenny the rabbit has few friends in his farming community, so when one, bookstore owner George, is sent to kill another, gentle dragon Grahame, Kenny must find a way to prevent their battle while satisfying the dragon-crazed townspeople.

"DiTerlizzi's novel is lighthearted and his informal pencil sketches enhance the creative interpretation of what would otherwise be a simple animal story." Publ Wkly

★ The **search** for WondLa; with illustrations by the author. Simon & Schuster Books for Young Readers 2010 477p il $17.99

Grades: 5 6 7 8 **Fic**

1. Science fiction 2. Extraterrestrial beings -- Fiction

ISBN 978-1-4169-8310-1; 1-4169-8310-4

LC 2010-01326

Living in isolation with a robot on what appears to be an alien world populated with bizarre life forms, a twelve-year-old human girl called Eva Nine sets out on a journey to find others like her.

"The abundant illustrations, drawn in a flat, two-tone style, are lush and enhance readers' understanding of this unique universe. . . . DiTerlizzi is pushing the envelope in his latest work, nearly creating a new format that combines a traditional novel with a graphic novel and with the interactivity of the computer. Yet, beneath this impressive package lies a theme readers will easily relate to: the need to belong, to connect, to figure out one's place in the world. The novel's ending is a stunning shocker that will leave kids frantically awaiting the next installment." SLJ

Divakaruni, Chitra Banerjee

The **conch** bearer. Roaring Brook Press 2003 265p (Brotherhood of the conch) $16.95; lib bdg $23.90

Grades: 5 6 7 8 **Fic**

1. India -- Fiction 2. Magic -- Fiction

ISBN 978-0-7613-1935-1; 0-7613-1935-2; 978-0-7613-2793-6 lib bdg; 0-7613-2793-2 lib bdg

LC 2003-8578

In India, a healer invites twelve-year-old Anand to join him on a quest to return a magical conch to its safe and rightful home, high in the Himalayan mountains

"Divakaruni keeps her tale fresh and riveting." Publ Wkly

Other titles in this series are:

The mirror of fire and dreaming (2005)

Shadowland (2009)

Donovan, Gail

In loving memory of Gorfman T. Frog; [illustrated by Janet Pedersen] Dutton Children's Books 2009 180p il $15.99

Grades: 3 4 5 **Fic**

1. School stories 2. Frogs -- Fiction 3. Family life -- Fiction

ISBN 978-0-525-42085-9; 0-525-42085-1

LC 2008-13897

When irrepressible fifth-grader Josh finds a five-legged frog in his backyard pond, it leads to him learning a lot about amphibians—and himself.

"Pedersen's full-page illustrations ramp up the comedy and action, and Donovan ably shows how the school world of kids is separate and little understood by adults." Booklist

Doodler, Todd H.

Super Fly! the world's smallest superhero. by Todd H. Doodler. Bloomsbury 2015 128 p. (hardcover) $14.99

Grades: 2 3 4 **Fic**

1. Flies -- Fiction 2. Insects -- Fiction 3. Bullying -- Fiction 4. Superheroes -- Fiction

ISBN 1619633795; 9781619633780; 9781619633797

LC 2014029077

This story, by Todd H. Doodler, "is the story of Eugene Flystein, a small and nerdy, mild-mannered housefly, who also happens to be the world's smallest superhero and humanity's greatest crime fighter. . . . Can this four-eyed little bugger, along with his trusty sidekick Fantastic Flea, take on Crazy Cockroach and his army of insect baddies? It's housefly vs. cockroach in this epic battle of good vs. evil." (Publisher's note)

Dorris, Michael

Morning Girl. Hyperion Bks. for Children 1992 74p hardcover o.p. pa $4.99

Grades: 4 5 6 7 **Fic**

1. Taino Indians -- Fiction 2. America -- Exploration -- Fiction

ISBN 0-7868-1358-X pa

LC 92-52989

Twelve year old Morning Girl, a Taino Indian who loves the day, and her younger brother Star Boy, who loves the night, take turns describing their life on a Bahamian island in 1492; in Morning Girl's last narrative, she witnesses the arrival of the first Europeans to her world

"The author uses a lyrical, yet easy-to-follow, style to place these compelling characters in historical context. . . . Dorris does a superb job of showing that family dynamics are complicated, regardless of time and place. . . . A touching glimpse into the humanity that connects us all." Horn Book

Sees Behind Trees. Hyperion Bks. for Children 1996 104p hardcover o.p. pa $4.99

Grades: 4 5 6 7   **Fic**
1. Native Americans -- Fiction 2. Vision disorders -- Fiction
ISBN 0-7868-1357-1 pa

LC 96-15859

"For the partially sighted Walnut, it is impossible to prove his right to a grown-up name by hitting a target with his bow and arrow. With his highly developed senses, however, he demonstrates that he can do something even better: he can see 'what cannot be seen' which earns him the name Sees Behind Trees. . . . Set in sixteenth-century America, this richly imagined and gorgeously written rite-of-passage story has the gravity of legend. Moreover, it has buoyant humor and the immediacy of a compelling story that is peopled with multidimensional characters." Booklist

Dowd, Siobhan
★ The **London** Eye mystery. David Fickling Books 2008 322p $15.99; lib bdg $18.99; pa $7.50
Grades: 5 6 7 8   **Fic**
1. Mystery fiction 2. Cousins -- Fiction 3. Siblings -- Fiction 4. London (England) -- Fiction 5. Missing children -- Fiction 6. Asperger's syndrome -- Fiction
ISBN 978-0-375-84976-3; 0-375-84976-9; 978-0-375-94976-0 lib bdg; 0-375-84976-3 lib bdg; 978-0-385-75184-1 pa; 0-385-75184-2 pa

LC 2007-15119

First published 2007 in the United Kingdom
When Ted and Kat's cousin Salim disappears from the London Eye ferris wheel, the two siblings must work together—Ted with his brain that is "wired differently" and impatient Kat—to try to solve the mystery of what happened to Salim.
"Everything rings true here, the family relationships, the quirky connections of Ted's mental circuitry, and . . . the mystery. . . . A page turner with heft." Booklist

Dowell, Frances O' Roark
★ **Chicken** boy. Atheneum Books for Young Readers 2005 201p $15.95; pa $5.99
Grades: 4 5 6 7   **Fic**
1. Chickens -- Fiction 2. Friendship -- Fiction 3. Family life -- Fiction
ISBN 0-689-85816-7; 1-4169-3482-0 pa

LC 2004-10928

Since the death of his mother, Tobin's family life and school life have been in disarray, but after he starts raising chickens with his seventh-grade classmate, Henry, everything starts to fall into place. "Intermediate, middle school." (Horn Book)
"There is no glib resolution here. But the strong narration and the child's struggle with forgiveness make for poignant, aching drama." Booklist

★ **Dovey** Coe. Atheneum Bks. for Young Readers 2000 181p $16; pa $5.99
Grades: 5 6 7 8   **Fic**
1. Mountain life -- Fiction 2. North Carolina -- Fiction
ISBN 0-689-83174-9; 0-689-84667-3 pa

LC 99-46870

When accused of murder in her North Carolina mountain town in 1928, Dovey Coe, a stronged-willed twelve-year-old girl, comes to a new understanding of others, including her deaf brother

"Dowell has created a memorable character in Dovey, quick-witted and honest to a fault. . . . This is a delightful book, thoughtful and full of substance." Booklist

★ **Falling** in. Atheneum Books for Young Readers 2010 245p il $16.99
Grades: 4 5 6 7   **Fic**
1. Fantasy fiction
ISBN 978-1-4169-5032-5; 1-4169-5032-X

LC 2009-10412

Middle-schooler Isabelle Bean follows a mouse's squeak into a closet and falls into a parallel universe where the children believe she is the witch they have feared for years, finally come to devour them.
"This perfectly paced story has enough realistic elements to appeal even to nonfantasy readers." Booklist

The **kind** of friends we used to be. Atheneum Books for Young Readers 2009 234p $16.99
Grades: 5 6 7 8   **Fic**
1. School stories 2. Friendship -- Fiction
ISBN 978-1-4169-5031-8; 1-4169-5031-1

LC 2008-22245

Sequel to: The secret language of girls (2004)
Twelve-year-olds Kate and Marylin, friends since preschool, draw further apart as Marylin becomes involved in student government and cheerleading, while Kate wants to play guitar and write songs, and both develop unlikely friendships with other girls and boys.
"Dowell gets middle-school dynamics exactly right, and while her empathetic portraits of Kate and Marylin are genuine and heartfelt, even secondary characters are memorable. A realistic and humorous look at the trials and tribulations of growing up and growing independent." SLJ

Phineas L. Macguire erupts! the first experiment. Atheneum Books for Young Readers 2006 167p il (From the highly scientific notebooks of Phineas L. MacGuire) $15.95; pa $4.99
Grades: 2 3 4   **Fic**
1. School stories 2. Science -- Experiments -- Fiction
ISBN 978-1-4169-0195-2; 1-4169-0195-7; 978-1-4169-4734-9 pa; 1-4169-4734-5 pa

LC 2005-12605

Fourth-grade science whiz Phineas MacGuire is forced to team up with the new boy in class on a science fair project, but the boy's quirky personality causes Phineas to wonder if they have any chance of winning.
"The type is large and well spaced, and black-and-white art playfully captures the characters. . . . Budding scientists will find instructions for their own experiments at the end of the book." Booklist
Other titles in this series are:
Phineas L. MacGuire . . . gets slimed! (2007)
Phineas L. MacGuire . . . blasts off! (2008)

★ The **second** life of Abigail Walker; Frances O'Roark Dowell. Atheneum Books for Young Readers 2012 228 p. (hardcover) $16.99
Grades: 4 5 6 7   **Fic**
1. Self-confidence -- Fiction 2. Friendship -- Juvenile fiction 3. Middle schools -- Juvenile fiction 4. Friendship -- Fiction 5. Overweight persons -- Fiction

6. Human-animal relationships -- Fiction
ISBN 1442405937; 9781442405936
LC 2012010646

This novel, by Frances O'Roark Dowell, follows a youth struggling with popularity. "Seventeen pounds. That's the difference between . . . chubby and slim, between teased and taunting. Abby is fine with her body, . . . so she speaks out against Kristen and her groupies--and becomes officially unpopular. Embracing her new status, Abby heads to an abandoned lot across the street and crosses an unfamiliar stream that leads her to a boy who's as different as they come." (Publisher's note)

The **secret** language of girls. Atheneum Books for Young Readers 2004 247p $15.95; pa $5.99
Grades: 5 6 7 8 **Fic**
1. School stories 2. Friendship -- Fiction
ISBN 0-689-84421-2; 978-1-4169-0717-6 pa
LC 2003-12026

Marylin and Kate have been friends since nursery school, but when Marylin becomes a middle school cheerleader and Kate begins to develop other interests, their relationship is put to the test.

"Excellent characterization, an accurate portrayal of the painful and often cruel machinations of preteens, and evocative dialogue will make this tale resonate with most readers." SLJ

Followed by: The kind of friends we used to be (2009)

★ **Shooting** the moon. Atheneum Books for Young Readers 2008 163p $16.99; pa $5.99
Grades: 4 5 6 7 **Fic**
1. Soldiers -- Fiction 2. Family life -- Fiction 3. Vietnam War, 1961-1975 -- Fiction
ISBN 978-1-4169-2690-0; 1-4169-2690-9; 978-1-4169-7986-9 pa; 1-4169-7986-7 pa
LC 2006-100347

Boston Globe-Horn Book Award honor book: Fiction and Poetry (2008)

When her brother is sent to fight in Vietnam, twelve-year-old Jamie begins to reconsider the army world that she has grown up in.

"The clear, well-paced first-person prose is perfectly matched to this novel's spare setting and restrained plot. . . . This [is a] thoughtful and satisfying story. . . . Readers will find beauty in its resolution, and will leave this eloquent heroine reluctantly." SLJ

The **sound** of your voice, only really far away; by Frances O'Roark Dowell. Atheneum Books for Young Readers 2013 192 p. (hardcover) $16.99
Grades: 5 6 7 8 **Fic**
1. Friendship -- Fiction 2. High school students -- Fiction 3. Interpersonal relations -- Fiction 4. Schools -- Fiction 5. Popularity -- Fiction 6. Best friends -- Fiction 7. Middle schools -- Fiction
ISBN 1442432896; 9781442432895; 9781442432918
LC 2012030308

Sequel to: The kind of friends we used to be
In this novel by Frances O'Roark Dowell "Marylin and Kate find that boys can be just as complicated as friendship. As a middle school cheerleader . . . Marylin [learns] there are also rules about whom she's allowed to like—and Benjamin,

the student body president, is . . . unnacceptable. She'll pretend that she's using him to get new cheerleading uniforms. When Matthew tells Kate that the school's Audio Lab needs funding . . ., she decides to . . . help him get it. There isn't enough money to go around, and it soon becomes clear that only one of the two girls can get her way." (Publisher's note)

Downer, Ann
The **dragon** of Never-Was. Atheneum Books for Young Readers 2006 305p il hardcover o.p. pa $5.99
Grades: 4 5 6 7 **Fic**
1. Magic -- Fiction 2. Dragons -- Fiction 3. Scotland -- Fiction
ISBN 978-0-689-85571-9; 0-689-85571-0; 978-1-4169-5453-8 pa; 1-4169-5453-8 pa
LC 2005017727

Sequel to Hatching magic (2003)
With the help of a bottle of blue fire and a magical brooch, Theodora searches for a dragon on an island off the coast of Scotland before it causes any harm.

"Smart, observant, and self-aware, Theodora makes a sympathetic character, convincing even in the most supernatural circumstances." Booklist

★ **Hatching** magic. Atheneum Bks. for Young Readers 2003 242p $16.95; pa $5.99
Grades: 4 5 6 7 **Fic**
1. Magic -- Fiction 2. Dragons -- Fiction
ISBN 0-689-83400-4; 0-689-87057-4 pa
LC 00-56570

When a thirteenth-century wizard confronts twenty-first century Boston while seeking his pet dragon, he is followed by a rival wizard and a very unhappy demon, but eleven-year-old Theodora Oglethorpe may hold the secret to setting everything right

"With likable characters, and laced with plenty of humor and adventure, Downer's fantasy will have solid appeal for young genre fans." Booklist

Another title about Theodora is:
The dragon of never-was (2006)

Downey, Jen Swann
The **ninja** librarians; the accidental keyhand. Jen Swann Downey. Sourcebooks Jabberwocky 2014 384 p. (hc: alk. paper) $16.99
Grades: 4 5 6 7 **Fic**
1. Adventure fiction 2. Libraries -- Fiction 3. Librarians -- Fiction 4. Censorship -- Fiction 5. Space and time -- Fiction 6. Secret societies -- Fiction
ISBN 1402287704; 9781402287701
LC 2013049956

Kirkus (March 15, 2014)
In this adventure story by Jen Swann Downey, "when Dorrie and her brother Marcus chase Moe--an unusually foul-tempered mongoose--into the janitor's closet of their local library, they make an astonishing discovery: the headquarters of a secret society of ninja librarians. Their mission: protect those whose words get them into trouble, anywhere in the world and at any time in history." (Publisher's note)

"Delightfully funny from the first page, where Dorrie laments having never been bitten by anything more bloodthirsty than her little sister, this middle-grade time-travel adventure is surprisingly full of fun and action (and a madcap mongoose). Downey's hilarious debut is perfect for any library-loving reader as well as those who never considered librarians to be cool.". - Booklist

Accidental keyhand

Drago, Ty

The **Undertakers**: rise of the Corpses. Sourcebooks Jabberwocky 2011 465p pa $10.99

Grades: 4 5 6 7   Fic

1. Horror fiction 2. Zombies -- Fiction

ISBN 978-1-4022-4785-9; 1-4022-4785-0

"Whatever you do, do not call them zombies! These are Corpses 'reanimated bodies that have been possessed,' and they are everywhere, although they are only visible to a select few, including 12-year-old Will Ritter. After realizing suddenly that he is able to see, Will is taken in by the Undertakers, a rogue group that rescues other, similarly targeted teens and fights to defeat the Corpses' evil plans to conquer Phildelphia and, ultimately, the world. . . . Calling into action a cast of distinctive characters with authentic voices and behaviors, . . . Will's breathless adventures . . . are thoughtful and exciting, and the descriptions of decaying flesh will likely both disgust and delight readers." Booklist

Drake, Salamanda

★ **Dragonsdale**; illustrations by Gilly Marklew. Chicken House/Scholastic 2007 269p il (Dragonsdale) $16.99

Grades: 3 4 5   Fic

1. Fantasy fiction 2. Dragons -- Fiction

ISBN 978-0-439-87173-0; 0-439-87173-5

LC 2006-32890

Cara yearns to ride her beloved Skydancer, a rare Goldenbrow dragon, but her father refuses to permit her to fly and she must be content with mucking out stalls and helping raise young dragons at the famed stud and training farm known as Dragonsdale.

"This will delight precisely the audience it's meant to— young girls who find tame dragons captivating." Booklist

Followed by: Riding the storm (2008)

Draper, Sharon M. (Sharon Mills), 1948-

Little Sister is not my name. Scholastic Press 2009 102p (Sassy) $14.99

Grades: 3 4 5   Fic

1. Size -- Fiction 2. Family life -- Fiction 3. African Americans -- Fiction

ISBN 978-0-545-07151-2; 0-545-07151-8

LC 2008-15634

Fashion-savy Sassy does not like being the smallest student in her fourth-grade class, until a family emergency calls for a pint-sized hero.

"Draper hits her middle-grade target in this cheerful yet reflective novel about feeling appreciated and finding one's place. . . . Filled with energy and opinion, Sassy more than lives up to her name." Publ Wkly

Other titles in this series are:

The birthday storm (2009)

The silver secret (2010)

The dazzle disaster dinner party (2010)

★ **Out** of my mind. Atheneum 2010 295p $16.99

Grades: 5 6 7 8   Fic

1. Cerebral palsy -- Fiction 2. Young adult literature -- Works 3. Children's literature -- Works -- Grades two

through six

ISBN 978-1-4169-7170-2; 1-4169-7170-X

LC 2009-18404

Josette Frank Award for Fiction, 2011

"Fifth-grader Melody has cerebral palsy, a condition that affects her body but not her mind. Although she is unable to walk, talk, or feed or care for herself, she can read, think, and feel. A brilliant person is trapped inside her body, determined to make her mark in the world despite her physical limitations. . . . Told in Melody's voice, this highly readable, compelling novel quickly establishes her determination and intelligence and the almost insurmountable challenges she faces. . . . Uplifting and upsetting." Booklist

★ **Stella** by starlight; Sharon Draper. Atheneum Books for Young Readers 2015 336 p. (hardcover) $16.99

Grades: 4 5 6 7 8   Fic

1. Ku Klux Klan 2. Segregation -- Fiction 3. Southern States -- Fiction 4. Prejudices -- Fiction 5. Civil rights -- Fiction 6. African Americans -- Fiction 7. Ku Klux Klan (1915-) -- Fiction 8. North Carolina -- History -- 20th century -- Fiction

ISBN 1442494972; 9781442494978; 9781442494985

LC 2014038728

In this novel by Sharon M. Draper "when the Ku Klux Klan's unwelcome reappearance rattles Stella's segregated southern town, bravery battles prejudice in this Depression-era tour de force. As Stella's community--her world--is upended, she decides to fight fire with fire. And she learns that ashes don't necessarily signify an end." (Publisher's note)

"Coretta Scott King Award winner Draper draws inspiration from her grandmother's journal to tell the absorbing story of a young girl growing up in Depression-era, segregated North Carolina...This is an engrossing historical fiction novel with an amiable and humble heroine who does not recognize her own bravery or the power of her words. She provides inspiration not only to her fellow characters but also to readers who will relate to her and her situation. Storytelling at its finest." SLJ

Du Bois, William Pene

The **twenty**-one balloons; written and illustrated by William Pène Du Bois. Viking 1947 179p il $16.99; pa $5.99

Grades: 5 6 7 8   Fic

1. Balloons -- Fiction

ISBN 0-670-73441-1; 0-14-032097-0 pa

Awarded the Newbery Medal, 1948

"Professor Sherman set off on a flight across the Pacific in a giant balloon, but three weeks later the headlines read 'Professor Sherman in wrong ocean with too many balloons.' This book is concerned with the professor's explanation of this phenomenon. His account of his one stopover on the island of Krakatoa which blew up with barely a minute to spare to allow time for his escape, is the highlight of this hilarious narrative." Ont Libr Rev

Dudley, David L.

The **bicycle** man. Clarion Books 2005 249p $16

Grades: 4 5 6   Fic

1. Georgia -- Fiction 2. Country life -- Fiction 3. African Americans -- Fiction

ISBN 0-618-54233-7

LC 2005-06409

In poor, rural Georgia in 1927, twelve-year-old Carrisa and her suspicious mama take in an elderly drifter with a shiny bicycle, never expecting how profoundly his wise and patient ways will affect them.

Readers "will find complex characters and rich themes. . . . There is much here to digest and a wealth of material for book discussions." SLJ

Duey, Kathleen

Lara and the gray mare; by Kathleen Duey. Dutton Children's Books 2005 140p (Hoofbeats) hardcover o.p. pa $4.99

Grades: 4 5 6   Fic

1. Horses -- Fiction 2. Ireland -- Fiction

ISBN 0-525-47332-7; 0-14-240230-3 pa

LC 2004-53521

While her father is away fighting the Normans and other Irish clans, nine-year-old Lara works hard to help harvest food and also cares for the pregnant gray mare that she loves

"Writing with a keen appreciation for everyday goings-on in thirteenth-century Ireland and an unusual ability to bring the past to life, Duey creates a convincing setting, a thoroughly likable heroine, and a strong narrative." Booklist

Other titles in the Hoofbeats series are:

Lara and the Moon-colored filly (book two) (2005)

Lara at Athnery Castle (book three) (2005)

Lara at the silent place (book four) (2005)

Silence and Lily (2007)

Silence and stone; illustrated by Sandara Tang. Aladdin 2010 109p il (The faeries' promise) $15.99; pa $4.99

Grades: 3 4 5   Fic

1. Magic -- Fiction 2. Fairies -- Fiction

ISBN 978-1-4169-8456-6; 1-4169-8456-9; 978-1-4169-8457-3 pa; 1-4169-8457-7 pa

LC 2009-42542

Kidnapped and confined to a room in a castle before she can develop her flying and magical skills, Alida the faerie patiently plans her escape—with the help of a human boy.

"With its magical tone, sturdy characters, and predictable yet satisfying plot, this simple fantasy will engage young readers and leave them eager to read the next book." SLJ

Other titles in this series are:

Following magic (2010)

The full moon (2011)

Wishes and wings (2011)

Dunrea, Olivier

Hanne's quest; [by] Olivier Dunrea. Philomel Books 2005 95p il $16.99

Grades: 3 4 5   Fic

1. Fairy tales 2. Chickens -- Fiction 3. Scotland -- Fiction

ISBN 0-399-24216-3

LC 2004-9091

On an island off the coast of Scotland, a young hen must prove herself pure, wise, and brave in a quest to help her beloved owner, Mem Pocket, from losing her family's farm.

"Beautifully composed and often darkly atmospheric, the handsome full-page paintings rival . . . those in the best picture books. This handsome, well-written book will find a rapt audience among children who prefer sturdy, homespun fairy tales." Booklist

DuPrau, Jeanne

The **city** of Ember. Random House 2003 270p (Books of Ember) $15.95; lib bdg $17.99; pa $6.99

Grades: 5 6 7 8   Fic

1. Science fiction

ISBN 0-375-82273-9; 0-375-92274-1 lib bdg; 0-385-73628-2 pa

LC 2002-10239

"The writing and storytelling are agreeably spare and remarkably suspenseful." Horn Book

Other titles in this series are:

The people of Sparks (2004)

The prophet of Yonwood (2006)

The diamond of Darkhold (2008)

Durand, Hallie

Dessert first; illustrations by Christine Davenier. Atheneum Books for Young Readers 2009 153p il $14.99

Grades: 3 4 5   Fic

1. School stories 2. Family life -- Fiction 3. Restaurants -- Fiction

ISBN 978-1-4169-6385-1; 1-4169-6385-5

LC 2008-11390

Third-grader Dessert's love of treats leads to a change in her large family's dinner routine, then an awful mistake, and later a true sacrifice after her teacher, Mrs. Howdy Doody, urges students to march to the beat of their own drums

"Experiences are delightfully imagined through Dessert's realistic, child-centered perspective. Short chapters interspersed with Davenier's pen-and-ink washes add immediacy to the text." Kirkus

Other titles about Dessert are:

Just desserts (2010)

No room for Dessert (2011)

Durango, Julia

The **walls** of Cartagena; by Julia Durango; illustrated by Tom Pohrt. Simon & Schuster Books for Young Readers 2008 152p il $15.99

Grades: 5 6 7 8   Fic

1. Leprosy -- Fiction 2. Slavery -- Fiction 3. Colombia -- Fiction 4. Catholic Church -- Fiction

ISBN 978-1-4169-4102-6; 1-4169-4102-9

LC 2007041861

Thirteen-year-old Calepino, an African slave in the seventeenth-century Caribbean city of Cartagena, works as a translator for a Jesuit priest who tends to newly-arrived slaves and, after working for a Jewish doctor in a leper colony and helping an Angolan boy and his mother escape, he realizes his true calling

"Illustrated with occasional small ink sketches, the ultimate rescue adventure is gripping, but more compelling is the authentic history of people desperate and brave." Booklist

Durham, Paul

Fork-tongue charmers; Paul Durham; illustrations by Petur Antonsson. Harper, an imprint of HarperCollinsPublishers 2015 416 p. illustrations, maps (The Luck Uglies) (hardcover) $16.99

Grades: 4 5 6 7 8   Fic

1. Magic -- Fiction 2. Criminals -- Fiction 3. Fantasy 4. Monsters -- Fiction 5. Secret societies -- Fiction 6.

Adventure and adventurers -- Fiction

ISBN 0062271539; 9780062271532

LC 2014038648

Sequel to: The Luck Uglies (2014)

In this novel by Paul Durham, illustrated by Petur Antonsson, "Rye O'Chanter was shocked to discover that her father was the leader . . . of outlaws known as the Luck Uglies. Now she too has been declared a criminal . . . and she must flee to the strange and remote Isle of Pest while her father faces off against . . . the Fork-Tongue Charmers, on the mainland. When the battle moves to the shores of Pest . . . Rye must . . . lead the charge in defending the island." (Publisher's note)

"The second volume in Durham's spirited series starts with a mysterious summons for Rye O'Chanter from her father, Harmless, now known to her as the High Chieftain of the Luck Uglies. . . . There is not a single dull moment in this story, which packs in as many clever twists and fully fleshed characters as the first book. And the writing remains a total delight: witty, richly layered, and capable of creating a world as real as this one. A bittersweet ending assures the reader that Rye's adventures are not over yet." Booklist

The **luck** uglies; Paul Durham; illustrations by Petur Antonsson. Harper, an imprint of HarperCollinsPublishers 2014 400 p. (hardback) $16.99

Grades: 4 5 6 7 8   **Fic**

1. Fantasy fiction 2. Secret societies -- Fiction 3. Monsters -- Fiction 4. Adventure and adventurers -- Fiction

ISBN 0062271504; 9780062271501

LC 2013047720

In this book, by Paul Durham, "a terrifying encounter has eleven-year-old Rye O'Chanter convinced that the monstrous, supposedly extinct Bog Noblins have returned. Now Rye's only hope is an exiled secret society so notorious its name can't be spoken aloud: the Luck Uglies. As Rye dives into Village Drowning's maze of secrets, rules, and lies, she'll discover the truth behind the village's legends of outlaws and beasts . . . and that it may take a villain to save them from the monsters." (Publisher's note)

"Rye O'Chanter and her friends Quinn and Folly live in Drowning, which is ruled by the tyrannical Earl Longchance, who bans women from reading. When the earl does nothing to protect the villagers from marauding monsters, Drowning's only hope is the Luck Uglies, a notorious outlaw gang--that may or may not exist. Durham's fast-paced narrative and clever characters enhance this humorous and engaging tale." Horn Book

Dutton, Sandra

Mary Mae and the gospel truth. Houghton Mifflin Books for Children 2010 134p $15

Grades: 4 5 6   **Fic**

1. School stories 2. Ohio -- Fiction 3. Family -- Fiction 4. Creationism -- Fiction 5. Christian life -- Fiction 6. Mother-daughter relationship -- Fiction

ISBN 978-0-547-24966-7; 0-547-24966-7

LC 2009-49706

Ten-year-old Mary Mae, living with her parents in fossil-rich southern Ohio, tries to reconcile, despite her mother's strong disapproval, her family's Creationist beliefs with the prehistoric fossils she studies in school.

"Very few books for this age group tackle religious subjects as this one does, in a way that shows respect for all sides. Dutton allows Mary Mae to retain both her questions and her faith; instead of a definitive answer, she shows evolutionists and creationists working to find a small, shared piece of middle ground. Mary Mae is a memorable character—spunky but not defiant—whose search for truth drives the narrative." Kirkus

Dyer, Heather

Ibby's magic weekend; illustrated by Peter Bailey. Chicken House 2008 140p il $16.99

Grades: 2 3 4 5   **Fic**

1. Magic -- Fiction 2. Cousins -- Fiction 3. Magicians -- Fiction

ISBN 0-545-03209-1; 978-0-545-03209-4

While visiting her two troublemaking cousins, Ibby learns about a magic box the boys found in the attic in their country home. She soon stumbles upon the strange tale of Uncle Godfrey, a professional magician who mysteriously vanished many years ago.

"This action-filled story is just right for beginning chapter book readers, who will be fascinated with the magic as well as the personalities. Bailey's black-and-white line drawings help make the book accessible to reluctant readers." SLJ

Eager, Edward

★ **Half** magic; illustrated by N.M. Bodecker; introduction by Jack Gantos. 50th anniversary ed.; Harcourt 2004 217p il $18.95

Grades: 4 5 6   **Fic**

1. Fantasy fiction

ISBN 0-15-205302-6

A reissue with a new introduction of the title first published 1954

Faced with a dull summer in the city, Jane, Mark, Katharine, and Martha suddenly find themselves involved in a series of extraordinary adventures after Jane discovers an ordinary-looking coin that seems to grant wishes

"Entertaining and suspenseful fare for readers of make-believe." Booklist

Other titles in this series are:

Knight's castle (1956)

Magic by the lake (1957)

The time garden (1958)

Eames, Brian

The **dagger** Quick. Simon & Schuster Books for Young Readers 2011 320p $15.99

Grades: 4 5 6 7   **Fic**

1. Sea stories 2. Adventure fiction 3. Pirates -- Fiction 4. People with disabilities -- Fiction

ISBN 978-1-4424-2311-4; 1-4424-2311-0

LC 2011-04405

Twelve-year-old Christopher "Kitto" Wheale, a club-footed boy seemingly doomed to follow in the boring footsteps of his father as a cooper in seventeenth-century England, finds himself on a dangerous seafaring adventure with his newly discovered uncle, the infamous pirate William Quick.

"Thoroughly researched, fast-paced, and tense, this coming-of-age adventure doesn't sugarcoat the dangers of the era, even as it embraces the mythical glamour of a pirate's life." Publ Wkly

Easton, Kelly

The **outlandish** adventures of Liberty Aimes; illustrated by Greg Swearingen. Wendy Lamb Books 2009 214p il $15.99; lib bdg $18.99

Grades: 3 4 5 6   **Fic**

1. Adventure fiction 2. Inventors -- Fiction 3. Family life -- Fiction 4. Runaway children -- Fiction

ISBN 978-0-375-83771-5; 0-375-83771-X; 978-0-375-93771-2 lib bdg; 0-375-93771-4 lib bdg

LC 2008-22119

Ten-year-old Libby Aimes escapes her prison-like home by using a strange concoction of her father's, then tries to make her way to the boarding school of her dreams, aided by various people and animals.

"The understated humor and friendly, imperturbable tone of the narration bring to mind the fantasies of Eva Ibbotson. The charming illustrations sprinkled throughout add immense appeal to this warm, delightfully odd fantasy." SLJ

Eckert, Allan W.

Incident at Hawk's Hill; with illustrations by John Schoenherr. Little, Brown 1998 173p il hardcover o.p. pa $5.95

Grades: 6 7 8 9   **Fic**

1. Badgers -- Fiction 2. Saskatchewan -- Fiction 3. Wilderness survival -- Fiction

ISBN 0-316-21905-3; 0-316-20948-1 pa

First published 1971

A Newbery Medal honor book, 1972

This account of an actual incident in Saskatchewan at the turn of the century tells of six-year-old Ben Macdonald, more attuned to animals than to people, who gets lost on the prairie and is nurtured by a female badger for two months before being found. Although a strange bond continues between the boy and the badger, the parents' understanding of their son and his communication with them improve as a result of the bizarre experience

"A very deeply moving, well written book." Jr Bookshelf

Followed by Return to Hawk's Hill (1998)

Edgar, Elsbeth

The **Visconti** house. Candlewick Press 2011 287p $16.99

Grades: 4 5 6 7   **Fic**

1. Houses -- Fiction 2. Australia -- Fiction 3. Family life -- Fiction

ISBN 0-7636-5019-6; 978-0-7636-5019-3

LC 2010-39172

Laura Horton has always been an outsider, more interested in writing, drawing, or spending time with her free-spirited family than in her fellow teens, but she is drawn to Leon, a new student, as together they explore the mysteries of her eccentric old house.

"Convincing dialogue and well-drawn characters, both major and minor, bring energy to the story. . . . A fine, sensitive first novel." Booklist

Edge, Christopher

Twelve minutes to midnight; Christopher Edge; illustrations by Eric Orchard. Albert Whitman & Company 2014 256 p. $16.99

Grades: 4 5 6 7   **Fic**

1. Orphans -- Fiction 2. Supernatural -- Fiction 3. Psychiatric hospitals -- Fiction 4. Great Britain -- History -- Victoria, 1837-1901 -- Fiction 5. Authorship -- Fiction 6. Mystery and detective stories 7. Publishers and publishing -- Fiction 8. London (England) -- History -- 19th century -- Fiction

ISBN 080758133X; 9780807581339

LC 2013029481

In this book, by Christopher Edge, "Penelope Tredwell is the . . . orphan heiress of Victorian Britain's bestselling magazine, the Penny Dreadful. Her . . . tales–concealed under the pen name Montgomery Finch–are gripping the public. One day she receives a letter from the governor of the Bedlam madhouse requesting Finch's help to investigate the asylum's strange goings-on. Every night at precisely twelve minutes to midnight, the inmates all begin feverishly writing-incoherent ramblings." (Publisher's note)

"In Twelve Minutes to Midnight, readers meet Penelope Tredwell, the 13-year-old newspaper heiress and ghostwriter who pens tales of horror and mystery as Montgomery Flinch. She must keep her true identity secret, going so far as to hire an actor to play Montgomery at public appearances. In Shadows of the Silver Screen, a filmmaker wants to transform Penelope's stories into a motion picture. The protagonist soon finds that her terrifying tales are bleeding into reality. An atmospheric and spine-tingling series for middle graders who love old-fashioned mysteries." SLJ

Egan, Kate

The **incredible** twisting arm; Kate Egan and Mike Lane, illustrated by Eric Wight. Feiwel & Friends 2014 150 p. $14.99

Grades: 3 4 5   **Fic**

1. Magic -- Fiction 2. Magicians -- Fiction 3. Responsibility -- Fiction

ISBN 1250029155; 9781250029157

In this children's book by Kate Egan and Mike Lane, illustrated by Eric Wight, "Life is a little easier for Mike now that he's found The White Rabbit magic shop. But after missing a special show from a visiting magician, Mike realizes he needs a way to get to the shop for himself. Unfortunately, he's exhausted after only a week of being a model student, and Nora, his magician assistant and expert on good behavior, is distracted by a new friendship." (Publisher's note)

"After finding the magic shop in The Vanishing Coin (Feiwel & Friends, 2014), Mike decides he wants to ride his bike downtown to the shop by himself. But convincing his parents that he is mature enough to ride alone may take quite a bit of magic. Includes ample black-and-white illustrations and instructions on how to do several fun magic tricks." SLJ

Other titles in the series include:

Great Escape (2014)

Vanishing Coin (2014)

Ehrlich, Amy

★ The **Snow** Queen; [by] Hans Christian Andersen; retold by Amy Ehrlich; [illustrated by] Susan Jeffers. Dutton Children's Books 2006 40p il $16.99

Grades: 2 3 4   **Fic**

1. Authors 2. Novelists 3. Dramatists 4. Fairy tales 5. Children's authors 6. Short story writers

ISBN 0-525-47694-6

LC 2006004415

A revised reissue of the edition published 1982 by Dial Books

The strength of a little girl's love enables her to overcome many obstacles and free a boy from the Snow Queen's spell

Elfman, Eric

Tesla's attic; by Neal Shusterman and Eric Elfman. Disney-Hyperion Books 2014 256 p. (Accelerati trilogy) $16.99

Grades: 5 6 7 8   **Fic**

1. Houses -- Fiction 2. Tesla, Nikola, 1856-1943 3. Science fiction 4. Inventions -- Fiction 5. Colorado Springs (Colo.) -- Fiction

ISBN 1423148037; 9781423148036

LC 2012039773

This children's novel, by Eric Elfman and Neal Shusterman, is the first book of "The Accelerati Trilogy." "After getting rid of . . . odd antiques in a garage sale, Nick befriends some local kids . . . and they discover that all of the objects have extraordinary properties. What's more, Nick figures out that the attic is a strange magnetic vortex, which attracts all sorts of trouble. It's as if the attic itself has an intelligence . . . and a purpose." (Publisher's note)

"Lively, intelligent prose elevates this story of teenagers versus mad scientists, the third-person point of view offering a stage to various players in their play of galactic consequence." Kirkus

Elish, Dan

The attack of the frozen woodchucks; by Dan Elish; illustrations by Greg Call. Laura Geringer Books 2008 247p il $16.99; lib bdg $17.89; pa $6.99

Grades: 4 5 6   **Fic**

1. Science fiction 2. Marmots -- Fiction 3. New York (N.Y.) -- Fiction 4. Extraterrestrial beings -- Fiction

ISBN 978-0-06-113870-6; 0-06-113870-3; 978-0-06-113871-3 lib bdg; 0-06-113871-1 lib bdg; 978-0-06-113872-0 pa; 0-06-113872-X pa

LC 2006-102962

When extraterrestrial woodchucks attack, ten-year-old Jimmy, his two-and-a-half-year-old sister, friend William, and an eccentric classmate who has built a flying saucer in her Manhattan brownstone, join forces to save the universe.

"This is ridiculous, over-the-top fun all the way. . . . Science fiction fans who welcome absurdity as much as planet-hopping in their reads will find this an ideal balance of both." Bull Cent Child Books

The family Hitchcock; story by Jennifer Flackett and Mark Levin; written by Dan Elish. HarperChildren's 2011 288p $16.99

Grades: 4 5 6   **Fic**

1. Adventure fiction 2. Family life -- Fiction 3. Paris (France) -- Fiction

ISBN 978-0-06-189394-0; 0-06-189394-3

LC 2011016610

When they agree to a summertime house swap with an unknown family in Paris, the four members of the Hitchcock family inadvertently get mixed up in a ring of international espionage.

"The plot-driven story is preposterous fun with genuine touches of emotion about family dynamics." SLJ

The School for the Insanely Gifted. Harper 2011 289p $15.99

Grades: 3 4 5 6   **Fic**

1. School stories 2. Genius -- Fiction 3. Missing persons -- Fiction 4. Voyages and travels -- Fiction

ISBN 978-0-06-113873-7; 0-06-113873-8

LC 2010-21962

Eleven-year-old musical genius Daphna Whispers embarks on a global journey to find her missing mother, only to uncover a shocking secret about the Blatt School for the Insanely Gifted where she is a student.

"Elish has created a school story with genius students and a likable main character. . . . This lively adventure parades enough gadgets to capture readers' imaginations" SLJ

Elliott, Laura

Give me liberty; [by] L. M. Elliott. Katherine Tegen Books 2006 376p $16.99; lib bdg $17.89; pa $7.99

Grades: 5 6 7 8   **Fic**

1. Virginia -- Fiction 2. United States -- History -- 1775-1783, Revolution -- Fiction

ISBN 0-06-074421-9; 0-06-074422-7 lib bdg; 0-06-074423-5 pa

Follows the life of thirteen-year-old Nathaniel Dunn, from May 1774 to December 1775, as he serves his indentureship with a music teacher in Williamsburg, Virginia, and witnesses the growing rift between patriots and loyalists, culminating in the American Revolution.

"Elliott packs a great deal of historical detail into a novel already filled with action, well-drawn characters, and a sympathetic understanding of many points of view." Booklist

Ellis, Deborah

I am a taxi. Groundwood Books/House of Anansi Press 2006 205p (The cocalero novels) $16.95; pa $9.95

Grades: 5 6 7 8   **Fic**

1. Bolivia -- Fiction 2. Cocaine -- Fiction

ISBN 978-0-88899-735-7; 0-88899-735-3; 978-0-88899-736-4 pa; 0-88899-736-1 pa

"Diego, 12, lives in prison in the city of Cochabamba, Bolivia, stuck there with his parents, who have been falsely arrested for smuggling drugs. He attends school and works as a 'taxi,' running errands for the inmates in the great street market. Then his friend, Mando, persuades him to make big money, and the boys find themselves stomping coca leaves in cocaine pits in the jungle. . . . Readers will be caught up by the nonstop action in the prison, and also in the jungle survival adventure." Booklist

Followed by Sacred leaf (2007)

★ No ordinary day. Groundwood Books 2011 160p $16.95

Grades: 5 6 7   **Fic**

1. India -- Fiction 2. Leprosy -- Fiction 3. Orphans -- Fiction 4. Poverty -- Fiction 5. Homeless persons -- Fiction

ISBN 978-1-55498-134-2; 1-55498-134-4

"Valli, about 10, lives in the poverty-stricken town of Jharia, India, where she is a coal picker. When she makes a shocking discovery about her family, she runs away and, after a series of harrowing events, reaches the bustling city of Kolkata. . . . While begging for change one day, she is befriended by a kind doctor who recognizes Valli's symptoms of leprosy. . . . With the help of the doctor and other leprosy patients, Valli gets treatment and education, learns tolerance for people different from herself, and simultaneously realizes her own self-worth. Although many important lessons are presented in this even-paced, clearly written story, it is never heavyhanded or didactic. Valli is a well-developed, realistic, and engaging narrator. . . . An important, inspiring tale." SLJ

Sacred leaf. Groundwood Books/House of Anansi Press 2007 206p (The cocalero novels) $16.95; pa $9.95 Grades: 5 6 7 8   Fic

1. Bolivia -- Fiction 2. Cocaine -- Fiction

ISBN 978-0-88899-751-7; 978-0-88899-808-8 pa

Sequel to: I am a taxi (2006)

Twelve year old Diego escapes from slavery at an illegal cocaine operation and is taken in by the Ricardos, coca farmers.

"An easy read that touches on issues seldom addressed for young teens." SLJ

Ellis, Sarah

Outside in; by Sarah Ellis. Pgw 2014 206 p. $16.95 Grades: 5 6 7 8   Fic

1. Canada -- Fiction 2. Teenage girls -- Fiction 3. Mother-daughter relationship -- Fiction 4. Eccentrics and eccentricities -- Fiction 5. Friendship -- Fiction 6. Homeless girls -- Fiction

ISBN 1554983673; 9781554983674

In this book, by Sarah Ellis, "Lynn is a typical 13-year-old Canadian, navigating through life. . . . Things start to fall apart when her mom wrecks her relationship with the only man who has ever stuck around and Lynn's passport doesn't come in time for her to take the choir trip with the rest of her friends, who leave for Portland. . . . Then a mysterious girl named Blossom is thrust into her life and introduces her to a wonderful world within their city called the Underland." (Publisher's note)

"With the exception of her quirky, unmarried mother, Lynn is a typical 13-year-old Canadian, navigating through life filled with choir practice, projects, best friends, and school...Lynn's difficult relationship with her mother and her strong bonds with friends make this story very relatable. A thoughtful, exciting read that makes everything ordinary suddenly have the possibility to be extraordinary." (SLJ

The **several** lives of Orphan Jack; pictures by Bruno St-Aubin. Douglas & McIntyre 2003 84p il hardcover o.p. pa $7.95 Grades: 3 4 5 6   Fic

1. Adventure fiction 2. Orphans -- Fiction

ISBN 0-88899-529-6; 0-88899-618-7 pa

When, at the age of twelve, he is sent out from the Opportunities School for Orphans and Foundlings to be a bookkeeper's apprentice, Jack finds his heretofore predictable life full of unusual adventures.

"Ellis has created a small gem here, with messages about following your heart tucked into the sentences, phrases, thoughts, and ideas that she seamlessly weaves together." Booklist

Enderle, Dotti

Crosswire. Calkins Creek 2010 143p $17.95 Grades: 5 6 7 8   Fic

1. Texas -- Fiction 2. Brothers -- Fiction 3. Droughts -- Fiction 4. Ranch life -- Fiction 5. Father-son

relationship -- Fiction

ISBN 978-1-59078-751-9; 1-59078-751-X

LC 2010-07522

When an 1883 drought drives free-range cattlemen to shred Texas ranchers' barbed wire fences and steal water, thirteen-year-old Jesse works hard to help while dealing with his father and brother's falling-out and his own fear of guns.

"Enderle writes with restraint, her research neatly woven into the story, her characters carefully drawn. A small gem of a story." Kirkus

Includes bibliographical references

Engle, Margarita

Silver people; voices from the Panama Canal. Margarita Engle. Houghton Mifflin Harcourt 2014 272 p. (hardback) $17.99 Grades: 5 6 7 8   Fic

1. Panama Canal 2. Novels in verse 3. Rain forests -- Fiction 4. Migrant labor -- Fiction 5. Racism -- Fiction 6. Segregation -- Fiction 7. Panama Canal (Panama) -- History -- Fiction

ISBN 0544109414; 9780544109414

LC 2013037485

This children's book, by Margarita Engle, is an "exploration of the construction of the Panama Canal. . . . Mateo, a 14-year-old Cuban lured by promises of wealth, journeys to Panama only to discover the recruiters' lies and a life of harsh labor. However, through his relationships with Anita, an 'herb girl,' Henry, a black Jamaican worker, and Augusto, a Puerto Rican geologist, Mateo is able to find a place in his new land." (Kirkus Reviews)

"In melodic verses, Engle offers the voices of the dark-skinned workers (known as the 'silver people'), whose back-breaking labor helped build the Panama Canal, along with the perspective of a local girl. Interspersed are occasional echoes from flora and fauna as well as cameo appearances by historical figures. Together, they provide an illuminating picture of the project's ecological sacrifices and human costs." Horn Book

Includes bibliographical references

The **wild** book; Margarita Engle. Harcourt Children's Books 2012 133p $16.99 Grades: 5 6 7 8   Fic

1. Novels in verse 2. Children's stories 3. Dyslexia -- Fiction 4. Cuba -- History -- 1909-1933 -- Fiction

ISBN 9780547581316

LC 2011027320

This book tells the story of "Josefa 'Fefa' de la Caridad Uría Peña. . . . Diagnosed with 'word blindness' (a misnomer for dyslexia), Fefa struggles at school. . . . Discounting a doctor's opinion . . . her mother gives her a blank diary: 'Let the words sprout / like seedlings, / then relax and watch / as your wild diary / grows.' . . . Her reading difficulties are heightened when bandits begin roving the countryside, kidnapping local children for ransom." (Kirkus Reviews)

English, Karen

Francie. Farrar, Straus & Giroux 1999 199p hardcover o.p. $17 Grades: 5 6 7 8   Fic

1. Alabama -- Fiction 2. Race relations -- Fiction 3.

African Americans -- Fiction **Fic**
ISBN 0-374-32456-5; 0-374-42459-4 pa
LC 98-53047
Coretta Scott King honor book for text, 2000

"The best student in her small, all-black school in pre-integration Alabama, 12-year-old Francie hopes for a better life. . . . When Jessie, an older school friend who is without family, is forced on the run by a racist employer, Francie leaves her mother's labeled canned food for him in the woods. Only when the sheriff begins searching their woods . . . does she realize the depth of the danger she may have brought to her family. Francie's smooth-flowing, well-paced narration is gently assisted by just the right touch of the vernacular. Characterization is evenhanded and believable, while place and time envelop readers." SLJ

Nikki & Deja; wedding drama. by Karen English; illustrated by Laura Freeman. Clarion Books 2012 108 p.
Grades: 1 2 3 **Fic**
1. Weddings -- Fiction 2. Friendship -- Fiction 3. Women teachers -- Fiction 4. African American children -- Fiction 5. Teacher-student relationship -- Fiction 6. Schools -- Fiction 7. Teachers -- Fiction 8. Best friends -- Fiction 9. African Americans -- Fiction
ISBN 0547615647; 9780547615646
LC 2011027484

In this book, part of the "Nikki & Deja" series from author Karen English, main characters Niki and Deja find out that "[t]heir beloved teacher, Ms. Shelby, is getting married. The excitement reaches a new high when she announces two last-minute guest cancellations and says she would like two students to attend. She draws names out of a hat, and Nikki and Deja are chosen "fair and square." The rest of the class is jealous but soon moves on to invent a classroom contest to see which team can create the best imaginary wedding. Meanwhile, Nikki and her mother revel in finding a dress and the perfect panini press, while Deja worries about Auntie Dee's new jobless status and fears what a homemade dress might look like." (Kirkus)

Nikki and Deja, wedding drama
Wedding drama

Nikki & Deja: birthday blues; illustrated by Laura Freeman. Clarion Books 2009 92p il $15
Grades: 2 3 4 **Fic**
1. School stories 2. Aunts -- Fiction 3. Parties -- Fiction 4. Birthdays -- Fiction 5. Friendship -- Fiction 6. African Americans -- Fiction
ISBN 978-0-618-97787-1; 0-618-97787-2
LC 2007-50189

As her eighth birthday approaches, Deja's biggest concern is whether her father will attend her party, until her aunt is called away on business and a classmate schedules a "just because party" on the same afternoon.

"Early chapter-book readers will relate to the protagonist's authentic emotions as English acknowledges the challenges and complexities of classroom life." SLJ

Companion volume to:
Nikki & Deja (2007)

Nikki & Deja: the newsy news newsletter. Clarion Books 2010 91p $15

Grades: 2 3 4 **Fic**
1. School stories 2. Friendship -- Fiction 3. Newspapers -- Fiction
ISBN 978-0-547-22247-9; 0-547-22247-5
LC 2009015845

When Nikki and her best friend, Deja, start a newsletter about what is happening on their street and in their school, they focus more on writing exciting stories than on finding the truth.

"English writes with wit, feeling, and a spot-on voice that acknowledges the realistic friendship and problems of the protagonists. Freeman's cartoon illustrations enhance the story." SLJ

Nikki and Deja: election madness; illustrated by Laura Freeman. Clarion Books 2011 108p il $14.99
Grades: 2 3 4 **Fic**
1. School stories 2. Elections -- Fiction 3. Friendship -- Fiction 4. African Americans -- Fiction
ISBN 978-0-547-43558-9; 0-547-43558-4
LC 2011008151

When Carver Elementary holds school-wide elections for the first time, third-grader Deja puts all her efforts into running for school president, ignoring her best friend Nikki's problems.

"Freeman's occasional black-and-white illustrations capture the dramatic tension between the girls." Kirkus

Skateboard party; by Karen English; illustrated by Laura Freeman. Clarion Books, Houghton Mifflin Harcourt 2014 128 p. illustrations (The Carver chronicles) (hardback) $14.99
Grades: 2 3 4 **Fic**
1. School stories 2. Parties -- Fiction 3. Skateboarding -- Fiction 4. Schools -- Fiction 5. African Americans -- Fiction
ISBN 0544283066; 9780544283060
LC 2013048934

In this children's book, part of Karen English's Carver Chronicles series, "Richard can't wait to show off his flat-ground Ollies at a friend's birthday party at the skate park, but a note home from his teacher threatens to ruin his plans. He really meant to finish his assignment on howler monkeys, but he just got . . . distracted. Can Richard manage to put off getting the note signed (and facing the consequences) until after the party, or will the deception make things even worse?" (Publisher's note)

"Skateboarder Richard spends so much time mastering a flat-ground Ollie that other things fall by the wayside. After blowing off his report on howler monkeys--again--Richard finds himself staying in for recess; readers will cheer when he finally tackles the report. Kids will recognize themselves in this series entry (including the occasional black-and-white illustrations) starring a realistic, likable boy of color." Horn Book

Epstein, Adam Jay
The **familiars**; [by] Adam Jay Epstein [and] Andrew Jacobson; art by Peter Chan & Kei Acedera. Harper 2010 360p il $16.99
Grades: 4 5 6 **Fic**
1. Adventure fiction 2. Cats -- Fiction 3. Magic --

Fiction
ISBN 978-0-06-196108-3; 0-06-196108-6
LC 2010-13686

When a scrappy alley cat named Aldwyn passes himself off as a magical animal companion to Jack, a young wizard in training, Aldwyn and his fellow "familiars," a know-it-all blue jay and bumbling tree frog, must save the kingdom after the evil queen of Vastia kidnaps Jack and two other wizards.

"The consistently suspenseful narrative moves quickly and is full of twists and turns. . . . This winning combination of action and humor will keep readers turning pages right up to the ending." SLJ

Followed by: Secrets of the crown (2011)

Secrets of the crown; [by] Adam Jay Epstein, Andrew Jacobson; art by Peter Chan & Kei Acedera. Harper 2011 374p il (The familiars) $16.99

Grades: 4 5 6 **Fic**

1. Fantasy fiction 2. Magic -- Fiction 3. Animals -- Fiction

ISBN 978-0-06-196111-3; 0-06-196111-6
LC 2011002086

Sequel to: The familiars (2010)

When human magic is destroyed, familiars Aldwyn the cat, Skylar the blue jay, and Gilbert the tree frog set out without their wizards to seek the Crown of the Snow Leopard, the only object that can save the kingdom of Vastia from the evil hare Paksahara.

"The familiars' adventures are exciting, and the revelations about Aldwyn's long-lost parents are touching. Fans of the first book will be pleased." SLJ

Erdrich, Louise, 1954-

★ The **birchbark** house. Hyperion Bks. for Children 1999 244p il hardcover o.p. pa $6.99

Grades: 5 6 7 8 **Fic**

1. Ojibwa Indians -- Fiction

ISBN 0-7868-0300-2; 0-7868-1454-3 pa
LC 98-46366

Omakayas, a seven-year-old Native American girl of the Ojibwa tribe, lives through the joys of summer and the perils of winter on an island in Lake Superior in 1847.

"Erdrich crafts images of tender beauty while weaving Ojibwa words seamlessly into the text. Her gentle spot art throughout complements this first of several projected stories that will 'attempt to retrace [her] own family's history.'" Horn Book Guide

Followed by: The game of silence (2004)

★ **Chickadee**; Louise Erdrich. Harper 2012 256p. (trade bdg.) $16.99

Grades: 5 6 7 8 **Fic**

1. Brothers -- Fiction 2. Ojibwe Indians -- Fiction 3. Voyages and travels -- Fiction 4. Kidnapping -- Fiction 5. Family life -- Fiction 6. Métis -- Fiction 7. Ojibwa Indians -- Fiction 8. Great Plains -- History -- 19th century -- Fiction 9. Superior, Lake, Region -- History -- 19th century -- Fiction

ISBN 9780060577902; 9780060577919
LC 2012006565

Sequel to: The porcupine year.

Scott O'Dell Award for Historical Fiction (2013)

This book is the "fourth book of The Birchbark House Series. Omakayas is now a young mother with lively 8-year-

old twins named Chickadee and Makoons." Makoons plays a trick on the tribe's bully, resulting in the bully's sons kidnapping Chickadee. He escapes, then "runs into his Uncle Quill driving an ox cart of furs to sell in St. Paul. Quill and Chickadee travel with fellow traders on the Red River ox cart trail, arriving in Pembina to find Makoons seriously ill." (Kirkus)

★ The **game** of silence; [by] Louise Erdrich. HarperCollins 2004 256p $15.99; lib bdg $16.89; pa $5.99

Grades: 5 6 7 8 **Fic**

1. Ojibwa Indians -- Fiction

ISBN 0-06-029789-1; 0-06-029790-5 lib bdg; 0-06-441029-3 pa
LC 2004-6018

Sequel to: The birchbark house (1999)

Nine-year-old Omakayas, of the Ojibwa tribe, moves west with her family in 1849

"Erdrich's captivating tale of four seasons portrays a deep appreciation of our environment, our history, and our Native American sisters and brothers." SLJ

Followed by: The porcupine year (2008)

★ The **porcupine** year. HarperCollinsPublishers 2008 193p $15.99; lib bdg $16.89

Grades: 5 6 7 8 **Fic**

1. Family life -- Fiction 2. Ojibwa Indians -- Fiction 3. Voyages and travels -- Fiction

ISBN 978-0-06-029787-9; 0-06-029787-5; 978-0-06-029788-6 lib bdg; 0-06-029788-3 lib bdg
LC 2008000757

Sequel to: The game of silence (2004)

In 1852, forced by the United States government to leave their beloved Island of the Golden Breasted Woodpecker, fourteen-year-old Omokayas and her Ojibwe family travel in search of a new home.

"Based on Erdrich's own family history, this celebration of life will move readers with its mischief, its anger, and its sadness. What is left unspoken is as powerful as the story told." Booklist

Erskine, Kathryn

The **absolute** value of Mike. Philomel Books 2011 247p $16.99

Grades: 5 6 7 8 **Fic**

1. Pennsylvania -- Fiction 2. Business enterprises -- Fiction 3. Father-son relationship -- Fiction 4. Eccentrics and eccentricities -- Fiction

ISBN 978-0-399-25505-2; 0-399-25505-2
LC 2010-13333

Fourteen-year-old Mike, whose father is a brilliant mathematician but who has no math aptitude himself, spends the summer in rural Pennsylvania with his elderly and eccentric relatives Moo and Poppy, helping the townspeople raise money to adopt a Romanian orphan.

"Erskine weaves together a large but entertaining cast of characters. . . . Despite many laugh-out-loud moments, the heart of the book is essentially serious." Horn Book

The **badger** knight; Kathryn Erskine. Scholastic Press 2014 352 p. illustrations $17.99

Grades: 5 6 7 8 **Fic**

1. Paganism 2. War stories 3. Medieval civilization 4. Adventure stories 5. Archers -- Fiction 6. Runaways

-- Fiction 7. Friendship -- Fiction 8. Albinos and albinism -- Fiction 9. Great Britain -- History -- Edward III, 1327-1377 -- Fiction

ISBN 0545464420; 9780545464420; 9780545464437; 9780545662932

LC 2013042527

In this book by Kathryn Erskine, "13-year-old Adrian--small, asthmatic, and an albino--dreams of becoming a soldier and fighting the 'pagan Scots' that threaten 1346 England. Perceived as weak and touched by the devil, the self-dubbed 'Badger' is a skilled archer and has the rare ability to read and write. When his amiable friend Hugh joins the English army, Adrian runs away to follow him." (Publishers Weekly)

"Erskine hits the bull's-eye in her retelling of the hero's journey through the eyes of a young, medieval archer determined to prove his worth through battle... Erskine excels at combining action, historical tidbits (Badger hides in an ancient Roman latrine and muses on the soldiers who came before him), and thoroughly likable characters with modern sensibilities. Much like Karen Cushman's notable books, Erskine's latest deserves a place in most middle school libraries." SLJ

★ **Mockingbird**. Philomel Books 2010 235p

Grades: 4 5 6   **Fic**

1. School stories 2. Siblings -- Fiction 3. Bereavement -- Fiction 4. Asperger's syndrome -- Fiction 5. Father-daughter relationship -- Fiction

ISBN 0-399-25264-9; 978-0-399-25264-8

LC 2009-06741

National Book Award, 2010

Ten-year-old Caitlin, who has Asperger's Syndrome, struggles to understand emotions, show empathy, and make friends at school, while at home she seeks closure by working on a project with her father. "Age ten and up." (Publisher's note)

"The sharp insights into Caitlyn's behavior enhance this fine addition to the recent group of books with narrators with autism and Asbergers." Booklist

Seeing red; by Kathryn Erskine. Scholastic Press 2013 352 p. $16.99

Grades: 5 6 7 8   **Fic**

1. Family -- Fiction 2. Friendship -- Fiction 3. Race relations -- Fiction 4. Grief -- Fiction 5. Bereavement -- Fiction 6. Family life -- Virginia -- Fiction

ISBN 0545464404; 9780545464406; 9780545464413; 9780545576451

LC 2013004261

Author Kathryn Erskin presents a "story of family, friendship, and race relations in the South. Red's daddy, his idol, has just died, leaving Red and Mama with some hard decisions and a whole lot of doubt. Should they sell the Porter family business? When Red discovers the injustices that have been happening in Rocky Gap since before he was born, he's faced with unsettling questions about his family's legacy." (Publisher's note)

Estes, Eleanor

Ginger Pye; with illustrations by the author. Harcourt 2000 306p il $17; pa $6

Grades: 4 5 6   **Fic**

1. Dogs -- Fiction

ISBN 0-15-202499-9; 0-15-202505-7 pa

LC 00-26700

A reissue of the title first published 1951

Awarded the Newbery Medal, 1952

The disappearance of a new puppy named Ginger and the appearance of a mysterious man in a mustard yellow hat bring excitement into the lives of the Pye children

Estes' drawings are "vivid, amusing sketches that point up and confirm the atmosphere of the story. It is a book to read and reread." Saturday Rev

Another title about the Pye family is:

Pinky Pye (1958)

★ The **hundred** dresses; illustrated by Louis Slobodkin. New ed; Harcourt 2004 80p il $16; pa $7

Grades: 4 5 6   **Fic**

1. Friendship -- Fiction 2. Polish Americans -- Fiction

ISBN 0-15-205170-8; 0-15-205260-7 pa

LC 2003-57037

A reissue of the title first published 1944

A Newbery honor book, 1945

"The 100 dresses are just dream dresses, pictures Wanda Petronski has drawn, but she describes them in self-defense as she appears daily in the same faded blue dress. Not until Wanda, snubbed and unhappy, moves away leaving her pictures at school for an art contest, do her classmates realize their cruelty." Books for Deaf Child

Etchemendy, Nancy

The **power** of Un. Front St./Cricket Bks. 2000 148p $16.95; pa $4.99

Grades: 4 5 6 7   **Fic**

1. Fantasy fiction

ISBN 0-8126-2850-0; 0-439-31331-7 pa

LC 99-58281

When he is given a device that will allow him to "undo" what has happened in the past, Gib Finney is not sure what event from the worst day in his life he should change in order to keep his sister from being hit by a truck

The author has a "knack for writing hilarious dialogue that perfectly paints the funny, poignant, and altogether unpredictable world of eleven and twelve year olds. . . . A unique, thought-provoking book." Voice Youth Advocates

Evans, Lissa

Horten's incredible illusions; magic, mystery & another very strange adventure. by Lissa Evans. Sterling Children's Books 2012 349 p. $14.95

Grades: 3 4 5 6 7   **Fic**

1. Adventure fiction 2. Magic -- Juvenile fiction 3. Magicians -- Juvenile literature

ISBN 1402798709; 9781402798702

In this sequel to "Horten's Miraculous Mechanisms" by Lissa Evans, "10-year-old Stuart Horten is catapulted on yet another adventure left to him by his Great-Uncle Tony. . . . It is up to Stuart to follow clues to locate the great magician's will. He and his friend April soon discover, however, that Tony's Tricks are truly magic: each one transports them to another time or place, where a puzzle must be solved." (School Library Journal)

Horten's miraculous mechanisms; magic, mystery & a very strange adventure. by Lissa Evans. Sterling 2012 270 p. $14.95

Grades: 3 4 5 6 7　　　　　　　　　　　　　**Fic**

1. Mystery fiction 2. Adventure fiction 3. Children's stories 4. Inventors -- Fiction 5. Magicians -- Fiction
ISBN 9781402798061

In this book, author Lissa "Evans borrows several classic tropes and themes--magic, riddles, a quest, and even a night at a museum--for the . . . story of 10-year-old Stuart Horten . . . who stumbles into a family mystery when he and his parents move to the small British town of Beeton. There, Stuart discovers that his Great-Uncle Tony Horten, who disappeared years ago without a trace, was both an inventor of mechanical devices and a magician. A chance phone call in a broken phone booth is the first step in a journey that leads Stuart around town, as he unearths his great-uncle's legacy and secrets. Stuart also draws the attention of April, May, and June (the journalistically inclined triplets next door), as well as Beeton residents with more sinister intentions." (Publishers Weekly)

Evans, Nate

Meet the beast; [by] Nate Evans and [illustrated by] Vince Evans. Soucebooks Jabberwocky 2010 111p il (Beast friends forever) pa $4.99

Grades: 2 3 4　　　　　　　　　　　　　　　**Fic**

1. Monsters -- Fiction 2. Siblings -- Fiction
ISBN 978-1-4022-4050-8 pa; 1-4022-4050-3 pa

"This well-plotted and fanciful opener promises a series that early chapter-book readers will appreciate. . . . Bouncy cartoon illustrations and a few passages in comic-strip format punctuate the brief chapters, but the narrative is seamless despite these multiple storytelling approaches." Booklist

Fagan, Cary

Banjo of destiny; pictures by Selçuk Demirel. Groundwood Books/House of Anansi Press 2011 127p il $14.95

Grades: 4 5 6　　　　　　　　　　　　　　　**Fic**

1. Banjos -- Fiction 2. Wealth -- Fiction
ISBN 978-1-55498-085-7; 1-55498-085-2; 978-1-55498-086-4 pa

"Jeremiah's nouveau riche parents want only the best for their gawky son—private school plus lessons in etiquette, dancing, art, and piano. When Jeremiah hears a banjo playing he becomes obsessed with following his true destiny. Fagan's straightforward, nondidactic narrative hints at the fact that individualism has its own rewards." Horn Book Guide

The **big** swim. Groundwood Books 2010 128p $14.95

Grades: 4 5 6　　　　　　　　　　　　　　　**Fic**

1. Camps -- Fiction 2. Summer -- Fiction 3. Friendship -- Fiction
ISBN 978-0-88899-969-6; 0-88899-969-0

"Ethan works hard to integrate himself into summer-camp routine. Much to his surprise, he makes friends easily and succeeds at not being the worst at any activity. Everything changes, though, when Zachary arrives, shrouded in a bad attitude and a mysterious past. . . . The setting is rich and the characters are interesting and fresh." SLJ

Fagan, Deva

Fortune's folly. Henry Holt 2009 260p $17.95

Grades: 5 6 7 8　　　　　　　　　　　　　　**Fic**

1. Fairy tales 2. Adventure fiction 3. Prophecies -- Fiction
ISBN 978-0-8050-8742-0; 0-8050-8742-7

LC 2008-36780

Ever since her mother died and her father lost his shoe-making skills, Fortunata has survived by pretending to tell fortunes, but when she is tricked into telling the fortune of a prince, she is faced with the impossible task of fulfilling her wild prophecy to save her father's life.

"Fagan's language evokes images of fairy tales and legends, and the protagonist's first-person narrative sparkles with humor. In this book, words are powerful, impressive, mystical, and, sometimes, downright silly." SLJ

Fairlie, Emily

The **lost** treasure of Tuckernuck; Emily Fairlie. Katherine Tegen Books 2012 283 p. (hardback) $16.99

Grades: 4 5 6 7 8　　　　　　　　　　　　　**Fic**

1. Mystery fiction 2. Buried treasure -- Fiction 3. Historic buildings -- Fiction 4. Schools -- Fiction
ISBN 0062118900; 9780062118905

LC 2012025279

This book by Emily Fairlie "tells the story of Bud and Laurie's quest to find the infamous Tutweiler Treasure. They're hot (or at least lukewarm) on the trail of clues, but time is running out -- the school board wants to tear down Tuckernuck Hall. Can Bud and Laurie find the treasure before it's lost forever?" (Publisher's note)

The **magician's** bird; a Tuckernuck mystery. Emily Fairlie; Illustrated by Antonio Javier Caparo. Katherine Tegen Books, an imprint of HarperCollinsPublishers 2013 288 p. (hardcover bdg.) $16.99

Grades: 4 5 6　　　　　　　　　　　　　　　**Fic**

1. Schools -- Fiction 2. Historic buildings -- Fiction 3. Mystery and detective stories 4. Treasure hunt (Game) -- Fiction
ISBN 0062118935; 9780062118936

LC 2012051738

In this book, by Emily Fairlie, "the mystery Bud and Laurie must solve is much more serious than a treasure hunt—their beloved school founder, Maria Tutweiler, has been accused of murdering Marchetti the Magician! Can Bud and Laurie—with the help of enthusiastic Misti and evil but useful Calliope—prove Maria Tutweiler's innocence? Or will Tuckernuck Hall be closed down for good?" (Publisher's note)

"Tuckernuck Hall students Bud, Laurie, and friends (The Lost Treasure of Tuckernuck) return to defend their founder from accusations of murder and reveal the truth about a vanished magician and his mechanical bird. Fairlie supplements her narrative with characters' notes, emails, texts, etc., a device which occasionally forces the tone but effectively displays the kids working through clues." (Horn Book)

Falls, Kat

Dark life. Scholastic Press 2010 297p $16.99; pa $6.99

Grades: 4 5 6 7　　　　　　　　　　　　　　**Fic**

1. Science fiction 2. Ocean -- Fiction
ISBN 978-0-545-17814-3; 0-545-17814-2; 978-0-545-17815-0 pa; 0-545-17815-0 pa

LC 2009-24907

"Ty has lived subsea his entire life. His family members moved below the water to make a better life for themselves. In this future, the climate changes on Earth have been so drastic that hardly any solid ground exits anymore. . . . This book will appeal to middle grade readers, who will enjoy the novel's mystery and suspense. It is a definite must-read for SF fans." Voice Youth Advocates

Followed by: Rip tide (2011)

Rip tide. Scholastic Press 2011 320p $16.99
Grades: 4 5 6 7   **Fic**
1. Science fiction 2. Ocean -- Fiction
ISBN 0-545-17843-6; 978-0-545-17843-3
Sequel to: Dark life (2010)

"While preparing to sell the season's seaweed crop, Ty stumbles across an abandoned township, its doors chained shut and its residents murdered. Soon after, the colonists' deal with another township goes bad, and Ty's parents are kidnapped. As Ty and Gemma try to track down those responsible and save their loved ones, they're forced to join up with the notorious Seablite Gang, infiltrate the rough-and-tumble town of Rip Tide, fight for their lives against sea monsters and human predators, and discover who's killing entire townships—and why. . . . There's no shortage of action, intrigue, or daring exploits in this aquatic thriller. Atmospheric and tense, built around an expertly used postapocalyptic meets Wild West setting, this story's a whole lot of fun." Publ Wkly

Farber, E. S.
Seagulls don't eat pickles; by Erica Farber; illustrated by Jason Beene. Chronicle Books 2013 184 p. (Fish Finelli) (alk. paper) $15.99
Grades: 4 5 6 7   **Fic**
1. Pirates -- Fiction 2. Adventure fiction -- Fiction 3. Librarians -- Fiction 4. Historic sites -- Fiction 5. Buried treasure -- Fiction 6. Mystery and detective stories 7. Treasure troves -- Fiction
ISBN 145210820X; 9781452108209
                         LC 2012027739
This is the first book in E.S. Farber's Fish Finelli series. "Fish Finelli wants nothing more . . . than to fix up his boat with a supercharged Seagull motor and win Whooping Hollow's annual Captain Kidd Classic boat race," but has only saved half the necessary funds. "When local bully Bryce Billings baits Fish into a bet that he and his friends Roger and T.J. can't find Captain Kidd's fabled lost treasure, . . . Fish finds himself knee-deep in a mysterious pirate adventure." (School Library Journal)

Farley, Walter
The **Black** Stallion; by Walter Farley; illustrated by Keith Ward. Random House 2008 275p il $15.99; lib bdg $18.99
Grades: 4 5 6 7   **Fic**
1. Horses -- Fiction
ISBN 978-0-375-85582-5; 0-375-85582-3; 978-0-375-95578-5 lib bdg; 0-375-95578-X lib bdg
A reissue of the title first published 1941
Young Alec Ramsay is shipwrecked on a desert island with a horse destined to play an important part in his life. Following their rescue their adventure continues in America.
Other titles in this series are:
The Black Stallion and Flame (1960)

The Black Stallion and the shape-shifter (2008) by Steven Farley
The Black Stallion returns (1945)
The Black Stallion's ghost (1969)
The Black Stallion's shadow (1996) by Steven Farley
The Black Stallion's steeplechaser (1997) by Steven Farley
Son of the Black Stallion (1947)
The young Black Stallion (1989)

Farmer, Nancy
★ The **Ear,** the Eye, and the Arm; a novel. Puffin Books 1995 311p pa $6.99
Grades: 6 7 8 9 10   **Fic**
1. Science fiction 2. Zimbabwe -- Fiction
ISBN 978-0-14-131109-8; 0-14-131109-6
                         LC 95019982
First published 1994 by Orchard Books
A Newbery Medal honor book, 1995
In 2194 in Zimbabwe, General Matsika's three children are kidnapped and put to work in a plastic mine while three mutant detectives use their special powers to search for them
"Throughout the story, it's the thrilling adventure that will grab readers, who will also like the comic, tender characterizations." Booklist

★ A **girl** named Disaster. Orchard Bks. 1996 309p $19.95; pa $7.99
Grades: 6 7 8 9   **Fic**
1. Adventure fiction 2. Zimbabwe -- Fiction 3. Mozambique -- Fiction 4. Supernatural -- Fiction
ISBN 0-531-09539-8; 0-14-038635-1 pa
                         LC 96-15141
A Newbery Medal honor book, 1997
While journeying from Mozambique to Zimbabwe to escape an arranged marriage, eleven-year-old Nhamo struggles to escape drowning and starvation and in so doing comes close to the luminous world of the African spirits
"This story is humorous and heartwrenching, complex and multilayered." SLJ

★ The **Sea** of Trolls. Atheneum Books for Young Readers 2004 459p $17.95; pa $9.99
Grades: 5 6 7 8 9   **Fic**
1. Fantasy fiction 2. Vikings -- Fiction 3. Norse mythology -- Fiction 4. Druids and Druidism -- Fiction
ISBN 0-689-86744-1; 0-689-86746-8 pa
                         LC 2003-19091
After Jack becomes apprenticed to a Druid bard, he and his little sister Lucy are captured by Viking Berserkers and taken to the home of King Ivar the Boneless and his half-troll queen, leading Jack to undertake a vital quest to Jotunheim, home of the trolls.
"This exciting and original fantasy will capture the hearts and imaginations of readers." SLJ
Includes bibliographical references
Other titles in this series are:
The Land of the Silver Apples (2007)
The Islands of the Blessed (2009)

Farrant, Natasha
After Iris; by Natasha Farrant. Dial Books for Young Readers 2013 272 p. (hardcover) $16.99

Grades: 5 6 7 8   **Fic**
1. Grief -- Fiction 2. Babysitters -- Fiction 3. Twins -- Fiction 4. Diaries -- Fiction 5. Au pairs -- Fiction 6. Brothers and sisters -- Fiction 7. Family life -- England -- London -- Fiction 8. Video recordings -- Production and direction -- Fiction
ISBN 0803739826; 9780803739826
                                    LC 2012039136

In this book, 12-year-old "Bluebell Gadsby's family has been collapsing ever since Blue's twin sister, Iris, died three years ago. Blue's father is working on the other side of the country, and their mother is traveling overseas, which leaves new au pair Zoran in charge. Between Blue's older sister Flora's rebelliousness, her two younger siblings' antics, and the family's pet rats, which live in the garden of their London home, Zoran has his hands full." (Publishers Weekly)

Farrey, Brian

The **Grimjinx** rebellion; Brian Farrey. HarperCollins 2014 432 p. illustrations (hardcover) $16.99
Grades: 4 5 6 7   **Fic**
1. Fantasy fiction 2. Magic -- Fiction 3. Brothers and sisters -- Fiction 4. Swindlers and swindling -- Fiction 5. Fantasy
ISBN 0062049348; 9780062049346
                                    LC 2013043194

In this book, by Brian Farrey, "Jaxter Grimjinx and his family haven't had much time for thieving. Through no fault of their own, they've been too busy saving the day. But the danger in the Five Provinces is only just beginning. The Palatinate Mages are almost ready to unveil their master plan, and legendary monsters will soon roam the land once more. Then Jaxter's sister, Aubrin, is kidnapped by the Mages." (Publisher's note)

"When mage sentinels carry off Jaxter Grimjinx's little sister Aubrin to be their new augur, the family's quest to get her back leads to the opening elements of a prophecy in which Jaxter will save the Five Provinces from a deadly scourge but die doing so. The twisted but coherent puzzle plot unfolds swiftly, speeded along by irreverent Grimjinx humor." Horn Book

Other titles in the series include:
The Vengekeep Prophecies (2012)
The Shadowhand Covenant (2013)

Federle, Tim

★ **Better** Nate than ever; Tim Federle. Simon & Schuster Books for Young Readers 2013 288 p. (hardcover) $16.99
Grades: 5 6 7 8   **Fic**
1. Theater -- Fiction 2. Musicals -- Fiction 3. New York (N.Y.) -- Fiction 4. Auditions -- Fiction 5. New York (N.Y.) -- Fiction 6. Broadway (New York, N.Y.) -- Fiction
ISBN 1442446897; 9781442446892; 9781442446908
                                    LC 2011050388
Odyssey Honor Recording (2014)
Rainbow List (2014)
Stonewall Honor Book: Children and Young Adult (2014)
Lambda Literary Awards Finalist (2014)

In author Tim Federle's book, "Nate Foster has big dreams. His whole life, he's wanted to star in a Broadway show. (Heck, he'd settle for seeing a Broadway show.) But how is Nate supposed to make his dreams come true when he's stuck in Jankburg, Pennsylvania . . . ? With Libby's help, Nate plans a daring overnight escape to New York. There's an open casting call for 'E.T.: The Musical,' and Nate knows this could be the difference between small-town blues and big-time stardom." (Publisher's note)

Five, six, seven, Nate! by Tim Federle. Simon & Schuster Books for Young Readers 2014 304 p. (hardcover) $16.99
Grades: 5 6 7 8   **Fic**
1. Theater 2. Actors -- Fiction 3. Theater -- Fiction 4. Musicals -- Fiction 5. Friendship -- Fiction 6. Best friends -- Fiction 7. New York (N.Y.) -- Fiction 8. Broadway (New York, N.Y.) -- Fiction
ISBN 1442446935; 9781442446939
                                    LC 2012051239
Sequel to: Better Nate than ever

In this book, by Tim Federle, "Nate is off to start rehearsals for 'E.T.: The Broadway Musical.' It's everything he ever practiced his autograph for! But as thrilling as Broadway is, rehearsals are nothing like Nate expects: full of intimidating child stars, cut-throat understudies, and a director who can't even remember Nate's name." (Publisher's note)

"Nate successfully auditioned for Broadway's E.T.: The Musical in Better Nate Than Ever. Of course, he's actually only an understudy's understudy, his chorus part keeps diminishing, and rehearsals are going poorly, but good-humored Nate takes it all in stride. Federle addresses his likable character's burgeoning interest in boys in a laudably straightforward way, making this entertaining backstage pass especially rewarding." (Horn Book)

Feiffer, Kate

The **problem** with the Puddles; illustrated by Tricia Tusa. Simon & Schuster Books for Young Readers 2009 193p il $16.99
Grades: 3 4 5   **Fic**
1. Dogs -- Fiction 2. Family life -- Fiction 3. Lost and found possessions -- Fiction
ISBN 978-1-4169-4961-9; 1-4169-4961-5
                                    LC 20080-51388
The Puddle parents cannot seem to agree about anything, but when their dogs go missing the whole family embarks on an unlikely quest that eventually answers many unasked questions.

"The kid-friendly humor . . . the full cast of eccentric characters and Tusa's . . . lively b&w spot art should readily win fans for the Puddle family." Publ Wkly

Fenner, Carol

Snowed in with Grandmother Silk; illustrated by Amanda Harvey. Dial Books for Young Readers 2003 75p il hardcover o.p. pa $6.99
Grades: 2 3 4   **Fic**
1. Snow -- Fiction 2. Grandmothers -- Fiction
ISBN 0-8037-2857-3; 0-14-240472-1 pa
                                    LC 2002-152296
Ruddy is disappointed when his parents go on a cruise and he must stay with his fussy grandmother for a whole week, but an unexpected snowstorm reveals a surprising side of Grandmother Silk

"Harvey's pencil-and-watercolor artwork extends the warmth and gentle humor in this chapter book, which will be a good choice for beginning readers as well as for reading aloud." Booklist

Yolonda's genius. Margaret K. McElderry Bks. 1995 211p $18.95; pa $5.99

Grades: 4 5 6   Fic
1. Siblings -- Fiction 2. Musicians -- Fiction 3. African Americans -- Fiction
ISBN 0-689-80001-0; 0-689-81327-9 pa

LC 94-46962

A Newbery Medal honor book, 1996

After moving from Chicago to Grand River, Michigan, fifth grader Yolonda, big and strong for her age, determines to prove that her younger brother is not a slow learner but a true musical genius

"In this brisk and appealing narrative, readers are introduced to a close-knit, middle-class African-American family.... [This novel] is suffused with humor and spirit." Horn Book

Fergus, Maureen
Ortega. Kids Can Press 2010 224p $16.95

Grades: 5 6 7 8   Fic
1. Science fiction 2. Gorillas -- Fiction
ISBN 978-1-55453-474-6; 1-55453-474-7

Eleven years ago, an infant lowland gorilla was acquired by a privately funded laboratory. An elite surgical team undertook a series of radical procedures designed to make it physically possible for the infant gorilla to acquire speech.

"The story's excitement and suspense as well as the emotional drama will ensnare readers. This interesting, affecting novel will definitely find an audience." SLJ

Ferraiolo, Jack D.
The **big** splash; by Jack D. Ferraiolo. Amulet Books 2008 277p $15.95

Grades: 4 5 6 7   Fic
1. School stories 2. Mystery fiction
ISBN 978-0-8109-7067-0; 0-8109-7067-8

LC 2007-49978

Matt Stevens, an average middle schooler with a glib tongue and a knack for solving crimes, uncovers a mystery while working with "the organization," a mafia-like syndicate run by seventh-grader Vincent "Mr. Biggs" Biggio, specializing in forged hall passes, test-copying rings, black market candy selling, and taking out hits with water guns.

This "novel delivers plenty of laughs, especially in the opening chapters, and fans of private-eye spoofs will enjoy this entertaining read." Booklist

Ferrari, Michael
Born to fly. Delacorte Press 2009 212p $15.99; lib bdg $18.99

Grades: 4 5 6   Fic
1. Sex role -- Fiction 2. Air pilots -- Fiction 3. Friendship -- Fiction 4. Family life -- Fiction 5. Rhode Island -- Fiction 6. World War, 1939-1945 -- Fiction
ISBN 0-385-73715-7; 0-385-90649-8 lib bdg; 978-0-385-73715-9; 978-0-385-90649-4 lib bdg

LC 2008035664

This novel takes place at the start of World War II. Eleven-year-old Bird has always loved flying with her mechanic dad, but now he has enlisted. She makes friends with

newcomer Kenji, the son of Japanese parents who have been interned. "Intermediate." (Horn Book)

"Ferrari's fast-paced plot and well-developed characters will keep readers engaged until the last page." Booklist

Ferris, Jean
Much ado about Grubstake. Harcourt 2006 265p $17

Grades: 5 6 7 8   Fic
1. Orphans -- Fiction 2. Colorado -- Fiction 3. City and town life -- Fiction 4. Gold mines and mining -- Fiction
ISBN 0-15-205706-4

When two city folks arrive in the depressed mining town of Grubstake, Colorado in 1888, sixteen-year-old orphaned Arley tries to discover why they want to buy the supposedly worthless mines in the area

"Ferris combines adventure, love, and off-the-wall characters in a page-turning story full of good laughs and common sense messages." Voice Youth Advocates

Once upon a Marigold; by Jean Ferris. Harcourt 2002 266 p. $17

Grades: 5 6 7 8   Fic
1. Love -- Fiction 2. Princesses -- Fiction 3. Triangles (Interpersonal relations) -- Fiction 4. Fairy tales
ISBN 0152050841; 0152167919; 9780152167912

LC 2002000311

Marigold series

This novel by Jean Ferris focuses on Christian, who did not know "love could be so amazing. He was clueless when he started spying on the royal family. He lives in a cave with a troll for a dad. If his dad had only warned him about all that mind-boggling love stuff, maybe things wouldn't be such a mess. But then, maybe, Princess Marigold would be dead. And now that he's fallen for the princess, it's up to him to untwist an odd love triangle . . . and foil a scheming queen." (Publisher's note)

"This complex, fast-paced plot, a mixture of fantasy, romance, comedy, and coming-of-age novel, succeeds because these characters are compelling, well developed, and sympathetic." SLJ

Followed by: Twice upon a Marigold (2008)

Field, Rachel
Hitty: her first hundred years; [by] Rachel Field; with illustrations by Dorothy P. Lathrop. Macmillan 1929 207p il $19.99; pa $6.99

Grades: 4 5 6 7   Fic
1. Dolls -- Fiction
ISBN 0-02-734840-7; 0-689-82284-7 pa

Awarded the Newbery Medal, 1930

"Hitty, a doll of real character carved from a block of mountain ash, writes a story of her eventful life from the security of an antique-shop window which she shares with Theobold, a rather over-bearing cat.... The illustrations by Dorothy P. Lathrop are the happiest extension of the text." Cleveland Public Libr

Fine, Anne
The **diary** of a killer cat; [by] Anne Fine; pictures by Steve Cox. Farrar, Straus and Giroux 2006 58p il $15

Grades: 2 3 4   **Fic**

1. Cats -- Fiction

ISBN 0-374-31779-8

           LC 2004-56212

First published 2001 in the United Kingdom

Tuffy the pet cat tries to defend himself against accusations of terrifying other animals and murdering the neighbor's rabbit

"The book is funny throughout, . . . The black-and-white sketches, some full page, bring movement and personality to the characters." SLJ

Another title about the killer cat is:

The return of the killer cat (2007)

Jamie and Angus together; illustrated by Penny Dale. Candlewick Press 2007 102p il $15.99

Grades: PreK K 1 2   **Fic**

1. Play -- Fiction 2. Toys -- Fiction 3. Friendship -- Fiction

ISBN 978-0-7636-3374-5; 0-7636-3374-7

           LC 2007-25166

Best friends Jamie and his toy Highland bull Angus tackle a lively playmate, become muddled by a pretend game, and discover that playing is not fun unless they are doing it together.

"Fine renders another pitch-perfect transitional chapter book. . . . Spare yet vivid language captures Jamie's perspective while supplying humor for adult readers. . . . Soft pencil illustrations . . . capture Jamie's loving family and convey his deep friendship with Angus." Booklist

Another title about Jamie and Angus is:

The Jamie and Angus stories (2002)

Fireside, Bryna J.

Private Joel and the Sewell Mountain seder; by Bryna J. Fireside; illustrations by Shawn Costello. Kar-Ben Pub. 2008 47p il lib bdg $16.95; pa $6.95

Grades: 2 3 4   **Fic**

1. Passover -- Fiction 2. Jews -- United States -- Fiction 3. United States -- History -- 1861-1865, Civil War -- Fiction

ISBN 978-0-8225-7240-4 lib bdg; 0-8225-7240-0 lib bdg; 978-0-8225-9050-7 pa; 0-8225-9050-6 pa

           LC 2007005275

A group of Jewish soldiers, and three freed slaves, have a Passover seder in 1862 on the battlefields of the Civil War

The book is based "on a true story. . . . Costello's impressionistic artwork seems well suited to this nostalgic story. Although respectful in tone, the illustrations also pick up on occasional humor." Booklist

Fitzgerald, John D.

★ The **Great** Brain; illustrated by Mercer Mayer. Dial Bks. for Young Readers 1967 175p il $17.99; pa $5.99

Grades: 4 5 6 7   **Fic**

1. Utah -- Fiction

ISBN 0-8037-2590-6; 0-14-240058-0 pa

"The Great Brain was Tom Dennis ('T.D.') Fitzgerald, age ten, of Adenville, Utah; the time, 1896. . . . This autobiographical yarn is spun by his brother John Dennis ('J.D.'), age seven . . . who can tell stories about himself and his family with enough tall-tale exaggeration to catch the imagination." Horn Book

Other titles about the Great Brain are:

The Great Brain at the academy (1972)

The Great Brain does it again (1975)

The Great Brain is back (1995)

The Great Brain reforms (1973)

Me and my little brain (1971)

More adventures of the Great Brain (1969)

The return of the Great Brain (1974)

Fitzhugh, Louise

★ **Harriet,** the spy; written and illustrated by Louise Fitzhugh. Delacorte Press 2000 300p il $15.95

Grades: 4 5 6 7   **Fic**

1. School stories

ISBN 0-385-32783-8

           LC 00712298

A reissue of the title first published 1964 by Harper & Row

Eleven-year-old Harriet keeps notes on her classmates and neighbors in a secret notebook, but when some of the students read the notebook, they seek revenge.

"A very, very funny and a very, very affective story; the characterizations are marvelously shrewd, the pictures of urban life and of the power structure of the sixth grade class are realistic." Bull Cent Child Books

Another title about Harriet is:

The long secret (1965)

Fitzmaurice, Kathryn

A **diamond** in the desert; Kathryn Fitzmaurice. Viking 2012 258 p. (hardcover) $16.99

Grades: 5 6 7 8   **Fic**

1. Baseball -- Fiction 2. Father-son relationship -- Fiction 3. World War, 1939-1945 -- United States -- Fiction 4. Japanese Americans -- Evacuation and relocation, 1942-1945 -- Fiction 5. Guilt -- Fiction 6. Gila River Relocation Center -- Fiction

ISBN 0670012920; 9780670012923

           LC 2011012041

In this book, "Tetsu is twelve when he and his mother and sister are relocated by World War II's infamous Executive Order 9066, which justified the internment of Japanese-Americans, to the camp at Gila River. His father, a leader in the Japanese-American community, is detained separately in another location, and Tetsu generally takes his responsibility as the oldest male in the immediate family very seriously. He's particularly solicitous of his younger sister, Kimi, who is . . . traumatized by the lack of privacy in the camp. . . . Kimi . . . wanders out into the desert, where she nearly dies. Guilt-stricken, Tetsu withdraws from baseball and from his friends, until his father arrives at Gila River and rekindles his son's interest in life." (Bulletin of the Center for Children's Books)

Includes bibliographical references (p. 255)

The **year** the swallows came early. Bowen Press 2009 277p $16.99; lib bdg $17.89

Grades: 4 5 6   **Fic**

1. Prisoners -- Fiction 2. Father-daughter relationship -- Fiction

ISBN 978-0-06-162497-1; 0-06-162497-7; 978-0-06-162499-5 lib bdg; 0-06-162499-3 lib bdg

           LC 2008-20156

After her father is sent to jail, eleven-year-old Groovy Robinson must decide if she can forgive the failings of someone she loves.

This "novel is peopled with three-dimensional characters whose imperfections make them believable and interesting. . . . The well-structured plot is underscored by clear writing and authentic dialogue." SLJ

Fixmer, Elizabeth

★ **Saint** training. Zonderkidz 2010 239p $14.99
Grades: 5 6 7 8   **Fic**
1. School stories 2. Catholics -- Fiction 3. Family life -- Fiction 4. Christian life -- Fiction
ISBN 978-0-310-72018-8; 0-310-72018-4
LC 2010010831

During the turbulent 1960s, sixth-grader Mary Clare makes a deal with God: she will try to become a saint if He provides for her large, cash-strapped family.

"The politically fervent period of the late 1960s, with its dramatic upheavals in family, gender, social, and religious conventions, comes to life with pathos and humor in this powerful debut." Publ Wkly

Flake, Sharon G.

★ The **broken** bike boy and the Queen of 33rd Street. Jump at the Sun/Hyperion Books for Children 2007 132p il $15.99; pa $5.99
Grades: 4 5 6 7   **Fic**
1. School stories 2. Friendship -- Fiction 3. African Americans -- Fiction
ISBN 978-1-4231-0032-4; 1-4231-0032-8; 978-1-4231-0035-5 pa; 1-4231-0035-2 pa
LC 2006-35590

Ten-year-old Queen, a spoiled and conceited African American girl who is disliked by most of her classmates, learns a lesson about friendship from an unlikely "knight in shining armor."

"Complex intergenerational characters and a rich urban setting defy stereotyping. . . . Infrequent detailed pencil illustrations . . . add a welcome dimension." Horn Book

Flanagan, John

The **hunters**; John Flanagan. Philomel 2012 403 p. (hardback) $18.99
Grades: 5 6 7 8   **Fic**
1. Fantasy 2. Courage -- Fiction 3. Pirates -- Fiction 4. Friendship -- Fiction 5. Seafaring life -- Fiction 6. Adventure and adventurers -- Fiction
ISBN 0399256210; 9780399256219
LC 2012020986

This book by John Flanagan is part of the Brotherband Chronicles series. "Hal and his brotherband crew are hot on the trail of the pirate Zavac and they have one thing only on their minds: Stopping the bloodthirsty thief before he can do more damage. Of course, they also know Zavac has the Andomal, the priceless Skandian artifact stolen when the brotherband let down their guard. The chase leads down mighty rivers, terrifying rapids, to the lawless fortress of Ragusa." (Publisher's note)

The **invaders**; John Flanagan. Philomel Books 2012 429 p. (The Brotherband chronicles) (hardback) $18.99
Grades: 5 6 7 8   **Fic**
1. Fantasy 2. Courage -- Fiction 3. Pirates -- Fiction 4.

Friendship -- Fiction 5. Seafaring life -- Fiction
ISBN 0399256202; 9780399256202
LC 2012000424

This book by John Flanagan is part of the Brotherband Chronicles series. "Hal and the Herons have done the impossible. This group of outsiders has beaten out the strongest, most skilled young warriors in all of Skandia to win the Brotherband competition. But their celebration comes to an abrupt end when the Skandians' most sacred artifact, the Andomal, is stolen--and the Herons are to blame." (Publisher's note)

★ The **outcasts**. Philomel Books 2011 434p (Brotherband chronicles) $18.99
Grades: 5 6 7 8   **Fic**
1. Fantasy fiction 2. Adventure fiction 3. Friendship -- Fiction
ISBN 978-0-399-25619-6; 0-399-25619-9

Hal, who does not fit into Skandian society, ends up in a brotherband, a group of boys learning the skills that they need to become warriors, with other outcasts, and they compete with other brotherbands in a series of challenges.

"This enjoyable, old-fashioned tale should have easy appeal for Flanagan's many fans, who are already invested in the world he's created." Publ Wkly

★ The **royal** ranger; John Flanagan. Philomel Books, an imprint of Penguin Group (USA) Inc. 2013 464 p.
Grades: 5 6 7 8   **Fic**
1. Apprentices -- Juvenile fiction 2. Fantasy fiction -- Juvenile fiction 3. Adventure and adventurers -- Juvenile fiction 4. Fantasy 5. Apprentices -- Fiction
ISBN 9780399163609
LC 2013015910

In this book, by John Flanagan, "Will Treaty has come a long way from the small boy with dreams of knighthood. Life had other plans for him, and as an apprentice Ranger under Halt, he grew into a legend. . . . The time has come to take on an apprentice of his own, and it's the last person he ever would have expected. Fighting his personal demons, Will has to win the trust and respect of his difficult new companion—a task that at times seems almost impossible." (Publisher's note)

"Taking place at least 16 years after the original 10 volumes of the Ranger's Apprentice series, this sequel sees Will training 15-year-old Maddie, the first girl to become a ranger's apprentice... Series fans will hang on every word of this adventure; Maddie emerges as a strong character and could easily develop a following among readers who enjoy Tamora Pierce's books about Alanna, another resourceful, independent-minded heroine." (Booklist)

★ The **ruins** of Gorlan. Philomel Books 2005 249p (Ranger's apprentice) $15.99; pa $7.99
Grades: 5 6 7 8   **Fic**
1. Fantasy fiction
ISBN 0-399-24454-9; 0-14-240663-5 pa

When fifteen-year-old Will is rejected by battleschool, he becomes the reluctant apprentice to the mysterious Ranger Halt, and winds up protecting the kingdom from danger.

"Flanagan concentrates on character, offering readers a young protagonist they will care about and relationships that develop believably over time." Booklist

Other titles in this series are:
The burning bridge (2006)
The icebound land (2007)
The battle for Skandia (2008)
The socerer of the north (2008)
The siege of Macindaw (2009)
Erak's ransom (2010)
The kings of Clonmel (2010)
Halt's peril (2010)
The Emperor of Nihon-Ja (2011)

Fleischman, Paul

Bull Run; woodcuts by David Frampton. HarperCollins Pubs. 1993 104p il pa $4.99

Grades: 6 7 8 9   **Fic**

1. Bull Run, 1st Battle of, 1861 -- Fiction 2. United States -- History -- 1861-1865, Civil War -- Fiction
ISBN 0-06-440588-5 pa

LC 92-14745

"Abandoning the conventions of narrative fiction, Fleischman tells a vivid, many-sided story in this original and moving book. An excellent choice for readers' theater in the classroom or on stage." Booklist

"In a sequence of sixty one- to two-page narratives, fifteen fictional characters (and one real general) recount their experiences during the Civil War. A few encounter each other, most meet unawares or not at all, but they have in common a battle, Bull Run, that affects—and sometimes ends—their lives." Bull Cent Child Books

The **dunderheads**; illustrated by David Roberts. Candlewick Press 2009 54p il

Grades: 2 3 4 5   **Fic**

1. School stories 2. Teachers -- Fiction
ISBN 0-7636-2498-5; 978-0-7636-2498-9; 978-0-7636-5239-5 pa

When Miss Breakbone confiscates Junkyard's crucial find, Wheels, Pencil, Spider, and the rest of the Dunderheads plot to teach her a lesson.

"Roberts's quirky watercolor and ink interpretations of Fleischman's deadpan humor and impeccable pacing produce hilarious results." SLJ

Followed by: The Dunderheads behind bars (2012)

★ The **Half**-a-Moon Inn; illustrated by Kathy Jacobi. Harper & Row 1980 88p il hardcover o.p. pa $4.99

Grades: 4 5 6   **Fic**

1. Kidnapping -- Fiction 2. Hotels and motels -- Fiction 3. Children with physical disabilities -- Fiction
ISBN 0-06-440364-5 pa

LC 79-2010

"Despite the grimness of Aaron's predicament, accentuated by dark scratch drawings of figures in grotesque proportion, the story's tone is hopeful and its style concrete and brisk. Elements of folklore exist in the story's characterization, structure, and narration." SLJ

Fleischman, Sid

The **13th** floor; a ghost story. illustrations by Peter Sís. Greenwillow Bks. 1995 134p il $15.99; pa $5.99

Grades: 4 5 6   **Fic**

1. Fantasy fiction 2. Pirates -- Fiction
ISBN 0-688-14216-8; 0-06-134503-2 pa

LC 94-42806

When his older sister disappears, twelve-year-old Buddy Stebbins follows her back in time and finds himself aboard a seventeenth-century pirate ship captained by a distant relative

"Liberally laced with dry wit and thoroughly satisfying. . . . Readers could hardly ask for more." Publ Wkly

★ **By** the Great Horn Spoon! illustrated by Eric von Schmidt. Little, Brown 1963 193p il hardcover o.p. pa $6.99

Grades: 4 5 6   **Fic**

1. California -- Gold discoveries -- Fiction
ISBN 0-316-28577-3; 0-316-28612-5 pa

"Jack and his aunt's butler, Praiseworthy, stow away on a ship bound for California. Here are their adventures aboard ship and in the Gold Rush of '49." Publ Wkly

★ The **dream** stealer; pictures by Peter Sís. Greenwillow Books 2009 89p il $16.99; lib bdg $17.89 **Fic**

1. Dreams -- Fiction 2. Mexico -- Fiction 3. Mythical animals -- Fiction
ISBN 978-0-06-175563-7; 0-06-175563-X; 978-0-06-175564-4 lib bdg; 0-06-175564-8 lib bdg

LC 2008-47694

A plucky Mexican girl tries to recover her dream from the Dream Stealer who takes her to his castle where countless dreams and even more adventures await

"The range of imaginative inventions . . . will delight children, as will the narrator's expertly modulated storyteller's cadence." Booklist

Here comes McBroom! three more tall tales. illustrated by Quentin Blake. Greenwillow Bks. 1992 79p il hardcover o.p. pa $4.95

Grades: 3 4 5   **Fic**

1. Tall tales 2. Farm life -- Fiction
ISBN 0-688-16364-5 pa

LC 91-32689

The stories were originally published separately by Grosset and Dunlap

The tall tale adventures of a farm family

Fleischman's "humor is still as fresh as ever, and Quentin Blake's illustrations continue to delight." Booklist

Other titles about McBroom are:
McBroom tells a lie (1976)
McBroom tells the truth (1981)
McBroom's wonderful one-acre farm: three tall tales (1992)

★ The **whipping** boy; illustrations by Peter Sís. Greenwillow Bks. 1986 90p il $16.99; pa $5.99

Grades: 5 6 7 8   **Fic**

1. Adventure fiction 2. Thieves -- Fiction
ISBN 0-688-06216-4; 0-06-052122-8 pa

LC 85-17555

Awarded the Newbery Medal, 1987

"A round tale of adventure and humor, this follows the fortunes of Prince Roland (better known as Prince Brat) and his whipping boy, Jemmy, who has received all the hard knocks for the prince's mischief. . . . There's not a moment's lag in pace, and the stock characters, from Hold-Your-Nose

Billy to Betsy's dancing bear Petunia, have enough inventive twists to project a lively air to it all." Bull Cent Child Books

★ The **white** elephant; [illustrated by] Robert Mc-Guire. Greenwillow Books 2006 95p il $15.99; lib bdg $16.89

Grades: 3 4 5   **Fic**

1. Thailand -- Fiction 2. Elephants -- Fiction
ISBN 978-0-06-113136-3; 0-06-113136-9; 978-0-06-113137-0 lib bdg; 0-06-113137-7 lib bdg

LC 2005-46793

In old Siam, young elephant trainer Run-Run and his old charge, Walking Mountain, must deal with the curse of a sacred white elephant.

"Fleischman successfully immerses readers in this ancient culture, creating clever and believable plot twists that bring the story to a satisfying but open-ended conclusion." SLJ

Fleming, Candace

The **fabled** fifth graders of Aesop Elementary School. Schwartz & Wade Books 2010 170p $15.99; lib bdg $18.99

Grades: 3 4 5   **Fic**

1. School stories
ISBN 978-0-375-86334-9; 0-375-86334-6; 978-0-375-96334-6 lib bdg; 0-375-96334-0 lib bdg

Throughout their fifth-grade year, a group of rambunctious students learns fable-like lessons from extraordinary activities, singing hamsters, and eccentric teachers, led by the inimitable Mr. Jupiter.

"A rare adventure—one that many teachers and students will take to heart." Horn Book

Lowji discovers America. Atheneum Books for Young Readers 2005 152p $15.95; pa $5.99

Grades: 3 4 5   **Fic**

1. Moving -- Fiction 2. Immigrants -- Fiction 3. East Indians -- United States -- Fiction
ISBN 0-689-86299-7; 1-4169-5832-0 pa

LC 2004-6899

A nine-year-old East Indian boy tries to adjust to his new life in suburban America

"Fleming tells a gentle, effective story about the loneliness and bewilderment that come with moving, and her brisk, lively sentences make this a good choice for readers gaining confidence with chapter books." Booklist

Fleming, David

★ The **Saturday** boy; by David Fleming. Viking Children's 2013 240 p. (hardcover) $16.99

Grades: 5 6 7 8   **Fic**

1. School stories 2. Bullies -- Fiction 3. Schools -- Fiction 4. Behavior -- Fiction 5. Family life -- Fiction 6. Families of military personnel -- Fiction
ISBN 0670785512; 9780670785513

LC 2012029680

In this book, Derek is the son of "a soldier who flies Apache helicopters and is stationed in Afghanistan for another tour. . . . Derek is a good-hearted kid who just naturally attracts trouble--he doesn't mean to, but he's always in the wrong place at the wrong time and often the victim. He's also impulsive and has a hard time staying focused, which

adds to his problems." Then one day, "he sees his dad on the news and his world falls apart." (School Library Journal)

Fletcher, Charlie

Ironhand. Hyperion Books for Children 2008 400p (Stoneheart trilogy) lib bdg $16.99

Grades: 5 6 7 8   **Fic**

1. Fantasy fiction
ISBN 978-1-4231-0177-2 lib bdg; 1-4231-0177-4 lib bdg

LC 2007-42073

Sequel to: Stoneheart (2007)

Having upset the balance between the warring statues of London, twelve-year-old George is confronted with new challenges as he tries to free his captured friends Edie and The Gunner from the formidable Walker and deal with the three strange veins of marble, bronze, and stone that have begun to grow out of his hand.

"Cliff-hanger chapters . . . will leave readers breathless. George's story is particularly vivid." Booklist

Followed by: Silvertongue (2009)

Silvertongue. Hyperion Books for Children 2009 (Stoneheart trilogy) $16.99

Grades: 5 6 7 8   **Fic**

1. Fantasy fiction
ISBN 978-1-4231-0179-6; 1-4231-0179-0
Sequel to: Ironhand (2008)

The battle between the statues and gargoyles of London rages on-and 12-year-old George Chapman and his friend Edie are caught in the middle. With the Walker intent on forcing his evil designs on the city and the world, George realizes that his destiny is inextricably tied to the Walker's destruction.

"George and Edie's action-packed experiences are told in alternate chapters. . . . The book does not stand on its own, but those familiar with the earlier titles will be satisfied." SLJ

Fletcher, Ralph

★ **Flying** solo. Clarion Bks. 1998 138p $15; pa $5.99

Grades: 5 6 7 8   **Fic**

1. School stories 2. Death -- Fiction
ISBN 0-395-87323-1; 0-547-07652-5 pa

LC 98-10775

Rachel, having chosen to be mute following the sudden death of a classmate, shares responsibility with the other sixth-graders who decide not to report that the substitute teacher failed to show up

"Fletcher expertly balances a wide variety of emotions, giving readers a story that is by turns sad, poignant, and funny." Booklist

Fletcher, Susan

Shadow spinner. Atheneum Bks. for Young Readers 1998 219p hardcover o.p. pa $4.99

Grades: 6 7 8 9   **Fic**

1. Iran -- Fiction 2. Storytelling -- Fiction 3. People with physical disabilities
ISBN 0-689-81852-1; 0-689-83051-3 pa

LC 97-37346

When Marjan, a thirteen-year-old crippled girl, joins the Sultan's harem in ancient Persia, she gathers for Shahrazad the stories which will save the queen's life

"An elegantly written novel that will delight and entertain even as it teaches." SLJ

Flores-Gabis, Enrique

★ **90** miles to Havana. Roaring Brook Press 2010 292p $17.99

Grades: 5 6 7 8 **Fic**

1. Cuba -- Fiction 2. Florida -- Fiction 3. Cuban refugees -- Fiction 4. Young adult literature -- Works
ISBN 978-1-59643-168-3; 1-59643-168-7

"Drawing on his own experience as a child refugee from Cuba, Flores-Galbis offers a gripping historical novel about children who were evacuated from Cuba to the U.S. during Operation Pedro Pan in 1961. Julian, a young Cuban boy, experiences the violent revolution and watches mobs throw out his family's furniture and move into their home. For his safety, his parents send him to a refugee camp in Miami. . . . This is a seldom-told refugee story that will move readers with the first-person, present-tense rescue narrative, filled with betrayal, kindness, and waiting for what may never come." Booklist

Foley, Lizzie K.

Remarkable; a novel. by Lizzie K. Foley. Dial Books for Young Readers 2012 325 p. (hardcover) $16.99

Grades: 3 4 5 6 7 **Fic**

1. Fantasy fiction 2. Humorous fiction 3. Ability -- Fiction 4. Young adult literature 5. Community life -- Fiction 6. Humorous stories 7. Pirates -- Fiction 8. Secrets -- Fiction 9. Eccentrics and eccentricities -- Fiction
ISBN 9780803737068

LC 2011021641

This book presents the story of an average girl named Jane Doe who lives in "the town of Remarkable, so named for its abundance of talented citizens, everyone lives up to its reputation. . . . Jane should be just as remarkable. Instead, this average 10-year-old girl is usually overlooked. . . . Mix in a rival town's dispute over jelly, hints of a Loch Ness Monster-like creature and a psychic pizzeria owner who sees the future in her reflective pizza pans. . . . With the help of her quiet Grandpa John, who's also forgotten most of the time, Jane learns to be true to herself and celebrate the ordinary in life." (Kirkus)

Fombelle, Timothee de

Toby alone; translated by Sarah Ardizzone; illustrated by François Place. Candlewick Press 2009 384p il $17.99; pa $8.99

Grades: 5 6 7 8 **Fic**

1. Fantasy fiction 2. Trees -- Fiction
ISBN 978-0-7636-4181-8; 0-7636-4181-2; 978-0-7636-4815-2 pa; 0-7636-4815-9 pa
Original French edition 2006

Toby is just one and a half millimeters tall, and he's the most wanted person in his world of the great oak Tree. When Toby's father discovers that the Tree is alive, he realizes that exploiting it could do damage to their world. Refusing to reveal the secret to an enraged community, Toby's parents have been imprisoned. Only Toby has managed to escape, but for how long?

"The impressive debut novel from French playwright de Fombelle deftly weaves mature political commentary, broad humor and some subtle satire into a thoroughly enjoyable adventure." Publ Wkly

Toby and the secrets of the tree; illustrated by François Place; translated by Sarah Ardizzone. Candlewick Press 2010 414p il $16.99

Grades: 5 6 7 8 **Fic**

1. Fantasy fiction 2. Trees -- Fiction
ISBN 978-0-7636-4655-4; 0-7636-4655-5

LC 2009014833

Sequel to: Toby alone (2009)

Thirteen-year-old Toby's tiny world is under greater threat than ever as Leo Blue holds Elisha prisoner while hunting the Grass People and anyone who stands in the way of his devastating plans for the oak Tree in which they all live, but this time Toby is not alone.

"Place's pen-and-ink illustrations are scattered generously throughout and enhance the overall quirkiness. This interesting piece of eco-fantasy provides a satisfying conclusion for those who enjoyed the first book." SLJ

Forbes, Esther

Johnny Tremain; a novel for old & young. with illustrations by Lynd Ward. Houghton Mifflin Books for Children 1943 256p il $17; pa $6.99

Grades: 5 6 7 8 **Fic**

1. United States -- History -- 1775-1783, Revolution -- Fiction
ISBN 978-0-395-06766-6; 0-395-06766-9; 978-0-440-44250-9 pa; 0-440-44250-8 pa

Awarded the Newbery Medal, 1944

"Johnny, an orphan, works as a favored apprentice to an aging silversmith until he burns his hand severely while working on an important project. During the Revolutionary War he serves as a dispatch rider for the Committee on Public Safety, meeting such men as Paul Revere and John Hancock. An outcast for a time, he finally learns on the battlefield of Lexington that his crippled hand can be put to use." Shapiro. Fic for Youth. 3d edition

Forester, Victoria

★ **The girl** who could fly. Feiwel and Friends 2008 329p $16.95

Grades: 4 5 6 7 **Fic**

1. School stories 2. Science fiction 3. Flight -- Fiction
ISBN 978-0-312-37462-4; 0-312-37462-3

LC 2008-06882

When homeschooled farm girl Piper McCloud reveals her ability to fly, she is quickly taken to a secret government facility to be trained with other exceptional children, but she soon realizes that something is very wrong and begins working with brilliant and wealthy Conrad to escape.

"The story soars, just like Piper, with enough loop-de-loops to keep kids uncertain about what will come next. . . . Best of all are the book's strong, lightly wrapped messages about friendship and authenticity and the difference between doing well and doing good." Booklist

Fox, Helen

★ **Eager**. Wendy Lamb Books 2004 280p hardcover o.p. pa $6.50

Grades: 5 6 7 8   **Fic**
1. Science fiction 2. Robots -- Fiction
ISBN 0-385-74672-5; 0-553-48795-7 pa

LC 2003-19489

Unlike Grumps, their old-fashioned robot, the Bell family's new robot, Eager, is programmed to not merely obey but to question, reason, and exercise free will.

"There is a lot of warmth and humor in this engaging . . . novel. . . . The characters are well developed and the action moves quickly. The author also raises thought-provoking questions about what it means to be human, the dangers of technology, and the concept of free will." SLJ

Another title about Eager is:
Eager's nephew (2006)

Fox, Paula
★ The **slave** dancer. Atheneum 2001 176p $18.99; pa $6.99
Grades: 5 6 7 8   **Fic**
1. Sea stories 2. Slave trade -- Fiction
ISBN 978-0-689-84505-5; 0-689-84505-7; 978-1-4169-7139-9 pa; 1-4169-7139-4 pa

A reissue of the title first published 1973 by Bradbury Press

Awarded the Newbery Medal, 1974

"Thirteen-year-old Jessie Bollier is kidnapped from New Orleans and taken aboard a slave ship. Cruelly tyrannized by the ship's captain, Jessie is made to play his fife for the slaves during the exercise period into which they are forced in order to keep them fit for sale. When a hurricane destroys the ship, Jessie and Ras, a young slave, survive. They are helped by an old black man who finds them, spirits Ras north to freedom, and assists Jessie to return to his family." Shapiro. Fic for Youth. 3d edition

The **stone**-faced boy. Front Street 2005 83p pa $8.95
Grades: 4 5 6   **Fic**
1. Dogs -- Fiction 2. Siblings -- Fiction 3. Family life -- Fiction
ISBN 978-1-932425-42-0 pa; 1-932425-42-X pa

LC 2005-12056

First published 1968 by Bradbury Press

Only his strange great-aunt seems to understand the thoughts behind a young boy's expressionless face as he returns on an eerie, snowy night from rescuing a dog that dislikes him

Foxlee, Karen
★ **Ophelia** and the marvelous boy; by Karen Foxlee. Alfred A. Knopf 2014 240 p. $16.99
Grades: 4 5 6 7 8   **Fic**
1. Snow -- Fiction 2. Museums -- Fiction 3. Prisoners -- Fiction 4. Magic -- Fiction 5. Heroes -- Fiction 6. Wizards -- Fiction 7. Kings, queens, rulers, etc. -- Fiction
ISBN 0385753543; 9780385753548; 9780385753555

LC 2013012236

In this book, by Karen Foxlee, "Ophelia Jane Worthington-Whittard . . . and her sister Alice are still grieving for their dead mother when their father takes a job in a strange museum in a city where it always snows. On her very first day in the museum Ophelia discovers a boy locked away in a long forgotten room. He is a prisoner of Her Majesty the Snow Queen. As Ophelia embarks on an incredible journey to rescue the boy everything that she believes will be tested." (Publisher's note)

"Ophelia discovers a boy who's imprisoned...by the Snow Queen; to rescue him, Ophelia must find the boy s missing sword. This is a fable of psychic healing, in which Ophelia, mourning her mother, must battle the Queen armed only with her powers as "defender of goodness and happiness and hope." Foxlee's deftness with characterization and setting makes this a satisfying fantasy." (Horn Book)

Fraustino, Lisa Rowe
The **Hole** in the Wall. Milkweed Editions 2010 214p $16.95
Grades: 4 5 6   **Fic**
1. Twins -- Fiction 2. Siblings -- Fiction 3. Family life -- Fiction 4. Supernatural -- Fiction 5. Coal mines and mining -- Fiction
ISBN 978-1-57131-696-7; 1-57131-696-5

LC 2010017732

An imaginative eleven-year-old named Sebby discovers that the strange things he has been seeing are real, and connected somehow with the strip-mining operation that has destroyed his town, but getting help from his bickering family seems unlikely.

"More than the science-fiction elements, it's the urgent details of conservation that will pull readers, and when the issues reach right to Sebby's home, the questions increase. . . . This title will capture young environmentalists." Boolist

Frazier, Angie
The **mastermind** plot; by Angie Frazier. Scholastic Press 2012 231 p. (Suzanna Snow mysteries) (hardcover: alk. paper) $16.99
Grades: 4 5 6 7   **Fic**
1. Mystery fiction 2. Adventure fiction 3. Children's stories 4. Arson -- Fiction 5. Uncles -- Fiction 6. Schools -- Fiction 7. Grandmothers -- Fiction 8. Mystery and detective stories 9. Family life -- Massachusetts -- Boston -- Fiction 10. Boston (Mass.) -- History -- 20th century -- Fiction
ISBN 0545208645; 9780545208642

LC 2011003770

Sequel to: The midnight tunnel

This children's mystery by Angie Frazier continues the adventures of Suzanna Snow. "She's just arrived in Boston, the city she's wanted to visit for as long as she can remember. . . . Her grandmother and cousin, Will, welcome her warmly, but her famous detective uncle, Bruce Snow, seems anything but pleased. He doesn't want [her] meddling in his current case involving a string of mysterious warehouse fires along the harbor. But Zanna can't help herself. Is someone setting the fires? Just when she thinks she's on to something, a strange man starts following her. Is he a threat? Zanna needs to solve the case before she has the chance to find out." (Publisher's note)

The **midnight** tunnel; a Suzanna Snow mystery. Scholastic Press 2011 283p $16.99
Grades: 4 5 6 7   **Fic**
1. Mystery fiction 2. Canada -- Fiction 3. Uncles -- Fiction 4. Missing children -- Fiction 5. Hotels and motels -- Fiction
ISBN 978-0-545-20862-8; 0-545-20862-9

LC 2010-26770

In 1905, Suzanna is in training to be a well-mannered hostess at a Loch Harbor, New Brunswick, hotel, but her dream of being a detective gets a boost when a seven-year-old guest goes missing and Suzanna's uncle, a famous detective, comes to solve the case.

"What Zanna lacks in grace and composure, she makes up for in pluck, persistence and cleverness, emerging a likely and likable Edwardian Nancy Drew." Kirkus

Frazier, Sundee Tucker

★ The **other** half of my heart; [by] Sundee T. Frazier. Delacorte Press 2010 296p $16.99

Grades: 5 6 7 8   **Fic**

1. Twins -- Fiction 2. Sisters -- Fiction 3. Prejudices -- Fiction 4. Grandmothers -- Fiction 5. Beauty contests -- Fiction 6. African Americans -- Fiction 7. Racially mixed people -- Fiction

ISBN 978-0-385-73440-0; 0-385-73440-9

LC 2009013209

Twin daughters of interracial parents, eleven-year-olds Keira and Minna have very different skin tones and personalities, but it is not until their African American grandmother enters them in the Miss Black Pearl Pre-Teen competition in North Carolina that red-haired and pale-skinned Minna realizes what life in their small town in the Pacific Northwest has been like for her more outgoing, darker-skinned sister.

"Frazier addresses issues faced by mixed-race children with a grace and humor that keep her from being pedantic. The story is enjoyable in its own right, and will also encourage readers to rethink racial boundries and what it means to be black or white in America." SLJ

Freedman, Paula J.

★ **My** basmati bat mitzvah; by Paula J. Freedman. Harry N. Abrams 2013 256 p. (alk. paper) $16.95

Grades: 4 5 6   **Fic**

1. Bat mitzvah -- Fiction 2. Jewish children -- Juvenile fiction 3. Judaism -- Fiction 4. East Indian Americans -- Fiction 5. Jews -- United States -- Fiction

ISBN 1419708066; 9781419708060

LC 2013005791

In this book, by Paula J. Freedman, "during the fall leading up to her bat mitzvah, Tara Feinstein has a lot more than her Torah portion on her mind. Between Hebrew school and study sessions with the rabbi, there doesn't seem to be enough time to hang out with her best friend Ben-O--who might also be her boyfriend--and her other best friend, Rebecca. Amid all this drama, Tara considers how to balance her Indian and Jewish identities and what it means to have a bat mitzvah while questioning her faith." (Publisher's note)

"How could Tara let know-it-all Sheila Rosenberg get away with saying, 'You're not even Jewish,' when Tara's Indian-born mother converted 'way before I was even born'? With her bat mitzvah on the horizon, Tara secretly wonders: 'Was I about to become more Jewish, or less Indian?' A light, warm, humorous story about cultural identity, inner harmony, and ordinary middle-school trials and tribulations. Glos." (Horn Book)

Freeman, Martha

The **trouble** with cats; illustrated by Cat Bowman Smith. Holiday House 2000 77p il $15.95

Grades: 2 3 4   **Fic**

1. School stories 2. Cats -- Fiction 3. Stepfathers --

Fiction 4. San Francisco (Calif.) -- Fiction

ISBN 0-8234-1479-5

LC 99-29291

After a difficult first week of third grade, Holly begins to adjust to her new school and living in her new stepfather's tiny apartment with his four cats

"Bowman contributes pen-and-ink drawings with lines that quiver with energy. . . . Freeman has a knack for wholesome, undemanding fiction . . . with enough action and humor to carry the plot." Bull Cent Child Books

Other titles about Holly are:

The trouble with babies (2002)

The trouble with twins (2007)

Who stole Halloween? Holiday House 2005 232p il (The Chickadee Court mysteries) $16.95; pa $7.95

Grades: 4 5 6   **Fic**

1. Mystery fiction 2. Cats -- Fiction 3. Halloween -- Fiction

ISBN 0-8234-1962-2; 0-8234-2170-8 pa

When nine-year-old Alex and his friend Yasmeen investigate the disappearance of cats in their neighborhood, they stumble onto a larger mystery involving a haunted house and a ghostly cat.

"The story unfolds to a satisfying resolution . . . Characters are well drawn, and the book will entice even reluctant readers with its action and humor." SLJ

Other titles about Alex and Yasmeen are:

Who is stealing the 12 days of Christmas (2003)

Who stole Uncle Sam? (2008)

Who stole Grandma's million-dollar pumpkin pie? (2009)

Who stole New Year's Eve? by Martha Freeman and illustrated by Eric Brace. Holiday House 2013 224 p. (A Chickadee Court mystery) (hardcover) $16.95

Grades: 4 5 6   **Fic**

1. Mystery fiction 2. Sculpture -- Fiction 3. Friendship -- Juvenile fiction 4. Carnivals -- Fiction 5. Ice carving -- Fiction 6. Pennsylvania -- Fiction

ISBN 0823427501; 9780823427505

LC 2012019674

In this book by Martha Freeman, part of the "Chickadee Court Mystery" series, "twelve-year-old sleuths, Yasmeen and Alex, are having friendship issues. Yasmeen thinks that she's being replaced by a new girl who has come to Chickadee Court. Then, the whole gang comes together to solve the frosty mystery [of stolen ice sculptures]. The clues lead to a fracking operation and the laboratory of a professor who is racing to invent a new alternative fuel before his competitors do." (Publisher's note)

"When all the ice sculptures intended for the town's annual Ice Carnival are stolen, eleven-year-old Alex Parakeet and his sleuth friends follow clues (water containing volatile chemicals; a dog that doesn't bark) to solve the case. This fifth series mystery is solid and satisfying, set against a background of holiday celebrations and enhanced with much humor and intrigue." (Horn Book)

Freymann-Weyr, Garret

★ **French** ducks in Venice; illustrated by Erin McGuire. Candlewick Press 2011 il $16.99

Grades: 2 3 4   **Fic**

1. Ducks -- Fiction 2. Canals -- Fiction 3. California

-- Fiction
ISBN 978-0-7636-4173-3; 0-7636-4173-1

LC 2010047672

When Polina Panova's "prince" moves out of their Venice, California, house, two ducks that live on the canals but believe themselves to be French try to help Polina, a designer of magical dresses of thread, silk, velvet, grass, and pieces of night sky, by giving her something to make her stop being sad.

"Freymann-Weyr's mannered narrative voice keeps emotions firmly in check . . . , and her storytelling gifts are unmistakable. . . . There's virtue in presenting a portrait of loss with a spoonful of sugar; readers learn how to talk about hurt . . . while McGuire's cinematically lit pictures recall classic Disney images of winsome animals consoling star-crossed heroines." Publ Wkly

Friedman, Laurie B.

Campfire Mallory; by Laurie Friedman; illustrations by Jennifer Kalis. Carolrhoda Books 2008 175p il lib bdg $15.95; pa $5.95

Grades: 2 3 4   Fic

1. Camps -- Fiction 2. Friendship -- Fiction
ISBN 978-0-8225-7657-0 lib bdg; 0-8225-7657-0 lib bdg; 978-1-58013-841-3 pa; 1-58013-841-1 pa

LC 2007022218

Nine-and-a-half-year-old Mallory's trepidation about going to sleepaway camp is multiplied when she and her best friend are assigned to different cabins, and a new "friend" seems determined to get Mallory in trouble

"The plot is believable, and the language is well suited to the intended audience. Mallory's diary entries and black-and-white cartoons appear throughout. The action is well paced. . . . A lighthearted, enjoyable read." SLJ

Other titles about Mallory are:
Back to school Mallory (2004)
Mallory on the move (2004)
Mallory vs. Max (2005)
Happy birthday, Mallory (2005)
In business with Mallory (2006)
Heart-to-heart with Mallory (2006)
Mallory on board (2007)
Honestly, Mallory (2007)
Step fourth, Mallory (2008)
Happy New Year, Mallory (2009)
Red, white & true blue Mallory (2009)
Mallory goes green (2010)
Mallory in the spotlight (2010)
Mallory's super sleepover (2011)
Mallory's guide to boys, brothers, dads, and dogs (2011)

Play it again, Mallory; by Laurie B. Friedman; illustrations by Jennifer Kalis. Darby Creek 2013 159 p. (Mallory) (trade hard cover: alk. paper) $15.95

Grades: 2 3 4   Fic

1. School stories 2. Bands (Music) -- Fiction 3. Musical instruments -- Fiction 4. Music -- Fiction 5. Schools -- Fiction
ISBN 0761360751; 9780761360759

LC 2012048866

In this book by Laurie B. Friedman "Mallory is excited about the six-week arts electives program at Fern Falls Elementary—until she gets stuck in her last-choice class, band. To make matters worse, she is assigned to the tuba. But with

some good guidance from her mom and her band teacher, Mallory learns the meaning of 'practice makes perfect' and that, in fact, making music can be lots of fun." (Publisher's note)

Too good to be true; by Laurie Friedman. Darby Creek 2014 158 p. (The mostly miserable life of April Sinclair) (trade hard cover: alk. paper) $17.95

Grades: 5 6 7 8   Fic

1. Diaries -- Fiction 2. Friendship -- Fiction 3. Dating (Social customs) -- Fiction 4. Interpersonal relations -- Fiction
ISBN 1467709263; 9781467709262

LC 2013026434

In this book, by Laurie Friedman, "eighth grade is off to a surprisingly promising start for April Sinclair. . . Making the dance team is the icing on the cake. But with one unexpected move from her hot neighbor, Matt Parker, April's life starts to spin out of control. In the blink of an eye, her best friend is furious, her boyfriend dumps her, and the girls on the dance team don't want anything to do with her. How could things go so wrong so fast?" (Publisher's note)

"April (Can You Say Catastrophe?) begins eighth grade with great news: she's selected for a highly coveted spot on the high school dance team. The team's grueling schedule, however, leads to hard feelings between April and her boyfriend, and her best friend. Readers will relate to April's struggle to maintain old friendships while forging new ones, and cheer for her as she navigates the aftermath of a bad romantic decision." Horn Book

Friend, Catherine

Barn boot blues. Marshall Cavendish 2011 142p $16.99

Grades: 5 6 7 8   Fic

1. Moving -- Fiction 2. Farm life -- Fiction 3. Minnesota -- Fiction
ISBN 978-0-7614-5827-2; 0-7614-5827-1

LC 2011001909

When her parents swap urban life in Minneapolis for rural life on a farm 100 miles away, twelve-year-old Taylor feels as if she is living on another planet.

"In this refreshingly compact novel, readers learn interesting, authentic details about everything from spinning wool to collecting eggs to in a kind-of-gross, kind-of-wonderful climax birthing lambs. In Taylor, Friend has created a plucky, lightly sarcastic protagonist whose frustration at her situation is palpable but who never comes off as unlikable or bratty." Horn Book

Friesen, Jonathan

The last Martin. Zonderkidz 2011 266p $14.99

Grades: 4 5 6 7   Fic

1. Family life -- Fiction
ISBN 978-0-310-72080-5; 0-310-72080-X

LC 2010-48275

Thirteen-year-old Martin Boyle struggles to break a family curse after discovering that he has twelve weeks to live.

"Spiced with plenty of slapstick, the yarn speeds its protagonist through a succession of highs, lows and improbable triumphs on the way to a hilariously melodramatic finish." Kirkus

Frost, Helen

★ **Salt**; by Helen Frost. Farrar, Straus, and Giroux 2013 160 p. (hardcover) $17.99

Grades: 5 6 7 8   **Fic**

1. War stories 2. Native Americans 3. Historical fiction 4. War of 1812 -- Fiction 5. Novels in verse 6. Friendship -- Fiction 7. Miami Indians -- Fiction 8. Trading posts -- Fiction 9. Frontier and pioneer life -- Indiana -- Fiction 10. United States -- History -- War of 1812 -- Fiction 11. Fort Wayne (Ind.) -- History -- 19th century -- Fiction

ISBN 0374363870; 9780374363871

LC 2012029521

This book, by Helen Frost, "set during the War of 1812 . . . is the story of the friendship between Anikwa, a Miami Indian boy, and James, the son of a trader. As both British and American armies advance on the area, other Native American peoples arrive hoping to fight with the British against the Americans. The plan fails, and Anikwa's peaceful people must flee. Will they have to abandon their traditional home, and will the friendship between the boys be sundered?" (Publisher's note)

Spinning through the universe; a novel in poems from room 214. Farrar, Straus and Giroux 2004 93p $16

Grades: 4 5 6 7   **Fic**

1. Poetry 2. School stories

ISBN 0-374-37159-8

LC 2003-48056

A collection of poems written in the voices of Mrs. Williams of room 214, her students, and a custodian about their interactions with each other, their families, and the world around them. Includes notes on the poetic forms represented

"Interwoven dramatic stories and interesting poetic patterns give this book extra appeal. A boon for poetry classes." SLJ

Fry, Michael

The **Odd** Squad; Bully Bait. by Michael Fry. Disney Hyperion 2013 224 p. (hardcover) $12.99

Grades: 4 5 6 7   **Fic**

1. Bullies -- Juvenile fiction 2. Friendship -- Juvenile fiction 3. School stories -- Juvenile fiction 4. Bullies -- Fiction 5. Schools -- Fiction 6. Middle schools -- Fiction 7. Interpersonal relations -- Fiction

ISBN 1423169247; 9781423169246

LC 2012014286

This children's story, by Michael Fry, is part of the "Odd Squad" series. "Nick is the shortest seventh-grader in the history of the world . . . , doesn't fit in . . . , and spends more time inside than outside his locker. . . . When a well-intentioned guidance counselor forces Nick to join the school's lamest club . . . , what starts off as a reluctant band of hopeless oddballs morphs into an effective and empowered team ready to face whatever middle school throws at them." (Publisher's note)

"Cartoonist Fry humorously mines the world of middle school as seen through the eyes of bullied Nick to answer the question: Can three oddballs team together to take down the school bully? ...Abundant cartoon-style illustrations enhance the book's silly yet sensitive portrayal of bullying and unlikely friendships." Kirkus

Funke, Cornelia Caroline

Dragon rider; [by] Cornelia Funke; translated by Anthea Bell. Scholastic 2004 523p il $12.95

Grades: 5 6 7 8   **Fic**

1. Fantasy fiction 2. Dragons -- Fiction

ISBN 0-439-45695-9

LC 2004-45419

Original German edition 1997

After learning that humans are headed toward his hidden home, Firedrake, a silver dragon, is joined by a brownie and an orphan boy in a quest to find the legendary valley known as the Rim of Heaven, encountering friendly and unfriendly creatures along the way, and struggling to evade the relentless pursuit of an old enemy.

"Funke proves she knows how to tickle the imaginations of younger readers. . . . This is a good, old-fashioned ensemble-cast quest." Booklist

★ **Inkheart**; [by] Cornelia Funke; translated from the German by Anthea Bell. Scholastic 2003 534p $19.95; pa $9.99

Grades: 5 6 7 8   **Fic**

1. Fantasy fiction 2. Books and reading -- Fiction

ISBN 0-439-53164-0; 0-439-70910-5 pa

LC 2003-45844

Twelve-year-old Meggie learns that her father, who repairs and binds books for a living, can "read" fictional characters to life when one of those characters abducts them and tries to force him into service.

The author "proves the power of her imagination; readers will be captivated by the chilling and thrilling world she has created here." Publ Wkly

Other titles in this series are:

Inkspell (2005)

Inkdeath (2008)

Fusco, Kimberly Newton

★ The **wonder** of Charlie Anne. Alfred A. Knopf 2010 272p $16.99; lib bdg $19.99

Grades: 5 6 7 8   **Fic**

1. Farm life -- Fiction 2. Friendship -- Fiction 3. Massachusetts -- Fiction 4. Race relations -- Fiction 5. African Americans -- Fiction 6. Great Depression, 1929-1939 -- Fiction

ISBN 978-0-375-86104-8; 0-375-86104-1; 978-0-375-96104-5 lib bdg; 0-375-96104-6 lib bdg

LC 2009-38831

In a 1930s Massachusetts farm town torn by the Depression, racial tension, and other hardships, Charlie Anne and her black next-door neighbor Phoebe form a friendship that begins to transform their community.

"Good humor, kindness and courage triumph in this warm, richly nuanced novel that cheers the heart like a song sweetly sung." Kirkus

Gaiman, Neil, 1960-

★ **Coraline**; [by] Neil Gaiman; with illustrations by Dave McKean. HarperCollins Pubs. 2002 162p il pa $6.99; $16.99

Grades: 5 6 7 8   **Fic**

1. Horror fiction 2. Supernatural -- Fiction

ISBN 0-380-80734-3 pa; 0-380-97778-8

LC 2002-18937

Looking for excitement, Coraline ventures through a mysterious door into a world that is similar, yet disturbingly different from her own, where she must challenge a gruesome entity in order to save herself, her parents, and the souls of three others

"Gaiman twines his taut tale with a menacing tone and crisp prose fraught with memorable imagery . . . yet keeps the narrative just this side of terrifying." Publ Wkly

★ **Fortunately,** the milk; by Neil Gaiman; illustrated by Skottie Young. Harper, an imprint of HarperCollinsPublishers 2013 128 p. (hardcover bdgs) $14.99
Grades: 4 5 6 7   **Fic**
1. Humorous stories 2. Fathers -- Fiction 3. Space and time -- Fiction 4. Adventure and adventurers -- Fiction
ISBN 0062224077; 9780062224071
         LC 2012050670
This children's picture book by Neil Gaiman is "about a father who has taken an excessively long time to return from the corner store with milk for his children's breakfast." He "is abducted by aliens, made to walk the plank by pirates, and rescued by a stegosaurus in a balloon, among other outrageous escapades." (Publishers Weekly)

★ The **graveyard** book; with illustrations by Dave McKean. HarperCollins 2008 312p il $17.99; lib bdg $18.89
Grades: 5 6 7 8 9 10   **Fic**
1. Death -- Fiction 2. Cemeteries -- Fiction 3. Supernatural -- Fiction
ISBN 0-06-053092-8; 0-06-053093-6 lib bdg; 978-0-06-053092-1; 978-0-06-053093-8 lib bdg
         LC 2008-13860
Awarded the Newbery Medal (2009)
Nobody Owens, nicknamed Bod, is a normal boy, except that he has been raised by in a graveyard by ghosts. "Grades five to nine." (Bull Cent Child Books)
"Gaiman writes with charm and humor, and again he has a real winner." Voice Youth Advocates

Odd and the Frost Giants; illustrated by Brett Helquist. HarperCollinsPublishers 2009 117p il $14.99
Grades: 3 4 5 6   **Fic**
1. Norse mythology -- Fiction
ISBN 978-0-06-167173-9; 0-06-167173-8
         LC 2009014574
An unlucky twelve-year-old Norwegian boy named Odd leads the Norse gods Loki, Thor, and Odin in an attempt to outwit evil Frost Giants who have taken over Asgard.
"Along with Gaiman's deft humor, lively prose, and agile imagination, a few unexpected themes—the double-edged allure of beauty, the value of family—sneak into this slim tale with particular appeal to kids drawn to Norse mythology, but suitable for any readers of light fantasy." Booklist

Galante, Cecilia
  Willowood. Simon & Schuster 2010 265p $16.99
Grades: 4 5 6 7   **Fic**
1. Geckos -- Fiction 2. Moving -- Fiction 3. Friendship -- Fiction 4. Single parent family -- Fiction
ISBN 978-1-4169-8022-3; 1-4169-8022-9
Eleven-year-old Lily has trouble leaving her best friend behind and moving to the city when her mother changes

jobs, but she makes some very unlikely friends that soon become like family members.
"The characters . . . are fully realized individuals. . . . [This book has a] finely tuned plot and poetic language. . . . Children will enjoy the story of Lily's first few months in the big city." SLJ

Gale, Eric Kahn
  The **Bully** Book; Eric Kahn Gale. Harpercollins Childrens Books 2012 240 p. $16.99
Grades: 4 5 6 7 8   **Fic**
1. School stories 2. Bullies -- Fiction 3. Friendship -- Fiction 4. Middle schools -- Fiction 5. Diaries -- Fiction
ISBN 0062125117; 9780062125118
         LC 2012050677
Originally published in a different format as an ebook by the author
"When the author was eleven, he was bullied. This book is loosely based on incidents that happened to him in sixth grade. Eric Haskins, the new sixth-grade bully target, is searching for answers. And unlike many of us who experienced something awful growing up, he finds them. Though they may not be what he expected." (Publisher's note)
"The juxtaposition of Eric's journal against the Bully Book allows readers to see both the bullies' methodology and Eric's unwitting complicity. . . . A compelling and unusual look at a complex and intractable problem that succeeds admirably as story as well." Kirkus

  The **Zoo** at the Edge of the World; by Eric Kahn Gale; illustrations by Matthew Howley. Balzer + Bray, an imprint of HarperCollinsPublishers 2014 240 p. illustrations (hardback) $16.99
Grades: 4 5 6 7   **Fic**
1. Zoos -- Fiction 2. Stuttering -- Fiction 3. Jungle animals -- Fiction 4. Human-animal communication -- Fiction
ISBN 0062125168; 9780062125163
         LC 2014002144
In this book, by Eric Kahn Gale, "Marlin is not slow, or mute; what he is is a stutterer, and that makes it impossible for him to convince people otherwise. What he is also is a Rackham: the youngest son of the world-famous explorer Roland Rackham, who is the owner and proprietor of the Zoo at the Edge of the World, a resort where the well-to-do from all over the world can come to experience the last bit of the wild left in the world at the end of the nineteenth century." (Publisher's note)
"The stuttering son of a famous explorer discovers a new ability that will change his life and his world forever. Marlin Rackham doesn't have an ordinary childhood. He works alongside his brother, Tim, and father, Ronan, in the family's exotic South American zoo, a zoo so renowned that rich and famous people from all over the world travel to visit the resort. But Marlin has a problem: He stutters. His stutter is so bad he can barely communicate with people. Many think he's mute. However, there is one group Marlin can talk to with no problem: the animals. And when his father brings a jaguar back from an expedition, the beast's mystical ways make it possible for the animals to talk back. . . . A secondary plot concerning Marlin's relationships with his father and brother is equally nuanced and powerful, making the book a formidable read on two fronts. The romantic setting and

striking prose are icing on the cake, creating an intoxicatingly charming book. Beautiful and fully absorbing." Kirkus

Gantos, Jack

★ **Dead** end in Norvelt; Jack Gantos. Farrar Straus Giroux 2011 341p. $15.99

Grades: 4 5 6 7   **Fic**

1. Old age -- Fiction 2. Pennsylvania -- Fiction
ISBN 978-0-374-37993-3; 0-374-37993-9

        LC 2010054009

Newbery Medal (2012)

Scott O'Dell Historical Fiction Award (2012)

In the historic town of Norvelt, Pennsylvania, twelve-year-old Jack Gantos spends the summer of 1962 grounded for various offenses until he is assigned to help an elderly neighbor with a most unusual chore involving the newly dead, molten wax, twisted promises, Girl Scout cookies, underage driving, lessons from history, typewriting, and countless bloody noses.

This is a "wildly entertaining meld of truth and fiction. . . . Memorable in every way." Publ Wkly

★ **From** Norvelt to nowhere; Jack Gantos. Farrar, Straus and Giroux 2013 288 p. (hardback) $16.99

Grades: 4 5 6 7   **Fic**

1. Old age -- Fiction 2. Friendship -- Fiction 3. Humorous stories 4. Mystery and detective stories 5. Norvelt (Pa.) -- History -- 20th century -- Fiction
ISBN 0374379947; 9780374379940

        LC 2013022251

Sequel to: Dead end in Norvelt

Author Jack Gantos' book "opens deep in the shadow of the Cuban missile crisis. But . . . other kinds of trouble are raining down on young Jack Gantos. . . . After an explosion, a new crime by an old murderer, and the sad passing of the town's founder, twelve-year-old Jack will soon find himself launched on a mission that takes him hundreds of miles away, escorting his slightly mental elderly mentor, Miss Volker, on her relentless pursuit of the oddest of outlaws." (Publisher's note)

★ **Heads** or tails; stories from the sixth grade. Farrar, Straus Giroux 1994 151p il $16; pa $4.95

Grades: 5 6 7 8   **Fic**

1. School stories 2. Diaries -- Fiction 3. Family life -- Fiction
ISBN 0-374-32909-5; 0-374-42923-5 pa

        LC 93-43117

"Jack is trying to survive his sixth-grade year, and he narrates, through a series of short-stories-cum-chapters, his difficulties in dodging the obstacles life throws in his path. . . . The writing is zingy and specific, with snappily authentic dialogue and a vivid sense of juvenile experience. . . . Jack and his family have a recognizably thorny relationship. This is a distinctive and lively sequence of everyday-life stories." Bull Cent Child Books

Other titles about Jack are:

Jack adrift (2003)

Jack on the tracks (1999)

Jack's black book (1997)

Jack's new power (1995)

★ **Joey** Pigza swallowed the key. Farrar, Straus & Giroux 1998 153p $16.99

Grades: 5 6 7 8   **Fic**

1. School stories 2. Schools -- Fiction 3. Single-parent families -- Fiction 4. Attention deficit disorder -- Fiction 5. Attention-deficit hyperactivity disorder -- Fiction
ISBN 0-374-33664-4

        LC 98-24264

To the constant disappointment of his mother and his teachers, Joey has trouble paying attention or controlling his mood swings when his prescription meds wear off and he starts getting worked up and acting wired

This "frenetic narrative pulls at heartstrings and tickles funny bones." SLJ

Other titles about Joey Pigza are:

Joey Pigza loses control (2000)

What would Joey do? (2002)

I am not Joey Pigza (2007)

★ **The key** that swallowed Joey Pigza; Jack Gantos. Fararr, Straus & Giroux 2014 160 p. (hardback) $16.99

Grades: 4 5 6 7   **Fic**

1. Boys -- Fiction 2. Family life -- Fiction 3. Babies -- Fiction 4. Brothers -- Fiction 5. Single-parent families -- Fiction 6. Attention-deficit hyperactivity disorder -- Fiction

ISBN 0374300836; 9780374300838

        LC 2014023370

First edition

This book by Jack Gantos is "the fifth and final book in the groundbreaking Joey Pigza series. . . . With his dad MIA in the wake of appearance-altering plastic surgery, Joey must give up school to look after his new baby brother and fill in for his mom, who hospitalizes herself to deal with a bad case of postpartum blues." (Publisher's note)

"Joey's indomitable spirit, grounded in his fierce, tender devotion to baby Carter and expressed through Gantos' inimitable comic tone, shows the fragile adults around him just what it looks like to be the man of the house." Booklist

Gardiner, John Reynolds

Stone Fox; illustrated by Marcia Sewall. Crowell 1980 81p il $15.99; lib bdg $16.89; pa $5.50

Grades: 2 3 4 5   **Fic**

1. Dogs -- Fiction 2. Sled dog racing -- Fiction
ISBN 0-690-03983-2; 0-690-03984-0 lib bdg; 0-06-440132-4 pa

        LC 79-7895

This story "is rooted in a Rocky Mountain legend, a locale faithfully represented in Sewall's wonderful drawings. . . . In Gardiner's bardic chronicle, the tension is teeth rattling, with the tale flying to a conclusion that is almost unbearably moving, one readers won't soon forget." Publ Wkly

Gardner, Lyn

★ **Into** the woods; pictures by Mini Grey. David Fickling Books 2007 427p il $16.99; lib bdg $19.99; pa $7.50

Grades: 4 5 6 7 8   **Fic**

1. Fantasy fiction 2. Sisters -- Fiction
ISBN 978-0-385-75115-5; 0-385-75115-X; 978-0-385-75116-2 lib bdg; 0-385-75116-8 lib bdg; 978-0-440-42223-5 pa; 0-440-42223-X pa

        LC 2006-24350

Pursued by the sinister Dr. DeWilde and his ravenous wolves, three sisters—Storm, the inheritor of a special musical pipe, the elder Aurora, and the baby Any—flee into the woods and begin a journey filled with danger as they try to find a way to defeat their pursuer and keep him from taking the pipe and control of the entire land. "Grades five to eight." (Bull Cent Child Books)

"Gardner's fast-paced fantasy-adventure cleverly borrows from well-known fairy tales, and astute readers will enjoy identifying the many folkloric references. . . . Grey's appealing black-and-white illustrations add humor and detail to the story." Booklist

Followed by: Out of the woods (2010)

Out of the woods; pictures by Mini Grey. David Fickling Books 2010 348p il $17.99; lib bdg $20.99
Grades: 4 5 6 7 8   Fic
1. Fantasy fiction 2. Sisters -- Fiction
ISBN 978-0-385-75154-4; 0-385-75154-0; 978-0-385-75156-8 lib bdg; 0-385-75156-7 lib bdg
Sequel to: Into the woods (2007)

This is a sequel to Into the Woods (2007). The Eden sisters "are being lured into a wicked witch's lair. . . . Belladonna wants Aurora's heart and Storm's all-powerful musical pipe, and she will stop at nothing to get them." (Publisher's note) "Grades five to eight." (Bull Cent Child Books)

"Aurora, Storm, and Any Eden thought their troubles were over when Storm tossed the Pied Piper's powerful, seductive pipe . . . into the sea and defeated the pipe's erstwhile owner, the villainous Dr. DeWilde. . . . But it seems their troubles have only begun. . . . A missing prince, a cowardly lion, a marauding dragon, seven dwarfs, and even the Grimm brothers all make appearances, and while the fractured fairy-tale stew is considerably more haphazard than that of the sisters' first outing, it's a well-conceived and entertaining mash-up nonetheless." Horn Book

Garland, Sarah
Azzi in Between; by Sarah Garland. Frances Lincoln Children's Books 2013 40 p. $17.99
Grades: 1 2 3 4   Fic
1. Refugees -- Fiction 2. Immigrants -- Fiction
ISBN 1847802613; 9781847802613

In this book, illustrated by Sarah Garland, "Azzi and her parents . . . have to leave their home and escape to another country. . . In the new country they must learn to speak a new language, find a new home and Azzi must start a new school. . . . Azzi begins to learn English and understand that she is not the only one who has had to flee her home. . . . But Grandma has been left behind and Azzi misses her more than anything. Will Azzi ever see her grandma again?" (Publisher's note)

"[T]his sensitive tale of a young war refugee slowly adapting to a new life will strike chords of sympathy and recognition almost anywhere." Kirkus

Garlick, Nick
Aunt Severe and the dragons; illustrated by Nick Maland. Andersen 2010 120p il pa $7.99
Grades: 2 3 4   Fic
1. Aunts -- Fiction 2. Dragons -- Fiction
ISBN 978-1-8493-9055-2; 1-8493-9055-X
LC 2011290327

"Eight years old when his explorer parents disappear, Daniel goes to live with the relative he secretly names Aunt Severe. She packs away his books, feeds him cold spinach

sandwiches, and forces him to help her collect rubbish from the gutters. Daniel's life brightens considerably when he befriends four young runaway dragons, who are hiding in his aunt's garden. . . . Garlick . . . infuses this appealing, eventful story with a childlike sense of imagination, humor, and justice. Well designed for readers new to chapter books, this attractive paperback features short chapters, a good-size type, and many engaging, crosshatched ink drawings." Booklist

Garretson, Dee
Wildfire run. Harper 2010 261p $16.99; pa $6.99
Grades: 5 6 7 8   Fic
1. Adventure fiction 2. Fires -- Fiction 3. Presidents -- Fiction 4. Earthquakes -- Fiction 5. Wilderness survival -- Fiction
ISBN 978-0-06-195347-7; 0-06-195347-4; 978-0-06-195350-7 pa; 0-06-195350-4 pa
LC 2009049482

A relaxing retreat to Camp David turns deadly after a faraway earthquake sets off a chain of disastrous events that traps the president's twelve-year-old son, Luke, and his two friends within the compound.

"Along with a breathlessly paced plot, Garretson crafts a preteen protagonist who grows out of being a whiny, moody sort and, with his companions, displays generous measures of courage and ingenuity in rising to the occasion." Booklist

Garza, Xavier
★ **Lucha** libre: the Man in the Silver Mask; a bilingual cuento. written & illustrated by Xavier Garza. Cinco Puntos Press 2005 un il $17.95
Grades: 2 3 4 5   Fic
1. Mexico -- Fiction 2. Uncles -- Fiction 3. Wrestling -- Fiction 4. Bilingual books -- English-Spanish
ISBN 0-938317-92-X
LC 2004-29756

When Carlitos attends a wrestling match in Mexico City with his father, his favorite masked-wrestler has eyes that are strangely familiar.

"Smoothly integrated information in fluid colloquial English and Spanish combines with grainy graphic-novel-style illustrations executed in acrylic to create an oddly compelling and sophisticated package. An informative endnote, in English only, presents a brief but engrossing history of lucha libre." SLJ

Maximilian and the mystery of the Guardian Angel; a bilingual lucha libre thriller. written and illustrated by Xavier Garza. 1st ed. Cinco Puntos Press 2011 207 p. ill. (paperback) $12.95
Grades: 3 4 5 6   Fic
1. Adventure fiction 2. Texas -- Fiction 3. Heroes -- Fiction 4. Uncles -- Fiction 5. Wrestling -- Fiction 6. Mexican Americans -- Fiction 7. Family life -- Texas -- Fiction 8. Spanish language materials -- Bilingual
ISBN 1933693983; 9781933693989
LC 2010037400

In this book, "eleven-year-old Max is fascinated with the world of Lucha Libre and the great wrestler known as the Guardian Angel. . . . Max lives in Texas, where it has become tremendously popular. Much to his great joy, he is given the opportunity to attend a match . . . where his hero will be challenging the ruthless Red Devil. In all the emotion of attending the event, Max falls into the ring and thus into the Guardian Angel's path," discovering a familial connection with him. (School Library Journal)

Gassman, Julie

You can't spike your serves; illustrated by Jorge Santillan. Stone Arch Books 2011 49p il (Sports Illustrated kids) lib bdg $25.32; pa $5.95

Grades: 1 2 3 4   **Fic**

1. Volleyball -- Fiction

ISBN 978-1-4342-2231-2 lib bdg; 1-4342-2231-4 lib bdg; 978-1-4342-3080-5 pa; 1-4342-3080-5 pa

LC 2010048182

"Alicia wants to help her pen pal, Jenny, earn money to purchase new pom-poms, and when an Olympic volleyball player comes to school to teach the fourth graders her sport, Alicia comes up with the idea of a tournament to raise the needed funds.... She discovers how hard serving is without being able to jump, but Reese suggests the perfect technique for her. Manga-style graphics give this book a cutting-edge look and enhance understanding of the text. Short chapters, colorful cartoon illustrations, and engaging subject matter make this title appropriate for those new to chapter books as well as older readers." SLJ

Includes glossary and bibliographical references

Gates, Doris

Blue willow; illustrated by Paul Lantz. Viking 1940 172p il hardcover o.p. pa $5.99

Grades: 4 5 6 7   **Fic**

1. California -- Fiction 2. Migrant labor -- Fiction

ISBN 0-14-030924-1 pa

"Having to move from one migrant camp to another intensifies Janey Larkin's desire for a permanent home, friends, and school. The only beautiful possession the family has is a blue willow plate handed down from generation to generation. It is a reminder of happier days in Texas and represents dreams and promises for a better future. Reading about this itinerant family's ways of life, often filled with despair and yet always hopeful, leaves little room for the reader's indifference." Read Ladders for Hum Relat. 6th edition

Gauch, Patricia Lee

★ **This** time, Tempe Wick? illustrated by Margot Tomes. Boyds Mills Press 2003 43p il hardcover o.p. $16.95

Grades: 3 4 5   **Fic**

1. United States -- History -- 1775-1783, Revolution -- Fiction

ISBN 1-59078-179-1; 1-59078-185-6 pa

A reissue of the title first published 1974 by Coward, McCann & Geoghegan

Everyone knows Tempe Wick is a most surprising girl, but she exceeds even her own reputation when two mutinous Revolutionary soldiers try to steal her beloved horse.

"The writing is the perfect vehicle for the illustrations— in the artist's inimitable style—which capture the down-to-earth, unpretentious, and humorous quality of the storytelling." Horn Book

George, Jean Craighead

Charlie's raven; written and illustrated by Jean Craighead George. Dutton Children's Books 2004 190p il hardcover o.p. pa $6.99

Grades: 5 6 7 8   **Fic**

1. Ravens -- Fiction 2. Naturalists -- Fiction 3. Grandfathers -- Fiction

ISBN 0-525-47219-3; 0-14-240547-7 pa

Charlie's friend, Singing Bird, a Teton Sioux, tells him that ravens have curing powers, so Charlie steals a baby bird from its nest, hoping to heal his ailing Granddad, a retired naturalist.

"The story is technically accurate and offers a vivid sense of place and a window into Native American beliefs through storytelling." SLJ

★ **My** side of the mountain trilogy; written and illustrated by Jean Craighead George. Dutton Children's Books 2000 177, 170, 258p il $24.99

Grades: 5 6 7 8   **Fic**

1. Falcons -- Fiction 2. New York (State) -- Fiction 3. Wilderness survival -- Fiction

ISBN 0-525-46269-4

LC 00-712305

Originally published as three separate volumes, 1959, 1990, and 1999 respectively

My side of the mountain was a Newbery honor book, 1960

In My Side of the Mountain Sam Gribley tells of his year in the wilderness of the Catskill Mountains. In On the Far Side of the Mountain Sam's peaceful existence in his wilderness home is disrupted when his sister runs away and his pet falcon is confiscated by a conservation officer. In Frightful's Mountain Sam's pet falcon must learn to live as a wild bird

There's an owl in the shower; illustrated by Christine Herman Merrill. HarperCollins Pubs. 1995 133p il hardcover o.p. pa $5.99

Grades: 3 4 5   **Fic**

1. Owls -- Fiction 2. Endangered species -- Fiction

ISBN 0-06-024891-2; 0-06-440682-2 pa

LC 94-38893

Because protecting spotted owls has cost Borden's father his job as a logger in the old growth forest of northern California, Borden intends to kill any spotted owl he sees, until he and his father find themselves taking care of a young owlet

"George's writing skill and knowledge of animal behavior turn what could have been nothing but a message into an absorbing story that shows both sides of the controversy.... Merrill's drawings perfectly capture the engaging bird and the family's affection for it." SLJ

George, Jessica Day

Dragon flight; [by] Jessica Day George. 1st U.S. ed.; Bloomsbury Children's Books 2008 262p $16.95

Grades: 5 6 7 8   **Fic**

1. Fantasy fiction 2. Dragons -- Fiction

ISBN 978-1-59990-110-7; 1-59990-110-2

LC 2007050762

Sequel to: Dragon slippers (2007)

Young seamstress Creel finds herself strategizing with the dragon king Shardas once again when a renegade dragon in a distant country launches a war against their country, bringing an entire army of dragons into the mix.

"Fans of the first book will find the same strengths here: the imaginatively detailed scenes; the thrilling, spell-fueled action; the possibility of romance with a prince; and the appealing, brave heroine." Booklist

Thursdays with the crown; by Jessica Day George. Bloomsbury 2014 224 p. (hardback) $16.99

Grades: 3 4 5 6   **Fic**

1. Fantasy fiction 2. Castles -- Fiction 3. Fairy tales 4. Princesses -- Fiction 5. Brothers and sisters -- Fiction
ISBN 1619632993; 9781619632998

LC 2014005015

Sequel to: Wednesdays in the tower

"Castle Glower has been acting weird, so it's no surprise when two towers transport Celie and her siblings to an unknown land. When they realize that no one from home is coming to get them, the kids--along with Celie's pet griffin Rufus--set out through the forest to figure out where they are and what's happened to their beloved Castle." (Publisher's note)

"Like the protagonist, readers will come away with the valuable lesson that there are multiple sides to every story and that there isn't always a clear right or wrong side in a conflict between groups of people." SLJ

Tuesdays at the castle. Bloomsbury 2011 $16.99

Grades: 3 4 5 6   **Fic**

1. Fairy tales 2. Castles -- Fiction 3. Princesses -- Fiction 4. Kings and rulers -- Fiction
ISBN 978-1-59990-644-7; 1-59990-644-9

LC 2011016739

Eleven-year-old Princess Celie lives with her parents, the king and queen, and her brothers and sister at Castle Glower, which adds rooms or stairways or secret passageways most every Tuesday, and when the king and queen are ambushed while travelling, it is up to Celie—the castle's favorite—with her secret knowledge of its never-ending twists and turns, to protect their home and save their kingdom.

"Castle Glower is the true star of this charming story of court intrigue and magic. A satisfying mix of Hogwarts and Howl's Moving Castle, . . . Castle Glower helps its true citizens, but never at the expense of plot or character development." SLJ

Gephart, Donna

★ **How** to survive middle school. Delacorte Press 2010 247p $15.99; lib bdg $18.99

Grades: 5 6 7 8   **Fic**

1. School stories 2. Family life -- Fiction
ISBN 978-0-385-73793-7; 0-385-73793-9; 978-0-385-90701-9 lib bdg; 0-385-90701-X lib bdg

LC 2009-21809

When thirteen-year-old David Greenberg's best friend makes the start of middle school even worse than he feared it could be, David becomes friends with Penny, who shares his love of television shows and posts one of their skits on YouTube, making them wildly popular—online, at least.

"Gephart crafts for her likable protagonist an engaging, feel-good transition into adolescence that's well stocked with tears and laughter." Booklist

Olivia Bean, trivia queen; Donna Gephart. Delacorte Press 2012 278 p. $16.99

Grades: 3 4 5 6 7   **Fic**

1. Game shows -- Fiction 2. Children of divorced parents -- Fiction 3. Father-daughter relationship -- Fiction 4. Divorce -- Fiction 5. Fathers -- Fiction 6. Curiosities and wonders -- Fiction 7. Jeopardy (Television program) -- Fiction
ISBN 0385740522; 9780385740524

LC 2011006023

In this book, "Olivia Bean has watched 'Jeopardy!' every evening since she was a little girl, but the nightly tradition just hasn't been the same since her father . . . took off for California two years ago. When the show announces auditions for Kids Week, Olivia is intent on making the cut, not only to compete but, more importantly, to get a plane ticket out to the show's taping in L.A. with the hopes of meeting up with her estranged dad." (Bulletin of the Center for Children's Books).

Gewirtz, Adina Rishe

Zebra forest; Adina Rishe Gewirtz. Candlewick Press 2013 208 p. (reinforced) $15.99

Grades: 5 6 7 8   **Fic**

1. Hostages -- Fiction 2. Siblings -- Fiction
ISBN 0763660418; 9780763660413

LC 2012947251

In this novel, by Adina Rishe Gewirtz, "an escaped fugitive upends everything two siblings think they know about their family, their past, and themselves. . . . A rattling at the back door, an escapee from the prison holding them hostage in their own home, four lives that will never be the same. . . . [The book] portrays an unfolding standoff of truth against family secrets." (Publisher's note)

"Debut author Gewirtz successfully conveys the terror and tedium of being trapped. . . While the situation may frighten some readers, the matter-of-fact way [the protagonists] make the best of difficult circumstances . . . may be comforting to those whose families don't match the ideal. An emotionally honest family story with an ending that's hopeful without being implausibly upbeat." Pub Wkly

Gibbs, Stuart

Belly up. Simon & Schuster Books for Young Readers 2010 294p $15.99; pa $6.99

Grades: 4 5 6 7   **Fic**

1. Mystery fiction 2. Zoos -- Fiction 3. Hippopotamus -- Fiction
ISBN 1-4169-8731-2; 1-4169-8732-0 pa; 978-1-4169-8731-4; 978-1-4169-8732-1 pa

LC 2009-34860

Twelve-year-old Teddy investigates when a popular Texas zoo's star attraction, Henry the hippopotamus, is murdered.

"The characters are well-developed and believable, making this book appealing to reluctant readers and those who enjoy animal stories and mysteries." Libr Media Connect

The last musketeer. Harper 2011 244p $16.99

Grades: 5 6 7 8   **Fic**

1. Cardinals 2. Statesmen 3. Adventure fiction 4. Time travel -- Fiction 5. France -- History -- 1589-1789, Bourbons -- Fiction
ISBN 978-0-06-204838-7; 0-06-204838-4

LC 2011019376

In Paris with his parents to sell family heirlooms, fourteen-year-old Greg Rich suddenly finds himself four hundred years in the past, and is aided by boys who will one day be known as 'The Three Musketeers.'

"From the gripping first sentence . . . the excitement never flags in this newly imagined Musketeer adventure. . . . Using Alexandre Dumas' stories as a jumping-off point, Gibbs mixes fact, fantasy and thrills to create a galloping swashbuckler." Kirkus

Poached; Stuart Gibbs. Simon & Schuster Books for Young Readers 2014 329 pages (hardcover) $15.99
Grades: 4 5 6 7   **Fic**
1. Mystery fiction 2. Zoos -- Fiction 3. Koalas -- Fiction 4. Bullies -- Fiction 5. Texas -- Fiction 6. Zoo animals -- Fiction 7. Mystery and detective stories 8. Family life -- Texas -- Fiction
ISBN 1442467770; 9781442467774
LC 2013000539

In this sequel to "Belly Up," by Stuart Gibbs, "12-year-old trouble-magnet Teddy is still living at FunJungle, a massive zoo and amusement park, with his primatologist mother and wildlife photographer father. . . . When the school bully, Vance, forces Teddy to throw a fake arm into the shark tank . . . [it] has a large-scale snowball effect that positions Teddy as the key suspect in the theft of Kazoo, a koala on loan from Australia." (Kirkus Reviews)

"In Belly Up's sequel, twelve-year-old Teddy contends with bullies at school. At FunJungle, the zoo where he lives with his primatologist mother and wildlife-photographer father, things are even worse: Teddy's the prime suspect in a koala kidnapping. Gibbs weaves interesting trivia (newborn koalas are jellybean-size) and plenty of humor (a poop-throwing chimp helps ID an industrial spy/saboteur) into his action-packed mystery." Horn Book

Space case; Stuart Gibbs. Simon & Schuster Books for Young Readers 2014 352 p. (hardcover) $16.99
Grades: 4 5 6 7   **Fic**
1. Mystery fiction 2. Space colonies -- Fiction 3. Moon -- Fiction 4. Science fiction 5. Mystery and detective stories 6. Human-alien encounters -- Fiction
ISBN 1442494867; 9781442494862; 9781442494879
LC 2013033587

This middle grades book by Stuart Gibbs describes how "like his fellow lunarnauts--otherwise known as Moonies--living on Moon Base Alpha, twelve-year-old Dashiell Gibson is famous the world over for being one of the first humans to live on the moon. . . . Then Moon Base Alpha's top scientist turns up dead. Dash senses there's foul play afoot, but no one believes him." (Publisher's note)

"It's 2041, and 12-year-old Dash Gibson lives with his family in Moon Base Alpha, the first lunar outpost. Life is mostly dull (watching TV, going to the gym to keep fit, and playing video games—not much variety) until Ronald Holtz, beloved base physician, dies under suspicious circumstances...Recommended as a breezy read, especially for the budding space scientist." SLJ

Spy camp; Stuart Gibbs. 1st ed. Simon & Schuster Books for Young Readers 2013 336 p. (hardcover) $17.99
Grades: 4 5 6 7   **Fic**
1. Spies -- Fiction 2. Camping -- Fiction 3. Camps -- Fiction 4. Survival -- Fiction
ISBN 1442457538; 9781442457539
LC 2012019416
Sequel to: Spy school

In this story by Stuart Gibbs, "Ben Ripley is a middle-schooler . . . [who] spent the last year training to be a top-level spy and dodging all sorts of associated danger. So now that summer's finally here, Ben's ready to have some fun and relax. Except . . . a spy-in-training's work is never done, and the threats from SPYDER, an enemy spy organization, are as unavoidable as the summer heat. Will Ben be able to keep his cover--and his cool?" (Publisher's note)

"After escaping assassination by the top-secret organization SPYDER, Ben Ripley (Spy School) is looking forward to chilling out this summer. But SPYDER is turning up the heat, insisting that Ben come to work for them. Gorgeous fellow-spy-in-training Erica is ready to help, and her legendary grandfather also appears on the scene. Clever descriptions and plot twists make this a top-notch summer read." Horn Book

Giblin, James

The **boy** who saved Cleveland; based on a true story. [by] James Cross Giblin; illustrated by Michael Dooling. Henry Holt and Company 2006 64p il $15.95
Grades: 3 4 5   **Fic**
1. Ohio -- Fiction 2. Malaria -- Fiction 3. Epidemics -- Fiction 4. Frontier and pioneer life -- Fiction
ISBN 0-8050-7355-8; 978-0-8050-7355-3
LC 2005021695

During a malaria epidemic in late eighteenth-century Cleveland, Ohio, ten-year-old Seth Doan surprises his family, his neighbors, and himself by having the strength to carry and grind enough corn to feed everyone.

"Young readers will enjoy the clear writing and plot-driven pace. Dooling's full-page pencil-on-paper illustrations convey the time period as well as the emotional tone. A solid choice for those seeking pioneer fiction and strong characters." Booklist

Gibson, Julia Mary

Copper magic; Julia Mary Gibson. Starscape 2014 336 p. map (hardback) $16.99
Grades: 4 5 6 7 8   **Fic**
1. Magic -- Fiction 2. Historical fiction 3. Great Lakes region -- Fiction 4. Talismans -- Fiction 5. Teenage girls -- Fiction 6. United States -- History -- 20th century -- Fiction
ISBN 0765332116; 9780765332110
LC 2014014660

"The year is 1906, and on the shores of Lake Michigan twelve-year-old Violet Blake unearths an ancient talisman--a copper hand. Violet's touch warms the copper hand and it begins to reveal glimpses of another time." (Publisher's note)

"The summer of 1906 promises to be an exciting one for twelve-year-old Violet Blake: she gets her first job as an assistant for a visiting photographer; she meets a new friend; and best of all, she discovers an ancient copper talisman in the shape of a hand buried near the creek where her mother used to harvest medicinal herbs. . . . The presence of magic is subtle in the story, but in the end, it matters little whether the copper hand has magical power or not. Instead it is Violet's growth from a self-centered child to one who carefully considers the feelings and needs of those around her that give this story weight." VOYA

Gidwitz, Adam

The **Grimm** conclusion; by Adam Gidwitz and illustrated by Hugh D'Andrade. Dutton Children's Books 2013
368 p. (hardcover) $16.99
Grades: 4 5 6   **Fic**

1. Fairy tales 2. Horror fiction 3. Humorous stories 4.
Brothers and sisters -- Fiction 5. Characters in literature
-- Fiction 6. Adventure and adventurers -- Fiction
ISBN 0525426159; 9780525426158

LC 2013021686

In this book by Adam Gidwitz and illustrated by Hugh
D'Andrade, "two children venture through forests, flee kingdoms, face ogres and demons and monsters, and, ultimately,
find their way home. Oh yes, and they may die. Just once
or twice." (Publisher's note) "An omniscient narrator comments throughout, offering warnings, consolation, and ex-
planations." (Horn Book Magazine)

In a glass Grimmly; Adam Gidwitz. Dutton Juvenile
2012 314 p. (hardback) $16.99
Grades: 4 5 6 7 8   **Fic**

1. Horror fiction 2. Occult fiction 3. Fractured fairy
tales 4. Fairy tales 5. Frogs -- Fiction 6. Humorous
stories 7. Cousins -- Fiction 8. Characters in literature
-- Fiction 9. Adventure and adventurers -- Fiction
ISBN 0525425810; 9780525425816

LC 2012015515

This book is Adam Gidwitz's second collection of reimagined fairy tales. "The protagonists in this installment
are Jack, Jill, and a talking frog, whose adventures begin
separately in reworkings of 'The Frog Prince' and 'The Emperor's New Clothes,' before the three join forces in 'Jack
and the Bean-stalk.'" (Publishers Weekly)

★ A **tale** dark & Grimm. Dutton 2010 256p il $16.99
Grades: 5 6 7 8   **Fic**

1. Fairy tales 2. Siblings -- Fiction
ISBN 978-0-525-42334-8; 0-525-42334-6;
9780525425816

LC 2009-53289

This book follows Hansel and Gretel as they walk out of
their own story and into eight more tales. "Age ten and up."
(N Y Times Book Rev)

"An audacious debut that's wicked smart and wicked
funny." Publ Wkly

Giff, Patricia Reilly

Eleven. Wendy Lamb Books 2008 164p $15.99; lib
bdg $18.99; pa $6.50
Grades: 4 5 6 7   **Fic**

1. Woodwork -- Fiction 2. Friendship -- Fiction 3.
Kidnapping -- Fiction 4. Learning disabilities -- Fiction
ISBN 978-0-385-73069-3; 978-0-385-90098-0 lib
bdg; 978-0-440-23802-7 pa

LC 2007-12638

When Sam, who can barely read, discovers an old newspaper clipping just before his eleventh birthday, it brings
forth memories from his past, and, with the help of a new
friend at school and the castle they are building for a school
project, his questions are eventually answered.

This is an "exquisitely rendered story of self-discovery."
Publ Wkly

Flying feet; illustrated by Alasdair Bright. Wendy
Lamb Books 2011 71p il (Zigzag kids) $11.99; lib bdg
$14.99; pa $4.99
Grades: 2 3 4   **Fic**

1. School stories 2. Inventors -- Fiction
ISBN 978-0-385-73887-3; 0-385-73887-0; 978-0-
385-90754-5 lib bdg; 0-385-90754-0 lib bdg; 978-0-
375-89637-8 e-book; 978-0-375-85911-3 pa; 0-375-
85911-X pa

LC 2010022645

Charlie often thinks of inventions that seldom work, but
his latest idea just might be able to help Jake the Sweeper
get rid of a big pile of trash and save "Come as a Character"
day, too.

"The cheerful drawings offer levity to the spare, straightforward prose laid out in one- or two-sentence paragraphs.
The tension builds mildly, exploring the concept of individuality and the expanding pressures of growing up, demonstrating Giff's keen understanding of chapter-book readers."
Kirkus

Lily's crossing. Delacorte Press 1997 180p $15.95;
pa $6.50; $15.95
Grades: 4 5 6 7   **Fic**

1. Friendship -- Fiction 2. World War, 1939-1945 --
Fiction
ISBN 0-385-32142-2; 0-440-41453-9 pa;
9780385321426

LC 96-23021

A Newbery Medal honor book, 1998

"Set during World War II, this . . . story tells of the war's
impact on two children, one an American and one a Hungarian refugee. Lily Mollahan, a spirited, sensitive youngster
being raised by her grandmother and Poppy, her widower
father, has a comfortable routine that includes the family's
annual summer migration to Gram's beach house in Rocka-
way, NY. Lily looks forward to summer's freedom and
fishing outings with Poppy. She meets Albert, a Hungarian
boy who is staying at a neighbor's house. . . . Eventually
the two become good friends. The war interferes directly
with Lily's life when Poppy, an engineer, is sent to Europe
to help with clean-up operations." (SLJ) "Grades five to
eight." (Booklist)

"Gentle elements of danger and suspense . . . keep the
plot moving forward, while the delicate balance of characters and setting gently coalesces into an emotional whole
that is fully satisfying." Bull Cent Child Books

Maggie's door. Wendy Lamb Bks. 2003 158p pa
$6.50
Grades: 5 6 7 8   **Fic**

1. Ireland -- Fiction 2. Immigrants -- Fiction
ISBN 0-385-32658-0; 0-385-90095-3 lib bdg; 0-440-
41581-0 pa

LC 2003-2415

Sequel to: Nory Ryan's song (2000)

In the mid-1800s, Nory and her neighbor and friend,
Sean, set out separately on a dangerous journey from fam-
ine-plagued Ireland, hoping to reach a better life in America

"Giff uses vivid language and precisely detailed observation to convey both experience and emotion." Horn Book

Nory Ryan's song. Delacorte Press 2000 148p hardcover o.p. pa $5.99

Grades: 5 6 7 8   **Fic**
    1. Famines -- Fiction 2. Ireland -- Fiction
    ISBN 0-385-32141-4; 0-440-41829-1 pa
                                            LC 00-27690

When a terrible blight attacks Ireland's potato crop in 1845, twelve-year-old Nory Ryan's courage and ingenuity help her family and neighbors survive

"Giff brings the landscape and the cultural particulars of the era vividly to life and creates in Nory a heroine to cheer for. A beautiful, heart-wrenching novel that makes a devastating event understandable." Booklist

Another title about Nory is:

Maggie's door (2003)

Pictures of Hollis Woods. Wendy Lamb Bks. 2002 166p $15.95; pa $6.50

Grades: 5 6 7 8   **Fic**
    1. Artists -- Fiction 2. Old age -- Fiction 3. Foster home care -- Fiction
    ISBN 0-385-32655-6; 0-440-41578-0 pa
                                           LC 2002-426

A Newbery Medal honor book, 2003

"She was named for the place where she was found as an abandoned baby. Twelve-year-old Hollis Woods has been through many foster homes—and she runs away, every time. In her latest placement, with an artist named Josie, the tightly wound Hollis begins to relax ever so slightly. . . . But Josie is slowly slipping into dementia, and Hollis knows that she'll be taken away from her if Josie is found out. . . . Giff has a sure hand with language, and the narrative is taut and absorbing." Booklist

R my name is Rachel. Wendy Lamb Books 2011 166p $15.99; lib bdg $18.99; e-book $10.99

Grades: 4 5 6 7   **Fic**
    1. Moving -- Fiction 2. Siblings -- Fiction 3. Farm life -- Fiction 4. Great Depression, 1929-1939 -- Fiction
    ISBN 978-0-375-83889-7; 0-375-83889-9; 978-0-375-93889-4 lib bdg; 0-375-93889-3; 978-0-375-98389-4 e-book
                                          LC 2011004303

Three city siblings, now living on a farm during the Great Depression, must survive on their own when their father takes a construction job miles away.

"Rachel's searing, present-tense narrative exposes her fears, determination, and hopefulness in the face of wrenching challenges. Recurring motifs—color, flowers, and drawings by a neighbor that Rachel discovers in unlikely places—add lyricism to this story of family solidarity." Publ Wkly

Storyteller. Wendy Lamb Books 2010 166p $15.99; lib bdg $18.99

Grades: 5 6 7 8   **Fic**
    1. Aunts -- Fiction 2. Family life -- Fiction 3. New York (State) -- Fiction 4. Father-daughter relationship -- Fiction 5. United States -- History -- 1775-1783, Revolution -- Fiction
    ISBN 978-0-375-83888-0; 0-375-83888-0; 978-0-375-93888-7 lib bdg; 0-375-93888-5 lib bdg
                                          LC 2009-48130

Forced to spend months at an aunt's house, Elizabeth feel a connection to her ancestor Zee, whose picture hangs on the wall, and who reveals her story of hardships during the Revolutionary War as Elizabeth comes to terms with her own troubles

"As she brings these characters and history alive, Giff again demonstrates her own gift for storytelling." Publ Wkly

Water Street. Wendy Lamb Books 2006 164p $15.95; lib bdg $17.99; pa $6.50

Grades: 5 6 7 8   **Fic**
    1. Family life -- Fiction 2. Irish Americans -- Fiction 3. Brooklyn (New York, N.Y.) -- Fiction
    ISBN 978-0-385-90097-3; 0-385-73068-3; 978-0-385-90097-3 lib bdg; 0-385-90097-X lib bdg; 978-0-440-41921-1 pa; 0-440-41921-2 pa
                                          LC 2006-02024

In the shadow of the construction of the Brooklyn Bridge, eighth-graders and new neighbors Bird Mallon and Thomas Neary make some decisions about what they want to do with their lives.

"Continuing the Irish American immigration story begun in Nory Ryan's Song (2000) and Maggie's Door (2003), [this] novel, set in 1875, is about the next generation. . . . A poignant immigration story of friendship, work, and the meaning of home." Booklist

Winter sky; by Patricia Reilly Giff. Wendy Lamb Books, an imprint of Random House Children's Books 2014 160 p. illustrations (hardback) $15.99

Grades: 4 5 6 7   **Fic**
    1. Courage -- Fiction 2. Friendship -- Fiction 3. Family life -- Fiction 4. Fire fighters -- Fiction
    ISBN 0375838929; 9780375838927; 9780385371926
                                          LC 2013022399

In this book, by Patricia Reilly Giff, "Siria's dad is a firefighter who doesn't know that someone special watches out for him; each time his daughter hears a siren, she sneaks out of her apartment building to chase his fire truck and make sure he is safe. During one such nightly pursuit, Siria discovers evidence of what she believes to be arson. Who could be purposely setting fires? When clues point to someone close to home, Siria must find the strength to unravel the mystery." (School Library Journal)

"Worried about her firefighter father's safety, every time a siren wails eleven-year-old Siria sneaks out and chases the truck, watching to make sure he escapes harm. Over Christmas break, Siria notices small fires being set all over town and decides to investigate on her own. Unadorned but engaging prose and Giff's well-drawn characters add depth to a simple story about courage and friendship." Horn Book

Giles, Stephen M.

The **body** thief. Sourcebooks Jabberwocky 2010 221p il (The death (and further adventures) of Silas Winterbottom) $12.99

Grades: 3 4 5 6   **Fic**
    1. Mystery fiction 2. Uncles -- Fiction 3. Cousins -- Fiction 4. Australia -- Fiction 5. Immortality -- Fiction 6. Inheritance and succession -- Fiction
    ISBN 978-1-4022-4090-4; 1-4022-4090-2
                                          LC 2010-14380

First published 2009 in Australia

Lured to their sick Uncle Silas's home under the pretense of becoming heirs to his vast fortune, cousins Adele, Isabella, and Milo soon learn that the old man has a diabolical plan to prevent his own death.

"Giles delivers even the macabre twists of the tale with a light touch, giving readers plenty of incentive to stick with the series." Publ Wkly

Gilman, Laura Anne

Grail quest: the Camelot spell; book one. HarperCollins 2006 291p $10.99; lib bdg $14.89

Grades: 5 6 7 8   **Fic**

1. Kings 2. Magic -- Fiction 3. Middle Ages -- Fiction 4. Knights and knighthood -- Fiction

ISBN 0-06-077279-4; 0-06-077280-8 lib bdg

Three teenagers living in Camelot are forced to undertake a dangerous mission when King Arthur's court falls under a mysterious enchantment on the eve of the quest for the Holy Grail.

"The believable dialogue, succint plot, and uncomplicated references to court life will appeal to middle graders who are beginning to explore Aurthurian legend." Voice Youth Advocates

Other titles in this series are:

Grail quest: Morgain's revenge (2006)

Grail quest: The shadow companion (2006)

Gilson, Jamie

Bug in a rug; illustrated by Diane deGroat. Clarion Books 1998 69p il hardcover o.p. $15

Grades: 2 3 4   **Fic**

1. School stories 2. Uncles -- Fiction 3. Clothing and dress -- Fiction

ISBN 0-395-86616-2; 0-618-31670-1

LC 97-16437

Seven-year-old Richard is self-conscious when he receives a pair of purple pants from his aunt and uncle and has to wear them to school, but he is even more worried when his uncle shows up for a visit to his classroom

"Gilson captures the thoughts and fears of second graders through authentic dialogue and solid characterization." SLJ

Other titles about Richard are:

Chess! I love it, I love it, I love it! (2008)

Gotcha! (2006)

It goes Eeeeeeeeeeeee! (1994)

Itchy Richard (1991)

Gipson, Frederick Benjamin

Old Yeller; [by] Fred Gipson; drawings by Carl Burger. Harper & Row 1956 158p il $23; pa $5.99

Grades: 6 7 8 9   **Fic**

1. Dogs -- Fiction 2. Texas -- Fiction 3. Frontier and pioneer life -- Fiction

ISBN 0-06-011545-9; 0-06-440382-3 pa

LC 56-8780

A Newbery Medal honor book, 1957

"Travis at fourteen was the man of the family during the hard summer of 1860 when his father drove his herd of cattle from Texas to the Kansas market. It was the summer when an old yellow dog attached himself to the family and won Travis' reluctant friendship. Before the summer was over, Old Yeller proved more than a match for thieving raccoons, fighting bulls, grizzly bears, and mad wolves. This is a skill-

ful tale of a boy's love for a dog as well as a description of a pioneer boyhood and it can't miss with any dog lover." Horn Book

Glaser, Linda

Bridge to America; based on a true story. Houghton Mifflin Co. 2005 200p $16

Grades: 4 5 6   **Fic**

1. Jews -- Fiction 2. Immigrants -- Fiction

ISBN 0-618-56301-6

Eight-year-old Fivel narrates the story of his family's Atlantic Ocean crossing to reunite with their father in the United States, from its desperate beginning in a shtetl in Poland in 1920 to his stirrings of identity as an American boy.

"Even reluctant readers will enjoy this riveting account and sensitive portrayal of what it means to be an immigrant." SLJ

Glatstein, Jacob

Emil and Karl; by Yankev Glatshteyn; translated by Jeffrey Shandler. Roaring Brook Press 2006 194p $17.95; pa $6.99

Grades: 5 6 7 8   **Fic**

1. Jews -- Fiction 2. Friendship -- Fiction 3. Vienna (Austria) -- Fiction 4. Holocaust, 1933-1945 -- Fiction

ISBN 1-59643-119-9; 0-312-37387-2 pa

LC 2005-26800

Original Yiddish edition 1940

A story about the dilemma faced by two young boys—one Jewish, the other not—when they suddenly find themselves without homes or families in Vienna on the eve of World War II.

"The fast-moving prose is stark and immediate. Glatshteyn was, of course, writing about what was happening to children in his time. . . . The translation, 65 years after the novel's original publication, is nothing short of haunting." Booklist

Glatt, Lisa

Abigail Iris: the one and only. Walker & Co. 2009 148p $14.99

Grades: 2 3 4   **Fic**

1. Siblings -- Fiction 2. Friendship -- Fiction 3. Family life -- Fiction

ISBN 978-0-8027-9782-7; 0-8027-9782-2

LC 2008007391

Abigail Iris thinks she would rather be an only child but after going on vacation with her best friend, who is an "Only," she realizes there are benefits of being one of many.

"Told in the first person from Abigail Iris' point of view, this chapter book comes to life through her ingenuous voice and reflections. Appealing black-and-white drawings show the characters' personalities, attitudes, and emotions." Booklist

Another title about Abigail Iris is:

Abigail Iris: the pet project (2010)

Abigail Iris: the pet project; [by] Lisa Glatt and Suzanne Greenberg; illustrated by Joy Allen. Walker 2010 164p il $14.99; pa $6.99

Grades: 2 3 4   **Fic**

1. Cats -- Fiction 2. Family life -- Fiction

ISBN 978-0-8027-8657-9; 0-8027-8657-X; 978-0-8027-2235-5 pa; 0-8027-2235-0 pa

When Abigail Iris finally gets the new kitten she has been wanting, she learns about the responsibilities that come with pet ownership, as well as the impact a kitten can have on a large family like hers.

"Fast-paced conversation, coupled with realistic events, creates a fun read while full-page black-and-white illustrations add interest." SLJ

Gliori, Debi

Witch Baby and me. Corgi 2010 246p il pa $7.99

Grades: 4 5 6   **Fic**

1. Magic -- Fiction 2. Infants -- Fiction 3. Sisters -- Fiction 4. Witches -- Fiction 5. Scotland -- Fiction

ISBN 978-0-552-55676-7; 0-552-55676-9

"Three witches from Ben Screeeiiighe, a wildly remote area of Scotland, are searching for a baby. Their plan, at first, is to cast a spell on an infant, allow the human parents to raise her, then take over her witchy education when she becomes older. . . . But the witches do not foresee that Baby Daisy MacRae's sister [Lily] . . . can see their magic, and knows that her sister is a witch even if no one believes her. . . . Readers will laugh at Lily's imagination and her attempts to keep people from finding out that her sister is really a spell-casting witch-in-training. Entertaining line drawings complement the [text]." SLJ

Other titles in this series are:

Witch Baby and me after dark (2010)

Witch Baby and me at school (2009)

Witch Baby and me on stage (2011)

Godden, Rumer

The doll's house; illustrated by Tasha Tudor. Viking 1962 136p il hardcover o.p. pa $5.99

Grades: 2 3 4   **Fic**

1. Dolls -- Fiction 2. Dollhouses -- Fiction

ISBN 0-14-030942-X pa

First published 1947 in the United Kingdom; first United States edition illustrated by Dana Saintsbury published 1948

Adventures of a brave little hundred-year-old Dutch farthing doll, her family, their Victorian dollhouse home and the two little English girls to whom they all belonged. Tottie's great adventure was when she went to the exhibition, Dolls through the ages, and was singled out for notice by the Queen who opened the exhibition

"Each doll has a firmly drawn, recognizably true character; the children think and behave convincingly. . . . The story is enthralling, and complete in every detail." Spectator

Godwin, Laura

The Doll people set sail; by Ann M. Martin and Laura Godwin; with pictures by Brett Helquist. Disney-Hyperion Books 2014 304 p. (The Doll people) $17.99

Grades: 3 4 5   **Fic**

1. Sea stories 2. Dolls -- Fiction

ISBN 1423136837; 9781423136835

LC 2013041937

In this fourth installment of the Doll People series, by Ann M. Martin and Laura Godwin, "Annabelle Doll, Tiffany Funcraft, and their families are whisked out to sea when the Palmers accidentally place them in a box destined for charity donation. And it turns out they're not alone-there are plenty of other doll people on the ship, too. After traveling thousands of miles, will they be able to find their way home?" (Publisher's note)

"The fourth installment of "The Doll People" series is an adventure on the high seas. Annabelle Doll, her best friend, Tiffany Funcraft, and the other doll people are packed away in anticipation of their human owners, Katie and Nora's, room renovation...Familiarity with the other books in the series would be helpful, but is not necessary. This is a good choice for independent readers ready to try something longer." SLJ

Other titles in the series include:

The Doll People (2000)

The Meanest Doll in the World (2003)

The Runaway Dolls (2008)

Going, K. L.

The garden of Eve. Harcourt 2007 234p $17; pa $6.99

Grades: 4 5 6 7   **Fic**

1. Death -- Fiction 2. Magic -- Fiction 3. Bereavement -- Fiction 4. New York (State) -- Fiction

ISBN 978-0-15-205986-6; 0-15-205986-5; 978-0-15-206614-7 pa; 0-15-206614-4 pa

LC 2007-05074

Eve gave up her belief in stories and magic after her mother's death, but a mysterious seed given to her as an eleventh-birthday gift by someone she has never met takes her and a boy who claims to be a ghost on a strange journey, to where their supposedly cursed town of Beaumont, New York, flourishes.

"Believably and with delicacy, Going paints a suspenseful story suffused with the poignant questions of what it means to be alive, and what might await on the other side." Horn Book

Goldblatt, Mark

Finding the worm; Mark Goldblatt. Random House Inc 2015 352 p. (lib. bdg.) $19.99

Grades: 5 6 7 8   **Fic**

1. School discipline 2. Teenagers -- Fiction 3. Vandalism -- Fiction 4. Friendship -- Fiction 5. Bar mitzvah -- Fiction 6. Conduct of life -- Fiction 7. Jews -- United States -- Fiction 8. Queens (New York, N.Y.) -- History -- 20th century -- Fiction

ISBN 0385391099; 9780385391085; 9780385391092

LC 2014004052

Sequel to: Twerp

In this novel by Mark Goldblatt "trouble always seems to find thirteen-year-old Julian Twerski. He's been accused of vandalizing a painting. The principal doesn't want to suspend him again, so instead, he asks Julian to write a 200-word essay on good citizenship. Being falsely accused is bad enough, but outside of school, Julian's dealing with even bigger issues. His friend Quentin has been really sick. How can life be fair when the nicest guy in your group has cancer?" (Publishers' note)

"Julian Twerski and the gang from Twerp (Random, 2013) are now in seventh grade, and it seems like they're dealing with an even bigger set of challenges than last year. When Julian is accused of vandalizing a painting at school, he gets locked into a battle with his new principal that he surely can't win.An excellent companion to Twerp, this novel also stands alone." SLJ

Goscinny, Rene

Nicholas; [by] Rene Goscinny & [illustrated by] Jean-Jacques Sempe; translated by Anthea Bell. Phaidon 2005 126p il $19.95

Grades: 4 5 6   **Fic**

1. School stories

ISBN 0-7148-4529-9

"This classic book about a mischievous schoolboy and his friends, originally published in French in 1959, is now available in English. The expertly translated text is enlivened by artwork by a New Yorker cartoonist to create the unforgettable milieu of Nicholas and his rowdy friends. A collection of 19 escapades, the stories introduce the protagonist and his cohorts as they wreak havoc out of simple, everyday situations at school, on the playground, and at home." SLJ

Other titles about Nicholas are:

Nicholas again (2006)

Nicholas on vacation (2007)

Grabenstein, Chris

The black heart crypt; a haunted mystery. Random House 2011 328p (Haunted places mystery) $16.99; lib bdg $19.99; e-book $16.99

Grades: 5 6 7 8   **Fic**

1. Ghost stories 2. Mystery fiction 3. Demonology -- Fiction

ISBN 978-0-375-86900-6; 0-375-86900-X; 978-0-375-96900-3 lib bdg; 0-375-96900-4 lib bdg; 978-0-375-89987-4 e-book

LC 2011001939

A 200-year-old ghost inhabits a living ancestor in order to take revenge on eleven-year-old Zack and his family.

"The pace never flags. Through flurries of ultrashort chapters, events spiral to a suspenseful climax, and the mix of corpses and comedy add up to a faintly macabre tone that isn't dispelled even by the end's just deserts and happy outcomes." Kirkus

The crossroads. Random House 2008 325p (Haunted places mystery) $16.99; lib bdg $19.99; pa $6.99

Grades: 5 6 7 8   **Fic**

1. Ghost stories 2. Connecticut -- Fiction 3. Stepmothers -- Fiction

ISBN 978-0-375-84697-7; 0-375-84697-2; 978-0-375-94697-4 lib bdg; 0-375-94697-7 lib bdg; 978-0-375-84698-4 pa; 0-375-84698-0 pa

LC 2007024803

When eleven-year-old Zack Jennings moves to Connecticut with his father and new stepmother, they must deal with the ghosts left behind by a terrible accident, as well as another kind of ghost from Zack's past

"An absorbing psychological thriller . . . as well as a rip-roaring ghost story, this switches points of view among humans, trees, and ghosts with astonishing élan." Booklist

Other titles in this series are:

The Hanging Hill (2009)

The smoky corridor (2010)

The Black Heart Crypt (2011)

Escape from Mr. Lemoncello's library; Chris Grabenstein. 1st ed. Random House Inc. 2013 304 p. (hardcover) $16.99; (library) $19.99

Grades: 5 6 7   **Fic**

1. Contests -- Fiction 2. Games -- Fiction 3. Libraries

-- Fiction 4. Books and reading -- Fiction

ISBN 037587089X; 9780375870897; 9780375970894

LC 2012048122

In this book, twelve "seventh-graders win a chance to spend an overnight lock-in previewing their town's new public library," which was "conceived by Luigi Lemoncello, the . . . founder of Mr. Lemoncello's Imagination Factory, which is a source for every kind of game imaginable. During the lock-in the winners . . . are offered a further challenge: 'Find your way out of the library using only what's in the library.' The winner will become spokesperson for the Imagination Factory." (Publishers Weekly)

The Hanging Hill. Random House 2009 322p (Haunted places mystery) $16.99; lib bdg $19.99

Grades: 5 6 7 8   **Fic**

1. Ghost stories 2. Theater -- Fiction 3. Criminals -- Fiction 4. Connecticut -- Fiction 5. Stepmothers -- Fiction

ISBN 978-0-375-84699-1; 0-375-84699-9; 978-0-375-94699-8 lib bdg; 978-0-375-84700-4 pa

LC 2008027274

While working at a summer stock theater, eleven-year-old Zack and his stepmother encounter the ghost of one of Connecticut's most notorious criminals.

"The story line is hauntingly delicious as the fully fleshed-out creepiness comes tempered with humor." SLJ

My brother the robot; James Patterson and Chris Grabenstein; illustrated by Juliana Neufeld. Little, Brown & Co. 2014 352 p. illustrations

Grades: 4 5 6 7 8   **Fic**

1. School stories 2. Robots -- Fiction 3. Humorous stories 4. Schools -- Fiction 5. Inventors -- Fiction 6. Family life -- Fiction 7. Middle schools -- Fiction

ISBN 9780316405911

LC 2013041672

In this graphic novel by James Patterson and Chris Grabenstein, "an extraordinary robot signs up for an ordinary fifth grade class. It was never easy for Sammy Hayes-Rodriguez to fit in, so he's dreading the day when his genius mom insists he bring her newest invention to school: a walking, talking robot he calls E--for 'Error.' Sammy's no stranger to robots--his house is full of a colorful cast of them. But this one not only thinks it's Sammy's brother... it's actually even nerdier than Sammy." (Publisher's note)

"Sammy Hayes-Rodriguez has never had an easy time fitting in at school. His mother is an inventor, his father is a graphic novel artist, and his beloved little sister has an immune condition that keeps her confined to the house. His best friend Trip has a talent for saying the wrong thing at the wrong time. And then, there are the robots: a houseful of his mother's creations, programmed to do everything from housework to tutoring, plus some that don't do anything useful at all...A fast-moving plot, lots of jokes, and a host of weird robots will draw readers in, especially those looking for books similar to series such as "Diary of a Wimpy Kid" (Abrams/Amulet) and "Timmy Failure" (Candlewick)." SLJ

Grabien, Deborah

Dark's tale. Egmont USA 2010 300p $15.99

Grades: 4 5 6   **Fic**

1. Cats -- Fiction 2. Parks -- Fiction 3. Animals --

Fiction 4. San Francisco (Calif.) -- Fiction
ISBN 978-1-60684-037-5; 1-60684-037-1

"Dark, a house cat abandoned in San Francisco's Golden Gate Park, must learn to survive in her new habitat. Befriended by a raccoon, she learns to recognize park inhabitants she must fear, like the 'crazybad' people, and those she can trust, including a wise owl named Memorie and a magical woman in rags who calls herself Streetwise Sal. . . . Written in first person from Dark's point of view, the novel creates a believable natural world, where predators hunt smaller animals and a cat must rely on her senses, her skills, and her friends for survival." Booklist

Graff, Lisa

★ **Absolutely** almost; Lisa Graff. Philomel Books, an imprint of Penguin Group (USA) 2014 304 p. $16.99
Grades: 4 5 6 7　　　　　　　　　　　　　　**Fic**
1. Self-esteem -- Fiction 2. Ability -- Fiction 3. Ability -- Fiction 4. Schools -- Fiction 5. Babysitters -- Fiction 6. Racially mixed people -- Fiction 7. Family life -- New York (State) -- Fiction
ISBN 0399164057; 9780399164057
　　　　　　　　　　　　　　　　　LC 2013023620

In this book, by Lisa Graff, "Albie has never been the smartest kid in his class. He has never been the tallest. Or the best at gym. Or the greatest artist. Or the most musical. In fact, Albie has a long list of the things he's not very good at. But then Albie gets a new babysitter, Calista, who helps him figure out all of the things he is good at and how he can take pride in himself." (Publisher's note)

"Ten-year-old New Yorker Albie is a middle-of-the-road (at best) student. He's buoyed by small successes in math club and on spelling tests, and by his new babysitter's low-key approach to confidence-boosting. Albie is a sweet, vulnerable kid who just needs a little extra help and to whom readers may well relate. Short chapters add to the story's accessibility and keep the pace moving." (Horn Book)

★ Lost in the sun; Lisa Graff. Philomel Books, an imprint of Penguin Group (USA) 2015 304 p. $16.99
Grades: 4 5 6 7 8 9　　　　　　　　　　　　**Fic**
1. Guilt -- Fiction 2. Brothers -- Fiction 3. Friendship -- Fiction 4. Remarriage -- Fiction 5. Tricks -- Fiction
ISBN 0399164065; 9780399164064
　　　　　　　　　　　　　　　　　LC 2014027868

In this book by Lisa Graff, "Trent knows nothing could be worse than the year he had in fifth grade, when a freak accident on Cedar Lake left one kid dead, and Trent with a brain full of terrible thoughts he can't get rid of. Trent's pretty positive the entire disaster was his fault. . . . . It isn't until Trent gets caught up in the whirlwind that is Fallon Little--the girl with the mysterious scar across her face--that things begin to change." (Publisher's note)

"Trent Zimmerman is consumed by rage. The universe has been manifestly unfair to him and he doesn't know how to handle it. Seven months ago, he struck a hockey puck at a bad angle, sending it like a missile into the chest of a boy with a previously undiagnosed heart ailment. That boy died and Trent feels responsible...Weighty matters deftly handled with humor and grace will give this book wide appeal." SLJ

Sophie Simon solves them all; pictures by Jason Beene. Farrar, Straus & Giroux 2010 103p il $14.99

Grades: 2 3 4　　　　　　　　　　　　　　　**Fic**
1. School stories 2. Friendship -- Fiction
ISBN 978-0-374-37125-8; 0-374-37125-3

Sophie Simon, a third-grade genius, wants a graphing calculator so she can continue to study calculus while she rides the bus to school, but her parents are more concerned that she does not have any friends.

"Sometimes exaggerated for comic effect and occasionally poignant, the black-and-white illustrations capture the story's sense of humor as well as its sense of style. A fresh, funny chapter book for young readers." Booklist

A **tangle** of knots; Lisa Graff. Philomel Books 2013 240 p. $16.99
Grades: 3 4 5 6　　　　　　　　　　　　　　**Fic**
1. Baking -- Fiction 2. Ability -- Fiction 3. Orphans -- Fiction 4. Identity -- Fiction 5. Poughkeepsie (N.Y.) -- Fiction 6. Family life -- New York -- Fiction
ISBN 0399255176; 9780399255175
　　　　　　　　　　　　　　　　　LC 2012009573
Parents' Choice: Gold Medal Fiction (2013)

This juvenile novel, by Lisa Graff, is set "in a slightly magical world where everyone has a Talent. . . . Eleven-year-old Cady is an orphan with a phenomenal Talent for cake baking. . . . And her destiny leads her to a mysterious address that houses a lost luggage emporium, an old recipe, a family of children searching for their own Talents, and a Talent Thief who will alter her life forever. However, these encounters hold the key to Cady's past and how she became an orphan." (Publisher's note)

The **thing** about Georgie; a novel. by Lisa Graff. Laura Geringer Books 2006 220p $15.99; lib bdg $16.89; pa $5.99
Grades: 3 4 5 6　　　　　　　　　　　　　　**Fic**
1. School stories 2. Dwarfism -- Fiction 3. Friendship -- Fiction 4. Family life -- Fiction
ISBN 978-0-06-087589-3; 0-06-087589-5; 978-0-06-087590-9 lib bdg; 0-06-087590-9 lib bdg; 978-0-06-087591-6 pa; 0-06-087591-7 pa
　　　　　　　　　　　　　　　　　LC 2006000393

Georgie's dwarfism causes problems, but he could always rely on his parents, his best friend, and classmate Jeanie the Meanie's teasing, until a surprising announcement, a new boy in school, and a class project shake things up

"An upbeat and sensitive look at what it's like to be different, this novel will spark discussion." Booklist

Umbrella summer. Laura Geringer Books 2009 235p $15.99
Grades: 4 5 6　　　　　　　　　　　　　　　**Fic**
1. Death -- Fiction 2. Worry -- Fiction 3. Bereavement -- Fiction
ISBN 978-0-06-143187-6; 0-06-143187-7
　　　　　　　　　　　　　　　　　LC 2008-26015

After her brother Jared dies, ten-year-old Annie worries about the hidden dangers of everything, from bug bites to bicycle riding, until she is befriended by a new neighbor who is grieving her own loss.

"Annie's story deals with death with sensitivity, love, and understanding." SLJ

Grahame, Kenneth, 1859-1932

★ The **reluctant** dragon; by Kenneth Grahame; illustrated by Ernest H. Shepard. Holiday House 2013 64 p. (hardcover) $16.95

Grades: 3 4 5   **Fic**

1. Dragons -- Fiction 2. Villages -- Fiction

ISBN 0823428206; 9780823428205; 9780823428212

       LC 2012030238

In this book, by Kenneth Grahame and illustrated by Ernest H. Shepard, "a young boy befriends a poetry-loving dragon living in the Downs above his home. When the townfolk send for St. George to slay the dragon, the boy needs to come up with a clever plan to save his friend and convince the townsfolk to accept him." (Publisher's note)

The **wind** in the willows. Palazzo 2008 224p col. ill. $19.95

Grades: 3 4 5 6   **Fic**

1. Animals -- Fiction

ISBN 978-0-9553046-3-7; 0-9553046-3-6

       LC 2008425442

First published 1908

"This handsomely illustrated, unabridged edition celebrates the 100th anniversary of Grahame's classic animal fantasy. Ingpen's detailed paintings blend earthy tones with firelit highlights to create a warm mood. . . . Both the woodland scenes and animal abodes are charmingly depicted, and the characters, costumed in 19th-century garb, have loads of personality." SLJ

Grant, Katy

Hide and seek. Peachtree 2010 230p $15.95

Grades: 5 6 7 8   **Fic**

1. Arizona -- Fiction 2. Divorce -- Fiction 3. Kidnapping -- Fiction 4. Family life -- Fiction 5. Wilderness survival -- Fiction

ISBN 978-1-56145-542-3; 1-56145-542-3

       LC 2009040519

In the remote mountains of Arizona where he lives with his mother, stepfather, and two sisters, fourteen-year-old Chase discovers two kidnapped boys and gets caught up in a dangerous adventure when he comes up with a plan to get them to safety.

"Mystery and adventure propel this readable survival story that will hit the spot with Gary Paulsen's fans and may also entice reluctant readers." SLJ

Grant, Michael, 1954-

★ The **call**; Michael Grant. 1st ed. Katherine Tegen Books 2010 243 p. ill. (hardcover) $16.99

Grades: 4 5 6   **Fic**

1. Fantasy fiction 2. Adventure fiction 3. Fantasy 4. Humorous stories 5. Good and evil -- Fiction 6. Adventure and adventurers -- Fiction

ISBN 0061833665; 9780061833663

       LC 2009044815

A seemingly average twelve-year-old learns that he is destined to gather a team of similarly gifted children to try to save the world from a nameless evil, which is threatening to reappear after an absence of three thousand years. "Age ten and up." (Publisher's note)

"The author keeps the story moving at a brisk pace with suspenseful action and laugh-out-loud humor." Kirkus

Followed by: The trap (2011)

The **trap**. Katherine Tegen Books 2011 294p (The Magnificent 12) $16.99

Grades: 4 5 6   **Fic**

1. Fantasy fiction 2. Adventure fiction 3. Good and evil -- Fiction

ISBN 0-06-183368-1; 978-0-06-183368-7

       LC 2010040580

Sequel to: The call (2010)

Mack MacAvoy, an average-seeming twelve-year-old boy who happens to have special powers, travels to China in an effort to assemble an elite team of his peers to help him thwart the evil Pale Queen.

Gratz, Alan

The **Brooklyn** nine; a novel in nine innings. Dial Books 2009 299p $16.99

Grades: 5 6 7 8 9   **Fic**

1. Baseball -- Fiction 2. Family life -- Fiction 3. German Americans -- Fiction 4. United States -- History -- Fiction 5. Brooklyn (New York, N.Y.) -- Fiction

ISBN 978-0-8037-3224-7; 0-8037-3224-4

       LC 2008-21263

This novel follows the fortunes of a German immigrant family through nine generations, beginning in 1845, as they experience American life and play baseball. "Grades five to nine." (Bull Cent Child Books)

Gratz "builds this novel upon a clever . . . conceit . . . and executes it with polish and precision." Booklist

The **League** of Seven; Alan Gratz; illustrated by Brett Helquist. Starscape 2014 352 p. map (hardback) $16.99

Grades: 5 6 7 8   **Fic**

1. Steampunk fiction 2. United States -- History -- Fiction 3. Science fiction 4. Monsters -- Fiction 5. Secret societies -- Fiction 6. Adventure and adventurers -- Fiction

ISBN 076533822X; 9780765338228

       LC 2014015435

"'The League of Seven' is the first book in [a] steampunk series by the acclaimed author of 'Samurai Shortstop,' Alan Gratz. In an alternate 1875 America electricity is forbidden, Native Americans and Yankees are united, and eldritch evil lurks in the shadows. Young Archie Dent knows there really are monsters in the world. His parents are members of the Septemberist Society, whose job it is to protect humanity from hideous giants called the Mangleborn." (Publisher's note)

"This hybrid of steampunk and alternate American history features a hell-raising girl's school, Atlantis, and three highly likable leads in a yarn rip-roaring from start to finish. . . . Moments of humor and pathos enliven the history and fantasy." Booklist

Graves, Keith

The **orphan** of Awkward Falls. Chronicle Books 2011 337p $16.99

Grades: 4 5 6 7   **Fic**

1. Mystery fiction 2. Orphans -- Fiction 3. Homicide -- Fiction 4. Inventors -- Fiction 5. Mentally ill -- Fiction 6. Science -- Experiments -- Fiction

ISBN 978-0-8118-7814-2; 0-8118-7814-7

       LC 2011008008

Josephine Cravitz, the new girl in Awkward Falls, and her neighbor Thaddeus Hibble, a reclusive and orphaned boy inventor, become the targets of a mad cannibal from the local asylum for the criminally insane.

"Graves crafts a quick-moving plot composed of macabre twists. . . . Wordless opening and closing sequences, plus a handful of interior illustrations, both fill in background detail and intensify the overall macabre atmosphere." Kirkus

Green, Tim
Baseball great. HarperCollinsPublishers 2009 250p $16.99; lib bdg $17.89
Grades: 5 6 7 8   **Fic**
1. School stories 2. Baseball -- Fiction 3. Father-son relationship -- Fiction
ISBN 978-0-06-162686-9; 0-06-162686-4; 978-0-06-162687-6 lib bdg; 0-06-162687-2 lib bdg
LC 2008051778

All twelve-year-old Josh wants to do is play baseball but when his father, a minor league pitcher, signs him up for a youth championship team, Josh finds himself embroiled in a situation with potentially illegal consequences.

"Issues of peer and family pressure are well handled, and the short, punchy chapters and crisp dialogue are likely to hold the attention of young baseball fans." SLJ

Other titles in this series are:
Rivals (2010)
Best of the best (2011)

Deep zone. Harper Collins 2011 265p (Football genius) $15.99
Grades: 5 6 7 8   **Fic**
1. Football -- Fiction
ISBN 978-0-06-201244-9; 0-06-201244-4

Twelve-year-old football stars Troy White and Ty Lewis are eager to face each other in a seven-on-seven tournament being held at the Super Bowl in Miami, unaware that bad choices made by members of their families will put both boys in danger.

"The football insights are the best part, as both professional games and seven-on-seven play are described in satisfying detail." Kirkus

Football genius. HarperCollinsPublishers 2007 244p $16.99; lib bdg $17.89; pa $6.99
Grades: 5 6 7 8   **Fic**
1. Football -- Fiction 2. Atlanta (Ga.) -- Fiction
ISBN 978-0-06-112270-5; 0-06-112270-X; 978-0-06-112272-9 lib bdg; 0-06-112272-6 lib bdg; 978-0-06-112273-6 pa; 0-06-112273-4 pa
LC 2006-29470

Troy, a sixth-grader with an unusual gift for predicting football plays before they occur, attempts to use his ability to help his favorite team, the Atlanta Falcons, but he must first prove himself to the coach and players.

The author "imparts many insider details that football fans will love. Green makes Troy a winning hero, and he ties everything together with a fast-moving plot." Booklist

Other titles in this series are:
Football champ (2009)
The big time (2010)
Deep zone (2011)

Football hero. HarperCollinsPublishers 2008 297p $16.99; lib bdg $17.89; pa $6.99
Grades: 5 6 7 8   **Fic**
1. Mafia -- Fiction 2. Football -- Fiction 3. New Jersey -- Fiction
ISBN 978-0-06-112274-3; 0-06-112274-2; 978-0-06-112275-0 lib bdg; 0-06-112275-0 lib bdg; 978-0-06-112276-7 pa; 0-06-112276-9 pa
LC 2007-24184

When twelve-year-old Ty's brother Thane is recruited out of college to play for the New York Jets, their Uncle Gus uses Ty to get insider information for his gambling ring, landing Ty and Thane in trouble with the Mafia.

"The novel is briskly paced and undemanding, and might be a good bet for sports-minded reluctant readers." SLJ

Force out; Tim Green. 1st ed. Harper 2013 288 p. (hardcover) $16.99
Grades: 4 5 6   **Fic**
1. Baseball -- Juvenile fiction 2. Friendship -- Juvenile fiction 3. Baseball -- Fiction 4. Friendship -- Fiction 5. Best friends -- Fiction 6. Conduct of life -- Fiction 7. Competition (Psychology) -- Fiction
ISBN 0062089595; 9780062089595
LC 2012026752

In this juvenile novel, by Tim Green, "Joey and Zach have always been best friends. They're also two of the best baseball players in their league, and shoo-ins for the all-star team at the end of the season. Their dream is to play together on the Center State select team, and they will do anything to help each other get there. . . . Then the unthinkable happens: The boys learn there's only one open spot on the select team." (Publisher's note)

"Though Green is no stylist, he does a better job of avoiding the sports fantasy and sticking to real life than usual. There's plenty of play-by-play for those who want the sports to be the focus, but the interactions off the field are never shortchanged. . . . A slice of life for middle school readers who know that their sport is a microcosm of the larger world." Kirkus

New kid; Tim Green. HarperCollins 2014 320 p. (hardback) $16.99
Grades: 4 5 6 7 8   **Fic**
1. School stories 2. Moving -- Fiction 3. Baseball players -- Fiction 4. Schools -- Fiction 5. Baseball -- Fiction 6. Fathers and sons -- Fiction 7. Moving, Household -- Fiction 8. Interpersonal relations -- Fiction
ISBN 0062208721; 9780062208729
LC 2013032816

In this "baseball novel," by Tim Green, "Tommy's the new kid in town--who now goes by the name Brock--and he's having a hard time fitting in. Thanks to a prank gone wrong, he may be able to settle in on the baseball team. But can he prove himself before he becomes a new kid . . . again?" (Publisher's note)

"A teenage baseball star struggles not only with gameday stress, but also with the ever-present fear that his world is about to end. . . . His dad's job is mysterious and dangerous, and it requires them to stay on the run. Moving abruptly has only gotten harder as Brock gets older, and when he finds a great baseball coach and a good friend—and a potential girlfriend—the thought of leaving it all behind terrifies him even more. Best-selling author and former NFL defensive end Green delivers a riveting book about the complexities of being a teenager caught in unusual circumstances beyond his control. His writing is both compelling and intelligent, and even the implausible scenes—like a visit from a baseball great—still maintain a feel of authenticity. Even readers who aren't sports fans will find plenty of familiar drama and entertainment in this book. Exciting, romantic and thought-provoking, this book scores a home run." Kirkus

Greene, Bette

Philip Hall likes me, I reckon maybe; pictures by Charles Lilly. Dial Bks. for Young Readers 1974 135p il hardcover o.p. pa $5.99

Grades: 4 5 6   **Fic**

1. Arkansas -- Fiction 2. Friendship -- Fiction 3. African Americans -- Fiction

ISBN 0-14-130312-3 pa

A Newbery Medal honor book, 1975

Eleven-year-old Beth, an African American girl from Arkansas, thinks that Philip Hall likes her, but their on-again, off-again relationship sometimes makes her wonder

"The action is sustained; . . . the illustrations are excellent black-and-white pencil sketches." Read Teach

Other titles about Beth and Philip Hall are:

Get out of here, Philip Hall (1981)

I've already forgotten your name, Philip Hall (2004)

Greene, Jacqueline Dembar

★ The **secret** shofar of Barcelona; illustrated by Doug Chayka. Kar-Ben 2009 un il lib bdg $17.95

Grades: 2 3 4 5   **Fic**

1. Spain -- Fiction 2. Musicians -- Fiction 3. Jews -- Spain -- Fiction 4. Rosh ha-Shanah -- Fiction

ISBN 978-0-8225-9915-9 lib bdg; 0-8225-9915-5 lib bdg

LC 2008031197

In the late 1500s, while the conductor of the Royal Orchestra of Barcelona prepares for a concert to celebrate Spain's colonies in the New World, his son secretly practices playing the Shofar to help Jews, who must hide their faith from the Inquisition, to celebrate Rosh Hashanah. Includes historical facts and glossary

"Based on a legend, this intriguing slice of converso life offers a thoughtful hero and a suspenseful plot. The warm opaque paintings are expressive and create a strong sense of place." SLJ

Greene, Stephanie

Happy birthday, Sophie Hartley. Clarion Books 2010 127p $16

Grades: 3 4 5   **Fic**

1. Siblings -- Fiction 2. Birthdays -- Fiction 3. Family life -- Fiction

ISBN 978-0-547-25128-8; 0-547-25128-9

A girl in a large family is looking forward to her first "double digit" birthday, but soon discovers that growing up brings some unwanted changes.

"All the plot strands merge in a satisfying denouement that's tidy but not in the least predictable. Greene explores her themes of identity, ambivalence about growing up, and friendship with an unusual naturalness and depth, yet the themes never trump story or character." Horn Book

★ **Owen** Foote, frontiersman; illustrated by Martha Weston. Clarion Bks. 1999 88p il $14; pa $4.95

Grades: 2 3 4   **Fic**

1. Outdoor life -- Fiction

ISBN 0-395-61578-X; 0-618-24620-7 pa

LC 98-44843

Second grader Owen Foote is looking forward to spending time with his friend Joseph in their tree fort, until some bullies visiting his neighbor, Mrs. Gold, threaten to wreck the fort

"Real-boy characters with an appealingly loyal friendship, a good balance of narrative and dialogue, and an honestly childlike sense of the way the world works." Horn Book

Other titles about Owen Foote are:

Owen Foote, mighty scientist (2004)

Owen Foote, money man (2000)

Owen Foote, second grade strongman (1997)

Owen Foote, super spy (2001)

Owen Foote, soccer star (1998)

Princess Posey and the first grade parade; illustrated by Stephanie Roth Sisson. G.P. Putnam's Sons 2010 83p il $12.99

Grades: K 1 2   **Fic**

1. School stories 2. Fear -- Fiction

ISBN 978-0-399-25167-2; 0-399-25167-7

LC 2009-12471

Posey's fear of starting first grade is alleviated when her teacher invites the students to wear their most comfortable clothes to school on the first day.

"Emergent readers can be anxious as they make the transition from easy readers to early chapter books and, like Posey, can be overwhelmed by new challenges. Short sentences, a generous font, ample white space and Sisson's charming, expressive black-and-white illustrations make this sweet story just right for them." Kirkus

Other titles about Princess Posey are:

Princess Posey and the perfect present (2011)

Princess Posey and the next-door dog (2011)

Princess Posey and the perfect present; illustrated by Stephanie Roth Sisson. G. P. Putnam's Sons 2011 85p il $12.99

Grades: K 1 2   **Fic**

1. School stories 2. Teachers -- Fiction 3. Friendship -- Fiction

ISBN 0-399-25462-5; 978-0-399-25462-8

LC 2010001476

For first-grader Posey, every school day is great until her teacher's birthday, when her best friend's gift of an enormous bouquet puts Posey's few, home-grown roses to shame.

"Very short chapters, generous font, lots of eye-saving white space on each page and frequent black-and-white illustrations make this longish early chapter book accessible to the very earliest reader. Posey is flawed in a way that is absolutely perfect." Kirkus

The **show-off**; by Stephanie Greene; illustrated by Joe Mathieu. 1st ed.; Marshall Cavendish 2007 50p il $14.99

Grades: 1 2 3   **Fic**

1. Pigs -- Fiction 2. Moose -- Fiction 3. Friendship -- Fiction

ISBN 978-0-7614-5374-1

LC 2007000253

Hildy looks forward to a visit from her cousin, Winston, but when he arrives he bores her and annoys all of her friends by declaring his superior intelligence and expertise on every subject, until Moose convinces him to try something different.

"This beginning chapter book is full of gentle humor. The pencil-and-gray-wash illustrations work well with the story." SLJ

Sophie Hartley and the facts of life; by Stephanie Greene. Clarion Books, Houghton Mifflin Harcourt 2013 144 p. (hardcover) $16.99

Grades: 3 4 5   **Fic**
1. Puberty -- Fiction 2. Family life -- Fiction 3. Maturation (Psychology) -- Fiction
ISBN 0547976526; 9780547976525

LC 2012041489

In this book, by Stephanie Greene, "Sophie Hartley, age ten, does not want to be a teenager. She vows she'll never be like her older sister, Nora, who has tantrums about her hair and almost everything else. . . . Next year Sophie's class will see the movie about body changes, and her classmates are already buzzing about it. Sophie doesn't want to know about that embarrassing stuff yet. Does that mean she's immature? How can she prove otherwise?" (Publisher's note)

"Upbeat middle child Sophie, ten, has no interest in puberty or the teenage obsessions of older siblings Thad and Nora. But her fellow fourth graders accuse her of being immature. Meanwhile, her mother goes on a business trip, leaving Mr. Hartley with the bickering kids. The messages in this fourth book are somewhat overt but nevertheless useful, and Sophie remains an engaging character." (Horn Book)

Sophie Hartley, on strike. Clarion Books 2006 152p $15

Grades: 3 4 5   **Fic**
1. Family life -- Fiction
ISBN 978-0-618-71960-0; 0-618-71960-1

LC 2006-08375

After their mother sets up a new list of household chores for them to do, Sophie and her siblings argue about housekeeping and finally go on strike

"Readers will empathize with this spunky youngster and her true-to-life problems." SLJ

Greenfield, Eloise

★ The **friendly** four; illustrations by Jan Spivey Gilchrist. HarperCollins/Amistad 2006 47p il $16.99; lib bdg $17.89

Grades: 2 3 4   **Fic**
1. Summer -- Fiction 2. Friendship -- Fiction 3. African Americans -- Fiction
ISBN 978-0-06-000759-1; 0-06-000759-1; 978-0-06-000760-7 lib bdg; 0-06-000760-5 lib bdg

LC 2005-18588

"Free-verse poems tell the story of a group of children who find each other during one otherwise lonely summer. . . . The African-American friends all bond, play, and build and paint an elaborate cardboard town they call Goodsummer. The simple watercolors work well at setting scenes of tidy streets lined with homes and lots of backyards and parks. Gilchrist's talent shows in her use of color, splashed with light. . . . For a younger audience than most novels-in-verse,

this accessible and well-written book has a nostalgic tone." SLJ

Sister; drawings by Moneta Barnett. Crowell 1974 83p il hardcover o.p. pa $4.99

Grades: 4 5 6 7   **Fic**
1. Sisters -- Fiction 2. African Americans -- Fiction 3. Single parent family -- Fiction
ISBN 0-690-00497-4; 0-06-440199-5 pa

A 13-year-old black girl whose father is dead watches her 16-year-old sister drifting away from her and her mother and fears she may fall into the same self-destructive behavior herself. While waiting for her sister's return home, she leafs through her diary, reliving both happy and unhappy experiences while gradually recognizing her own individuality

"The book is strong . . . strong in perception, in its sensitivity, in its realism." Bull Cent Child Books

Greenwald, Lisa

Dog Beach; The Seagate Summers Book One. Lisa Greenwald. Amulet Books 2014 272 p. (alk. paper) $15.95

Grades: 5 6 7 8   **Fic**
1. Dogs -- Fiction 2. Summer -- Fiction 3. Beaches -- Fiction 4. Friendship -- Fiction 5. Vacations -- Fiction 6. Dog walking -- Fiction
ISBN 1419710184; 9781419710186

LC 2013023282

In this book, by Lisa Greenwald, "Eleven-year-old Remy loves Seagate, the island where her grandmother had a house and where her family spends every summer vacation. But this year's different. Remy misses her dog, Danish, who recently passed away. The usual Seagate traditions don't feel the same—and neither does her relationship with her two best friends, Micayla and Bennett. . . . Remy takes comfort in the company of Dog Beach." (Publisher's note)

"For 11-year-old Remy, Seagate Island, where her family vacations every year, is perfect because "summer after summer, it always stays the same." But this summer is different. Her beloved dog, Danish, has died, and Remy misses him terribly...Greenwald's gentle read is tailor-made for those on the cusp of friendship misunderstandings, burgeoning popularity awareness, awkward crushes, and the wobbly feeling that can come from deviating from comfortable routine. All of Remy's worries are soothed eventually, and happiness is well earned. This sweet series opener promises an agreeable journey." Booklist

My life in pink and green. Amulet Books 2010 288 p. (hbk.) $16.95

Grades: 4 5 6 7   **Fic**
1. Cosmetics -- Fiction 2. Environmental protection -- Fiction 3. Mother-daughter relationship -- Fiction
ISBN 0810983524; 0810989840 pa; 9780810983526; 9780810989849

LC 2008025577

When the family's drugstore is failing, seventh-grader Lucy uses her problem solving talents to come up with solution that might resuscitate the business, along with helping the environment.

"Greenwald deftly blends eco-facts and makeup tips, friendship dynamics, and spot-on middle-school politics into a warm, uplifting story." Booklist

Greenwald, Tommy

★ **Charlie** Joe Jackson's guide to not reading. Roaring Brook Press 2011 220p il $14.99

Grades: 4 5 6 7 **Fic**

1. School stories 2. Books and reading -- Fiction

ISBN 978-1-59643-691-6; 1-59643-691-3

LC 2010-24079

Middle schooler Charlie Joe is proud of his success at avoiding reading, but eventually his schemes go too far.

"With its subversive humor and contemporary details drawn straight from kids' worlds, this clever title should attract a wide following." Booklist

Charlie Joe Jackson's guide to summer vacation; by Tommy Greenwald; illustrated by J. P. Coovert. 1st ed. Roaring Brook Press 2013 231 p. ill. (hardcover) $14.99

Grades: 4 5 6 7 **Fic**

1. Reading -- Fiction 2. Vacations -- Fiction 3. Camps -- Fiction 4. Humorous stories 5. Interpersonal relations -- Fiction

ISBN 159643757X; 9781596437579; 9781596438804

LC 2012034249

In this graphic novel by Tommy Greenwald "Charlie Joe Jackson finds himself in a terrible dream he can't wake up from: Camp Rituhbukkee . . . a place filled with grammar workshops, Read-a-Ramas, and kids who actually like reading. But Charlie Joe is determined to convince the entire camp to hate reading and writing—one genius at a time. Tommy Greenwald's 'Charlie Joe Jackson's Guide to Summer Vacation' is another . . . installment in the life of a reluctant reader." (Publisher's note)

Griffin, Peni R.

The **ghost** sitter. Dutton Children's Bks. 2001 131p $14.99; pa $5.99

Grades: 4 5 6 7 **Fic**

1. Ghost stories

ISBN 0-525-46676-2; 0-14-230216-3 pa

LC 00-65859

When she realizes that her new house is haunted by the ghost of a ten-year-old girl who used to live there, Charlotte tries to help her find peace

"Griffin's book has several strong appeals: new best friends solving a mystery together, a just-scary-enough ghost girl, and a deathless bond between sisters that provides the book with its resoundingly satisfying conclusion and bang-up last sentence." Horn Book

Griffiths, Andy

The **13**-story Treehouse; Any Griffiths; illustrated by Terry Denton. Feiwel & Friends 2013 256 p. ill. (hardcover) $13.99

Grades: 3 4 5 **Fic**

1. Graphic novels 2. Treehouses -- Graphic novels

ISBN 1250026903; 9781250026903

In this children's graphic novel, "Andy and Terry live in a treehouse. In addition to the normal rooms found in a house, it has a theater and library, a bowling alley, and a games room. The boys write and illustrate books, and are far behind on their deadline for their publisher, Mr. Big Nose. They bicker and procrastinate and experience many adventures and misadventures." (School Library Journal)

The **26**-story treehouse; Andy Griffiths; illustrated by Terry Denton. 1st US edition Feiwel & Friends 2014 352 p. illustrations $13.99

Grades: 3 4 5 **Fic**

1. Imagination -- Fiction 2. Tree houses -- Fiction

ISBN 9781250073273; 1250026911; 9781250026910

LC 2014430138

Sequel to: The 13-Story Treehouse (2013)

In this children's story, by Andy Griffiths, illustrated by Terry Denton, "Andy and Terry live in a 26-story treehouse. (It used to be 13 stories, but they've expanded.) It has a bumper car rink, a skate ramp, an antigravity chamber, an ice cream parlor with 78 flavors, and the Maze of Doom--a maze so complicated that nobody who has gone in has ever come out again. Well, not yet, anyway." (Publisher's note)

"Griffiths and Denton follow the uproarious The 13-Story Treehouse with another cartoon-laden carnival of slapstick and self-referential humor--this time, with pirates. . . . Denton's furiously scrawled line drawings milk the silly, gross-out gags for everything they're worth." Pub Wkly

Grimes, Nikki

Chasing freedom; the life journeys of Harriet Tubman and Susan B. Anthony, inspired by historical facts. Nikki Grimes; [illustrations by] Michele Wood. Orchard Books, an imprint of Scholastic Inc. 2015 56 p. color illustrations $18.99

Grades: 3 4 5 6 **Fic**

1. Slavery -- Fiction 2. Women's rights -- Fiction 3. African Americans -- Fiction 4. Women -- Suffrage -- Fiction 5. Underground Railroad -- Fiction

ISBN 0439793386; 9780439793384

LC 2014014835

This juvenile biographical book, by Nikki Grimes, illustrated by Michele Wood, "offers a glimpse into the inspiring lives of Susan B. Anthony and Harriet Tubman. . . . [It] richly imagines the experiences of Tubman and Anthony, set against the backdrop of the Underground Railroad, the Civil War, and the Women's Suffrage Movement. Additional back matter invites curious young readers to further explore this period in history--and the larger-than-life figures who lived it." (Publisher's note)

"Two iconic women recount their stories. In New York state in 1904, a suffragist convention is about to begin, and Susan B. Anthony is scheduled to introduce Harriet Tubman. But first the two women meet at Anthony's home for tea and talk. Grimes artfully creates an afternoon of conversation and reminiscence in carefully constructed, fact-based vignettes that allow each to recount her life, accomplishments and continuing dreams...A tremendous opportunity for children to understand what these women worked so hard to accomplish—one succeeding and one coming close. (capsule biographies, additional notes, bibliography, author's note) ." Kirkus

Includes bibliographical references

Make way for Dyamonde Daniel; illustrated by R. Gregory Christie. G.P. Putnam's Sons 2009 74p il $10.99

Grades: 2 3 4 **Fic**

1. Moving -- Fiction 2. Friendship -- Fiction 3. African Americans -- Fiction

ISBN 978-0-399-25175-7; 0-399-25175-8

LC 2008-26788

Spunky third-grader Dyamonde Daniel misses her old neighborhood, but when she befriends a boy named Free, another new student at school, she finally starts to feel at home.

"Dyamonde . . . is a memorable main character. . . . Her actions and feelings ring true. Christie's illustrations flesh out the characters, and along with patterned page borders, contribute child appeal." SLJ

Other titles about Dyamonde Daniel are:

Rich (2009)

Almost zero (2010)

★ **Planet** Middle School. Bloomsbury Childrens 2011 154p $15.99

Grades: 4 5 6 7   **Fic**

1. School stories 2. Novels in verse 3. Basketball -- Fiction 4. Friendship -- Fiction 5. Family life -- Fiction

ISBN 978-1-59990-284-5; 1-59990-284-2

LC 2010050744

A series of poems describes all the baffling changes at home and at school in twelve-year-old Joylin's transition from tomboy basketball player to not-quite-girly girl.

"In freeflowing free-verse poems, multi–awardwinning author and poet Grimes . . . explores the riot of hormones and expected gender roles that can make negotiating the preteen years such a challenge. . . . A work that should help adolescent readers find the courage and humor to grow into the individuals they already are." Kirkus

The **road** to Paris. G. P. Putnam's Sons 2006 153p $15.99; pa $6.99

Grades: 4 5 6 7   **Fic**

1. Siblings -- Fiction 2. Foster home care -- Fiction 3. Racially mixed people -- Fiction

ISBN 0-399-24537-5; 978-0-399-24537-4; 978-0-14-241082-0 pa; 0-14-241082-9 pa

LC 2005-28920

Inconsolable at being separated from her older brother, eight-year-old Paris is apprehensive about her new foster family but just as she learns to trust them, she faces a life-changing decision.

"In clear, short chapters, Grimes tells a beautiful story of family, friendship, and faith from the viewpoint of a child in search of home in a harsh world." Booklist

★ **Words** With Wings; by Nikki Grimes. Boyds Mills Press 2013 96 p. $15.95

Grades: 2 3 4   **Fic**

1. Child authors -- Fiction 2. Dreams -- Juvenile fiction 3. Imagination -- Juvenile fiction

ISBN 1590789857; 9781590789858

Coretta Scott King Honor Book: Author (2014)

In this book, by Nikki Grimes, "Gabby . . . is a daydreamer, and words fire her imagination, creating new worlds for her to inhabit. After her parents separate and Gabby must go to a different school, her daydreams become increasingly vivid, intruding on the realities of the classroom and schoolwork. To Gabby's occasional puzzlement, her mother worries . . . but her wonderful new teacher is more patient, wisely helping her capture her daydreams on paper and inspiring a new dream to become an author." (Booklist)

Grisham, John

Theodore Boone: the abduction. Dutton Children's Books 2011 217p $16.99

Grades: 4 5 6 7   **Fic**

1. Lawyers -- Fiction 2. Kidnapping -- Fiction

ISBN 978-0-525-42557-1; 0-525-42557-8

LC 2011006060

When his best friend disappears from her bedroom in the middle of the night, thirteen-year-old Theo uses his legal knowledge and investigative skills to chase down the truth and save April.

"The book is smoothly written, and there's a mild tutorial on the criminal justice system." Publ Wkly

Theodore Boone: kid lawyer. Dutton Children's Books 2010 263p $16.99

Grades: 4 5 6 7   **Fic**

1. Mystery fiction 2. Lawyers -- Fiction

ISBN 0-525-42384-2; 978-0-525-42384-3

With two attorneys for parents, thirteen-year-old Theodore Boone knows more about the law than most lawyers do. But when a high profile murder trial comes to his small town and Theo gets pulled into it, it's up to this amateur attorney to save the day.

"Grisham serves up a dandy legal adventure that moves along quickly. Without intruding on the story's trajectory, he gives plenty of background about the legal process and explores various ethical questions." Horn Book Guide

Gunderson, Jessica

Stranger on the silk road; a story of ancient China. by Jessica Gunderson; illustrated by Caroline Hu. Picture Window Books 2009 64p il (Read-it! chapter books: historical tales) lib bdg $21.26

Grades: 2 3 4   **Fic**

1. Silk -- Fiction 2. China -- Fiction

ISBN 978-1-4048-4736-1 lib bdg; 1-4048-4736-7 lib bdg

LC 2008006308

Song Sun likes to talk but never listens. After talking too much to a stranger, Song Sun accidentally gives away the Chinese secret of silk making

"Sassy, graphic-novel-style illustrations give [this] great little first chapter [book] extra appeal. . . . [This is a] wonderful [introduction] to historical fiction." SLJ

Guo Yue

★ **Little** Leap Forward; a boy in Beijing. by Guo Yue and Clare Farrow; illustrated by Helen Cann. Barefoot Books 2008 126p il $16.99

Grades: 3 4 5 6   **Fic**

1. Communism -- Fiction 2. Friendship -- Fiction 3. Family life -- Fiction 4. China -- History -- 1949-1976 -- Fiction

ISBN 978-1-84686-114-7; 1-84686-114-4

LC 2007-42676

In Communist China in 1966, eight-year-old Leap Forward learns about freedom while flying kites with his best friend, by trying to get a caged wild bird to sing, and through the music he is learning to play on a bamboo flute. Includes author's notes on his childhood in Beijing, life under Mao Zedong, and the Cultural Revolution.

"The simple prose is quiet and physical. . . . The beautifully detailed, clear illustrations in ink and brilliant watercolors combine realistic group scenes with spare, individual portraits." Booklist

Gutman, Dan

The **Christmas** genie; illustrated by Dan Santat. Simon & Schuster Books for Young Readers 2009 150p il $15.99

Grades: 3 4 5   Fic

1. School stories 2. Wishes -- Fiction 3. Christmas -- Fiction 4. Meteorites -- Fiction

ISBN 978-1-4169-9001-7; 1-4169-9001-1

LC 2009017765

When a meteorite crashes into a fifth-grade classroom at Lincoln School in Oak Park, Illinois, the genie inside agrees to grant the class a Christmas wish—if they can agree on one within an hour.

This is "lively, thought-provoking, and hilarious. . . . Gutman packs plenty of history, science, and ethics lessons in this fun, well-paced fantasy." SLJ

The **homework** machine. Simon & Schuster Books for Young Readers 2006 146p $15.95; pa $5.99

Grades: 4 5 6   Fic

1. School stories

ISBN 0-689-87678-5; 0-689-87679-3 pa

LC 2005-19785

Four fifth-grade students—a geek, a class clown, a teacher's pet, and a slacker—as well as their teacher and mothers, each relate events surrounding a computer programmed to complete homework assignments.

"This fast-paced, entertaining book has something for everyone: convincing characters deftly portrayed . . . points of discussion on ethics and student computer use; and every child's dream machine." Booklist

Followed by: Return of the homework machine (2009)

Mission unstoppable. Harper 2011 293p (The genius files) $16.99; lib bdg $17.89

Grades: 5 6 7 8   Fic

1. Adventure fiction 2. Twins -- Fiction 3. Genius -- Fiction 4. Siblings -- Fiction 5. Family life -- Fiction

ISBN 0-06-182764-9; 0-06-182765-7 lib bdg; 978-0-06-182764-8; 978-0-06-182765-5 lib bdg

LC 2010-09390

On a cross-country vacation with their parents, twins Coke and Pepsi, soon to be thirteen, fend off strange assassins as they try to come to terms with their being part of a top-secret government organization known as The Genius Files.

"Gutman's novel offers a quirky look at Americana that will engage curious minds. . . . Those looking for a fun and suspenseful read . . . will not be disappointed." Booklist

Another title in this series is:

Never say genius (2012)

Never say genius. Harper 2012 (Genius files) $16.99; lib bdg $17.89

Grades: 5 6 7 8   Fic

1. Adventure fiction 2. Twins -- Fiction 3. Genius -- Fiction 4. Siblings -- Fiction 5. Family life -- Fiction

ISBN 978-0-06-182767-9; 0-0-6182767-3; 978-0-06-182768-6 lib bdg; 0-06-182768-1 lib bdg

LC 2011019363

As their cross-country journey with their parents continues through the midwest, twins Coke and Pepsi, now thir-

teen, again face strange assassins at such places as the first McDonald's restaurant and Cedar Point amusement park.

"The author brings his confused but resourceful youngsters to an explosive climax and a shocking revelation that guarantees further adventures on the road back to the left coast." Kirkus

The **return** of the homework machine. Simon & Schuster Books for Young Readers 2009 162p $15.99

Grades: 4 5 6   Fic

1. School stories 2. Arizona -- Fiction 3. Grand Canyon (Ariz.) -- Fiction

ISBN 978-1-4169-5416-3; 1-4169-5416-3

LC 2008029543

Sequel to: The homework machine (2006)

After discarding their infamous homework machine, four friends, now in sixth grade, find themselves once again at the police station, this time giving testimony about an incident involving a powerful computer chip, a Grand Canyon treasure, and a dead body.

Shoeless Joe & me; a baseball card adventure. HarperCollins Pubs. 2002 163p (Baseball card adventures) hardcover o.p. lib bdg $17.89; pa $5.99

Grades: 4 5 6 7   Fic

1. Baseball players 2. Baseball -- Fiction

ISBN 0-06-029253-9; 0-06-029254-7 lib bdg; 0-06-447259-0 pa

LC 2001-24638

Joe Stoshack travels back to 1919, where he meets Shoeless Joe Jackson and tries to prevent the fixing of the World Series in which Jackson was wrongly implicated

"Shoeless Joe is compelling, and Joe's adventures are exciting." Voice Youth Advocates

Other titles in the Baseball card adventures series are:

Abner & me (2005)

Babe & me (2000)

Honus & me (1997)

Jackie & me (1999)

Jim & me (2008)

Mickey & me (2003)

Ray & me (2009)

Roberto & me (2010)

Satch & me (2006)

Haas, Jessie

Bramble and Maggie; horse meets girl. Jessie Haas; illustrated by Alison Friend. Candlewick Press 2012 51 p. $3.99

Grades: 1 2 3   Fic

1. Horses -- Fiction 2. Human-animal relationship -- Fiction

ISBN 0763662518; 9780763649555; 9780763662516

LC 2011018625

In this children's story, by Jessie Haas and illustrated by Alison Friend, "Maggie wants a pony to ride and take care of, and to prepare she's been reading a big book on horse care. Meanwhile, Bramble is bored with giving riding lessons and walking in circles. She's looking for just the right person to take her away from her routine. Is it a perfect match?" (Publisher's note)

"Maggie and her horse, Bramble, are back in another beginning chapter book. With a slightly mischievous, frisky attitude in the cooler fall weather, Bramble takes risks and pretends to be fearful, while Maggie introduces her to the sights and sounds of autumn...Dialogue, Maggie's occasional reflections, and a bit of onomatopoeia allow the narrative text to flow nicely as a trusting relationship develops between horse and rider. A solid addition for general purchase." SLJ

Other titles include:

Give and Take (2013)

Spooky Season (2014)

Horse meets girl

Bramble and Maggie give and take; give and take. Jessie Haas, Alison Friend. Candlewick Press 2013 56 p. col. ill. (Bramble and Maggie.) $14.99

Grades: 1 2 3   **Fic**

1. Horses -- Fiction 2. Horsemanship -- Fiction 3. Human-animal relationship -- Fiction 4. Friendship -- Fiction 5. Human-animal relationships -- Fiction

ISBN 0763650218; 9780763650216

LC 2012942618

In this book, by Jessie Haas, "Bramble, an opinionated mare, isn't about to be taken advantage of. For instance, she knows all about rides: 'The rider sat in the saddle. The horse did all the hard work.' Young Maggie, as always, has Bramble's number, and with a little judicious bribery (give-and-take, thinks Bramble), they are soon having adventures together, Maggie in the saddle, Bramble content." (Kirkus Reviews)

"When Maggie attempts to saddle and bridle her horse, Bramble, she finds her uncooperative until they reach a solution she sees as give-and-take...Portraying human and animal characters empathetically, the narrative features moments of humor as well as insight. Expressive watercolor artwork will draw horse lovers to this highly satisfying book for beginning readers." Booklist

Other titles in the series include:

Horse meets Girl (2012)

Spooky Season (2014)

Give and take

Bramble and maggie spooky season; spooky season. Jessie Haas, illustrated by Alison Friend. First edition 2014 Candlewick Press 2014 56 p. colour illustrations $14.99

Grades: 1 2 3   **Fic**

1. Autumn -- Fiction 2. Horses -- Fiction 3. Halloween -- Fiction 4. Horsemanship -- Fiction 5. Children's stories 6. Human-animal relationships

ISBN 0763664502; 9780763664503

LC 2013952844

In this book, by Jessie Haas, "Bramble and Maggie explore a new season together—fall! Leaves crunch underfoot. Acorns ping off rooftops. It all makes Bramble feel wonderfully spooky. But Bramble's frisky-pretend-scary gait makes Maggie jumpy, and soon Bramble really is nervous. . . . When Maggie takes a fall, will she want to get back in the saddle? And when Halloween comes, can Maggie trust Bramble to brave the tricks and lead them both safely to the treats?" (Publisher's note)

"'Bramble loved fall . . . The weather made Bramble feel spooky. It made her feel frisky and full of fun.' In their third first-chapter-book entry, Maggie (girl) helps Bramble (horse) overcome her fear of scarecrows; Bramble helps Maggie get back in the saddle after a fall; and the two have a Halloween-y good time. Clear, lively prose and soft, expres-

sive gouache illustrations combine for a Halloween friendship story." Horn Book

Haddix, Margaret Peterson, 1964-

Caught; Book 5 Margaret Peterson Haddix. Simon & Schuster Books for Young Readers 2012 343 p. (The Missing) (hardcover: alk. paper) $16.99

Grades: 5 6 7 8   **Fic**

1. Science fiction 2. Time travel -- Fiction 3. Einstein, Albert, 1879-1955 -- Fiction 4. Space and time -- Fiction 5. Serbia -- History -- 1804-1918 -- Fiction 6. Switzerland -- History -- 20th century -- Fiction

ISBN 141698982X; 9781416989820; 9781442422889

LC 2011018654

In this fifth installment of Margaret Peterson Haddix's "Missing" series, "Jonah and Katherine are accustomed to traveling through time, but when learn they next have to return Albert Einstein's daughter to history, they think it's a joke -- they've only heard of his sons. But it turns out that Albert Einstein really did have a daughter, Lieserl, whose 1902 birth and subsequent disappearance was shrouded in mystery." (Publisher's note)

★ **Found**. Simon & Schuster Books for Young Readers 2008 314p (The missing) $15.99; pa $6.99

Grades: 5 6 7 8 9   **Fic**

1. Science fiction 2. Adoption -- Fiction

ISBN 978-1-4169-5417-0; 1-4169-5417-1; 978-1-4169-5421-7 pa; 1-4169-5421-X pa

LC 2007-23614

When thirteen-year-olds Jonah and Chip, who are both adopted, learn they were discovered on a plane that appeared out of nowhere, full of babies with no adults on board, they realize that they have uncovered a mystery involving time travel and two opposing forces, each trying to repair the fabric of time.

This is "a tantalizing opener to a new series. . . . Readers will be hard-pressed to wait for the next installment." Publ Wkly

Other titles in this series are:

Sent (2009)

Sabotaged (2010)

Torn (2011)

Risked; Margaret Peterson Haddix. Simon & Schuster Books for Young Readers 2013 320 p. (The missing) (hardcover: alk. paper) $16.99

Grades: 5 6 7 8 9   **Fic**

1. Time travel -- Fiction 2. Soviet Union -- History -- 1917-1921, Revolution -- Fiction 3. Science fiction 4. Time travel -- Fiction 5. Soviet Union -- History -- Revolution, 1917-1921 -- Fiction

ISBN 1416989846; 9781416989844; 9781442426474

LC 2012006770

In this book, by Margaret Peterson Haddix, "When Jonah and Katherine find themselves on a mission to return Alexei and Anastasia Romanov to history and then save them from the Russian Revolution, they are at a loss. Because in their own time, the bones of Alexei and Anastasia have been positively identified through DNA testing. What hope do they have of saving Alexis and Anastasia's lives when the twenty-first century has proof of their deaths?" (Publisher's note)

Haddon, Mark

Boom! (or 70,000 light years) David Fickling Books 2010 194p $15.99; lib bdg $18.99

Grades: 4 5 6 7   **Fic**

1. Science fiction 2. Great Britain -- Fiction 3. Interplanetary voyages -- Fiction 4. Extraterrestrial beings -- Fiction

ISBN 978-0-385-75187-2; 0-385-75187-7; 978-0-385-75188-9 lib bdg; 0-385-75188-5 lib bdg

First published 1992 in the United Kingdom with title: Gridzbi spudvetch

When Jim and Charlie overhear two of their teachers talking in a secret language and the two friends set out to solve the mystery, they do not expect the dire consequences of their actions.

"Adventure and quirky humor keep the pages turning, and readers will connect to Jimbo with little difficulty. If they can overcome some of the cultural differences, they will appreciate the simple and engaging tale." SLJ

Hagen, George

★ **Gabriel** Finley and the raven's riddle; George Hagen. Schwartz & Wade Books 2014 384 p. illustrations, maps (lib bdg) $19.99

Grades: 5 6 7 8   **Fic**

1. Fantasy fiction 2. Ravens -- Fiction 3. Magic -- Fiction 4. Missing persons -- Fiction 5. Voyages and travels -- Fiction 6. Adventure and adventurers -- Fiction

ISBN 9780385371049; 0385371047; 9780385371032

LC 2013032533

This fantasy by George Hagen follows the "twelve-year-old Gabriel [trying to] find his missing father, who seems to have vanished without a trace. . . . With the help of Paladin--a young raven with whom he has a magical bond that enables them to become one creature--he flies to the foreboding land of Aviopolis, where he must face a series of difficult challenges and unanswerable riddles that could lead to his . . . or to his death." (Publisher's note)

"The world-building and narrative tension are solid, fairly fresh, and rich, forgiving the obvious plot and slightly cardboard characters." Horn Book

Gabriel Finley and the raven's riddle

Hahn, Mary Downing

All the lovely bad ones; a ghost story. Clarion Books 2008 182p $16; pa $5.99

Grades: 4 5 6 7   **Fic**

1. Ghost stories 2. Vermont -- Fiction 3. Siblings -- Fiction 4. Hotels and motels -- Fiction

ISBN 978-0-618-85467-7; 978-0-547-24878-3 pa

LC 2007-37932

While spending the summer at their grandmother's Vermont inn, two prankster siblings awaken young ghosts from the inn's distant past who refuse to "rest in peace."

"In addition to crafting some genuinely spine-chilling moments, the author takes a unique approach to a well-traversed genre." Publ Wkly

★ The **ghost** of Crutchfield Hall. Clarion Books 2010 153p $17

Grades: 5 6 7 8   **Fic**

1. Ghost stories 2. Cousins -- Fiction 3. Orphans -- Fiction 4. Great Britain -- History -- 19th century

-- Fiction

ISBN 978-0-547-38560-0; 0-547-38560-9

In the nineteenth century, ten-year-old Florence Crutchfield leaves a London orphanage to live with her great-uncle, great-aunt, and sickly cousin James, but she soon realizes the home has another resident, who means to do her and James harm.

"A deliciously spine-tingling tale that even the most reluctant readers will enjoy." SLJ

★ **Hear** the wind blow. Clarion Bks. 2003 212p $15

Grades: 5 6 7 8   **Fic**

1. Siblings -- Fiction 2. United States -- History -- 1861-1865, Civil War -- Fiction

ISBN 0-618-18190-3

LC 2002-15977

With their mother dead and their home burned, a thirteen-year-old boy and his little sister set out across Virginia in search of relatives during the final days of the Civil War

The author "gives readers an entertaining and thought-provoking combination: a strong adventure inextricably bound to a specific time and place, but one that resonates with universal themes." Horn Book

★ **Wait** till Helen comes; a ghost story. Clarion Bks. 1986 184p $15; pa $5.95; pa $6.99

Grades: 4 5 6   **Fic**

1. Ghost stories 2. Stepchildren -- Fiction

ISBN 0-89919-453-2; 0-547-02864-4 pa; 9780380704422 pa

LC 86-2648

"Molly, the 12-year-old narrator, and her brother Michael dislike their bratty 5-year-old stepsister Heather and resent the family move to an isolated converted church in the country. The adjourning graveyard frightens Molly, but Heather seems drawn to it. Molly discovers that the ghost of a child (Helen) who died in a fire a century ago wants to lure Heather to her doom. Molly determines to save her stepsister. In so doing, she learns that Heather's strange behavior stems from her feelings of guilt at having accidentally caused her mother's death by playing near a stove and starting a fire. Eventually, Molly wrests Heather from Helen's arms as the ghost attempts to drown them. The girls discover the skeletons of Helen's parents, and their burial finally puts to rest Helen's spirit. . . . Grades four to seven." (SLJ)

"Intertwined with the ghost story is the question of Molly's moral imperative to save a child she truly dislikes. Though the emotional turnaround may be a bit quick for some, this still scores as a first-rate thriller." Booklist

★ **Witch** catcher. Clarion Books 2006 236p $16

Grades: 3 4 5 6   **Fic**

1. Fairies -- Fiction 2. Witches -- Fiction 3. West Virginia -- Fiction 4. Father-daughter relationship -- Fiction

ISBN 0-618-50457-5

LC 2005-24795

Having just moved into the West Virginia home they inherited from a distant relative, twelve-year-old Jen is surprised that her father is already dating a local antiques dealer, but more surprised by what the spooky woman really wants.

"A fast-paced, suspenseful fantasy in which an appealing heroine stands against forces seemingly beyond her control." Booklist

Hahn, Rebecca

A **creature** of moonlight; Rebecca Hahn. Houghton Mifflin Harcourt 2014 224 p. $17.99

Grades: 7 8 9 10 11 12   Fic

1. Fantasy fiction 2. Dragons -- Fiction 3. Fantasy 4. Magic -- Fiction 5. Flowers -- Fiction 6. Identity -- Fiction 7. Princesses -- Fiction 8. Forests and forestry -- Fiction

ISBN 054410935X; 9780544109353

LC 2013020188

In this novel, by Rebecca Hahn, "as the only heir to the throne, Marni should have been surrounded by wealth and privilege, not living in exile--but now the time has come when she must choose between claiming her birthright as princess of a realm whose king wants her dead, and life with the father she has never known: a wild dragon who is sending his magical woods to capture her." (Publisher's note)

"Marni lives in a shack at the edge of the woods with her Gramps, where she tends flowers, as she's done for most of her life. Yet change is afoot... This book's greatest strength lies in the vivid woodland scenes and the rich detail that describes the mystical pieces of Marni's tale." (School Library Journal)

Hale, Shannon

Princess Academy; the forgotten sisters. by Shannon Hale. Bloomsbury 2015 336 p. (hardcover) $17.99

Grades: 5 6 7 8   Fic

1. School stories 2. Mystery fiction 3. Telepathy -- Fiction 4. Princesses -- Fiction 5. Self-confidence -- Fiction 6. Kings and rulers -- Fiction 7. Schools -- Fiction 8. Mountains -- Fiction 9. Mystery and detective stories 10. Kings, queens, rulers, etc. -- Fiction

ISBN 1619634856; 9781619634855

LC 2014013744

In this book, by Shannon Hale, "Miri has learned all about being a proper princess. But the tables turn when the student must become the teacher! Instead of returning to her beloved Mount Eskel, Miri is ordered to journey to a distant swamp and start a princess academy for three sisters, cousins of the royal family. . . . As Miri spends more time with the sisters, she realizes the king and queen's interest in them hides a long-buried secret." (Publisher's note)

" On the day that Miri is to return to her beloved Mount Eskel, she is summoned by King Bjorn of Danland, requesting her to travel to outer territorial Lesser Alva, where she is to tutor three royal sisters. If the King of Stora chooses one to marry, war will be prevented, and it's up to Miri to succeed...Action-packed and well paced, the story's depth incorporates artful negotiation, the importance of education, and citizens' equality and rights. This final installment of the Princess Academy trilogy certainly leaves room for more books if Hale were so inclined. Won't she reconsider?" Booklist

Other titles in the triology are:

Princess Academy (2005)

Palace of Stone (2012)

Forgotten sisters

The **storybook** of legends; by Shannon Hale. Little Brown & Co 2013 320 p. (Ever After High) (hardback) $14.99

Grades: 4 5 6 7   Fic

1. Fairy tales 2. School stories 3. Schools -- Fiction 4. Friendship -- Fiction 5. Boarding schools -- Fiction 6. Fate and fatalism -- Fiction 7. Characters in literature -- Fiction

ISBN 0316401226; 9780316401227

LC 2013024496

In this middle grades story by Shannon Hale, "At Ever After High, an enchanting boarding school, the children of fairytale legends prepare themselves to fulfill their destinies as the next generation of Snow Whites, Prince Charmings and Evil Queens . . . whether they want to or not. Each year on Legacy Day, students sign the Storybook of Legends to seal their scripted fates." (Publisher's note)

"Raven Queen and Apple White, the daughters of famous fairy-tale characters, begin their much-anticipated Legacy Year at Ever After High. They investigate the mystery of a lost story, and Raven realizes that being evil might not be her only path. Fans of the Inkheart and Sisters Grimm series will enjoy the "hexellent" fairy-tale-infused lingo and lively characters." Horn Book

Hall, Teri

Away. Dial Books 2011 234 p. $16.99

Grades: 5 6 7 8   Fic

1. Science fiction 2. Resistance to government -- Fiction

ISBN 9780803735026; 0803735022

LC 2011001163

Sequel to: The Line (2010)

After helping heal Malgam, Rachel learns that her father is still living in the devastated territory of Away, captured by members of another clan who are planning to use him to make a deal with the government on the other side of the Line, and she joins the rescue party that must risk much to save him.

"This worthy sequel . . . continues to build a dystopian world rich with suspense and moral choices." Kirkus

The **Line**. Dial Books 2010 219p $16.99

Grades: 5 6 7 8   Fic

1. Science fiction

ISBN 978-0-8037-3466-1; 0-8037-3466-2

LC 2009-12301

Rachel thinks that she and her mother are safe working for Ms. Moore at her estate close to The Line, an invisible border of the Unified States, but when Rachel has an opportunity to Cross into the forbidden zone, she is both frightened and intrigued

This "sets readers up for a series about another world that might have come from situations too close to our own." Libr Media Connect

Followed by: Away (2011)

Hamilton, Virginia

Drylongso; illustrated by Jerry Pinkney. Harcourt Brace Jovanovich 1992 54p il hardcover o.p. pa $10

Grades: 3 4 5   Fic

1. Droughts -- Fiction 2. Farm life -- Fiction 3. African

Americans -- Fiction

ISBN 0-15-201587-6 pa

LC 91-25575

As a great wall of dust moves across their drought-stricken farm, a family's distress is relieved by a young man called Drylongso, who literally blows into their lives with the storm

"In an understand story of drought and hard times and longing for rain, a great writer and a great artists have pared down their rich, exuberant styles to something quieter but no less intense." Booklist

★ The **house** of Dies Drear; illustrated by Eros Keith. Macmillan 1968 246p il hardcover o.p. pa $5.99

Grades: 5 6 7 8   **Fic**

1. Mystery fiction 2. Ohio -- Fiction 3. African Americans -- Fiction

ISBN 0-02-742500-2; 1-4169-1405-6 pa

"The answer to the mystery comes in a startling dramatic dénouement that is pure theater. This is gifted writing; the characterization is unforgettable, the plot imbued with mounting tension." Saturday Rev

"A hundred years ago, Dies Drear and two slaves he was hiding in his house, an Underground Railroad station in Ohio, had been murdered. The house, huge and isolated, was fascinating, Thomas thought, but he wasn't sure he was glad Papa had bought it—funny things kept happening, frightening things." Bull Cent Child Books

Followed by The mystery of Drear House (1987)

★ **M.C.** Higgins, the great; 25th anniversary ed; Simon & Schuster 1999 232p $18; pa $5.99

Grades: 5 6 7 8   **Fic**

1. Family life -- Fiction 2. African Americans -- Fiction 3. Appalachian region -- Fiction

ISBN 0-689-83074-2; 1-4169-1407-2 pa

LC 99014288

Awarded the Newbery Medal, 1975

As a slag heap, the result of strip mining, creeps closer to his house in the Ohio hills, fifteen-year-old M.C. is torn between trying to get his family away and fighting for the home they love

"This is a deeply involving story possessing a folklorish quality." Child Book Rev Serv

Han, Jenny

★ **Clara** Lee and the apple pie dream; with pictures by Julia Kuo. Little, Brown and Company 2011 149p il $14.99

Grades: 2 3 4   **Fic**

1. School stories 2. Family life -- Fiction 3. Korean Americans -- Fiction

ISBN 978-0-316-07038-6; 0-316-07038-6

LC 2010-06900

Korean American fourth-grader Clara Lee longs to be Little Miss Apple Pie, and when her luck seems suddenly to change for the better, she overcomes her fear of public speaking and enters the competition.

Han "captures an 8-year-old's perspective perfectly. . . . The message shines through but doesn't overwhelm this engaging chapter book that will be welcomed by middle-grade fans of Clementine." Kirkus

Hanlon, Abby

★ **Dory** Fantasmagory; by Abby Hanlon. Dial Books for Young Readers, an imprint of Penguin Group (USA) Inc. 2014 160 p. illustrations (hardcover) $14.99

Grades: 1 2 3   **Fic**

1. Family life -- Fiction 2. Imagination -- Fiction 3. Imaginary playmates -- Fiction 4. Brothers and sisters -- Fiction

ISBN 0803740883; 9780803740884

LC 2013034996

In this book by Abby Hanlon, "Dory really wants attention, and more than anything she wants her brother and sister to play with her. But she's too much of a baby for them, so she's left to her own devices. . . . Her siblings may roll their eyes at her childish games, but Dory has lots of things to do: outsmarting the monsters all over the house, escaping from prison (aka time-out), and exacting revenge on her sister's favorite doll." (Publisher's note)

"The frequent kidlike illustrations integrate seamlessly with the text, adding another layer of madcap humor. Try this as a lively group read-aloud." Horn Book

Hannigan, Katherine

★ **Emmaline** and the bunny. Greenwillow Books 2009 94p il $14.99

Grades: 1 2 3   **Fic**

1. Rabbits -- Fiction 2. Loneliness -- Fiction 3. Cleanliness -- Fiction

ISBN 978-0-06-162654-8; 0-06-162654-6

LC 2008012639

Everyone and everything in the town of Neatasapin is tidy, except Emmaline who likes to dig dirt and jump in puddles, and wants to adopt an untidy bunny.

"Told in very short chapters and using language in unusual ways, this is a small delight, cunningly illustrated by Hannigan's own sweet watercolors." Booklist

True (. . . sort of) Greenwillow Books 2011 360p $16.99; lib bdg $17.89

Grades: 4 5 6   **Fic**

1. School stories 2. Siblings -- Fiction 3. Friendship -- Fiction 4. Family life -- Fiction

ISBN 978-0-06-196873-0; 0-06-196873-0; 978-0-06-196874-7 lib bdg; 0-06-196874-9 lib bdg

For most of her eleven years, Delly has been in trouble without knowing why, until her little brother, R. B., and a strange, silent new friend, Ferris, help her find a way to be good—and happy—again.

"Told in carefully crafted language that begs to be read aloud, the story runs the gamut from laugh-out-loud funny to emotionally wrenching." SLJ

Hansen, Joyce

Home is with our family; [illustrated by] E. B. Lewis. Hyperion 2010 272p il (Black pioneers) $16.99

Grades: 4 5 6 7   **Fic**

1. Abolitionists -- Fiction 2. African Americans -- Fiction

ISBN 978-0-7868-5217-8; 0-7868-5217-8

Maria Peterson is looking forward to turning 13. She envisions new adult prestige and responsibility, like attending abolitionist meetings and listening to inspiring speakers like Sojourner Truth. However, she doesn't bank on all the unexpected changes that her 13th year brings.

"The plot flows quickly and has enough action to hold a reader's attention. Teachers can use this book to provide their students with a deeper understanding of the Fugitive Slave Act." Libr Media Connect

Haptie, Charlotte

Otto and the flying twins; the first book of the Karmidee. [by] Charlotte Haptie. Holiday House 2004 304p il $17.95

Grades: 4 5 6 7   **Fic**

1. Fantasy fiction 2. Magic -- Fiction

ISBN 0-8234-1826-X

                                   LC 2003-57135

First published 2002 in the United Kingdom

Young Otto comes to the rescue when he discovers that his family and city are the last remnants of an ancient magical world now under threat from the Normal Police

"The amazing oddities and quirks of this world and its residents are described with delicious nonchalance. . . . The characters are equally surprising and unpredictable. . . . The writing is as fresh and invigorating as the setting." SLJ

Another title about Otto is:

Otto and the bird charmers (2005)

Hardinge, Frances

Fly by night. HarperCollinsPublishers 2006 487p hardcover o.p. lib bdg $17.89; pa $7.99

Grades: 5 6 7 8   **Fic**

1. Fantasy fiction

ISBN 978-0-06-087627-2; 0-06-087627-1; 978-0-06-087629-6 lib bdg; 0-06-087629-8 lib bdg; 978-0-06-087630-2 pa; 0-06-087630-1 pa

                                   LC 2005-20598

Mosca Mye and her homicidal goose, Saracen, travel to the city of Mandelion on the heels of smooth-talking con-man, Eponymous Clent.

"Through rich, colorful language and a sure sense of plot and pacing, Hardinge has created a distinctly imaginative world full of engaging characters, robust humor, and true suspense." SLJ

Followed by: Fly trap (2011)

Fly trap. Harper 2011 584p $16.99

Grades: 5 6 7 8   **Fic**

1. Fantasy fiction

ISBN 978-0-06-088044-6; 0-06-088044-9

                                   LC 2010027755

Sequel to: Fly by night (2006)

Adventurous orphan Mosca Mye, her savage goose, Saracen, and their sometimes-loyal companion, Eponymous Clent, become embroiled in the intrigues of Toll, a town that changes entirely as day turns to night.

Crammed with eccentric, Dickensian characters, unexpected plot turns, and numerous very niche gods and goddesses . . . , Hardinge's world is rich enough to fuel two or three fantasy novels. It's a beautifully written tale, by turns humorous and heartbreaking and a sheer pleasure to read. Publ Wkly

Hardy, Janice

The **shifter**. Balzer + Bray 2009 370p (The Healing Wars) $16.99; pa $7.99

Grades: 5 6 7 8   **Fic**

1. War stories 2. Fantasy fiction 3. Orphans -- Fiction

4. Sisters -- Fiction

ISBN 978-0-06-174704-5; 0-06-174704-1; 978-0-06-174708-3 pa; 0-06-174708-4 pa

                                   LC 2008-47673

Nya is an orphan struggling for survival in a city crippled by war. She is also a Taker—with her touch, she can heal injuries, pulling pain from another person into her own body. But unlike her sister, Tali, and the other Takers who become Healers' League apprentices, Nya's skill is flawed: She can't push that pain into pynvium, the enchanted metal used to store it. All she can do is shift it into another person

"The ethical dilemmas raised . . . provide thoughtful discussion material and also make the story accessible to more than just fantasy readers." Booklist

Other titles in this series are:

Blue fire (2010)

Darkfall (2011)

Harkrader, Lisa

The **adventures** of Beanboy; written and illustrated by Lisa Harkrader. Houghton Mifflin Harcourt 2012 234p. ill.

Grades: 4 5 6 7 8   **Fic**

1. Family -- Fiction 2. Domestic relations 3. Superhero comic books, strips, etc. 4. Comic books, strips, etc. -- Fiction 5. Schools -- Fiction 6. Contests -- Fiction 7. Middle schools -- Fiction 8. Family problems -- Fiction

ISBN 9780547550787

                                   LC 2011012161

In this book, "Tucker MacBean is a collector and aspiring creator of comic books, a preoccupation that he realizes doesn't rank high 'on the sliding scale of middle-school coolness.' He enters a contest to create a sidekick for his favorite superhero, convinced that a win will jump-start his popularity; he plans to give the prize--a college scholarship--to his overextended single mother, who's juggling classes and work. Tucker joins the art club to prepare his entry, and Sam (a classmate who Tucker sees as 'arch nemesis to the world') is hired to babysit his special-needs brother after school. . . . Tucker displays his own heroism when he reaches out to Sam after discovering why she is so belligerent and defensive." (Publishers Weekly)

Harper, Charise Mericle

Alien encounter; Charise Mericle Harper. First edition Christy Ottaviano Books, Henry Holt & Company 2014 208 p. illustrations (Sasquatch and aliens) (hardback) $12.99

Grades: 3 4 5 6   **Fic**

1. Yeti -- Fiction 2. Friendship -- Fiction 3. Family life -- Fiction 4. Extraterrestrial beings -- Fiction 5. Humorous stories 6. Family life -- Northwest, Pacific -- Fiction

ISBN 0805096213; 9780805096217

                                   LC 2013039906

This book, the first in Charise Mericle Harper's "Sasquatch and Aliens" series, "introduces a pair of nine-year-old boys who are propelled into an adventure that may or may not involve otherworldly creatures. Anxiety-prone Morgan first meets new kid Lewis as Lewis is hanging from a tree by his underwear. After Morgan reluctantly rescues Lewis (whose family just bought a creepy motel), a tentative friendship is born." (Publishers Weekly)

"With an authentic, zany splash of fourth-grade humor, perspective, and imagination, this inaugural series title targets boys and will captivate elementary readers...Like

Grace in Harper's popular "Just Grace" series (Houghton Harcourt), Morgan is a spunky, verbal, resourceful protagonist whose nonstop adventures resonate with self-discovery, family relationships, friendships, and creative problem-solving." SLJ

Dreamer, wisher, liar; by Charise Mericle Harper. Balzer + Bray, an imprint of HarperCollinsPublishers 2014 352 p. (hardcover bdg.) $16.99

Grades: 4 5 6 **Fic**
 1. Babysitters -- Fiction 2. Magic tricks -- Fiction
 3. Female friendship -- Fiction 4. Mother-daughter relationship -- Fiction 5. Magic -- Fiction 6. Wishes -- Fiction 7. Babysitter -- Fiction 8. Mothers and daughters -- Fiction
ISBN 0062026755; 9780062026750
LC 2013008222

This book is a "story about one girl's transformative summer full of friendship, secret magic, and family. . . . When her best friend is moving away and her mom has arranged for some strange little girl to come and stay with them, Ash . . . is expecting the worst summer of her life. Then seven-year-old Claire shows up. Armed with a love of thrift-store clothes and an altogether too-sunny disposition, Claire proceeds to turn Ash's carefully constructed life upside down." (Publisher's note)

"When a best friend is leaving you, what can you do? Ashley dreads the upcoming summer and her last few weeks at camp with her best friend, Lucy, who is moving away... Through Harper's skillful combination of fantastical and wholly realistic situations, readers are presented with gently larger-than-life characters, who are magnified through Ash's eyes and take on the roles she needs them to as she steps into her coming-of-age journey. As sweet and tart as a strawberry lemonade, readers will want to sip slowly and savor every page." Booklist

Just Grace. Houghton Mifflin 2007 138p il $15; pa $4.99

Grades: 2 3 4 **Fic**
 1. School stories
ISBN 978-0-618-64642-5; 0-618-64642-6; 978-0-547-01440-1 pa; 0-547-01440-6 pa
LC 2006-17062

Misnamed by her teacher, seven-year-old Just Grace prides herself on being empathetic, but when she tries to help a neighbor feel better, her good intentions backfire.

"Grace is a funny, mischievous protagonist who should easily find a place in the pantheon of precocious third graders." SLJ

Other titles about Just Grace are:
Still Just Grace (2007)
Just Grace walks the dog (2008)
Just Grace goes green (2009)
Just Grace and the snack attack (2009)
Just Grace and the Terrible Tutu (2011)
Just Grace and the double surprise (2011)

Harper, Jessica
 ★ **Uh-oh,** Cleo; illustrated by Jon Berkeley. G. P. Putnam's Sons 2008 58p il $14.99

Grades: K 1 2 3 **Fic**
 1. Twins -- Fiction 2. Illinois -- Fiction 3. Siblings -- Fiction 4. Family life -- Fiction 5. Medical care --

Fiction 6. Wounds and injuries -- Fiction
ISBN 978-0-399-24671-5; 0-399-24671-1
LC 2007027507

What starts out as a perfectly ordinary day in the Small house turns into Stitches Saturday when Cleo gets a cut on the head after her twin brother, Jack, accidentally pulls down their "Toy House."

This is an "engaging early chapter book. . . . The story is studded with observations, incidents, and conversations that reflect true-to-life sibling relationships and realistic individual foibles. . . . Large type, spacious design, and appealing drawings add to the accessiblity." Booklist

Other titles about Cleo re:
Underpants on my head (2009)
I barfed on Mrs. Kenly (2010)

Harper, Suzanne
 A **gaggle** of goblins. Greenwillow Books 2011 300p (The unseen world of Poppy Malone) $16.99

Grades: 4 5 6 **Fic**
 1. Texas -- Fiction 2. Goblins -- Fiction 3. Family life -- Fiction
ISBN 0-06-199607-6; 978-0-06-199607-8
LC 2010025558

Eleven-year-old Poppy's parents are paranormal investigators who have never actually found anything, but that may change when they move to Austin, Texas, and Poppy meets a goblin in the attic of their new house.

"The book shines through the consistently amusing dynamics and dialogue among the Malones; Harper has abundant fun with the Malone parents' eccentricities, and kids will too. Readers will want more from this family." Publ Wkly

Harrington, Karen
 Courage for beginners; by Karen Harrington. Little, Brown and Co. 2014 304 p. (hardcover) $17

Grades: 4 5 6 7 8 **Fic**
 1. Texas -- Fiction 2. Friendship -- Fiction 3. Schools -- Fiction 4. Agoraphobia -- Fiction 5. Middle schools -- Fiction 6. Family problems -- Fiction
ISBN 031621048X; 9780316210485
LC 2013021596

Sequel to: Sure Signs of Crazy (2013)

"Twelve-year-old Mysti Murphy wishes she were a character in a book. If her life were fictional, she'd magically know how to deal with the fact that her best friend, Anibal Gomez, has abandoned her in favor of being a 'hipster.' She'd be able to take care of everyone when her dad has to spend time in the hospital. And she'd certainly be able to change her family's secret." (Publisher's note)

"Mysti's curatorial narration--as if she were describing paintings or book characters--works on multiple levels, showing off her snark and emphasizing her mother's sheltered influence. Her mother is flawed but sympathetic; she knows her fears are disproportionate, but their debilitating effect is real.With gallows humor and believable small victories, this unusual novel is a window into making friends and facing fears." Kirkus

Sure signs of crazy; by Karen Harrington. 1st ed. Little Brown & Co 2013 288 p. (hardcover) $17

Grades: 4 5 6 7 8 **Fic**
 1. Adolescence -- Fiction 2. Parent-child relationship

-- Fiction 3. Texas -- Fiction 4. Coming of age -- Fiction 5. Mental illness -- Fiction 6. Family problems -- Fiction

ISBN 0316210587; 9780316210584

LC 2012030683

Parents' Choice: Silver Medal Fiction (2013)

In this book, "worried that she will grow up to be crazy like her mother or alcoholic like her father, rising seventh-grader Sarah Nelson takes courage from Harper Lee's 'To Kill a Mockingbird,' writing letters to Atticus Finch and discovering her own strengths. . . . She describes the events of the summer she turns 12, gets her period, develops a crush on a neighbor and fellow word lover, and comes to terms with her parents' failings." (Kirkus Reviews)

Harris, Lewis

A **taste** for red. Clarion Books 2009 169p $16

Grades: 4 5 6   Fic

1. Vampires -- Fiction 2. Friendship -- Fiction 3. Missing children -- Fiction

ISBN 978-0-547-14462-7; 0-547-14462-8

LC 2008-25318

When some of her classmates disappear, sixth-grader Svetlana, along with her new friends go in search of the missing students using her newfound ability as an Olfactive, one who has heightened smell, hearing, and the ability to detect vampires.

"Svetlana comes across as a strong character. . . . Her first-person narrative is fast-paced and witty, and her mild scorn for everything she encounters at school will appeal to angst-ridden tweens. Sure to be a crowd-pleaser." SLJ

Harris, Teresa E.

The **perfect** place; Teresa E. Harris. Clarion Books 2014 272 p. (hardcover) $16.99

Grades: 5 6 7 8   Fic

1. Aunts -- Fiction 2. Family life -- Fiction 3. African Americans -- Fiction 4. Home -- Fiction 5. Virginia -- Fiction 6. Great-aunts -- Fiction 7. Segregation -- Fiction 8. Moving, Household -- Fiction 9. Family life -- Virginia -- Fiction

ISBN 0547255195; 9780547255194

LC 2013036214

In this book, "12-year-old Treasure is tired of moving from place to place every time her unreliable father leaves the family. At the opening of the novel, Treasure's father is gone and her mother leaves her and her younger sister, Tiffany, with their Great-Aunt Grace in the small town of Black Lake, Virginia. Treasure does not want to be there, and her introduction to her no-nonsense relative only strengthens her resolve to stay detached during her mother's absence." (School Library Journal)

"Two months after 12-year-old Treasure's dad left without further word, her mom decides to search for him, and she takes Treasure and her younger sister to stay with their cantankerous Great-Aunt Grace in Black Lake, Virginia... Readers will find sly humor here as well as the pleasure of seeing justice done on several levels. A satisfying first novel with a realistic but heartening ending." Booklist

Harrison, Michelle

13 curses. Little, Brown 2011 486p (13 Treasures Trilogy) $15.99; pa $6.99

Grades: 5 6 7 8   Fic

1. Magic -- Fiction 2. Fairies -- Fiction 3. Orphans -- Fiction 4. Kidnapping -- Fiction

ISBN 978-0-316-04150-8; 0-316-04150-5; 978-0316041492 pa

Sequel to: 13 treasures (2010)

When fairies steal her brother, thirteen-year-old Rowan Fox promises that in exchange for his return she will find the thirteen charms that the fairies have enchanted and hidden in the human world.

"The sure-handed storytelling creates a completely credible setting—by turns violent and tender, sinister and poignant. . . . Contrasts between human emotion and commitment and the cold, often cruel magic and mischief of the fairy realm create terrific tension and afford opportunities for heroism for the young protagonists." Kirkus

★ **13** treasures. Little, Brown Books for Young Readers 2010 355p il $15.99

Grades: 5 6 7 8   Fic

1. Mystery fiction 2. Fairies -- Fiction 3. Grandmothers -- Fiction 4. Great Britain -- Fiction

ISBN 978-0-316-04148-5; 0-316-04148-3

LC 2008-45511

Bedeviled by evil fairies that only she can see, thirteen-year-old Tanya is sent to stay with her cold and distant grandmother at Elvesden Manor, where she and the caretaker's son solve a disturbing mystery that leads them to the discovery that Tanya's life is in danger.

"Harrison writes with great assuredness, creating a seductive setting and memorable, fully developed characters. . . . It's an excellent choice for fans of the Spiderwick Chronicles and other modern-day fairy tales." Publ Wkly

Followed by: 13 curses (2011)

Harrold, A. F.

The **imaginary**; by A.F. Harrold; illustrations by Emily Gravett. Bloomsbury 2015 224 p. illustrations (some color) (hardcover) $16.99

Grades: 4 5 6 7 8   Fic

1. Friendship -- Fiction 2. Supernatural -- Fiction 3. Adventure and adventurers 4. Imaginary playmates -- Fiction 5. Mother-daughter relationship -- Fiction 6. Best friends -- Fiction 7. Mothers and daughters -- Fiction 8. Adventure and adventurers -- Fiction

ISBN 0802738117; 9780802738110; 9781619636965

LC 2014016677

"Rudger is Amanda Shuffleup's imaginary friend. Nobody else can see Rudger-until the evil Mr. Bunting arrives at Amanda's door. Mr. Bunting hunts imaginaries. Rumor has it that he even eats them. And now he's found Rudger. Soon Rudger is alone, and running for his imaginary life. He needs to find Amanda before Mr. Bunting catches him-and before Amanda forgets him and he fades away to nothing." (Publisher's note)

"This inventive mix of humor and suspense starts with the amusing appearance of Amanda's imaginary friend, Rudger. Their summer of make-believe adventures quickly darkens, though, when Mr. Bunting shows up. He's a grown-up who can not only see "Imaginaries" like Rudger, but also eats them to prolong his own life. . . . A great choice for readers who like fantastic tales with a dose of true scariness." SLJ

Hartnett, Sonya, 1968-

★ The **children** of the King; Sonya Hartnett. 1st U.S. edition Penguin Books (Australia) 2012 265 p. ill. $16.99
Grades: 5 6 7 8   **Fic**
1. Historical fiction 2. Friendship -- Fiction 3. World War, 1939-1945 -- Great Britain -- Fiction 4. World War, 1939-1945 -- Evacuation of civilians -- Fiction 5. England -- Fiction 6. World War, 1939-1945 -- Children -- Great Britain -- Fiction 7. World War, 1939-1945 -- Evacuation of civilians -- England -- Fiction
ISBN 0763667358; 9780670076130; 9780763667351
LC 2013414845

This book, by Sonya Hartnett, "takes place in England during World War II. . . . Siblings Cecily and Jeremy, along with their mother Heloise, are sent to the northern countryside to live with Heloise's brother, Peregrine Lockwood, in mysterious Heron Hall. . . . The family winds up taking in May Bright, a 10-year-old refugee from London. The two girls become fast friends and . . . come across two boys in the ruins of a nearby castle." (School Library Journal)

"Twelve-year-old Cecily, her older brother Jeremy, and their mother flee WWII London for the safety of Uncle Peregrine's country manor. Once there, Cecily discovers two boys hiding in some nearby ruins. Hartnett's gift for language deftly conveys both the sublime and the mundane in life. She grounds the book's fantasy elements with a heartfelt examination of the hardships endured by civilians in wartime." Horn Book

Sadie and Ratz; Sonya Hartnett; illustrated by Ann James. 1st U.S. ed. Candlewick Press 2012 59 p. ill. (reinforced) $14.99
Grades: K 1 2 3   **Fic**
1. Hand -- Fiction 2. Imagination -- Fiction 3. Sibling rivalry -- Fiction
ISBN 0763653152; 9780763653156
LC 2011045899

"Sadie and Ratz are the names of Hannah's hands. . . . They're always after four-year-old Baby Boy (whom Sadie wishes were a dog). . . . Baby Boy knows how to turn the tables, though, and when he spills milk on the carpet, he tells Grandma that Sadie and Ratz pushed him. But when Baby Boy goes too far, Hannah may have to send Sadie and Ratz on vacation to prove their innocence." (Publisher's note)

★ The **silver** donkey; illustrated by Don T. Powers. Candlewick Press 2006 266p il $15.99; pa $7.99
Grades: 5 6 7 8   **Fic**
1. France -- Fiction 2. Soldiers -- Fiction 3. World War, 1914-1918 -- Fiction
ISBN 978-0-7636-2937-3; 0-7636-2937-5; 978-0-7636-3681-4 pa; 0-7636-3681-9 pa
LC 2006-42582

First published 2004 in Australia

In France during World War I, four French children learn about honesty, loyalty, and courage from an English army deserter who tells them a series of stories related to his small, silver donkey charm

"Occasional full-page black-and-white art deftly suggests setting and mood without intruding on readers' imaginations. Provocative, timely, and elegantly honed." Horn Book

Hartry, Nancy

Watching Jimmy. Tundra Books 2009 152p $16.95
Grades: 5 6 7 8   **Fic**
1. Child abuse -- Fiction 2. Brain -- Wounds and injuries -- Fiction
ISBN 0-88776-871-7; 978-0-88776-871-2

This story takes place in Canadia in 1958. Eleven-year-old Carolyn walks an emotional tightrope knowing what really happened to her best friend, Jimmy, the day his Uncle Ted chose to teach him a lesson that left Jimmy brain-damaged. But when Uncle Ted threatens his beleaguered family with even more abuse and the loss of their home, Carolyn must find the courage to match wits with him and to speak out, using the truth as her only weapon. "Age nine and up." (Quill Quire)

"Like a steady beat that pulses louder and louder, the story unfolds against a backdrop of postwar social and political concerns and Remembrance Day. Carolyn is a passionate and feisty character, delineated with love and precision, and readers will be drawn to her. A compelling and satisfying novel." SLJ

Harvey, Matthea

Cecil the pet glacier; Matthea Harvey; illustrated by Giselle Potter. Schwartz & Wade Books 2012 40 p. $17.99
Grades: PreK K 1 2   **Fic**
1. Pets -- Fiction 2. Glaciers -- Fiction 3. Picture books for children 4. Norway -- Fiction 5. Eccentrics and eccentricities -- Fiction
ISBN 9780375867736; 9780375967733
LC 2011018657

This book is "[Matthea] Harvey's . . . tale of a misunderstood child and her equally misunderstood glacier. Lonely Ruby has flamboyantly eccentric parents who run a topiary and tiara business. . . . A family trip to Norway nets Ruby a pet, a pint-size glacier named Cecil who follows her everywhere; Ruby--who wanted a dog--scorns him." It isn't until "Cecil . . . performs a daring rescue. . . that Ruby realizes how wrong she's been." (Publishers Weekly)

Haskell, Merrie

The **princess** curse. Harper 2011 325p $16.99
Grades: 4 5 6 7   **Fic**
1. Fairy tales 2. Magic -- Fiction 3. Princesses -- Fiction
ISBN 978-0-06-200813-8; 0-06-200813-7
LC 2010040424

"Author Haskell has her way with the story of 'The Twelve Dancing Princesses,' incorporating references to other myths and legends and adding many twists of her own, not least of which is making the royals' attempted rescuer a strong-willed, 13-year-old apprentice herbalist, Reveka. . . . When Vasile offers the hand of any of his daughters in marriage to anyone who banishes the curse (or a 'fabulous dowry' if the curse-breaker is female), Reveka is determined to win the reward. . . . With a good sense of humor, an able and empowered protagonist, and a highly original take on this tale, Haskell's story gives readers much to enjoy." Publ Wkly

Hattemer, Kate

The **vigilante** poets of Selwyn Academy; Kate Hattemer. Alfred A. Knopf 2014 336 p. $16.99

Grades: 8 9 10 11 12 **Fic**

1. School stories 2. Poetry -- Fiction 3. Young adult literature 4. Arts -- Fiction 5. Schools -- Fiction 6. Minnesota -- Fiction 7. Friendship -- Fiction 8. Creative ability -- Fiction 9. Family life -- Minnesota -- Fiction 10. Reality television programs -- Fiction
ISBN 0385753780; 9780385753784; 9780385753791
LC 2013014325
Kirkus (March 1, 2014); Booklist (March 15, 2014)

"Witty, sarcastic Ethan and his three friends decide to take down the reality TV show, 'For Art's Sake,' that is being filmed at their high school, the esteemed Selwyn Arts Academy, where each student is more talented than the next. While studying Ezra Pound in English class, the friends are inspired to write a vigilante long poem and distribute it to the student body, detailing the evils of 'For Art's Sake.'" (Publisher's note)

"In this place of immense talent, Ethan is immensely relatable as the voice of the average (that is, socially awkward) teen. Hattemer writes with a refreshing narrative style, crafting both believable characters and a cohesive, well-plotted story. Romance, while in the air, takes a sideline to friendship, which proves to be the book's heart and soul. Relying on the passion and ideals that drive adolescence, this has a vibrancy and authenticity that will resonate with anyone who has fought for their beliefs—or who has loved a hamster." Booklist

Hawkins, Aaron R.

The **year** money grew on trees; written and illustrated by Aaron R. Hawkins. Houghton Mifflin 2010 293p il $16
Grades: 5 6 7 8 **Fic**

1. Apples -- Fiction 2. Cousins -- Fiction 3. Siblings -- Fiction 4. Farm life -- Fiction 5. New Mexico -- Fiction 6. Money-making projects for children -- Fiction
ISBN 978-0-547-27977-0; 0-547-27977-9

In early 1980s New Mexico, thirteen-year-old Jackson Jones recruits his cousins and sisters to help tend an elderly neighbor's neglected apple orchard for the chance to make big money and, perhaps, to own the orchard.

"Hawkins's children's book debut is rich with details that feel drawn from memory, . . . and Jackson's narration sparkles. His hard work, setbacks, and motivations make this a highly relatable adventure in entrepreneurship." Publ Wkly

Hayles, Marsha

Breathing room; Marsha Hayles. Henry Holt and Co. 2012 244 p. (hc) $17.99
Grades: 5 6 7 8 **Fic**

1. Bildungsromans 2. Historical fiction 3. Teenagers -- Fiction 4. Tuberculosis -- Fiction 5. Sick -- Fiction 6. Hospitals -- Fiction 7. Coming of age -- Fiction 8. Minnesota -- History -- 20th century -- Fiction
ISBN 0805089616; 9780805089615
LC 2011034055

Author Marsha Hayles' book is "set in 1940 at a sanitarium in Loon Lake, Minn. . . . Thirteen-year-old Evvy Hoffmeister has tuberculosis and feels abandoned by her family when she's sent to the sanitarium to be cured. The cold nurses, strict rules, mind-numbing routines, and endless bed rest are dispiriting for Evvy and her roommates: kind Beverly, glamorous Pearl, and defensive Dena. . . . Nonetheless, the girls find strength in each other and discover creative ways to bring cheer." (Publishers Weekly)

Hazen, Lynn E.

The **amazing** trail of Seymour Snail; illustrated by Doug Cushman. Henry Holt and Co. 2009 64p il $16.95
Grades: 1 2 3 **Fic**

1. Snails -- Fiction 2. Artists -- Fiction 3. New York (N.Y.) -- Fiction
ISBN 978-0-8050-8698-0; 0-8050-8698-6
LC 2008036939

Hoping to become a famous artist one day, Seymour Snail takes a job in a New York City art gallery, where everyone is buzzing about a "magnificent mystery artist."

"With only a few sentences and at least one illustration per page, this title is perfect for students transitioning to chapter books. . . . Cushman's black-and-white cartoons delineate the characters and add humor and perspective." SLJ

Cinder Rabbit; [by] Lynn E. Hazen; illustrated by Elyse Pastel. Henry Holt & Co. 2008 64p il $15.95
Grades: K 1 2 **Fic**

1. School stories 2. Rabbits -- Fiction 3. Theater -- Fiction
ISBN 978-0-8050-8194-7; 0-8050-8194-1
LC 2007027318

Zoe is chosen for the role of Cinder Rabbit in her school play and is also supposed to lead the class in the Bunny Hop at the end, but ever since wicked Winifred laughed at her for landing in a mud puddle, Zoe has forgotten how to hop

"This simple, sweet beginning chapter book contains the right amount of story for children just starting to read longer books; and the charming black-and-white illustrations, decorating every page, will engage kids." Booklist

Healy, Christopher

The **Hero's** Guide to Being an Outlaw; Christopher Healy, illustrated by Todd Harris. Harpercollins Childrens Books 2014 528 p. illustrations (The Hero's guide; book 3) $16.99
Grades: 4 5 6 7 **Fic**

1. Fantasy fiction 2. Princes -- Fiction
ISBN 006211848X; 9780062118486
LC 2014018251

"The League of Princes returns in the hilariously epic conclusion to the hit series that began with Christopher Healy's 'The Hero's Guide to Saving Your Kingdom.' . . . Posters plastered across the thirteen kingdoms are saying that Briar Rose has been murdered--and the four Princes Charming are the prime suspects. Now they're on the run in a desperate attempt to clear their names." (Publisher's note)

"Throughout the heroes' and heroines' travels, the anti-prince conspiracy is revealed in each kingdom—it's directly related to loose ends from The Hero's Guide to Storming the Castle (2013). Side characters make comedic final appearances, and a surprise villain team-up provides closure to the trilogy. Part screwball comedy, part sly wit and all fun." Kirkus

The **hero's** guide to saving your kingdom; written by Christopher Healy; with drawings by Todd Harris. Walden Pond Press 2012 438 p. ill., map $16.99
Grades: 4 5 6 7 **Fic**

1. Princes -- Fiction 2. Fairy tales -- Fiction 3. Heroes and heroines -- Fiction 4. Fairy tales 5. Humorous

stories 6. Witches -- Fiction
ISBN 0062117432; 9780062117434

LC 2011053347

In this book, "four Princes . . . must team up on a . . . quest to save their kingdoms. . . . Cinderella wants adventure more than sheltered Prince Frederic does. Prince Gustav's pride is still badly damaged from having needed Rapunzel's teary-eyed rescue. Through Sleeping Beauty, Prince Liam learns kissing someone out of enchanted sleep doesn't guarantee compatibility. . . . Although she loves wacky Prince Duncan, Snow White needs some solitude." (Kirkus Reviews)

The **hero's** guide to storming the castle; by Christopher Healy; with drawings by Todd Harris. Walden Pond Press, an imprint of HarperCollinsPublishers 2013 496 p. (Hero's Guide) (hardcover) $16.99

Grades: 4 5 6 7   **Fic**

1. Fractured fairy tales 2. Humorous fiction 3. Fairy tales 4. Humorous stories 5. Heroes -- Fiction 6. Princes -- Fiction 7. Characters in literature -- Fiction
ISBN 0062118455; 9780062118455

LC 2012050668

Sequel to: The hero's guide to saving your kingdom

In this humorous, middle-grade fantasy story, by Christopher Healy, illustrated by Todd Harris, "the charming princes from the fairy tales of Cinderella, Rapunzel, Snow White, and Briar Rose, saved the countryside from an evil witch in 'The Hero's Guide to Saving Your Kingdom.' And now, they have to save the day again, by keeping a magical object from falling into the hands of power-mad warlords who would use it for evil." (Publisher's note)

Heide, Florence Parry

Dillweed's revenge; a deadly dose of magic. [by] Florence Parry Heide, with Roxanne Heide Pierce, David Fisher Parry, and Jeanne McReynolds Parry; illustrated by Carson Ellis. Harcourt Children's Books 2010 un il $16.99

Grades: 2 3 4 5   **Fic**

1. Monsters -- Fiction
ISBN 978-0-15-206394-8; 0-15-206394-3

LC 2009-27599

An adventure-deprived young boy's neglectful parents and abusive servants receive their just desserts.

"Terse sentences and repeated refrains inject humor while leaving room for the playful ink and gouache illustrations, which recall Edward Gorey's work, to fill in the details. . . . The mixture of humor and gruesomeness may offend some, but for fans of Roald Dahl, Lemony Snicket, or Hilaire Belloc, it's right on target." SLJ

The **shrinking** of Treehorn; drawings by Edward Gorey. Holiday House 1971 un il lib bdg $16.95; pa $6.95

Grades: 2 3 4 5   **Fic**

ISBN 0-8234-0189-8 lib bdg; 0-8234-0975-9 pa

Treehorn spends an unhappy day and night shrinking. Yet when he tells his mother, father, teacher and principal of his problem they're all too busy to do anything about it. To Treehorn's great relief he finally discovers a magical game that restores him to his natural size, but then he starts turning green!

This "is an imaginative little whimsy, whose sly humor and macabre touches are perfectly matched in Edward Gorey's illustrations." Book World

Heinz, Brian

★ **Mocha** Dick; the legend and fury. by Brian Heinz; illustrated by Randall Enos. Creative Editions 2014 32 p. (hardcover: alk. paper) $18.99

Grades: 2 3 4 5   **Fic**

1. Whales 2. Whaling -- History 3. Whales -- Fiction 4. Whaling -- Fiction 5. Sperm whale -- Fiction
ISBN 1568462425; 9781568462424

LC 2013040661

"Believed to have been active from 1810 to 1859, Mocha Dick was infamous for the ferocity of his retaliations. . . . From the first recorded encounter near the South American island of Mocha till the fatal harpoon blow, Mocha Dick was a legend in his own time. In language befitting a sea lore, author Brain Heinz describes characteristic episodes of the great whale's life, as illustrator Randall Enos animates the tale in a textured style evocative of scrimshaw." (Publisher's note)

" For almost 50 years, a huge albino sperm whale spotted off Isla Mocha (whence the name Mocha Dick) antagonized whalers by aggressively attacking and evading their ships, and tales of this legendary leviathan went on to inspire Herman Melville to write Moby Dick. Heinz and Enos dramatize a few accounts of Mocha Dick's activity in this beautifully designed picture book...The whale appears both vicious and mischievous, adding an extra dose of drama to Heinz's descriptive lines. While a list of sources or further reading would have been useful, most kiddos will be utterly entranced by the folk art–style illustrations, which seem to tell the story enough on their own." Booklist

Helgerson, Joseph

Crows & cards; a novel. written with diligence by Mr. Joseph Helgerson; to which are added fine illustrations by Mr. Peter Desève; also included is Dictionarium Americannicum; being the words herein most arcane and alien and their definitions. Houghton Mifflin Harcourt 2009 344p il $16; pa $5.99

Grades: 4 5 6 7   **Fic**

1. Slavery -- Fiction 2. Gambling -- Fiction 3. Apprentices -- Fiction 4. Native Americans -- Fiction 5. Saint Louis (Mo.) -- Fiction
ISBN 978-0-618-88395-0; 0-618-88395-9; 978-0-547-33909-2 pa; 0-547-33909-7 pa

LC 2008013308

In 1849, Zeb's parents ship him off to St. Louis to become an apprentice tanner, but the naive twelve-year-old rebels, casting his lot with a cheating riverboat gambler, while a slave and an Indian medicine man try to get Zeb back on the right path. Includes historical notes, glossary, and bibliographical references

"Helgerson surrounds Zeb with a lively cast. . . . A solid choice for fans of high-spun yarns and not-too-tall tales." Booklist

★ **Horns** & wrinkles. Houghton Mifflin 2006 357p il $16; pa $4.95

Grades: 4 5 6 7   **Fic**

1. Magic -- Fiction 2. Trolls -- Fiction 3. Bullies -- Fiction 4. Mississippi River -- Fiction
ISBN 0-618-61679-9; 0-618-98178-0 pa

LC 2005025448

Along a magic-saturated stretch of the Mississippi River near Blue Wing, Minnesota, twelve-year-old Claire and her bullying cousin Duke are drawn into an adventure involving Bodacious Deepthink the Great Rock Troll, a helpful fairy, and a group of trolls searching for their fathers.

"Tongue-in-cheek humor brings a delightful zing to the playfully inventive storytelling and fast-paced plot. Enchanting sketches foreshadow each chapter, adding to the wonder." SLJ

Hemingway, Edith Morris

Road to Tater Hill; [by] Edith M. Hemingway. Delacorte Press 2009 213p map $16.99; lib bdg $19.99
Grades: 5 6 7 8   **Fic**
1. Friendship -- Fiction 2. Bereavement -- Fiction 3. Grandparents -- Fiction 4. Mountain life -- Fiction 5. North Carolina -- Fiction 6. Depression (Psychology) -- Fiction
ISBN 978-0-385-73677-0; 0-385-73677-0; 978-0-385-90627-2 lib bdg; 0-385-90627-7 lib bdg
LC 2008-24906

At her grandparents' North Carolina mountain home during the summer of 1963, eleven-year-old Annie Winters, grief-stricken by the death of her newborn sister and isolated by her mother's deepening depression, finds comfort in holding an oblong stone 'rock baby' and in the friendship of a neighbor boy and a reclusive mountain woman with a devastating secret

"Drawing on the author's childhood roots, the heart of this first novel is the sense of place, described in simple lyrical words. . . . True to Annie's viewpoint, the particulars tell a universal drama of childhood grief, complete in all its sadness, anger, loneliness, and healing." Booklist

Hemphill, Helen

The **adventurous** deeds of Deadwood Jones. Front Street 2008 228p $16.95
Grades: 5 6 7 8   **Fic**
1. Cousins -- Fiction 2. Cowhands -- Fiction 3. West (U.S.) -- Fiction 4. Race relations -- Fiction 5. African Americans -- Fiction
ISBN 978-1-59078-637-6; 1-59078-637-8
LC 2008005422

Thirteen-year-old Prometheus Jones and his eleven-year-old cousin Omer flee Tennessee and join a cattle drive that will eventually take them to Texas, where Prometheus hopes his father lives, and they find adventure and face challenges as African Americans in a land still recovering from the Civil War.

"Prometheus is an always sympathetic and engaging character, and the dangers and misadventures he encounters . . . make for compelling reading." Booklist

Hemphill, Michael

Stonewall Hinkleman and the Battle of Bull Run; [by] Michael Hemphill and Sam Riddleburger. Dial Books for Young Readers 2009 168p $16.99
Grades: 4 5 6   **Fic**
1. Time travel -- Fiction 2. Bull Run, 1st Battle of, 1861 -- Fiction 3. United States -- History -- 1861-1865, Civil War -- Fiction
ISBN 978-0-8037-3179-0; 0-8037-3179-5
LC 2008-15795

While participating in a reenactment of the Battle of Bull Run, twelve-year-old Stonewall Hinkleman is transported back to the actual Civil War battle by means of a magic bugle.

This is a "well-paced time-travel novel. . . . Stonewall is a likable character whose attitude changes for the better in the story. . . . A good choice for historical fiction fans." SLJ

Henham, R. D.

The **red** dragon codex. Mirrorstone 2008 244p il map (Dragon condices) pa $9.95
Grades: 4 5 6   **Fic**
1. Fantasy fiction 2. Dragons -- Fiction
ISBN 978-0-7869-4925-0 pa; 0-7869-4925-2 pa
LC 2007014679

Mudd must seek a silver dragon's help to rescue Shemnara, an old woman who is practically his mother, when she is kidnapped by a red dragon.

"Inventive details, dimensional characterizations, and fast-paced action make this a good introduction to the fantasy genre." Booklist

Henkes, Kevin

★ **Bird** Lake moon. Greenwillow Books 2008 179p $15.99; lib bdg $16.89; pa $5.99
Grades: 4 5 6 7   **Fic**
1. Lakes -- Fiction 2. Divorce -- Fiction 3. Wisconsin -- Fiction 4. Friendship -- Fiction 5. Bereavement -- Fiction 6. Family life -- Fiction
ISBN 978-0-06-147076-9; 0-06-147076-7; 978-0-06-147078-3 lib bdg; 0-06-147078-3 lib bdg; 978-0-06-147079-0 pa; 0-06-147079-1 pa
LC 2007-36564

Twelve-year-old Mitch and his mother are spending the summer with his grandparents at Bird Lake after his parents separate, and ten-year-old Spencer and his family have returned to the lake where Spencer's little brother drowned long ago, and as the boys become friends and spend time together, each of them begins to heal

"Characters are gently and believably developed as the story weaves in and around the beautiful Wisconsin setting. The superbly crafted plot moves smoothly and unhurriedly, mirroring a slow summer pace." SLJ

The **birthday** room. Greenwillow Bks. 1999 152p $15.99; pa $5.99
Grades: 5 6 7 8   **Fic**
1. Uncles -- Fiction 2. Family life -- Fiction
ISBN 0-688-16733-0; 0-06-443828-7 pa
LC 98-39887

"Told in spare, unobtrusive prose, a story that helps us see our own chances for benefiting from mutual tolerance, creative conflict resolution, and other forms of good will." Horn Book

"For his twelfth birthday, Ben Hunter receives a room that he can use as an art studio and a letter from his uncle—the one responsible for the loss of Ben's little finger when Ben was a toddler. . . . Mrs. Hunter, who has been angry at her brother since the accident, reluctantly agrees to go to Oregon with Ben." Booklist

★ **Olive's** ocean. Greenwillow Bks. 2003 217p $15.99; pa $6.99

Grades: 5 6 7 8 **Fic**
1. Family life -- Fiction 2. Grandmothers -- Fiction
ISBN 0-06-053543-1; 0-06-053545-8 pa

LC 2002-29782

A Newbery Medal honor book, 2004

On a summer visit to her grandmother's cottage by the ocean, twelve-year-old Martha gains perspective on the death of a classmate, on her relationship with her grandmother, on her feelings for an older boy, and on her plans to be a writer.

"Rich characterizations move this compelling novel to its satisfying and emotionally authentic conclusion." SLJ

Protecting Marie. Greenwillow Bks. 1995 195p $18.99; pa $5.99
Grades: 5 6 7 8 **Fic**
1. Dogs -- Fiction 2. Father-daughter relationship -- Fiction
ISBN 0-688-13958-2; 0-06-053545-8 pa

LC 94-16387

Relates twelve-year-old Fanny's love-hate relationship with her father, a temperamental artist, who has given Fanny a new dog

"The characters ring heartbreakingly true in this quiet, wise story; they are complex and difficult—like all of us— and worthy of our attention." Horn Book

★ **Sun** & Spoon. Greenwillow Bks. 1997 135p $15.99; pa $5.99
Grades: 4 5 6 7 **Fic**
1. Death -- Fiction 2. Grandmothers -- Fiction
ISBN 0-688-15232-5; 0-06-128875-6 pa

LC 96-46259

"Sensitively placed metaphors enrich the narrative, embuing its perceptive depictions of grief with a powerful message of affirmation." Publ Wkly

"Spoon, 10, spends his summer trying to reconfigure his world, which seems strangely out of kilter since his grandmother's death." SLJ

Words of stone. Greenwillow Bks. 1992 152p $18.99; pa $6.99
Grades: 5 6 7 8 **Fic**
1. Friendship -- Fiction
ISBN 0-688-11356-7; 0-06-078230-7 pa

LC 91-28543

Busy trying to deal with his many fears and his troubled feelings for his dead mother, ten-year-old Blaze has his life changed when he meets the boisterous and irresistible Joselle

"A story rich in characterization, dramatic subplots, and some very creepy moments." SLJ

★ The **year** of Billy Miller; by Kevin Henkes. 1st ed. Harpercollins Childrens Books 2013 240 p. (hardcover) $16.99; (library) $17.89
Grades: 2 3 4 5 **Fic**
1. Siblings -- Fiction 2. School stories 3. Parent-child relationship -- Fiction 4. Humorous stories 5. Schools -- Fiction 6. Wisconsin -- Fiction 7. Family life -- Wisconsin -- Fiction
ISBN 0062268120; 9780062268129; 9780062268136

LC 2012050373

Newberry Honor Book (2014)

This book follows second-grader Billy Miller. It's the "year of several dilemmas for the boy, including the fear he might 'start forgetting things' due to bumping his head while on vacation over the summer. Then there's the habitat diorama that Billy is assigned--the bat cave he creates doesn't turn out quite like he'd hoped." His relationships with his teacher, father, mother, and sister are examined. (Publishers Weekly)

Henry, Marguerite
Brighty of the Grand Canyon; illustrated by Wesley Dennis. Macmillan 1991 222p il hardcover o.p. pa $3.95
Grades: 4 5 6 7 **Fic**
1. Donkeys -- Fiction 2. Grand Canyon (Ariz.) -- Fiction
ISBN 0-02-743664-0; 0-689-71485-8 pa

LC 90-28636

First published 1953 by Rand McNally

"Only those who are unfamiliar with the West would say it is too packed with drama to be true. And the author's understanding warmth for all of God's creatures still shines through her superb ability as a story teller making this a vivid tale." Christ Sci Monit

★ **King** of the wind; illustrated by Wesley Dennis. Macmillan 1991 172p il $18.95; pa $5.99
Grades: 4 5 6 7 **Fic**
1. Horses -- Fiction
ISBN 0-02-743629-2; 0-689-71486-6 pa

LC 91-13474

A reissue of the title first published 1948 by Rand McNally

Awarded the Newbery Medal, 1949

"A beautiful, sympathetic story of the famous [ancestor of a line of great thoroughbred horses] . . . and the little mute Arabian stable boy who accompanies him on his journey across the seas to France and England [in the eighteenth century]. The lad's fierce devotion to his horse and his great faith and loyalty are skillfully woven into an enthralling tale which children will long remember. The moving quality of the writing is reflected in the handsome illustrations." Wis Libr Bull

★ **Misty** of Chincoteague; illustrated by Wesley Dennis. Macmillan 1991 173p il hardcover o.p. pa $5.99
Grades: 4 5 6 7 **Fic**
1. Horses -- Fiction 2. Chincoteague Island (Va.) -- Fiction
ISBN 0-02-743622-5; 1-4169-2783-2 pa

LC 90-27237

First published 1947 by Rand McNally

A Newbery Medal honor book, 1948

"The beauty and pride of the wild horses is the highpoint in the story, and skillful drawings of them reveal their grace and swiftness." Ont Libr Rev

Other titles about the ponies of Chincoteague Island are:
Sea star, orphan of Chincoteague (1949)
Stormy, Misty's foal (1963)

Herlong, M.H.
Buddy; by M. H. Herlong. Viking Childrens Books 2012 p. cm.
Grades: 4 5 6 **Fic**
1. Hurricane Katrina, 2005 -- Fiction 2. Dogs -- Fiction

3. African Americans -- Fiction 4. New Orleans (La.)
-- Fiction 5. Family life -- Louisiana -- Fiction 6. Lost
and found possessions -- Fiction
ISBN 9780670014033

LC 2011042854

This book tells the story of Li'l T Roberts, who "meets
Buddy when his family's car accidentally hits the stray dog.
. . . Buddy turns out to be the dog Li'l T's always wished
for--until Hurricane Katrina comes to New Orleans and he
must leave Buddy behind. . . . But Li'l T refuses to give up
his quest to find his best friend." (Publisher's Note)

Hermes, Patricia

Emma Dilemma and the new nanny. Marshall Cavendish 2006 106p il $15.95
Grades: 2 3 4   **Fic**
1. Family life -- Fiction
ISBN 0-7614-5286-9; 978-0-7614-5286-7

LC 2005024668

Emma tries to help her parents understand that, although
their beloved new nanny has made a few mistakes, no one
can behave perfectly responsibly all the time

"The tumult in a family with five preteen children, several pets, and two working parents provides a lively setting,
and the author lightly but effectively conveys the ideas that
adults aren't perfect and that admitting mistakes is often
the first step toward solutions that leave everyone pleased."
Booklist

Other titles about Emma are:

Emma Dilemma and the two nannies (2007)
Emma Dilemma and the soccer nanny (2008)
Emma Dilemma and the camping nanny (2009)
Emma Dilemma, the nanny, and the secret ferret (2010)
Emma Dilemma, the nanny, and the best horse ever
(2011)

Herrera, Robin

Hope is a ferris wheel; Robin Herrera. Amulet Books
2014 272 p. (alk. paper) $16.95
Grades: 4 5 6 7   **Fic**
1. Clubs -- Fiction 2. Moving -- Fiction 3. Poetry
-- Fiction 4. Trailer parks -- Fiction 5. Trailer camps
-- Fiction
ISBN 1419710397; 9781419710391

LC 2013026392

In this book, by Robin Herrera, "ten-year-old Star Mackie lives in a trailer park with her flaky mom and her melancholy older sister. . . . Moving to a new town has made it
difficult for Star to make friends, when her classmates tease
her because of where she lives and because of her layered
blue hair. But when Star starts a poetry club, she develops a
love of Emily Dickinson and . . . learns some important lessons about herself and comes to terms with her hopes for the
future." (Publisher's note)

"Star Mackie is a fifth-grader overflowing with hope—
especially for friends. But that seems impossible at her new
school since she is teased for living in a pink trailer and having strangely layered blue hair. In her debut, Herrera has
created a delightful narrator with a memorable voice and
surrounded her with a unique supporting cast. Got fans of
Joan Bauer in your neck of the woods? Send them this way.;
Booklist

Herrick, Steven

Naked bunyip dancing; pictures by Beth Norling.
Front Street 2008 201p il $16.95
Grades: 3 4 5 6   **Fic**
1. School stories 2. Novels in verse 3. Teachers --
Fiction 4. Australia -- Fiction
ISBN 978-1-59078-499-0

LC 2007-18353

First published 2005 in Australia

This novel in verse follows the school year of Australian
students in classroom 6C, as their unconventional teacher
encourages them to discover their own strengths and talents
and perform in a memorable concert.

"The novel captures the humor and unpredictability of
11 and 12-year-olds. . . . The terse free verse, in short clear
lines, is easily accessible. Funny, with some touches of poignancy. . . . The childlike, black-and-white illustrations are
reminiscent of the drawings of Shel Silverstein and complement the narrative." SLJ

Hesse, Karen

★ **Brooklyn** Bridge; a novel. Feiwel and Friends
2008 229p il map $17.95
Grades: 5 6 7 8 9 10   **Fic**
1. Immigrants -- Fiction 2. Family life -- Fiction 3.
Social classes -- Fiction 4. Homeless persons -- Fiction
5. Russian Americans -- Fiction 6. Brooklyn (New
York, N.Y.) -- Fiction
ISBN 978-0-312-37886-8; 0-312-37886-6

LC 2008-05624

In 1903 Brooklyn, fourteen-year-old Joseph Michtom's
life changes for the worse when his parents, Russian immigrants, invent the teddy bear and turn their apartment
into a factory, while nearby the glitter of Coney Island contrasts with the dismal lives of children dwelling under the
Brooklyn Bridge.

Hesse "applies her gift for narrative voice to this memorable story. . . . The novel explodes with dark drama before
its eerie but moving resolution." Publ Wkly

★ **Letters** from Rifka. Holt & Co. 1992 148p $16.95;
pa $6.99
Grades: 5 6 7 8   **Fic**
1. Jews -- Fiction 2. Letters -- Fiction 3. Immigrants
-- Fiction
ISBN 0-8050-1964-2; 0-312-53561-9 pa

LC 91-48007

In letters to her cousin, Rifka, a young Jewish girl,
chronicles her family's flight from Russia in 1919 and her
own experiences when she must be left in Belgium for a
while when the others emigrate to America

"Based on the true story of the author's great-aunt, the
moving account of a brave young girl's story brings to life
the day-to-day trials and horrors experienced by many immigrants as well as the resourcefulness and strength they found
within themselves." Horn Book

★ **Out** of the dust. Scholastic 1997 227p $16.95;
pa $6.99
Grades: 5 6 7 8   **Fic**
1. Novels in verse 2. Oklahoma -- Fiction 3. Farm life
-- Fiction 4. Dust storms -- Fiction 5. Great Depression,

1929-1939 -- Fiction
ISBN 0-590-36080-9; 0-590-37125-8 pa
LC 96-40344
Awarded the Newbery Medal, 1998
"Hesse's writing transcends the gloom and transforms it into a powerfully compelling tale of a girl with enormous strength, courage, and love. The entire novel is written in very readable blank verse." Booklist

★ **Witness**. Scholastic Press 2001 161p $16.95; pa $5.99
Grades: 6 7 8 9   **Fic**
1. Novels in verse 2. Vermont -- Fiction 3. Prejudices -- Fiction 4. Ku Klux Klan -- Fiction
ISBN 0-439-27199-1; 0-439-27200-9 pa
LC 00-54139
A series of poems express the views of eleven people in a small Vermont town, including a young black girl and a young Jewish girl, during the early 1920s when the Ku Klux Klan is trying to infiltrate the town
"The story is divided into five acts, and would lend itself beautifully to performance. The plot unfolds smoothly, and the author creates multidimensional characters." SLJ

Hest, Amy
★ **Remembering** Mrs. Rossi; [illustrated by] Heather Maione. Candlewick Press 2007 184p il $14.99; pa $6.99
Grades: 3 4 5   **Fic**
1. Death -- Fiction 2. Mothers -- Fiction 3. Teachers -- Fiction 4. New York (N.Y.) -- Fiction 5. Father-daughter relationship -- Fiction
ISBN 978-0-7636-2163-6; 0-7636-2163-3; 978-0-7636-4089-7 pa
LC 2006-41649
Although she loves her father, their home in New York City, and third-grade teacher Miss Meadows, Annie misses her mother who died recently
"Hest imbues her characters with warmth, humor, and realistic imperfections. . . . Maione's ink sketches highlight the tender affections." Booklist
Followed by: Letters to Leo (2012)

Hiaasen, Carl
★ **Flush**. Knopf 2005 263p $16.95; lib bdg $18.99; pa $8.99
Grades: 5 6 7 8   **Fic**
1. Florida -- Fiction 2. Boats and boating -- Fiction 3. Environmental protection -- Fiction
ISBN 0-375-82182-1; 0-375-92182-6 lib bdg; 0-375-84185-7 pa
LC 2005-05259
With their father jailed for sinking a river boat, Noah Underwood and his younger sister, Abbey, must gather evidence that the owner of this floating casino is emptying his bilge tanks into the protected waters around their Florida Keys home
"This quick-reading, fun, family adventure harkens back to the Hardy Boys in its simplicity and quirky characters." SLJ

★ **Hoot**. Knopf 2002 292p $15.95; pa $8.95
Grades: 5 6 7 8   **Fic**
1. Owls -- Fiction 2. Florida -- Fiction 3. Environmental

protection -- Fiction
ISBN 0-375-82181-3; 0-375-82916-4 pa
LC 2002-25478
A Newbery Medal honor book, 2003
Roy, who is new to his small Florida community, becomes involved in another boy's attempt to save a colony of burrowing owls from a proposed construction site
"The story is full of offbeat humor, buffoonish yet charming supporting characters, and genuinely touching scenes of children enjoying the wildness of nature." Booklist

★ **Scat**. Knopf 2009 371p $16.99; lib bdg $19.99; pa $8.99
Grades: 5 6 7 8   **Fic**
1. Florida -- Fiction 2. Teachers -- Fiction 3. Missing persons -- Fiction 4. Wildlife conservation -- Fiction
ISBN 978-0-375-83486-8; 0-375-83486-9; 978-0-375-93486-5 lib bdg; 0-375-93486-3 lib bdg; 978-0-375-83487-5 pa; 0-375-83487-7 pa
LC 2008-28266
Nick and his friend Marta decide to investigate when a mysterious fire starts near a Florida wildlife preserve and an unpopular teacher goes missing
"Once again, Hiaasen has written an edge-of-the-seat eco-thriller. . . . From the first sentence, readers will be hooked. . . . This well-written and smoothly plotted story, with fully realized characters, will certainly appeal to mystery lovers." SLJ

Hicks, Betty
Basketball Bats; illustrated by Adam McCauley. Roaring Brook Press 2008 55p il (Gym shorts) $15.95
Grades: 2 3 4   **Fic**
1. Basketball -- Fiction
ISBN 978-1-59643-243-7; 1-59643-243-8
LC 2007-019501
Henry and his basketball teammates, the Bats, take on the Tigers, and Henry learns a lesson about working as a team.
"Hicks finds just the right balance between story line, play-by-play action, and wry humor. . . . Nearly every double-page spread includes a droll illustration by McCauley, the illustrator of Scieszka's Time Warp Trio series." Booklist
Other titles in this series are:
Goof-off goalie (2008)
Swimming with sharks (2008)
Scaredy-cat catcher (2009)
Track attack (2009)
Doubles troubles (2010)

Out of order. Roaring Brook Press 2005 169p $15.95; pa $6.99
Grades: 4 5 6   **Fic**
1. Stepfamilies -- Fiction
ISBN 1-59643-061-3; 0-312-37355-4 pa
LC 2004-30107
Four youngsters, ages nine to fifteen, narrate one side of the story of their newly blended family's adjustment, interwoven with grief and loss.
"Hicks provides readers with a fresh look at blended families, offering much food for thought and several multi-layered characters." SLJ

The **worm** whisperer; Betty Hicks; illustrated by Ben Hatke. Roaring Brook Press 2012 192 p. (hardcover) $16.99

Grades: 4 5 6 **Fic**
1. Picture books for children 2. Caterpillars -- Fiction 3. Worms -- Fiction 4. Racing -- Fiction 5. Insects -- Fiction 6. Human-animal communication -- Fiction
ISBN 1596434902; 9781596434905; 9781596438460
LC 2012013790

In this children's book by Betty Hicks, illustrated by Ben Hatke, "Ellis Coffey loves animals. He spends so much time outdoors that sometimes he thinks he can talk with them. When he discovers a caterpillar that seems to follow his directions, he knows he has a chance to win the annual Woolly Worm race. The prize money is $1,000--exactly the amount of the deductible for his dad's back surgery." (Publisher's note)

Higgins, F. E.

The **Black** Book of Secrets. Feiwel and Friends 2007 273p $14.95

Grades: 4 5 6 7 **Fic**
1. Apprentices -- Fiction 2. Pawnbrokers -- Fiction
ISBN 978-0-312-36844-9; 0-312-36844-5
LC 2007-32559

When Ludlow Fitch runs away from his thieving parents in the City, he meets up with the mysterious Joe Zabbidou, who calls himself a secret pawnbroker, and who takes Ludlow as an apprentice to record the confessions of the townspeople of Pagus Parvus, where resentments are many and trust is scarce.

This is "an intriguing blend of adventure and historical fiction spiced with a light touch of the fantastic." Voice Youth Advocates

The **bone** magician. Feiwel and Friends 2008 272p $14.95

Grades: 4 5 6 7 **Fic**
1. Mystery fiction 2. Magicians -- Fiction 3. Undertakers and undertaking -- Fiction
ISBN 978-0-312-36845-6; 0-312-36845-3
LC 2008-6777

With his father, a fugitive, falsely accused of multiple murders and the real serial killer stalking the wretched streets of Urbs Umida, Pin Carpue, a young undertaker's assistant, investigates and soon discovers that all of the victims may have attended the performance of a stage magician who claims to be able to raise corpses and make the dead speak.

This offers "no end of picaresque charms, creepy turns, and beguiling cast members." Booklist

Higgins, Simon

Moonshadow; rise of the ninja. Little Brown & Co. 2010 325p il $15.99

Grades: 4 5 6 7 **Fic**
1. Japan -- Fiction 2. Ninja -- Fiction 3. Spies -- Fiction 4. Secret societies -- Fiction
ISBN 978-0-316-05531-4; 0-316-05531-X

First published 2008 in Australia with title: Moonshadow: eye of the beast

It's the dawn of an age of peace in medieval Japan. But a power-hungry warlord is plotting to plunge the national into a deadly civil war. Enter Moonshadow, the newest agent for the Grey Light Order, a secret brotherhood of ninja spy war-

riors. Can Moonshadow defeat the evil warlord or will his first mission be his last?

"The swordplay is fast and furious, and Japanese terms and places are integrated in a manner that reluctant readers will find accessible. This adventure is part spy novel, part magic, and all fun." SLJ

Followed by: The nightmare ninja (2011)

The **nightmare** ninja. Little, Brown 2011 368p (Moonshadow) $15.99

Grades: 4 5 6 7 **Fic**
1. Japan -- Fiction 2. Ninja -- Fiction 3. Orphans -- Fiction 4. Supernatural -- Fiction
ISBN 978-0-316-05533-8; 0-316-05533-6
LC 2010043177

Sequel to: Moonshadow: rise of the ninja (2010)

Battling a power-hungry warlord in medieval Japan, teenaged Moonshadow, an orphaned ninja in the shogun's secret service with the ability to see through the eyes of animals, encounters a weaponless assassin who enters the mind of his victims during their sleep.

"Higgins effectively uses this work to set the stage for a compelling third installment." Kirkus

Hill, Kirkpatrick

Bo at Ballard Creek; Kirkpatrick Hill; illustrated by LeUyen Pham. Henry Holt and Co. 2013 288 p. (hardcover) $15.99

Grades: 3 4 5 6 **Fic**
1. Historical fiction 2. Adopted children -- Fiction 3. Eskimos -- Fiction 4. Fathers -- Fiction 5. Adoption -- Fiction 6. Alaska -- History -- 1867-1959 -- Fiction
ISBN 0805093516; 9780805093513
LC 2012046055

Scott O'Dell Award for Historical Fiction (2014)

In this historical novel, "Bo, a 5-year-old girl, was adopted as a newborn by two gruff but tenderhearted blacksmiths who've toiled in the mining camps of the Yukon for years. These unlikely fathers smoke a bit and swear a bit, but they love Bo with all their hearts. Theirs is an extraordinarily generous, solicitous, close-knit community, comprised of indigenous neighbors and workers from around the world." (Kirkus)

The **year** of Miss Agnes. Margaret K. McElderry Bks. 2000 115p $16; pa $5.99

Grades: 3 4 5 **Fic**
1. School stories 2. Alaska -- Fiction 3. Teachers -- Fiction 4. Athaspascan Indians -- Fiction
ISBN 0-689-82933-7; 0-689-85124-3 pa
LC 99-46912

Ten-year-old Fred (short for Frederika) narrates the story of school and village life among the Athapascans in Alaska during 1948 when Miss Agnes arrived as the new teacher

"Hill has created more than just an appealing cast of characters; she introduces readers to a whole community and makes a long-ago and faraway place seem real and very much alive. This is an inspirational story." SLJ

Hilmo, Tess

Skies like these; Tess Hilmo. Margaret Ferguson Books, Farrar Straus Giroux 2014 240 p. (hardback) $16.99

Grades: 4 5 6 7 **Fic**
1. Western stories 2. Friendship -- Fiction 3. Aunts

-- Fiction 4. Wyoming -- Fiction 5. Eccentrics and eccentricities -- Fiction
ISBN 0374369984; 9780374369989
LC 2013033675
"Twelve-year-old Jade's perfect summers have always been spent reading and watching TV reruns, so she's not happy when her parents send her off to Wyoming to her aunt's house. She meets a boy who calls himself Roy Parker--just like the real name of the legendary rebel cowboy Butch Cassidy. . . . Jade wants to be a good friend, but she's not so sure about Roy's schemes." (Publisher's note)

"In Hilmo's second middle-grade novel, a 12-year-old city girl spends a month in Wyoming and finds big skies, a boy who idolizes Butch Cassidy, and her own sense of adventure. . . . But rest assured, if there's a sequel, their future big plans will likely center around climbing Grand Teton rather than robbing banks." Booklist

★ **With** a name like Love. Margaret Ferguson Books/ Farrar Straus Giroux 2011 249p $16.99
Grades: 5 6 7 8   **Fic**
1. Mystery fiction 2. Arkansas -- Fiction 3. Country life -- Fiction 4. Christian life -- Fiction 5. Conduct of life -- Fiction
ISBN 978-0-374-38465-4; 0-374-38465-7
LC 2010036314
Thirteen-year-old Olivene Love gets tangled up in a murder mystery when her itinerant preaching family arrives in the small town of Binder, Arkansas in 1957.

"Hilmo creates a family, town and a mystery that readers won't soon forget." Kirkus

Himmelman, John, 1959-
Tales of Bunjitsu Bunny; written and illustrated by John Himmelman. Henry Holt & Co. 2014 128 p. color illustrations (hardcover) $13.99
Grades: 1 2 3   **Fic**
1. Rabbits -- Fiction 2. Martial arts -- Fiction 3. Animals -- Fiction
ISBN 0805099700; 9780805099706
LC 2013048431
In this children's book, author John Himmelman is "introducing Isabel, aka Bunjitsu Bunny! She is the BEST bunjitsu artist in her school, and she can throw farther, kick higher, and hit harder than anyone else! But she never hurts another creature . . . unless she has to. This series of brief stories about Isabel's adventures are a beguiling combination of child-friendly scenarios and Eastern wisdom perfect for the youngest readers." (Publisher's note)

"Himmelman (Duck to the Rescue) draws on his own experience as a martial arts instructor in 12 brief tales about a rabbit named Isabel, "the best bunjitsu artist in her school.". . . Spare ink illustrations appear on every page, skillfully balancing humor, bunjitsu action, and understated grace. Like Isabel herself, this one's a winner in unexpected ways." PW

Hirsch, Jeff
The **39** clues: Breakaway; unstoppable: breakaway. Jeff Hirsch. Scholastic 2014 192 p. (The 39 clues: unstoppable) (paper over board) $12.99
Grades: 4 5 6 7   **Fic**
1. Betrayal 2. Adventure stories 3. Brothers and sisters

-- Fiction
ISBN 0545521424; 9780545521420
LC 2013942298
In this 39 Clues series book by Jeff Hirsch, "Dan and Amy are facing their greatest threat yet, an enemy who has found a way to use the source of the Cahill family power against them. To stop him, Dan and Amy must set out on a desperate mission that will take them from one of the world's hottest regions all the way to the frozen blast of the Arctic Circle. But with the enemy closing in, Dan finds himself facing the one terror he never imagined--being betrayed by his own sister." (Publisher's note)

Hirsch, Odo
Darius Bell and the glitter pool. Kane/Miller 2010 214p $15.99
Grades: 4 5 6 7   **Fic**
1. Gifts -- Fiction 2. Poverty -- Fiction
ISBN 978-1-935279-65-5; 1-935279-65-3
First published 2009 in Australia
The Bell family's ancestors were showered with honours, gifts and grants of land. In exchange, they have bestowed a Gift, once every 25 years, on the town. Now it's Darius's father's turn and there is no money for an impressive gift. When an earthquake reveals a glorious cave, with the most beautiful minerals lining the walls, he thinks he's found the answer.

"With an inventive cast of characters and a surprise twist at the end, this gentle, appealing story would make a terrific read-aloud for a young audience." Booklist

Hitchcock, Shannon
The **ballad** of Jessie Pearl; Shannon Hitchcock. 1st ed. Namelos llc 2012 131 p. ill. (hardcover) $18.95
Grades: 5 6 7 8   **Fic**
1. Love stories 2. Historical fiction 3. Tuberculosis -- Fiction
ISBN 160898141X; 9781608981410; 9781608981427
LC 2012936706
In this novel, by Shannon Hitchcock, "it's 1922, and Jessie has big plans for her future, but that's before tuberculosis strikes. Though she has no talent for cooking, cleaning, or nursing, Jessie puts her dreams on hold to help her family. She falls in love for the first time ever, and suddenly what she wants is not so simple anymore." (Publisher's note)

Hobbs, Valerie
Defiance. Farrar, Straus and Giroux 2005 116p $16; pa $7.99
Grades: 5 6 7 8   **Fic**
1. Death -- Fiction 2. Cancer -- Fiction 3. Country life -- Fiction
ISBN 0-374-30847-0; 0-312-53581-3 pa
LC 2004-61524
While vacationing in the country, eleven-year-old Toby, a cancer patient, learns some important lessons about living and dying from an elderly poet and her cow.

"Spare, graceful writing, with just enough detail to bring the characters and setting to life, skillfully paces the action and keeps the focus on Toby's conflicted feelings. . . . A quiet, yet resonant story." SLJ

★ The **last** best days of summer. Frances Foster Books 2010 197p $16.99

Grades: 5 6 7 8   **Fic**

1. Artists -- Fiction 2. Old age -- Fiction 3. Popularity -- Fiction 4. Grandmothers -- Fiction 5. Down syndrome -- Fiction

ISBN 978-0-374-34670-6; 0-374-34670-4

LC 2008-47145

During a summer visit, twelve-year-old Lucy must come to terms with both her grandmother's failing memory and how her mentally-challenged neighbor will impact her popularity when both enter the same middle school in the fall.

"The story's finely tuned realism is refreshing, particularly in Lucy's yearning for social acceptance and in the fully drawn and wholly memorable characters." Booklist

Maggie and Oliver, or, A bone of one's own; art by Jennifer Thermes. Henry Holt and Company 2011 181p il $15.99

Grades: 4 5 6   **Fic**

1. Dogs -- Fiction 2. Orphans -- Fiction 3. Poverty -- Fiction 4. Boston (Mass.) -- Fiction 5. Homeless persons -- Fiction

ISBN 978-0-8050-9294-3; 0-8050-9294-3

LC 2011005791

A dog whose beloved owner has died and an orphaned ten-year-old girl find each other while enduring poverty and homelessness in early-twentieth-century Boston.

"Thermes' black-and-white illustrations quietly match both tone and period. A touching and emotionally satisfying foundling tale." Kirkus

Hobbs, Will

Crossing the wire. HarperCollins 2006 216p $15.99; lib bdg $16.89; pa $5.99

Grades: 5 6 7 8   **Fic**

1. Mexicans -- Fiction 2. Illegal aliens -- Fiction

ISBN 978-0-06-074138-9; 0-06-074138-4; 978-0-06-074139-6 lib bdg; 0-06-074139-2 lib bdg; 978-0-06-074140-2 pa; 0-06-074140-6 pa

LC 2005-19697

Fifteen-year-old Victor Flores journeys north in a desperate attempt to cross the Arizona border and find work in the United States to support his family in central Mexico.

This is "an exciting story in a vital contemporary setting." Voice Youth Advocates

★ **Jason's** gold. Morrow Junior Bks. 1999 221p $16.99; pa $5.99

Grades: 5 6 7 8   **Fic**

1. Orphans -- Fiction 2. Voyages and travels -- Fiction 3. Klondike River Valley (Yukon) -- Gold discoveries -- Fiction

ISBN 0-688-15093-4; 0-380-72914-8 pa

LC 99-17973

When news of the discovery of gold in Canada's Yukon Territory in 1897 reaches fifteen-year-old Jason, he embarks on a 10,000-mile journey to strike it rich

"The successful presentation of a fascinating era, coupled with plenty of action, makes this a good historical fiction choice." SLJ

Followed by Down the Yukon (2001)

Never say die; by Will Hobbs. HarperCollins Children's Books 2012 224 p. (trade bdg.) $16.99

Grades: 4 5 6 7   **Fic**

1. Canada -- Fiction 2. Wilderness survival -- Fiction 3. Adventure fiction 4. Bears -- Fiction 5. Caribou -- Fiction 6. Eskimos -- Fiction 7. Brothers -- Fiction 8. Inuit -- Canada -- Fiction 9. Photojournalism -- Fiction 10. Aklavik (N.W.T.) -- Fiction 11. Climatic changes -- Fiction 12. Adventure and adventurers -- Fiction

ISBN 006170878X; 9780061708787; 9780061708794

LC 2011053289

This juvenile adventure novel, by Will Hobbs, is set "in Canada's Arctic, [where] Nick Thrasher is an accomplished Inuit hunter at fifteen. . . . Ryan Powers . . . invites Nick to come along and help him find the caribou. Barely down the river, disaster strikes. . . . With nothing but the clothes on his back and the knife on his hip, Nick is up against it in a world of wolves, caribou, and grizzlies. All the while, the monstrous grolar bear stalks the land." (Publisher's note)

Take me to the river. HarperCollins 2011 184p $15.99; lib bdg $16.89

Grades: 5 6 7 8   **Fic**

1. Texas -- Fiction 2. Cousins -- Fiction 3. Canoes and canoeing -- Fiction

ISBN 978-0-06-074144-0; 0-06-074144-9; 978-0-06-074145-7 lib bdg; 0-06-074145-7 lib bdg

LC 2010003147

When North Carolina fourteen-year-old Dylan Sands joins his fifteen-year-old cousin Rio in running the Rio Grande River, they face a tropical storm and a fugitive kidnapper.

"The story unfolds in a disarming manner. The pace is quick, and the challenges are relentless, but the writing is so grounded in physical details and emotional realism that every turn of events seems convincing within the context of the story." Booklist

Hof, Marjolijn

Against the odds; translated by Johanna H. Prins and Johanna W. Prins. Groundwood Books/House of Anansi Press 2009 125p $17.95

Grades: 3 4 5   **Fic**

1. War stories 2. Worry -- Fiction 3. Fathers -- Fiction 4. Physicians -- Fiction

ISBN 978-0-88899-935-1; 0-88899-935-6; 978-0-88899-950-4 pa

"Kiki's father is traveling to a war zone as a doctor, and the child and her mother worry that he won't return. As soon as he leaves, Kiki starts planning to increase the odds that he will be safe. . . . The language and writing style are a bit old-fashioned, yet comforting. The story is engaging and gives readers a chance to develop empathy." SLJ

Mother number zero. Groundwood Books 2011 179p $16.95

Grades: 4 5 6 7   **Fic**

1. Adoption -- Fiction 2. Siblings -- Fiction 3. Family life -- Fiction 4. Netherlands -- Fiction

ISBN 978-1-55498-078-9; 1-55498-078-X

Fay "and his older sister An Bing Wa were both adopted; she was an abandoned baby in China, and he was born to a mother traumatized in the Bosnian conflict. A new girl in the neighborhood, Maud, takes a keen interest in Fay's story and urges him to find his birth mother. . . . Hof . . . writes Fay's narration with a calm, matter-of-fact voice that possesses a literalness and simplicity in keeping with his youth. . . . The story nonetheless treats the characters with quiet percipience. . . . Younger fans of domestic novels who like a tale with more gravitas if not reading difficulty will appreciate this thoughtful family story." Bull Cent Child Books

Hoffmann, E. T. A.

Nutcracker; pictures by Maurice Sendak; translated by Ralph Manheim. Crown 1984 102p il $40

Grades: 4 5 6 7   **Fic**

1. Fairy tales 2. Christmas -- Fiction

ISBN 0-609-61049-X

LC 83-25266

"The smooth, elegant, new translation re-creates the flavor of the period and does justice to the story. . . . The occasional quirkiness of the pictures . . . eerily reflect the mysterious story. Altogether a magnificent, splendid combination of talents." Horn Book

Holczer, Tracy

The **secret** hum of a daisy; Tracy Holczer. G.P. Putnam's Sons, an imprint of Penguin Group (USA) 2014 320 p. (hardback) $16.99

Grades: 5 6 7 8   **Fic**

1. Home -- Fiction 2. Death -- Fiction 3. Moving -- Fiction 4. Grandmothers -- Fiction 5. Treasure hunt (Game) -- Fiction 6. Moving, Household -- Fiction

ISBN 039916393X; 9780399163937

LC 2013039962

In this book, by Tracy Holczer, "twelve-year-old Grace and her mother . . . [travel] from place to place like gypsies. But Grace wants to finally have a home all their own. Just when she thinks she's found it her mother says it's time to move again. Grace summons the courage to tell her mother how she really feels and will always regret that her last words to her were angry ones. After her mother's sudden death, Grace is forced to live with a grandmother she's never met." (Publisher's note)

"Twelve-year-old Grace, mourning her mother's death, goes to live with her grandmother in Mama's hometown. Grace refuses to forgive Grandma for sending Mama away as a pregnant teen. In talking to townspeople, who help fill in gaps about her family's past, Grace finds the hope, peace, and home she's been looking for. Holczer weaves healing symbols (birds, daisies) and poetry into her lyrical text." Horn Book

Holling, Holling C.

Paddle-to-the-sea; written and illustrated by Holling Clancy Holling. Houghton Mifflin 1941 un il lib bdg $20; pa $11.95

Grades: 4 5 6   **Fic**

1. Great Lakes region -- Fiction

ISBN 0-395-15082-5 lib bdg; 0-395-29203-4 pa

A Caldecott Medal honor book, 1942

A toy canoe with a seated Indian figure is launched in Lake Nipigon by the Indian boy who carved it and in four years travels through all the Great Lakes and the St. Lawrence River to the Atlantic. An interesting picture of the shore life of the lakes and the river with striking full page pictures in bright colors and marginal pencil drawings

"The canoe's journey is used to show the flow of currents and of traffic, and each occurrence is made to seem plausible. . . . There are also diagrams of a sawmill, a freighter, the canal locks at the Soo, and Niagara Falls." Libr J

Holm, Jennifer L.

★ The **fourteenth** goldfish; Jennifer L. Holm. Random House Inc 2014 208 p. (hardcover) $16.99; (library binding) $19.99

Grades: 4 5 6 7   **Fic**

1. Scientists -- Fiction 2. Grandfathers -- Fiction 3. Aging -- Fiction 4. Family life -- Fiction

ISBN 0375870644; 9780375870644; 9780375970641

LC 2013035052

"Eleven-year-old Ellie has never liked change. She misses fifth grade. She misses her old best friend. She even misses her dearly departed goldfish. Then one day a strange boy shows up. He's bossy. He's cranky. And weirdly enough . . . he looks a lot like Ellie's grandfather, a scientist who's always been slightly obsessed with immortality." (Publisher's note)

"With humor and heart, Holm has crafted a story about life, family, and finding one's passion that will appeal to readers willing to imagine the possible." SLJ

Includes bibliographical references

★ **Middle** school is worse than meatloaf; a year told through stuff. by Jennifer L. Holm; pictures by Elicia Castaldi. Atheneum Books for Young Readers 2007 un il $12.99

Grades: 5 6 7 8   **Fic**

1. School stories 2. Family life -- Fiction

ISBN 0-689-85281-9

"Ginny Davis begins seventh grade with a list of items to accomplish. This list, along with lots of other 'stuff'—including diary entries, refrigerator notes, cards from Grandpa, and IM screen messages—convey a year full of ups and downs. Digitally rendered collage illustrations realistically depict the various means of communication, and the story flows easily from one colorful page to the next. . . . The story combines honesty and humor to create a believable and appealing voice." SLJ

★ **Our** only May Amelia. HarperCollins Pubs. 1999 253p il hardcover o.p. pa $5.99

Grades: 5 6 7 8   **Fic**

1. Family life -- Fiction 2. Finnish Americans -- Fiction 3. Washington (State) -- Fiction 4. Frontier and pioneer life -- Fiction

ISBN 0-06-027822-6; 0-06-440856-6 pa

LC 98-47504

A Newbery Medal honor book, 2000

As the only girl in a Finnish American family of seven brothers, May Amelia Jackson resents being expected to act like a lady while growing up in Washington State in 1899

"The voice of the colloquial first-person narrative rings true and provides a vivid picture of frontier and pioneer life. . . . An afterword discusses Holm's research into her own family's history and that of other Finnish immigrants." Horn Book Guide

Followed by: The trouble with May Amelia (2011)

★ **Penny** from heaven. Random House 2006 274p il $15.95; lib bdg $17.99; pa $6.99

Grades: 5 6 7 8   **Fic**

1. New Jersey -- Fiction 2. Family life -- Fiction 3.

Italian Americans -- Fiction

ISBN 0-375-83687-X; 0-375-93687-4 lib bdg; 0-375-83689-6 pa

LC 2005-13896

A Newbery Medal honor book, 2007

As she turns twelve during the summer of 1953, Penny gains new insights into herself and her family while also learning a secret about her father's death.

"Holm impressively wraps pathos with comedy in this coming-of-age story, populated by a cast of vivid characters." Booklist

The **trouble** with May Amelia; illustrated by Adam Gustavson. Atheneum Books for Young Readers 2011 204p il $15.99

Grades: 5 6 7 8   **Fic**

1. Sex role -- Fiction 2. Siblings -- Fiction 3. Finnish Americans -- Fiction 4. Washington (State) -- Fiction 5. Frontier and pioneer life -- Fiction

ISBN 1-4169-1373-4; 978-1-4169-1373-3

LC 2010042092

Sequel to: Our only May Amelia (1999)

Living with seven brothers and her father, who thinks girls are useless, a thirteen-year-old Finnish American farm girl is determined to prove her worth when a enterprising gentleman tries to purchase their cash-strapped family settlement in Washington State in 1900.

"Holm gets her heroine just right. Narrating events in dryly witty, plainspoken first-person, this indomitable teen draws readers in with her account, through which her world comes alive." Kirkus

★ **Turtle** in paradise. Random House 2010 191p $16.99; lib bdg $19.99

Grades: 3 4 5   **Fic**

1. Adventure fiction 2. Cousins -- Fiction 3. Florida -- Fiction 4. Family life -- Fiction 5. Great Depression, 1929-1939 -- Fiction

ISBN 978-0-375-83688-6; 0-375-83688-8; 978-0-375-93688-3 lib bdg; 0-375-93688-2 lib bdg

LC 2009-19077

A Newbery Medal honor book, 2011

In 1935, when her mother gets a job housekeeping for a woman who does not like children, eleven-year-old Turtle is sent to stay with relatives she has never met in far away Key West, Florida.

"Holm's voice for Turtle is winning and authentic—that of a practical, clear-eyed observer—and her nimble way with dialogue creates laugh-out-loud moments. Sweet, funny and superb." Kirkus

Holmes, Sara Lewis

★ **Operation** Yes. Arthur A. Levine Books 2009 234p $16.99

Grades: 5 6 7 8   **Fic**

1. School stories 2. Acting -- Fiction 3. Cousins -- Fiction 4. Teachers -- Fiction 5. Military bases -- Fiction

ISBN 978-0-545-10795-2; 0-545-10795-4; 978-0-545-10796-9 pa; 0-545-10796-2 pa

LC 2008053732

In her first ever teaching job, Miss Loupe uses improvisational acting exercises with her sixth-grade students at an Air Force base school, and when she experiences a

family tragedy, her previously skeptical class members use what they have learned to help her, her brother, and other wounded soldiers

"Quick, funny, sad, full of heart, and irresistibly absorbing." Booklist

Holt, Kimberly Willis

★ **Dancing** in Cadillac light. Putnam 2001 167p hardcover o.p. pa $5.99

Grades: 5 6 7 8   **Fic**

1. Texas -- Fiction 2. Old age -- Fiction 3. Grandfathers -- Fiction

ISBN 0-399-23402-0; 0-698-11970-3 pa

LC 00-40267

In 1968, eleven-year-old Jaynell's life in the town of Moon, Texas, is enlivened when her eccentric Grandpap comes to live with her family

"This nostalgic parable about loss and redemption is at once gritty and poetic, stark and sentimental, howlingly funny and depressingly sad, but it is a solid page-turner." SLJ

Piper Reed, Navy brat. Henry Holt 2007 146p il $14.95; pa $6.99

Grades: 3 4 5   **Fic**

1. Moving -- Fiction 2. Florida -- Fiction 3. Family life -- Fiction

ISBN 978-0-8050-8197-8; 0-8050-8197-6; 978-0-312-38020-5 pa; 0-312-38020-8 pa

LC 2006-35467

Piper is sad about leaving her home and friends behind when her father, a Navy aircraft mechanic, is transferred yet again, but with help from her often-annoying sisters and a surprise from their parents, she finds happiness in their new home in Pensacola, Florida.

"Holt tells a lively family story. . . . Davenier's occasional black-and-white pictures capture the daily family dramas." Booklist

Other titles about Piper Reed are:

Piper Reed, the great gypsy (2008)

Piper Reed gets a job (2009)

Piper Reed, campfire girl (2011)

★ **When** Zachary Beaver came to town. Holt & Co. 1999 227p $17.99

Grades: 5 6 7 8   **Fic**

1. Texas -- Fiction 2. Obesity -- Fiction 3. Friendship -- Fiction

ISBN 0-8050-6116-9

LC 99-27998

During the summer of 1971 in a small Texas town, thirteen-year-old Toby and his best friend Cal meet the star of a sideshow act, 600-pound Zachary, the fattest boy in the world

"Holt writes with a subtle sense of humor and sensitivity, and reading her work is a delightful experience." Voice Youth Advocates

Holub, Joan

Bed, bats, and beyond; by Joan Holub; illustrated by Mernie Gallagher-Cole. Darby Creek Pub. 2008 64p il $14.95

Grades: 1 2 3   **Fic**

1. Bats -- Fiction 2. Bedtime -- Fiction 3. Storytelling

-- Fiction

ISBN 978-1-58196-077-8; 1-58196-077-8

It's dawn and time for bats to go to bed, but Fang's brother Fink can't sleep. Soon the whole family tries different bedtime stories to lull Fink to sleep

"The narrative as a whole feels satisfying. . . . Gallagher-Cole's illustrations add humorous details. . . . With no more than 15 lines per page and illustrations on every spread, the story is ideal for students who have just graduated to chapter books. Charming and full of humor." SLJ

Holyoke, Polly

The **Neptune** Project; Polly Holyoke. 1st ed. Disney-Hyperion Books 2013 352 p. (reinforced) $16.99

Grades: 4 5 6 7   **Fic**

1. Science fiction 2. Ocean -- Fiction 3. Genetic engineering -- Fiction 4. Survival -- Fiction 5. Undersea colonies -- Fiction 6. Environmental degradation -- Fiction

ISBN 1423157567; 9781423157564

LC 2013000353

In this novel, by Polly Holyoke, "Nere . . . . is one of a group of kids who . . . . have been genetically altered to survive in the ocean. . . . In order to reach the safe haven of the Neptune colony, Nere and her fellow mutates must swim through hundreds of miles of dangerous waters, relying only on their wits, dolphins, and each other to evade terrifying undersea creatures and a government that will stop at nothing to capture the Neptune kids." (Publisher's note)

Hopkins, Karen Leigh

Labracadabra; [by Jessie Nelson & Karen Leigh Hopkins; illustrated by Deborah Melmon] Viking 2011 36p il $14.99

Grades: 1 2 3   **Fic**

1. Dogs -- Fiction 2. Magic -- Fiction

ISBN 978-0-670-01251-0; 0-670-01251-3

LC 2010-25109

Zach always wanted a dog but Larry, the full-grown mongrel his parents choose, is not it, however, he soon discovers that there is something very special—even magical—about Larry's tail.

"This early chapter book is a beaut of brevity and pacing. . . . With plenty of illustrations and white space, this five-chapter romp flies along. . . . Transitioning independent readers will enjoy getting to know the unnamed narrator and watching his attitude progress as Larry changes from a 'used dog' to 'my dog.'" Kirkus

Hopkinson, Deborah

Birdie's lighthouse; written by Deborah Hopkinson; illustrated by Kimberly Bulcken Root. Atheneum Bks. for Young Readers 1997 un il hardcover o.p. pa $6.99

Grades: 1 2 3   **Fic**

1. Maine -- Fiction 2. Lighthouses -- Fiction

ISBN 0-689-81052-0; 0-689-83529-9 pa

LC 94-24097

"With an exemplary assemblage of genre paintings perfectly attuned to the flow of the text, the whole is restrained yet charged with emotion." Horn Book

A **boy** called Dickens; Deborah Hopkinson; illustrations by John Hendrix. 1st ed. Schwartz & Wade Books

2012 40 p. col. ill. (hardcover) $17.99; (lib. bdg.) $20.99; (ebook) $17.99

Grades: 4 5 6   **Fic**

1. Authors 2. Child labor 3. Novelists 4. Authors -- Fiction 5. London (England) -- Fiction 6. Great Britain -- History -- 19th century -- Fiction

ISBN 037596732X; 9780375867323; 9780375967320; 9780375987403

LC 2010048531

This book presents an "account of Charles Dickens' boyhood, specifically his tenure wrapping and labeling bottles of boot blacking while his father and family languish in debtors' prison. Here young Charles passes the ten-hour days by regaling a fellow worker with made-up stories, elements of which would later appear in his best-known novels. . . . A closing note comments more fully on autobiographic references in Dicken's work." (Bulletin of the Center for Children's Books)

The **Great** Trouble; a mystery of London, the blue death, and a boy called Eel. by Deborah Hopkinson. Alfred A. Knopf 2013 256 p. (hard cover) $16.99

Grades: 4 5 6 7 8   **Fic**

1. Cholera 2. Orphans -- Fiction 3. London (England) -- Fiction 4. Cholera -- Fiction 5. Epidemics -- Fiction 6. London (England) -- History -- 19th century -- Fiction 7. Great Britain -- History -- Victoria, 1837-1901 -- Fiction

ISBN 0375848185; 9780375848186; 9780375948183

LC 2012032799

Author Deborah Hopkinson's book, "equal parts medical mystery, historical novel, and survival story about the 1854 London cholera outbreak, . . . introduces Eel, a boy trying to make ends meet on Broad Street. When he visits one of his regular employers, he learns the man has fallen ill. Eel enlists the help of Dr. Snow, and together they work to solve the mystery of what exactly is causing the spread of cholera and how they can prevent it." (Booklist)

Includes bibliographical references (p. 245-247)

Into the firestorm; a novel of San Francisco, 1906. Alfred A. Knopf 2006 200p hardcover o.p. pa $5.99

Grades: 5 6 7 8   **Fic**

1. Orphans -- Fiction 2. Earthquakes -- Fiction 3. San Francisco (Calif.) -- Fiction

ISBN 0-375-83652-7; 0-440-42129-2 pa

LC 2005-37189

Days after arriving in San Francisco from Texas, eleven-year-old orphan Nicholas Dray tries to help his new neighbors survive the 1906 San Francisco earthquake and the subsequent fires.

"The terror of the 1906 disaster is brought powerfully alive in this fast-paced tale. . . . Nick is a thoroughly developed protagonist, as are the supporting characters." SLJ

Includes bibliographical references

Horowitz, Anthony

★ **Public** enemy number two; a Diamond brothers mystery. Philomel Books 2004 190p $16.99; pa $5.99

Grades: 5 6 7 8   **Fic**

1. Mystery fiction

ISBN 0-399-24154-X; 0-14-240218-4 pa

LC 2004-10418

When thirteen-year-old Nick is framed for a jewel robbery, he and his brother, the bumbling detective Tim Diamond, attempt to clear his name by capturing the master
criminal known as the Fence.

"Horowitz has a knack for puns and humor, and he successfully combines it with a nonstop action mystery that
has everything from hydraulically controlled buses to secret
caverns. A readable and exciting adventure." SLJ

Other titles in the Diamond Brothers Mystery series are:
The falcon's Maltester (2004)
South by southeast (2005)
Three of Diamonds (2005)
The Greek who stole Christmas (2008)

★ **Stormbreaker**. Philomel Books 2001 192p (An
Alex Rider adventure) $17.99; pa $7.99
Grades: 5 6 7 8   Fic
1. Adventure fiction 2. Spies -- Fiction 3. Orphans
-- Fiction 4. Terrorism -- Fiction 5. Great Britain --
Fiction
ISBN 0-399-23620-1; 0-14-240611-2 pa
LC 00-63683
First published 2000 in the United Kingdom
After the death of the uncle who had been his guardian,
fourteen-year-old Alex Rider is coerced to continue his un-
cle's dangerous work for Britain's intelligence agency, MI6

"Horowitz thoughtfully balances Alex's super-spy finesse with typical teen insecurities to create a likable hero
living a fantasy come true. An entertaining, nicely layered
novel." Booklist

Other titles about Alex Rider are:
Point blank (2002)
Skeleton key (2003)
Eagle strike (2004)
Scorpia (2005)
Alex Rider, the gadgets (2006)
Ark angel (2006)
Snakehead (2007)
Crocodile tears (2009)
Scorpia rising (2011)

The **switch**; [by] Anthony Horowitz. Philomel Books
2009 162p $16.99
Grades: 5 6 7 8   Fic
1. Wealth -- Fiction 2. Criminals -- Fiction 3.
Supernatural -- Fiction 4. Great Britain -- Fiction
ISBN 978-0-399-25062-0; 0-399-25062-X
LC 2008-32380
When wealthy, spoiled, thirteen-year-old Tad Spencer
wishes he were someone else, he awakens as Bob Snarby,
the uncouth, impoverished son of carnival workers, and as
he is drawn into a life of crime he begins to discover truths
about himself and his family.

"A fun, tongue-in-cheek read that will captivate children
who like adventure and mystery." SLJ

Horvath, Polly
Everything on a waffle. Farrar, Straus & Giroux 2001
149p hardcover o.p. $16
Grades: 4 5 6 7   Fic
1. Uncles -- Fiction 2. British Columbia -- Fiction
ISBN 0-374-32236-8; 0-374-42208-7 pa
LC 00-35399
A Newbery Medal honor book, 2002

Eleven-year-old Primrose living in a small fishing village in British Columbia recounts her experiences and all
that she learns about human nature and the unpredictability
of life in the months after her parents are lost at sea

"The story is full of subtle humor and wisdom, presented
through the eyes of a uniquely appealing young protagonist." SLJ

Lord and Lady Bunny -- almost royalty! by Mr. & Mrs.
Bunny; translated from the Rabbit by Polly Horvath; illus-
trated by Sophie Blackall. Schwartz & Wade books 2014
304 p. illustrations $16.99
Grades: 3 4 5 6   Fic
1. Rabbits -- Fiction 2. Kings and rulers -- Fiction 3.
England -- Fiction 4. Hippies -- Fiction 5. Voyages
and travels -- Fiction 6. Human-animal communication
-- Fiction
ISBN 0307980650; 9780307980656; 9780307980663;
9780307980670
LC 2012027442
Sequel to Mr. and Mrs. Bunny--Detectives Extraordinaire! (2012)

"Madeleine wants nothing more than to save money for
college, but her impractical, ex-hippie parents are broke.
When the family unexpectedly inherits a sweet shoppe in
England that has the potential to earn serious profit, they see
an answer to all their problems." (Publisher's note)

"The plot is unapologetically preposterous, but the truly
witty banter, near-constant conflict and palpable love between Mr. and Mrs. Bunny are both genuinely affecting and
uproariously funny. Blackall's elegant, expressive black-
and-white illustrations add whimsy to an already effervescent adventure." Kirkus

★ **Mr.** and Mrs. Bunny-- detectives extraordinaire! by
Mrs. Bunny; translated from the Rabbit by Polly Horvath;
illustrated by Sophie Blackall. Schwartz & Wade Books
2011 248 p.
Grades: 3 4 5 6   Fic
1. Mystery fiction 2. Children's stories 3. Ciphers --
Fiction 4. Rabbits -- Fiction 5. Kidnapping -- Fiction
6. Foxes -- Fiction 7. Hippies -- Fiction 8. Marmots
-- Fiction 9. Mystery and detective stories 10. Human-
animal communication -- Fiction 11. Hornby Island
(B.C.: Island) -- Fiction
ISBN 9780375867552; 9780375898273;
9780375967559
LC 2010024133
In this book, "middle-schooler Madeline has learned to
be resourceful, a skill upon which she calls when her [hip-
pie] parents are kidnapped by foxes who want a bunch of
coded recipes . . . . decoded by Madeline's . . . uncle Runyon,
a code-savvy spy. Madeline first seeks out Runyon herself,
but he suddenly falls into a coma, so she turns for help to a
pair of fedora-wearing rabbits, taking them for detectives.
Mr. and Mrs. Bunny are only too happy to assist." (Bulletin
of the Center for Children's Books)

★ **My** one hundred adventures. Schwartz & Wade
Books 2008 260p $16.99; lib bdg $19.99; pa $7.99
Grades: 4 5 6 7   Fic
1. Summer -- Fiction 2. Beaches -- Fiction 3. Siblings
-- Fiction 4. Babysitters -- Fiction 5. Single parent

family -- Fiction

ISBN 978-0-375-84582-6; 0-375-84582-8; 978-0-375-95582-2 lib bdg; 0-375-95582-8 lib bdg; 978-0-375-85526-9 pa; 0-375-85526-2 pa

LC 2008-02243

Twelve-year-old Jane, who lives at the beach in a run-down old house with her mother, two brothers, and sister, has an eventful summer accompanying her pastor on bible deliveries, meeting former boyfriends of her mother's, and being coerced into babysitting for a family of ill-mannered children.

With writing as foamy as waves, as gritty as sand, or as deep as the sea, this book may startle readers with the freedom given the heroine. . . . Unconventionality is Horvath's stock and trade, but here the high quirkiness quotient rests easily against Jane's inner story with its honest, childlike core. Booklist

Followed by: Northward to the Moon (2010)

The **Pepins** and their problems; pictures by Marylin Hafner. Farrar Straus Giroux 2004 179p il $16; pa $6.99

Grades: 3 4 5 6 **Fic**

1. Family life -- Fiction

ISBN 0-374-35817-6; 0-312-37751-7 pa

LC 2003-60196

The reader is invited to help solve the Pepin family's unusual problems, which include having a cow who creates lemonade rather than milk and having to cope with a competitive neighbor

"Horvath spins a delightful yarn. . . . Absurd characters and situations and witty repartee are Horvath's strengths, and . . . the wordplay is a great argument for reading this aloud." Booklist

House, Silas

★ **Eli** the Good. Candlewick Press 2009 295p $16.99

Grades: 5 6 7 8 **Fic**

1. Aunts -- Fiction 2. Veterans -- Fiction 3. Friendship -- Fiction 4. Family life -- Fiction 5. Post-traumatic stress disorder -- Fiction

ISBN 978-0-7636-4341-6; 0-7636-4341-6

LC 2009004589

In the summer of 1976, ten-year-old Eli Book's excitement over Bicentennial celebrations is tempered by his father's flashbacks to the Vietnam War and other family problems, as well as concern about his tough but troubled best friend, Edie.

"House writes beautifully, with a gentle tone. He lays out Eli's world in exquisite detail. . . . The story flows along as steadily as a stream. . . . Eli is good company and children will enjoy accompanying him on his journey." SLJ

Howard, Ellen

The **crimson** cap. Holiday House 2009 177p $16.95

Grades: 5 6 7 8 **Fic**

1. Explorers 2. Texas -- Fiction 3. Explorers -- Fiction 4. Native Americans -- Fiction 5. America -- Exploration -- Fiction

ISBN 978-0-8234-2152-7; 0-8234-2152-X

LC 2009-25551

In 1684, wearing his father's faded cap, eleven-year-old Pierre Talon joins explorer Rene-Robert Cavelier on an ill-fated expedition to seek the Mississippi River, but after the expedition falls apart Pierre, deathly ill, is taken in by Hasinai Indians. Includes historical facts.

"A riveting adventure that will prove to be hard to put down. Howard's fast-paced writing brings the story to life. This solid coming-of-age story is based on real events and historical figures." SLJ

Howe, Deborah

★ **Bunnicula**; a rabbit-tale of mystery. by Deborah and James Howe; illustrated by Alan Daniel. 25th anniversary edition; Atheneum Books for Young Readers 2004 92p il $16.95

Grades: 4 5 6 **Fic**

1. Mystery fiction 2. Animals -- Fiction

ISBN 0-689-86775-1

A reissue of the title first published 1979

Though scoffed at by Harold the dog, Chester the cat tries to warn his human family that their foundling baby bunny must be a vampire

This book is "blithe, sophisticated, and distinguished for the wit and humor of the dialogue." Bull Cent Child Books

Howe, James, 1946-

★ **Addie** on the inside; James Howe. Atheneum Books for Young Readers 2011 206 p. $16.99

Grades: 5 6 7 8 **Fic**

1. School stories 2. Novels in verse 3. Self-acceptance -- Fiction 4. Interpersonal relations -- Fiction 5. Grandmothers -- Fiction 6. Identity (Psychology) -- Fiction

ISBN 141691384X; 9781416913849

LC 2010024497

This book, by James Howe, "follows 13-year-old Addie's struggles to define herself according to her own terms. Through her poems, Addie reflects on her life and life in general: her first boyfriend, what it means to be accepted and her endeavors to promote equality. Addie is at her most fragile when she examines her relationship with her boyfriend and the cruel behavior of her former best friend. Her forthright observations address serious topics with a maturity beyond her age." (Kirkus Reviews)

"Howe's artfully crafted lines show Addie's intelligence and wit, and his imagery evokes the aura of sadness surrounding 'this purgatory of/ the middle school years/ when so many things/ that never mattered before/ and will never matter again/ matter.' Readers will empathize with Addie's anguish and admire her courage to keep fighting." Publ Wkly

Dew drop dead; a Sebastian Barth mystery. Atheneum Pubs. 1990 156p hardcover o.p. pa $4.99

Grades: 4 5 6 **Fic**

1. Mystery fiction 2. Homeless persons -- Fiction

ISBN 0-689-31425-6; 0-689-80760-0 pa

LC 89-34697

"The story is well crafted and has substance beyond escapist fare as a result of Howe's inclusion of secondary storylines involving the homeless and Sebastian's own worries about his father's pending job loss." Booklist

Other titles about Sebastian Barth are:

Eat your poison, dear (1986)

Stage fright (1986)

What Eric knew (1985)

★ **Totally** Joe; James Howe. Atheneum Books for Young Readers 2005 189 p. $17.99
Grades: 5 6 7 8 9 **Fic**
1. School stories 2. Friendship -- Fiction 3. Adolescence -- Fiction 4. Homosexuality -- Fiction
ISBN 068983957X; 9780689839573
LC 2004022242

In this book, by James Howe, "Joe's teacher asks his seventh-grade class to write an alphabiography throughout the year, presenting themselves and their lives in entries from A to Z. Joe's essays begin and end with friends, from Addie, a long-time pal and confidant, to Zachary, a new student who, like Joe, has a unique approach to life. . . . Joe demonstrates that he truly is a one-of-a-kind kid, mostly comfortable with himself but still struggling with common adolescent issues." (School Library Journal)

"Joe, one of the characters in The Misfits (2001), has his say, in a voice uniquely his own. Twelve-year-old Joe knows he is gay. He played with Barbies as a young child, prefers cooking to sports, and has a crush on a male classmate...Joe himself often comes off as a cross between Niles Crane and Harvey Fierstein. But he also reacts like a kid, and readers in his situation will wish for the love and support he receives from friends and family, as well as the happy life he so clearly envisions." Booklist

Howe, Peter
Waggit again; drawings by Omar Rayyan. HarperCollinsPublishers 2009 292p il $16.99; lib bdg $17.89
Grades: 5 6 7 **Fic**
1. Dogs -- Fiction
ISBN 978-0-06-124264-9; 0-06-124264-0; 978-0-06-124265-6 lib bdg; 0-06-124265-9 lib bdg
LC 2008020213
Sequel to: Waggit's tale (2008)

After being left in the country by his owner, Waggit sets out on the long journey to New York City and meets some unexpected friends along the way.

Felicia's "relationship with the dogs is made wonderfully plausible. Waggit's growth in self-understanding is also fully developed and well handled, and the ending will satisfy readers deeply." Kirkus

Waggit's tale; drawings by Omar Rayyan. HarperCollinsPublishers 2008 288p il $16.99; lib bdg $17.89; pa $6.99
Grades: 5 6 7 **Fic**
1. Dogs -- Fiction
ISBN 978-0-06-124261-8; 0-06-124261-6; 978-0-06-124262-5 lib bdg; 0-06-124262-4 lib bdg; 978-0-06-124263-2 pa; 0-06-124263-2 pa
LC 2007020878
Followed by: Waggit again (2009)

When Waggit is abandoned by his owner as a puppy, he meets a pack of wild dogs who become his friends and teach him to survive in the city park, but when he has a chance to go home with a kind woman who wants to adopt him, he takes it

"The novel celebrates the wild freedom of the feral dog pack, while also emphasizing the many hazards of urban life for homeless companion animals." Voice Youth Advocates

Warriors of the black shroud. Harper 2012 $16.99

Grades: 3 4 5 **Fic**
1. Fantasy fiction
ISBN 978-0-06-172987-4; 0-06-172987-6
LC 2011026147

A shy, bookish boy is pulled into an underground land called Nebula and asked to lead a kingdom in its fight against darkness.

This is a "fast-paced fantasy novel. . . . The climax and resolution have just enough surprise to satisfy readers. This attractive world (warriors ride unicorns!) and likable characters—boy heroes with a strong girl sidekick—will give fledgling readers of fantasy a treat." Kirkus

Howell, Troy
The **dragon** of Cripple Creek; a novel. Amulet Books 2011 385p $19.95
Grades: 5 6 7 8 **Fic**
1. Fantasy fiction 2. Adventure fiction 3. Gold -- Fiction 4. Dragons -- Fiction 5. Colorado -- Fiction
ISBN 978-0-8109-9713-4; 0-8109-9713-4
LC 2010-34362

When Kat, her father, and brother visit an old gold mine that has been turned into an amusement park, she falls down a shaft and meets an ancient dragon, the last of his kind, and inadvertently triggers a twenty-first century gold rush.

"Writing in Kat's first person narrative, which is wry and funny, clipped and eloquent, Howell, best known as an illustrator, mixes fantasy adventure with a moving conservation story in a debut that blends sadness, secrecy, and pure fantasy." Booklist

Hughes, Shirley, 1927-
★ **Hero** on a bicycle; Shirley Hughes. Candlewick Press 2013 224 p. $15.99
Grades: 5 6 7 **Fic**
1. Historical fiction 2. World War, 1939-1945 -- Fiction
ISBN 076366037X; 9780763660376
LC 2012943650

This book is set in Italy during World War II. "The narrative focuses on a city under German occupation, events being perceived principally through the eyes of three members of the Crivelli family: teenager Paolo, his older sister Constanza and Rosemary, their English-born mother. . . . When an opportunity arises for Paolo, Constanza and Rosemary to lend their practical support to the Partisan cause Paolo, in particular, seizes it enthusiastically." (School Librarian)

Hughes, Ted, 1930-1998
The **iron** giant; illustrated by Laura Carlin. Knopf 2011 104p il $19.99
Grades: 4 5 6 **Fic**
1. Science fiction
ISBN 978-0-375-87149-8; 0-375-87149-7
A newly illustrated edition of the title first published 1968 by Harper & Row; published in the United Kingdom with title: The iron man

The fearsome iron giant becomes a hero when he challenges a huge space monster.

"Hughes's 1968 story of unexpected friendships and redemptions returns with new artwork from Carlin in a polished and well-designed edition that uses occasional gatefolds and die-cuts to amplify key moments. Carlin's mixedmedia artwork emphasizes the giant's innate otherness. . . . It's an elegant and thoughtful treatment of a story that, with its hopeful message of global unity, feels as important and timely as ever." Publ Wkly

Hulme, John

★ The **glitch** in sleep; [by] John Hulme and Michael Wexler; illustrations by Gideon Kendall. Bloomsbury Children's Books 2007 277p il (The Seems) $16.95; pa $7.99
Grades: 4 5 6 7   **Fic**

1. Science fiction 2. Sleep -- Fiction
ISBN 978-1-59990-129-9; 1-59990-129-3; 978-1-59990-298-2 pa; 1-59990-298-2 pa
                                                    LC 2007-2598

When twelve-year-old Becker Drane is recruited by The Seems, a parallel universe that runs everything in The World, he must fix a disastrous glitch in the Department of Sleep that threatens everyone's ability to ever fall asleep again

"The story is upbeat and full of humor. . . . Dynamic full-page illustrations appear throughout." SLJ

Another title in this series is:

The split second (2008)

The **split** second; by John Hulme and Michael Wexler; illustrations by Gideon Kendall. 1st U.S. ed.; Bloomsbury Children's Books 2008 301p il (The Seems) $16.99
Grades: 5 6 7 8   **Fic**

1. Science fiction 2. Terrorism -- Fiction
ISBN 978-1-599-90130-5; 1-599-90130-7
                                                    LC 2008012241

Sequel to: The glitch in sleep (2007)

Now thirteen-years-old and still a Fixer in the parallel universe called the Seems, Becker Drane is called upon to repair the damage caused by an enormous bomb planted in the Department of Time, an act of terrorism perpetrated by the evil members of the Tide, a group that is trying to destroy the World.

"This sequel continues to develop a truly ingenious setting while proving every bit as much of a nail-biter as the first." Booklist

Hunt, Irene

Across five Aprils. Berkley Jam Books 2002 212p pa $5.99
Grades: 5 6 7 8   **Fic**

1. Illinois -- Fiction 2. Farm life -- Fiction 3. United States -- History -- 1861-1865, Civil War -- Fiction
ISBN 978-0-425-18278-9; 0-425-18278-9

First published 1964 by Follett

A Newbery Medal honor book, 1965

Young Jethro Creighton grows from a boy to a man when he is left to take care of the family farm in Illinois during the difficult years of the Civil War.

"Authentic background, a feeling for the people of that time, and a story that never loses the reader's interest." Wilson Libr Bull

Hunt, Lynda Mullaly

One for the Murphys; Lynda Mullaly Hunt. Nancy Paulsen Books 2012 224 p. (hardback) $16.99
Grades: 5 6 7 8   **Fic**

1. Girls -- Fiction 2. Connecticut -- Fiction 3. Stepfathers -- Fiction 4. Family problems -- Fiction 5. Foster home care -- Fiction 6. Mothers and daughters

-- Fiction 7. Family life -- Connecticut -- Fiction
ISBN 0399256156; 9780399256158
                                                    LC 2011046708

This book by Lynda Mullaly Hunt follows "eighth-grader Carley Connors [as she] learns about a different kind of family life, first resisting and then resisting having to leave the loving, loyal Murphys. . . . She's torn between her love for her mother and her memory of the fight that sent her to the hospital, when her mother caught and held her for her stepfather. Slowly won over at home . . . Carley also finds a friend at school in the prickly, Wicked-obsessed Toni." (Kirkus Reviews)

Hurd, Thacher

Bongo fishing. Henry Holt 2011 233p il $16.99
Grades: 3 4 5   **Fic**

1. Science fiction 2. California -- Fiction 3. Family life -- Fiction 4. Space flight -- Fiction 5. Extraterrestrial beings -- Fiction
ISBN 978-0-8050-9100-7; 0-8050-9100-9
                                                    LC 2010-11696

Berkeley, California, middle-schooler Jason Jameson has a close encounter of the fun kind when Sam, a bluish alien from the Pleiades, arrives in a 1960 Dodge Dart spaceship and invites Jason to go fishing.

"The funniest moments come through twists of Earth conventions. . . . Intriguing gadgets and amusing descriptions of alien technology add to the fun, as do the lively illustrations. . . . Sam and his wife are delightfully atypical aliens . . . and the moments of humor are consistently strong throughout." SLJ

Hurst, Carol Otis

You come to Yokum; with illustrations by Kay Life. Houghton Mifflin Co. 2005 137p il $15
Grades: 3 4 5   **Fic**

1. Feminism -- Fiction 2. Family life -- Fiction 3. Massachusetts -- Fiction 4. Women -- Suffrage -- Fiction
ISBN 0-618-55122-0

Twelve-year-old Frank witnesses his mother's struggles to muster support for women's right to vote even as the family's life is transformed by a year running a lodge in western Massachusetts in the early 1920s.

"With mostly short chapters and charming black-and-white illustrations, this is a satisfying read." SLJ

Hurwitz, Johanna

★ The **adventures** of Ali Baba Bernstein; illustrated by Gail Owens. Morrow 1985 82p il hardcover o.p. pa $5.99
Grades: 2 3 4   **Fic**

1. Personal names -- Fiction
ISBN 0-688-04161-2; 0-380-72349-2 pa
                                                    LC 84-27387

"Hurwitz' characters, as always, are believable, the situations realistic and the plot well developed." SLJ

Another title about Ali Baba Bernstein is:

Hurray for Ali Baba Bernstein (1989)

★ **Baseball** fever; illustrated by Ray Cruz. Morrow 1981 128p il hardcover o.p. pa $4.99
Grades: 3 4 5   **Fic**

1. Baseball -- Fiction 2. Father-son relationship --

Fiction
ISBN 0-380-73255-6 pa

LC 81-5633

"A brisk, breezy story about a believable family is told with warmth and humor." Bull Cent Child Books

Fourth-grade fuss; illustrated by Andy Hammond. HarperCollins 2004 132p $15.99; lib bdg $16.89
Grades: 2 3 4   **Fic**
1. School stories
ISBN 0-06-052343-3; 0-06-052344-1 lib bdg

LC 2003-22216

A yard sale, ice skating, class pictures, and a surprise party are a few of the things that make fourth grade fun for Julio and his friends, but they must get serious about studying as the statewide end-of-year test approaches.

"Fans of this series as well as young test takers everywhere are sure to appreciate the humorous, reassuring story." Booklist

Mostly Monty. Candlewick Press 2007 86p il $15.99; pa $5.99
Grades: 1 2 3   **Fic**
1. Asthma -- Fiction 2. Friendship -- Fiction
ISBN 978-0-7636-2831-4; 0-7636-2831-X; 978-0-7636-4062-0 pa; 0-7636-4062-X pa

LC 2006-49024

Because he suffers from asthma, six-year-old Monty is nervous about starting first grade but he soon learns to cope with his illness and use his special talents to make friends.

"Watercolor illustrations . . . appear every few pages, breaking up the text with pictures of cheerful button-nose children. More reserved children . . . will appreciate seeing themselves reflected in this gently funny story about learning to like oneself." Booklist

Other titles about Monty are:
Mighty Monty (2008)
Magical Monty (2012)

Hurwitz, Michele Weber
Calli be gold. Wendy Lamb Books 2011 198p $15.99; lib bdg $18.99
Grades: 4 5 6   **Fic**
1. School stories 2. Family life -- Fiction
ISBN 978-0-385-73970-2; 0-385-73970-2; 978-0-385-90802-3 lib bdg; 0-385-90802-4 lib bdg

LC 2010-13157

Eleven-year-old Calli, the third child in a family of busy high-achievers, likes to take her time and observe rather than rush around, and when she meets an awkward, insecure second-grader named Noah and is paired with him in the Peer Helper Program, she finds satisfaction and strength in working with him.

"Callie's often-insightful first-person narration provides a thoughtful, child-eyed view look at how adults too often try to find success through their children's achievements. The sometimes over-the-top depiction of stage parents pokes gentle but oh-so-true fun at them, adding to the appeal of this amusing debut." Kirkus

The **summer** I saved the world-- in 65 days; by Michele Weber Hurwitz. Wendy Lamb Books, an imprint of Random House Children's Books 2014 272 p. (trade) $16.99

Grades: 5 6 7 8   **Fic**
1. Summer -- Fiction 2. Neighbors -- Fiction 3. Family life -- Fiction 4. Helping behavior -- Fiction 5. Illinois -- Fiction 6. Friendship -- Fiction 7. Helpfulness -- Fiction 8. Conduct of life -- Fiction 9. Family life -- Illinois -- Fiction
ISBN 0385371063; 9780385371063; 9780385371070; 9780385371094

LC 2013016843

In this book, by Michele Weber Hurwitz, "thirteen-year-old Nina Ross is feeling kind of lost. . . . This summer, Nina decides to change things. She hatches a plan. There are sixty-five days of summer. Every day, she'll anonymously do one small but remarkable good thing for someone in her neighborhood, and find out: does doing good actually make a difference? Along the way, she discovers that her neighborhood, and her family, are full of surprises and secrets." (Publisher's note)

"The summer before ninth grade, Nina is adrift: she's growing apart from her best friend, and her family hardly speaks to one another. Then she decides to do one small, anonymous kind act each day, hoping to bring some good to her neighborhood. Nina is a thoughtful, inspiring hero who proves that one person really can make a difference." Horn Book

Hyde, Natalie
I owe you one. Orca 2011 125p (Orca young readers) pa $7.95
Grades: 3 4 5   **Fic**
1. Canada -- Fiction 2. Friendship -- Fiction
ISBN 978-1-55469-414-3; 1-55469-414-0

"After old Mrs. Minton saves him from drowning, Wes strikes up an unexpected friendship with her. His friend says that he owes Mrs. Minton a 'life debt,' and Wes worries how he could ever repay it. His chance comes when the town's aspiring pyrotechnic blows up the television tower. . . . The plot moves quickly from one humorous situation to another. Quirky but believable characters populate the small Canadian town. . . . With its slim length, fast pace, and humor, this title will appeal to a wide range of readers." Booklist

★ **Saving** ARM PIT. Fitzhenry & Whiteside 2011
Grades: 3 4 5 6   **Fic**
1. Letters -- Fiction 2. Baseball -- Fiction 3. Postal service -- Fiction
ISBN 1-55455-151-X; 978-1-55455-151-4

The Harmony Point baseball team hasn't won a game in two seasons, and vandals have deleted letters on the the town sign so that it says "arm Pit." A new postmaster becomes the new ball coach, but it takes a letter-writing campaign to save the coach's job and the baseball team.

"This book would be a terrific read-aloud for students to learn about citizenship, community service, and collaboration. Sportsmanship and hard work, respect for coaches are also valuable lessons within the story." SLJ

Ibbotson, Eva
The **beasts** of Clawstone Castle; illustrated by Kevin Hawkes. Dutton Children's Books 2006 243p il hardcover o.p. $16.99
Grades: 4 5 6   **Fic**
1. Ghost stories 2. Cattle -- Fiction 3. Castles -- Fiction

4. Great Britain -- Fiction

ISBN 0-14-240931-6 pa; 0-525-47719-5

LC 2005-29188

While spending the summer with elderly relatives at Clawstone Castle in northern England, Madlyn and her brother Rollo, with the help of several ghosts, attempt to save the rare cattle that live on the castle grounds. "Grades four to seven." (Bull Cent Child Books)

"Ibbotson's charismatic ghosts are great . . .—as human as they are horrific—and there's plenty of quirky humor in this energetic, diverting read, loaded with charm." Booklist

Dial-a-ghost. Dutton Children's Bks. 2001 195p hardcover o.p. pa $5.99

Grades: 4 5 6   Fic

1. Ghost stories 2. Orphans -- Fiction 3. Great Britain -- Fiction

ISBN 0-525-46693-2; 0-14-250018-6 pa

LC 00-52287

A family of nice ghosts protects a British orphan from the diabolical plans of his evil guardians

"The book is filled with a large and delightful cast of characters. . . . The black-and-white illustrations have an eerie charm." SLJ

Another title about the nice ghosts is:

The great ghost rescue (2002)

★ The **dragonfly** pool; illustrated by Kevin Hawkes. Dutton Children's Books 2008 377p il $17.99; pa $7.99

Grades: 5 6 7 8   Fic

1. School stories 2. World War, 1939-1945 -- Fiction

ISBN 978-0-525-42064-4; 0-525-42064-9; 978-0-14-241486-6 pa; 0-14-241486-7 pa

"Ibbotson's trademark eccentric characters and strongly contrasted principles of right and wrong brighten and broaden this uplifting tale." Booklist

★ The **Ogre** of Oglefort; [illustrations by Lisa K. Weber] Dutton Children's Books 2011 246p il $16.99

Grades: 4 5 6   Fic

1. Fairy tales 2. Magic -- Fiction 3. Orphans -- Fiction 4. Princesses -- Fiction

ISBN 978-0-525-42382-9; 0-525-42382-6

LC 2010038137

When the Hag of Dribble, an orphan boy, and a troll called Ulf are sent to rescue a princess from an ogre, it turns out to be far from the routine magical mission they expect.

"Magical creatures abound in this effervescent fairy tale that effectively merges classic tropes with modern sensibilities." Bull Cent Child Books

One dog and his boy; by Eva Ibbotson. Scholastic Press 2012 271 p. $16.99

Grades: 3 4 5 6   Fic

1. Children's stories 2. Dogs -- Fiction 3. Wealth -- Fiction 4. England -- Fiction 5. London (England) -- Fiction 6. Voyages and travels -- Fiction 7. Human-animal relationships -- Fiction 8. Family life -- England -- London -- Fiction

ISBN 0545351960; 9780545351966

LC 2011003773

In this book, by Eva Ibbotson, "[all] Hal has ever wanted is a dog. His busy parents, hoping that he'll tire of the idea,

rent a dog from Easy Pets, run by the heartless Mr. and Mrs. Carker. Hal and Fleck, the dog he chooses, bond immediately, and they are both heartbroken when Hal's mother, realizing that Hal's interest isn't waning, sneaks the dog back to Easy Pets. Hal decides to get Fleck back and run away to his grandparents." (Bulletin of the Center for Children's Books)

★ The **secret** of platform 13; illustrated by Sue Porter. Dutton Children's Bks. 1998 231p il hardcover o.p. pa $5.99

Grades: 5 6 7 8   Fic

1. Fantasy fiction

ISBN 0-525-45929-4; 0-14-130286-0 pa

LC 97-44601

First published 1994 in the United Kingdom

Odge Gribble, a young hag, accompanies an old wizard, a gentle fey, and a giant ogre on their mission through a magical tunnel from their Island to London to rescue their King and Queen's son who had been stolen as an infant

"Lively, funny fantasy with a case of mistaken identity and a cast of eccentric characters." SLJ

★ The **star** of Kazan; illustrated by Kevin Hawkes. Dutton 2004 405p il $16.99; pa $7.99

Grades: 5 6 7 8   Fic

1. Mystery fiction 2. Germany -- Fiction 3. Vienna (Austria) -- Fiction

ISBN 0-525-47347-5; 0-14-240582-5 pa

LC 2004-45455

After twelve-year-old Annika, a foundling living in late nineteenth-century Vienna, inherits a trunk of costume jewelry, a woman claiming to be her aristocratic mother arrives and takes her to live in a strangely decrepit mansion in Germany

"This is a rich saga . . . full of stalwart friends, sly villains, a brave heroine, and good triumphing over evil. . . . An intensely satisfying read." SLJ

Iggulden, Conn

★ **Tollins**; explosive tales for children. illustrated by Lizzy Duncan. Harper 2009 172p il $16.99

Grades: 3 4 5 6   Fic

1. Fantasy fiction

ISBN 978-0-06-173098-6; 0-06-173098-X

"Tollins are tiny, nectar-eating woodland creatures with elf ears and wings but bigger than the fairies they casually use as handkerchiefs. They enjoy an idyllic existance until a fireworks factory is built in the village of Chorleywood. . . . The men of the village hunt the Tollins down to use as fodder for their fireworks. . . . Duncan's full-color illustrations and maps bring the world to witty life. A note at the end likens the Tollin's fate to child labor during the Industrial Revolution. There is much to think about and love in this beautifully realized world." Booklist

Ignatow, Amy

★ The **popularity** papers; research for the social improvement and general betterment of Lydia Goldblatt & Julie Graham-Chang. Amulet Books 204p il $15.95

Grades: 3 4 5 6   Fic

1. School stories 2. Popularity -- Fiction

ISBN 978-0-8109-8421-9; 0-8109-8421-0

LC 2009-39741

"Before they leave elementary school behind, two fifth-grade best friends are determined to uncover the secrets of popularity by observing, recording, discussing, and replicating the behaviors of the cool girls.... In a notebook format, this heavily illustrated title shows their research in dramatic, alternating, handwritten entries and colorful, hilarious drawings.... Ignatow offers a quick, fun, well-developed story that invites repeated readings." Booklist

Other titles about Lydia and Julie are:

The long distance dispatch between Lydia Goldblatt and Julie Graham-Chang (2011)

Words of (questionable) wisdom from Lydia Goldblatt & Julie Graham-Chang (2011)

Irving, Washington

The **Legend** of Sleepy Hollow; illustrated by Gris Grimly. Atheneum Books for Young Readers 2007 un il $16.99

Grades: 4 5 6 **Fic**

1. Ghost stories 2. New York (State) -- Fiction
ISBN 1-4169-0625-8; 978-1-4169-0625-4

LC 2005-27502

A superstitious schoolmaster, in love with a wealthy farmer's daughter, has a terrifying encounter with a headless horseman.

"The tale, ... slightly condensed but with language and ambiguities intact, is reimagined here with humor, vigor, [and] clarity. . . . Irving's language is challenging . . . but Grimly's numerous Halloween-hued panel and spot illustrations . . . parse it into comprehensible tidbits. The comically amplified emotions and warm yellow and orange tones balance the horror aspects of the text." Horn Book

Washington Irving's Rip van Winkle; illustrated by Arthur Rackham. Dover Publications 2005 19p pa $12.95

Grades: 5 6 7 8 **Fic**

1. Catskill Mountains (N.Y.) -- Fiction
ISBN 0-486-44242-X

LC 2004063543

A reissue of the edition first published 1905 by Doubleday

Rip Van Winkle "is based on a folk tale. Henpecked Rip and his dog Wolf wander into the Catskill mountains before the Revolutionary War. There they meet a dwarf, whom Rip helps to carry a keg. They join a group of dwarfs playing ninepins. When Rip drinks from the keg, he falls asleep and wakes 20 years later, an old man. Returning to his town, he discovers his termagant wife dead, his daughter married, and the portrait of King George replaced by one of George Washington. Irving uses the folk tale to present the contrast between the new and old societies." Reader's Ency. 3d edition

Jackson, Alison

★ **Eggs** over Evie; illustrated by Tuesday Mourning. Henry Holt 2010 215p il $16.99

Grades: 4 5 6 **Fic**

1. Pets -- Fiction 2. Cooking -- Fiction 3. Divorce -- Fiction 4. Stepfamilies -- Fiction
ISBN 978-0-8050-8294-4; 0-8050-8294-8

LC 2009-50762

Evie feels unsettled and sad after her parents divorce, her father remarries and takes the family dog, and his new wife becomes pregnant, but a cooking class and helping the elderly lady next door with her cat give Evie a way to cope with the changes in her life. Includes recipes.

"Evie tells her story with a pinch of humor and a dash of vulnerability, sifting together the people in her life and blending them into a surprising new family.... Sweet and savory." Kirkus

Includes bibliographical references

Rainmaker. Boyds Mills Press 2005 192p $16.95

Grades: 5 6 7 8 **Fic**

1. Florida -- Fiction 2. Droughts -- Fiction 3. Great Depression, 1929-1939 -- Fiction
ISBN 1-59078-309-3

"For 13-year-old Pidge Martin, the summer of 1939 brings changes and challenges. Her town, Frostfree, Florida, faces its longest drought in 40 years, and if it doesn't rain soon, area families . . . may lose their farms. A miracle is in order, and Pidge's father hopes a rainmaker can provide one. . . . Pidge is a well-characterized, sympathetic protagonist that readers will connect with." Booklist

Jacobson, Andrew

Palace of dreams; Adam Jay Epstein & Andrew Jacobson. Harper, an imprint of HarperCollinsPublishers 2013 336 p. illustrations (The familiars) (hardback) $16.99

Grades: 4 5 6 **Fic**

1. Fantasy fiction 2. Magic -- Fiction 3. Animals -- Fiction 4. Blessing and cursing -- Fiction
ISBN 0062120298; 9780062120298

LC 2013032810

In this book, by Adam Jay Epstein & Andrew Jacobson, "their reputation as heroes is short-lived for the Prophesized Three-cat Aldwyn, blue jay Skylar, and tree frog Gilbert-when they are suspected of poisoning Queen Loranella and promptly sent to the dungeon. After a daring escape, the familiars quickly go from being Vastia's most celebrated to its most wanted. Intent on clearing their names and saving Loranella's life, the three embark on an adventuresome journey to find a magical spell." (School Library Journal)

"The signature mixture of dry humor and gripping action makes this a worthy addition to the series." Horn Book

Jacobson, Jennifer

Andy Shane and the very bossy Dolores Starbuckle; [by] Jennifer Richard Jacobson; illustrated by Abby Carter. Candlewick Press 2005 56p il $13.99; pa $4.99

Grades: 1 2 3 **Fic**

1. School stories 2. Grandmothers -- Fiction
ISBN 0-7636-1940-X; 0-7636-3044-6 pa

LC 2004-57040

Andy Shane hates school, mainly because of a tattletale know-it-all named Dolores Starbuckle, but Granny Webb, who has taken care of him all his life, joins him in class one day and helps him solve the problem

"The characters are complex and realistic. . . . The narrative voice is fresh and whimsical. . . . The pen-and-ink illustrations effectively depict Andy's frustration, Dolores's temper, and Granny's zany self-assuredness." SLJ

Other titles about Andy Shane are:

Andy Shane and the pumpkin trick (2006)

Andy Shane and the Queen of Egypt (2008)

Andy Shane is NOT in love (2008)

Andy Shane and the barn sale mystery (2009)

Andy Shane, hero at last (2010)

★ **Small** as an elephant; [by] Jennifer Richard Jacobson. Candlewick Press 2011 275p $15.99

Grades: 5 6 7 8 **Fic**

1. Adventure fiction 2. New England -- Fiction 3. Abandoned children -- Fiction

ISBN 0-7636-4155-3; 978-0-7636-4155-9

LC 2010039175

When his mother disappears from an Acadia National Park campground, Jack tries to make his way back home to Boston, with only a small toy elephant for company. "Intermediate, middle school." (Horn Book)

"Jacobson masterfully puts readers into Jack's mind—he loves and understands his mother, but sometimes his judgments are not always good, and readers understand. . . . Jack's journey to a new kind of family is inspiring and never sappy." Kirkus

Jacques, Brian

★ **Redwall**; illustrated by Gary Chalk. 20th anniversary ed.; Philomel 2007 351p il $23.99; pa $7.99

Grades: 5 6 7 8 9 **Fic**

1. Fantasy fiction 2. Mice -- Fiction 3. Animals -- Fiction

ISBN 978-0-399-24794-1; 0-399-24794-7; 978-0-441-00548-2 pa; 0-441-00548-9 pa

First published 1986

"Thoroughly engrossing, this novel captivates despite its length. . . . The theme will linger long after the story is finished." Booklist

Other titles in this series are:

The Bellmaker (1995)
Doomwyte (2008)
Eulalia! (2007)
High Rhulain (2005)
The legend of Luke (2000)
Loamhedge (2003)
The long patrol (1998)
Lord Brocktree (2000)
Mariel of Redwall (1992)
Marlfox (1998)
Martin the Warrior (1994)
Mattimeo (1990)
Mossflower (1998)
The outcast of Redwall (1996)
Pearls of Lutra (1997)
Rakkety Tam (2004)
The Rogue Crew (2011)
Sable Quean (2009)
Salamandastron (1993)
Taggerung (2001)
Triss (2002)

James, Helen Foster

Paper son; Lee's journey to America. written by Helen Foster James and Virginia Shin-Mui Loh; illustrated by Wilson Ong. Sleeping Bear Press 2013 32 p. ill. (reinforced) $16.99

Grades: 5 6 7 8 **Fic**

1. Historical fiction 2. Orphans -- Fiction 3. Immigrants -- Fiction 4. Chinese Americans -- Fiction 5. Emigration and immigration -- Fiction 6. Angel Island Immigration Station (Calif.) -- Fiction 7. Angel Island (Calif.) -- History -- 20th century -- Fiction

ISBN 1585368334; 9781585368334

LC 2012033691

This historical novel, by Helen Foster James, Virginia Shin-Mui Loh, and illustrated by Wilson Ong, is part of the "Tales of Young Americans" series. "In 1926, 12-year-old Fu Lee['s] . . . parents . . . spent all of their money buying a 'paper son slot' for Lee to go to America. Being a 'paper son' means pretending to be the son of a family already in America. . . . But first he must pass the test at Angel Island Immigration Station in San Francisco." (Publisher's note)

Janisch, Heinz

Fantastic adventures of Baron Munchausen; traditional and newly discovered tales of Karl Friedrich Hieronymus von Munchausen. with illustrations by Aljoscha Blau; translated by Belinda Cooper. Enchanted Lion Books 2010 30p il $17.95

Grades: 1 2 3 **Fic**

1. Soldiers 2. Tall tales 3. Voyages and travels -- Fiction

ISBN 978-1-59270-091-2; 1-59270-091-8

LC 2010001115

Retells Baron Munchausen's boastful account of some of his incredible adventures around the world, including riding a cannonball during a spy mission and entering a whale's mouth to hear a musical concert.

"In his retellings of the Baron's tall tales, Janisch . . . combines the bravura of Paul Bunyan with the elegance of Voltaire's Candide. Each story appears on the left, accompanied by a painting on the right of the beak-nosed Baron. . . . Children with a romantic streak will be taken both with the Baron and his courtly fictions and by Blau's misty, stately portraits." Publ Wkly

Jaramillo, Ann

La linea. Roaring Brook Press 2006 131p $16.95; pa $7.99

Grades: 5 6 7 8 **Fic**

1. Mexicans -- Fiction 2. Siblings -- Fiction 3. Immigrants -- Fiction

ISBN 1-59643-154-7; 0-312-37354-6 pa

LC 2005-20133

When fifteen-year-old Miguel's time finally comes to leave his poor Mexican village, cross the border illegally, and join his parents in California, his younger sister's determination to join him soon imperils them both.

"A gripping contemporary survival adventure, this spare first novel is also a heart-wrenching family story of courage, betrayal, and love." Booklist

Jarrell, Randall

★ The **animal** family; decorations by Maurice Sendak. HarperCollins Pubs. 1996 179p il $16.99; pa $8.95

Grades: 4 5 6 7 **Fic**

1. Fantasy fiction 2. Animals -- Fiction

ISBN 0-06-205088-5; 0-06-205904-1 pa

LC 94-76270

A reissue of the title first published 1965 by Pantheon Bks. A lonely hunter living in the wilderness beside the sea gains a family made up of a mermaid, a bear, a lynx, and a boy

This story is "sensitively related with touches of humor and wisdom. A delight for the imaginative reader." Booklist

The **bat**-poet; pictures by Maurice Sendak. HarperCollins Pubs. 1996 42p il $15.95; pa $7.95
Grades: 2 3 4   **Fic**
1. Bats -- Fiction 2. Poetry -- Fiction
ISBN 0-06-205084-2; 0-06-205905-X pa
LC 94-76271
A reissue of the title first published 1964 by MacMillan
A bat who can't sleep days makes up poems about the woodland creatures he now perceives for the first time
"A lovely book, perfectly illustrated—one well worth a child's attention and affection." Publ Wkly

Jeffrey, Mark
  Max Quick: the pocket and the pendant. Harper 2011 294p $15.99
Grades: 4 5 6 7   **Fic**
1. Science fiction 2. Time -- Fiction 3. Voyages and travels -- Fiction 4. Identity (Psychology) -- Fiction
ISBN 978-0-06-198892-9; 0-06-198892-8
LC 2010-42663
First released 2005 as a podcast audiobook
Young Max, a troubled boy with a mysterious past, joins two other youths unaffected when the rest of the world was frozen in time on a journey across America—and time itself—seeking the source of the "Time-stop."
"This fast-paced adventure . . . will keep readers turning pages." SLJ

Jenkins, Emily
  Invisible Inkling; illustrations by Harry Bliss. Balzer + Bray 2011 154p il
Grades: 3 4 5   **Fic**
1. Bullies -- Fiction 2. Imaginary playmates -- Fiction 3. Brooklyn (New York, N.Y.) -- Fiction
ISBN 0-06-180220-4; 978-0-06-180220-1
LC 2010-46238
When Hank Wolowitz runs into trouble in the form a of lunch-stealing bully, he finds an unlikely ally in an invisible refugee pumpkin-loving bandapat named Inkling.
"Jenkins' possible series starter . . . is a gently humorous and nicely realistic . . . tale about coping with the loss of a lifelong best friend. . . . Anyone who has ever had an imaginary friend will appreciate sassy Inkling (who's invisible—not imaginary)." Kirkus

  ★ **Toys** go out; being the adventures of a knowledgeable Stingray, a toughy little Buffalo, and someone called Plastic. illustrated by Paul O. Zelinsky. Schwartz & Wade Bks. 2006 116p il $16.95; lib bdg $18.99; pa $5.99
Grades: 1 2 3   **Fic**
1. Toys -- Fiction 2. Friendship -- Fiction
ISBN 0-375-83604-7; 0-375-93604-1 lib bdg; 0-385-73661-4 pa
"For beginning chapter-book readers, this . . . relates the experiences of three engaging toy best friends: Lumphy the buffalo, plush StingRay, and Plastic. . . . The simple prose is clever and often hilarious, incorporating dialogue and musings that ring kid-perspective true, and Zelinsky's charming black-and-white illustrations, wonderfully detailed and textured, expressively portray character situations and feelings." Booklist

Other titles about Lumphy, StingRay, and Plastic are:
Toy dance party (2008)
Toys come home (2011)

Jennings, Patrick
  Guinea dog. Egmont USA 2010 135p $15.99; lib bdg $18.99
Grades: 3 4 5   **Fic**
1. School stories 2. Family life -- Fiction 3. Guinea pigs -- Fiction
ISBN 1-60684-053-3; 1-60684-069-X lib bdg; 978-1-60684-053-5; 978-1-60684-069-6 lib bdg
LC 2009-25117
When his mother brings home a guinea pig instead of the dog he has always wanted, fifth-grader Rufus is not happy—until the rodent starts acting exactly like a dog. "Grades three to five." (Bull Cent Child Books)
"Children will have no problem accepting the absurdity of the situation. Early chapter-book readers will enjoy this humorous tale." SLJ

  Guinea dog 2; by Patrick Jennings. Egmont USA 2013 164 p. (hardback) $15.99
Grades: 3 4 5   **Fic**
1. Pets -- Fiction 2. Guinea pigs -- Fiction 3. Schools -- Fiction 4. Family life -- Fiction
ISBN 1606844520; 9781606844526
LC 2013000979
In this book by Patrick Jennings, "when his classmates learn about Fido, the guinea pig that acts like a dog, they all want a piece of Rufus, her owner. But Rufus hates the attention. So he decides to make Fido learn how to be an actual guinea pig. But when she goes missing, he feels terrible. Was she lost, 'dognapped,' or did she run away, because he no longer liked her just the way she was?" (Publisher's note)

  Odd, weird, and little; Patrick Jennings. Egmont USA 2014 160 p. (hardcover) $15.99
Grades: 4 5 6 7   **Fic**
1. Owls -- Fiction 2. Bullies -- Fiction 3. Schools -- Fiction 4. Friendship -- Fiction 5. Middle schools -- Fiction 6. Eccentrics and eccentricities -- Fiction
ISBN 1606843745; 9781606843741
LC 2013018248
In this book, by Patrick Jennings, "Woodrow and his classmates are surprised at the old-fashioned clothing and the tiny, delicate appearance of Toulouse, a newly arrived student from Canada. . . . Woodrow risks regaining his place as top [bullying] victim as he decides to befriend and protect Toulouse. . . . Readers also learn about the psychology behind bullying and about self-empowerment." (Kirkus Reviews)

  Out standing in my field. Scholastic Press 2005 165p hardcover o.p. pa $5.99
Grades: 4 5 6   **Fic**
1. Baseball -- Fiction 2. Father-son relationship -- Fiction
ISBN 0-439-46581-8; 0-439-48749-8 pa
LC 2004-41619
Although fifth-grader Ty Cutter is named after baseball great Ty Cobb, he is the worst player on the Brewer's team—which happens to be coached by his overly-competitive father—

"The book is funny, poignant, and deeper than one might think at first glance." SLJ

Jennings, Richard W.
★ Orwell's luck; [by] Richard Jennings. Houghton Mifflin 2000 146p $15; pa $6.95
Grades: 5 6 7 8   **Fic**
1. Magic -- Fiction 2. Rabbits -- Fiction
ISBN 0-618-03628-8; 0-618-69335-1 pa
LC 99-33501

While caring for an injured rabbit which becomes her confidant, horoscope writer, and source of good luck, a thoughtful seventh grade girl learns to see things in more than one way

"This absolutely captivating tale is about everyday magic . . . filled with quiet humor and seamless invention. The characters . . . are the sort that readers fall in love with." Booklist

Jensen, Marion
Almost super; by Marion Jensen. Harper, an imprint of HarperCollinsPublishers 2014 256 p. (hardback) $14.99
Grades: 4 5 6   **Fic**
1. Brothers -- Fiction 2. Superheroes -- Fiction 3. Families -- Fiction 4. Supervillains -- Fiction
ISBN 0062209612; 9780062209610
LC 2013032145

This book, by Marion Jensen, is an "adventure about two brothers in a family of superheroes who must find a way to be heroic despite receiving powers that are total duds. Along with Rafter's algebra class nemesis, Juanita Johnson, Rafter and Benny realize that what they thought they knew about superheroes and supervillains may be all wrong. And it's up to the three of them to put aside their differences and make things right." (Publisher's note)

"In a family where your dad can fly and your great-aunt can breath fire, finding out that your superpower is worthless is, well, devastating. Such is the misfortune of Rafter and Benny Bailey...Packed with action and humor, this is a superhero tale in the spirit of The Incredibles. Jensen's wit and light tone give the story a playful quality while still managing to incorporate a healthy dose of suspense. Family dynamics and teamwork drive a plot that has, above all, a super amount of heart. " (Booklist)

Jinks, Catherine
★ How to catch a bogle; by Catherine Jinks; illustrated by Sarah Watts. Harcourt Children's Books 2013 320 p. ill. (hardcover) $16.99
Grades: 5 6 7 8   **Fic**
1. Fantasy fiction 2. Alternative histories 3. Orphans -- Fiction 4. Monsters -- Fiction 5. Apprentices -- Fiction 6. Supernatural -- Fiction 7. London (England) -- History -- 19th century -- Fiction 8. Great Britain -- History -- Victoria, 1837-1901 -- Fiction
ISBN 0544087089; 9780544087088
LC 2012045936

This is the first in a historical fantasy trilogy from Catherine Jinks. Here, "child-eating bogles infest Victorian London, providing work aplenty for 'Go-Devil Man' Alfred Bunce and his intrepid young apprentice, Birdie." Birdie is kidnapped by "would-be warlock Roswell Morton, out to capture one of the monsters for his own evil uses." She also must deal with the unwanted "attentions of Miss Edith

Eames," who wants "to see Birdie cleaned up and educated in the social graces." (Kirkus Reviews)

Saving Thanehaven; by Catherine Jinks. Egmont USA 2013 384 p. (hardcover) $17.99
Grades: 4 5 6 7   **Fic**
1. Fantasy fiction 2. Science fiction 3. Computer games -- Fiction 4. Virtual reality -- Fiction 5. Knights and knighthood -- Fiction
ISBN 1606842749; 9781606842744
LC 2012046190

In this book, "Noble is just an earnest knight in the computer game 'Thanehaven Slayer' when he encounters young Rufus, who strongly suggests that he may be doomed if he doesn't drop all the heroics and start thinking for himself. With Rufus' mantra 'you don't have to do this' ringing in his ears, Noble sets out to change his computer world." (Kirkus Reviews)

Jobling, Curtis
The rise of the wolf. Viking Childrens Books 2011 412p (Wereworld) $16.99
Grades: 4 5 6 7   **Fic**
1. Fantasy fiction 2. Adventure fiction 3. Werewolves -- Fiction
ISBN 978-0-670-01330-2; 0-670-01330-7
LC 2010049517

When a vicious beast invades his father's farm and sixteen-year-old Drew suddenly transforms into a werewolf, he runs away from his family, seeking refuge in the most out of the way parts of Lyssia, only to be captured by Lord Bergan's men and forced to battle numerous werecreatures while trying to prove that he is not the enemy.

"Jobling's characterizations are solid, his world-building is complex and fascinating, and the combat scenes are suitably exciting. The book's themes are familiar—lost prince in exile, voyage of self-discovery, young heroes rebelling against injustice and evil—but Jobling uses them to tell a thoroughly enjoyable adventure that makes particularly inventive use of its shapeshifter elements and mythology." Publ Wkly

Jocelyn, Marthe
Viminy Crowe's comic book; Marthe Jocelyn, Richard Scrimger. Tundra Books of Northern New York 2014 317 p. illustrations (hardcover) $17.99
Grades: 4 5 6 7   **Fic**
1. Adventure fiction 2. Comic books, strips, etc. 3. Adventure stories 4. Steampunk fiction 5. Caricatures and cartoons -- Fiction. 6. Congresses and conventions -- Fiction
ISBN 1770494790; 9781770494794; 9781770494800
LC 2013943886

"Is there a personality conflict? Oh, yes. Addy wants to go home; Wylder wants to stay and explore the world of Viminy Crowe's comic book. Do things go wrong? You bet they do, from the very start, when Addy loses her pet rat, Catnip, and almost gets shot by a Red Rider. All the while the actual comic book story is going on around them." (Publisher's note)

"A bathroom portal at ComicFest launches two kids, Wylder Wallace and Addy Crowe, into the pages of a comic book. Suspense builds as the kids' presence affects the story, their adventures shown (in interspersed comic panels) in

Davila's clear, humorous illustrations. It's a clever concept that's well executed by Jocelyn and Scrimger." Horn Book

Johnson, Angela

★ A **cool** moonlight. Dial Bks. 2003 133p hardcover o.p. pa $6.99

Grades: 4 5 6   **Fic**

1. Skin -- Diseases -- Fiction

ISBN 0-8037-2846-8; 0-14-240284-2 pa

LC 2002-31521

Nine-year-old Lila, born with xeroderma pigmentosum, a skin disease that make her sensitive to sunlight, makes secret plans to feel the sun's rays on her tenth birthday

"The book's real magic resides in the spell cast by Johnson's spare, lucid, lyrical prose. Using simple words and vivid sensory images, she creates Lila's inner world as a place of quiet intensity." Booklist

Johnson, Jaleigh

★ The **mark** of the dragonfly; Jaleigh Johnson. First edition Delacorte Press 2014 400 p. map (glb) $19.99; (hc) $16.99

Grades: 5 6 7 8 9 10   **Fic**

1. Magic 2. Fantasy fiction 3. Adventure and adventurers 4. Fantasy

ISBN 0385376456; 9780385376457; 9780385376150

LC 2013019716

This book, by Jaleigh Johnson, is an "adventure story about a mysterious girl and a fearless boy, set in a magical world. . . . Piper has never seen the Mark of the Dragonfly until she finds the girl amid the wreckage of a caravan in the Meteor Fields. The girl doesn't remember a thing about her life, but the intricate tattoo on her arm is proof that she's from the Dragonfly Territories and that she's protected by the king. Which means a reward for Piper if she can get the girl home." (Publisher's note)

"Heart, brains and courage find a home in a steampunk fantasy worthy of a nod from Baum. . . . A well-imagined world of veritable adventure." Kirkus

Johnson, Peter

The **amazing** adventures of John Smith, Jr., aka Houdini; by Peter Johnson. HarperCollins Children's Books 2012 168p.

Grades: 4 5 6   **Fic**

1. Domestic relations 2. Teenagers -- Fiction 3. Child authors -- Fiction 4. Authorship -- Fiction 5. Neighborliness -- Fiction 6. Providence (R.I.) -- Fiction 7. Moneymaking projects -- Fiction 8. Interpersonal relations -- Fiction 9. Family life -- Rhode Island -- Fiction

ISBN 9780061988905

LC 2011019387

In this book, "thirteen-year-old John Smith, Jr., also known as Houdini, meets the author of a children's book . . . [and] decides to try . . . . writing a novel. . . . [Peter] Johnson offers this title as Houdini's own work, wherein he shares stories about . . . his rough and tumble neighborhood in Providence, Rhode Island; his older brother who is fighting in Iraq; Angel Dimitri, the local bully; and Jackson, the neighborhood crazy/Vietnam vet." (Bulletin of the Center for Children's Books)

Includes bibliographical references

Johnson, Terry Lynn

Ice dogs; by Terry Lynn Johnson. Houghton Mifflin, Houghton Mifflin Harcourt 2013 288 p. $16.99

Grades: 5 6 7 8 9   **Fic**

1. Wilderness survival -- Fiction 2. Sled dog racing 3. Dogs -- Fiction 4. Alaska -- Fiction 5. Survival -- Fiction 6. Sled dogs -- Fiction 7. Dogsledding -- Fiction 8. Wilderness areas -- Fiction

ISBN 0547899262; 9780547899268

LC 2012045061

In this book, by Terry Lynn Johnson, "Victoria Secord, a fourteen-year-old Alaskan dogsled racer, loses her way on a routine outing with her dogs. With food gone and temperatures dropping, her survival and that of her dogs and the mysterious boy she meets in the woods is entirely up to her." (Publisher's note)

Johnson, Varian

★ The **great** Greene heist; by Varian Johnson. Arthur A. Levine Books 2014 240 p. (hardcover) $16.99

Grades: 5 6 7 8   **Fic**

1. School stories 2. Schools -- Fiction 3. Elections -- Fiction 4. Friendship -- Fiction 5. Best friends -- Fiction 6. Middle schools -- Fiction 7. Practical jokes -- Fiction

ISBN 0545525527; 9780545525534; 0545525535; 9780545525527

LC 2013029145

"Jackson Greene has reformed. No, really he has. He was once the best con artist at Maplewood Middle School, and everyone still talks about his Blitz at the Fitz.... But after Principal Kelsey caught him in his office, Jackson swore off scheming for good. Then Keith Sinclair--loser of the Blitz--announces he's running for school president, against Jackson's former almost-girlfriend Gaby de la Cruz." (Publisher's note)

"This fast-paced caper reads like Ocean's 11 for the middle-school set, and that's no coincidence: Johnson (Saving Maddie, 2010) openly credits the film as inspiration, and he has pretty much pulled it off, right down to the dizzying plot twists, incredulous access to the latest tech, and unflappable swagger. " Booklist

Johnson-Shelton, Nils

The **Invisible** Tower. HarperCollins 2011 335p (Otherworld chronicles) $16.99

Grades: 4 5 6 7   **Fic**

1. Adventure fiction 2. Kings

ISBN 978-0-06-207086-9; 0-06-207086-X

LC 2011022928

A twelve-year-old boy learns that he is actually King Arthur brought back to life in the twenty-first century—and that the fate of the universe rests in his hands.

"This new take on the Arthurian legends, told in third-person, pits wisecracking contemporary teens with their contemporary banter. . . . against all manner of obstacles. . . . It's always high-spirited and fun. Gives new life to Arthurian legends and may just send readers back to more traditional tellings." Kirkus

The **seven** swords; Nils Johnson-Shelton. HarperCollins 2013 368 p. (Otherworld chronicles) (hardback) $16.99

Grades: 4 5 6 7   Fic
1. Arthurian romances -- Adaptations 2. Fantasy fiction
3. Adventure fiction
ISBN 0062070940; 9780062070944

LC 2012019088

This juvenile adventure fantasy, by Nils Johnson-Shelton, second in the "Otherworld Chronicles," follows "Artie Kingfisher, the new King Arthur. On a quest to recover seven magical swords of the Dark Ages, Artie and Kay gather 'New Knights of the Round Table' and try to unite two worlds. Standing in their way is Lordess Morgaine. . . . Artie and his band travel from Ohio via crossover points between worlds in search of swords in Sweden, France and Japan." (Kirkus Reviews)

Johnston, Julie
A **very** fine line. Tundra Books 2006 198p $18.95; pa $10.95
Grades: 5 6 7 8   Fic
1. Canada -- Fiction 2. Clairvoyance -- Fiction
ISBN 978-0-88776-746-3; 0-88776-746-X; 978-0-88776-829-3 pa; 0-88776-829-6 pa

Then thirteen-year-old Rosalind's "aunt informs her that as the seventh daughter of a seventh daughter, she can . . . see glimpses of the future, she balks. . . . The story begins in Kepston, Ontario, in 1941. . . . Readers who come to the book intrigued by the idea of clairvoyance will fine much more: several vivid characters, a well-realized setting, and a sensitively nuanced resolution." Booklist

Jonell, Lynne
★ **Emmy** and the incredible shrinking rat. Henry Holt 2007 346p il $16.95; pa $6.99
Grades: 3 4 5 6   Fic
1. Rats -- Fiction
ISBN 978-0-8050-8150-3; 0-8050-8150-X; 978-0-312-38460-9 pa; 0-312-38460-2 pa

LC 2006-35461

When Emmy discovers that she and her formerly loving parents are being drugged by their evil nanny with rodent potions that can change people in frightening ways, she and some new friends must try everything possible to return things to normal.

"This tale turns smoothly on its fanciful premise and fabulous characters." Booklist

Other titles about Emmy are:
Emmy and the Home for Troubled Girls (2008)
Emmy and the rats in the Belfry (2011)

Jones, Diana Wynne
★ **Castle** in the air. Greenwillow Bks. 1991 199p hardcover o.p. pa $6.99
Grades: 6 7 8 9   Fic
1. Fantasy fiction
ISBN 0-688-09686-7; 0-06-447345-7 pa

LC 90-30266

In this "follow-up to Howl'sMoving Castle . . . the protagonist is a young carpet merchant called Abdullah, who spends much of his time creating a richly developed daydream in which he is the long-lost son of a great prince, kidnapped as a child by a villainous bandit. . . . Feisty Sophie and the Wizard Howl (from Howl's Moving Castle do not become apparent till late in the story, but their fortunes do link up with those of Abdullah and his love. Jones maintains

both suspense and wit throughout, demonstrating once again that frequently nothing is what it seems to be." Booklist

Earwig and the witch; illustrator, Paul O. Zelinsky. Greenwillow Books 2012 140p il
Grades: 2 3 4   Fic
1. Orphans -- Fiction 2. Witches -- Fiction
ISBN 0-06-207511-X; 978-0-06-207511-6

LC 2010048999

This book tells the story of Earwig, who "rules the roost at St. Morwald's Home for Children until she is adopted by a witchy woman named Bella Yaga with 'one brown eye and one blue one, and a raggety, ribby look to her face.' Earwig hopes to learn magic from Bella Yaga, but is trapped in the woman's decrepit house, sharing it with the Mandrake, an impossibly tall and grouchy being. Powerful and evil, Bella Yaga uses Earwig as a second pair of hands for grinding up disgusting things in bowls ('The only thing wrong with magic is that it smells so awful,' Earwig quips)." (Publishers Weekly)

"Earwig, illustrated with marvelous vitality by Zelinsky, is not to be trifled with. There's just the right level of grotesquerie and scariness . . . in this utterly charming chapter book." Kirkus

House of many ways. Greenwillow Books 2008 404p $17.99; lib bdg $18.89; pa $8.99
Grades: 5 6 7 8   Fic
1. Fantasy fiction 2. Magic -- Fiction 3. Houses -- Fiction 4. Uncles -- Fiction
ISBN 978-0-06-147795-9; 0-06-147795-8; 978-0-06-147796-6 lib bdg; 0-06-147796-6 lib bdg; 978-0-06-147797-3 pa; 0-06-147797-4 pa

LC 2007036147

Sequel to: Howl's moving castle (1986)

When Charmain is asked to housesit for Great Uncle William, the Royal Wizard of Norland, she is ecstatic to get away from her parents, but finds that his house is much more than it seems.

This is "a buoyantly entertaining read. . . . [Jones'] comic pacing and wit are amply evident." Horn Book

★ **Howl's** moving castle. Greenwillow Books 1986 212p hardcover o.p. pa $6.99
Grades: 5 6 7 8   Fic
1. Fantasy fiction
ISBN 0-06-147878-4 pa; 0-688-06233-4; 978-0-06-147878-9 pa

LC 85-21981

Sophie "resigns herself to making a living as a hatter and helping her younger sisters prepare to make their fortunes. But adventure seeks her out in the shop where she sits alone dreaming over her hats. The wicked Witch of the Waste, angered by 'competition' in the area, turns her into an old woman, so she seeks refuge inside the strange moving castle of the wizard Howl. Howl, advertised by his apprentice as an eater of souls, lives a mad, frantic life trying to escape the curse the witch has placed on him, find the perfect girl of his dreams and end the contract he and his fire demon have entered. Sophie, against her best instincts and at first unaware of her own powers, falls in love. . . . Grade six and up." (SLJ)

"Satisfyingly, Sophie meets a fate far exceeding her dreary expectations. This novel is an exciting, multi-faceted puzzle, peopled with vibrant, captivating characters. A generous sprinkling of humor adds potency to this skillful author's spell." Voice Youth Advocates

Followed by: House of many ways (2008)

Jones, Kelly

Unusual chickens for the exceptional poultry farmer; by Kelly Jones; Illustrated by Katie Kath. Alfred A. Knopf 2015 224 p. illustrations (trade) $16.99

Grades: 4 5 6   **Fic**
1. Chickens -- Fiction 2. Farm life -- Fiction 3. California -- Fiction 4. Supernatural -- Fiction 5. Letters -- Fiction 6. Racially mixed people -- Fiction 7. Farm life -- California -- Fiction
ISBN 038575552X; 9780385755528; 9780385755535
                                            LC 2013050736

In this book, by Kelly Jones, "Sophie Brown feels like a fish out of water when she and her parents move from Los Angeles to the farm they've inherited from a great-uncle. But farm life gets more interesting when a cranky chicken appears and Sophie discovers the hen can move objects with the power of her little chicken brain." (Publisher's note)

"The epistolary format consists mostly of letters in Sophie's earnest voice; often the addressee is either her late abuelita or her great-uncle Jim in various iterations of the afterlife. . . . Sophie's unique way of figuring life out on her own makes her easy to root for and provides entertainment beyond the inherent humor of chickens." Horn Book

Jones, Traci L.

★ **Silhouetted** by the blue. Farrar, Straus & Giroux 2011 200p $16.99

Grades: 5 6 7 8   **Fic**
1. School stories 2. Theater -- Fiction 3. Bereavement -- Fiction 4. African Americans -- Fiction 5. Depression (Psychology) -- Fiction
ISBN 978-0-374-36914-9; 0-374-36914-3
                                            LC 2010008419

After the death of her mother in an automobile accident, seventh-grader Serena, who has gotten the lead in her middle school play, is left to handle the day-to-day challenges of caring for herself and her younger brother when their father cannot pull himself out of his depression.

"Jones has written another winner with this beautiful, haunting tale rich in story and characterization." Booklist

Jones, Ursula

The **islands** of Chaldea; by Diana Wynne Jones; completed by Ursula Jones. Greenwillow Books, an imprint of HarperCollinsPublishers 2013 368 p. (trade ed.) $17.99

Grades: 4 5 6 7 8   **Fic**
1. Cats -- Fiction 2. Fantasy fiction 3. Aunts -- Fiction 4. Magic -- Fiction 5. Fantasy 6. Self-confidence -- Fiction 7. Voyages and travels -- Fiction
ISBN 0062295071; 9780062295071
                                            LC 2013036422

In this book, by Diana Wynne Jones and Ursula Jones, "Aileen comes from a long line of magic makers, and her Aunt Beck is the most powerful magician on Skarr. But even though she is old enough, Aileen's magic has yet to reveal itself. When Aileen is sent over the sea on a mission for the King, she worries that she'll be useless and in the way. A

powerful (but mostly invisible) cat changes all of that—and with every obstacle Aileen faces, she becomes stronger and more confident and her magic blooms." (Publisher's note)

"Diana Wynne Jones's humor, insight, and brisk, inventive style shine in this posthumously published novel. Aileen is embarrassed when she fails her Wise Woman initiation. She discovers her own "very vigorous" powers on a quest with her Wise Aunt Beck, a prince, and his attendant through the islands of Chaldea. Jones's imaginative vigor is unabated in this last, picaresque novel." Horn Book

Jordan, Rosa

Lost Goat Lane. Peachtree Publisher 2004 197p $14.95

Grades: 5 6 7 8   **Fic**
1. Goats -- Fiction 2. Florida -- Fiction 3. Race relations -- Fiction 4. African Americans -- Fiction
ISBN 1-56145-325-0
                                            LC 2004-5343

Two families—one white, one black—living near one another in rural Florida overcome their suspicions of each other and find ways to work together, with the help of their children and a few goats

"The fully realized characters and the warmth of the story make up for the small sermons. A tender, satisfying offering." SLJ

Other titles in this series are:
The goatnappers (2007)
The last wild place (2008)

Jung, Mike

Geeks, girls, and secret identities; by Mike Jung; with illustrations by Mike Maihack. Arthur A. Levine Books 2012 307 p. (hardcover: alk. paper) $16.99

Grades: 3 4 5 6 7   **Fic**
1. Boys' clubs 2. Secrecy -- Fiction 3. Friendship 4. Science fiction 5. Clubs -- Fiction 6. Humorous stories 7. Robots -- Fiction 8. Schools -- Fiction 9. Superheroes -- Fiction 10. Middle schools -- Fiction
ISBN 0545335485; 9780545335485; 9780545335492; 9780545392518
                                            LC 2011042548

In author Mike Jung's book, "Vincent Wu is Captain Stupendous's No. 1 Fan, but even he has to admit that Captain Stupendous has been a little off lately. During Professor Mayhem's latest attack, Captain Stupendous barely made it out alive, although he did manage to save Vincent from a giant monster robot. It's Vincent's dream come true . . . until he finds out Captain Stupendous's secret identity: It's Polly Winnicott-Lee, the girl Vincent happens to have a crush on." (Publisher's note)

Juster, Norton

★ The **phantom** tollbooth; illustrated by Jules Feiffer. Random House 1961 255p il $19.95; pa $6.50

Grades: 5 6 7 8   **Fic**
1. Fantasy fiction
ISBN 0-394-81500-9; 0-394-82037-1 pa

"It's all very clever. The author plays most ingeniously on words and phrases . . . and on concepts of averages and infinity and such . . . while the pictures are even more diverting than the text, for they add interesting details." N Y Her Trib Books

Kadohata, Cynthia

★ **Cracker!** the best dog in Vietnam. Atheneum Books for Young Readers 2007 312p $16.99; pa $7.99
Grades: 5 6 7 8   **Fic**
1. Dogs -- Fiction 2. Vietnam War, 1961-1975 -- Fiction
ISBN 978-1-4169-0637-7; 1-4169-0637-1; 978-1-4169-0638-4 pa; 1-4169-0638-X pa
                                      LC 2006-22022
The author "tells a stirring, realistic story of America's war in Vietnam, using the alternating viewpoints of an army dog named Cracker and her 17-year-old handler, Rick Hanski. . . . The heartfelt tale explores the close bond of the scout-dog team." Booklist

★ **Kira-**Kira. Atheneum Bks. for Young Readers 2004 244p $15.95; pa $6.99
Grades: 5 6 7 8   **Fic**
1. Death -- Fiction 2. Georgia -- Fiction 3. Sisters -- Fiction 4. Japanese Americans -- Fiction
ISBN 0-689-85639-3; 0-689-85640-7 pa
Awarded the Newbery Medal, 2005
Chronicles the close friendship between two Japanese-American sisters growing up in rural Georgia during the late 1950s and early 1960s, and the despair when one sister becomes terminally ill.
"This beautifully written story tells of a girl struggling to find her own way in a family torn by illness and horrendous work conditions. . . . All of the characters are believable and well developed." SLJ

★ **A million** shades of gray. Atheneum Books for Young Readers 2010 216p $16.99
Grades: 5 6 7 8   **Fic**
1. Vietnam -- Fiction 2. Elephants -- Fiction 3. Wilderness survival -- Fiction
ISBN 1-4169-1883-3; 978-1-4169-1883-7
                                      LC 2009-33307
In 1975 after American troops pull out of Vietnam, a thirteen-year-old boy and his beloved elephant escape into the jungle when the Viet Cong attack his village. "Grades five to eight." (Bull Cent Child Books)
"Kadohata delves deep into the soul of her protagonist while making a faraway place and stark consequences of war seem very near." Publ Wkly

Outside beauty. Atheneum Books for Young Readers 2008 265p $16.99; pa $8.99
Grades: 5 6 7 8   **Fic**
1. Sisters -- Fiction 2. Japanese Americans -- Fiction 3. Father-daughter relationship -- Fiction 4. Mother-daughter relationship -- Fiction
ISBN 978-0-689-86575-6; 0-689-86575-9; 978-1-4169-9818-1 pa; 1-4169-9818-7 pa
                                      LC 2007-39711
Thirteen-year-old Shelby and her three sisters must go to live with their respective fathers while their mother, who has trained them to rely on their looks, recovers from a car accident that scarred her face
Kadohata's "gifts for creating and containing drama and for careful definition of character prove as powerful as ever in this wise, tender and compelling novel." Publ Wkly

★ The **thing** about luck; Cynthia Kadohata; illustrated by Julia Kuo. 1st ed. Atheneum Books for Young Readers 2013 288 p. (hardcover) $16.99
Grades: 5 6 7 8   **Fic**
1. Luck -- Fiction 2. Japanese Americans -- Fiction 3. Brothers and sisters -- Fiction 4. Kansas -- Fiction 5. Grandparents -- Fiction 6. Farm life -- Kansas -- Fiction
ISBN 1416918825; 9781416918820; 9781442474673
                                      LC 2012021287
National Book Award Finalist (2013)
Parents' Choice: Silver Medal Fiction (2013)
Asian/Pacific American Awards for Literature: Children's Literature Winner (2014)
In this novel, by Newbery Medalist Cynthia Kadohata, "Summer knows that kouun means 'good luck' in Japanese, and this year her family has none of it. Just when she thinks nothing else can possibly go wrong, an emergency whisks her parents away to Japan--right before harvest season. Summer and her little brother, Jaz, are left in the care of their grandparents, who come out of retirement in order to harvest wheat and help pay the bills." (Publisher's note)
"Kadohata expertly captures the uncertainties of the tween years as Summer navigates the balance of childlike concerns with the onset of increasingly grown-up responsibilities." (SLJ)

★ **Weedflower**. Atheneum Books for Young Readers 2006 260p $16.95; pa $5.99
Grades: 5 6 7 8   **Fic**
1. Arizona -- Fiction 2. World War, 1939-1945 -- Fiction 3. Japanese Americans -- Evacuation and relocation, 1942-1945 -- Fiction
ISBN 0-689-86574-0; 1-4169-7566-7 pa
                                      LC 2004-24912
After twelve-year-old Sumiko and her Japanese-American family are relocated from their flower farm in southern California to an internment camp on a Mojave Indian reservation in Arizona, she helps her family and neighbors, becomes friends with a local Indian boy, and tries to hold on to her dream of owning a flower shop.
Sumiko "is a sympathetic heroine, surrounded by well-crafted, fascinating people. The concise yet lyrical prose conveys her story in a compelling narrative." SLJ

Kang, Hildi
Chengli and the Silk Road caravan. Tanglewood 2011 178p $14.95
Grades: 5 6 7 8   **Fic**
1. China -- Fiction 2. Fathers -- Fiction 3. Princesses -- Fiction 4. Trade routes -- Fiction
ISBN 978-1-933718-54-5; 1-933718-54-4
                                      LC 2010047359
Called to follow the wind and search for information about his father who disappeared many years ago, thirteen-year-old Chengli, carrying a piece of jade with strange writing that had belonged to his father, joins a caravan charged with giving safe passage to the Emperor's daughter as it navigates the constant dangers of the Silk Road in 630 A.D.
"This fast-paced adventure is filled with friendship, historical detail, changing scenery, and action. It will appeal to a wide range of readers." SLJ

Kehret, Peg

The **ghost's** grave. Dutton Children's Books 2005
210p $16.99; pa $5.99

Grades: 5 6 7 8   **Fic**

1. Ghost stories 2. Coal miners -- Fiction 3. Washington
(State) -- Fiction

ISBN 0-525-46162-0; 0-14-240819-0 pa

LC 2004022064

Apprehensive about spending the summer in Washington State with his Aunt Ethel when his parents get an overseas job, twelve-year-old Josh soon finds adventure when he meets the ghost of a coal miner.

"This fast-paced and engaging book should be a hit with fans of ghost stories. Josh is a rich character to whom readers can relate." SLJ

Keith, Harold

Rifles for Watie. Crowell 1957 332p lib bdg $16.89;
pa $5.99

Grades: 6 7 8 9   **Fic**

1. Generals 2. Indian leaders 3. United States --
History -- 1861-1865, Civil War -- Fiction

ISBN 0-690-04907-2 lib bdg; 0-06-447030-X pa

Awarded the Newbery Medal, 1958

"Young Jeff Bussey longs for the life of a Union soldier during the Civil War, but before long he realizes the cruelty and savagery of some men in the army situation. The war loses its glamor as he sees his very young friends die. When he is made a scout, his duties take him into the ranks of Stand Watie, leader of the rebel troops of the Cherokee Indian Nation, as a spy." Stensland. Lit By & About the Am Indian

Keller, Laurie

Invasion of the Ufonuts; Laurie Keller. Henry Holt and
Company 2014 126 p. (hardback) $12.99

Grades: 2 3 4 5   **Fic**

1. Humorous fiction 2. Doughnuts -- Fiction 3. Aliens
(Fictional characters) 4. Humorous stories 5. Alien
abduction -- Fiction

ISBN 0805090754; 9780805090758

LC 2013042139

In this book, by Laurie Keller, "Arnie finds himself in trouble when his neighbor, Loretta Schmoretta, begins telling news reporters that she was the victim of an alien abduction. And not just any aliens—alien doughnuts from outer spastry, who will continue the abductions until people stop eating doughnuts! Although Arnie thinks this is a ridiculous story, he notices that everyone is treating him differently, as if he is an alien doughnut rather than just a doughnut-dog." (Publisher's note)

"Arnie the Doughnut narrates his second adventure with caretaker Mr. Bing and friend Peezo (a pizza slice), in which Earth is threatened by a bizarre invasion. When wacky puns, eccentric characters, and doughnuts from outer space mix together with Keller's recognizable illustrations, it's a recipe for a deliciously zany story. Keller even works in a secret alien-doughnut language (think Pig Latin)." Horn Book

Other titles in this series include:

Bowling Alley Bandit (2013)

Kelley, Jane

The **girl** behind the glass; [by] Jane Kelley. Random
House 2011 183p $16.99; lib bdg $19.99; e-book $16.99

Grades: 4 5 6 7   **Fic**

1. Ghost stories 2. Twins -- Fiction 3. Moving --
Fiction 4. Sisters -- Fiction 5. Family life -- Fiction

ISBN 978-0-375-86220-5; 0-375-86220-X; 978-0-
375-96220-2 lib bdg; 0-375-96220-4 lib bdg; 978-0-
375-88996-7 e-book

LC 2010-43568

Moving from Brooklyn to a rental house in the country strains the relationship between eleven-year-old identical twins Hannah and Anna Zimmer, a situation made worse by the ghost of a girl who is trapped in the house because of problems with her own sister eighty years before.

"Both chilling and lyrical. . . . The tensions within the Zimmer family are especially well-observed, and Kelley . . . conveys an impressive amount of emotion with few words. The ethereal tone and steady parceling out of warning, clues, and bits of information . . . maintain the novel's intrigue and will keep readers invested in the unfolding mystery." Publ Wkly

Kelly, David A.

The **Fenway** foul-up; illustrated by Mark Meyers.
Random House 2011 101p il (Ballpark mysteries) lib bdg
$12.99; pa $4.99

Grades: 2 3 4   **Fic**

1. Mystery fiction 2. Cousins -- Fiction 3. Baseball
-- Fiction 4. Fenway Park (Boston, Mass.)

ISBN 978-0-375-96703-0 lib bdg; 0-375-96703-6 lib
bdg; 978-0-375-86703-3 pa; 0-375-86703-1 pa; 978-
0-375-89816-7 e-book

LC 2010-08521

"Two nine-year-old sleuths bring sharp powers of observation and deduction into play when a Red Sox slugger's favorite bat disappears. Cousins Mike and Kate are thrilled when Kate's sports-reporter mom brings them to a game, and they are up to the challenge when star player Big D's bat goes missing after batting practice. Folding information about Fenway Park and its colorful history into the tale, Kelly also artfully slips in simple red herrings along with real clues to the thief's identity and the bat's whereabouts. . . . This book should draw baseball fans as well as budding whodunit aficionados." Booklist

Other titles in this series are:

The pinstripe ghost (2011)

The L.A. Dodger (2011)

Kelly, Erin Entrada

Blackbird fly; by Erin Entrada Kelly. Greenwillow
Books, an imprint of HarperCollinsPublishers 2015 304 p.
(hardback) $16.99

Grades: 4 5 6 7 8   **Fic**

1. School stories 2. Music -- Fiction 3. Bullies --
Fiction 4. Guitar -- Fiction 5. Middle schools -- Fiction
6. Filipino Americans -- Fiction

ISBN 0062238612; 9780062238610

LC 2014029444

In this novel by Erin Entrada Kelly, "Apple has always felt a little different from her classmates. . . . It becomes unbearable in middle school, when the boys . . . in Apple's class put her name on the Dog Log, the list of the most unpopular girls in school. When Apple's friends turn on her and everything about her life starts to seem weird and embarrassing, Apple turns to music." (Publisher's note)

"Debut author Kelly skillfully weaves together the story of misfit Apple, her love of music, and a budding romance with a new boy at school, while never losing focus on the central issue of what it is like to be the 'other. . ..'" Booklist

Kelly, Jacqueline

★ The **evolution** of Calpurnia Tate. Henry Holt and Co. 2009 340p $16.99

Grades: 4 5 6 7   **Fic**

1. Texas -- Fiction 2. Nature -- Fiction 3. Family life -- Fiction 4. Naturalists -- Fiction 5. Grandfathers -- Fiction

ISBN 978-0-8050-8841-0; 0-8050-8841-5

LC 2008-40595

A Newbery Medal honor book (2010)

In central Texas in 1899, eleven-year-old Callie Vee Tate is instructed to be a lady by her mother, learns about love from the older three of her six brothers, and studies the natural world with her grandfather, the latter of which leads to an important discovery.

"Callie is a charming, inquisitive protagonist; a joyous, bright, and thoughtful creation. . . . Several scenes . . . mix gentle humor and pathos to great effect." SLJ

Kelly, Katy

Lucy Rose, here's the thing about me; illustrated by Adam Rex. Delacorte Press 2004 137p il hardcover o.p. pa $5.99

Grades: 2 3 4   **Fic**

1. School stories 2. Moving -- Fiction 3. Family life -- Fiction 4. Washington (D.C.) -- Fiction

ISBN 0-385-73203-1; 0-440-42026-1 pa

LC 2003-20754

Eight-year-old Lucy Rose keeps a diary of her first year in Washington, D.C., her home since her parents separation, where she spends time with her grandparents, makes new friends, and longs to convince her teacher to let her take care of the class pet during a holiday

"There's something especially endearing about Lucy Rose, and her interactions with her parents, grandparents, teacher, and friends seem believable and comfortable." Booklist

Other titles about Lucy Rose are:

Lucy Rose, big on plans (2005)

Lucy Rose, busy like you can't believe (2006)

Lucy Rose, working myself to pieces and bits (2007)

Melonhead; illustrated by Gillian Johnson. Delacorte Press 2009 209p il $12.99; lib bdg $15.99

Grades: 3 4 5   **Fic**

1. Inventors -- Fiction 2. Washington (D.C.) -- Fiction

ISBN 978-0-385-73409-7; 0-385-73409-3; 978-0-385-90426-1 lib bdg; 0-385-90426-6 lib bdg

LC 2007-46076

In the Washington, D.C. neighborhood of Capitol Hill, Lucy Rose's friend Adam "Melonhead" Melon, a budding inventor with a knack for getting into trouble, enters a science contest that challenges students to recycle an older invention into a new invention.

This is "laugh-out-loud funny. . . . The capital setting and a unique cast of characters round out this strong chapterbook offering." SLJ

Other titles about Melonhead are:

Melonhead and the big stink (2010)

Melonhead and the undercover operation (2011)

Kelly, Lynne

Chained; Lynne Kelly. Farrar Straus Giroux 2012 248 p. (hardcover) $16.99

Grades: 4 5 6   **Fic**

1. Debt 2. Circus performers -- Fiction 3. Human-animal relationship -- Fiction 4. India -- Fiction 5. Circus -- Fiction 6. Elephants -- Fiction 7. Child labor -- Fiction 8. Conduct of life -- Fiction 9. Animals -- Treatment -- Fiction

ISBN 0374312370; 9780374312374; 9780374312503

LC 2011031767

In author Lynne Kelly's book, "after ten-year-old Hastin's family borrows money to pay for his sister's hospital bill, he leaves his village in northern India to take a job as an elephant keeper and work off the debt. . . . The crowds that come to the circus see a lively animal . . . but Hastin sees Nandita, a sweet elephant and his best friend, who is chained when she's not performing and hurt with a hook until she learns tricks perfectly. Hastin protects Nandita as best as he can, knowing that the only way they will both survive is if he can find a way for them to escape." (Publisher's note)

Kelsey, Marybeth

A **recipe** 4 robbery. Greenwillow Books 2009 282p $16.99; lib bdg $17.89

Grades: 4 5 6   **Fic**

1. Mystery fiction

ISBN 978-0-06-128843-2; 0-06-128843-8; 978-0-06-128845-6 lib bdg; 0-06-128845-4 lib bdg

LC 2008-29145

An unsupervised goose, missing family heirlooms, and some suspicious characters turn the annual cucumber festival into a robbery investigation for three sixth-grade friends.

"The novel is full of likable characters and fun twists and turns. The plot moves quickly, and Kelsey writes with wit and verve." SLJ

Kennedy, Emma

Wilma Tenderfoot: the case of the frozen hearts. Dial Books for Young Readers 2011 335p $16.99

Grades: 4 5 6   **Fic**

1. Mystery fiction 2. Orphans -- Fiction 3. Great Britain -- Fiction

ISBN 978-0-8037-3540-8; 0-8037-3540-5

LC 2009040050

Wilma Tenderfoot, a ten-year-old orphan who lives at Cooper Island's Lowside Institute for Woeful Children, dreams of escape and of becoming the apprentice of the world-famous detective Theodore P. Goodman, whose every case she follows devotedly in the newspaper.

"Wilma is an appealing character, ever-hopeful that Goodman will take her on as an apprentice and help her find out more about her origins. The fast-paced plot twists and turns, but the conflict between good and evil is clear." Kirkus

Another title in this series is:

Wilma Tenderfoot: the case if the putrid poison (2011)

Wilma Tenderfoot: the case of the putrid poison. Dial Books for Young Readers 2011 314p $16.99

Grades: 4 5 6   **Fic**

1. Mystery fiction 2. Actors -- Fiction 3. Orphans -- Fiction 4. Theater -- Fiction 5. Great Britain -- Fiction

6. Missing persons -- Fiction 7. Poisons and poisoning
-- Fiction
ISBN 978-0-8037-3541-5; 0-8037-3541-3
LC 2011001165

Companion volume to: Wilma Tenderfoot: the case of
the frozen hearts (2001)

"The writing is straightforward, but Kennedy includes
language that may challenge younger readers, irresistible
new words like 'irascible,' 'wafting,' 'sordid' and 'mania-
cally.' A couple of pages of summary of the events of the
first book will bring newcomers into the long-term story,
but this title stands on its own. Both familiar and fresh, this
English import is likely to appeal to American readers as
well." Kirkus

Kennedy, Marlane
The **dog** days of Charlotte Hayes. Greenwillow Books
2009 233p $15.99; lib bdg $16.89
Grades: 4 5 6   **Fic**
1. Dogs -- Fiction 2. Old age -- Fiction 3. Family life
-- Fiction 4. West Virginia -- Fiction
ISBN 978-0-06-145241-3; 0-06-145241-6; 978-0-06-
145242-0 lib bdg; 0-06-145242-4 lib bdg
LC 2008-07507

Eleven-year-old Charlotte is not a dog person but does
not like that the rest of her family neglects their Saint Bernard puppy, and so with a lot of determination and a little
sneakiness, she works on finding a good home for the
gentle giant.

This is a "gentle, appealing story.... The familiar family
and friendship issues and satisfying resolution make this an
agreeable read." Booklist

Kerrin, Jessica Scott
★ **Martin** Bridge: ready for takeoff! written by Jessica
Scott Kerrin; illustrated by Joseph Kelly. Kids Can Press
2005 120p il $14.95; pa $4.95
Grades: 2 3 4   **Fic**
ISBN 1-55337-688-9; 1-55337-772-9 pa

"Martin Bridge usually has a scheme or project under
way. In the three school and home stories presented in this
beginning chapter book, he sees how a happy surprise intended for one person makes a positive difference for another, figures out what to say to a little girl whose hamster has
died, and suffers the consequences of jealousy.... [Martin's]
responses are on target for a third grader. Kerrin relates the
episodes in a straightforward way that incorporates rich language. Kelly's full-page illustrations and spot art follow the
narrative closely enough to support the newly independent
readers for whom this book is written." SLJ

Other titles about Martin Bridge are:
Martin Bridge on the lookout! (2005)
Martin Bridge blazing ahead! (2006)
Martin Bridge out of orbit! (2007)
Martin Bridge sound the alarm (2007)
Martin Bridge in high gear! (2008)
Martin Bridge: the sky's the limit (2008)
Martin Bridge: onwards and upwards! (2009)

Kerz, Anna
Better than weird. Orca Book Publishers 2011 218p
pa $9.95
Grades: 4 5 6 7   **Fic**
1. School stories 2. Autism -- Fiction 3. Bullies --

Fiction 4. Father-son relationship -- Fiction
ISBN 978-1-55469-362-7 pa; 1-55469-362-4 pa

When Aaron's long-absent father returns, Aaron must
cope with bullying at school, his grandmother's illness and
his father's pregnant new wife.

"Yet another in a long line of recent books about kids
with autism, Kerz's effort nevertheless shines. . . . A heartwarming read for fans of realistic fiction." Booklist

The **gnome's** eye. Orca Book Publishers 2010 210p
pa $12.95
Grades: 4 5 6 7   **Fic**
1. Fear -- Fiction 2. Canada -- Fiction 3. Immigrants
-- Fiction
ISBN 978-1-55469-195-1 pa; 1-55469-195-8 pa

When Theresa and her family immigrate to Canada after
World War II, she confronts her many fears with the help of
a talisman given to her by a friend in Austria.

"Both laughter and genuine concern will be evident
through Theresa's imaginative storytelling and descriptive
narrative." SLJ

Ketchum, Liza
Where the great hawk flies. Clarion Books 2005 264p
$16
Grades: 5 6 7 8   **Fic**
1. Vermont -- Fiction 2. Prejudices -- Fiction 3. Pequot
Indians -- Fiction
ISBN 0-618-40085-0
LC 2004-29832

Years after a violent New England raid by the Redcoats
and their Revolutionary War Indian allies, two families, one
that suffered during that raid and one with an Indian mother
and Patriot father, become neighbors and must deal with past
trauma and prejudices before they can help each other in the
present. Based on the author's family history. Includes historical notes and notes on the Pequot Indians.

The author writes "in prose as sturdy and well crafted as
a cedar-frame wigwam or hand-pegged pine barn." Booklist

Key, Watt
Alabama moon. Farrar, Straus & Giroux 2006 294p
$16; pa $6.99
Grades: 5 6 7 8   **Fic**
1. Alabama -- Fiction 2. Orphans -- Fiction 3.
Wilderness survival -- Fiction
ISBN 0-374-30184-0; 0-312-38428-9 pa
LC 2005-40165

After the death of his father, ten-year-old Moon leaves
their forest shelter home and is sent to an Alabama institution, becoming entangled in the outside world he has never
known and making good friends, a relentless enemy, and
finally a new life

"The book is well written with a flowing style, plenty of
dialogue, and lots of action. The characters are well drawn
and three-dimensional." SLJ

Followed by: Dirt road home (2010)

Kibuishi, Kazu
Explorer; the lost islands. Kazu Kibuishi. Abrams
Books 2013 128 p. (Explorer) (hardcover) $19.95; (pbk.)
$10.95

Grades: 4 5 6 7 8 **Fic**
1. Islands 2. Graphic novels
ISBN 1419708813; 141970883X; 9781419708817; 9781419708831
LC 2013935794

In this follow-up to "Explorer: The Mystery Boxes," Kazu Kibuishi and a crew of cartoonists again take turns weaving seven tales based around a loose theme. This time the motif is islands, and the contributors are left to interpret it in illustrated shorts. Some, by using their strange and remote settings as microcosms, underscore the value of hard work . . . or finding one's niche , . . , while others examine more abstract concepts such as exploration and isolation." (Publishers Weekly)

Kilworth, Garry
Attica. Little, Brown 2009 334p pa $11.95
Grades: 5 6 7 8 **Fic**
1. Fantasy fiction 2. Stepfamilies -- Fiction
ISBN 978-1-904233-56-5 pa; 1-904233-56-2 pa

"The children have distinct personalities and react to Attica in realistic ways, finding their own strengths in this exhilarating, unpredictable environment. This book is a rare find." Booklist

Kimmel, Elizabeth Cody
★ The **reinvention** of Moxie Roosevelt. Dial Books for Young Readers 2010 256p $16.99
Grades: 4 5 6 7 **Fic**
1. School stories
ISBN 978-0-8037-3303-9; 0-8037-3303-8
LC 2009-37939

On her first day of boarding school, a thirteen-year-old girl who feels boring and invisible decides to change her personality to match her unusual name.

"Kimmel's sharply observed novel reflects a keen understanding of the agony of self-definition that is adolescence. Readers will cheer for Moxie as she charts her path toward self-acceptance." Kirkus

School spirit. Little, Brown and Co. 2008 316p (Suddenly supernatural) $15.99
Grades: 5 6 7 8 **Fic**
1. Ghost stories 2. School stories 3. Popularity -- Fiction 4. Clairvoyance -- Fiction 5. Mother-daughter relationship -- Fiction
ISBN 978-0-316-06683-9; 0-316-06683-4
LC 2007-031542

Like her mother, a professional medium, Kat has been able to see dead people since turning thirteen, and although they would prefer to be normal, Kat and her best friend come to terms with their own talents while helping free the spirit of a girl trapped at their middle school.

"This delightfully fun and well-written story is a fast, clean read. . . . Its nice blend of supernatural and reality will attract fantasy and non-fantasy readers alike." Voice Youth Advocates

Other titles in this series are:
Scaredy Kat (2009)
Unhappy medium (2009)

Kinard, Kami
The **boy** prediction; (notes and observations of Tabitha Reddy) Kami Kinard. Scholastic Press 2014 272 p. illustrations $12.99
Grades: 6 7 8 9 **Fic**
1. Girls -- Fiction 2. Middle schools -- Fiction 3. Humorous stories 4. Schools -- Fiction 5. Friendship -- Fiction 6. Best friends -- Fiction 7. Dating (Social customs) -- Fiction
ISBN 0545575869; 9780545575867
LC 2013025996

"Full of asides about classmates and the kind of detailed gossip only 11 to 13-year-olds can truly follow, this giddy, giggly book reads like a diary and is aimed at tween girls who like their literature frothy. Tabbi, short for Tabitha, is a middle-school student looking for the right guy, a crush who will elevate her status and help her put aside the feeling that she is just a third wheel when she hangs out with her bestie Kara and Kara's boyfriend, Chip. But how is she going to find the guy of her dreams? Tabbi is sure that everything, from the cheese that slid off her pizza and formed the shape of a male face (well, kind of) to a Magic 8 Ball, will predict her future." (Booklist)

" the girls struggle to make their fundraising goal, they learn about handling competition, working in partnership and even a little something about cyberbullying. For any spirited, entrepreneurial teen that's ever had a crush, this sweet read is sprinkled with lessons on life, love and business." - Kirkus

King, Caro
Seven sorcerers; Caro King. Aladdin 2011 324 p. (hbk.) $15.99
Grades: 5 6 7 8 **Fic**
1. Fantasy 2. Missing children -- Fiction 3. Brothers and sisters -- Fiction 4. Adventure and adventurers -- Fiction
ISBN 1442420421; 9781442420427
LC 2011001432

Sequel: Shadow spell
First published 2009 in the United Kingdom

"Nineveh 'Nin' Redstone is 11 years old and resolutely ordinary. Her four-year-old brother is nothing but a nuisance until the awful Wednesday when she wakes up and he's gone. Worse, no one but Nin remembers he exists. It's left to her to reclaim him from Skerridge (a bogeyman) and the Terrible House of Strood." (Publishers Weekly)

A "complex, intelligent fantasy that is at turns funny and terrifying." Booklist

King, Thomas
A **Coyote** solstice tale; pictures by Gary Clement. Groundwood Books 2009 un il $14.95
Grades: 1 2 3 4 **Fic**
1. Stories in rhyme 2. Animals -- Fiction 3. Coyotes -- Fiction 4. Shopping -- Fiction 5. Winter solstice -- Fiction
ISBN 978-0-88899-929-0; 0-88899-929-1

ALA America Indian Library Association American Indian Youth Literature Award (2010)

"Coyote is expecting Beaver, Bear, Otter, and Moose for a solstice dinner at his small house in the woods but a little girl in a reindeer costume shows up first. When the friends follow her tracks to discover where she came from, they discover a huge and frenzied mall just beyond the woods, where Coyote goes wild shopping until he discovers that he has to pay for the stuff. The humor is dry and affectionate, the rhyming text delights with sly turns of phrase, the water-color cartoons are whimsical, and the small size of the book (a bit bigger than a DVD case) adds to the charm." SLJ

King-Smith, Dick

★ **Babe**; the gallant pig. illustrated by Maggie Kneen. Twentieth anniversary edition; Knopf 2005 130p il $16.95
Grades: 3 4 5   Fic
1. Pigs -- Fiction
ISBN 0-375-82970-9
LC 2004-5832
First published 1983 in the United Kingdom with title: The sheep-pig; first United States edition 1985 by Crown
A piglet destined for eventual butchering arrives at the farmyard, is adopted by an old sheep dog, and discovers a special secret to success
"Mary Rayner's engaging black-and-white drawings capture the essence of Babe and the skittishness of sheep and enhance this splendid book-which should once and for all establish the intelligence and nobility of pigs." Horn Book

Dinosaur trouble; [by] Dick King-Smith; illustrated by Nick Bruel. Roaring Brook Press 2008 118p il $14.95
Grades: 2 3 4   Fic
1. Dinosaurs -- Fiction
ISBN 978-1-59643-324-3; 1-59643-324-8
Young dinosaurs Nosy, a pterodactyl, and Banty, an apatosaurus, become friends, despite their parents' prejudices
"Much of the book's humor relies on wordplay and the juxtaposition of the clever mothers next to their dim-witted husbands. Frequent black-and-white cartoon illustrations . . . enliven the text and add a light comic touch." Booklist

The **mouse** family Robinson; [by] Dick King-Smith; illustrated by Nick Bruel. Roaring Brook Press 2008 71p il $15.95
Grades: 3 4 5   Fic
1. Mice -- Fiction 2. Family life -- Fiction
ISBN 978-1-59643-326-7; 1-59643-326-4
LC 2008011139
After a close call with the cat who stalks the hallways, a family of wild mice, including adventurous, young Beaumont and elderly Uncle Brown, emigrates to a more mouse-friendly house down the block
"The lively, often droll narrative, divided into short chapters, and the many captivating illustrations . . . provide an accessible, engaging read filled with everyday details of imagined mouse life and appealing characters." Booklist

Kingfisher, Rupert

Madame Pamplemousse and her incredible edibles; [by] Rupert Kingfisher; illustrated by Sue Hellard. Bloomsbury Children's Books 2008 138p il $15.99
Grades: 2 3 4   Fic
1. Food -- Fiction 2. Restaurants -- Fiction 3. Paris (France) -- Fiction
ISBN 978-1-59990-306-4; 1-59990-306-7
LC 2008-10409
Forced to work in her unpleasant uncle's horrible restaurant, a Parisian girl finds comfort and companionship in

a shop nearby that sells otherworldly foods prepared by a mysterious cook and her cat
"Kingfisher writes in whimsical, humorous prose, creating vivid scenarios and intriguing characters. . . . This droll title is sprinkled with fanciful line drawings and topped with a moral about the magical power and rewards of following one's heart." Booklist

Kinney, Jeff

Diary of a wimpy kid; hard luck. by Jeff Kinney. Harry N Abrams Inc 2013 217 p. (hardback) $13.95
Grades: 5 6 7 8   Fic
1. School stories 2. Chance -- Fiction 3. Friendship -- Fiction 4. Luck -- Fiction 5. Humorous stories 6. Diaries -- Fiction 7. Schools -- Fiction 8. Middle schools -- Fiction
ISBN 1419711326; 9781419711329
LC 2013033173
In this book by Jeff Kinney, "Greg Heffley's on a losing streak. His best friend, Rowley Jefferson, has ditched him, and finding new friends in middle school is proving to be a tough task. To change his fortunes, Greg decides to take a leap of faith and turn his decisions over to chance. Will a roll of the dice turn things around, or is Greg's life destined to be just another hard-luck story?" (Publisher's note)
"Greg Heffley's eighth adventure (but who's counting?) centers on his relationship with his best friend, Rowley —more specifically, the demise of that relationship when Rowley gets a girlfriend... As ever, Kinney strikes his comic target in the bull's-eye, exaggerating the trials of adolescence just enough to make them real while deftly exposing the insecurities behind Greg's bravado with his super, simple drawings. Will Greg and Rowley make up? Either way, devotees need not worry; there is plenty more angst in store." (Booklist)
Hard luck

★ **Diary** of a wimpy kid: Greg Heffley's journal. Amulet Books 2007 217p pa $14.95
Grades: 5 6 7 8   Fic
1. School stories 2. Friendship -- Fiction
ISBN 978-0-8109-9313-6 pa; 0-8109-9313-9 pa
LC 2006-31847
Greg records his sixth grade experiences in a middle school where he and his best friend, Rowley, undersized weaklings amid boys who need to shave twice daily, hope just to survive, but when Rowley grows more popular, Greg must take drastic measures to save their friendship
"Kinney's background as a cartoonist is apparent in this hybrid book that falls somewhere between traditional prose and graphic novel. . . . The pace moves quickly. The first of three installments, it is an excellent choice for reluctant readers, but more experienced readers will also find much to enjoy and relate to." SLJ
Other titles about Greg are:
Diary of a wimpy kid: Rodrick rules (2008)
Diary of a wimpy kid: the last straw (2009)
Diary of a wimpy kid: dog days (2009)

The **third** wheel; Jeff Kinney. Amulet Books 2012 217 p. (Diary of a wimpy kid) $13.95; $13.95
Grades: 5 6 7 8   Fic
1. Dance -- Juvenile fiction 2. School stories -- Juvenile

fiction 3. Humorous fiction -- Juvenile fiction
ISBN 1419705849; 9781419705847

This children's story, by Jeff Kinney, is book 7 in the "Diary of a Wimpy Kid" series. "A dance at Greg's middle school has everyone scrambling to find a partner, and Greg is determined not to be left by the wayside. So he concocts a desperate plan to find someone . . . to go with on the big night. But Greg's schemes go hilariously awry, and his only option is to attend the dance with his best friend, Rowley Jefferson, and a female classmate as a 'group of friends.'" (Publisher's note)

Kinsey-Warnock, Natalie
True colors; by Natalie Kinsey-Warnock. Alfred A. Knopf Books for Young Readers 2012 242 p. (hard cover) $15.99
Grades: 4 5 6 7   **Fic**
1. Absent mothers -- Fiction 2. Orphans -- Fiction 3. Abandoned children -- Fiction 4. Identity -- Fiction 5. Foundlings -- Fiction 6. Farm life -- Vermont -- Fiction 7. People with mental disabilities -- Fiction 8. Vermont -- History -- 20th century -- Fiction
ISBN 0375860991; 9780375854538; 9780375860997; 9780375897061; 9780375960994
LC 2011037863

This book by Natalie Kinsey-Warnock "tells the story of one girl's journey to find the mother she never had, set against the period backdrop of a small farming town in 1950s Vermont. For her entire life, 10-year-old Blue has never known her mother. . . . Over the course of one summer, she resolves to finally find out who she is. . . . Her search leads her down a road of self-discovery that will change her life forever." (Publisher's note)

Kirby, Matthew J.
★ The **clockwork** three. Scholastic Press 2010 391p $17.99
Grades: 5 6 7 8   **Fic**
1. Fantasy fiction 2. Friendship -- Fiction 3. Clocks and watches -- Fiction
ISBN 978-0-545-20337-1; 0-545-20337-6
LC 2009-37879

As mysterious circumstances bring Giuseppe, Frederick, and Hannah together, their lives soon interlock like the turning gears in a clock and they realize that each one holds a key to solving the others' mysteries

This is a "riveting historical fantasy. . . . Kirby has assembled all the ingredients for a rousing adventure, which he delivers with rich, transporting prose." Publ Wkly

Icefall. Scholastic Press 2011 325p $17.99
Grades: 5 6 7 8   **Fic**
1. Fantasy fiction 2. Ice -- Fiction 3. Winter -- Fiction 4. Storytelling -- Fiction
ISBN 978-0-545-27424-1; 0-545-27424-9
LC 2011000890

"Kirby turns in a claustrophobic, thought-provoking coming-of-age adventure that shows a young woman growing into her own, while demonstrating the power of myth and legend. Kirby's attention to detail and stark descriptions make this an effective mood piece." Publ Wkly

Klages, Ellen
★ The **green** glass sea. Viking 2006 321p $16.99; pa $7.99
Grades: 5 6 7 8   **Fic**
1. New Mexico -- Fiction 2. Scientists -- Fiction 3. Atomic bomb -- Fiction 4. World War, 1939-1945 -- Fiction
ISBN 0-670-06134-4; 0-14-241149-3 pa

It is 1943, and 11-year-old Dewey Kerrigan is traveling west on a train to live with her scientist father—but no one will tell her exactly where he is. When she reaches Los Alamos, New Mexico, she learns why: he's working on a top secret government program.

"Many readers will know as little about the true nature of the project as the girls do, so the gradual revelation of facts is especially effective, while those who already know about Los Alamos's historical significance will experience the story in a different, but equally powerful, way." SLJ

Followed by: White sands, red menace (2008)

White sands, red menace. Viking 2008 337p $16.99
Grades: 5 6 7 8   **Fic**
1. Cold war -- Fiction 2. New Mexico -- Fiction 3. Scientists -- Fiction 4. Atomic bomb -- Fiction
ISBN 978-0-670-06235-5; 0-670-06235-9
Sequel to: The green glass sea (2006)

"The groundbreaking science is part of daily life for the smart techno-teens, and the adult characters are as compelling as the kids. . . . Along with . . . global issues, Klages' compelling story explores personal relationships and what it means to be a family." Booklist

Klass, David
★ **Stuck** on Earth. Farrar Straus & Giroux 2010 227p $16.99
Grades: 4 5 6 7   **Fic**
1. Science fiction 2. Bullies -- Fiction 3. Extraterrestrial beings -- Fiction
ISBN 978-0-374-39951-1; 0-374-39951-4
LC 2008--48133

On a secret mission to evaluate whether the human race should be annihilated, a space alien inhabits the body of a bullied fourteen-year-old boy.

"Klass's . . . thoughtful, often wrenching book offers plenty to think about, from what's really going on in Tom's head to questions about human responsibility to the planet and each other. It takes 'alienation' to a whole new level." Publ Wkly

Klimo, Kate
The **dragon** in the sock drawer; with illustrations by John Schroades. Random House Childrens Books 2008 159p il (Dragon keepers) $14.99; lib bdg $17.99
Grades: 3 4 5   **Fic**
1. Eggs -- Fiction 2. Cousins -- Fiction 3. Dragons -- Fiction
ISBN 978-0-375-85587-0; 0-375-85587-4; 978-0-375-95587-7 lib bdg; 0-375-95587-9 lib bdg
LC 2007-42306

Cousins Jesse and Daisy always knew they would have a magical adventure, but they are not prepared when the "thunder egg" Jesse has found turns out to be a dragon egg that is about to hatch

"Illustrated with small black-and-white drawings to introduce each of the 11 chapters, this novel, with its unique and modern twists, is a great addition to the dragon genre for younger readers." SLJ

Other titles in this series are:

The dragon in the driveway (2009)

The dragon in the library (2010)

The dragon in the volcano (2011)

Kline, Suzy

★ **Horrible** Harry in room 2B; pictures by Frank Remkiewicz. Viking Kestrel 1988 56p il hardcover o.p. pa $3.99

Grades: 2 3 4   **Fic**

1. School stories

ISBN 0-14-038552-5 pa

LC 88-14204

Harry "is the devilish second grader who plays pranks and gets into mischief but can still end up a good friend. In a series of brief scenes, children meet Harry as he shows a garter snake to Song Lee and later ends up being a snake himself for Halloween. His trick to make scary people out of pencil stubs backfires when no one is scared, and his budding romance with Song Lee goes nowhere on the trip to the aquarium. . . . This story should prove to be popular with those just starting chapter books." SLJ

Other titles about Horrible Harry and Song Lee are:

Horrible Harry and the ant invasion (1989)

Horrible Harry and the Christmas surprise (1991)

Horrible Harry and the dragon war (2002)

Horrible Harry and the Drop of Doom (1998)

Horrible Harry and the dungeon (1996)

Horrible Harry and the goog (2005)

Horrible Harry and the green slime (1989)

Horrible Harry and the holidaze (2003)

Horrible Harry and the June box (2011)

Horrible Harry and the kickball wedding (1992)

Horrible Harry and the locked closet (2004)

Horrible Harry and the missing diamond (2013)

Horrible Harry and the mud gremlins (2003)

Horrible Harry and the purple people (1997)

Horrible Harry and the scarlet scissors (2012)

Horrible Harry and the secret treasure (2011)

Horrible Harry and the stolen cookie (2013)

Horrible Harry and the triple revenge (2006)

Horrible Harry at Halloween (2000)

Horrible Harry bugs the three bears (2008)

Horrible Harry goes to the moon (2000)

Horrible Harry moves up to third grade (1998)

Horrible Harry takes the cake (2006)

Horrible Harry's secret (1990)

Song Lee and Leech Man (1995)

Song Lee and the hamster hunt (1994)

Song Lee and the I hate you notes (1999)

Song Lee in Room 2B; pictures by Frank Remkiewicz. Viking 1993 56p il hardcover o.p. pa $3.99

Grades: 2 3 4   **Fic**

1. School stories 2. Korean Americans -- Fiction

ISBN 0-670-84772-0; 0-14-130408-1 pa

LC 92-41523

Spring becomes a memorable time for Miss Mackle's second-grade classroom because of the antics of Horrible Harry and the special insights of shy Song Lee

"The school setting has great appeal, and the familiar 2B kids deliver lots of funny moments." Booklist

Klise, Kate

Dying to meet you; illustrated by M. Sarah Klise. Harcourt 2009 147p il (43 Old Cemetery Road) $15

Grades: 3 4 5 6   **Fic**

1. Ghost stories 2. Authors -- Fiction 3. Letters -- Fiction

ISBN 978-0-15-205727-5; 0-15-205727-7

LC 2007-28534

In this story told mostly through letters, children's book author, I. B. Grumply, gets more than he bargained for when he rents a quiet place to write for the summer.

"This first title in a new series will appeal to readers, especially reluctant ones, as it moves quickly and leaves its audience eager for book two, which is announced in this ghastly and fun tale." SLJ

Other titles in this series are:

Over my dead body (2009)

Till death do us bark (2011)

The **Greatest** Star on Earth; Kate Klise; illustrated by M. Sarah Klise. Algonquin Young Readers 2014 144 p. (Three-ring rascals) $15.95

Grades: 2 3 4 5   **Fic**

1. Mice -- Fiction 2. Circus -- Fiction 3. Contests -- Fiction 4. Authorship -- Fiction

ISBN 1616202459; 9781616202453

LC 2013044900

Written by Kate Klise and illustrated by M. Sarah Klise, this children's book, part of the Three-Ring Rascals series, describes how "Everyone knows Sir Sidney's Circus is the best in the world. But who's the star of the show? The Circus Times is having a contest to find out. Just thinking about it gives Sir Sidney a worrywart, and it's quickly clear why. Soon after he goes off to rest, the performers start thinking too much about winning the trophy and not enough about putting on a good show." (Publisher's note)

"The performers in Sir Sidney's Circus are thrown off their game when a newspaper proposes a contest to determine the best performer. Pun- and gag-filled narration, gentle messaging about teamwork and kindness, and frequent expressive spot art enrich the quirky, accessible story. Characters' struggles to live up to Sir Sidney's expectations are understatedly complex and will resonate with readers." Horn Book

★ **Grounded.** Feiwel and Friends 2010 196p $16.99

Grades: 4 5 6 7   **Fic**

1. Death -- Fiction 2. Missouri -- Fiction 3. Bereavement -- Fiction 4. Swindlers and swindling -- Fiction

ISBN 978-0-312-57039-2; 0-312-57039-2

LC 2010013008

After her father, brother, and sister are killed in a plane crash, twelve-year-old Daralynn's life in tiny Digginsville, Missouri, proceeds as her mother turns angry and embittered, her grandmother becomes senile, and her flamboyant aunt continues to run the Summer Sunset Retirement Home for Distinguished Gentlemen, while being courted by the owner of the town's new crematorium.

"Dark humor melds with genuine pathos in Klise's moving novel. . . . This quiet story illuminates and celebrates the human need for connection beyond the grave." Booklist

Homesick; Kate Klise. 1st ed. Feiwel and Friends 2012 192 p. (hardcover) $16.99

Grades: 4 5 6 7 8   **Fic**

1. Divorce -- Fiction 2. Family life -- Fiction

ISBN 1250008425; 9781250008428

In this book by Kate Klise, "Benny's parents are splitting up. . . . Benny's dad has always liked clutter, but now, he begins hoarding everything. . . . As his house grows more cluttered and his father grows more distant, Benny tries to sort out whether he can change anything at all. Meanwhile, a local teacher enters their quiet Missouri town in America's Most Charming Small Town contest, and the pressure is on to clean up the area, especially Benny's ramshackle of a house." (Publisher's note)

Regarding the sink; where, oh where, did Waters go? illustrated by M. Sarah Klise. Harcourt 2004 127p il $15

Grades: 4 5 6 7   **Fic**

1. School stories

ISBN 0-15-205019-1

LC 2003-26560

A series of letters reveals the selection of the famous fountain designer, Florence Waters, to design a new sink for the Geyser Creek Middle School cafeteria, her subsequent disappearance, and the efforts of a class of sixth-graders to find her

"Piecing the story and clues together is satisfying. Introduce this book to savvy readers who are ready for the jump to a clever, unconventional reading experience." SLJ

Other titles in this series are:

Regarding the bathrooms (2006)

Regarding the bees (2007)

Regarding the fountain (1998)

Regarding the trees (2005)

The **show** must go on! Kate Klise; illustrated by M. Sarah Klise. Algonquin Young Readers 2013 160 p. (Three-ring rascals) $15.95

Grades: 2 3 4 5   **Fic**

1. Animals -- Fiction 2. Circus -- Fiction

ISBN 1616202440; 9781616202446

LC 2013008940

In this book, "elderly Sir Sidney loves his circus, and he pampers his animals and performers, as well as the two mice and crow who are part of its extended family. When he decides to take some time off, he hires brash Barnabas Brambles, who promises to care for the circus with the same doting attention as Sir Sidney. As soon as the kindhearted owner leaves, though, Barnabas" turns out to be greedy and self-serving. "Things look grim, but the circus folk hold onto their humor." (Publishers Weekly)

Kluger, Jeffrey

★ **Freedom** stone. Philomel Books 2011 316p $16.99

Grades: 4 5 6   **Fic**

1. Magic -- Fiction 2. Slavery -- Fiction 3. African Americans -- Fiction 4. United States -- History -- 1861-1865, Civil War -- Fiction

ISBN 978-0-399-25214-3; 0-399-25214-2

LC 2010-06028

With the help of a magical stone from Africa, a thirteen-year-old slave travels to the battle of Vicksburg to clear her father's name and free her family from bondage.

Kluger "adeptly mixes drama, fantasy, romance, and history, while creating characters so determined to survive that readers can't help being drawn into their plights. In a climax that breaks with reality but that will keep readers hungry to learn the outcome, Kluger proves his storytelling prowess." Publ Wkly

Knight, Joan

Charlotte in Giverny; by Joan MacPhail Knight; watercolor illustrations by Melissa Sweet. Chronicle Bks. 2000 un il $16.95; pa $6.95

Grades: 3 4 5   **Fic**

1. France -- Fiction 2. Artists -- Fiction

ISBN 0-8118-2383-0; 0-8118-5803-0 pa

LC 99-6878

While living in France in 1892, Charlotte, a young American girl, writes a journal of her experiences including those among the Impressionist painters at the artist colony of Giverny. Includes profiles of artists who appear in the journal and a glossary of French words

"The profuse illustrations , a mix of 1890s postcards and other memorabilia, reproductions of (mostly) impressionistic paintings by the mentioned artists, and Melissa Sweet's delicately drawn vignettes of vegetables and other items, lay an air of sunny, well-bred tranquility over the scene." Booklist

Other titles in this series are:

Charlotte in New York (2006)

Charlotte in Paris (2003)

Charlotte in London (2009)

Knudsen, Michelle

The **dragon** of Trelian. Candlewick Press 2009 407p $16.99

Grades: 4 5 6 7   **Fic**

1. Fantasy fiction 2. Magic -- Fiction 3. Dragons -- Fiction 4. Princesses -- Fiction

ISBN 978-0-7636-3455-1; 0-7636-3455-7

LC 2008025378

A mage's apprentice, a princess, and a dragon combine their strength and magic to bring down a traitor and restore peace to the kingdom of Trelian.

"Knudsen does a fantastic job of creating sympathetic and realistic characters that really drive the story. The tale is adventurous and exciting with many twists and turns along the way." SLJ

Followed by: The princess of Trelian (2012)

The **princess** of Trelian; Michelle Knudsen. Candlewick Press 2012 437 p. (reinforced) $16.99

Grades: 4 5 6 7   **Fic**

1. Fantasy 2. Magic -- Fiction 3. Dragons -- Fiction 4. Princesses -- Fiction

ISBN 0763650625; 9780763650629

LC 2011047174

Sequel to: The dragon of Trelian (2009)

In this juvenile fantasy novel, by Michelle Knudsen, a "sequel to 'The Dragon of Trelian,' . . . Princess Meg is now heir to the throne, but her subjects are uneasy about her . . . dragon, and it only becomes worse when a neighboring king accuses the dragon of ravaging the countryside. . . . Meanwhile, Meg's best friend Calen has earned his mage's mark, but a mysterious, magical attack occurs. . . . [T]he deposed villain from the previous book is behind all the mischief." (Horn Book Magazine)

Knudson, Mike

Raymond and Graham rule the school; by Mike Knudson and Steve Wilkinson; illustrated by Stacy Curtis. Viking Childrens Books 2008 136p il $14.99; pa $6.99

Grades: 2 3 4   **Fic**

1. School stories 2. Theater -- Fiction 3. Friendship -- Fiction

ISBN 978-0-670-01101-8; 0-670-01101-0; 978-0-14-241426-2 pa; 0-14-241426-3 pa

LC 2007033350

Best friends Raymond and Graham have looked forward to being the "oldest, coolest, toughest" boys at East Mill-creek Elementary School, but from the start of fourth grade everything goes wrong, from getting the scary teacher to not getting the lead in the school play

"This story is filled with nonstop action and kid-friendly humor. Done in an exaggerated cartoon style, Curtis's occasional black-and-white illustrations perfectly suit the tone of the text." SLJ

Other titles about Raymond and Graham are:
Raymond and Graham; dancing dudes (2008)
Raymond and Graham: bases loaded (2010)
Raymond and Graham: cool campers (2010)

Konigsburg, E. L.

★ **From** the mixed-up files of Mrs. Basil E. Frankweiler. Atheneum Pubs. 1967 162p il $16; pa $9.99

Grades: 4 5 6   **Fic**

1. Metropolitan Museum of Art (New York, N.Y.) -- Fiction

ISBN 0-689-20586-4; 1-4169-4975-5 pa

Awarded the Newbery Medal, 1968

"Claudia, feeling misunderstood at home, takes her younger brother and runs away to New York where she sets up housekeeping in the Metropolitan Museum of Art, making ingenious arrangements for sleeping, bathing, and laundering. She and James also look for clues to the authenticity of an alleged Michelangelo statue, the true story of which is locked in the files of Mrs. Frankweiler, its former owner. Claudia's progress toward maturity is also a unique introduction to the Metropolitan Museum." Moorachian. What is a City?

Jennifer, Hecate, Macbeth, William McKinley, and me, Elizabeth. Atheneum Pubs. 1967 117p il $16; pa $5.99

Grades: 4 5 6   **Fic**

1. Friendship -- Fiction 2. Witchcraft -- Fiction 3. African Americans -- Fiction

ISBN 0-689-30007-7; 1-4169-3396-4 pa

A Newbery Medal honor book, 1968

"Two fifth grade girls, one of whom is the first black child in a middle-income suburb, play at being apprentice witches in this amusing and perceptive story." NY Public Libr. Black Exper in Child Books

The **mysterious** edge of the heroic world. Atheneum Books for Young Readers 2007 244p il $16.99; pa $5.99

Grades: 5 6 7 8   **Fic**

1. Florida -- Fiction 2. Friendship -- Fiction 3. Art

museums -- Fiction

ISBN 978-1-4169-4972-5; 1-4169-4972-0; 978-1-4169-5353-1 pa; 1-4169-5353-1 pa

"This humorous, poignant, tragic, and mysterious story has intertwining plots that peel away like the layers of an onion." SLJ

"Amedeo Kaplan (son of characters met in The Outcasts of 19 Schuyler Place) has just moved to coastal Florida and made friends with William Wilcox, son of an estate sale manager. . . . As the boys help William's mother pack up the palatial home of Amedeo's next-door neighbor, a larger-than-life retired opera singer, Amedeo finds a signed Modigliani drawing. . . . Amedeo is primed to uncover the history behind the drawing—a dark provenance that links the retired opera singer, the Vanderwaals and the Nazi occupation of Amsterdam." Publ Wkly

A **proud** taste for scarlet and miniver. Atheneum Pubs. 1973 201p il $18.95; pa $5.99

Grades: 5 6 7 8   **Fic**

1. Queens

ISBN 0-689-30111-1; 0-689-84624-X pa

This is an historical novel about the 12th century queen, Eleanor of Aquitaine, wife of kings of France and England and mother of King Richard the Lion Hearted and King John. Impatiently awaiting the arrival of her second husband, King Henry II, in heaven, she recalls her life with the aid of some contemporaries

The author "has succeeded in making history amusing as well as interesting. . . . The characterization is superb. . . . The black-and-white drawings are skillfully as well as appropriately modeled upon medieval manuscript illuminations and add their share of joy to the book." Horn Book

Up from Jericho Tel. Atheneum Pubs. 1986 178p hardcover o.p. pa $4.99

Grades: 5 6 7 8   **Fic**

1. Mystery fiction 2. Actors -- Fiction

ISBN 0-689-31194-X; 0-689-82332-0 pa

LC 85-20061

"Konigsburg always provides fresh ideas, tart wit and humor, and memorable characters. As for style, she is a natural and gifted storyteller. . . . This is a lively, clever, and very funny book." Bull Cent Child Books

"Jeanmarie and Malcolm are both unpopular, both bossy, both latchkey children; both live in a trailer park, and both want to be famous. Jeanmarie knows that she will be a famous actress and that Malcolm will one day be a famous scientist. These two friends embark on a series of adventures encouraged by the spirit of the long dead actress, Tallulah. Yes, presumbably 'the' Tallulah! Tallulah, as a ghost, has the ability to make them invisible, and in that state the kids are sent to find the missing Regina Stone." Voice Youth Advocates

★ The **view** from Saturday. Atheneum Bks. for Young Readers 1996 163p $16.95; pa $5.99

Grades: 4 5 6 7   **Fic**

1. School stories 2. Friendship -- Fiction 3. People with physical disabilities -- Fiction

ISBN 0-689-80993-X; 0-689-81721-5 pa

LC 95-52624

Awarded the Newbery Medal, 1997

Four students, with their own individual stories, develop a special bond and attract the attention of their teacher, a paraplegic, who choses them to represent their sixth-grade class in the Academic Bowl competition

"Glowing with humor and dusted with magic. . . . Wrought with deep compassion and a keen sense of balance." Publ Wkly

Koppe, Susanne

The **Nutcracker**; [by] E. T. A. Hoffmann; illustrated by Lisbeth Zwerger; retold by Susanne Koppe; translated from the German by Anthea Bell; North-South Books 2004 un il $15.95; lib bdg $16.50

Grades: 3 4 5   **Fic**
  1. Fairy tales 2. Christmas -- Fiction
  ISBN 0-7358-1733-2; 0-7358-1734-0 lib bdg

In this retelling of the original 1816 German story, Godfather Drosselmeier gives young Marie a nutcracker for Christmas, and she finds herself in a magical realm where she saves a boy from an evil curse

"This version features somewhat surreal, almost theatrically presented tableaux, delicately and darkly rendered in pen and ink and watercolor. . . . Koppe's retelling is . . . accessible and detailed." SLJ

Korman, Gordon

Framed. Scholastic Press 2011 234p $16.99

Grades: 3 4 5 6   **Fic**
  1. School stories 2. Adventure fiction 3. Theft -- Fiction 4. Friendship -- Fiction
  ISBN 978-0-545-17849-5; 0-545-17849-5
                                                   LC 2010002583

Sequel to: Zoobreak (2009)

Griffin Bing is in big trouble when a Super Bowl ring disappears from his middle school's display case, replaced by Griffin's retainer, and the more he and his friends investigate, the worse his situation becomes.

"This mystery will draw readers in with its quickly developing plot that combines unconventional characters and situations with believable dialogue and plot twists." SLJ

Masterminds; Gordon Korman. Balzer + Bray 2015 336 p. (hardback) $16.99

Grades: 4 5 6   **Fic**
  1. Criminals -- Fiction 2. Cloning -- Fiction 3. Experiments -- Fiction
  ISBN 0062299964; 9780062299963
                                                   LC 2014026839

In this book by Gordon Korman, "when 13-year-old Eli Frieden attempts to bike past the town limits for the first time, he is struck with paralyzing nausea and pain that makes him wonder if Serenity is less of a paradise and more of a prison." He and his friends "decide to investigate. They find that Serenity, which holds honesty and integrity above all else, is built on a lie." (Kirkus Reviews)

"Tiny Serenity, New Mexico, is idyllic as it gets—everyone has a job and a home, the kids are well behaved, and the genial community spirit is intoxicating. Sure, it's boring, and it's suspicious that a town of 185 people has its own helicopter-equipped security force, but 13-year-old Eli is content... The compelling, twisty mystery has a truly gratifying payoff, and the emotional depth of the characters, not to mention the steadily building pace, will keep readers en-

gaged to the final page, which happily lays the groundwork for a sequel. " Booklist

No more dead dogs. Hyperion Bks. for Children 2000 180p $15.99; pa $5.99

Grades: 5 6 7 8   **Fic**
  1. School stories 2. Theater -- Fiction
  ISBN 0-7868-0531-5; 0-7868-1601-5 pa
                                                   LC 00-24313

"Humor abounds here, but underlying is the true angst of the middle school student." Voice Youth Advocates

"Truthful Wallace gives a thumbs-down to a book much to the chagrin of his English teacher, who sentences him to help with a stage version of the book but is unaware that Wallace's plot-improvement suggestions will wind up changing the entire production." (Publisher's note)

Swindle. Scholastic Press 2008 252p (Swindle)

Grades: 4 5 6   **Fic**
  1. Baseball cards -- Fiction 2. Swindlers and swindling -- Fiction
  ISBN 0-439-90344-0; 0-439-90345-9 pa; 978-0-439-90344-8; 978-0-439-90345-5 pa
                                                   LC 2007-17225

After unscrupulous collector S. Wendell Palomino cons him out of a valuable baseball card, sixth-grader Griffin Bing puts together a band of misfits to break into Palomino's store and steal the card back, planning to use the money to finance his father's failing invention, the SmartPick fruit picker. "Grades four to six." (Bull Cent Child Books)

"The plot is the main attraction, and its clever intricacies—silly, deceptively predictable, and seasoned with the occasional unexpected twist—do not disappoint." Booklist

Zoobreak. Scholastic Press 2009 230p $16.99; pa $6.99

Grades: 3 4 5 6   **Fic**
  1. Adventure fiction 2. Zoos -- Fiction 3. Theft -- Fiction 4. Long Island (N.Y.) -- Fiction 5. Lost and found possessions -- Fiction
  ISBN 978-0-545-12499-7; 0-545-12499-9; 978-0-545-12500-0 pa; 0-545-12500-6 pa
                                                   LC 2009015456

Sequel to: Swindle (2008)

After a class trip to a floating zoo where animals are mistreated and Savannah's missing pet monkey is found in a cage, Long Island sixth-grader Griffin Bing and his band of misfits plan a rescue.

"Both children and adults will find the story fast moving and enjoyable. The often-unpredictable plot is interesting, full of humor, and good fun." Voice Youth Advocates

Kornblatt, Marc

Izzy's place. Margaret K. McElderry Bks. 2003 118p $16.95

Grades: 4 5 6   **Fic**
  1. Death -- Fiction
  ISBN 0-689-84639-8
                                                   LC 2002-6185

While spending the summer at his grandmother's Indiana home, ten-year-old Henry Stone gets help from a new friend in coping with the recent death of his grandfather and the possibility of his parents getting divorced

"In straightforward language, Kornblatt writes a realistic, affecting account of the challenges of coming to terms with grief and family difficulties and the process of acceptance and healing." Booklist

Krensky, Stephen

Dangerous crossing; the revolutionary voyage of John Quincy Adams. by Stephen Krensky; illustrated by Greg Harlin. Dutton Children's Books 2005 un il $16.99
Grades: 2 3 4   **Fic**
1. Presidents 2. Vice-presidents 3. Senators 4. Members of Congress 5. Secretaries of state 6. Voyages and travels -- Fiction 7. United States -- History -- 1775-1783, Revolution -- Fiction
ISBN 0-525-46966-4
                   LC 2003-40852
In 1778, ten-year-old Johnny Adams and his father make a dangerous midwinter voyage from Massachusetts to Paris in hopes of gaining support for the colonies during the American Revolution

"Harlin's richly atmospheric paintings dramatize scene after scene with subtle hues and lighting effects. . . . The story offers a stirring account of life aboard ship, spiced with details from the voyage. An appended author's note comments on the story's source and the illustrious careers of the two Adamses." Booklist

Krieg, Jim

★ **Griff** Carver, hallway patrol. Razorbill 2010 224p $15.99
Grades: 4 5 6 7   **Fic**
1. School stories 2. Counterfeits and counterfeiting -- Fiction
ISBN 978-1-59514-276-4; 1-59514-276-2
                   LC 2009-32553
Legendary Griff Carver joins the Rampart Middle School Hallway Patrol and, with the help of his friend Tommy, Griff solves the case of counterfeit hall passes.

"With comically over-the-top cop lingo . . . Griff and Tommy tell their stories through incident reports and interviews, adding drama and humor to the most mundane aspects of school. . . . Krieg will keep readers chuckling through the hilarious but action-packed showdown." Publ Wkly

Krishnaswami, Uma

The **Girl** of the Wish Garden; A Thumbelina Story. Pgw 2013 32 p. (hardcover) $17.95
Grades: K 1 2   **Fic**
1. Fairy tales 2. Picture books for children
ISBN 155498324X; 9781554983247
In this picture book, the "thumb-size Lina begins her journey when she is captured by a giant frog and then the story loosely follows the path of the original [Hans Christian Andersen] tale. She is swept along at the mercy of the winds and follows the tunes of the birds, and each new encounter is foreshadowed by her sung cries for help." (School Library Journal)

★ The **grand** plan to fix everything; [illustrations by Abigail Halpin] Atheneum Books for Young Readers 2011 224p il $16.99
Grades: 4 5 6 7   **Fic**
1. India -- Fiction 2. Actors -- Fiction 3. Moving -- Fiction 4. Friendship -- Fiction 5. East Indian Americans -- Fiction
ISBN 978-1-4169-9589-0; 1-4169-9589-7
                LC 2010035145
Eleven-year-old Dini loves movies, and so when she learns that her family is moving to India for two years, her devastation over leaving her best friend in Maryland is tempered by the possibility of meeting her favorite actress, Dolly Singh.

"An out-of-the-ordinary setting, a distinctive middle-grade character with an unusual passion, and the pace of a lively Bollywood 'fillum' make this novel a delight." Publ Wkly

Krull, Kathleen

Fartiste; [by] Kathleen Krull and Paul Brewer; illustrated by Boris Kulikov. Simon & Schuster Books for Young Readers 2008 un il $16.99
Grades: 3 4 5   **Fic**
1. Entertainers 2. Stories in rhyme 3. Entertainers -- Fiction 4. Paris (France) -- Fiction
ISBN 978-1-4169-2828-7; 1-4169-2828-6
                LC 2007-37526
In nineteenth-century France, Joseph Pujol, a little boy who can control his farts, grows up to become Le Petomaine, making audiences laugh at the Moulin Rouge in Paris with his animal noises, songs, and other sounds. Includes facts about Joseph Pujol and life in turn-of-the-century Paris.

"Written in well-rhymed couplets, this gleefully tasteless tale reads easily. Kulikov's illustrations allude to the age of vaudevillian stage performance, painted playbills, and fire-hazard footlights that bronzed everything nearest them in golden warmth." SLJ

Krumgold, Joseph

Onion John; illustrated by Symeon Shimin. Crowell 1959 248p il lib bdg $15.89; pa $5.95
Grades: 5 6 7 8   **Fic**
1. Friendship -- Fiction
ISBN 0-690-04698-7 lib bdg; 0-06-440144-8 pa
Awarded the Newbery Medal, 1960
"The writing has dignity and strength. There is conflict, drama, and excellent character portrayal." SLJ

The story "of Andy Rusch, twelve, and European-born Onion John, the town's odd-jobs man and vegetable peddler who lives in a stone hut and frequents the dump. Andy . . . tells of their . . . friendship and of how he and his father, as well as Onion John, are affected when the Rotary Club, at his father's instigation, attempts to transform Onion John's way of life." Booklist

Kuhlman, Evan

The **last** invisible boy; written by Evan Kuhlman; illustrated by J. P. Coovert. Atheneum Books for Young Readers 2008 233p il $16.99; pa $5.99
Grades: 4 5 6 7   **Fic**
1. School stories 2. Ohio -- Fiction 3. Bereavement -- Fiction 4. Family life -- Fiction 5. Father-son relationship -- Fiction
ISBN 978-1-4169-5797-3; 1-4169-5797-9; 978-1-4169-6089-8 pa; 1-4169-6089-9 pa
                LC 2007-40258
In the wake of his father's sudden death, twelve-year-old Finn feels he is becoming invisible as his hair and skin become whiter by the day, and so he writes and illustrates a

book to try to understand what is happening and to hold on to himself and his father

"Vivid details . . . add depth to the characterizations and grow in meaning as the story progresses. . . . Finn's distinct narrative voice, and the sweet precision with which the story unfolds, give this title a touching resonance." Booklist

Kuijer, Guus
The **book** of everything; a novel. translated by John Nieuwenhuizen. Arthur A. Levine Books 2006 101p hardcover o.p. $16.99
Grades: 5 6 7 8   **Fic**
1. Family life -- Fiction 2. Netherlands -- Fiction 3. Christian life -- Fiction
ISBN 0-439-74918-2; 0-439-74919-0 pa
LC 2005-18717
Nine-year-old Thomas receives encouragement from many sources, including candid talks with Jesus, to help him tolerate the strict family life dictated by his deeply-religious father.

"Set in Amsterdam in 1951, this slender Dutch novel is filled with quirky characters, frightening family confrontations, and laugh-out-loud moments. Dark humor and a wry, ironic tone . . . give the story a sharp edge." Booklist

Kurtz, Chris
The **adventures** of a South Pole pig; a novel of snow and courage. Chris Kurtz; illustrations by Jennifer Black Reinhardt. Harcourt Children's Books, Houghton Mifflin Harcourt 2013 288 p. $16.99
Grades: 4 5 6 7   **Fic**
1. Adventure fiction 2. Dogs -- Fiction 3. Pigs -- Fiction 4. Sled dogs -- Fiction 5. Antarctica -- Fiction
ISBN 0547634552; 9780547634555
LC 2012027226
In this children's story, by Chris Kurtz, illustrated by Jennifer Black Reinhardt, "the day Flora spots a team of sled dogs is the day she sets her heart on becoming a sled pig. Before she knows it, she's on board a ship to Antarctica for the most exhilarating--and dangerous--adventure of her life." (Publisher's note)

The **pup** who cried wolf; illustrations by Guy Francis. Bloomsbury 2010 132p il (Animal tales) $15.99; pa $5.99
Grades: 2 3 4   **Fic**
1. Dogs -- Fiction 2. Wolves -- Fiction
ISBN 978-1-59990-497-9; 1-59990-497-7; 978-1-59990-492-4 pa; 1-59990-492-6 pa
Lobo, a Chihuahua from New York City who feels he is truly a wolf in an undersized body, goes to Yellowstone National Park with his mistress and dreams of running wild with his wolf brothers.

"Children will love this humorous story and empathize with feisty, misguided Lobo. . . . A few black-and-white illustrations, some full page, are scattered throughout. This story will appeal to beginning chapter book and reluctant readers alike." SLJ

Kurtz, Jane
The **storyteller's** beads. Harcourt Brace & Co. 1998 154p $15
Grades: 5 6 7 8   **Fic**
1. Blind -- Fiction 2. Ethiopia -- Fiction 3. Friendship

-- Fiction 4. Prejudices -- Fiction
ISBN 0-15-201074-2
LC 97-42312
During the political strife and famine of the 1980's, two Ethiopian girls, one Christian and the other Jewish and blind, struggle to overcome many difficulties, including their prejudices about each other, as they make the dangerous journey out of Ethiopia

"The novel presents an involving portrait of Ethiopian culture through the eyes of two well-defined characters." Horn Book Guide

Kushner, Ellen
The **golden** dreydl; [by] Ellen Kushner; illustrations by Ilene Winn-Lederer. Charlesbridge 2007 126p il $15.95
Grades: 3 4 5   **Fic**
1. Jews -- Fiction 2. Magic -- Fiction 3. Hanukkah -- Fiction
ISBN 978-1-58089-135-6
LC 2006021257
After receiving a magic dreydl at Aunt Leah's Chanukah party, Sara is catapulted into an alternate world of demons, fools, sorcerers, and sages

"The chatty storytelling is fast, furious, and sometimes funny, . . . and scattered throughout are delicate black-and-white illustrations that capture the magical realism." Booklist

L'Engle, Madeleine
Meet the Austins. Farrar, Straus & Giroux 1997 216p hardcover o.p. pa $6.99
Grades: 5 6 7 8   **Fic**
1. Orphans -- Fiction 2. Family life -- Fiction
ISBN 0-374-34929-0; 0-312-37931-5 pa
LC 96-27655
A revised edition of the title first published 1960 by Vanguard Press
ALA YALSA Margaret A. Edwards Award (1998)
A "story of the family of a country doctor, told by the twelve-year-old daughter, during a year in which a spoiled young orphan, Maggy, comes to live with them. . . . [This is an] account of the family's adjustment to Maggy and hers to them." Horn Book
Other titles about the Austins are:
The moon by night (1963)
A ring of endless light (1980)
Troubling a star (1994)

A **swiftly** tilting planet. Farrar, Straus & Giroux 1978 278p $18; pa $6.99
Grades: 5 6 7 8 9 10   **Fic**
1. Fantasy fiction
ISBN 978-0-374-37362-7; 0-374-37362-0; 978-0-312-36856-2 pa; 0-312-36856-9 pa
LC 78-9648
Sequel to: A wind in the door (1973)
ALA YALSA Margaret A. Edwards Award (1998)
The youngest of the Murry children must travel through time and space in a battle against an evil dictator who would destroy the entire universe

A **wind** in the door. Farrar, Straus & Giroux 1973 211p $17.99; pa $6.99

Grades: 5 6 7 8 9 10 **Fic**
1. Fantasy fiction
ISBN 0-374-38443-6; 0-312-36854-2 pa
LC 73-751176
Sequel to: A wrinkle in time (1962)

This episode about the Murrys begins "when Charles Wallace has difficulty adjusting to school. Meg tries to straighten things out, but her help only leads to another adventure in space involving alien creatures." Roman. Sequences

Followed by: A swiftly tilting planet (1978)

★ A **wrinkle** in time. Farrar, Straus & Giroux 1962 211p $17; pa $7.99
Grades: 5 6 7 8 9 10 **Fic**
1. Fantasy fiction
ISBN 0-374-38613-7; 0-312-36754-6 pa
ALA YALSA Margaret A. Edwards Award (1998)
Awarded The Newbery Medal, 1963
This book "makes unusual demands on the imagination and consequently gives great rewards." Horn Book
Other titles in this series are:
A swiftly tilting planet (1978)
A wind in the door (1973)

La Fevers, R. L.
Theodosia and the Serpents of Chaos; illustrated by Yoko Tanaka. Houghton Mifflin 2007 343p il $16; pa $6.99
Grades: 4 5 6 7 **Fic**
1. Adventure fiction 2. Egypt -- Fiction 3. Magic -- Fiction 4. Museums -- Fiction 5. London (England) -- Fiction
ISBN 978-0-618-75638-4; 0-618-75638-8; 978-0-618-99976-7 pa; 0-618-99976-0 pa
LC 2006-34284
Set in 1906 London and Cairo, this mystery adventure introduces an intrepid heroine—Theodosia Throckmorton, who is thrust into the heart of a mystery when she learns an ancient Egyptian amulet carries a curse that threatens to crumble the British Empire

"It's the delicious, precise, and atmospheric details (nicely extended in Tanaka's few, stylized illustrations) that will capture and hold readers." Booklist

Other titles about Theodosia are:
Theodosia and the Staff of Osiris (2008)
Theodosia and the Eyes of Horus (2010)
Theodosia and the last Pharoah (2011)

The **unicorn's** tale; by R.L. LaFevers; illustrated by Kelly Murphy. Houghton Mifflin Books for Children 2011 153p il (Nathaniel Fludd, Beastologist) $14.99
Grades: 3 4 5 **Fic**
1. Adventure fiction 2. Aunts -- Fiction 3. France -- Fiction 4. Unicorns -- Fiction 5. Mythical animals -- Fiction
ISBN 978-0-547-48277-4; 0-547-48277-9
LC 2010025118
Beastologist-in-training Nathaniel Fludd and his Aunt Phil nurse a mysteriously ill unicorn, try to stop Obediah from taking the unicorn's horn, and finally get a solid lead on the whereabouts of Nathaniel's parents.

La Valley, Josanne
The **Vine** basket; by Josanne La Valley. Clarion Books 2013 252 p. (hardcover) $16.99
Grades: 4 5 6 7 8 **Fic**
1. China -- Fiction 2. Farm life -- Fiction 3. Basket making -- Fiction 4. Ethnic relations -- Fiction 5. Farm life -- China -- Fiction 6. Fathers and daughters -- Fiction 7. Uighur (Turkic people) -- Fiction
ISBN 0547848013; 9780547848013
LC 2012021007
Asian/Pacific American Awards for Literature: Children's Literature Honor (2014)

In this novel, by Josanne La Valley, "things aren't looking good for fourteen-year-old Mehrigul. She yearns to be in school, but she's needed on the family farm. . . . Her only hope is an American woman who buys one of her decorative vine baskets for a staggering sum and says she will return in three weeks for more. Mehrigul must brave terrible storms, torn-up hands from working the fields, and her father's scorn to get the baskets done." (Publisher's note)

"The vivid and authentic sense of place, custom, and politics serves as an effective vehicle for the skillfully characterized, emotionally charged story. . . . The realistic and satisfying resolution will resonate with readers . . . An absorbing read and an excellent choice for expanding global understanding." SLJ

Lacey, Josh
Island of Thieves; Josh Lacey. Houghton Mifflin 2012 228 p.
Grades: 4 5 6 7 8 **Fic**
1. Peru -- Fiction 2. Adventure fiction 3. Uncles -- Fiction 4. Pirates -- Fiction 5. Buried treasure -- Fiction 6. Islands -- Fiction 7. Mystery and detective stories 8. Adventure and adventurers -- Fiction
ISBN 0547763271; 9780547763279
LC 2011033893
In this children's novel, a boy takes part in "swashbuckling adventures in faraway places, freed from the strictures of parents, school, siblings and caregivers. . . . Tom nearly ruins his parents' vacation by accidentally burning down the shed in his backyard. . . . Harvey welcomes Tom . . . but as soon as Tom's parents leave, he starts packing for Peru. . . . When he tells Tom it's because he has an opportunity to hunt for pirate treasure, Tom blackmails his uncle into taking him along." (Kirkus)

LaFaye, A.
Water steps. Milkweed Editions 2009 175p $16.95; pa $6.95
Grades: 4 5 6 7 **Fic**
1. Water -- Fiction 2. Phobias -- Fiction 3. Irish Americans -- Fiction
ISBN 978-1-57131-687-5; 1-57131-687-6; 978-1-57131-686-8 pa; 1-57131-686-8 pa
LC 2008011684
Eleven-year-old Kyna, terrified of water since her family drowned in a storm that nearly took her life as well, works to overcome her phobia when her adoptive parents, Irish immigrants with a mysterious past, rent a cabin on Lake Champlain for the summer.

"The language is almost poetic with its use of sensory detail, alliteration, and precise word choices. A satisfying

story of overcoming one's fears and discovering secrets."
SLJ

Worth. Simon & Schuster Books for Young Readers
2004 144p $15.95; pa $5.99

Grades: 5 6 7 8   **Fic**
1. Orphans -- Fiction 2. Nebraska -- Fiction 3. Frontier
and pioneer life -- Fiction
ISBN 0-689-85730-6; 1-4169-1624-5 pa
       LC 2003-8101
After breaking his leg, eleven-year-old Nate feels useless
because he cannot work on the family farm in nineteenth-
century Nebraska, so when his father brings home an orphan
boy to help with the chores, Nate feels even worse.
"This short tale has a quietly epic sweep." Horn
Book Guide

LaFleur, Suzanne
     Eight keys; by Suzanne LaFleur. Wendy Lamb Books
2011 216p $16.99; lib bdg $19.99

Grades: 3 4 5 6   **Fic**
1. School stories 2. Orphans -- Fiction 3. Friendship
-- Fiction 4. Family life -- Fiction
ISBN 978-0-385-74030-2; 0-385-74030-1; 978-0-385-
90833-7 lib bdg; 978-0-375-89905-8 e-book
       LC 2010040137
When twelve-year-old Elise, orphaned since age nine,
becomes disheartened by middle school, with its bullies,
changing relationships, and higher expectations, keys to
long-locked rooms and messages from her late father help
her cope.
LaFleur "writes with uncommon sensitivity to the
fraught period between childhood and the teenage years,
when friendships balance on a razor's edge and nothing feels
certain. The heart of the story lies in the layered relationships and characters that give the novel its powerful sense of
realism." Publ Wkly

    ★ **Listening** for Lucca; by Suzanne LaFleur. Wendy
Lamb Books 2013 240 p. (trade) $16.99

Grades: 4 5 6 7   **Fic**
1. Diaries -- Fiction 2. Mute persons -- Fiction 3.
Supernatural -- Fiction 4. Maine -- Fiction 5. Visions
-- Fiction 6. Selective mutism -- Fiction 7. Moving,
Household -- Fiction 8. Brothers and sisters -- Fiction
9. Family life -- Maine -- Fiction 10. Maine -- History
-- 20th century -- Fiction
ISBN 0385742991; 9780307980304; 9780307980311;
9780375990885; 9780385742993
       LC 2012030911
In this novel by Suzanne LaFleur Sienna's "two-year-
old brother Lucca stopped talking. Now Mom and Dad are
moving the family from Brooklyn to Maine hoping that it
will mean a whole new start for Lucca and Siena. When Siena writes in her diary with an old pen she found . . . the pen
writes its own story, of Sarah and Joshua, a brother and sister who lived in the same house during World War II. Siena
senses that Sarah and Joshua's story might contain the key to
unlocking Lucca's voice." (Publisher's note)

    ★ **Love,** Aubrey. Wendy Lamb Books 2009 262p
$15.99; lib bdg $18.99

Grades: 5 6 7 8   **Fic**
1. School stories 2. Letters -- Fiction 3. Vermont

-- Fiction 4. Friendship -- Fiction 5. Bereavement
-- Fiction 6. Grandmothers -- Fiction 7. Abandoned
children -- Fiction 8. Depression (Psychology) -- Fiction
ISBN 978-0-385-73774-6; 0-385-73774-2; 978-0-385-
90686-9 lib bdg; 0-385-90686-2 lib bdg
       LC 2008-31742
While living with her Gram in Vermont, eleven-year-old
Aubrey writes letters as a way of dealing with losing her
father and sister in a car accident, and then being abandoned
by her grief-stricken mother.
Aubrey's "detailed progression from denial to acceptance makes her both brave and credible in this honest and
realistic portrayal of grief." Kirkus

Lai, Thanhha
    ★ **Inside** out and back again. Harper 2011 262p
$15.99

Grades: 4 5 6 7   **Fic**
1. Novels in verse 2. Alabama -- Fiction 3. Vietnam
-- Fiction 4. Immigrants -- Fiction 5. Vietnamese
Americans -- Fiction
ISBN 978-0-06-196278-3; 0-06-196278-3
       LC 2010007855
"Based on Lai's personal experience, this first novel captures a child-refugee's struggle with rare honesty. Written in
accessible, short free-verse poems." Booklist
"For all the ten years of her life, Hà has only known Saigon: the thrills of its markets, the joy of its traditions, and the
warmth of her friends close by. But now the Vietnam War
has reached her home. Hà and her family are forced to flee
as Saigon falls, and they board a ship headed toward hope.
In America, Hà discovers the foreign world of Alabama: the
coldness of its strangers, the dullness of its food . . . and the
strength of her very own family." (Publisher's note)

    ★ **Listen,** Slowly; Thanhha Lai. Harpercollins Child-
rens Books 2015 272 p. illustration $16.99

Grades: 4 5 6 7 8   **Fic**
1. Culture 2. Family -- Fiction 3. Vietnam -- Fiction
4. Families -- Fiction 5. Grandmothers -- Fiction 6.
Vietnam War, 1961-1975 -- Missing in action -- Fiction
ISBN 0062229184; 9780062229182
"A California girl born and raised, Mai . . . has to travel
to Vietnam with her grandmother, who is going back to find
out what really happened to her husband during the Vietnam
War. Mai's parents think this trip will be a great opportunity for their out-of-touch daughter to learn more about her
culture. But to Mai, those are their roots, not her own. To
survive her trip, Mai must find a balance between her two
completely different worlds." (Publisher's note)
"Gracefully written and enriched by apposite figures of
speech, Listen, Slowly is a superb, sometimes humorous,
always thought-provoking coming-of-age story." Booklist

Lairamore, Dawn
    Ivy and the meanstalk. Holiday House 2011 227p
$16.95

Grades: 4 5 6 7   **Fic**
1. Fairy tales 2. Giants -- Fiction 3. Dragons -- Fiction
4. Princesses -- Fiction
ISBN 978-0-8234-2392-7; 0-8234-2392-1
       LC 2010048627
Sequel to: Ivy's ever after (2010)

Fourteen-year-old Princess Ivy wants nothing more than to have a little fun in the company of her dragon friend, Elridge, but unless she can recover the magical harp snatched by a thieving youth named Jack long ago, her entire kingdom will suffer an unspeakable fate.

This is "delightful and humorous. . . . Lairamore's well-developed characters are excellent riffs on fairy-tale traditions. . . . Various settings are depicted in rich detail while never detracting from the narrative. The plot is filled with action-packed scenes." SLJ

★ Ivy's ever after. Holiday House 2010 311p $16.95
Grades: 4 5 6 7 **Fic**
1. Fairy tales 2. Dragons -- Fiction 3. Princesses -- Fiction
ISBN 978-0-8234-2261-6; 0-8234-2261-5
LC 2009-43288
Fourteen-year-old Ivy, a most unroyal princess, befriends Elridge, the dragon sent to keep her in a tower, and together they set out on a perilous quest to find Ivy's fairy godmother, who may be able to save both from their dire fates.

"Ivy is an engaging alternative to the standard damsel-in-distress figure, and with a lushly vivid setting, witty dialogue, and lots of adventure, this well-plotted first novel will appeal to fans of Vivian Vande Velde's A Hidden Magic (1985) and A Well-Timed Enchantment (1990)." Booklist

Followed by: Ivy and the meanstalk (2011)

Landy, Derek
★ Skulduggery Pleasant. HarperCollinsPublishers 2007 392p $17.99; lib bdg $18.89; pa $7.99
Grades: 4 5 6 7 **Fic**
1. Fantasy fiction 2. Magic -- Fiction
ISBN 978-0-06-123115-5; 0-06-123115-0; 978-0-06-123116-2 lib bdg; 0-06-123116-9 lib bdg; 978-0-06-123117-9 pa; 0-06-123117-7 pa
LC 2006-29403
When twelve-year-old Stephanie inherits her weird uncle's estate, she must join forces with Skulduggery Pleasant, a skeleton mage, to save the world from the Faceless Ones.

This "is a rich fantasy that is as engaging in its creative protagonists and villains as it is in the lightning-paced plot and sharp humor." Bulletin Cent Child Books

Other titles in this series are:
Playing with fire (2008)
The faceless ones (2009)

Lane, Andrew
Black ice; Andrew Lane. Farrar Straus Giroux 2013 288 p. (Sherlock Holmes. The legend begins) (hardcover) $17.99
Grades: 5 6 7 8 **Fic**
1. Mystery fiction 2. Holmes, Sherlock (Fictional character) -- Fiction 3. Murder -- Fiction 4. Mystery and detective stories 5. Moscow (Russia) -- History -- 19th century -- Fiction 6. Russia -- History -- Alexander II, 1855-1881 -- Fiction 7. Great Britain -- History -- Victoria, 1837-1901 -- Fiction
ISBN 0374387699; 9780374387693
LC 2012004996
This novel, by Andrew Lane, is the third book of the "Sherlock Holmes: The Legend Begins" series. "When Sherlock and Amyus Crowe, his American tutor, visit Sherlock's brother, Mycroft, in London, all they are expecting is

lunch and some polite conversation. What they find shocks both of them to the core: a locked room, a dead body, and Mycroft holding a knife. . . . Threatened with the gallows, Mycroft needs Sherlock to save him." (Publisher's note)

Rebel fire; Andrew Lane. Farrar Straus Giroux 2012 343 p. (Sherlock Holmes. The legend begins) $16.99
Grades: 5 6 7 8 **Fic**
1. Mystery fiction 2. Holmes, Sherlock (Fictional character) -- Fiction 3. Mystery and detective stories 4. Great Britain -- History -- Victoria, 1837-1901 -- Fiction
ISBN 0374387680; 9780374387686
LC 2011000124
This novel, by Andrew Lane, is part of the "Sherlock Holmes: The Legend Begins" series. "Fourteen-year-old Sherlock Holmes knows that Amyus Crowe, his mysterious American tutor, has some dark secrets. But he didn't expect to find John Wilkes Booth, the notorious assassin, apparently alive and well in England--and Crowe somehow mixed up in it. . . . And so begins an adventure that will take Sherlock across the Atlantic, to the center of a deadly web." (Publisher's note)

Includes bibliographical references

Langton, Jane
The fledgling. Harper & Row 1980 182p il lib bdg $15.89; pa $5.95
Grades: 5 6 7 8 **Fic**
1. Fantasy fiction 2. Geese -- Fiction
ISBN 0-06-023679-5 lib bdg; 0-06-440121-9 pa
LC 79-2008
A Newbery Medal honor book, 1981

"The writing is alternately solemn and funny, elevated and colloquial. It is mythic, almost sacred, in passages involving Georgie and the goose; it is satiric, almost irreverent, when it relates to Mr. Preek and Miss Prawn." Horn Book

Larson, Kirby
Dash; Kirby Larson. Scholastic Press 2014 256 p. (hardcover) $16.99
Grades: 4 5 6 7 **Fic**
1. Dogs -- Fiction 2. Japanese Americans -- Evacuation and relocation, 1942-1945 3. World War, 1939-1945 -- Fiction 4. Japanese American children -- Fiction 5. Puyallup Assembly Center (Puyallup, Wash.) -- Fiction
ISBN 0545416353; 9780545416351
LC 2013042525
"Although Mitsi Kashino and her family are swept up in the wave of anti-Japanese sentiment following the attack on Pearl Harbor, Mitsi never expects to lose her home--or her beloved dog, Dash. But, as World War II rages and people of Japanese descent are forced into incarceration camps, Mitsi is separated from Dash, her classmates, and life as she knows it." (Publisher's note)

"Spot-on dialogue, careful cultural details and the inclusion of specific historical characters such as artist Eddie Sato make this an educational read as well as a heartwarming one. An author's note adds further authenticity. This emotionally satisfying and thought-provoking book will have readers pulling for Mitsi and Dash." Kirkus

Duke; Kirby Larson. Scholastic Press 2013 240 p. (jacketed hardcover) $16.99

Grades: 4 5 6 7 **Fic**
1. World War, 1939-1945 -- United States 2. Dogs --
War use -- Fiction 3. German shepherd dog -- Fiction
4. Human-animal relationships -- Fiction
ISBN 054541637X; 9780545416375
LC 2012046636

In this World War II story by Kirby Larson, "when fifth-
grader Hobie Hanson's father leaves his fishing boat in Seattle to pilot a B-24 in Europe, he tells Hobie 'to step up and
do what needs to be done.' Whether it is buying war bonds,
collecting rubber or simply making due with less, Hobie
is giving all he can to the war effort. But when he begins
to feel the pressure to lend his beloved German shepherd,
Duke, to the Army, Hobie realizes he still has more to give."
(Kirkus Reviews)

Lucky dog; twelve tales of rescued dogs. [by Kirby
Larson ... et al.] Scholastic Press 2013 192 p. $15.99
Grades: 4 5 6 7 **Fic**
1. Short stories 2. Dogs -- Fiction 3. Dog rescue --
Fiction 4. Dog adoption -- Fiction
ISBN 0545554519; 9780545554510
LC 2013011309

This book is a collection of dog stories for children by
authors such as Kirby Larson, Tui T. Sutherland, and Ellen
Miles. "You'll meet Foxtrot, a feisty Pomeranian who can't
bear the thought of leaving her best friend. And Beatrice,
whose bark is definitely worse than her bite. And then there's
Pumpkin, one of the 101 Chihuahuas who turn life at the
center upside down." (Publisher's note)

"Troy, 'the new kid in town,' is comforted when he
adopts a new dog at the shelter; Tilly is afraid of dogs and
Buddy is happy at the shelter, but somehow the two bond.
Each short story by a different popular author is connected
through the Pawley Rescue Center, which places dogs with
their families. Some of the stories lack a strong emotional
core." Horn Book

Larson, M. A.
Pennyroyal Academy; M. A. Larson. G. P. Putnam's
Sons, an imprint of Penguin Group (USA) 2014 304 p.
maps (hardback) $16.99
Grades: 5 6 7 8 **Fic**
1. Schools 2. Princesses -- Fiction 3. Knights and
knighthood -- Fiction 4. Fantasy 5. Dragons -- Fiction
6. Schools -- Fiction 7. Witches -- Fiction 8. Military
education -- Fiction 9. Adventure and adventurers --
Fiction
ISBN 0399163247; 9780399163241
LC 2014014516

In this novel by M.A. Larson, "a girl from the forest arrives in a bustling kingdom with no name and no idea why
she is there, only to find herself at the center of a world at
war. She enlists at Pennyroyal Academy, where princesses
and knights are trained to battle the two great menaces of the
day: witches and dragons. As Evie learns what it truly means
to be a princess, she realizes surprising things about herself
and her family." (Publisher's note)

"Forget the notion of traditional princesses. At Pennyroyal Academy, princesses are trained to fight witches and
save kingdoms, and, yes, knights learn to slay dragons...the
focus and detailed character development is on the young
women, their hopes and dreams (sometimes dreadfully
scary), their real fears, and their disappointments in them-

selves, their friends, and the adults around them. Since the
book ends with some of the princesses and knights selected
to return for another school year, Larson has left the door
open for a welcome second year at Pennyroyal with Evie and
her friends." Booklist

Larwood, Kieran
Freaks; Kieran Larwood. Chicken House/Scholastic
2013 256 p. $16.99
Grades: 5 6 7 8 **Fic**
1. Mystery fiction 2. Circus performers -- Fiction
3. Freak shows -- Fiction 4. Mystery and detective
stories 5. Abnormalities, Human -- Fiction 6. London
(England) -- History -- 19th century -- Fiction 7. Great
Britain -- History -- Victoria, 1837-1901 -- Fiction
ISBN 0545474248; 9780545474245; 9780545474252
LC 2012002639

In this book, 10-year-old "Sheba, better known as the
Wolfgirl for her layer of fur and ability to sprout fangs and
claws, is an orphan who ends up as part of Plumpscuttle's
Peculiars, a freak show that also stars a teenage ninja, a
trash-talking monkey boy, a romance-writing strongman,
and a woman who talks to rats. This gang of unlikely heroes
gets caught up in a mystery involving missing street urchins,
steampunk monstrosities, and a fiendish set of villains."
(Publishers Weekly)

Lasky, Kathryn
The **escape**; Kathryn Lasky. Scholastic Press 2014 240
p. illustrations (Horses of the dawn) (hardcover) $16.99
Grades: 4 5 6 7 8 **Fic**
1. Horses -- Fiction 2. Mother-daughter relationship
-- Fiction 3. Responsibility -- Fiction 4. North America
-- History -- Fiction
ISBN 9780545397162; 0545397162
LC 2013037215

This book "reimagines the history of the reintroduc-
tion of horses to North America by Spanish conquistadors
through the eyes of the horses they brought with them. Es-
trella, a plucky foal unexpectedly born on board a Spanish
ship bound for the New World, is strong, brave, and wise beyond her years. She, along with three others, survives being
tossed overboard into shark-infested waters by swimming to
the Yucatan Peninsula. Thus begins her quest to find the land
of the sweet grass only she can smell." (Booklist)

"Lasky successfully fuses fantasy and fact as she gives
her equine characters credible emotional depth and under-
scores the tensions and disparity between Old and New
World sensibilities." Pub Wkly

Felix takes the stage; illustrated by Stephen Gilpin.
Scholastic Press 2010 142p il (The Deadlies) $15.99
Grades: 3 4 5 **Fic**
1. Moving -- Fiction 2. Spiders -- Fiction
ISBN 978-0-545-11681-7; 0-545-11681-3

Having been discovered, a family of poisonous but
friendly brown recluse spiders must flee their cozy home in
a symphony hall and go searching for a new place to live.

"Humor and action seamlessly blend as these arachnids
struggle for survival against the scary E-Men who threaten
them with extermination. Vivid characters, from the theatrical godspider Fat Cat to the pompous orb weaver Oliphant
Uxbridge, make up the clever supporting cast. Genuinely
funny dialogue helps move the brief chapters along, and Gil-

pin's lively black-and-white drawings provide an animated accompaniment." Kirkus

Hawksmaid; the untold story of Robin Hood and Maid Marian. Harper 2010 292p $16.99

Grades: 5 6 7 8   Fic

1. Falconry -- Fiction 2. Robin Hood (Legendary character) -- Fiction 3. Maid Marian (Legendary character) -- Fiction 4. Great Britain -- History -- 1154-1399, Plantagenets -- Fiction

ISBN 978-0-06-000071-4; 0-06-000071-6

In twelfth-century England, Matty grows up to be a master falconer, able to communicate with the devoted birds who later help her and Fynn, also known as Robin Hood, to foil Prince John's plot to steal the crown.

"Lasky nicely weaves details of 12th-century life into this suspenseful adventure whose fantasy ending may surprise but will certainly please readers." SLJ

Spiders on the case; illustrated by Stephen Gilpin. Scholastic Press 2011 171p il (The Deadlies) $15.99

Grades: 3 4 5   Fic

1. Mystery fiction 2. Spiders -- Fiction 3. Libraries -- Fiction 4. Boston (Mass.) -- Fiction 5. Books and reading -- Fiction 6. Boston Public Library -- Fiction

ISBN 978-0-545-11682-4; 0-545-11682-1

LC 2010047587

Buster, a walnut orb weaving spider, enlists the help of Jo Beth, one of a family of poisonous but friendly brown recluse spiders, to help stop humans who are stealing from the rare books room of the Boston Public Library, where the spiders live.

"Young readers will relate to the family drama and rivalry between Jo Bell and her siblings. There are moments of good humor. The spiders in the illustrations are full of expression, and the drawings help move the story along." SLJ

Latham, Irene

Leaving Gee's Bend. G.P. Putnam's Sons 2010 230p $16.99

Grades: 5 6 7 8   Fic

1. Quilts -- Fiction 2. Alabama -- Fiction 3. African Americans -- Fiction

ISBN 978-0-399-25179-5; 0-399-25179-0

LC 2009-08732

Ludelphia Bennett, a determined, ten-year-old African American girl in 1932 Gee's Bend, Alabama, leaves home in an effort to find medical help for her sick mother, and she recounts her ensuing adventures in a quilt she is making.

"Ludelphia's voice is authentic and memorable, and Latham captures the tension of her dangerous journey and the racism she encounters." Booklist

Law, Ingrid

★ **Savvy**. Dial Books for Young Readers 2008 342p $16.99

Grades: 4 5 6 7   Fic

1. Magic -- Fiction 2. Family life -- Fiction 3. Voyages and travels -- Fiction

ISBN 978-0-8037-3306-0; 0-8037-3306-2

LC 2007-39814

A Newbery Medal honor book, 2009

Boston Globe-Horn Book Award honor book: Fiction and Poetry (2008)

Recounts the adventures of Mississippi (Mibs) Beaumont, whose thirteenth birthday has revealed her "savvy"—a magical power unique to each member of her family—just as her father is injured in a terrible accident.

"Short chapters and cliffhangers keep the pace quick, while the mix of traditional language and vernacular helps the story feel both fresh and timeless. . . . [This is] a vibrant and cinematic novel that readers are going to love." Publ Wkly

Followed by: Scumble (2010)

★ **Scumble**. Dial Books for Young Readers 2010 400p il $16.99

Grades: 4 5 6 7   Fic

1. Magic -- Fiction 2. Wyoming -- Fiction 3. Ranch life -- Fiction

ISBN 978-0-8037-3307-7; 0-8037-3307-0

LC 2010-02444

Mibs's cousin Ledge is disappointed to discover that his "savvy" —the magical power unique to each member of their family—is to make things fall apart, which endangers his uncle Autry's ranch and reveals the family secret to future reporter Sarah.

This provides a "satisfying plot, delightful characters, alliterative language, and rich imagery." Booklist

Lawlor, Laurie

He will go fearless; [by] Laurie Lawlor. Simon & Schuster Books for Young Readers 2006 210p $15.95

Grades: 5 6 7 8   Fic

1. Father-son relationship -- Fiction 2. Overland journeys to the Pacific -- Fiction 3. United States -- History -- 1865-1898 -- Fiction

ISBN 0-689-86579-1

LC 2005-06129

With the Civil War ended and Reconstruction begun, fifteen-year-old Billy resolves to make the dangerous and challenging journey West in search of real fortune – his true father.

"Danger, adventure, and survival combine to make this a richly detailed story." SLJ

The **school** at Crooked Creek; illustrated by Ronald Himler. Holiday House 2004 83p il map $15.95

Grades: 3 4 5   Fic

1. School stories 2. Indiana -- Fiction 3. Frontier and pioneer life -- Fiction

ISBN 0-8234-1812-X

LC 2003-56759

Living on the nineteenth-century Indiana frontier with his parents and irritable older sister Louise, six-year-old Beansie dreads his first day of school, but his resilience surprises even his sister.

"The book is rich with colloquial language, superstitions, and information about the lifestyle of this pioneer family. Nicely done shaded, pencil drawings help set the tone." SLJ

Lawrence, Caroline

★ **P.K.** Pinkerton and the petrified man; Caroline Lawrence. G.P. Putnam's Sons 2013 320 p. (hardcover) $16.99

Grades: 4 5 6 7 8   Fic

1. Mystery fiction 2. Western stories 3. Orphans -- Fiction 4. Disguise -- Fiction 5. Westerns 6. Mystery and detective stories 7. Racially mixed people -- Fiction

8. Nevada -- History -- 19th century -- Fiction
ISBN 0399256342; 9780399256349

LC 2012026737

This western mystery adventure novel, by Caroline Lawrence, is "starring Master-of-Disguise, P.K. Pinkerton. After vanquishing three notorious Desperados, twelve-year-old P.K. Pinkerton opens a private-eye business in Virginia City. P.K.'s skills are quickly put to the test: When a maid named Martha witnesses a murder, she hires the young detective to track the killer before he finds her too." (Publisher's note)

★ P.K. Pinkerton and the pistol-packing widows; Caroline Lawrence. G.P. Putnam's Sons, an imprint of Penguin Group (USA) Inc. 2014 304 p. maps (hardcover) $16.99
Grades: 4 5 6 7 8   Fic
1. Mystery fiction 2. Nevada -- Fiction 3. Disguise -- Fiction 4. Detectives -- Fiction 5. Orphans -- Fiction 6. Mystery and detective stories 7. Racially mixed people -- Fiction 8. Nevada -- History -- 19th century -- Fiction
ISBN 0399256350; 9780399256356

LC 2013000211

In this book, by Caroline Lawrence, "P.K. Pinkerton's detective agency is thriving in Virginia City--until the evening P.K. is abruptly stuffed into a turnip sack and tossed into the back of a wagon! Surfacing in Chinatown, P.K. is forced into taking a job trailing the abductor's fiancé in Carson City. Danger lurks at every turn. P.K. must battle quicksand, escape the despicable former Deputy Marshall, Jack Williams, and save Poker Face Jace from certain death." (Publisher's note)

"In this third rousing series entry, P.K. is going to Carson City to investigate Poker Face Jace, who Opal Blossom believes is her two-timing fianci. P.K. must navigate twists and turns in a case involving Nevada Territory's bid for statehood. A big reveal should have readers thinking about P.K.'s art of disguise and looking at our hero in a new light." Horn Book

Lawrence, Iain
The giant-slayer. Delacorte Press 2009 292p $16.99
Grades: 5 6 7 8   Fic
1. Imagination -- Fiction 2. Medical care -- Fiction 3. Storytelling -- Fiction 4. Poliomyelitis -- Fiction 5. Father-daughter relationship -- Fiction
ISBN 978-0-385-73376-2; 0-385-73376-3

LC 2008-35409

When her eight-year-old neighbor is stricken with polio in 1955, eleven-year-old Laurie discovers that there is power in her imagination as she weaves a story during her visits with him and other patients confined to iron lung machines.
This is "compelling. . . . This effectively shows how children face life-changing challenges with incredible determination." Booklist

★ The wreckers. Delacorte Press 1998 196p hardcover o.p. pa $5.99
Grades: 5 6 7 8   Fic
1. Adventure fiction 2. Shipwrecks -- Fiction 3. Great Britain -- History -- 1714-1837 -- Fiction
ISBN 0-385-32535-5; 0-440-41545-4 pa

LC 97-31625

"In 1799 fourteen-year-old John Spencer survives a shipwreck on the coast of Cornwall. To his horror, he soon learns that the villagers are not rescuers, but pirates who lure

ships ashore in order to plunder their cargoes. . . . Lawrence creates an edge-of-the-chair survival/mystery story. Fast-moving, mesmerizing." Horn Book Guide
Other titles in this series are:
The smugglers (1999)
The buccaneers (2001)

Lawson, Jessica
The actual & truthful adventures of Becky Thatcher; Jessica Lawson. Simon & Schuster Books for Young Readers 2014 224 p. (hardcover) $16.99
Grades: 4 5 6 7   Fic
1. Girls -- Fiction 2. Adventure fiction 3. Behavior -- Fiction 4. Mississippi River -- Fiction 5. Family life -- Missouri -- Fiction 6. Adventure and adventurers -- Fiction 7. Missouri -- History -- 19th century -- Fiction
ISBN 1481401505; 9781481401500; 9781481401531

LC 2013020560

This middle grades novel by Jessica Lawson, illustrated by Iacopo Bruno, describes how "In 1860, eleven-year-old Becky Thatcher is the new girl in town, determined to have adventures like she promised her brother Jon before he died. With her Mama frozen in grief and her Daddy busy as town judge, Becky spends much of her time on her own, getting into mischief. Before long, she joins the boys at school in a bet to steal from the Widow Douglas." (Publisher's note)

"As a more politically correct retelling of The Adventures of Tom Sawyer, Lawson's novel turns several ideas in Mark Twain's original story on their heads. Tom the tattle-tale lurks in the backdrop of 1860 St. Petersburg, MO, but the focus is on the adventures that Becky plans with her friend Amy Lawrence...Nevertheless, readers not familiar with Twain's work will find an enjoyable adventure story with glimmers of mystery. Fans of historical fiction will enjoy the charming heroine and fitting affirmations of family, friendship, and remembrance." SLJ
Actual and truthful adventures of Becky Thatcher

Lawson, Robert
Ben and me; a new and astonishing life of Benjamin Franklin, as written by his good mouse Amos. lately discovered, edited and illustrated by Robert Lawson. Little, Brown 1939 113p il hardcover o.p. pa $5.95
Grades: 5 6 7 8   Fic
1. Authors 2. Diplomats 3. Inventors 4. Statesmen 5. Scientists 6. Mice -- Fiction 7. Writers on science 8. Members of Congress
ISBN 0-316-51732-1; 0-316-51730-5 pa

"The sophisticated and clever story is illustrated by even more sophisticated and clever line drawings." Roundabout of Books

"How Amos, a poor church mouse, oldest son of a large family, went forth into the world to make his living, and established himself in Benjamin Franklin's old fur cap, 'a rough frontier-cabin type of residence,' and made himself indispensable to Ben with his advice and information, and incidentally let himself in for some very strange experiences is related here in a merry compound of fact and fancy." Bookmark

Mr. Revere and I; set down and embellished with numerous drawings by Robert Lawson. Little, Brown 1953 152p il hardcover o.p. pa $5.95

Grades: 5 6 7 8 **Fic**
1. Artisans 2. Metalworkers 3. Revolutionaries 4. Horses -- Fiction 5. United States -- History -- 1775-1783, Revolution -- Fiction
ISBN 0-316-51729-1 pa

"A delightful tale which is perfect for reading aloud to the whole family. The make-up is excellent, illustrations are wonderful, and the reader will get a very interesting picture of the American Revolution." Libr J

"Paul Revere didn't make his famous midnight ride alone. Meet a patriot unlike any other: Scheherazade, the mare who doesn't mind mentioning she was once the fastest and most admired horse in the King's army. But on arrival in America, "Sherry" is quickly let down by her British rider and recruited by Sam Adams to join the Sons of Liberty..." (Publisher's note)

Rabbit Hill. Viking 1944 127p il lib bdg $16.99; pa $5.99
Grades: 3 4 5 6 **Fic**
1. Animals -- Fiction 2. Rabbits -- Fiction
ISBN 0-670-58675-7 lib bdg; 0-14-240796-8 pa
Awarded the Newbery Medal, 1945

"Robert Lawson, because he loves the Connecticut country and the little animals of field and wood and looks at them with the eye of an artist, a poet and a child, has created for the boy and girl, indeed for the sensitive reader of any age, a whole, fresh, lively, amusing world." N Y Times Book Rev
Followed by The tough winter (1954)

Le Guin, Ursula K.
Gifts. Harcourt 2004 274p $17; $17; pa $7.95
Grades: 7 8 9 10 **Fic**
1. Fantasy fiction
ISBN 9780152051235; 0-15-205123-6; 0-15-205124-4 pa
LC 2003-21449

"Brantors, or chiefs, of the various clans of the Uplands have powers passed down through generations, powers to call animals to the hunt, start fires, cast a wasting disease, or undo the very essence of a life or thing. The clans live isolated from the inhabitants of the Lowland cities in an uneasy truce, where each people's ambitions are kept at bay by fear of the other's vengeance. Two Upland teenagers, Gry and Orrec, have grown from childhood friendship into romance and also into a repudiation of their hereditary powers. . . . Rejecting traditions that bind them to roles unwanted and undesired, Gry and Orrec decide to leave their homes and seek a freer if less privileged life in the Lowlands. . . . Grades seven to twelve." (Bull Cent Child Books)

"Although intriguing as a coming-of-age allegory, Orrec's story is also rich in . . . earthy magic and intelligent plot twists." Booklist

Leach, Sara
Count me in. Orca Book Publishers 2011 pa $9.95
Grades: 4 5 6 7 **Fic**
1. Hiking -- Fiction 2. Cousins -- Fiction
ISBN 978-1-55469-404-4; 1-55469-404-3

"The characters and their motivations are well developed. The plot is simple, but entertaining, and the survival aspects of the story are realistic and suspenseful. Chapter transitions are smooth and easy to follow." SLJ

"When 12-year-old Tabitha is forced by her parents to go backpacking with her two cousins and recently widowed Aunt Tess, she ends up with more of an adventure than any of them planned." Kirkus

Jake Reynolds: chicken or eagle? Orca Book Publishers 2009 101p (Orca young readers) pa $7.95
Grades: 3 4 5 **Fic**
1. Fear -- Fiction 2. Wolves -- Fiction 3. Courage -- Fiction 4. Islands -- Fiction
ISBN 978-1-55469-145-6 pa; 1-55469-145-1 pa

Jake dreams of being a superhero, but he's not exactly brave, especially when it comes to wolves living on the island where he and his family are staying

"The theme of confronting fear is made vivid in this chapter book. . . . [The book offers] a heart-pounding climax and a very satisfying resolution." Booklist

Leal, Ann Haywood
A **finders**-keepers place. Henry Holt 2010 259p $16.99
Grades: 5 6 7 **Fic**
1. School stories 2. Sisters -- Fiction 3. Mental illness -- Fiction 4. Missing persons -- Fiction 5. Single parent family -- Fiction 6. Manic-depressive illness -- Fiction
ISBN 978-0-8050-8882-3; 0-8050-8882-2
LC 2009-50771

As their mother's manic-depression grows worse, eleven-year-old Esther and her sister Ruth visit various churches hoping to find their father, a preacher named Ezekiel who left them seven years before in 1966.

"Leal excels in pithy characterization, mainly through spot-on dialogue, yielding sympathetic characters, a gripping plot, and no shortage of heartbreaking moments." Publ Wkly

Lean, Sarah
★ A **dog** called Homeless; Sarah Lean. Katherine Tegen Books 2012 202 p. (trade bdg) $16.99
Grades: 3 4 5 6 7 **Fic**
1. Dogs -- Juvenile fiction 2. Grief -- Juvenile fiction 3. People with disabilities -- Juvenile fiction 4. Dogs -- Fiction 5. Blind -- Fiction 6. Grief -- Fiction 7. Hearing impaired -- Fiction 8. Selective mutism -- Fiction 9. Single-parent families -- Fiction 10. People with disabilities -- Fiction
ISBN 0062122207; 9780062122209
LC 2011044628
Schneider Family Book Award (2013)

In this book by Sarah Lean, "a girl grieving for her dead mother gives up talking when she becomes convinced that what she says doesn't matter. . . . Cally begins to see her mother . . . dressed in a red raincoat and sometimes accompanied by a very large dog. . . . Cally also meets Mrs. Cooper, a neighbor in their new apartment building who lovingly cares for her blind, nearly deaf 11-year-old son, Sam." (Kirkus Reviews)

A **hundred** horses; Sarah Lean. Katherine Tegen Books, an imprint of HarperCollinsPublishers 2014 224 p. (hardcover bdg.) $16.99
Grades: 5 6 7 8 **Fic**
1. Farms 2. Female friendship 3. Horses -- Fiction 4. England -- Fiction 5. Runaways -- Fiction 6. Conduct

of life -- Fiction 7. Farm life -- England -- Fiction 8.
Family life -- England -- Fiction
ISBN 0062122290; 9780062122292
LC 2013008060

In this book by Sarah Lean, "Nell isn't happy about
spending her vacation on a farm, but when she meets a half-
wild and mysterious girl named Angel, the two girls are tied
in an adventure that may help Nell discover something special about herself--and the most special of a hundred horses." (Publisher's note)

"-Eleven-year-old Nell Green is unhappy about having
to spend her school vacation on a farm with her aunt and
two younger cousins whom she hardly knows...he author in-
tertwines the characters and story line with finesse, keeping
readers guessing about Angel's identity and the appearance
of the hundredth horse until the end of the evenly paced plot.
A touch of magic delivers a satisfying and positive conclusion." (School Library Journal)

Leck, James

★ The **adventures** of Jack Lime; written by James
Leck. Kids Can Press 2010 126p $16.95; pa $8.95
Grades: 5 6 7 8   Fic
1. Mystery fiction 2. Narcolepsy -- Fiction
ISBN 978-1-55453-364-0; 1-55453-364-3; 978-1-
55453-365-7 pa; 1-55453-365-1 pa

"Jack Lime is the guy you come to if you've got a problem. . . . He'll find out what needs finding out. . . . This
slim volume contains three cases. In the first, Jack susses
out the whereabouts of a missing bike. In the second, he
shakes down a hamster-napping and blackmail scheme. And
in the final, he recounts his first case on the job. . . . All
the touchstones that make for great noir are translated for
kids. . . . The lingo that makes hard-boiled reading so much
fun is here, but never schticky, and Leck knows that a great
hero needs a debilitating flaw: for Jack, it's his narcolepsy."
Booklist

Lee, Jenny

Elvis and the underdogs; by Jenny Lee; illustrations by
Kelly Light. Balzer + Bray 2013 304 p. ill. (Elvis and the
Underdogs) (hardcover bdg) $16.99
Grades: 4 5 6   Fic
1. Pet therapy 2. Service dogs 3. Sick -- Fiction 4.
Dogs -- Juvenile fiction 5. Dogs -- Fiction 6. Bullies
-- Fiction 7. Schools -- Fiction 8. Family life --
Fiction 9. Service dogs -- Fiction 10. Human-animal
communication -- Fiction
ISBN 0062235540; 9780062235541
LC 2012028329

This book, by Jenny Lee, "is about a sickly boy whose
life is turned upside down when he gets a therapy dog who
can talk. Elvis brings out the dog lover in the most surprising
people and shows Benji that making new friends may not be
as scary as he once thought." (Publisher's note)

Lee, Milly

Landed; [by] Milly Lee; pictures by Yangsook Choi.
Farrar, Straus & Giroux 2006 un il $16 **Fic**
1. Immigrants -- Fiction 2. Chinese Americans --
Fiction 3. San Francisco (Calif.) -- Fiction
ISBN 0-374-34314-4
LC 2004-47216

After leaving his village in southeastern China, twelve-
year-old Sun is held at Angel Island, San Francisco, before
being released to join his father, a merchant living in the
area. Includes historical notes

"The story is told with quiet restraint. . . . Choi's beautiful, full-page oil paintings, in sepia tones and shades of
green, are quiet and packed with feeling." Booklist

Leeds, Constance

The **unfortunate** son; by Constance Leeds. Viking
Childrens Books 2012 302 p. (hardcover) $16.99
Grades: 4 5 6 7   **Fic**
1. Bildungsromans 2. Historical fiction 3. Pirates --
Fiction 4. Kidnapping -- Fiction 5. Luck -- Fiction 6.
Fishing -- Fiction 7. Slavery -- Fiction 8. Identity --
Fiction 9. Abnormalities, Human -- Fiction 10. Africa
-- History -- To 1498 -- Fiction 11. France -- History
-- 15th century -- Fiction
ISBN 0670013986; 9780670013982
LC 2011027530

This book is the story of Luc, whose "father hates him,
seemingly without reason, so" the boy runs away "to apprentice with a local fisherman. . . . Living with the fisherman's
family he grows close to their ward, the beautiful Beatrice,
and things seem to be looking up . . . until he's kidnapped
by pirates and sold to a Tunisian in North Africa. While Luc
receives an education from his learned master, Beatrice" attempts to unravel Luc's past. (Kirkus Reviews)

Lendroth, Susan

Calico Dorsey; mail dog of the mining camps. illustrations by Adam Gustavson. Tricycle Press 2010 un il
$16.99; lib bdg $19.99
Grades: 2 3 4 5   **Fic**
1. Dogs -- Fiction 2. California -- Fiction 3. Postal
service -- Fiction 4. Silver mines and mining -- Fiction
ISBN 978-1-58246-318-6; 1-58246-318-2; 978-1-
58246-367-4 lib bdg; 1-58246-367-0 lib bdg

A Border Collie named Dorsey works with Al to deliver
the mail and carry supplies to the miners living in Calico,
California, during the nineteenth century, but on the morning
that Al decides to postpone his duties Dorsey has other plans.

"Gustavson's paintings are intergrated into the text,
flowing from page through the centerfold to page, making
this obscure story larger than life. The vitality of the characters is enhanced by the artist's accurate, yet expressive
details that add humor and sweetness to the faces of both the
people and Dorsey." SLJ

Lerangis, Peter

Tomb of shadows; Peter Lerangis, Torstein Norstrand;
[edited by] David Linker. HarperCollins 2014 352 p. (Sev-
en wonders) (hardcover) $17.99
Grades: 4 5 6 7 8 9   **Fic**
1. Fantasy fiction 2. Seven Wonders of the World --
Fiction 3. Adventure stories 4. Betrayal -- Fiction
ISBN 0062070460; 9780062070463
LC 2014931071

This middle grades fantasy novel by Peter Lerangis, illustrated by Torstein Norstrand, part of the Seven Wonders
series, "chronicles the adventures of Jack McKinley and his
friends in a life-or-death race to the Mausoleum at Halicar-
nassus. In the rubble of this Wonder of the Ancient World,

they have to face down their own demons and engage in an epic battle with foes long gone." (Publisher's note)

"Jack, Ally, and Cass continue their quest to save the world—even as their friend Marco joins the enemy's side. Epic battles and fast-moving chapters will keep fans of this "Percy Jackson"-like series engaged." SLJ

Other titles in the series include:

The Colossus Rises (2013)

Lost in Bablyon (2013)

Lester, Julius

★ The **old** African; illustrated by Jerry Pinkney. Dial Bks. 2005 79p il $19.99

Grades: 3 4 5 6   **Fic**

1. Slavery -- Fiction 2. African Americans -- Fiction 3. Extrasensory perception -- Fiction

ISBN 0-8037-2564-7

LC 2003-15671

An elderly slave uses the power of his mind to ease the suffering of his fellow slaves and eventually lead them back to Africa.

"The stirring illustrations, glowing with color and swirling with action, beautifully depict the dramatic escape fantasy (which is based on legend), but they never deny the horror." Booklist

Levine, Gail Carson

Ella enchanted. HarperCollins Pubs. 1997 232p $16.99; lib bdg $17.89; pa $6.50

Grades: 5 6 7 8   **Fic**

1. Fantasy fiction

ISBN 0-06-027510-3; 0-06-027511-1 lib bdg; 0-06-440705-5 pa

LC 96-30734

A Newbery Medal honor book, 1998

"Ella is blessed by a fairy at birth with the gift of obedience. But the blessing is a horror for Ella, who must literally do what everyone tells her, from sweeping the floor to giving up a beloved heirloom necklace. After her mother dies, and her covetous, caustic father leaves on a trading trip, Ella's world is turned upside down. She battles both ogres and wicked stepsisters, makes friends and loses them, and must deny her love for her prince, Charmont, to save his life and his realm. In making this ultimate sacrifice, she breaks the curse." (Booklist) "Grades five to eight." (Bull Cent Child Books)

"As finely designed as a tapestry, Ella's story both neatly incorporates elements of the original tale and mightily expands them." Booklist

★ **Ever**. HarperCollinsPublishers 2008 256p $16.99; lib bdg $17.89; pa $6.99

Grades: 5 6 7 8   **Fic**

1. Winds -- Fiction 2. Immortality -- Fiction 3. Fate and fatalism -- Fiction 4. Gods and goddesses -- Fiction

ISBN 978-0-06-122962-6; 0-06-122962-8; 978-0-06-122963-3 lib bdg; 0-06-122963-6 lib bdg; 978-0-06-122964-0 pa; 0-06-122964-4 pa

LC 2007-32289

Fourteen-year-old Kezi and Olus, Akkan god of the winds, fall in love and together try to change her fate—to be sacrificed to a Hyte god because of a rash promise her father made—through a series of quests that might make her immortal.

"Levine conducts a riveting journey, offering passion and profound pondering along the way." Publ Wkly

★ A **tale** of Two Castles. Harper 2011 328p $16.99; lib bdg $17.89

Grades: 4 5 6   **Fic**

1. Fantasy fiction 2. Mystery fiction 3. Dragons -- Fiction 4. Apprentices -- Fiction 5. Kings and rulers -- Fiction

ISBN 978-0-06-122965-7; 0-06-122965-2; 978-0-06-122966-4 lib bdg; 0-06-122966-0 lib bdg

LC 2010027756

"Hoping to apprentice as an actor, Elodie travels from her rural home to the city of Two Castles. . . . When she's robbed and then rejected as an actor, she apprentices herself to crafty dragon Meenore as a detective. Shape-shifting Count Jonty Um, a kindly ogre, is their first client. . . . But who is to be trusted and who isn't? . . . Intermediate, middle school." (Horn Book)

"Readers are certain to be pulled, like Elodie herself, right into the midst of the rich and swirling life of Two Castles." SLJ

The **two** princesses of Bamarre. HarperCollins Pubs. 2001 241p $15.99; pa $5.99

Grades: 5 6 7 8   **Fic**

1. Fantasy fiction 2. Sisters -- Fiction 3. Princesses -- Fiction

ISBN 0-06-029315-2; 0-06-440966-X pa

LC 00-47953

With her adventurous sister, Meryl, suffering from the Gray Death, meek and timid Princess Addie sets out to find a cure

"A lively tale with vivid characters and an exciting plot." Book Rep

Levine, Kristin

★ The **best** bad luck I ever had. Putnam 2009 266p $16.99

Grades: 5 6 7 8   **Fic**

1. Alabama -- Fiction 2. Friendship -- Fiction 3. Prejudices -- Fiction 4. Family life -- Fiction 5. Country life -- Fiction 6. Race relations -- Fiction

ISBN 978-0-399-25090-3; 0-399-25090-5

LC 2008-11570

In Moundville, Alabama, in 1917, twelve-year-old Dit hopes the new postmaster will have a son his age, but instead he meets Emma, who is black, and their friendship challenges accepted ways of thinking and leads them to save the life of a condemned man.

"Tension builds just below the surface of this energetic, seamlessly narrated . . . novel. . . . Levine handles the setting with grace and nuance." Publ Wkly

★ The **lions** of Little Rock; Kristin Levine. G. P. Putnam's Sons 2012 298p.

Grades: 5 6 7 8   **Fic**

1. School stories 2. African Americans -- Fiction 3. School integration -- Fiction 4. Schools -- Fiction 5. Friendship -- Fiction 6. Bashfulness -- Fiction 7. Middle schools -- Fiction 8. Race relations -- Fiction 9. Family life -- Arkansas -- Fiction 10. Little Rock (Ark.)

-- History -- 20th century -- Fiction
ISBN 9780399256448

LC 2011031835

This book presents a "portrait of 1958 Little Rock, Ark., the tumultuous year when the governor refused integration by closing local high schools. The story is told through the . . . voice of painfully quiet 12-year-old Marlee Nisbett, who makes a rare friend in Liz, a new student at her middle school. Liz instills some much-needed confidence in Marlee, but when it's revealed that Liz is 'passing' as a white student, Liz must leave school abruptly, putting their friendship to the test. The girls meet in secret, and Marlee joins an antisegregationist organization, both actions inviting serious risk amid escalating racist threats." (Publishers Weekly)

Levitin, Sonia

Journey to America; illustrated by Charles Robinson. Atheneum Pubs. 1993 150p il hardcover o.p. pa $4.99
Grades: 4 5 6 7   **Fic**
1. Family life -- Fiction 2. Jewish refugees -- Fiction 3. World War, 1939-1945 -- Fiction
ISBN 0-689-71130-1 pa

LC 93-163980

A reissue of the title first published 1970

"In a strong immigration story, Lisa Platt, the middle daughter, tells how her family is forced to leave Nazi Germany and make a new life in the United States. First their father leaves, then the others escape to Switzerland, where they endure harsh conditions. After months of separation, the family is reunited in New York." Rochman. Against borders

Followed by Silver days (1989) and Annie's promise (1993)

Levy, Dana Alison

The **misadventures** of the family Fletcher; Dana Levy. Delacorte Press 2014 272 p. (glb) $18.99
Grades: 4 5 6 7   **Fic**
1. Interracial adoption 2. Children of gay parents -- Fiction 3. Humorous stories 4. Schools -- Fiction 5. Adoption -- Fiction 6. Brothers -- Fiction 7. Neighbors -- Fiction 8. Family life -- Fiction
ISBN 0385376545; 9780385376525; 9780385376549

LC 2013026320

In this middle grades book by Dana Alison Levy, "With four brothers, a dog, a cat, school projects, soccer matches, and a grumpy neighbor, the Fletchers are your typical American family . . . with two dads, and siblings who are adopted kids from various ethnic backgrounds. While 12-year-old Sam ponders . . . trying out for the school play . . . , 10-year-old Jax negotiates changing friendships and a veteran project that involves talking to the unfriendly Vietnam vet next door." (School Library Journal)

"Four adopted (and racially diverse) brothers and two dads star in this Penderwicks-esque chronicle of a year in their lives. Focusing each chapter on one boy while still keeping the whole family in the picture, Levy provides a compelling, compassionate, and frequently hilarious look at their daily concerns. Readers will want to be part of (or at least friends with) this delightful family." Horn Book

Lewis, C. S.

★ The **lion**, the witch, and the wardrobe; illustrated by Pauline Baynes. HarperCollins Pubs. 1994 189p il (The chronicles of Narnia) $17.99; lib bdg $18.89; pa $7.99

Grades: 4 5 6 7   **Fic**
1. Fantasy fiction
ISBN 0-06-023481-4; 0-06-023482-2 lib bdg; 0-06-440499-4 pa

LC 93-8889

A reissue of the title first published 1950 by Macmillan

Four English schoolchildren find their way through the back of a wardrobe into the magic land of Narnia and assist Aslan, the golden lion, to triumph over the White Witch, who has cursed the land with eternal winter

This begins "the 'Narnia' stories, outstanding modern fairy tales with an underlying theme of good overcoming evil." Child Books Too Good to Miss

Other titles in this series are:
Prince Caspian (1951)
The voyage of the Dawn Treader (1952)
The silver chair (1953)
The horse and his boy (1954)
The magician's nephew (1956)
The last battle (1956)

Lewis, Elizabeth Foreman

Young Fu of the upper Yangtze; [by] Elizabeth Foreman Lewis; illustrations by William Low. 75th anniversary ed.; Henry Holt 2007 302p il $17.95; pa $7.99
Grades: 4 5 6   **Fic**
1. China -- Fiction 2. City and town life -- Fiction
ISBN 978-0-8050-8113-8; 0-8050-8113-5; 978-0-312-38007-6 pa; 0-312-38007-0 pa

LC 2006049633

A newly illustrated edition of the title first published 1932 by The John C. Winston Company

Awarded the Newbery Medal, 1933

In the 1920's, a Chinese youth from the country comes to Chungking with his mother where the bustling city offers adventure and his apprenticeship to a coppersmith brings good fortune

This edition "features a foreword by Katherine Paterson, extensive end-notes comparing China then and now, and new, atmospheric black-and-white illustrations." Horn Book Guide

Lewis, Gill

Moon bear; Gill Lewis; illustrated by Alessandro Gottardo. Atheneum Books for Young Readers 2015 384 p. illustrations (hardcover) $16.99
Grades: 4 5 6 7 8   **Fic**
1. Laos -- Fiction 2. Bears -- Fiction 3. Asiatic black bear -- Fiction 4. Animals -- Treatment -- Fiction
ISBN 1481400940; 9781481400947; 9781481400954

LC 2013049285

In this book, by Gill Lewis, "[t]welve-year-old Tam, on a dare, ventures into a moon bear den in the mountains of Northern Laos. His goal is to steal the cub and sell it, making a fortune for his family. But the mother bear's unexpected return upends Tam's plan, and he barely escapes with his life. And then his life implodes anyway. . . . Tam is forced to work hundreds of miles away in the city, at a moon bear farm where bile from bear gall bladders is used for medicine." (Publisher's note)

"Through Tam's selfless quest to get the bear back to the wild, and his protection of the cub at the expense of his own well-being, readers witness the depths of his bravery, compassion, and strong moral compass." Pub Wkly

★ **Wild** wings; illustrated by Yuta Onoda. Atheneum Books for Young Readers 2011 287p il $15.99

Grades: 4 5 6 7   **Fic**

1. Gambia -- Fiction 2. Ospreys -- Fiction 3. Scotland -- Fiction 4. Farm life -- Fiction 5. Friendship -- Fiction

ISBN 1-4424-1445-6; 978-1-4424-1445-7

LC 2010-49228

Callum becomes friends with Iona, a practically feral classmate who has discovered an osprey, thought to be gone from Scotland, on Callum's family farm, and they eventually share the secret with others, including Jeneba who encounters the same bird at her home in Gambia.

This is a "rich, moving tale. . . . The suspenseful story line is surrounded with precise details. . . . Short chapters, some with cliffhanging endings, will read-aloud well. . . . A powerfully memorable story." Kirkus

Lewis, J. Patrick

★ **And** the soldiers sang; [written by] J. Patrick Lewis & [illustrations by] Gary Kelley. Creative Editions 2011 31p il $17.99

Grades: 2 3 4 5 6   **Fic**

1. Soldiers -- Fiction 2. Christmas -- Fiction 3. World War, 1914-1918 -- Fiction

ISBN 978-1-5684-6220-2; 1-5684-6220-4

LC 2010028644

A young Welsh soldier fights along the Western Front during World War I, experiencing the horrors of trench warfare before participating in the famed Christmas Truce of 1914.

This offers "a terse yet lyrical text and stark, dramatic illustrations. . . . Kelley's compelling artwork features mostly dark shades and strong, angular compositions. . . . Grim, upsetting and utterly beautiful, this is both a strong antiwar statement and a fascinating glimpse of a little-known historical event." Kirkus

Lewis, Maggie

★ **Morgy** makes his move; illustrated by Michael Chesworth. Houghton Mifflin 1999 74p il $15; pa $4.95

Grades: 2 3 4   **Fic**

1. School stories 2. Moving -- Fiction 3. Massachusetts -- Fiction

ISBN 0-395-92284-4; 0-618-19680-3 pa

LC 98-43245

When third-grader Morgy MacDougal-MacDuff moves from California to Massachusetts with his parents, he has a lot of new things to get used to before he feels comfortable

"Heavy issues are handled lightly; language is simple and straightforward; Michael Chesworth's illustrations are funny and exaggerated." Booklist

Other titles about Morgy are:

Morgy coast to coast (2005)

Morgy's musical summer (2008)

Lin, Grace

★ **Starry** River of the Sky; by Grace Lin. Little, Brown 2012 288 p. col. ill. $17.99

Grades: 3 4 5 6   **Fic**

1. Fairy tales 2. Moon -- Fiction 3. Villages -- Fiction 4. Storytelling -- Fiction

ISBN 0316125954; 9780316125956

LC 2012012651

In this novel by Grace Lin, "the moon is missing from the remote Village of Clear Sky, but only a young boy named Rendi seems to notice! Rendi has run away from home and is now working as a chore boy at the village inn. He can't help but notice the village's peculiar inhabitants and their problems . . . but one day, a mysterious lady arrives at the Inn with the gift of storytelling, and slowly transforms the villagers and Rendi himself." (Publisher's note)

Includes bibliographical references.

★ **Where** the mountain meets the moon. Little, Brown and Co. 2009 278p il $16.99

Grades: 4 5 6 7   **Fic**

1. Fairy tales 2. Moon -- Fiction 3. Dragons -- Fiction

ISBN 978-0-316-11427-1; 0-316-11427-8

LC 2008-32818

A Newbery Medal honor book, 2010

Minli, an adventurous girl from a poor village, buys a magical goldfish, and then joins a dragon who cannot fly on a quest to find the Old Man of the Moon in hopes of bringing life to Fruitless Mountain and freshness to Jade River

"With beautiful language, Lin creates a strong, memorable heroine and a mystical land. . . . Children will embrace this accessible, timeless story about the evil of greed and the joy of gratitude." Booklist

★ **The Year** of the Dog; a novel. Little, Brown 2006 134p il $14.99; pa $5.99

Grades: 3 4 5   **Fic**

1. Chinese New Year -- Fiction 2. Taiwanese Americans -- Fiction

ISBN 0-316-06000-3; 0-316-06002-X pa

LC 2005-02586

Frustrated at her seeming lack of talent for anything, Pacy, a young Taiwanese American girl, sets out to apply the lessons of the Chinese Year of the Dog, those of making best friends and finding oneself, to her own life.

"The story . . . is entertaining and often illuminating. Appealing, childlike decorative drawings add a delightful flavor to a gentle tale full of humor." Horn Book

Other titles about Pacy are:

The Year of the Rat (2008)

Dumpling days (2011)

Lindgren, Astrid

★ **Pippi** Longstocking; [by] Astrid Lindgren; translated by Tiina Nunnally; illustrated by Lauren Child. Viking Children's Books 2007 207p il $25

Grades: 3 4 5 6   **Fic**

1. Sweden -- Fiction

ISBN 978-0-670-06276-8

Original Swedish edition, 1945; first English language edition 1950

Escapades of a lucky little girl who lives with a horse and a monkey—but without any parents—at the edge of a Swedish village

"This oversize edition of the classic story has much to offer a new generation of readers. It has full-color illustrations . . . and a new translation. . . . Nunnally's language flows naturally and gives a fresh, modern feel to the line drawings, filled with color and pattern." SLJ

Other titles about Pippi Longstocking are:

Pippi goes on board (1957)

Pippi in the South Seas (1959)

Lindo, Elvira

Manolito Four-Eyes; illustrated by Emilio Urberuaga; translated by Joanne Moriarity. Marshall Cavendish Children 2008 144p il (Manolito Four-Eyes) $15.99

Grades: 4 5 6   **Fic**

1. School stories 2. Spain -- Fiction 3. Family life -- Fiction 4. Grandfathers -- Fiction

ISBN 978-0-7614-5303-1; 0-7614-5303-2

Original Spanish edition 2003

Recounts the exploits of the irrepressible Manolito as he navigates the world of his small Madrid neighborhood, along with his grandpa, his little brother, and his school friends.

"The protagonist is a wild, spunky, dramatic, comical sort of character sure to be popular with children, who will probably find him, in Manolito's own inimitable words, a 'whole lotta cool.' Lively cartoon illustrations are scattered throughout." SLJ

Other titles about Manolito are:

Manolito Four-Eyes: the 2nd volume of the great encyclopedia of my life (2009)

Manolito Four-Eyes: the 3rd volume of the great encyclopedia of my life (2010)

Lipsyte, Robert

The **twinning** project; by Robert Lipsyte. Clarion Books 2012 269 p. (hardback) $16.99

Grades: 4 5 6 7   **Fic**

1. Science fiction 2. Twins -- Fiction 3. Parallel universes -- Fiction 4. Schools -- Fiction 5. Middle schools -- Fiction 6. Space and time -- Fiction

ISBN 0547645716; 9780547645711

LC 2011050252

This book by Robert Lipsyte follows protagonist Tom, who has been "expelled from school after school for fighting bullies. . . . The boy's only comfort comes from talking through his problems with his imaginary twin, Eddie, a jock who lives on a version of Earth 50 years behind Tom's. . . . When the boys' 'grandfather' on both Earths reveals that the twin planets were created by alien scientists, the boys switch places to fight for the survival of both Earths." (Publishers Weekly)

Lisle, Holly

The **Ruby** Key. Orchard Books 2008 361p (Moon & sun) $16.99; pa $7.99

Grades: 5 6 7 8   **Fic**

1. Fantasy fiction 2. Siblings -- Fiction

ISBN 978-0-545-00012-3; 0-545-00012-2; 978-0-545-00013-0 pa; 0-545-00013-0 pa

LC 2007-30217

In a world where an uneasy peace binds Humans and Nightlings, fourteen-year-old Genna and her twelve-year-old brother Dan learn of their uncle's plot to gain immortality in exchange for human lives, and the two strike their own bargain with the Nightling lord, which sets them on a dangerous journey along the Moonroads in search of a key.

"Lisle's fertile imagination provides the nightworlds with monsters . . . but it is her clever plotting in this . . . fantasy, leading up to a thrilling finish . . . That will bewitch her audience." Horn Book

Followed by: The silver door (2009)

The **silver** door. Orchard Books 2009 366p (Moon & sun) $17.99

Grades: 5 6 7 8   **Fic**

1. War stories 2. Fantasy fiction

ISBN 978-0-545-00014-7; 0-545-00014-9

LC 2008-40153

When Genna is chosen as the Sunrider of prophecy, her destiny is to unite the magic of the sun and the moon for the good of both Nightlings and humans.

"This second book of the Moon & Sun series has jarring stop-start feel, but the complexities of the interlaced human and nightling societies continue to unfold in fascinating way, creating a multi-hued, fully realized world for readers to explore." Horn Book

Lisle, Janet Taylor

Afternoon of the elves. Orchard Bks. 1989 122p hardcover o.p. pa $6.99

Grades: 4 5 6   **Fic**

1. Friendship -- Fiction 2. Mentally ill -- Fiction

ISBN 0-531-05837-9; 0-698-11806-5 pa

LC 88-35099

A Newbery Medal honor book, 1990

"'Afternoon of the elves' is a distinctive portrayal of the way children figure out ways to inhabit the world when there aren't any adults around." N Y Times Book Rev

"Nine-year-old Hillary has a happy home, all the material possessions she wants, and plenty of friends at school. Eleven-year-old Sara-Kate is an outcast, thin, poorly dressed, with failing grades, a decrepit house, and a weedy yard adjoining Hillary's neat garden. But Sara-Kate has an elf village, and with it she hooks Hillary into a friendship that thrives on elf stories but suffers from Sara-Kate's stormy moods and prickly pride. It is for Hillary to discover that Sara-Kate alone is caring for a mother who is mentally ill, penniless, and unable to provide the most basic physical or emotional necessities." Bull Cent Child Books

★ The **art** of keeping cool. Atheneum Bks. for Young Readers 2000 207p hardcover o.p.

Grades: 5 6 7 8   **Fic**

1. Artists 2. Cousins 3. Grandparents 4. Rhode Island 5. Family problems 6. Rhode Island -- Fiction 7. World War, 1939-1945 -- Fiction 8. World War, 1939-1945 -- United States

ISBN 0689837879; 0689837887

LC 00-32778

In 1942, Robert and his cousin Elliot uncover long-hidden family secrets while staying in their grandparents' Rhode Island town. They also become involved with a German artist who is suspected of being a spy. "Ages ten to fourteen." (N Y Times Book Rev)

"Lisle develops an unforgettable cast of characters placed against a fully realized setting. Engrossing, challenging, and well paced." Horn Book

Little, Kimberley Griffiths

★ **Circle** of secrets. Scholastic Press 2011 326p $17.99

Grades: 5 6 7 8   **Fic**

1. Ghost stories 2. Guilt -- Fiction 3. Louisiana -- Fiction 4. Mother-daughter relationship -- Fiction

ISBN 978-0-545-16561-7; 0-545-16561-X

LC 2011000889

A year after her mother has deserted the family, eleven-year-old Shelby goes to stay with her, deep in the Louisiana bayou, where they both confront old hurts and regrets.

"The gently spooky ghost angle is handled nicely with some religious overtones. A very dramatic climax leads to a sweet, satisfying ending with some surprising twists and with reconciliation occurring for several characters." Kirkus

The **healing** spell. Scholastic Press 2010 354p $17.99
Grades: 5 6 7 8   **Fic**
1. Coma -- Fiction 2. Guilt -- Fiction 3. Mother-daughter relationship -- Fiction
ISBN 978-0-545-16559-4; 0-545-16559-8
LC 2009-28016

Twelve-year-old Livie is living with a secret and it's crushing her. She knows she is responsible for her mother's coma, but she can't tell anyone. It's up to her to find a way to wake her momma up.

"Little explores the extremes of childhood guilt and its consequences in this harsh yet well-crafted story about fully drawn people. The bayou, with its rich culture, is an atmospheric character that overlays the story with mystery and dread." Booklist

The **time** of the fireflies; Kimberley Griffiths Little. Scholastic Press 2014 368 p. (jacketed hardcover) $18.99
Grades: 5 6 7 8   **Fic**
1. Mystery fiction 2. Family secrets -- Fiction 3. Secrets -- Fiction 4. Fireflies -- Fiction 5. Louisiana -- Fiction 6. Family life -- Fiction 7. Time travel -- Fiction 8. Family problems -- Fiction
ISBN 0545165636; 9780545165631
LC 2013027396

In this middle grades book by Kimberley Griffiths Little, "When Larissa Renaud starts receiving eerie phone calls on a disconnected old phone in her family's antique shop, she knows she's in for a strange summer. A series of clues leads her to the muddy river banks. . . . It soon becomes clear that it is up to Larissa to prevent history from repeating itself and a fatal tragedy from striking the people she loves." (Publisher's note)

"Twelve-year-old Larissa's parents own Bayou Bridge Antiques, which features a wall of old phones. When one of the phones begins ringing, Larissa hesitantly picks it up. The female voice on the other end begs Larissa to find the fireflies. . . . [F]ans of Mary Downing Hahn's books will appreciate the spooky porcelain dolls and family curse." Booklist

Llewellyn, Sam
  Darksolstice. Orchard Books 2010 365p map (Lyonesse) $17.99
Grades: 5 6 7 8   **Fic**
1. Fantasy fiction 2. Kings
ISBN 978-0-439-93471-8; 0-439-93471-0
LC 2009006283
Sequel to: The well between the worlds (2009)

While Idris Limpet, Rightful King of the Land of Lyonesse, is making the treacherous journey to the distant land of Aegypt to rescue his dear friend and sister, Morgan, he meets a company of friends who shall become his Knights of the Round Table and lead armies to battle the evil regent, Fisheagle.

The **well** between the worlds. Orchard Books 2009 339p (Lyonesse) $17.99
Grades: 5 6 7 8   **Fic**
1. Fantasy fiction 2. Kings
ISBN 978-0-439-93469-5; 0-439-93469-9
LC 2008-20075

Eleven-year-old Idris Limpet, living with his family in the once noble but now evil and corrupt island country of Lyonesse, finds his life taking a dramatic turn when, after a near-drowning incident, he is accused of being allied to the feared sea monsters and is rescued from a death sentence by a mysterious and fearsome stranger.

"Seldom does one find a new fantasy that is so richly textured, so original in concept, and with such a wonderfully interesting story. . . . Fantasy lovers will be impatient to find out where their paths take them." Voice Youth Advocates
Followed by: Darksolstice (2010)

Lloyd Jones, Rob
  Wild boy; Rob Lloyd Jones. Candlewick Press 2013 304 p. $16.99
Grades: 5 6 7 8   **Fic**
1. Mystery fiction 2. Steampunk fiction
ISBN 0763662526; 9780763662523
LC 2013931467

In this book, "Wild Boy's head-to-toe fur has garnered him scorn and abuse from commoners, but his extraordinary intellectual gifts eventually win him a future with a powerful, elite group called the Gentlemen. . . . When Wild Boy is about to be hanged by the unseemly circus crew for a murder he did not commit, teen acrobat Clarissa helps him escape. Together, they follow clues through sewers and back alleys, learning about an extraordinary electrical device linked to the murder." (Kirkus Reviews)

  Wild boy and the black terror; Rob Lloyd Jones. Candlewick Press 2015 336 p. illustrations, map $16.99
Grades: 5 6 7 8   **Fic**
1. Serial killers -- Fiction 2. Circus performers -- Fiction 3. Great Britain -- History -- Victoria, 1837-1901 -- Fiction 4. Children's stories 5. Murderers--England--London 6. Detective and mystery stories
ISBN 0763662534; 9780763662530
LC 2014945722

This novel by Rob Lloyd Jones is set in "London, 1842. Wild Boy, master detective and former freak-show performer, and Clarissa, circus acrobat and troublemaker, are the secret last hope of a city beset by horror. A poisoner stalks the streets, leaving victims mad with terror--and then dead. Can the Black Terror be traced to a demon called Malphas? Can Wild Boy and Clarissa uncover a cure in time to save the queen and the city?" (Publisher's note)

"Adventure, conspiracy and adrenaline intermingle with dark deeds, devil worship and blood diamonds in this sequel to Wild Boy (2013). . . . The queen and the Gentlemen need them to unearth the cause of a mysterious sickness that blackens veins and sends victims into a stupor of madness before tragic death. . . . Can the duo save all of London from a hellbent killer? Diamonds are a Wild Boy's worst enemy in this steampunk romp not intended for the faint—or black—of heart." Kirkus

Lloyd, Alison
  Year of the tiger. Holiday House 2010 194p $16.95

Grades: 5 6 7 8 **Fic**
1. Adventure fiction 2. China -- Fiction 3. Archery -- Fiction 4. Social classes -- Fiction
ISBN 978-0-8234-2277-7; 0-8234-2277-1
LC 2009033651

First published 2008 in Australia

In ancient China, Hu and Ren forge an unlikely alliance in an effort to become expert archers and, ultimately, to save their city from invading barbarians.

"Brimming with details of daily life in the Han Dynasty, this fast-paced story alternates in the third person between Hu and Ren." Kirkus

Lloyd, Natalie
★ A **snicker** of magic; by Natalie Lloyd. Scholastic Press 2014 320 p. hbk $16.99
Grades: 4 5 6 7 **Fic**
1. Magic -- Fiction 2. Curses -- Fiction 3. Tennessee -- Fiction 4. Friendship -- Fiction 5. Family life -- Fiction 6. Mothers and daughters -- Fiction
ISBN 9780545552707; 0545552702
LC 2013027779

"Midnight Gulch used to be a magical place, a town where people could sing up thunderstorms and dance up sunflowers. But that was long ago, before a curse drove the magic away. Twelve-year-old Felicity knows all about things like that; her nomadic mother is cursed with a wandering heart. . . . But when she arrives in Midnight Gulch, Felicity thinks her luck's about to change." (Publisher's note)

"The unusual language, showing a tinge of Tennessee mountain dialect, spins a web around the story that touches on helping others, budding friendships, and strength of family." Booklist

Lobel, Arnold
★ **Fables**; written and illustrated by Arnold Lobel. Harper & Row 1980 40p il $16.99; lib bdg $18.89; pa $6.99
Grades: 3 4 5 **Fic**
1. Animals -- Fiction
ISBN 0-06-023973-5; 0-06-023974-3 lib bdg; 0-06-443046-4 pa
LC 79-2004

Awarded the Caldecott Medal, 1981

"Short, original fables, complete with moral, poke subtle fun at human foibles through the antics of 20 memorable animal characters. . . . Despite the large picture-book format, the best audience will be older readers who can understand the innuendos and underlying messages. Children of all ages, however, will appreciate and be intrigued by the artist's fine, full-color illustrations. Tones are deftly blended to luminescent shadings, and the pictorial simplicity of ideas, droll expressions, and caricature of behavior work in many instances as complete and humorous stories in themselves." Booklist

Lodding, Linda Ravin
A **gift** for Mama; by Linda Ravin Lodding; illustrated by Alison Jay. Alfred A. Knopf 2014 32 p. (hard cover) $17.99
Grades: PreK K 1 2 **Fic**
1. Gifts -- Fiction 2. Secondhand trade 3. Mother-child relationship -- Fiction 4. Barter -- Fiction 5. Austria -- History -- 1867-1918 -- Fiction 6. Viennna (Austria)

-- History -- 19th century -- Fiction
ISBN 0385753314; 9780385753319; 9780385753326
LC 2013006071

"In this lovely, circular story set in 19th-century Vienna, Oskar searches for the perfect gift for his mother, armed with a single coin. Each time he acquires a gift, starting with a perfect yellow rose, he meets someone who convinces him to trade it for something else. Finally, the day is over, and he is back where he started. In the concluding paragraph, Lodding states that most of the people Oskar meets are important figures from Viennese history-Gustav Klimt, Felix Salten, Johann Strauss II, and Empress Sisi-and that this is Vienna's story as well as Oskar's." (School Library Journal)

Loftin, Nikki
Nightingale's nest; Nikki Loftin. Razorbill 2014 256 p. 22 cm (hardcover) $16.99
Grades: 4 5 6 7 **Fic**
1. Boys -- Fiction 2. Friendship -- Fiction 3. Birds -- Fiction 4. Magic -- Fiction 5. Singing -- Fiction 6. Family problems -- Fiction 7. Foster home care -- Fiction 8. Dysfunctional families -- fiction
ISBN 159514546X; 9781595145468
LC 2013047556

"Twelve-year-old John Fischer Jr. . . . is spending his summer helping his father with his tree removal business, clearing brush for Mr. King, the wealthy owner of a chain of Texas dollar stores, when he hears a beautiful song that transfixes him. Inspired by a Hans Christian Andersen story, 'Nightingale's Nest' is a . . . novel about a boy with the weight of the world on his shoulders and a girl with the gift of healing in her voice." (Publisher's note)

"John narrates his story in fluid, lyrical prose, Loftin blending the raw realism of a boy who makes the wrong choice with the fairy-tale magic of a girl with a nightingale voice. Unusual, finely crafted story of loss, betrayal and healing." Kirkus

Wish girl; Nikki Loftin. Razorbill 2015 256 p. (hardcover) $16.99
Grades: 4 5 6 7 **Fic**
1. Friendship -- Fiction 2. Cancer patients -- Fiction 3. Runaway children -- Fiction 4. Texas -- Fiction 5. Cancer -- Fiction 6. Best friends -- Fiction 7. Individuality -- Fiction 8. Family problems -- Fiction 9. Family life -- Texas -- Fiction
ISBN 1595146865; 9781595146861
LC 2014031004

In this children's novel by Nikki Loftin "when his family moves to the Texas Hill Country, . . . Peter finds a tranquil, natural valley where he can, at last, hear himself think. There, he meets a girl his age: Annie Blythe . . . a 'Make-A-Wish Girl.' And in two weeks she will begin a dangerous treatment to try and stop her cancer from spreading. Annie and Peter hatch a plan to escape into the valley. But the pair soon discovers that the valley--and life--may have other plans for them." (Publisher's note)

"In this companion to Nightingale's Nest (Razorbill, 2014), 12-year-old Peter Stone's new home in rural Texas is completely unlike his previous life in San Antonio. Even in the quiet of the country, his family is too loud. They never stop to understand sensitive, introverted Peter...This emotional story will be loved by fans of Nightingale's Nest, as

the plot structure, atmosphere, and characters are similar."
SLJ

Companion to:

Nightingale's Nest (2014)

Lofting, Hugh

The **voyages** of Doctor Dolittle; told by Hugh Lofting;
illustrated by Michael Hague; edited with a foreword by Patricia C. McKissack and Fredrick L. McKissack; afterword
by Peter Glassman. HarperCollins Pubs. 2001 355p il
$22.95

Grades: 4 5 6 7   **Fic**

1. Fantasy fiction 2. Animals -- Fiction
    ISBN 0-688-14002-5

A newly illustrated and revised edition of the title first
published 1922 by Stokes

Awarded the Newbery Medal, 1923

When his colleague Long Arrow disappears, Dr. Dolittle
sets off with his assistant, Tommy Stubbins, his dog, Jip, and
Polynesia the parrot on an adventurous voyage over tropical
seas to floating Spidermonkey Island

Loizeaux, William

Clarence Cochran, a human boy; pictures by Anne
Wilsdorf. Farrar, Straus and Giroux 2009 152p il $16

Grades: 4 5 6   **Fic**

1. Toleration -- Fiction 2. Cockroaches -- Fiction 3.
    Environmental protection -- Fiction
    ISBN 978-0-374-31323-4; 0-374-31323-7

                                              LC 2007-35358

With the threat of extermination looming, a cockroach
who has been transformed into a tiny human learns to communicate with his human hosts, leading to an agreement
both sides can live with, and a friendship between Clarence
and ten-year-old Mimi, a human environmentalist.

"There's a serious message here about environmentalism
and the power of words, and the action and suspense make
this a good read-aloud or classroom-discussion choice." SLJ

Lombard, Jenny

★ **Drita,** my homegirl. G. P. Putnam's Sons 2006
135p $15.99; pa $5.99

Grades: 3 4 5   **Fic**

1. Refugees -- Fiction 2. Albanians -- Fiction 3.
    Friendship -- Fiction 4. New York (N.Y.) -- Fiction 5.
    African Americans -- Fiction
    ISBN 0-399-24380-1; 0-14-240905-7 pa

                                              LC 2005-13501

When ten-year-old Drita and her family, refugees from
Kosovo, move to New York, Drita is teased about not speaking English well, but after a popular student named Maxine
is forced to learn about Kosovo as a punishment for teasing
Drita, the two girls soon bond.

"Maxie's attempts to help Drita understand American
ways are touching, and Drita's understanding of her friend's
loss is a testament to the emotional intelligence of children."
SLJ

London, Alex

Proxy; Alex London. Philomel 2013 379 p. $17.99

Grades: 7 8 9 10   **Fic**

1. Science fiction 2. Dystopian fiction 3. Gays --

Fiction 4. Social classes -- Fiction
    ISBN 0399257764; 9780399257766

                                              LC 2012039704

In this book, "Knox is a 'patron,' a privileged and
wealthy citizen of Mountain City. His only concerns are
hacking, scoring with girls, and causing trouble while anger-
ing his bigwig dad. His proxy, a person who is contractually
obligated to serve out Knox's punishments, is a gay teen. In
exchange for working as a proxy, Syd is able to pay off his
debts. When Knox accidentally kills a girl, 16 years at the
Old Sterling Work Colony is too great a punishment for Syd
to bear, so he escapes." (School Library Journal)

We are not eaten by yaks; with art by Jonny Duddle.
Philomel Books 2011 355p il (An accidental adventure)
$12.99

Grades: 3 4 5 6   **Fic**

1. Adventure fiction 2. Twins -- Fiction 3. Parents
    -- Fiction 4. Siblings -- Fiction 5. Explorers -- Fiction
    6. Television -- Fiction
    ISBN 978-0-399-25487-1; 0-399-25487-0

                                              LC 2010-06020

As the children of two world-famous explorers, eleven-
year-old twins Celia and Oliver prefer television-watching
to adventure-seeking until their father takes them to Tibet to
help search for their long-lost mother.

"This text will appeal to reluctant readers who appreciate
magic, humor, and predicatble parental behaviors that will
cause any tween to roll their eyes. The improbable connection between ubiquitous television shows, poison witches,
talking yaks, and reluctant heroes works to make this a light
yet intriguing read." Libr Media Connect

Another title in this series is:

We dine with cannibals (2011)

We dine with cannibals. Philomel Books 2011 il (An
accidental adventure) $12.99

Grades: 3 4 5 6   **Fic**

1. Adventure fiction 2. Twins -- Fiction 3. Siblings --
    Fiction 4. Explorers -- Fiction 5. Television -- Fiction
    6. Rain forests -- Fiction 7. Amazon River valley --
    Fiction
    ISBN 978-0-399-25488-8; 0-399-25488-9

                                              LC 2010041993

All eleven-year-old twins Oliver and Celia Navel want
to do is watch television, but their explorer father takes them
in search of El Dorado, the Lost City of Gold, and their long-
lost mother.

"London's second in the Accidental Adventure series
has more thrills and more mystery (and naturally more complaining and more laughs) than the first." Kirkus

Look, Lenore

★ **Alvin** Ho: allergic to girls, school, and other scary
things; pictures by LeUyen Pham. Schwartz & Wade Books
2008 170p il $15.99; lib bdg $18.99

Grades: 2 3 4 5   **Fic**

1. Fear -- Fiction 2. Massachusetts -- Fiction 3.
    Chinese Americans -- Fiction
    ISBN 978-0-375-83914-6; 0-375-83914-3; 978-0-375-
    93914-3 lib bdg; 0-375-93914-8 lib bdg

                                              LC 2007-029456

Alvin Ho, a young boy in Concord, Massachusetts, who
loves superheroes and comes from a long line of brave Chi-

nese farmer-warriors, wants to make friends, but first he must overcome his fear of everything.

Look's "intuitive grasp of children's emotions is rivaled only by her flair for comic exaggeration." Publ Wkly

Other titles about Alvin Ho are:

Alvin Ho: allergic to camping, hiking, and other natural disasters (2009)

Alvin Ho: allergic to birthday parties, science projects, and other man-made catastrophies (2010)

Alvin Ho

allergic to dead bodies, funerals, and other fatal circumstances (2011)

★ **Ruby** Lu, brave and true; illustrated by Anne Wilsdorf. Atheneum Books for Young Readers 2004 105p il $15.95; pa $3.99

Grades: 1 2 3   **Fic**

1. Chinese Americans -- Fiction

ISBN 0-689-84907-9; 1-4169-1389-0 pa

LC 2003-3605

"Almost-eight-year-old" Ruby Lu spends time with her baby brother, goes to Chinese school, performs magic tricks and learns to drive, and has adventures with both old and new friends.

This is a "funny and charming chapter book. . . . [It offers] generous font, ample white space, and animated and active illustrations rendered in India ink." SLJ

Other titles about Ruby Lu are:

Ruby Lu, empress of everything (2006)

Ruby Lu, star of the show (2011)

Lopez, Diana

Ask my mood ring how I feel; by Diana Lopez. 1st ed. Little, Brown and Co. 2013 324 p. (hardcover) $17

Grades: 4 5 6 7   **Fic**

1. Breast cancer -- Fiction 2. Children of cancer patients -- Fiction 3. Cancer -- Fiction 4. Promises -- Fiction 5. Friendship -- Fiction 6. Fund-raising -- Fiction 7. Christian life -- Fiction 8. Hispanic Americans -- Fiction 9. San Antonio (Tex.) -- Fiction 10. Family life -- Texas -- Fiction

ISBN 0316209961; 9780316209960

LC 2012029856

In this book, Chia's "mother is diagnosed with breast cancer, which spurs . . . changes throughout their family. . . . After visiting the Basilica of Our Lady of San Juan del Valle in southern Texas, Chia dedicates herself to a promesa, vowing to secure 500 sponsors for a Walk for the Cure in exchange (she hopes) for her mother's recovery." (Publishers Weekly)

Confetti girl. Little, Brown and Company 2009 198p $15.99

Grades: 4 5 6 7   **Fic**

1. School stories 2. Texas -- Fiction 3. Friendship -- Fiction 4. Bereavement -- Fiction 5. Mexican Americans -- Fiction 6. Father-daughter relationship -- Fiction

ISBN 978-0-316-02955-1; 0-316-02955-6

LC 2008032819

After the death of her mother, Texas sixth-grader Lina's grades and mood drop as she watches her father lose himself more and more in books, while her best friend uses Lina as an excuse to secretly meet her boyfriend.

"Lopez effectively portrays the Texas setting and the characters' Latino heritage. . . . This . . . novel puts at its center a likable girl facing realistic problems on her own terms." Booklist

Lord, Bette Bao

In the Year of the Boar and Jackie Robinson; illustrations by Marc Simont. Harper & Row 1984 169p il lib bdg $15.89; pa $4.95

Grades: 4 5 6   **Fic**

1. School stories 2. Chinese Americans -- Fiction

ISBN 0-06-024004-0 lib bdg; 0-06-440175-8 pa

LC 83-48440

"Warm-hearted, fresh, and dappled with humor, the episodic book, which successfully encompasses both Chinese dragons and the Brooklyn Dodgers, stands out in the bevy of contemporary problem novels. And the unusual flavor of the text infiltrates the striking illustrations picturing the pert, pigtailed heroine making her way in 'Mei Guo'—her new 'Beautiful Country.'" Horn Book

Lord, Cynthia

Half a chance; Cynthia Lord. Scholastic Press 2014 224 p. (hc) $16.99

Grades: 4 5 6 7   **Fic**

1. Photography -- Fiction 2. Father-daughter relationship -- Fiction 3. Friendship -- Fiction 4. New Hampshire -- Fiction

ISBN 0545035333; 9780545035330

LC 2013013431

"When Lucy's family moves to an old house on a lake, Lucy tries to see her new home through her camera's lens, as her father has taught her--he's a famous photographer, away on a shoot. . . . When she discovers that he's judging a photo contest, Lucy decides to enter anonymously. She wants to find out if her eye for photography is really special--or only good enough." (Publisher's note)

"The story is moving, and readers will find themselves caught up in sensitive Lucy's honest and thoughtful narration." Horn Book

Jelly Bean; Cynthia Lord. Scholastic Press 2014 128 p. (alk. paper) $16.99

Grades: 1 2 3   **Fic**

1. Volunteer work -- Fiction 2. Animal shelters -- Fiction 3. Pets -- Fiction 4. Guinea pigs -- Fiction 5. Voluntarism -- Fiction 6. Responsibility -- Fiction

ISBN 0545635969; 9780545635967

LC 2014005097

In this children's book by Cynthia Lord, illustrated by Erin McGuire, part of the "Shelter Pet Squad" series, "Suzannah's always wanted a pet of her own, but she lives in an apartment where there are absolutely no pets allowed. What she CAN do is volunteer at a local pet shelter. There, although she's the youngest, Suzannah quickly finds herself making friends with the kids and bonding with the animals. She makes toys and treats for the animals." (Publisher's note)

"Second-grader Suzannah wants a live pet, but apartment-building rules won't allow any type of animal. Her mother, however, reads about a new program at the local animal shelter and thinks this might be the answer: the Shelter Pet Squad, where children volunteer to make toys and treats for homeless animals...Easy vocabulary, uncomplicated sentences, generous dialogue, large font, and friendly illustrations make the book accessible." Booklist

★ **Touch** blue. Scholastic Press 2010 186p $16.99
Grades: 4 5 6 7   **Fic**
1. Maine -- Fiction 2. Islands -- Fiction 3. Foster home care -- Fiction
ISBN 978-0-545-03531-6; 0-545-03531-7
LC 2009042306

When the state of Maine threatens to shut down their island's one-room schoolhouse because of dwindling enrollment, eleven-year-old Tess, a strong believer in luck, and her family take in a trumpet-playing foster child named Aaron to increase the school's population.

"Aaron's relationship with his foster family . . . develops believably. The tight-knit community and lobster-catching details make for a warm, colorful environment. This is a feel-good story." Booklist

Lottridge, Celia Barker

The **listening** tree. Fitzhenry & Whiteside 2011 172p $11.95
Grades: 4 5 6 7   **Fic**
1. Canada -- Fiction 2. Courage -- Fiction 3. Great Depression, 1929-1939 -- Fiction
ISBN 978-1-55455-052-4; 1-55455-052-1

It's 1935, and Ellen and her mother must leave their dried-up Saskatchewan farm to board with Aunt Gladys in Toronto. Intimidated by her new surroundings, Ellen chooses to hide in the branches of the large leafy tree outside her window and watch the neighbourhood children playing, rather than joining in their games. But when Ellen overhears a plan to evict the family-next-door from their home, she must overcome her fears and help her neighbours.

"Lottridge provides a wealth of well-developed, believable characters, especially Ellen. The story is a deftly-written, heartbreaking, and heartwarming tale of friendship and the perseverance to withstand hardships. This is a great book to introduce young readers to the impact of the Great Depression." Voice Youth Advocates

Love, D. Anne

Semiprecious. Margaret K. McElderry Books 2006 293p $16.95; pa $6.99
Grades: 5 6 7 8   **Fic**
1. Oklahoma -- Fiction 2. Family life -- Fiction
ISBN 978-0-689-85638-9; 0-689-85638-5; 978-0-689-87389-8 pa; 0-689-87389-1 pa
LC 2005-14906

Uprooted and living with an aunt in 1960s Oklahoma, thirteen-year-old Garnet and her older sister Opal brave their mother's desertion and their father's recovery from an accident, learning that "the best home of all is the one you make inside yourself"

"An involving novel of hurt, healing, and adjustment." Booklist

Lovelace, Maud Hart

Betsy-Tacy; illustrated by Lois Lenski. HarperCollins Pubs. 1994 112p il hardcover o.p. pa $5.99
Grades: 2 3 4   **Fic**
1. Minnesota -- Fiction 2. Friendship -- Fiction
ISBN 0-06-024415-1; 0-06-440096-4 pa

A reissue of the title first published 1940 by Crowell

Betsy and Tacy (short for Anastacia) were two little five-year-olds, such inseparable friends that they were regarded almost as one person. This is the story of their friendship in a little Minnesota town in the early 1900's

The author "has written a story of real literary merit as well as one with good story interest." Libr J

Other titles about Betsy through adolescence and young womanhood with reading levels to grade 5 and up are:
Betsy and Joe (1948)
Betsy and Tacy go downtown (1943)
Betsy and Tacy go over the big hill (1942)
Betsy and the great world (1952)
Betsy in spite of herself (1946)
Betsy, Tacy and Tib (1941)
Betsy was a junior (1947)
Betsy's wedding (1955)
Heavens to Betsy (1945)

Lowry, Lois

★ **Anastasia** Krupnik. Houghton Mifflin 1979 113p $17; pa $5.99
Grades: 4 5 6   **Fic**
1. Family life -- Fiction
ISBN 0-395-28629-8; 0-440-40852-0 pa

Anastasia's 10th year has some good things like falling in love and really getting to know her grandmother and some bad things like finding out about an impending baby brother

"Anastasia's father and mother—an English professor and an artist—are among the most humorous, sensible, and understanding parents to be found in . . . children's fiction, and Anastasia herself is an amusing and engaging heroine." Horn Book

Other titles about Anastasia Krupnik are:
Anastasia again! (1981)
Anastasia at your service (1982)
Anastasia, ask your analyst (1984)
Anastasia on her own (1985)
Anastasia has the answers (1986)
Anastasia's chosen career (1987)
Anastasia at this address (1991)
Anastasia, absolutely (1995)

★ **Autumn** Street. Houghton Mifflin 1980 188p $17; $16
Grades: 4 5 6 7   **Fic**
1. Friendship -- Fiction 2. World War, 1939-1945 -- Fiction
ISBN 9780395278123; 0-395-27812-0
LC 80-376

"Elizabeth, the teller of the story, feels danger around her when her father goes to fight in World War II. She, her older sister, and her pregnant mother go to live with her grandparents on Autumn Street. Tatie, the black cook-housekeeper, and her street-wise grandson Charley love Elizabeth and reassure her during this difficult time." Child Book Rev Serv

★ The **birthday** ball; illustrations by Jules Feiffer. Houghton Mifflin Harcourt 2010 186p il $16
Grades: 3 4 5   **Fic**
1. School stories 2. Birthdays -- Fiction 3. Princesses -- Fiction
ISBN 978-0-547-23869-2; 0-547-23869-X
LC 2009-32966

Princess Patricia Priscilla is bored with life as a royal life and the preparations for her 16th birthday ball. "Disguised as a peasant, she attends the village school . . . and attracts friends and the attention of the handsome school master. . . . What began as a cure for boredom, becomes a chance for [the princess] to break the rules and marry the man she loves." (Publisher's note) "Intermediate." (Horn Book)

"Lowry uses her knack for cleverly turning familiar stories on their heads . . . in this tale about a princess who's utterly bored with privileged palace life. . . . Feiffer's wiry ink illustrations paint the characters in offhand caricatures, adding to the merriment. Employing elements from the 'Prince and the Pauper' as well as ample doses of humor and slapstick, Lowry sets the stage for a rowdy denouement." Publ Wkly

Bless this mouse; illustrated by Eric Rohmann. Houghton Mifflin Books for Children 2011 151p il $15.99
Grades: 4 5 6   **Fic**
  1. Mice -- Fiction
  ISBN 978-0-547-39009-3; 0-547-39009-2
                  LC 2010-07331
Mouse Mistress Hildegarde musters all her ingenuity to keep a large colony of church mice safe from the exterminator and to see that they make it through the dangerous Blessing of the Animals. "Grades three to five." (Bull Cent Child Books)

"The book is an impeccably constructed, good-humored adventure filled with master plans, near disasters, and brave rescues, all gently frightening for readers even younger than the target audience. . . . Fun and lighthearted." Publ Wkly

★ The **giver**. Houghton Mifflin 1993 180p pa $8.95; $17
Grades: 6 7 8 9 10   **Fic**
  1. Science fiction
  ISBN 0-385-73255-4 pa; 0-395-64566-2
                  LC 92-15034
Awarded the Newbery Medal, 1994
This novel is set in a future society "without conflict, poverty, unemployment, divorce, injustice, or inequality. . . . December is the time of the annual Ceremony at which each twelve-year-old receives a life assignment determined by the Elders. . . . Jonas has been chosen for something special. When his selection leads him to an unnamed man—the man called only the Giver—he begins to sense the dark secrets that underlie the fragile perfection of his world." (Publisher's note) "Grades five to eight." (Bull Cent Child Books)
"A riveting, chilling story that inspires a new appreciation for diversity, love, and even pain. Truly memorable." SLJ

Gooney Bird and all her charms; by Lois Lowry and illustrated by Middy Thomas. Houghton Mifflin Harcourt 2014 160 p. $16.99
Grades: 2 3 4   **Fic**
  1. Anatomy 2. Skeleton 3. School stories 4. Schools -- Fiction 5. Skeleton -- Fiction 6. Human anatomy -- Fiction 7. Charm bracelets -- Fiction
  ISBN 0544113543; 9780544113541
                  LC 2012041887
In this book, by Lois Lowry, "Gooney Bird and her second-grade classmates are studying the human body. The

students are in for a surprise when her uncle, Dr. Walter Oglethorpe, an anatomy professor, loans them a skeleton to help them with their research. The skeleton, on display outside the school to show the location of the respiratory system, goes missing, and Gooney Bird becomes head detective, leading her class on an investigation to solve the mystery." (Publisher's note)

"In her sixth book, bossy but good-natured Gooney Bird Greene livens up the class human body unit with a real skeleton, on loan from her great-uncle, Dr. Oglethorpe. A parent's objection brings tension to the plot laden with amusingly precocious observations of second graders; ultimately, Gooney's charm bracelet helps the kids present their new anatomy knowledge. Simple line drawings illustrate the chapters." (Horn Book)

Gooney Bird and the room mother; illustrated by Middy Thomas. Houghton Mifflin 2005 80p il $15; pa $5.50
Grades: 2 3 4   **Fic**
  1. School stories 2. Thanksgiving Day -- Fiction
  ISBN 0-618-53230-7; 0440421330 pa
                  LC 2004-15511
Gooney Bird Greene, an entertaining second grader who introduces challenging vocabulary words and tells "absolutely true" stories, finds a surprise room mother to bring cupcakes for the Thanksgiving pageant.

"This is a fast-paced read, with Thomas's black-and-white drawings highlighting key moments." SLJ

Gooney Bird Greene; illustrated by Middy Thomas. Houghton Mifflin 2002 88p il $15
Grades: 2 3 4   **Fic**
  1. School stories 2. Storytelling -- Fiction
  ISBN 0-618-23848-4
                  LC 2002-1478
A most unusual new student who loves to be the center of attention entertains her teacher and fellow second graders by telling absolutely true stories about herself, including how she got her name

"Lowry's masterful writing style reaches directly into her audience, managing both to appeal to young listeners and to engage older readers." Bull Cent Child Books

Other titles about Gooney Bird are:
Gooney Bird and the room mother (2005)
Gooney Bird is so absurd (2009)
Gooney Bird on the map (2011)
Gooney the fabulous (2007)

★ **Number** the Stars; Lois Lowry. 25th Anniversary Edition Houghton Mifflin Harcourt 2014 137 p. $17.99
Grades: 4 5 6 7   **Fic**
  1. Jews -- Fiction 2. Denmark -- Fiction 3. Friendship -- Fiction 4. World War, 1939-1945 -- Fiction
  ISBN 0544340000; 9780544340008
                  LC 8837134
First published 1989
Newbery Medal (1990)
"As the German troops begin their campaign to 'relocate' all the Jews of Denmark, Annemarie Johansen's family takes in Annemarie's best friend, Ellen Rosen, and conceals her as part of the family. Through the eyes of ten-year-old Annemarie, we watch as the Danish Resistance smuggles almost the entire Jewish population of Denmark, nearly

seven thousand people, across the sea to Sweden." (Publisher's note)

"The appendix details the historical incidents upon which Lowry bases her plot. . . . The whole work is seamless, compelling, and memorable." Horn Book

Son; by Lois Lowry. Houghton Mifflin 2012 393 p. $17.99

Grades: 6 7 8 9 10 11 12   **Fic**

1. Science fiction 2. Dystopian fiction 3. Amnesia -- Fiction 4. Mothers -- Fiction 5. Secrecy -- Fiction 6. Identity -- Fiction 7. Mother-child relationship -- Fiction 8. Mother and child -- Fiction 9. Separation (Psychology) -- Fiction

ISBN 0547887205; 9780547887203

LC 2012014034

Author Lois Lowry tells the story of "14-year-old Claire, [who] has no contact with her baby Gabe until she surreptitiously bonds with him in the community Nurturing Center. . . . After living for years with Alys, a childless healer, Claire's memory returns. Intent on finding Gabe, she . . . encounters the sinister Trademaster and exchanges her youth for his help in finding her child, now living in the same village as middle-aged Jonas and his wife Kira. Elderly and failing, Claire reveals her identity to Gabe, who must use his unique talent to save the village." (Kirkus Reviews)

Stay! Keeper's story. Houghton Mifflin 1997 127p il $15

Grades: 5 6 7 8   **Fic**

1. Dogs -- Fiction

ISBN 0-395-87048-8

LC 97-1569

"The author proves she is as well versed in animal behavior as in human sensibilities. Her warm sense of humor and vivid imagination . . . accentuate Keeper's unorthodox perceptions of the world." Publ Wkly

"The canine narrator is a mongrel with class, a poetically inclined, refined animal of good upbringing if not bloodlines. He leaves the relative safety of his first home (an alley outside a French restaurant) for the perils of the wide world in search of a human friend." Bull Cent Child Books

A summer to die; illustrated by Jenni Oliver. Houghton Mifflin 1977 154p il $16

Grades: 5 6 7 8   **Fic**

1. Death -- Fiction 2. Sisters -- Fiction

ISBN 0-395-25338-1

LC 77-83

"As told by Meg, the chronicle of this experience is a sensitive exploration of the complex emotions underlying the adolescent's first confrontation with human mortality; the author suggests nuances of contemporary conversation and situations without sacrificing the finesse with which she limns her characters." Horn Book

Lunn, Janet Louise Swoboda

Laura Secord: a story of courage; [by] Janet Lunn; illustrated by Maxwell Newhouse. Tundra Bks. 2001 un il maps $16.95

Grades: 3 4 5   **Fic**

1. Pioneers 2. War of 1812 -- Fiction

ISBN 0-88776-538-6

"The folkloric rhythm of the tale is underscored in the dramatically colored, naively rendered illustrations." Horn Book Guide

Luper, Eric

Jeremy Bender vs. the Cupcake Cadets. Balzer + Bray 2011 235p $15.99

Grades: 4 5 6   **Fic**

1. Contests -- Fiction 2. Sex role -- Fiction 3. Boats and boating -- Fiction 4. Money-making projects for children -- Fiction

ISBN 978-0-06-201512-9; 0-06-201512-5

LC 2010-40808

When sixth-grader Jeremy Bender damages his father's prized boat and needs to come up with a lot of money to get it repaired, he and his best friend dress up as girls and infiltrate the Cupcake Cadet troop in an attempt to win the Windjammer Whirl model sailboat contest, and the prize money that comes with it.

"A not-so-lightweight tale rises above drag jokes to reveal surprising profundity." Kirkus

Lupica, Mike

The batboy. Philomel Books 2010 247p $17.99

Grades: 5 6 7 8   **Fic**

1. Baseball -- Fiction 2. Detroit (Mich.) -- Fiction 3. Mother-son relationship -- Fiction 4. Detroit Tigers (Baseball team) -- Fiction

ISBN 978-0-399-25000-2; 0-399-25000-X

LC 2009015067

Even though his mother feels baseball ruined her marriage to his father, she allows fourteen-year-old Brian to become a bat boy for the Detroit Tigers, who have just drafted his favorite player back onto the team.

Lupica gives "his readers a behind-the-scenes look at major league sports. In this novel, he adds genuine insights into family dynamics and the emotional state of his hero." Booklist

Fantasy league; Mike Lupica. Philomel, an imprint of Penguin Group (USA) 2014 304 p. (hardback) $17.99

Grades: 5 6 7 8   **Fic**

1. Football -- Fiction 2. Football teams -- fiction 3. Fantasy football -- fiction

ISBN 0399256075; 9780399256073

LC 2014007442

In this book, by Mike Lupica, "12-year-old Charlie is a fantasy football guru. He may be just a bench warmer for his school's football team, but when it comes to knowing and loving the game, he's first-string. He even becomes a celebrity when his podcast gets noticed by a sports radio host, who plays Charlie's fantasy picks for all of Los Angeles to hear. Soon Charlie befriends the elderly owner of the L.A. Bulldogs . . . and convinces him to take a chance on an aging quarterback." (Publisher's note)

"Usually a football book is about whether or not the kid makes the team and the problems that follow. So it's refreshing that those issues are only a part of 12-year-old Charlie Gains' story. See, Charlie is known as the Brain, because he is a football stats genius. He understands which players should be playing where and why. . . . There's a lot of football here: pro and fantasy teams and Charlie's own Pop Warner career. Veteran sportswriter Lupica handles it all very well. However, it's the heart and depth he adds to the story depicting Charlie's relationships with a sterling cast of characters that make this unique. This Moneyball story with kids is on the money." Booklist

Heat. Philomel Books 2006 220p $16.99
Grades: 5 6 7 8   **Fic**
1. Cubans -- Fiction 2. Orphans -- Fiction 3. Baseball -- Fiction 4. Illegal aliens -- Fiction
ISBN 0-14-240757-7 pa; 0-399-24301-1
                   LC 2005013521

Pitching prodigy Michael Arroyo is on the run from social services after being banned from playing Little League baseball because rival coaches doubt he is only twelve years old and he has no parents to offer them proof. "Grades five to eight." (Bull Cent Child Books)

"The dialogue crackles, and the rich cast of supporting characters' . . . nearly steals the show. Topnotch entertainment." Booklist

Heavy hitters; Mike Lupica. Scholastic 2014 219 p. hbk $16.99
Grades: 3 4 5 6 7   **Fic**
1. Baseball -- Fiction 2. Children of divorced parents -- Fiction 3. Fear -- Fiction 4. Friendship -- Fiction 5. Baseball players -- Fiction 6. Dysfunctional families -- Fiction
ISBN 0545381843; 9780545381840
                   LC 2014430128

In this middle grade book by Mike Lupica, part of the Game Changers series, "Ben and his friends, the Core Four Plus One, are so excited to play in their town's All-Star Baseball league. But in the first game of the season Ben gets hit by a pitch. It's never happened to him before and it shakes him up. . . . Ben discovers that Justin's parents are getting a divorce and Justin is thinking about quitting the team." (Publisher's note)

"Charismatic Ben McBain joins his favorite sidekicks . . . for another sports season, this time All-Star baseball. Conflict comes quickly when Ben slumps after being hit by a pitch and Justin struggles with his parent's divorce. By trying to help one another, the friends also help themselves. Lupica's captivating play-by-play details pull the reader into the games, right alongside these sports-loving characters." Horn Book

Other titles in this series are:
Game changers (2012)
Play makers (2013)

Hot hand; [by] Mike Lupica. Philomel Books 2007 165p (Comeback kids) $9.99; pa $6.99
Grades: 3 4 5   **Fic**
1. Bullies -- Fiction 2. Basketball -- Fiction 3. Father-son relationship -- Fiction
ISBN 978-0-399-24714-9; 978-0-14-241441-5 pa
                   LC 2006034562

In the wake of his parents' separation, ten-year-old Billy seems to have continual conflicts with his father, who is also his basketball coach, but his quiet, younger brother Ben, a piano prodigy, is having even more trouble adjusting, and only Billy seems to notice.

"The characters . . . are always sympathetic . . . and the adults have complexity and depth. . . . The strongest point .

. . is the quality of the sports play-by-play; Lupica portrays the action clearly and vividly." SLJ
Other titles in this series are:
Two-minute drill (2007)
Safe at home (2008)
Long shot (2008)
Shoot-out (2010)

Long shot. Philomel Books 2008 182p (Comeback kids) $9.99; pa $6.99
Grades: 3 4 5   **Fic**
1. School stories 2. Basketball -- Fiction 3. Mexican Americans -- Fiction
ISBN 978-0-399-24717-0; 0-399-24717-3; 978-0-14-241520-7 pa; 0-14-241520-0 pa
                   LC 2008001385

Pedro, an avid basketball player, decides to run for class president, challenging a teammate who is also one of the most popular boys in school.

Safe at home. Philomel Books 2008 175p (Comeback kids) $9.99; pa $6.99
Grades: 3 4 5   **Fic**
1. School stories 2. Orphans -- Fiction 3. Adoption -- Fiction 4. Baseball -- Fiction
ISBN 978-0-399-24716-3; 0-399-24716-5; 978-0-14-241460-6 pa; 0-14-241460-3 pa
                   LC 2007042100

Playing baseball was the one thing that made twelve-year-old Nick Crandall feel at home until he found acceptance with adoptive parents, but he faces a new struggle to fit in when he becomes the first seventh-grader ever to make the varsity baseball team.

Shoot-out. Philomel Books 2009 165p (Comeback kids) $10.99
Grades: 3 4 5   **Fic**
1. Moving -- Fiction 2. Soccer -- Fiction
ISBN 978-0-399-24718-7; 0-399-24718-1
                   LC 2008021588

Twelve-year-old Jake must leave his championship soccer team to play on a team with a losing record when his family moves to a neighboring town.

"An enjoyable sports story with lots of action." Booklist

Two-minute drill; [by] Mike Lupica. Philomel Books 2007 165p (Comeback kids) $9.99
Grades: 3 4 5   **Fic**
1. School stories 2. Dyslexia -- Fiction 3. Football -- Fiction 4. Friendship -- Fiction
ISBN 978-0-399-24715-6; 0-399-24715-7
                   LC 2007011745

Brainy Scott, a great kicker who otherwise struggles with football, and star quarterback Chris, who has dyslexia, team up to help each other succeed in both football and school.

"The characters . . . are always sympathetic . . . and the adults have complexity and depth. . . . The strongest point . . . is the quality of the sports play-by-play; Lupica portrays the action clearly and vividly." SLJ

Lyga, Barry
Archvillain. Scholastic Press 2010 180p $16.99
Grades: 4 5 6 7   **Fic**
1. Science fiction 2. Superheroes -- Fiction 3. Good

and evil -- Fiction 4. Extraterrestrial beings -- Fiction
ISBN 978-0-545-19649-9; 0-545-19649-3

LC 2010-05291

Twelve-year-old Kyle Camden develops greater mental agility and superpowers during a plasma storm that also brings Mighty Mike, an alien, to the town of Bouring, but while each does what he thinks is best, Kyle is labeled a villain and Mike a hero.

"Comic book fans in particular will appreciate this clever origin story, first in a new series. . . . Lyga . . . laces his story with ample humor. . . . Readers will find plenty to ponder." Publ Wkly

Lynch, Chris, 1962-
The **right** fight; Chris Lynch. Scholastic Press 2014
192 p.
Grades: 5 6 7 8   **Fic**
1. War stories 2. War -- Fiction 3. Soldiers -- Fiction 4. World War, 1939-1945 -- Fiction 5. Tanks (Military science) -- Fiction 6. World War, 1939-1945 -- Tank warfare 7. Africa, North -- History -- 20th century -- Fiction 8. World War, 1939-1945 -- Campaigns -- Africa, North -- Fiction
ISBN 9780545522946

LC 2013014034

In this book, by Chris Lynch, "there are few things Roman loves as much as baseball, but his country is at the top of the list. So when it looks like the United States will be swept up into World War II, he turns his back on baseball and joins the US Army. . . . As it turns out, he is far more talented with a tank than he ever was with a baseball. And he is eager to drive his tank right into the field of battle, where the Army is up against the . . . Nazis of the Afrika Korps." (Publisher's note)

"Roman loves playing semi-professional baseball. Unfortunately, he's not very good. When war breaks out, he volunteers for the army and finds something he can do better than anyone: drive a tank. Here's WWII lite, with fast-paced battle scenes in Northern Africa recalling video-game action. By book's end, however, Lynch has built a lucid, realistic setting for his powerful new war series." (Horn Book)

Lyons, Mary E.
★ **Letters** from a slave girl; the story of Harriet Jacobs.
Scribner 1992 146p il hardcover o.p. pa $5.99; pa $5.99
Grades: 6 7 8 9   **Fic**
1. Slaves 2. Authors 3. Domestics 4. Memoirists 5. Letters -- Fiction 6. Slavery -- Fiction 7. African Americans -- Fiction
ISBN 0-684-19446-5; 1-4169-3637-8 pa; 9781416936374 pa

LC 91-45778

This is a fictionalized version of the life of Harriet Jacobs, told in the form of letters that she might have written during her slavery in North Carolina and as she prepared for escape to the North in 1842. Glossary. Bibliography. "Age twelve and up." (Horn Book)

This "is historical fiction at its best. . . . Mary Lyons has remained faithful to Jacobs's actual autobiography throughout her readable, compelling novel. . . . Her observations of the horrors of slavery are concise and lucid. The letters are written in dialect, based on Jacobs's own writing and on other slave narrations of the period." Horn Book

Maberry, Jonathan
The **orphan** army; Jonathan Maberry. Simon & Schuster Books for Young Readers 2015 400 p. (The Nightsiders) (hardcover) $16.99
Grades: 5 6 7 8   **Fic**
1. Science fiction 2. Monsters -- Fiction 3. Heroes and heroines -- Fiction 4. Magic -- Fiction 5. Heroes -- Fiction 6. Supernatural -- Fiction 7. Extraterrestrial beings -- Fiction
ISBN 1481415751; 9781481415750

LC 2014014576

In this juvenile novel, by Jonathan Maberry, part of "The Nightsiders" series, set "in a slightly futuristic world, where ruthless insectlike monsters are exterminating humans and the Earth itself, Milo discovers secrets that change the tides of war in a serious way. The Nightsiders are a group of mystical beasts leading the fight to defend Earth and its inhabitants from the maleficent Bugs." (School Library Journal)

"Milo Silk is not a hero. This mantra of Milo's, repeated throughout much of this series opener, couldn't be further from the truth. In a slightly futuristic world, where ruthless insectlike monsters are exterminating humans and the Earth itself, Milo discovers secrets that change the tides of war in a serious way... must-have for fans of Maberry's previous books and middle grade sci-fi." SLJ

MacDonald, Amy
Too much flapdoodle! [illustrations by Cat Bowman Smith] Farrar Straus Giroux 2008 182p il $16.95
Grades: 3 4 5 6   **Fic**
1. Aunts -- Fiction 2. Uncles -- Fiction 3. Farm life -- Fiction 4. Country life -- Fiction
ISBN 978-0-374-37671-0; 0-374-37671-9

LC 2007033273

Twelve-year-old Parker reluctantly goes to spend the summer with his eccentric great-aunt and great-uncle on their dilapidated farm, where he discovers that there is more to life than the latest game system and the coolest cell phone

"Hilarious antics ensue as the boy matures and realizes that there is more to life than the latest video game. Black-and-white line drawings enhance the lighthearted text." SLJ

Other titles about these characters are:
No more nice (1996)
No more nasty (2001)

MacDonald, Bailey
The **secret** of the sealed room; a mystery of young Benjamin Franklin. Aladdin 2010 208p $16.99
Grades: 4 5 6 7   **Fic**
1. Authors 2. Diplomats 3. Inventors 4. Statesmen 5. Scientists 6. Mystery fiction 7. Writers on science 8. Members of Congress 9. Boston (Mass.) -- Fiction
ISBN 978-1-4169-9760-3; 1-4169-9760-1

When she runs away after her master dies, indentured servant Patience Martin is accused of stealing and needs the help of a young Benjamin Franklin to prove her innocence.

"MacDonald creates a series of events that could very well be factual and leaves the reader curious to know more. Replete with historical facts without being blatant, the well-developed plot will keep mystery lovers guessing until the very last chapter." Booklist

Wicked Will. Aladdin 2009 201p $16.99

Grades: 5 6 7   **Fic**
1. Poets 2. Authors 3. Dramatists 4. Mystery fiction
5. Orphans -- Fiction 6. Theater -- Fiction 7. Great
Britain -- History -- 1485-1603, Tudors -- Fiction
ISBN 1-4169-8660-X; 978-1-4169-8660-7
LC 2008-50818

Performing in the English town of Stratford-on-Avon in
1576, Viola, a young actress (disguised as a boy) and a local lad named Will Shakespeare uncover a murder mystery.

"The chapters themselves logically reveal the twists and
turns of the plot in concise, readable prose. The realistic details put flesh on the bones of not only the primary characters, but also of the secondary personages as well." SLJ

MacDonald, Betty

Nancy and Plum; illustrated by Mary Grandpre; with
an introduction by Jeanne Birdsall. Alfred A. Knopf 2010
222p il $15.99; lib bdg $18.99
Grades: 3 4 5   **Fic**
1. Orphans -- Fiction 2. Sisters -- Fiction
ISBN 978-0-375-86685-2; 0-375-86685-X; 978-0-
375-96685-9 lib bdg; 0-375-96685-4 lib bdg
A reissue of the title first published 1952

"Orphans Nancy and Plum lead deprived lives at cruel
Mrs. Monday's boarding school. . . . The sisters manage to
escape her clutches, find wonderful new guardians, redeem
their neglectful uncle, and even improve the lot of the other
orphans. . . . Their dialogue is full of humorous teasing, and
they pull no punches with their feelings about the villainous Mrs. Monday and her dreadful niece. . . . GrandPré's
pencil and wash illustrations strike just the right note: old-
fashioned yet cheeky." Horn Book

MacDonald, George

The **light** princess; with pictures by Maurice Sendak.
Farrar, Straus & Giroux 1969 110p il hardcover o.p. pa
$5.95
Grades: 3 4 5 6   **Fic**
1. Fairy tales
ISBN 0-374-44458-7 pa

This fairy story originally appeared 1864 in the author's
novel Adela Cathcart and was reprinted in his 1867 story
collection Dealings with the fairies

"The problems of the princess who had been deprived,
as an infant, of her gravity and whose life hung in the balance when she grew up are amusing as ever and the sweet
capitulation to love that brings her (literally) to her feet, just
as touching. All of the best of Macdonald is reflected in the
Sendak illustrations: the humor and wit, the sweetness and
tenderness, and the sophistication—and they are beautiful."
Sutherland. The Best in Child Books

MacHale, D. J.

SYLO; by D.J. MacHale. Penguin Group USA 2013
416 p. (hardcover) $17.99
Grades: 5 6 7 8 9   **Fic**
1. Dystopian Fiction 2. Adventure fiction
ISBN 1595146652; 9781595146656

This is the first book in a proposed trilogy from D.J.
MacHale. Here, Tucker Pierce has a small but satisfying life
on a small island. But when the island is quarantined by the
U.S. Navy, things start to fall apart. . . . People start dying.
The girl he wants to get to know a whole lot better, Tori, is
captured along with Tucker and imprisoned behind barbed

wire." They must escape to the mainland and try to figure
out what this SYLO organization that is imprisoning them
is. (Kirkus Reviews)

Mack, Tracy

The **fall** of the Amazing Zalindas; casebook no. 1. by
Tracy Mack and Michael Citrin; illustrations by Greg Ruth.
Orchard Books 2006 259p il (Sherlock Holmes and the
Baker Street irregulars) $16.99; pa $6.99
Grades: 4 5 6 7   **Fic**
1. Mystery fiction 2. Circus -- Fiction 3. Great Britain
-- Fiction
ISBN 0-439-82836-8; 0-545-06939-4 pa
LC 2005-34000

The ragamuffin boys known as the Baker Street Irregulars help Sherlock Holmes solve the mysterious deaths of a
family of circus tightrope walkers.

"Colorful, well-defined characters . . . and plenty of
historical detail, Cockney slang . . . and Sherlockian references bring Victorian England to life. Vintage-style design
elements and evocative black-and-white illustrations further
the effect." Booklist

The **mystery** of the conjured man; [by] Tracy Mack &
Michael Citrin; [illustrations by Greg Ruth] Orchard Books
2009 il (Sherlock Holmes and the Baker Street Irregulars)
hardcover o.p.
Grades: 4 5 6   **Fic**
1. Mystery fiction 2. Spiritualism -- Fiction 3. Great
Britain -- Fiction 4. Swindlers and swindling -- Fiction
ISBN 978-0-439-83667-8 pa
LC 2006035701

The ragtag group of orphan boys known as the Baker
Street Irregulars faces shady characters and seemingly real
ghosts when they assist the famous detective, Sherlock
Holmes, in investigating the mysterious death of Greta Ber-
linger during a seance.

"A great addition to an entertaining series." SLJ

Mackey, Heather

Dreamwood; Heather Mackey. G.P. Putnam's Sons
2014 336 p. (hardback) $16.99
Grades: 4 5 6 7 8   **Fic**
1. Supernatural -- Fiction 2. Missing persons -- Fiction
3. Runaway children -- Fiction 4. Forests and forestry
-- Fiction 5. Runaways -- Fiction 6. Adventure and
adventurers -- Fiction 7. Northwest, Pacific -- History
-- 19th century -- Fiction
ISBN 0399250670; 9780399250675
LC 2013039402

In this book, by Heather Mackey, "Lucy Darrington has
no choice but to run away from boarding school. Her father, an expert on the supernatural, has been away for too
long while doing research in Saarthe, a remote territory in
the Pacific Northwest populated by towering redwoods,
timber barons, and the Lupine people. But upon arriving,
she learns her father is missing: Rumor has it he's gone in
search of dreamwood, a rare tree with magical properties."
(Publisher's note)

"Lucy Darrington's adventures begin on a train as she
flees a starched ladies finishing school to join her ghost-
chasing father on the west coast of the vaguely Victorian,
slightly steampunk American States...Dialogue and perilous
situations nudge the story along at a steady clip, with the

second half a breathless page turner. Dreamwood will please character-focused readers. Hand this to children who want an environmental adventure like Eva Ibbotson's Journey to the River Sea (Dutton, 2002) or a character-grounded speculation like Kenneth Oppel's Airborn (HarperCollins, 2004)." SLJ

MacLachlan, Patricia

The **facts** and fictions of Minna Pratt. Harper & Row 1988 136p pa $4.95

Grades: 4 5 6 7   **Fic**

1. Musicians -- Fiction

ISBN 0-06-440265-7

LC 85-45388

"Ms. MacLachlan's skillful handling of her subject, and above all her vivid characterization . . . place her story in the ranks of outstanding middle-grade fiction." N Y Times Book Rev

"Minna Pratt plays the cello and wishes she would get her vibrato. She wishes someone would answer her questions about herself and life and love. . . . Then she meets Lucas Ellerby. His life seems so perfect and he has a vibrato. As their friendship develops Minna finds that life is not always as it seems and even when you think you know someone or something there may be a hidden side that will surprise you." Voice Youth Advocates

Fly away; Patricia MacLachlan. Margaret K. McElderry Books 2014 108 p. (hardcover: alk. paper) $15.99

Grades: 3 4 5   **Fic**

1. Floods -- Juvenile fiction 2. Siblings -- Juvenile fiction 3. Family life -- Juvenile fiction 4. Cows -- Fiction 5. Poets -- Fiction 6. Floods -- Fiction 7. Family life -- Fiction 8. Brothers and sisters -- Fiction

ISBN 1442460083; 9781442460089; 9781442460102

LC 2012040995

This children's story, by Patricia MacLachlan, is "a story about one brave girl who saves her family from losing everything. Everyone in Lucy's family sings. . . . Everyone, except Lucy. . . . Just like singing, helping Aunt Frankie prepare for flooding season is a family tradition. . . . And this year, when the flood arrives, danger finds its way into the heart of Lucy's family, and Lucy will need to find her voice to save her brother." (Publisher's note)

"Lucy and her family make their annual trip to visit Aunt Frankie in North Dakota just as floodwaters rise, threatening her home. Meanwhile, Lucy shares a secret with her little brother, Teddy: though the rest of the family thinks that he can't talk yet, she knows that he can...The appealing jacket art, large type, and wide-spaced lines of text make this volume an inviting choice for readers who are beginning to read longer chapter books." Booklist

Kindred souls; Patricia MacLachlan. HarperCollins 2012 119 p. (trade bdg.) $16.99

Grades: 4 5 6   **Fic**

1. Bereavement -- Fiction 2. Family life -- Fiction 3. Family farms -- Fiction 4. Grandfathers -- Fiction 5. Houses -- Remodeling -- Fiction 6. Dogs -- Fiction 7. Old age -- Fiction 8. Prairies -- Fiction 9. Farm life -- Fiction 10. Sod houses -- Fiction

ISBN 9780060522971; 9780060522988

LC 2011016617

This book follows narrator Jake and his 88-year-old grandfather Billy, the eponymous kindred souls of the story's title. The pair "live on a farm that their family has owned for generations; in fact, Billy was born in a sod house he remembers fondly, the ruins of which still exist on the property." To comfort their dying grandfather, "Jake and his siblings undertake a remarkably ambitious project: They rebuild the sod house; Billy moves into it, and he eventually passes away there." The "first-person account of a boy coping with his grandfather's death . . . portrays . . . the opportunity to grieve for a loved one even while he is still alive." (Kirkus)

★ **Sarah,** plain and tall. Harper & Row 58p $14.99; lib bdg $15.89; pa $4.99

Grades: 3 4 5   **Fic**

1. Stepmothers -- Fiction 2. Frontier and pioneer life -- Fiction

ISBN 0-06-024101-2; 0-06-024102-0 lib bdg; 0-06-440205-3 pa

LC 83-49481

Awarded the Newbery Medal, 1986

When their father invites a mail-order bride to come live with them in their prairie home, Caleb and Anna are captivated by their new mother and hope that she will stay

"It is the simplest of love stories expressed in the simplest of prose. Embedded in these unadorned declarative sentences about ordinary people, actions, animals, facts, objects and colors are evocations of the deepest feelings of loss and fear, love and hope." N Y Times Book Rev

Other titles in this series are:

Caleb's story (2001)

Grandfather's dance (2006)

More perfect than the moon (2004)

Skylark (1994)

★ **Snowflakes** fall; by Patricia MacLachlan; illustrated by Steven Kellogg. Random House 2013 32 p. (library binding) $20.99

Grades: PreK K 1 2 3   **Fic**

1. Snow 2. Life cycles (Biology) 3. Snow -- Fiction

ISBN 0375973281; 9780375973284; 9780385376938

LC 2013008622

This book, by Patricia MacLachlan and illustrated by Steven Kellogg "portray[s] life's natural cycle: its beauty, its joy, and its sorrow. Together, the words and pictures offer the promise of renewal that can be found in our lives--snowflakes fall, and return again as raindrops so that flowers can grow." (Publisher's note)

The **truth** of me; about a boy, his grandmother, and a very good dog. Patricia MacLachlan. Katherine Tegen Books, an imprint of HarperCollinsPublishers 2013 128 p. (hardcover bdg.) $16.99

Grades: 3 4 5   **Fic**

1. Grandmothers -- Juvenile fiction 2. Parent-child relationship -- Juvenile fiction 3. Dogs -- Fiction 4. Grandmothers -- Fiction 5. Parent and child -- Fiction

ISBN 0061998591; 9780061998591; 9780061998607

LC 2012040151

In this book, "Robbie is looking forward to spending the summer with his grandmother, Maddy. He likes her eccentric stories, he likes that wild animals come right up to her, and he likes how Maddy makes his parents nervous. Robbie often feels that his parents, accomplished professional musicians, love their instruments more than him. Over the course of the summer, Maddy helps him realize that he can be brave enough to express his feelings openly." (School Library Journal)

★ **Waiting** for the magic; illustrated by Amy June Bates. Atheneum Books for Young Readers 2011 143p il $15.99

Grades: 3 4 5 6 **Fic**

1. Cats -- Fiction 2. Dogs -- Fiction 3. Family life -- Fiction

ISBN 978-1-4169-2745-7; 1-4169-2745-X

LC 2010019668

When Papa goes away for a little while, his family tries to cope with the separation by adopting four dogs and a cat.

"MacLachlan tackles the familiar yet always heart-wrenching subject of parental separation in her venerable spare and moving style. . . . The characters are individualistic, believable, and likable." Publ Wkly

White fur flying; Patricia MacLachlan. 1st ed. Margaret K. McElderry Books 2013 128 p. (hardcover) $15.99

Grades: 2 3 4 5 **Fic**

1. Dogs -- Juvenile fiction 2. Human-animal relationship -- Juvenile fiction 3. Dogs -- Fiction 4. Rescue dogs -- Fiction 5. Family problems -- Fiction 6. Human-animal relationships -- Fiction

ISBN 1442421711; 9781442421714

LC 2011046125

In this children's book, by Newbery Medalist Patricia MacLachlan, "A young boy tries to find his voice with the help of some four-legged friends. . . . Zoe's family rescues dogs in need. . . . But the house across the street is always silent these days. A new family has moved in and Phillip, the boy, has stopped speaking. He doesn't even want to try. Zoe knows that saving dogs and saving boys are different jobs, but she learns that some parts are the same." (Publisher's note)

★ **Word** after word after word. HarperCollins 2010 128p $14.99; lib bdg $15.89

Grades: 2 3 4 5 **Fic**

1. School stories 2. Cancer -- Fiction 3. Poetry -- Fiction 4. Authorship -- Fiction 5. Mother-daughter relationship -- Fiction

ISBN 978-0-06-027971-4; 0-06-027971-0; 978-0-06-027972-1 lib bdg; 0-06-027972-9 lib bdg

"Mrs. Mirabel, a visiting poet, works with a fourth-grade class over several weeks as they first discuss why people write poetry and then attempt to express themselves in verse. . . . Narrator Lucy, whose mother is recovering from cancer treatments, often meets her friends to talk about their hopes, their fears, their families, and their charismatic mentor. . . . Showing great respect for both her readers and her craft, . . . MacLachlan makes every word count in Lucy's smooth-flowing economical narrative." Booklist

Maclear, Kyo

Virginia Wolf; Kyo Maclear; [illustrated by] Isabelle Arsenault. Kids Can Press 2012 32 p.

Grades: K 1 2 **Fic**

1. Wolves -- Fiction 2. Painting -- Fiction 3. Picture books for children 4. Depression (Psychology) --

Fiction

ISBN 9781554536498; 1554536499

This picture book tells the story of a girl named Virginia whose bad mood turns her into a wolf. Her sister Vanessa, the narrator, tries to help by painting pictures for her. "The wolf--previously a black near-silhouette with snout and tail, wearing a dress--morphs back into a girl. Wolf ears, silhouetted from behind, become a hair bow. Ink, pencil and paint . . . divide color from black-and-white as emotional symbolism." Kyo Maclear combines the real-life story of writer Virginia Woolf and her sister, painter Vanessa Bell, with "a bad-day/bad-mood or animal-transformation tale" that presents "literal and metaphorical glimpses of real depression." (Kirkus)

Madden, Kerry

Gentle's Holler. Viking 2005 237p $16.99; pa $6.99

Grades: 5 6 7 8 **Fic**

1. Poverty -- Fiction 2. Family life -- Fiction 3. North Carolina -- Fiction

ISBN 0-670-05998-6; 0-14-240751-8 pa

LC 2004-18424

In the early 1960s, twelve-year-old songwriter Livy Two Weems dreams of seeing the world beyond the Maggie Valley, North Carolina, holler where she lives in poverty with her parents and eight brothers and sisters, but understands that she must put family first.

"Livy's narration rings true and is wonderfully voiced, and Madden's message about the importance of forgiveness will be well received." SLJ

Other titles in this series are:

Louisiana's song (2007)

Jessie's mountain (2008)

Madison, Alan

100 days and 99 nights; illustrated by Julia Denos. Little, Brown 2008 137p il $14.99; pa $5.99

Grades: 3 4 5 **Fic**

1. Toys -- Fiction 2. Soldiers -- Fiction 3. Virginia -- Fiction 4. Imagination -- Fiction 5. Father-daughter relationship -- Fiction

ISBN 978-0-316-11354-0; 0-316-11354-9; 978-0-316-11798-2 pa; 0-316-11798-6 pa

As Esme introduces her stuffed animal collection that is alphabetically arranged from Alvin the aardvark to Zelda the zebra she also relates her family's military life and her father's deployment

"In this moving debut novel, wordplay is part of every chapter. . . . This is a mix of hilarious language and one child's terror that there could be bad news." Booklist

Magaziner, Lauren

The **only** thing worse than witches; Lauren Magaziner. Dial Books for Young Readers, an imprint of Penguin Group (USA) LLC 2014 272 p. (hardcover) $16.99

Grades: 4 5 6 **Fic**

1. Witches -- Fiction 2. Friendship -- Fiction 3. Magic -- Fiction 4. Witchcraft -- Fiction 5. Apprentices -- Fiction 6. Best friends -- Fiction 7. Mothers and sons -- Fiction

ISBN 0803739184; 9780803739185

LC 2013034310

In this middle grades book by Lauren Magaziner, "Rupert Campbell is fascinated by the witches who live nearby.

He dreams of broomstick tours and souvenir potions, but Rupert's mother forbids him from even looking at that part of town. The closest he can get to a witchy experience is sitting in class with his awful teacher Mrs. Frabbleknacker, who smells like bellybutton lint and forbids Rupert's classmates from talking to each other before, during, and after class." (Publisher's note)

"Rupert Campbell is a fifth grader in Mrs. Frabbleknacker's class. She's the meanest teacher in school; she discourages her students from becoming friends and forces them to participate in gross projects...A solid choice for libraries looking to bolster their collection of lower-reading-level, middle-grade fiction." SLJ

Magnin, Joyce
   Carrying Mason; [by] Joyce Magnin. Zonderkidz 2011 153p $14.99
Grades: 5 6 7 8   Fic
   1. Family life -- Fiction 2. Country life -- Fiction 3. Pennsylvania -- Fiction 4. People with mental disabilities -- Fiction
   ISBN 978-0-310-72681-4; 0-310-72681-6
                                         LC 2011014462
In rural Pennsylvania in 1958, when thirteen-year-old Luna's best friend Mason dies, she decides to move in with his mentally disabled mother and care for her as Mason did.

"Gently, deliberately paced, Luna's first-person tale provides a fresh look at mental disabilities and the additional burden of negative attitudes. While Ruby's disability is apparent, this effort also celebrates her capabilities. Although the primary focus is Luna, her quirky father, supportive mother and boy-crazy older sister are also sufficiently developed to provide additional depth. A quiet coming-of-age tale with heart offers a fresh look at mentally disabled adults." Kirkus

Magoon, Kekla
   Camo girl. Aladdin 2010 218p $16.99
Grades: 5 6 7 8   Fic
   1. Friendship -- Fiction 2. Prejudices -- Fiction 3. Racially mixed people -- Fiction
   ISBN 978-1-4169-7804-6; 1-4169-7804-6
A novel about a biracial girl living in the suburbs of Las Vegas examines the friendships that grow out of, and despite, her race.

"Magoon . . . offers a sensitive and articulate portrayal of a pair of middle-school outsiders. . . . This poetic and nuanced story addresses the courage it takes to truly know and support someone, as well as the difficult choices that come with growing up." Publ Wkly

Mahy, Margaret
   Maddigan's Fantasia. Margaret K. McElderry Books 2007 499p $15.99
Grades: 4 5 6 7   Fic
   1. Fantasy fiction 2. Magic -- Fiction 3. Circus -- Fiction
   ISBN 1-4169-1812-4; 978-1-4169-1817-7
                                         LC 2006-15512
In a world made uncertain by "the Chaos," two time-traveling boys, fifteen-year-old Timon and eleven-year-old Eden, seek to protect a magic talisman, aided by twelve-year-old Garland, a member of a traveling circus known as Maddigan's Fantasia.

"A well-drawn character, Garland resembles other Mahy protagonists—cranky, assertive and filled with self-doubt—and her adventures are invariably exciting." Publ Wkly

   Mister Whistler; Margaret Mahy. Lerner Pub Group 2013 32 p. $17.95
Grades: PreK K   Fic
   1. Dance -- Fiction 2. Humorous fiction 3. Lost and found possessions -- Fiction
   ISBN 187746791X; 9781877467912
In this humorous picture book for children, by Margaret Mahy, illustrated by Gavin Bishop, "Mister Whistler always has a song in his head and a dance in his legs. But when he has to catch the train, he is so distracted he loses his ticket--and has to dance his way out of his clothes to find it!" (Publisher's note)

Malaghan, Michael
   Greek ransom. Andersen Press 2010 264p pa $9.99
Grades: 5 6 7 8   Fic
   1. Adventure fiction 2. Greece -- Fiction 3. Siblings -- Fiction 4. Kidnapping -- Fiction
   ISBN 978-184270-786-9; 1-84270-786-8
"Nick and Callie Latham are on the Greek island of Theta with their archaeologist parents for a working vacation. Then the children discover that Mum and Dad have lost the family's money in a reckless bid to locate the lost treasure of King Akanon. A shifty businessman kidnaps the couple in order to acquire it for himself. After Nick and Callie barely escape capture themselves, it's up to them to find a way to free their parents. . . . Readers will be on the edge of their seats throughout to see what happens next. . . . The relationship between Nick and Callie is spot-on, and kids will enjoy this high-spirited tale." SLJ

Malaspina, Ann
   Yasmin's hammer; illustrated by Doug Chayka. Lee & Low Books 2010 un il $18.95
Grades: 2 3 4 5   Fic
   1. Bangladesh -- Fiction 2. Child labor -- Fiction
   ISBN 978-1-60060-359-4; 1-60060-359-9
"Swinging a hammer all day as she and her little sister break bricks in the city heat of Dhaka, Bangladesh, Yasmin dreams of going to school. In a moving voice true to her viewpoint, Yasmin speaks in smooth free verse about her longing. . . . Stirring oil paintings bring the setting to a close with images of the sisters in the brickyard and their father pedaling a rickshaw through the crowded streets. The back matter includes a clear map, a glossary, and a bibliography with online sites about how to help children like Yasmin." Booklist
   Includes glossary and bibliographical references

Malchow, Alex
   The **Sword** of Darrow; [by] Alex and Hal Malchow. BenBella 2011 531p map $17.99
Grades: 5 6 7 8   Fic
   1. Fantasy fiction 2. Magic -- Fiction 3. Fairies -- Fiction 4. Princesses -- Fiction
   ISBN 978-1-9356-1846-1; 1-9356-1846-6
                                         LC 2011012233
"For 10 years the people of Sonnencrest endured the cruel and tyrannical rule of the Goblins. Then Princess Babette, the only surviving member of the royal family, and

Darrow, a crippled boy, become the unlikely forces in the fight against the oppressors. The authors paint convincing portraits of the characters. . . . Readers will be drawn to this fledgling rebellion and follow it to its spectacular success. Magic, monsters, and wizards add to the excitement." SLJ

Manivong, Laura
Escaping the tiger. Harper 2010 216p il $15.99
Grades: 6 7 8 9   Fic
1. Laos -- Fiction 2. Refugees -- Fiction 3. Thailand -- Fiction 4. Family life -- Fiction
ISBN 978-0-06-166177-8; 0-06-166177-5
LC 2009-24095
In 1982, twelve-year-old Vonlai, his parents, and sister, Dalah, escape from Laos to a Thai refugee camp, where they spend four long years struggling to survive in hopes on one day reaching America.

"This compelling novel offers significant historical background. This is certainly a book to prompt purposeful discussion to increase historical and multicultural awareness." SLJ

Manley, Candace
Skeeter's dream; a novel. La Frontera Pub. 2010 183p pa $14.95
Grades: 4 5 6   Fic
1. Adventure fiction 2. Texas -- Fiction 3. Arkansas -- Fiction 4. Family life -- Fiction 5. Stepfamilies -- Fiction 6. Runaway children -- Fiction 7. Frontier and pioneer life -- Fiction
ISBN 978-0-9785634-8-6; 0-9785634-8-4
LC 2010027719
When thirteen-year-old Robert "Skeeter" Tates, fed up with his Yankee stepfather and stepbrothers, leaves his Arkansas home for Texas in 1867, he meets up with unexpected traveling companions as well as outlaws and the lawmen tracking them.

"This is a well-written story with believable characters and an intriguing plot. The dialog is authentic and the action is fast-paced. Give this book to fans of historical fiction or to boys looking for a thrilling adventure story." Libr Media Connect

Marciano, John Bemelmans
The **9** lives of Alexander Baddenfield; by John Bemelmans Marciano. Viking Published by Penguin Group 2013 144 p. (hardcover) $16.99
Grades: 4 5 6 7 8   Fic
1. Fantasy fiction 2. Cats -- Fiction 3. Death -- Fiction 4. Humorous stories 5. Wealth -- Fiction 6. Orphans -- Fiction 7. Reincarnation -- Fiction 8. Conduct of life -- Fiction
ISBN 0670014060; 9780670014064
LC 2012048448
In this book, "Alexander Baddenfield is a horrible boy . . . who is the last in a long line of lying, thieving scoundrels. One day, Alexander has an astonishing idea. Why not transplant the nine lives from his cat into himself? Suddenly, Alexander has lives to spare, and goes about using them up, attempting the most outrageous feats he can imagine. Only when his lives start running out, and he is left with only one just like everyone else, does he realize how reckless he has been." (Publisher's note)

Marentette, Meghan
The **stowaways**; by Meghan Marentette; illustrated by Dean Griffiths. Orca Book Pub 2014 240 p. $19.95
Grades: 3 4 5   Fic
1. Mice -- Fiction 2. Family -- Fiction 3. Secrets -- Fiction 4. Adventure stories
ISBN 1927485339; 9781927485330
In this book, by Meghan Marentette and illustrated by Dean Griffiths, "the Stowaways aren't like the other Weedle mice. They are inventive and curious, they go on adventures, and they are much too clever for their own good. In fact, everyone knows that Grampa Stowaway was killed in a trap on one of his adventures. . . . There's something else about the Stowaways. They keep secrets." (Publisher's note)

"Rory Stowaway comes from a long line of adventuring mice. He does not understand why his own papa is so against going out into the world beyond their cozy little home on Biggle's farm... Themes of courage, family, friendship, and accepting differences permeate the story. Intermittent and well-placed black-and-white illustrations lend a vintage feel to the overall design of the book. A fine debut that deserves a place alongside Cynthia Voight's Young Fredle (Knopf) and Richard Peck's Secrets at Sea (Dial, both 2011)." SLJ

Margolis, Leslie
Everybody bugs out. Bloomsbury Children's Books 2011 195p $15.99
Grades: 4 5 6   Fic
1. School stories 2. California -- Fiction 3. Friendship -- Fiction 4. Family life -- Fiction
ISBN 1-59990-526-4; 978-1-59990-526-6
LC 2010035628
Sixth-grader Annabelle realizes that she has a crush on Oliver, with whom she is doing a science fair project, just before the Valentine's Day dance—and just before her friend Claire announces her crush on him.

"Margolis' breezy tone nicely conveys the peaks and valleys of middle-school life." Kirkus

Girl's best friend. Bloomsbury USA Childrens Books 2010 261p $14.99
Grades: 4 5 6 7   Fic
1. School stories 2. Mystery fiction 3. Dogs -- Fiction 4. Twins -- Fiction 5. Siblings -- Fiction 6. Family life -- Fiction 7. Brooklyn (New York, N.Y.) -- Fiction
ISBN 978-1-59990-525-9; 1-59990-525-6
LC 2010000562
In Brooklyn, New York, twelve-year-old dog-walker Maggie, aided by her twin brother Finn and best friend Lucy, investigates someone she believes is stealing pets.

"Characters are well-developed, typical preteens. Readers will easily identify with these seventh graders, and they will love the eccentric landlady who adds a bit of humor. Mystery fans will enjoy this lighthearted whodunit." SLJ

Girls acting catty. Bloomsbury 2009 179p $15.99
Grades: 4 5 6   Fic
1. School stories 2. California -- Fiction 3. Remarriage -- Fiction 4. Family life -- Fiction
ISBN 978-1-59990-237-1; 1-59990-237-0
LC 2009002144
Sequel to: Boys are dogs (2008)
Sixth-grader Annabelle spends autumn coping with competing groups of friends at school, her mother's pre-

wedding stress, learning to get along with a cute stepbrother-to-be, and such momentous events as wearing her first bra and learning to shave her legs.

"Margolis handles Annabelle's minor crises with sensitivity and humor." SLJ

Marino, Nan

★ Neil Armstrong is my uncle; & other lies Muscle Man McGinty told me. Roaring Brook Press 2009 154p $16.95

Grades: 3 4 5 6   **Fic**

1. Bullies -- Fiction 2. Friendship -- Fiction 3. Foster home care -- Fiction 4. Long Island (N.Y.) -- Fiction
ISBN 978-1-59643-499-8; 1-59643-499-6

"It's the summer of 1969, when astronauts land on the moon, and Tamara Ann Simpson is not having a good time. Foster child and best friend Kebsie has suddenly moved away and now Douglas McGinty is in her spot with Mrs. Kutchner. Tammy dubs him 'Muscle Man' after one outrageous lie. . . . Fierce and plaintive, Tammy's voice crackles with originality and yet is completely childlike. The '60s setting comes to life with sharply honed details. . . . The authenticity of the time and the voice combine with a poignant plot to reveal a depth unusual in such a straightforward first-person narrative." Kirkus

Marr, Melissa, 1972-

Loki's wolves; by K.L. Armstrong and M.A. Marr. 1st ed. Little, Brown and Co. 2013 368 p. ill. (The Blackwell pages) (hardcover) $16.99

Grades: 4 5 6 7 8   **Fic**

1. Norse mythology -- Fiction 2. Adventure fiction -- Juvenile fiction 3. Gods -- Fiction 4. Monsters -- Fiction 5. Supernatural -- Fiction 6. Shapeshifting -- Fiction 7. Mythology, Norse -- Fiction 8. Adventure and adventurers -- Fiction
ISBN 031620496X; 9780316204965

LC 2012029851

This juvenile fantasy novel, by K. L. Armstrong and M. A. Marr, is the first book in the "Blackwell Pages" series. "Matt hears the words, but he can't believe them. He's Thor's representative? Destined to fight trolls, monstrous wolves and giant serpents . . . or the world ends? He's only thirteen. . . . But now Ragnarok is coming, and it's up to the champions to fight in the place of the long-dead gods." (Publisher's note)

"It is so methodically constructed that readers will welcome the action Ragnarök will offer. . . . Norse mythology brought to life with engaging contemporary characters and future volumes that promise explosive action; ideal for Percy Jackson fans who want to branch out." Kirkus

Odin's ravens; K.L. Armstrong; M.A. Marr. First edition Little, Brown and Co. 2014 352 p. illustrations (The Blackwell pages) (hardcover) $17

Grades: 4 5 6 7 8   **Fic**

1. Adventure fiction 2. Supernatural -- Fiction 3. Norse mythology -- Fiction 4. Gods and goddesses -- Fiction 5. Gods -- Fiction 6. Monsters -- Fiction 7. Valhalla -- Fiction 8. Shapeshifting -- Fiction 9. Mythology, Norse -- Fiction 10. Adventure and adventurers -- Fiction
ISBN 0316204986; 9780316204989

LC 2013018519

In this sequel to "Loki's Wolves," by K.L. Armstrong and M.A. Marr, "when thirteen-year-old Matt Thorsen, a modern day descendant of the Norse god Thor, was chosen to represent Thor in an epic battle to prevent the apocalypse he thought he knew how things would play out. Gather the descendants standing in for gods like Loki and Odin, defeat a giant serpent, and save the world. No problem, right?" (Publisher's note)

"This sequel stands by itself, as essential details of the first are neatly woven throughout. Intense action, well-crafted scenes and humor-laced dialogue add up to a sure winner. Just enough black-and-white illustrations add a visual dimension to the vivid text. What Riordan has done for Greek and Egyptian mythology, Armstrong and Marr are doing for Norse myths, and readers will come away knowing much about Valkyries, Berserkers, wulfenkind and draugr. A Hel of a good read." -Kirkus

Marsden, Carolyn, 1950-

★ The gold-threaded dress. Candlewick Press 2002 73p hardcover o.p. pa $5.99

Grades: 3 4 5   **Fic**

1. Friendship 2. Prejudices 3. School stories 4. Thai Americans 5. Identity 6. Moving, Household 7. Prejudices -- Fiction 8. Thai Americans -- Fiction
ISBN 0-7636-1569-2; 0-7636-2993-6 pa

LC 2001-25132

When Oy and her Thai American family move to a new neighborhood, her third-grade classmates tease and exclude her because she is different

"Marsden writes with keen observation and finesse about the social dynamics of the classroom and with simplicity reveals the layers of emotion experienced by Oy." Booklist

Another title about Oy is:
The Quail Club (2006)

★ Silk umbrellas; [by] Carolyn Marsden. Candlewick Press 2004 134p $15.99; pa $5.99

Grades: 3 4 5 6   **Fic**

1. Artists -- Fiction 2. Thailand -- Fiction 3. Family life -- Fiction
ISBN 0-7636-2257-5; 0-7636-3376-3 pa

LC 2003-55323

Eleven-year-old Noi worries that she will have to stop painting the silk umbrellas her family sells at the market near their Thai village and be forced to join her older sister in difficult work at a local factory instead.

"In simple, lucid prose, Marsden tells a story that is foreign in detail and texture but universal in appeal. . . . This gracefully told story will resonate with many young readers." Booklist

★ Take me with you. Candlewick Press 2010 160p $14.99

Grades: 4 5 6 7   **Fic**

1. Italy -- Fiction 2. Orphans -- Fiction 3. Friendship -- Fiction 4. Racially mixed people -- Fiction
ISBN 978-0-7636-3739-2; 0-7636-3739-4

LC 2009-38053

This story is set in "Italy after World War II. Pina and Susanna have lived at their Naples orphanage since they were babies. . . . Pina, pretty and blonde, . . . is sure the nuns tell prospective parents she is bad. Susanna is the daughter of an Italian woman and a black American solider. . . no one looks like her. Then two very different parents come into the girls' lives. . . . Both satisfy the girls' dreams in unexpected ways. Marsden often puts crafts like sewing or crocheting into her stories, and in many ways she is like a master craftsman, using words instead of stitches for her deceptively simple design." Booklist

When heaven fell. Candlewick Press 2007 183p $15.99; pa $8.99
Grades: 4 5 6   **Fic**
   1. Aunts -- Fiction 2. Vietnam -- Fiction 3. Family life -- Fiction
   ISBN 978-0-7636-3175-8; 0-7636-3175-2; 978-0-7636-4381-2 pa; 0-7636-4381-5 pa
               LC 2006-51712
When her grandmother reveals that the daughter that she had given up for adoption is coming from America to visit her Vietnamese family, nine-year-old Binh is convinced that her newly-discovered aunt is wealthy and will take care of all the family's needs.
   "Marsden sensitively portrays expectations and disappointments on both sides. . . . An unusually accessible introduction to the culture of modern Vietnam." Booklist

Martin, Ann M.
  ★ **Belle** Teal. Scholastic Press 2001 214p hardcover o.p. pa $5.99
Grades: 4 5 6 7   **Fic**
   1. School stories 2. Race relations -- Fiction
   ISBN 0-439-09823-8; 0-439-09824-6 pa
               LC 00-136292
Belle Teal Harper is from a poor family in the country, and beginning fifth-grade is a challenge as her grandmother's memory is slipping away, her brother and father are fighting again, and she becomes involved with the two new African American children in her class.
   "This is a solid piece of work with an absorbing plot." SLJ

Better to wish; Ann M. Martin. 1st ed. Scholastic 2013 240 p. (Family tree) (hardcover) $16.99
Grades: 3 4 5 6 7   **Fic**
   1. Discrimination -- Fiction 2. Historical fiction 3. Depressions -- 1929 -- Fiction 4. Family life -- Maine -- Fiction 5. Families -- Maine -- Fiction 6. Maine -- History -- 20th century -- Fiction 8
   ISBN 0545359422; 9780545359429
             LC 2012047940
This is the first book in Ann M. Martin's Family Tree series. "Growing up in Maine, eight-year-old Abby Nichols is the oldest daughter of an ambitious carpenter eager to realize the American Dream. But his prejudices are strong, too: he won't let Abby associate with her Irish Catholic neighbor, Orrin. . . . As Abby's father gains success, she enjoys more privileges, . . . but the family's newfound prosperity doesn't ease her outrage over her father's mistreatment of the less fortunate." (Publishers Weekly)

  ★ A **corner** of the universe. Scholastic Press 2002 189p $15.95; pa $5.99
Grades: 5 6 7 8   **Fic**
   1. Uncles -- Fiction 2. Friendship -- Fiction 3. People

with mental disabilities -- Fiction
   ISBN 0-439-38880-5; 0-439-38881-3 pa
              LC 2001-57611
   A Newbery Medal honor book, 2003
   The summer that Hattie turns twelve, she meets the childlike uncle she never knew and becomes friends with a girl who works at the carnival that comes to Hattie's small town
   "Martin delivers wonderfully real characters and an engrossing plot through the viewpoint of a girl who tries so earnestly to connect with those around her." SLJ

The **doll** people; by Ann M. Martin and Laura Godwin; with pictures by Brian Selznick. Hyperion Bks. for Children 2000 256p il $15.99; pa $6.99
Grades: 3 4 5   **Fic**
   1. Dolls -- Fiction
   ISBN 0-7868-0361-4; 0-7868-1240-0 pa
              LC 98-12344
A family of porcelain dolls that has lived in the same house for one hundred years is taken aback when a new family of plastic dolls arrives and doesn't follow The Doll Code of Honor
   "Superbly nuanced drawings echo the action that breathes life into these extraordinary playthings." SLJ
   Other titles about the doll family are:
   The meanest doll in the world (2003)
   The runaway dolls (2008)

  ★ **Rain** Reign; Ann M. Martin. Feiwel & Friends 2014 240 p. $16.99
Grades: 4 5 6 7   **Fic**
   1. Dogs -- Fiction 2. English language -- Homonyms 3. Lost items -- Fiction 4. Asperger's syndrome -- Fiction
   ISBN 0312643004; 9780312643003
   Schneider Family Book Award (Ages 11 - 13) (2015)
   In this middle grades novel by Ann M. Martin, "Rose Howard is obsessed with homonyms. She's thrilled that her own name is a homonym, and she purposely gave her dog Rain a name with two homonyms (Reign, Rein), which, according to Rose's rules of homonyms, is very special. . . . When a storm hits their rural town, rivers overflow, the roads are flooded, and Rain goes missing. . . . Now Rose has to find her dog, even if it means leaving her routines and safe places to search." (Publisher's note)
   "Rose, a fifth-grader who has been diagnosed with Asperger syndrome, is often teased at school about her obsession with homonyms and her steadfast conviction that everyone should follow the rules at all times. Rose lives with her harsh, troubled father, but it's Uncle Weldon who cares for her in the ways that matter most. Still, her father did give her Rain, a stray dog that comforts and protects Rose. After Rain is lost in a storm and recovered, Rose learns that her dog has an identification microchip...Rose is driven by the unwavering belief that she must follow the rules, find Rain's former owners, and give the dog back to them... Readers will be moved by the raw portrayal of Rose's difficult home life, her separation from other kids at school, and her loss of the dog that has loved her and provided a buffer from painful experiences. A strong story told in a nuanced, highly accessible way." (Booklist)

★ **Ten** rules for living with my sister. Feiwel & Friends 2011 228p $16.99

Grades: 3 4 5 6 **Fic**

1. Sisters -- Fiction 2. Family life -- Fiction 3. Grandfathers -- Fiction 4. New York (N.Y.) -- Fiction 5. Apartment houses -- Fiction

ISBN 978-0-312-36766-4; 0-312-36766-X

LC 2011009166

Nine-year-old Pearl and her popular, thirteen-year-old sister, Lexie, do not get along very well, but when their grandfather moves in and the girls have to share a room, they must find common ground.

"Credible characterizations, on-the-nail humor, and well-observed family dynamics add up to another hit from . . . author Martin." Publ Wkly

Martinez, Arturo O.

Pedrito's world. Texas Tech University Press 2007 131p il pa $16.95

Grades: 4 5 6 **Fic**

1. Texas -- Fiction 2. Farm life -- Fiction 3. Mexican Americans -- Fiction

ISBN 978-0-89672-600-0 pa; 0-89672-600-2 pa

LC 2006-21628

In southern Texas in 1941, six-year-old Pedrito holds onto his hope for a better future as he helps to grow watermelons on his parents' farm and sell them in San Antonio, and attends school five miles from home.

"Readers will be moved . . . through clean writing and well-chosen details that breathe life into the characters and give heft to the setting." Booklist

Mason, Simon

Moon pie. David Fickling Books 2011 327p $16.99

Grades: 3 4 5 6 **Fic**

1. Fathers -- Fiction 2. Alcoholism -- Fiction

ISBN 978-0-385-75235-0; 0-385-75235-0

LC 2010051354

Eleven-year-old Martha tries to keep her family together after her mother's death as her father struggles with alcoholism.

"Mason has conjured a rarity indeed—a tremendously charming, unflinching account of a parent's downward spiral. . . . While the dialogue is realistic and rat-a-tat-tat quick, lyrical prose wends its way throughout. . . . Love conquers all in this bighearted and heartbreaking story." Kirkus

Mason, Timothy

The **last** synapsid. Delacorte Press 2009 311p il $16.99; lib bdg $19.99

Grades: 5 6 7 8 **Fic**

1. Colorado -- Fiction 2. Time travel -- Fiction 3. Space and time -- Fiction 4. Prehistoric animals -- Fiction

ISBN 978-0-385-73581-0; 0-385-73581-2; 978-0-385-90567-1 lib bdg; 0-385-90567-X lib bdg

LC 2008-35678

On a mountain near their tiny town of Faith, Colorado, best friends Rob and Phoebe discover a squat, drooly creature from thirty million years before the dinosaurs, that needs their help in tracking down a violent carnivore that must be returned to its proper place in time, or humans will never evolve.

"Mason has written a highly engaging fantasy that includes something for all readers. . . . Readers will find it difficult to put this book down until they have reached the last page." Libr Media Connect

Mass, Wendy

11 birthdays. Scholastic Press 2009 267p $16.99; pa $6.99

Grades: 4 5 6 **Fic**

1. Time -- Fiction 2. Birthdays -- Fiction 3. Friendship -- Fiction

ISBN 978-0-545-05239-9; 0-545-05239-4; 978-0-545-05240-5 pa; 0-545-05240-8 pa

LC 2008-09784

After celebrating their first nine same-day birthdays together, Amanda and Leo, having fallen out on their tenth and not speaking to each other for the last year, prepare to celebrate their eleventh birthday separately but peculiar things begin to happen as the day of their birthday begins to repeat itself over and over again.

"From the double-entendre title to the solid character portrayals to the clarity and wit of the writing, this novel offers a fresh twist on the familiar themes of middle-grade family and school dynamics." Booklist

Other titles in this series are:

Finally (2010)

13 gifts (2011)

The **candymakers**. Little, Brown 2010 453p $16.99

Grades: 3 4 5 6 **Fic**

1. Candy -- Fiction 2. Contests -- Fiction 3. Friendship -- Fiction

ISBN 978-0-316-00258-5; 0-316-00258-5

LC 2010008621

When four twelve-year-olds, including Logan, who has grown up never leaving his parents' Life Is Sweet candy factory, compete in the Confectionary Association's annual contest, they unexpectedly become friends and uncover secrets about themselves during the process.

"Mass has crafted a solid mystery dipped in sweet candymaking details. Character development moves a lengthy story forward in smooth increments. As each child's story emerges, the mystery becomes one bit clearer, making this a real page-turner. The characters are intricate, flawed heroes with whom readers will identify." SLJ

★ **Every** soul a star; a novel. Little, Brown and Co. 2008 322p $15.99; pa $6.99

Grades: 5 6 7 8 **Fic**

1. Friendship -- Fiction 2. Solar eclipses -- Fiction

ISBN 978-0-316-00256-1; 0-316-00256-9; 978-0-316-00257-8 pa; 0-316-00257-7 pa

LC 2008009259

Ally, Bree, and Jack meet at the one place the Great Eclipse can be seen in totality, each carrying the burden of different personal problems, which become dim when compared to the task they embark upon and the friendship they find.

Mass "combines astronomy and storytelling for a well-balanced look at friendships and the role they play in shaping identity. . . . Information about solar eclipses and astronomy is carefully woven into the plot to build drama and will almost certainly intrigue readers." Publ Wkly

Includes bibliographical references

Jeremy Fink and the meaning of life. Little, Brown 2006 289p $15.99; pa $6.99
Grades: 5 6 7 8   **Fic**
1. Conduct of life -- Fiction 2. Father-son relationship
-- Fiction
ISBN 978-0-316-05829-2; 0-316-05829-7; 978-0-316-
05849-0 pa; 0-316-05849-1 pa
         LC 2005037291
Just before his thirteenth birthday, Jeremy Fink receives
a keyless locked box—set aside by his father before his
death five years earlier—that purportedly contains the meaning of life.
"Mass fashions an adventure in which both journey and
destination are worth the trip." Horn Book

The **last** present; Wendy Mass. Scholastic Press 2013
256 p. (hardcover) $16.99
Grades: 4 5 6   **Fic**
1. Paranormal fiction 2. Birthdays -- Fiction 3.
Friendship -- Fiction 4. Time travel -- Fiction 5. Best
friends -- Fiction 6. Supernatural -- Fiction 7. Blessing
and cursing -- Fiction
ISBN 0545310164; 9780545310161
         LC 2013014736
In this book, by Wendy Mass, "Amanda and Leo have a
history with birthdays. Now their friend's little sister, Grace,
has fallen into a strange frozen state on her birthday, and
Amanda and Leo must travel in time in order to fix whatever's wrong. As they journey back to each of Grace's birthdays, they start seeing all sorts of patterns . . . which raise all
sorts of questions." (Publisher's note)
"Amanda and Leo (11 Birthdays) travel back in time to
help their friend's little sister, Grace, who's become mysteriously catatonic after her tenth birthday. The answer lies
in Grace's past birthday parties, and Amanda and Leo--with
help from Rory (Finally) and Tara (13 Gifts)--must break the
curse. Action, magic, and interesting twists will keep readers
entranced until the end." (Horn Book)

Pi in the sky; Wendy Mass. 1st ed. Little, Brown and
Co. 2013 256 p. (hardcover) $17
Grades: 3 4 5 6 7   **Fic**
1. Creation -- Fiction 2. Science fiction 3. Earth --
Fiction 4. Universe -- Fiction
ISBN 0316089168; 9780316089166
         LC 2012030638
In this humorous children's novel, by Wendy Mass,
"Joss is the seventh son of the Supreme Overlord of the Universe, and all he gets to do is deliver pies. . . . But when Earth
suddenly disappears, Joss is tasked with the not-so-simple
job of bringing it back. With the help of an outspoken girl
from Earth named Annika, Joss embarks on the adventure
of a lifetime and learns that the universe is an even stranger
place than he'd imagined." (Publisher's note)

Matti, Truus
★ **Departure** time; translated from the Dutch by Nan-
cy Forest-Flier. Namelos 2010 214p $18.95; pa $9.95
Grades: 5 6 7 8   **Fic**
1. Memory -- Fiction 2. Father-daughter relationship
-- Fiction
ISBN 978-1-60898-087-1; 1-60898-087-1; 978-1-
60898-009-3 pa; 1-60898-009-X pa
Original Dutch edition 2009

"A 10-year-old girl is lost in a surrealistic landscape—a
red-earth desert threatened by an approaching storm. Nothing looks familiar. She can't remember how she got to this
place. Alternating with this classic bad-dream setting, which
is narrated in the third person, is a first-person, furious tirade
by a girl who feels abandoned by her father and neglected
by her mother. Readers will be intrigued by the way Matti
interweaves these stories and tantalizes with the possible
connections between them. . . . Remarkable and arresting
and wholly original, this novel lingers in the mind long after
the last page has been read." SLJ

★ **Mister** Orange; Truus Matti; translated from the
Dutch by Laura Watkinson. Enchanted Lion Books 2013
156 p. (hardcover) $16.95
Grades: 5 6 7 8   **Fic**
1. Historical fiction 2. Child-adult relationship --
Fiction 3. Artists -- Fiction 4. Friendship -- Fiction
ISBN 159270123X; 9781592701230
         LC 2012051313
Mildred L. Batchelder Award (2014)
This children's story, by Truus Matti, translated by Laura
Watkinson, is set in Manhattan in "1943. . . . Linus Muller
works at the family grocery store in the east 70s. . . . One of
his customers . . . arranges to have a crate of oranges delivered every other week. Over the course of these deliveries,
an intimacy develops between Linus and . . . Mister Orange.
In the peacefulness of Mister Orange's spare kitchen, they
discuss the war, the future, freedom and imagination." (Publisher's note)

Mayer, Mercer
What a good kitty; Mercer Mayer; edited by Mary-
Kate Gaudet. HarperCollins 2012 32 p. (trade bdg.) $3.99
Grades: K 1 2 3   **Fic**
1. Cats -- Fiction 2. Pets -- Fiction
ISBN 0060835656; 9780060835651; 9780060835668
         LC 2011941958
In this children's book by Mercer Mayer, "Little Crit-
ter loves his kitty, despite the cat's multiple naughty deeds.
Wreaking havoc with Dad's newspaper, Mom's knitting, and
Little Sister's dolls . . . the cat even disturbs the family dog
and pet fish. She is exiled to the yard, and the fire department must come when she and Dad get stuck in a tree. But
. . . when a mean dog scares Little Sister, Kitty successfully
chases him away." (School Library Journal)

McCall Smith, Alexander, 1948-
The **great** cake mystery; Precious Ramotswe's very
first case. Alexander McCall Smith; illustrations by Iain
McIntosh. Anchor Books 2012 73 p.
Grades: 2 3 4 5   **Fic**
1. School stories 2. Mystery fiction 3. Children's
stories 4. Botswana -- Fiction 5. Blacks -- Botswana
-- Fiction 6. Mystery and detective stories
ISBN 0307743896; 9780307743893
         LC 2011026494
This children's book by Alexander McCall Smith is part
of the "Number 1 Ladies' Detective Agency" series and tells
the story of an eight-year-old African school girl in Botswa-
na who wants to become a detective. "Her name is Precious.
When a piece of cake goes missing from her classroom . . .
Precious . . . sets out to find the real thief. Along the way she

learns that your first guess isn't always right. She also learns how to be a detective." (Publisher's note)

The **Mystery** of Meerkat Hill; A Precious Ramotswe Mystery for Young Readers. by Alexander Smith; illustrated by Iain McIntosh. Random House Inc 2013 112 p. $12.99
Grades: 2 3 4 5   **Fic**
1. Meerkats -- Fiction 2. Mystery fiction 3. Botswana -- Fiction 4. Mystery and detective stories 5. Lost and found possessions -- Fiction 6. Ramotswe, Precious (Fictitious character) -- Fiction
ISBN 0345804589; 9780345804587
LC 2013363878
In this book, by Alexander Smith and illustrated by Iain McIntosh, "Precious wants to be a detective when she grows up. She is always practicing at being a detective by asking questions and finding out about other people's lives. There are two new students in her class, a girl called Teb and a boy called Pontsho. She learns that they are brother and sister, and—even more exciting—that Pontsho has a clever pet meerkat named Kosi." (Publisher's note)
"Kind, clever, and compassionate Precious Ramotswe is always eager to hone her budding detective skills. When newcomers Pontsho and Teb can't find their much-needed cow, she uses her quick wit and clue-finding skills to come to their aid...The block-print style illustrations, done in black, gray, and white with lots of touches of red, create interest and intrigue, yet artfully allow readers the luxury of using their imaginations to develop the plot and characters fully. This book will enhance all library collections, especially those eager to include fiction that gives a slice of life in another country. Perfect as a read-aloud or for beginning chapter readers." (School Library Journal)

The **mystery** of the missing lion; a Precious Ramotswe mystery for young readers. by Alexander McCall Smith; illustrations by Iain McIntosh. Anchor Books, a division of Random House LLC 2014 112 p. color illustrations (hardcover) $12.99
Grades: 2 3 4 5   **Fic**
1. Mystery fiction 2. Lions -- Fiction 3. Jungles -- Fiction 4. Botswana -- Fiction 5. Mystery and detective stories
ISBN 1101872020; 9780804173278; 9781101872024
LC 2014021479
In this book by Alexander McCall Smith, "young Precious gets . . . a trip to visit her Aunty Bee at a safari camp. While there she makes a new friend, a boy named Khumo, and meets an actor-lion named Teddy, who is starring in a film. When Teddy disappears, Khumo and Precious will brave hippos and crocodiles as they search for the missing lion." (Publisher's note)
"This is an attractive package, with a compact but entertaining mystery full of fascinating details bolstered by McIntosh's intriguing graphic illustrations." Booklist

McCaughrean, Geraldine
★ The **death**-defying Pepper Roux. Harper 2010 328p $16.99; lib bdg $17.89
Grades: 5 6 7 8   **Fic**
1. Adventure fiction 2. France -- Fiction 3. Fate and fatalism -- Fiction
ISBN 978-0-06-183665-7; 0-06-183665-6; 978-0-06-183666-4 lib bdg; 0-06-183666-4 lib bdg
LC 2009-39665
Having been raised believing he will die before he reaches the age of fourteen, Pepper Roux runs away on his fourteenth birthday in an attempt to elude his fate, assumes another identity, and continues to try to outrun death, no matter the consequences.
"McCaughrean's exuberant prose and whirling humor animate an unforgettable cast of characters." Booklist

★ The **glorious** adventures of the Sunshine Queen. Harper 2011 325p $16.99
Grades: 5 6 7 8   **Fic**
1. Adventure fiction 2. Theater -- Fiction 3. Missouri River -- Fiction
ISBN 978-0-06-200806-0; 0-06-200806-4
LC 2010021958
Sequel to: Stop the train! (2003)
When a diphtheria outbreak forces twelve-year-old Cissy to leave her Oklahoma hometown in the 1890s, she and her two classmates embark on a wild adventure down the Missouri River with a team of traveling actors who are living on a dilapidated paddle steamer.
"McCaughrean invests her characters with humanity and shows a farcical sense for dialogue, while her arch narrative voice, includes the theatrical and clever turns of phrase." Booklist

The **kite** rider; a novel. HarperCollins Pubs. 2002 272p maps hardcover o.p. pa $6.99
Grades: 5 6 7 8   **Fic**
1. Kings 2. China -- Fiction 3. Kites -- Fiction
ISBN 0-06-623874-9; 0-06-441091-9 pa
LC 2001-39522
In thirteenth-century China, after trying to save his widowed mother from a horrendous second marriage, twelve-year-old Haoyou has life-changing adventures when he takes to the sky as a circus kite rider and ends up meeting the great Mongol ruler Kublai Khan
"The story is a genuine page-turner. . . . McCaughrean fully immerses her memorable characters in the culture and lore of the ancient Chinese and Mongols, which make this not only a solid adventure story but also a window to a fascinating time and place." Booklist

Peter Pan in scarlet; by Geraldine McCaughrean; illustrations by Scott M. Fischer. Margaret K. McElderry Books 2006 309p il $17.99; pa $6.99
Grades: 4 5 6 7   **Fic**
1. Fairy tales
ISBN 978-1-4169-1808-0; 1-4169-1808-6; 978-1-4169-1809-7 pa; 1-4169-1809-4 pa
In the 1930s, all is not well. Nightmares are leaking out of Neverland. Fearing for Peter Pan's life, Wendy and the Lost Boys go back to Neverland with the help of the fairy Fireflyer only to discover their worst nightmares coming true!
"McCaughrean's story, with its picaresque descriptions, faithfully rekindled characters and an ending that leaves room for sequels, will keep the pages turning." Publ Wkly

McCloskey, Robert

Centerburg tales. Viking 1951 190p il $17.99; pa $6.99

Grades: 4 5 6   **Fic**

ISBN 0-670-20977-5; 0-14-031072-X pa

LC 51-10675

Sequel to: Homer Price

"Pictures and story show a real, live American boy with a knack for getting into hilarious adventures that make perfect reading aloud." Horn Book

★ **Homer** Price. Viking 1943 149p il $16.99; pa $5.99

Grades: 4 5 6   **Fic**

ISBN 0-670-37729-5; 0-14-240415-2 pa

"Text and pictures are pure Americana, hilarious and convincing in their portrayal of midwestern small-town life." Child Books Too Good to Miss

Another title about Homer Price is:
Centerburg tales (1951)

McCrite, K. D.

In front of God and everybody. Thomas Nelson 2011 298p (Confessions of April Grace) pa $9.99

Grades: 4 5 6 7   **Fic**

1. Arkansas -- Fiction 2. Farm life -- Fiction 3. Christian life -- Fiction 4. Swindlers and swindling -- Fiction

ISBN 978-1-4003-1722-6; 1-4003-1722-3

LC 2011005583

In the summer of 1986, eleven-year-old April Grace, who lives on a rural Arkansas farm with her family, across a field from her grandmother, has her sense of Christian charity tested when a snooty couple from San Francisco moves into a dilapidated house down the road and her grandmother takes up with a loud, obnoxious, and suspicious-acting Texan.

"With keen eyes and good humor, April Grace notes the quirks, presumptions, and motivations of family and neighbors; she has plenty of fodder—the characters' personalities are dialed up to 11." Publ Wkly

McCulloch, Michael

The **other** Felix. Roaring Brook Press 2011 $16.99

Grades: 3 4 5 6   **Fic**

1. School stories 2. Fear -- Fiction 3. Dreams -- Fiction 4. Bullies -- Fiction

ISBN 978-1-5964-3655-8; 1-5964-3655-7

LC 2010050605

Worrying about his father losing his job and the bully at school, fourth-grader Felix has terrifying dreams of the same monster-filled place every night until he meets someone there who looks and sounds strangely familiar.

"The story has a beautifully crafted innocence. . . . This is a satisfying tale in and of itself, as well as a helpful and sensitive guide for those children who are just learning to confront life's sticky challenges. The ending is exquisite." SLJ

McDonald, Megan

Cloudy with a chance of boys. Candlewick Press 2011 260p il (The Sisters Club) $15.99; pa $5.99

Grades: 3 4 5 6   **Fic**

1. Clubs -- Fiction 2. Acting -- Fiction 3. Oregon --

Fiction 4. Sisters -- Fiction 5. Family life -- Fiction 6. Dating (Social customs) -- Fiction

ISBN 978-0-7636-4615-8; 0-7636-4615-6; 978-0-7636-5577-8 pa

LC 2010-39179

While older sister Alex is trying to orchestrate a perfect first kiss with her heartthrob and younger sister Joey prefers frogs to boys, Stevie Reel wonders if she is ready for a boyfriend while being pursued by a new boy in her class.

"The sisters are solidly developed, each with a distinctive narrative style made clear by formatting. . . . Breezy and light-hearted, this makes a nice recommendation for young readers looking for girl power." Bull Cent Child Books

Other titles in this series are:
The Sisters Club (2003)
Rule of three (2009)

★ **Judy** Moody; illustrated by Peter Reynolds. Candlewick Press 2000 160p il $15.99; pa $5.99

Grades: 2 3 4   **Fic**

1. School stories

ISBN 0-7636-0685-5; 0-7636-1231-6 pa

LC 99-13464

Third grader Judy Moody is in a first day of school bad mood until she gets an assignment to create a collage all about herself and begins creating her masterpiece, the Me collage.

"This beginning chapter book features large type; simple, expressive prose and dialogue; and plenty of child-appealing humor." Booklist

Other titles about Judy Moody are:
Judy Moody & Stink: the holly joliday (2007)
Judy Moody: around the world in 8 1/2 days (2006)
Judy Moody declares independence (2005)
Judy Moody gets famous (2001)
Judy Moody, girl detective (2010)
Judy Moody goes to college (2008)
Judy Moody M.D., the doctor is in (2004)
Judy Moody predicts the future (2003)
Judy Moody saves the world (2002)

The **rule** of three. Candlewick Press 2009 234p il (The Sisters Club) $15.99; pa $5.99

Grades: 3 4 5 6   **Fic**

1. Clubs -- Fiction 2. Acting -- Fiction 3. Baking -- Fiction 4. Oregon -- Fiction 5. Sisters -- Fiction 6. Theater -- Fiction 7. Family life -- Fiction

ISBN 978-0-7636-4153-5; 0-7636-4153-7; 978-0-7636-4830-5 pa; 0-7636-4830-2 pa

LC 2008028859

In Acton, Oregon, sisters Alex, Stevie, and Joey take turns telling about their lives, including auditioning for the same part in the school musical, baking contest-worthy cupcakes, and becoming obsessed with Little Women.

"The story is believable, as are the sisters' interactions. The different styles add to the fun and help move the plot along quickly." SLJ

★ **Stink**: the incredible shrinking kid; illustrated by Peter H. Reynolds. Candlewick Press 2005 102p il $12.99

Grades: 2 3 4   **Fic**
1. School stories
ISBN 0-7636-2025-4

LC 2003-65246

The shortest kid in the second grade, James Moody, also known as Stink, learns all about the shortest president of the United States, James Madison, when they celebrate Presidents' Day at school

"Delightful full-page and spot-art cartoons and playful language in large type bring the child's adventures to life." SLJ

Other titles about Stink are:
Judy Moody & Stink: the holly joliday (2007)
Stink and the great Guinea Pig Express (2008)
Stink and the incredible super-galactic jawbreaker (2006)
Stink and the world's worst super-stinky sneakers (2007)
Stink: solar system superhero (2010)
Stink and the ultimate thumb-wrestling smackdown (2011)

Stink and the Midnight Zombie Walk; Megan McDonald; illustrated by Peter H. Reynolds. Candlewick Press 2012 144 p.
Grades: K 1 2 3   **Fic**
1. Zombies -- Fiction 2. Books and reading -- Fiction 3. Moneymaking projects -- Fiction
ISBN 0763656925; 9780763656928

LC 2011018620

This children's story by Megan McDonald follows the friends Stink and Webster, who are waiting for "the new book in the Nightmare on Zombie Street series [to come out.] Of corpse Stink will be first in line at the Blue Frog Bookstore to buy his copy and join the town's Midnight Zombie Walk! Until then, Stink and his friends keep busy making ketchup-stained zombie costumes, trying to raise money to buy the book, and racking up points for Virginia Dare School's race to one million minutes of reading." (Publisher's note)

Stink and the shark sleepover; Megan McDonald, illustrated by Peter H. Reynolds. Candlewick Press 2014 176 p. $12.99
Grades: 2 3 4   **Fic**
1. Aquariums 2. Fear -- Fiction 3. Sleepovers -- Juvenile fiction 4. Squids -- Fiction 5. Treasure hunt (Game) -- Fiction
ISBN 076366474X; 9780763664749

LC 2013943081

In this children's story, by Megan McDonald, illustrated by Peter H. Reynolds, "when Stink's parents win tickets for the whole family to sleep over at the aquarium (along with Stink's two best friends), it sounds like a science freak's dream come true. . . . But after some spooky stories around the virtual campfire, can he manage to fall asleep thinking about the eating habits of the vampire squid? Especially Bloody Mary, the mutant, glowing Frankensquid that's supposed to be on the prowl?" (Publisher's note)

"When Stink goes to a sleepover at the aquarium, he's very excited (he loves sharks) but also nervous (he's a bit afraid of sleepovers). Although the children are constantly cracking each other up with silly second-grade jokes, readers will also glean lots of factual information about sea crea-

tures. Reynolds ably illustrates both the wondrous animals and the comical antics." Horn Book

McDonough, Yona Zeldis
The **cats** in the doll shop; illustrated by Heather Maione. Viking 2011 il $14.99
Grades: 2 3 4 5   **Fic**
1. Cats -- Fiction 2. Dolls -- Fiction 3. Cousins -- Fiction 4. Immigrants -- Fiction 5. New York (N.Y.) -- Fiction 6. Jews -- United States -- Fiction
ISBN 978-0-670-01279-4; 0-670-01279-3

LC 2011009312

With World War I raging in Europe, eleven-year-old Anna is thrilled to learn that her cousin Tania is coming from Russia to stay with Anna's family on the lower East Side of New York, and although Tania is shy and withdrawn when she arrives, her love of cats helps her adjust to her new family.

"Filled with references to Jewish traditions and the rich history of tenement life in New York City, these fully realized characters could be best friends with the girls from Sydney Taylor's All-of-a-Kind Family. A quiet treasure." Kirkus

The **doll** shop downstairs; illustrated by Heather Maione. Viking 2009 118p il $14.99
Grades: 2 3 4 5   **Fic**
1. Dolls -- Fiction 2. Immigrants -- Fiction 3. Family life -- Fiction 4. New York (N.Y.) -- Fiction 5. World War, 1914-1918 -- Fiction 6. Jews -- United States -- Fiction
ISBN 978-0-670-01091-2; 0-670-01091-X

LC 2009-01934

When World War I breaks out, nine-year-old Anna thinks of a way to save her family's beloved New York City doll repair shop. Includes brief author's note about the history of the Madame Alexander doll, a glossary, and timeline.

"Anna's first person narrative creates convincing portrayals of her sisters and parents as well as her personal ups and downs. . . . Pleasant black-and-white pictures illustrate the action while helping children to visualize the period setting." Booklist

Another title about Anna and the doll shop is:
The cats in the doll shop (2011)

★ The **doll** with the yellow star; illustrated by Kimberly Bulcken Root. Henry Holt and Co. 2005 90p il $16.95
Grades: 3 4 5   **Fic**
1. Jews -- Fiction 2. Dolls -- Fiction 3. Holocaust, 1933-1945 -- Fiction
ISBN 0-8050-6337-4

LC 2002-27554

When France falls to Germany at the start of World War II, nine-year-old Claudine must leave her beloved parents and friends to stay with relatives in America, accompanied by her doll, Violette

"This fiction book is informative, enjoyable, and passionately written." Libr Media Connect

McDowell, Marilyn Taylor
★ **Carolina** Harmony. Delacorte 2009 288p $16.99; lib bdg $19.99
Grades: 4 5 6 7   **Fic**
1. Orphans -- Fiction 2. Farm life -- Fiction 3. Blue

Ridge Mountains region -- Fiction

ISBN 978-0-385-73590-2; 0-385-73590-1; 978-0-385-90575-6 lib bdg; 0-385-90575-0 lib bdg

"After Carolina's beloved Auntie Shen suffers a stroke, Carolina escapes from an unpleasant foster placement. The orphaned 10-year-old finds love at Harmony Farm, but the web of lies she spins almost leads to losing that home too. . . This third-person narrative unwinds leisurely, with plenty of backtracking to fill in details of Carolina's life and the glories of her world in the Blue Ridge Mountains. . . . Mc-Dowell reveals her love for this part of the world, savoring the language, the environment, and the traditions of mountain culture." Booklist

McElligott, Matthew

Benjamin Franklinstein lives! [by] Matthew McElligott & Larry Tuxbury; illustrated by Matthew McElligott. G. P. Putnam's Sons 2010 121p il $12.99

Grades: 4 5 6 7   **Fic**

1. Authors 2. Diplomats 3. Inventors 4. Statesmen 5. Scientists 6. Science fiction 7. Writers on science 8. Zombies -- Fiction 9. Members of Congress

ISBN 978-0-399-25229-7; 0-399-25229-0

While working on a science fair project, a Philadelphia school boy discovers both a secret laboratory in his basement and Benjamin Franklin, who comes to life after receiving a jolt of electricity.

"It's a light fun read, and McElligott's many diagrams, graphs, and drawings are a nice addition." Booklist

Followed by: Benjamin Franklinstein meets the fright brothers (2011)

Benjamin Franklinstein meets the Fright brothers; by Matthew McElligott and Larry Tuxbury; [illustrated by Matthew McElligott] G. P. Putnam's Sons 2011 147p il $16.99

Grades: 4 5 6 7   **Fic**

1. Authors 2. Diplomats 3. Inventors 4. Statesmen 5. Scientists 6. Writers on science 7. Members of Congress 8. Scientists -- Fiction 9. Secret societies -- Fiction

ISBN 978-0-399-25480-2; 0-399-25480-3

LC 2010040431

Sequel to: Benjamin Franklinstein lives! (2010)

Victor and his friends, aided by Benjamin Franklin, uncover an evil scheme involving giant bats and two mysterious brothers, and learn more about the secretive Modern Order of Prometheus.

"Enhanced by frequent charts, diagrams, lists and other visual aids, a spirit of rational (if often reckless) scientific inquiry pervades the tale, as Ben and his allies translate coded messages, analyze evidence, get a lesson in meteorology and conduct experiments using both real and science-fictional gear on the way to a literally electrifying climax. . . The authors have way too much fun taking the opener's premise and evil conspiracy to the next level. Readers will too." Kirkus

McGraw, Eloise Jarvis

The **moorchild**; [by] Eloise McGraw. Margaret K. McElderry Bks. 1996 241p $17; pa $5.99

Grades: 4 5 6 7   **Fic**

1. Fantasy fiction 2. Fairies -- Fiction

ISBN 0-689-80654-X; 1-4169-2768-9 pa

LC 95-34107

A Newbery Medal honor book, 1997

"Incorporating some classic fantasy motifs and icons, McGraw . . . conjures up an appreciably familiar world that, as evidence of her storytelling power, still strikes an original chord." Publ Wkly

McKay, Hilary, 1959-

★ **Binny** for short; by Hilary McKay and illustrated by Micah Player. Margaret K. McElderry Books 2013 291 p. (hardcover) $16.99

Grades: 3 4 5 6   **Fic**

1. Aunts -- Fiction 2. Ghosts 3. Family life -- Fiction 4. Loss (Psychology) -- Fiction 5. Moving, Household -- Fiction

ISBN 1442482753; 9781442482753

LC 2013000053

In this book, by Hilary McKay and illustrated by Micah Player, "Aunty Violet has died, and left Binny and her family an old house in a seaside town. Binny is faced with a new crush, a new frenemy, and a ghost. It seems Aunty Violet may not have completely departed. [For Binny] it's odd being haunted by her aunt, but there is also the warmth of a busy and loving mother, a musical older sister, and a hilarious little brother, who is busy with his experiments." (Publisher's note)

Lulu and the hedgehog in the rain; Hilary McKay; illustrated by Priscilla Lamont. Albert Whitman & Company 2014 104 p. illustrations (hardback) $13.99

Grades: 2 3 4   **Fic**

1. Cousins -- Fiction 2. Hedgehogs -- Fiction 3. Animal rescue -- Fiction 4. Wildlife rescue -- Fiction

ISBN 080754812X; 9780807548127

LC 2014013381

In this children's book, by Hilary McKay, illustrated by Priscilla Lamont, "Lulu loves animals. She knows that the hedgehog she rescued isn't really a pet, but Lulu does want to make sure she's all right. And so the Hedgehog Club is born. Everyone on the street agrees to keep an eye on the little hedgehog and keep it away from the road. But come wintertime the hedgehog disappears! Where could she have gone?" (Publisher's note)

"After sneaking outdoors during a rainstorm, Lulu rescues a half-drowned hedgehog and makes a home for it in her family's garden...From the Bossy Man to the New Old Lady, the people in Lulu's multicultural neighborhood are well-drawn, distinctive characters. Lamont's sensitive graywash illustrations are as lively as the appealing story in this early chapter book from the celebrated Lulu series." Booklist

Other titles in the series include:

Lulu and the Rabbit Next Door (2012)

Lulu and the Duck in the Park (2012)

Lulu and the Cat in the Bag (2013)

Lulu and the Dog from the Sea (2013)

Lulu and the Hamster in the night (2015)

★ **Saffy's** angel. Margaret K. McElderry Bks. 2002 152p $16; pa $4.99

Grades: 5 6 7 8   **Fic**

1. Adoption -- Fiction 2. Family life -- Fiction 3. Great Britain -- Fiction

ISBN 0-689-84933-8; 0-689-84934-6 pa

LC 2001-44110

First published 2001 in the United Kingdom

After learning that she was adopted, thirteen-year-old Saffron's relationship with her eccentric, artistic family changes, until they help her go back to Italy where she was born to find a special momento of her past

"Like the Casson household itself, the plot is a chaotic whirl that careens off in several directions simultaneously. But McKay always skillfully draws each clearly defined character back into the story with witty, well-edited details; rapid dialogue; and fine pacing." Booklist

Other titles in this series are:

Indigo's star (2004)

Permanent Rose (2005)

Caddy ever after (2006)

Forever Rose (2008)

Wishing for tomorrow; the sequel to A little princess. illustrated by Nick Maland. Margaret K. McElderry Books 2010 273p il $16.99

Grades: 4 5 6   **Fic**

1. School stories 2. Friendship -- Fiction 3. London (England) -- Fiction

ISBN 978-1-4424-0169-3; 1-4424-0169-9

LC 2009-24868

Relates what becomes of Ermengarde and the other girls left behind at Miss Minchin's School after Sara Crewe leaves to live with her guardian, the Indian gentleman.

"Enhanced by Maland's period illustrations, the novel convincingly evokes the Victorian era, even as McKay interjects a contemporary sensibility. A surprising, dramatic denouement caps this droll and heartwarming tale, a very worthy follow-up to a well-loved classic." Publ Wkly

McKinlay, Meg

Below; Meg McKinlay. Candlewick Press 2013 224 p. (reinforced) $15.99

Grades: 4 5 6 7   **Fic**

1. Reservoirs -- Fiction 2. Extinct cities -- Fiction

ISBN 0763661260; 9780763661267

LC 2012943652

In this book by Meg McKinlay, "Cassie was . . . the first baby born in the Australian town of New Lower Grange, which was established after the intentional flooding of the previous town to accommodate a dam. . . . [S]he feels the pull of the forbidden lake above Old Lower Grange. There, she is joined by Liam, a classmate whose life was altered in a tragic accident, and together they search for the truth about the town's past as its centenary celebration approaches." (Publishers Weekly)

"Although the author does a masterful job of making sure all the pieces fit at the end, the central mystery is hard to buy. This is mitigated by a reasonably suspenseful climax, an earned family solidarity message and the lesson: that to find the truth, one must delve below the surface. A quietly intriguing meditation on history and truth." Kirkus

Duck for a day; illustrated by Leila Rudge. Candlewick Press 2012 89 p. $12.99

Grades: 1 2 3   **Fic**

1. Children and animals 2. Pets -- Fiction 3. Friendship -- Fiction 4. School stories 5. Ducks -- Fiction 6. Lost and found possessions -- Fiction

ISBN 0763657840; 9780763657840

LC 2011018608

In author Meg McKinlay's book, "class pet is a duck named Max, and pet-deprived Abby longs to earn the privilege of taking him home overnight. Active and involving right from the first, . . . the plot unfolds . . . to include a contest to build Max the ideal 'aquatic environment,' a well-deserved visit to Abby's house, and an exciting chase to find Max after he escapes from her backyard." (Horn Book Magazine)

McKinnon, Hannah Roberts

★ **Franny** Parker. Farrar Straus Giroux 2009 149p $16

Grades: 5 6 7 8   **Fic**

1. Droughts -- Fiction 2. Oklahoma -- Fiction 3. Violence -- Fiction 4. Family life -- Fiction

ISBN 978-0-374-32469-8; 0-374-32469-7

LC 2008-01702

Through a hot, dry Oklahoma summer, twelve-year-old Franny tends wild animals brought by her neighbors, hears gossip during a weekly quilting bee, befriends a new neighbor who has some big secrets, and learns to hope.

"Franny is a relatable and consistent narrator, the homey rural setting is throughtfully rendered and the easy prose should appeal to reluctant readers." Publ Wkly

The **properties** of water. Farrar, Straus, and Giroux 2010 166p $16.99

Grades: 5 6 7 8   **Fic**

1. Sisters -- Fiction 2. Accidents -- Fiction

ISBN 978-0-374-36145-7; 0-374-36145-2

When her older sister, Marni, is paralyzed jumping off the cliffs into the lake near their house, twelve-year-old Lace feels responsible for the accident and struggles to find a way to help heal her family.

McKinnon "has created a cast of believably imperfect characters, and Lace's emotions ring true." Publ Wkly

McKissack, Patricia C.

Abby takes a stand; illustrated [by] Gordon C. James. Viking 2005 104p il (Scraps of time) $14.99; pa $4.99

Grades: 2 3 4   **Fic**

1. Tennessee -- Fiction 2. African Americans -- Fiction 3. Civil rights demonstrations -- Fiction

ISBN 0-670-06011-9; 0-14-240687-2 pa

LC 2004-21641

Gee recalls for her grandchildren what happened in 1960 in Nashville, Tennessee, when she, aged ten, passed out flyers while her cousin and other adults held sit-ins at restaurants and lunch counters to protest segregation.

"Although short and simply told, the book gives readers a kid's-eye view of important happenings and reminds them that history is something that is always in the making. Fine black-and-white art adds to the ambience of the time." Booklist

Other titles in this series are:

Away west (2006)

A song for Harlem (2007)

The homerun king (2008)

The **clone** codes; [by] Patricia C. McKissack, Fredrick L. McKissack [and] John McKissack. Scholastic 2010 173p $16.99

Grades: 4 5 6 7   **Fic**

1. Science fiction 2. Cloning -- Fiction 3. Segregation

-- Fiction 4. Identity (Psychology) -- Fiction
ISBN 978-0-439-92983-7; 0-439-92983-0

LC 2009-24076

On the run from a bounty hunter who arrested her mother for being part of a secret society devoted to freeing clones, thirteen-year-old Leanna learns amazing truths about herself and her family as she is forced to consider the value of freedom and what it really means to be human in 2170 America.

"The story is tight and fast-paced, yet makes room for historical parallels that are vivid without being preachy. An intriguing start to a planned trilogy." Publ Wkly

Followed by: Cyborg (2011)

Cyborg; a Clone codes novel. [by] Patricia C. McKissack, Fredrick L. McKissack, John P. McKissack. Scholastic Press 2011 107p $16.99

Grades: 4 5 6 7   Fic

1. Science fiction 2. Civil rights -- Fiction 3. Artificial intelligence -- Fiction
ISBN 978-0-439-92985-1; 0-439-92985-7

LC 2010016075

Sequel to: Clone codes (2010)

Seventeen-year-old Houston, a cyborg since the age of seven, and a fugitive living on the Moon, joins with other cyborgs all over the world in non-violent protest marches to challenge the Cyborg Act 2130 and hopefully secure increased civil liberties.

"The McKissacks continue to successfully draw parallels between a futuristic world that tries to control those considered different and historic racial struggles. . . . The worldbuilding is intriguing, there is plenty of action and ethnic diversity in a science-fiction tale is welcome." Kirkus

★ **Let** my people go; Bible stories told by a freeman of color to his daughter, Charlotte, in Charleston, South Carolina, 1806-16. by Patricia and Fredrick McKissack; illustrated by James Ransome. Atheneum Bks. for Young Readers 1998 134p il $20

Grades: 4 5 6 7   Fic

1. Bible stories 2. Slavery -- Fiction 3. African Americans -- Fiction
ISBN 0-689-80856-9

LC 97-19983

Charlotte, the daughter of a free black man who worked as a blacksmith in Charleston, South Carolina, in the early 1800s recalls the stories from the Bible that her father shared with her, relating them to the experiences of African Americans

"The poignant juxtaposition of the Biblical characters and Charlotte's personal narrative is authentic and moving. The occasional illustrations are powerful oil paintings in rich colors, emotional and evocative." SLJ

Includes bibliographical references

★ **Never** forgotten. Schwartz & Wade Books 2011 un il $18.99; lib bdg $21.99

Grades: 3 4 5 6   Fic

1. Novels in verse 2. Slavery -- Fiction 3. African Americans -- Fiction
ISBN 978-0-375-84384-6; 0-375-84384-1; 978-0-375-94453-6 lib bdg; 0-375-94453-2 lib bdg

LC 2010024789

McKissack's "story about a Malian boy abducted and sold into slavery has frightening moments, but carries dignity and even triumph away from them. . . . The willingness to turn the dark history of the past into literature takes not just talent but courage. McKissack has both." Publ Wkly

Stitchin' and pullin' a Gee's Bend quilt. illustrated by Cozbi A. Cabrera. Random House 2008 un il $17.99; lib bdg $20.99

Grades: 2 3 4 5   Fic

1. Novels in verse 2. Quilts -- Fiction 3. Alabama -- Fiction 4. Family life -- Fiction 5. African Americans -- Fiction
ISBN 978-0-375-83163-8; 0-375-83163-0; 978-0-375-93163-5 lib bdg; 0-375-93163-5 lib bdg

LC 2007011066

As a young African American girl pieces her first quilt together, the history of her family, community, and the struggle for justice and freedom in Gee's Bend, Alabama unfolds.

"Rich naif-style paintings in a warm, deep palette bring the poems to life and reflect their tone and spirit. . . . It's marvelously clear that McKissack understands the creative pulse of the quilter and artist." Horn Book

★ **Tippy** Lemmey; illustrated by Susan Keeter. Simon & Schuster 2003 59p il (Ready-for-chapters) pa $3.99

Grades: 2 3 4   Fic

1. Dogs -- Fiction 2. Tennessee -- Fiction 3. African Americans -- Fiction
ISBN 0-689-85019-0

"In 1951, in Templeton, TN, Leanne Martin and her friends Paul and Jeannie are at war with Tippy Lemmey, a dog that frightens them. . . . The kids learn that Tippy is simply a puppy who wants to play, and that his owner is fighting in Korea. Leanne remains unconvinced about the dog's good intentions, but when the friends see thieves stealing him and other neighborhood dogs to sell across state, they rescue the animals and are rewarded when Tippy gets them out of a dangerous situation. . . . This charming and humorous story moves along at a fast pace, making it perfect for readers just venturing into chapter-book territory." SLJ

McMullan, Kate

School! adventures at the Harvey N. Trouble Elementary School. written by Kate McMullan; inspired and illustrated by George Booth. Feiwel and Friends 2010 149p il $12.99

Grades: 1 2 3 4   Fic

1. School stories
ISBN 978-0-312-37592-8; 0-312-37592-1

LC 2008-15263

"The story takes readers into Ron's week, from Hotsy-Totsy Monday to Hunky-Dory Thursday, at his outlandish school, where, through extreme silliness, little life lessons are learned. . . . The characters all have giggle-worthy names that relate to their personalities or attributes. . . . Booth's great cartoon illustrations add whimsy and pure fun to every page, a quality that, when paired with McMullan's simple, quirky story, may well draw in reluctant readers." SLJ

McMullan, Margaret

How I found the Strong; a Civil War story. Houghton Mifflin 2004 136p $15

Grades: 5 6 7 8   **Fic**
1. Slavery -- Fiction 2. Mississippi -- Fiction 3. United
States -- History -- 1861-1865, Civil War -- Fiction
ISBN 0-618-35008-X
                                    LC 2003-12294

Frank Russell, known as Shanks, wishes he could have
gone with his father and brother to fight for Mississippi and
the Confederacy, but his experiences with the war and his
changing relationship with the family slave, Buck, change
his thinking.

"The crisply written narrative is full of regional speech
and detail, creating a vivid portrait." Voice Youth Advocates

When I crossed No-Bob. Houghton Mifflin Company
2007 209p $16
Grades: 5 6 7 8   **Fic**
1. Farm life -- Fiction 2. Mississippi -- Fiction 3. Race
relations -- Fiction 4. Abandoned children -- Fiction 5.
Reconstruction (1865-1876) -- Fiction
ISBN 978-0-618-71715-6; 0-618-71715-3
                                    LC 2007-12753

Ten years after the Civil War's end, twelve-year-old
Addy, abandoned by her parents, is taken from the horrid
town of No-Bob by schoolteacher Frank Russell and his
bride, but when her father returns to claim her she must find
another way to leave her O'Donnell past behind.

"The simple prose can be pure poetry. . . . Readers will
be drawn by the history close-up and by the elemental moral
choice." Booklist

McNamara, Margaret

A **poem** in your pocket; by Margaret McNamara; illus-
trated by G. Brian Karas. Schwartz & Wade Books 2015 40
p. color illustrations (Mr. Tiffin's Classroom Series) (glb)
$19.99
Grades: K 1 2 3   **Fic**
1. School stories 2. Poetry -- Fiction 3. Authorship
-- Fiction 4. Schools -- Fiction 5. Self-confidence --
Fiction
ISBN 0307979482; 9780307979476; 9780307979483
                                    LC 2014005745

In this children's story, by Margaret McNamara, illustrated by G. Brian Karas, set "in the classroom, . . . poetry
- from metaphors to acrostics to haiku - is the name of the
game. The focus here is on Elinor, whose confidence falters
as she tries to write something 'perfect' for Poem in Your
Pocket Day and impress a visiting poet." (Publisher's note)

"The author/artist team behind How Many Seeds in a
Pumpkin? revisit Mr. Tiffin's warm, supportive classroom,
where this time his students are learning about poetry...Ex-
amples of poetry the kids come up with ("Buds are like tiny
red firecrackers...waiting to explode into flowers"; "Sadness
is a cracked sidewalk") may inspire young readers to attempt
their own writing, especially since Karas's gouache, acrylic,
and pencil pictures make the diverse group of classmates
look like they are having fun..." Horn Book

McNamee, Eoin

The **Ring** of Five. Wendy Lamb Books 2010 345p
$16.99; lib bdg $19.99

Grades: 5 6 7 8   **Fic**
1. School stories 2. Fantasy fiction 3. Spies -- Fiction
ISBN 978-0-385-73731-9; 0-385-73731-9; 978-0-385-
90658-6 lib bdg; 0-385-90658-7 lib bdg
                                    LC 2009-33345

Kidnapped on his way to boarding school, Danny Caul-
field, who has one blue eye and one brown eye, ends up at
a mysterious academy of spies, where he is to be trained in
the art of espionage in an effort to keep the Upper and Lower
worlds from colliding.

McQuerry, Maureen Doyle

★ **Beyond** the door; Maureen Doyle McQuerry. Amulet Books 2014 384 p. (Time out of time) $16.95
Grades: 4 5 6 7 8   **Fic**
1. Adventure fiction 2. Celtic mythology -- Fiction
3. Brothers and sisters -- Fiction 4. Magic -- Fiction
5. Space and time -- Fiction 6. Animals, Mythical --
Fiction 7. Mythology, Celtic -- Fiction 8. Adventure
and adventurers -- Fiction
ISBN 1419710168; 9781419710162
                                    LC 2013025513

This book, by Maureen Doyle McQuerry, "weaves a . .
. coming-of-age story with fantasy and mythology. With his
love of learning and the game of Scrabble, Timothy James
feels like the only person who understands him is his older
sister, Sarah. . . . One night, while his parents and sister are
away, the door opens, and mythical creatures appear in his
own living room! Soon, a mystery of unparalleled propor-
tions begins to unfold, revealing an age-old battle of Light
against Dark." (Publisher's note)

"Scrabble-loving loner Timothy and his older sister
Sarah access an ancient mythological prophecy when Timothy saves his school tormentor Jessica from being hunted
on Beltane, the Gaelic May Day festival. Heavy reliance on
Celtic mythology and symbolism doesn't help an awkwardly
disjointed plot, though the strong good/evil dichotomy will
attract fans to the new series. A code in Ogham script runs
along each page." Horn Book

McSwigan, Marie

★ **Snow** treasure; [by] Marie McSwigan; illustrated by
Mary Reardon. Dutton's Children's Books 2005 196p il
$10.99; pa $5.99
Grades: 3 4 5 6   **Fic**
1. Norway -- Fiction 2. World War, 1939-1945 --
Fiction
ISBN 0-525-47626-1; 0-14-240224-9 pa
                                    LC 2005042108

A reissue of the title first published 1942.

In 1940, when the Nazi invasion of Norway reaches their
village in the far north, twelve-year-old Peter and his friends
use their sleds to transport nine million dollars worth of gold
bullion past the German soldiers to the secret harbor where
Peter's uncle keeps his ship ready to take the gold for safe-
keeping in the United States.

"A dramatic reconstruction of an actual happening. . . .
Well written." Booklist

Mead, Alice

★ **Junebug**. Farrar, Straus & Giroux 1995 101p hardcover o.p. pa $6.99

Grades: 3 4 5   **Fic**

1. Sailing -- Fiction 2. African Americans -- Fiction
ISBN 0-374-33964-3; 0-312-56126-1 pa

LC 95-5421

"Junebug approaches his tenth birthday with fear because he knows he'll be forced by the older boys in his housing project to join a gang. On his birthday, with luck and persistence, Junebug realizes his secret dream of one day sailing a boat. The novel contains vivid descriptions of the grim realities of inner-city life but also demonstrates that strong convictions and warm hearts can bring about change." Horn Book Guide

Other titles about Junebug are:
Junebug and the Reverend (1998)
Junebug in trouble (2003)

Meloy, Colin

Under Wildwood; Colin Meloy; illustrated by Carson Ellis. Balzer + Bray 2012 559 p. (hardback) $17.99
Grades: 5 6 7 8   **Fic**

1. Fantasy fiction 2. Adventure fiction 3. Fantasy 4. Animals -- Fiction 5. Portland (Or.) -- Fiction
ISBN 006202471X; 9780062024718

LC 2012019040

Sequel to: Wildwood

This children's picture book is a sequel to "Wildwood." Here, bookish "Prue and bandit-in-training Curtis team up once again to fight a nefarious governess and evil science teacher in this fast-paced fantasy set in Oregon. . . . In this strange land, it can be difficult to tell friend from foe, making for deliciously suspenseful adventures with a rat named Septimus and a circus bear with hooks instead of paws." (Children's Literature)

★ **Wildwood**; illustrations by Carson Ellis. Balzer + Bray 2011 541p il $16.99
Grades: 5 6 7 8   **Fic**

1. Fantasy fiction 2. Animals -- Fiction 3. Siblings -- Fiction 4. Portland (Or.) -- Fiction 5. Missing persons -- Fiction
ISBN 978-0-06-202468-8; 0-06-202468-X

LC 2011010072

When her baby brother is kidnapped by crows, seventh-grader Prue McKeel ventures into the forbidden Impassable Wilderness—a dangerous and magical forest in the middle of Portland, Oregon—and soon finds herself involved in a war among the various inhabitants.

"Illustrations by Ellis . . . bring forest and inhabitants to gently whimsical life. A satisfying blend of fantasy, adventure story, eco-fable and political satire with broad appeal." Kirkus

Wildwood imperium; Colin Meloy; illustrations by Carson Ellis. Balzer + Bray 2014 592 p. ill (some col.), maps (Wildwood chronicles) (hardcover) $17.99
Grades: 5 6 7 8   **Fic**

1. Fairy tales 2. Fantasy fiction 3. Orphans -- Fiction 4. Friendship -- Fiction
ISBN 0062024744; 9780062024749

LC 2013953784

Kirkus (December 15, 2013)

This fairy tale, by Colin Meloy, is the third book in the fantasy "Wildwood" series. "A young girl's midnight séance awakens a long-slumbering malevolent spirit. . . . A band of runaway orphans allies with an underground collective of saboteurs and plans a daring rescue of their friends, imprisoned in . . . an industrial wasteland. . . . Two old friends draw closer to their goal of bringing together a pair of exiled toy makers in order to reanimate a mechanical boy prince." (Publisher's note)

"Dramatic shifts in tone and mood--by turns politically astute and subversively witty, elegiac, droll and philosophical--are par for the course, while narrative style ranges from intimate to intergalactically distant." Kirkus

Merrill, Jean

★ The **pushcart** war; by Jean Merrill; with illustrations by Ronni Solbert. Bantam Doubleday Dell Books for Young Readers 1987 222p il pa $6.50
Grades: 5 6 7 8   **Fic**

1. Trucks -- Fiction 2. New York (N.Y.) -- Fiction
ISBN 0-440-47147-8

A reissue of the title first published 1964 by W. R. Scott

The outbreak of a war between truck drivers and pushcart peddlers brings the mounting problems of traffic to the attention of both the city of New York and the world.

"A book that is both humorous and downright funny. . . . Such a lively book will need little introducing." Horn Book

The **toothpaste** millionaire; by Jean Merrill; prepared by the Bank Street College of Education. 35th anniversary ed.; Houghton Mifflin 2006 129p il $16; pa $5.95
Grades: 4 5 6   **Fic**

1. Mathematics -- Fiction 2. Cleveland (Ohio) -- Fiction 3. Business enterprises -- Fiction
ISBN 978-0-618-75924-8; 0-618-75924-7; 978-0-618-75925-5 pa; 0-618-75925-5 pa

A reissue of the title first published 1972

A young girl describes how her school friend made over a million dollars by creating and marketing a cheaper and better toothpaste

"The illustrations are engaging, the style is light, the project interesting (with more than a few swipes taken at advertising and business practices in our society) and Rufus a believable genius." Bull Cent Child Books

Messer, Stephen

The **death** of Yorik Mortwell; illustrated by Gris Grimly. Random House Children's Books 2011 173p il $15.99; lib bdg $18.99; e-book $15.95
Grades: 5 6 7 8   **Fic**

1. Ghost stories 2. Fantasy fiction 3. Magic -- Fiction 4. Siblings -- Fiction 5. Demonology -- Fiction 6. Good and evil -- Fiction 7. Social classes -- Fiction
ISBN 978-0-375-86858-0; 978-0-375-96858-7 lib bdg; 978-0-375-89928-7 e-book

LC 2010014255

Following his death at the hands of fellow twelve-year-old, Lord Thomas, Yorik returns as a ghost to protect his sister from a similar fate but soon learns of ancient magical beings, both good and evil, who are vying for power at the Estate.

"Full-page, macabre illustrations appear throughout. Lemony Snicket, Harry Potter, and Neil Gaiman enthusiasts will appreciate this engaging, eccentric adventure." SLJ

★ **Windblowne**. Random House 2010 304p $16.99

Grades: 4 5 6 7   **Fic**
1. Fantasy fiction 2. Kites -- Fiction 3. Uncles -- Fiction 4. Space and time -- Fiction
ISBN 978-0-375-86195-6; 0-375-86195-5
LC 2008-43777

Hapless Oliver, who lives in the trees in the town of Windblowne, seeks his eccentric great-uncle Gilbert's help in creating a kite for the all-important kite festival, but when Gilbert suddenly disappears, Oliver is guided by one of Gilbert's kites in a quest through different worlds to find him.

"Messer constructs a tale that moves along at a powerful, steady pace to a climactic faceoff, and Oliver's realization that the gateway to worlds is open for those who can truly listen to the wind's voices sparks a memorable sea change in his self-image." Kirkus

Messner, Kate
Marty McGuire; illustrated by Brian Floca. Scholastic Press 2011 129p il $15.99; pa $5.99
Grades: 2 3 4   **Fic**
1. School stories 2. Theater -- Fiction
ISBN 978-0-545-14244-1; 0-545-14244-X; 978-0-545-14246-5 pa; 0-545-14246-6 pa
LC 2010-31291

When tomboy Marty is cast as the princess in the third-grade play, she learns about improvisation, which helps her become more adaptable.

"Messner gets all the details of third grade right. . . . Floca's black-and-white sketches are filled with movement and emotion and are frequent enough to help new chapter-book readers keep up with this longer text. [The book features] believable and endearing characters in a realistic elementary-school setting." Kirkus

Followed by: Marty McGuire digs worms! (2012)

Marty McGuire digs worms! by Kate Messner; illustrated by Brian Floca. Scholastic Press 2012 161 p.
Grades: K 1 2 3   **Fic**
1. Worms -- Fiction 2. Compost -- Fiction 3. Recycling -- Fiction 4. School children -- Fiction 5. Environmental protection -- Fiction 6. Schools -- Fiction 7. Grandmothers -- Fiction 8. Recycling (Waste) -- Fiction
ISBN 0545142458; 9780545142458; 9780545142472
LC 2011016291

In this book, "Marty McGuire's third-grade class has a special assignment: Save the Earth! Even more exciting, the best project wins a special award. Marty's pretty sure her classmates' ideas won't stand a chance against her plan to turn the garbage from the school cafeteria into fertilizer. All she needs is a little help from her teammate and best friend, Annie—and the worms in her grandma's garden. . . . [W]hen the critters escape, the whole class starts grumbling. Can Marty save the Earth without losing her friends?" (Publisher's note)

Marty McGuire has too many pets! by Kate Messner; illustrated by Brian Floca. Scholastic Press 2014 168 p. illustrations (hc) $15.99
Grades: 2 3 4   **Fic**
1. Pets -- Fiction 2. Chimpanzees -- Fiction 3. Animal sanctuaries -- Fiction 4. Money-making projects for children 5. Pet sitting -- Fiction 6. Money-making projects -- Fiction
ISBN 054553559X; 9780545535595; 9780545535601
LC 2013010371

"Marty McGuire really has her hands full this time. . . . After visiting a sanctuary for retired lab chimpanzees, Marty wants to follow in the footsteps of her idol Jane Goodall and help with their care. But 'adopting a chimp' is expensive, so Marty and her third-grade pals hatch a plan to raise money by holding a talent show at school and opening a pet-sitting business in Marty's basement." (Publisher's note)

"Messner makes the most of Marty's story with a nicely differentiated cast of empathetic characters and plenty of dramatic range. The line-and-gray-wash illustrations by Caldecott Medal–winning artist Floca capture moments of anxiety, despair, and happiness with equal grace." (Booklist)

Sugar and ice. Walker & Co. 2010 275p $16.99
Grades: 4 5 6 7   **Fic**
1. Ice skating -- Fiction 2. New York (State) -- Fiction
ISBN 978-0-8027-2081-8; 0-8027-2081-1
LC 2009-54217

When Russian skating coach Andrei Grosheva offers farm girl Claire a scholarship to train with the elite in Lake Placid, she encounters a world of mean girls on ice, where competition is everything

"The dialogue between classmates and siblings is realistic, and the intergenerational or extended family relationships are interesting. The author shows the intensity of the world of competitive skating without dwelling on its rough edges, making it accessible not only to tween readers, but also to those who might have Olympic aspirations." SLJ

Meyer, Susan
Black radishes; [by] Susan Lynn Meyer. Delacorte Press 2010 228p map $16.99; lib bdg $19.99
Grades: 5 6 7 8   **Fic**
1. France -- Fiction 2. Jews -- France -- Fiction 3. Paris (France) -- Fiction 4. Holocaust, 1933-1945 -- Fiction
ISBN 978-0-385-73881-1; 0-385-73881-1; 978-0-385-90748-4 lib bdg; 0-385-90748-6 lib bdg
LC 2009-47613

"Set in France during World War II, this historical novel follows eleven-year-old Gustave as his family escapes Paris for safer quarters in the small, provincial town of Saint-Georges. . . . Not long after Gustave's family arrives in Saint-Georges, the Nazis invade and occupy Paris and establish a demarcation line between occupied northern France and unoccupied Vichy France in the south. . . . The episodic narrative offers abundant detail, and the wartime dangers, especially Gustave's father's illicit travel between occupied and unoccupied zones, adds considerable suspense. Gustave's growth over the course of the novel is both realistic and relatable, making this an appealing topical entry for the upper elementary/middle school set." Bull Cent Child Books

Miles, Miska
Annie and the Old One; illustrated by Peter Parnall. Little, Brown 1971 44p il lib bdg $16.95; pa $7.95
Grades: 1 2 3 4   **Fic**
1. Death -- Fiction 2. Navajo Indians -- Fiction
ISBN 0-316-57117-2 lib bdg; 0-316-57120-2 pa
A Newbery Medal honor book, 1972

This is "a poignant, understated, rather brave story of a very real child, set against a background of Navajo traditions and contemporary Indian life. Fine expressive drawings match the simplicity of the story." Horn Book

Milford, Kate

★ The **Boneshaker**; [illustrations by Andrea Offermann] Clarion Books 2010 372p il $17

Grades: 5 6 7 8 9   Fic

1. Bicycles -- Fiction 2. Missouri -- Fiction 3. Demonology -- Fiction 4. Supernatural -- Fiction

ISBN 978-0-547-24187-6; 0-547-24187-9

LC 2009-45350

When Jake Limberleg brings his traveling medicine show to a small Missouri town in 1913, thirteen-year-old Natalie senses that something is wrong and, after investigating, learns that her love of automata and other machines make her the only one who can set things right.

"Natalie is a well-drawn protagonist with sturdy supporting characters around her. The tension built into the solidly constructed plot is complemented by themes that explore the literal and metaphorical role of crossroads and that thin line between good and evil." Kirkus

The **Broken** Lands; by Kate Milford; with illustrations by Andrea Offermann. Clarion Books 2012 455 p. ill. (hardback) $16.99

Grades: 5 6 7 8 9 10   Fic

1. Bridges -- Fiction 2. Supernatural -- Fiction 3. New York (N.Y.) -- Fiction 4. Orphans -- Fiction 5. Demonology -- Fiction 6. Good and evil -- Fiction 7. New York (N.Y.) -- History -- 1865-1898 -- Fiction 8. Coney Island (New York, N.Y.) -- History -- 19th century -- Fiction

ISBN 0547739664; 9780547739663

LC 2011049466

This book, a prequel to "Kate Milford's 'The Boneshaker,' [is] set in . . . nineteenth-century Coney Island and New York City. Few crossroads compare to the one being formed by the Brooklyn Bridge and the East River, and as the bridge's construction progresses, forces of unimaginable evil seek to bend that power to their advantage. . . . Can the teenagers Sam, a card sharp, and Jin, a fireworks expert, stop them before it's too late?" (Publisher's note)

Greenglass House; by Kate Milford; with illustrations by Jaime Zollars. Clarion Books, Houghton Mifflin Harcourt 2014 384 p. (hardback) $17.99

Grades: 5 6 7 8   Fic

1. Mystery fiction 2. Hotels and motels -- Fiction 3. Magic -- Fiction 4. Adoption -- Fiction 5. Mystery and detective stories 6. Hotels, motels, etc. -- Fiction

ISBN 0544052706; 9780544052703

LC 2013036212

Edgar Award: Best Juvenile (2015)

In this middle grades book by Kate Milford, illustrated by Jaime Zollars, "it's wintertime at Greenglass House. The creaky smuggler's inn is always quiet during this season, and twelve-year-old Milo, the innkeepers' adopted son, plans to spend his holidays relaxing. . . . As objects go missing and tempers flare, Milo and Meddy, the cook's daughter, must decipher clues and untangle the web of deepening mysteries to discover the truth about Greenglass House--and themselves." (Publisher's note)

Millard, Glenda

Layla, Queen of hearts; illustrated by Patrice Barton. Farrar Straus Giroux 2010 119p il $16.99

Grades: 3 4 5   Fic

1. Old age -- Fiction 2. Australia -- Fiction 3. Friendship -- Fiction 4. Family life -- Fiction

ISBN 0-374-34360-8; 978-0-374-34360-6

LC 2008-38748

Sequel to: The naming of Tishkin Silk (2009)

First published 2006 in Australia

Even though she loves the family of her best friend, Griffin Silk, especially grandmother Nell, Layla Elliott, who no longer has a grandmother, determines, despite many difficulties, to find an old person of her own to bring to the school's Senior Citizens' Day.

"Barton's illustrations gently convey the bonds of affection among the author's eccentric, engaging characters." Kirkus

The **naming** of Tishkin Silk; illustrated by Patrice Barton. Farrar, Straus and Giroux 2009 101p il $15.99

Grades: 3 4 5   Fic

1. Death -- Fiction 2. Australia -- Fiction 3. Friendship -- Fiction 4. Family life -- Fiction 5. Personal names -- Fiction

ISBN 0-374-35481-2; 978-0-374-35481-7

LC 2008-16796

First published 2003 in Australia

Griffin Silk feels responsible for the absence of his mother and baby sister, but he and his new friend Layla find the perfect way to make everyone feel a little bit better. "Grades two to four." (Bull Cent Child Books)

"Illustrated with softly rendered black-and-white drawings, the gentle, descriptive narrative [is] touched with droll humor . . . and features a likable protagonist and other appealing, diverse characters." Booklist

Followed by: Layla, Queen of Hearts (2010)

Miller, Kirsten

Kiki Strike; the darkness dwellers. by Kirsten Miller. Bloomsbury 2013 416 p. (hardback) $17.99

Grades: 5 6 7 8   Fic

1. Girls -- Fiction 2. Adventure fiction 3. Teenagers -- Fiction 4. Crime -- Fiction 5. France -- Fiction 6. Identity -- Fiction 7. Paris (France) -- Fiction 8. New York (N.Y.) -- Fiction

ISBN 1599907364; 9781599907369

LC 2012023303

This teen adventure novel, by Kirsten Miller, is part of the "Kiki Strike" series. "First they ventured deep under New York to save the city itself. Then things got personal as the Irregulars ventured into a haunted mansion in Chinatown to uncover an evil twin. Now, . . . this . . . group of delinquent geniuses jump feet first into a[n] . . . international pursuit, going underground in Paris to pursue a pair of treacherous royals who have killed Kiki's parents." (Publisher's note)

Millet, Lydia

The **fires** beneath the sea. Big Mouth House 2011 256p (The dissenters) $16.95

Grades: 4 5 6 7   Fic

1. Otters -- Fiction 2. Mothers -- Fiction 3. Supernatural -- Fiction 4. Cape Cod (Mass.) -- Fiction

ISBN 978-1-931520-71-3; 1-931520-71-2

"Mom vanished two months ago, and summer's ending. While swimming in the ocean, Cara spots a sea otter—but sea otters don't belong on Atlantic beaches. Cara reaches out her fingertips, and the otter streams words into Cara's mind. . . . Millet's prose is lyrically evocative. . . . A lush and intelligent opener for a topical eco-fantasy series." Kirkus

Mills, Claudia, 1954-

★ **7** x 9; pictures by G. Brian Karas. Farrar, Straus & Giroux 2002 103p il $15; pa $6.95

Grades: 2 3 4   Fic

1. School stories 2. Mathematics -- Fiction

ISBN 0-374-36746-9; 0-374-46452-9 pa

LC 2001-16028

Third-grader Wilson struggles with his times-tables in order to beat the class deadline

"Mills' sympathetic and detailed treatment of Wilson's travails makes this both a suspenseful and satisfying beginning chapter book." Bull Cent Child Books

Followed by: Fractions = trouble! (2011)

Being Teddy Roosevelt; pictures by R.W. Alley. Farrar, Straus and Giroux 2007 89p il $16

Grades: 2 3 4   Fic

1. School stories

ISBN 978-0-374-30657-1; 0-374-30657-51

LC 2006-48978

When he is assigned Teddy Roosevelt as his biography project in school, fourth-grader Riley finds himself inspired by Roosevelt's tenacity and perseverance and resolves to find a way to get what he most wants—a saxophone and music lessons

"Lots of funny lines and comical situations enliven the simple story, which is also enriched by its portrait of grade-school friendships and goofy classroom happenings, depicted in Alley's appealing spot drawings." Booklist

Fractions; [pictures by G. Brian Karas] Farrar Straus Giroux 2011 113p il $15.99

Grades: 2 3 4   Fic

1. School stories 2. Fractions -- Fiction 3. Science projects -- Fiction

ISBN 978-0-374-36716-9; 0-374-36716-7

LC 2010-08395

Sequel to: 7 x 9 = trouble! (2002)

While trying to decide on a science fair project, third-grader Wilson struggles with with fractions and, much to his embarrassment, his parents sign him up to work with a math tutor.

"Familiar school concerns, nicely resolved, make this another excellent selection for early chapter-book readers." Kirkus

★ **How** Oliver Olson changed the world; pictures by Heather Maione. Farrar, Straus and Giroux 2009 103p il $15.95

Grades: 2 3 4   Fic

1. School stories 2. Colorado -- Fiction 3. Solar system -- Fiction 4. Science projects -- Fiction

ISBN 0-374-33487-0; 978-0-374-33487-1

LC 2007-48846

Afraid he will always be an outsider like ex-planet Pluto, nine-year-old Oliver finally shows his extremely overprotec-

tive parents that he is capable of doing great things without their help while his class is studying the solar system.

"An engaging and thought-provoking chapter book." Booklist

One square inch. Farrar, Straus and Giroux 2010 168p $16.99

Grades: 4 5 6 7   Fic

1. Mothers -- Fiction 2. Siblings -- Fiction 3. Imagination -- Fiction 4. Manic-depressive illness -- Fiction

ISBN 978-0-374-35652-1; 0-374-35652-1

When their mother's behavior changes and she starts to neglect her children, seventh-grader Cooper and his little sister take refuge in Inchland, an imaginary country inspired by deeds to one square inch of land that their grandfather gave them.

Mills "delivers a compassionate story about life with a bipolar parent. . . . The twist of [Cooper's] emotions and depth of his concern for his mother and sister are believable and deeply moving." Publ Wkly

Pet disasters. Alfred A. Knopf 2011 154p (Mason Dixon) $12.99; lib bdg $15.99

Grades: 3 4 5   Fic

1. Dogs -- Fiction 2. Pets -- Fiction 3. Friendship -- Fiction

ISBN 978-0-375-86873-3; 0-375-86873-9; 978-0-375-96873-0 lib bdg; 0-375-96873-3 lib bdg

LC 2010029724

Nine-year-old Mason's parents keep trying to get him a pet, but until he and his best friend Brody adopt a three-legged dog, he's not interested.

"Mills's account of this quirky kid and his trials and tribulations is both funny and touching. . . . An enjoyable read with cartoon-style pen-and-ink illustrations scattered throughout." SLJ

Other titles about Mason Dixon are:

Fourth grade disasters (2011)

Basketball disasters (2012)

The totally made-up Civil War diary of Amanda MacLeish. Farrar, Straus and Giroux 2008 197p $16

Grades: 3 4 5   Fic

1. School stories 2. Maryland -- Fiction 3. Family life -- Fiction 4. United States -- History -- 1861-1865, Civil War -- Fiction

ISBN 978-0-374-37696-3; 0-374-37696-4

LC 2007-09162

While dealing with her parents' separation and her best friend's distance, Amanda is able to work out some of her anxiety through her fifth-grade project—writing a diary from the point of view of a ten-year-old girl whose brothers fight on opposite sides in the Civil War.

"Mills handles the MacLeish family's separation realistically. . . . Subplots provide the novel's lighter moments. . . . This makes a good choice for Mills' many fans, as well as for children in search of a satisfying family story." Booklist

Mills, Rob

Charlie's key. Orca Book Publishers 2011 254p pa $9.99

Grades: 5 6 7 8 9 **Fic**

1. Mystery fiction 2. Orphans -- Fiction

ISBN 978-1-55469-872-1; 1-55469-872-3

A young orphan struggles to unlock the significance of an old key left by his dying father.

"A fast-paced, often riveting mystery with a plausible, thrilling climax." Kirkus

Milne, A. A.

★ The **House** at Pooh Corner; with decorations by Ernest H. Shepard. Dutton 1985 180p il $9.95; pa $4.99

Grades: 1 2 3 4 **Fic**

1. Toys -- Fiction 2. Bears -- Fiction 3. Animals -- Fiction

ISBN 0-525-32302-3; 0-14-036122-7 pa

First published 1928

"It is hard to tell what Pooh Bear and his friends would have been without the able assistance of Ernest H. Shepard to see them and picture them so cleverly. . . . They are, and should be, classics." N Y Times Book Rev

★ **Winnie**-the-Pooh; illustrated by Ernest H. Shepard, colored by Hilda Scott. Dutton 1974 161p il $10.99; pa $4.99

Grades: 1 2 3 4 **Fic**

1. Toys -- Fiction 2. Bears -- Fiction 3. Animals -- Fiction

ISBN 0-525-44443-2; 0-14-036121-9 pa

First published 1926

"The kindly, lovable Pooh is one of an imaginative cast of animal characters which includes Eeyore, the wistfully gloomy donkey, Tigger, Piglet, Kanga, and Roo, all living in a fantasy world presided over by Milne's young son, Christopher Robin. Many of the animals are drawn from figures in Milne's life, though each emerges as a universally recognizable type." Reader's Ency

Milway, Katie Smith

The **good** garden; how one family went from hunger to having enough. written by Katie Smith Milway; illustrated by Sylvie Daigneault. Kids Can Press 2010 30p il (CitizenKid) $18.95

Grades: 3 4 5 **Fic**

1. Honduras -- Fiction 2. Vegetable gardening -- Fiction 3. Sustainable agriculture -- Fiction

ISBN 978-1-55453-488-3; 1-55453-488-7

"When María Luz's Papa makes the tough decision to leave their hillside home in Honduras to seek employment elsewhere, he puts the girl in charge of planting and tending their winter garden. . . . A new teacher has arrived at her school with fresh ideas for how to feed and restore the soil. . . . [Maria] also learns that they need not rely on the unscrupulous 'coyotes' who have historically acted as loan sharks and middlemen. . . . Taken at a literal level, this is a story of how sustainable farming practices can nourish families and the earth simultaneously. On a deeper level, it is about social justice and self-sustaining economies. . . . The stylized colored-pencil artwork is appropriately lush and idealized." SLJ

Mimi's Village; And How Basic Health Care Transformed It. Katie Smith Milway. Kids Can Press 2012 32 p. $18.95

Grades: 1 2 3 4 **Fic**

1. Public health 2. Kenya -- Fiction 3. Malaria -- Fiction

ISBN 1554537223; 9781554537228

Author Katie Smith Milway presents a story on public health care in Kenya. "Mimi Malaho and her family help bring basic health care to their community. By making small changes like sleeping under mosquito nets and big ones like building a clinic with outside help, the Malahos and their neighbors transform their Kenyan village from one afraid of illness to a thriving community." (Publisher's note)

Mitchell, Stephen

The **nightingale**; [by] Hans Christian Andersen; retold by Stephen Mitchell; illustrated by Bagram Ibatoulline. Candlewick Press 2002 un il hardcover o.p. pa $6.95

Grades: 2 3 4 **Fic**

1. Nightingales -- Fiction

ISBN 0-7636-1521-8; 0-7636-2406-3 pa

LC 2001-25144

Though the emperor banishes the nightingale in preference of a jeweled mechanical imitation, the little bird remains faithful and returns years later when the emperor is near death and no one else can help him

"This is an elegant piece of bookmaking. Mixed-media illustrations (ink, gouache, watercolor) based on Chinese art and costume are rendered in a ceremonial, fairy-tale style." Bull Cent Child Books

The **tinderbox**; [by] Hans Christian Andersen; retold by Stephen Mitchell; illustrated by Bagram Ibatoulline. Candlewick Press 2007 un il $17.99

Grades: 2 3 4 5 **Fic**

1. Fairy tales

ISBN 978-0-7636-2078-3; 0-7636-2078-5

LC 2006-47554

With the help of a magic tinderbox, a soldier finds a fortune and pursues a princess imprisoned in a castle.

"The soldier may be handsome and the princess lovely, but the old witch and the three giant dogs along with the beautifully developed settings really create the superb fairy-tale ambience of this robust telling of Andersen's tale. Ibatoulline's finely hatched pen drawings, washed in muted tones, resemble lithographs." SLJ

Mobley, Jeannie

★ **Katerina's** wish; Jeannie Mobley. Margaret K. McElderry Books 2012 256 p. (hardcover) $15.99

Grades: 4 5 6 7 **Fic**

1. Wishes -- Fiction 2. Historical fiction 3. Immigrants -- Fiction 4. Czech Americans -- Fiction 5. Coal mines and mining -- Fiction 6. Family life -- Colorado -- Fiction 7. Colorado -- History -- 1876-1950 -- Fiction

ISBN 1442433434; 9781442433434; 9781442433458

LC 2011044392

In this young adult novel, Katerina and her family have immigrated from Bohemia and "settled in a coal mining camp, [where] they are still buried in work and trapped by debt. Then Trina sees a fish that reminds her of a fairy tale about a magic carp; soon after, her two younger sisters' frivolous wishes are granted. Initially skeptical, Trina eventually makes her wish: for a farm that will make her family happy." (Publishers Weekly)

Modugno, Maria

★ **Santa** Claus and the Three Bears; by Maria Modugno and illustrated by Jane Dyer and Brooke Dyer. Harpercollins Childrens Books 2013 40 p. $17.99

Grades: PreK K 1 2   **Fic**

1. Bears -- Fiction 2. Santa Claus -- Fiction

ISBN 0061700231; 9780061700231

In this book, "author Maria Modugno teams up with award-winning artists Jane and Brooke Dyer to deliver a festive twist on Goldilocks and the Three Bears, with Santa Claus stepping in as the cheerful intruder. Papa Bear, Mama Bear, and Baby Bear weren't expecting any company when they went for a walk on Christmas Eve, but that's exactly what they got!" (Publisher's note)

Moloney, James

The **Book** of Lies. HarperCollinsPublishers 2007 360p $16.99; lib bdg $17.89

Grades: 5 6 7 8   **Fic**

1. Fantasy fiction 2. Magic -- Fiction 3. Orphans -- Fiction

ISBN 978-0-06-057842-8; 0-06-057842-4; 978-0-06-057843-5 lib bdg; 0-06-057843-2 lib bdg

LC 2006-29874

On the night he was brought to an orphanage, Marcel's memories were taken by a sorceror and replaced with new ones by his Book of Lies, but Bea, a girl with the ability to make herself invisible, was watching and is determined to help him discover his true identity.

"Readers who enjoy the mixture of mystery, riddles, action, and camaraderie will be pleased that the open-ended conclusion leads to a planned sequel." Booklist

Mone, Gregory

Fish. Scholastic Press 2010 241p $16.99

Grades: 4 5 6 7   **Fic**

1. Adventure fiction 2. Ciphers -- Fiction 3. Pirates -- Fiction 4. Buried treasure -- Fiction

ISBN 978-0-545-11632-9; 0-545-11632-5

Eleven-year-old Fish, seeking a way to help his family financially, becomes a reluctant cabin boy on a pirate ship, where he soon makes friends—and enemies—and is asked to help decipher clues that might lead to a legendary treasure.

"Mone seamlessly integrates factual information into his tale of friendship, loyalty, and exploration. . . . Fish makes a splashing good addition to adventure fiction." SLJ

Montgomery, Lewis B.

The **case** of the stinky socks; by Lewis B. Montgomery; illustrated by Amy Wummer. Kane Press 2009 94p il (Milo & Jazz mysteries) pa $6.95; $22.60

Grades: 1 2 3 4   **Fic**

1. Mystery fiction 2. Baseball -- Fiction 3. Clothing and dress -- Fiction

ISBN 1-57565-285-4 pa; 1-57565-288-9; 978-1-57565-285-6 pa; 978-1-57565-288-7

LC 2008027536

Detectives-in-training Milo and Jazz join forces to tackle their first big case—finding out who stole the lucky socks from the high school baseball team's star pitcher.

This book "gets it just right: a fun, easy-to-solve mystery, readily identifiable young detectives, and some extras readers will enjoy. . . . The short chapters, written in a large

typeface, are punctuated by pen-and-ink illustrations of better quality than those often seen in series books." Booklist

Other titles in this series are:

The case of the poisoned pig (2009)

The case of the haunted haunted house (2009)

The case of the Amazing Zelda (2009)

The case of the July 4th jinx (2010)

The case of the missing moose (2011)

Montijo, Rhode

Chews your destiny; Rhode Montijo. 1st ed. Disney-Hyperion Books 2013 128 p. (The gumazing Gum Girl!) (alk. paper) $14.99

Grades: 2 3 4   **Fic**

1. Chewing gum -- Fiction 2. Superheroes -- Juvenile fiction 3. Bubble gum -- Fiction 4. Superheroes -- Fiction 5. Hispanic Americans -- Fiction

ISBN 1423157400; 9781423157403

LC 2012036706

In this book by Rhode Montijo, "Gabby Gomez loves to chew bubble gum even though her mother has warned her against it. It's not like she will turn into gum . . . except, that's exactly what happens! With her new, stretch-tastic powers Gabby can help save the day, but she will have to keep her gummy alter-ego a secret from her mother or else she'll find herself in a really sticky situation." (Publisher's note)

Moodie, Craig

Into the trap. Roaring Brook Press 2011 199p $15.99

Grades: 5 6 7 8   **Fic**

1. Adventure fiction 2. Islands -- Fiction 3. Thieves -- Fiction 4. Lobsters -- Fiction

ISBN 978-1-59643-585-8; 1-59643-585-2

LC 2010029238

Twelve-year-old Eddie Atwell accidentally learns who has been stealing lobsters from Fog Island lobstermen and enlists thirteen-year-old Briggs Fairfield, a summer visitor, to help foil their plans.

"Set over a single, tense day, the novel's chapter titles track the hours and give the book an immediate, real-time pace. An exciting drama." Booklist

Morey, Walt

Gentle Ben; illustrated by John Schoenherr. Dutton 1965 191p il hardcover o.p. pa $6.99

Grades: 5 6 7 8   **Fic**

1. Bears -- Fiction 2. Alaska -- Fiction

ISBN 0-14-240551-5 pa

Set in Alaska before statehood, this is the story of 13-year-old Mark Anderson who befriends a huge brown bear which has been chained in a shed since it was a cub. Finally Mark's father buys the bear, but Orca City's inhabitants eventually insist that the animal, named Ben, be shipped to an uninhabited island. However, the friendship of Mark and Ben endures

The author "has written a vivid chronicle of Alaska, its people and places, challenges and beauties. Told with a simplicity and dignity which befits its characters, human and animal, [it] is a memorable reading experience." SLJ

Morgenstern, Susie Hoch

★ A **book** of coupons; by Susie Morgenstern; illustrated by Serge Bloch; translated by Gill Rosner. Viking 2001 62p il $12.99

Grades: 3 4 5   **Fic**
1. School stories 2. Teachers -- Fiction
ISBN 0-670-89970-4
LC 00-11940
Original French edition, 1999

Elderly Monsieur Noel, the very unconventional new teacher, gives coupon books for such things as dancing in class and sleeping late, which are bound to get him in trouble with the military discipline of Principal Incarnation Perez

"Morgenstern's witty and poignant tribute to great teachers everywhere proclaims what education should be about. Her message may be pointed, but no reader will be unmoved." Horn Book Guide

Moriarty, Chris

The **inquisitor's** apprentice; illustrations by Mark Edward Geyer. Harcourt Children's Books 2011 345p il $16.99

Grades: 4 5 6 7   **Fic**
1. Inventors 2. Gangs -- Fiction 3. Magic -- Fiction 4. Witches -- Fiction 5. Apprentices -- Fiction 6. New York (N.Y.) -- Fiction 7. Jews -- United States -- Fiction
ISBN 978-0-547-58135-4; 0-547-58135-1

In early twentieth-century New York, Sacha Kessler's ability to see witches earns him an apprenticeship to the police department's star Inquisitor, Maximillian Wolf, to help stop magical crime and, with fellow apprentice Lily Astral, Sacha investigates who is trying to kill Thomas Edison, whose mechanical witch detector that could unleash the worst witch-hunt in American history.

"Sacha, Lily and Inspector Wolf are all fully developed and multilayered characters, as are the many other distinctive personalities that appear in the tale. The author employs rich language and syntax that please the ear and touch the senses, making it all come alive." Kirkus

The **watcher** in the shadows; Chris Moriarty; [illustrated by] Mark Edward Geyer. Harcourt Children's Books 2013 336 p. (hardcover) $16.99

Grades: 4 5 6 7   **Fic**
1. Fantasy fiction 2. Jews -- Fiction 3. Mystery fiction 4. New York (N.Y.) -- History -- 20th century -- Fiction
ISBN 0547466323; 9780547466323
LC 2013003919

This juvenile novel, by Chris Moriarty, is part of the "Inquisitor's Apprentice" series. "New York's Bowery District becomes the scene of a terrible murder when the Klezmer King gets fried to a crisp by his Electric Tuxedo--on stage! The Inquisitor's apprentice, thirteen-year-old Sacha Kessler, tries to help find the killer, but the closer he gets to solving the crime, the more it sounds as if the creature that haunted him in his first adventure is back." (Publisher's note)

"Rich language, colorful syntax, vivid description and a brilliant cast of characters beckon readers right into both the adventure and the heartfelt emotional landscape. Exciting, action-packed and absolutely marvelous." Kirkus

Morpurgo, Michael

★ **Kensuke's** kingdom. Scholastic Press 2003 164p hardcover o.p. pa $5.99

Grades: 4 5 6 7   **Fic**
1. Survival after airplane accidents, shipwrecks, etc. --

Fiction
ISBN 0-439-38202-5; 0-439-59181-3 pa
LC 2002-9078
First published 1999 in the United Kingdom

When Michael is swept off his family's yacht, he washes up on a desert island, where he struggles to survive—until he finds he is not alone

This is "highly readable. . . . The end is bittersweet but believable, and the epilogue is a sad commentary on the long-lasting effects of war." Booklist

★ **On** angel wings; illustrated by Quentin Blake. Candlewick Press 2007 un il $8.99

Grades: 3 4 5   **Fic**
1. Angels -- Fiction 2. Shepherds -- Fiction
ISBN 978-0-7636-3466-7; 0-7636-3466-2

"Morpurgo's tone blends reverence with wit, a combination matched in Blake's pen-and-ink and watercolor cartoons." Publ Wkly

Grandpa tells "of his boyhood recollection of being with the adult shepherds when the angel Gabriel . . . told them of the Baby Jesus's birth. . . . The adults follow and leave the boy behind to tend the sheep. Gabriel then reappears and offers to fly him to the stable to see the baby for himself." SLJ

Waiting for Anya. Viking 1991 172p hardcover o.p. pa $4.99

Grades: 5 6 7 8   **Fic**
1. Jews -- Fiction 2. France -- Fiction 3. World War, 1939-1945 -- Fiction
ISBN 0-670-83735-0; 0-14-038431-6 pa
LC 90-50560
First published 1990 in the United Kingdom

"A World War II adventure story set in Vichy, France, this centers on a young shepherd, Jo, who becomes involved in smuggling Jewish children across the border from his mountain village to Spain. Morpurgo has injected the basic conventions of heroism and villainy with some complexities of character. . . . Independent readers will appreciate the simple, clear style and fast-paced plot of the book, which will also hold up well in group read-alouds, commanding attention to ethics as well as action." Bull Cent Child Books

War horse; by Michael Morpurgo. Scholastic 2007 165p $16.99

Grades: 5 6 7 8   **Fic**
1. Horses -- Fiction 2. World War, 1914-1918 -- Fiction
ISBN 978-0-439-79663-7; 0-439-79663-6
LC 2006044368
First published 1982 in the United Kingdom

Joey the horse recalls his experiences growing up on an English farm, his struggle for survival as a cavalry horse during World War I, and his reunion with his beloved master

"At times deeply affecting, the story balances the horror with moments of respite and care." Horn Book Guide

Morris, Gerald

The **adventures** of Sir Lancelot the Great; illustrated by Aaron Renier. Houghton Mifflin Company 2008 92p il (The knights' tales) $15; pa $4.99

Grades: 3 4 5 6   **Fic**
1. Kings 2. Knights and knighthood -- Fiction 3. Lancelot (Legendary character) -- Fiction 4. Great

Britain -- History -- 0-1066 -- Fiction
ISBN 978-0-618-77714-3; 0-618-77714-8; 978-0-547-23756-5 pa; 0-547-23756-1 pa

LC 2007-41167

This novel relates the story of Sir Lancelot, the bravest knight in King Arthur's court.

"This trim novel, with simple vocabulary and brief, witty chapters, is an ideal fit for early readers. . . . Fans of the legendary characters may find particular delight in this irreverent and unabashedly silly exploration of Arthur's court and his most influential knight. . . . Frequent black-and-white illustrations supplement the text, highlighting (and in most cases, exaggerating) elements from humorous passages." Bull Cent Child Books

Other titles in this series are:

The adventures of Sir Givret the Short (2008)

The adventures of Sir Gawain the True (2011)

Morris, Jackie

East of the Sun, West of the Moon; Jackie Morris. Pgw 2013 176 p. (hardcover) $14.99
Grades: 6 7 8 9   **Fic**
1. Bears -- Fiction 2. Girls -- Fiction 3. Fantasy fiction
ISBN 184780294X; 9781847802941

This book, by Jackie Morris, describes a friendship between a girl and a bear. The girl goes "first to the bear's secret palace in faraway mountains, where she is treated so courteously, but where she experiences the bear's unfathomable sadness, and a deep mystery. . . As the bear's secret unravels, another journey unfolds . . . that takes the girl to the homes of the four Winds and beyond, to the castle east of the sun, west of the moon." (Publisher's note)

Morrison, Megan

Grounded; the tale of Rapunzel. Megan Morrison. Arthur A. Levine Books, an imprint of Scholastic Inc. 2015 384 p. (Tyme) (alk. paper) $17.99
Grades: 5 6 7 8   **Fic**
1. Fractured fairy tales 2. Fairy tales 3. Magic -- Fiction 4. Fairies -- Fiction 5. Witches -- Fiction 6. Robbers and outlaws -- Fiction 7. Characters in literature -- Fiction 8. Adventure and adventurers -- Fiction
ISBN 0545638267; 9780545638265; 9780545642699; 9780545642705; 9780545754682

LC 2014027138

This juvenile story, by Megan Morrison, is a retelling of the Rapunzel legend. "In all of Tyme, . . . no one is as lucky as Rapunzel. . . . And she knows this because Witch tells her so--her beloved Witch. . . . [Then] Rapunzel descends to the ground for the first time, and finds a world filled with more peril than Witch promised . . . and more beauty, wonder, and adventure than she could have dreamed." (Publisher's note)

Morse, Scott

Magic Pickle and the garden of evil. Graphix 2009 136p il pa $5.99
Grades: 2 3 4 5   **Fic**
1. Vegetables -- Fiction 2. Superheroes -- Fiction
ISBN 978-0-545-13580-1; 0-545-13580-X

LC 2008037614

Magic Pickle, a fearless, dill superhero, comes to the rescue when Jo Jo's class garden yields a monstrous lettuce plant bent on world domination.

"One of a series of illustrated chapter books coming on the heels of Morse's graphic novel. . . . The spot illustrations are lively, with crackling energy dots and a constant sense of action and movement. . . . The comic segments, typography sound effects, and the like are cues wtih which struggling readers can propel themselves along." SLJ

Moses, Shelia P.

★ **Sallie** Gal and the Wall-a-kee man; illustrated by Niki Daly. Scholastic 2007 152p il $15.99
Grades: 3 4 5   **Fic**
1. Family life -- Fiction 2. North Carolina -- Fiction 3. African Americans -- Fiction
ISBN 978-0-439-90890-0; 0-439-90890-6

LC 2006033171

More than anything, Sallie Gal wants pretty ribbons to wear in her hair, but she knows that they cannot afford them and Momma has too much dignity to accept charity.

"Appealing black-and-white illustrations in various sizes embellish the text. Moses takes a fond look at strong family ties and the values of honesty and hard work. Short paragraphs and peppy dialogue make this easy chapter book a candidate for reading aloud." SLJ

Moss, Marissa

Alien Eraser to the rescue. Candlewick Press 2009 52p il (Max Disaster) $16.99; pa $6.99
Grades: 3 4 5   **Fic**
1. Extraterrestrial beings -- Fiction
ISBN 978-0-7636-3577-0; 0-7636-3577-4; 978-0-7636-4407-9 pa; 0-7636-4407-2 pa

Welcome to Max's book of inventions, experiments, comic strips, and random thoughts about school, pimply older brothers, mutant marshmallows, erasers and good parents who get into bad fights.

"Moss is a master at verbalizing kids' anxieties and channeling their astute observations of family life—both as it breaks apart and begins to mend." Publ Wkly

Other titles in the Max Disaster series are:

Alien Eraser unravels the mystery of the pyramids (2009)

Alien Eraser reveals the secrets of evolution (2009)

Amelia writes again. Simon & Schuster Books for Young Readers 2006 un il $9.95
Grades: 3 4 5   **Fic**
1. School stories 2. Diaries -- Fiction 3. Family life -- Fiction
ISBN 978-1-416-90904-0; 1-416-90904-4

LC 2005051669

A reissue of the title first published 1996 by Tricycle Press

"Ten years old at last, Amelia finds that she has plenty to write about as she discusses the expressiveness of hands, the time she and her sister stuck marshmallows to the ceiling, her reactions to an arson fire at her school, and her discomfort when a friend wants to read her journal. Finally, she and the friend jointly write a story in the notebook. Naive ink-and-watercolor illustrations brighten the blue-lined, hand-printed pages. Many labels and side comments add to the fun." Booklist

★ **Amelia's** 6th-grade notebook. Simon & Schuster Books for Young Readers 2005 un il $9.95

Grades: 3 4 5 6 **Fic**

1. School stories

ISBN 0-689-87040-X

LC 2004-45309

Problems arise for Amelia when she starts sixth grade at the same middle school where her older sister Cleo is an eighth-grader, and she gets the school's meanest teacher for three of her classes

"Both insightful and entertaining, Amelia's first-person narrative rings true. . . . [This] features a handwritten format; colorful, cartoonlike illustrations; and charming doodles with descriptive asides." Booklist

Other titles about Amelia are:

The all-new Amelia (1999)

Amelia lends a hand (2002)

Amelia works it out (2000)

Amelia writes again (1996)

Amelia's are-we-there-yet longest ever car trip (1997)

Amelia's BFF (2011)

Amelia's book of notes & note passing (2006)

Amelia's boredom survival guide (1999)

Amelia's bully survival guide (1998)

Amelia's family ties (2000)

Amelia's 5th-grade notebook (2003)

Amelia's guide to gossip (2006)

Amelia's itchy-twitchy, lovey-dovey summer at Camp Mosquito (2008)

Amelia's longest, biggest, most-fights-ever family reunion (2006)

Amelia's most unforgettable embarrassing moments (2005)

Amelia's must-keep resolutions for the best year ever! (2007)

Amelia's notebook (1995)

Amelia's school survival guide (2002)

Amelia's science fair disaster (2009)

Luv, Amelia luv, Nadia (1999)

Oh boy, Amelia! (2001)

Vote 4 Amelia (2007)

Mira's Diary; Lost in Paris. Marissa Moss. Sourcebooks Inc 2012 224 p. $12.99

Grades: 4 5 6 **Fic**

1. Time travel -- Fiction 2. Missing persons -- Fiction

ISBN 1402266065; 9781402266065

In this children's story, by Marissa Moss, "when Mira receives a cryptic postcard from her missing mother, she sets off with her father and brother to find her in Paris. . . . With an innocent touch to a gargoyle sculpture on the roof of Notre Dame, Mira is whisked into the past. There she learns her mother isn't just avoiding the family, she's in serious trouble. Following her mother's clues, Mira travels through time to help change history and bring her mother home." (Publisher's note)

Mould, Chris

★ The **wooden** mile. Roaring Brook Press 2008 176p il (Something wickedly weird) $9.95

Grades: 3 4 5 6 **Fic**

1. Pirates -- Fiction 2. Werewolves -- Fiction 3. Supernatural -- Fiction

ISBN 978-1-59643-383-0; 1-59643-383-3

LC 2008011258

First published 2007 in the United Kingdom

Eleven-year-old Stanley Buggle, happily anticipating a long summer vacation in the house he inherits from his great-uncle, discovers, soon after arriving in the seemingly peaceful village of Crampton Rock, that along with the house he has also inherited some sinister neighbors, a talking stuffed fish, and a host of mysteries surrounding his great-uncle's death.

"With its fairly easy text, many black-and-white illustrations, and a dramatic scene silhouetted on the cover, this chapter book will appeal to young readers who like their fiction fast-paced and a bit scary. Mould's richly atmospheric ink drawings capture the rather macabre tone of the story." Booklist

Other titles in this series are:

The icy hand (2008)

The darkling curse (2009)

Smugglers' mine (2010)

Moulton, Erin E.

Flutter; the story of four sisters and an incredible journey. Philomel Books 2011

Grades: 4 5 6 **Fic**

1. Adventure fiction 2. Nature -- Fiction 3. Sisters -- Fiction 4. Vermont -- Fiction 5. Poaching -- Fiction 6. Family life -- Fiction

ISBN 0-399-25515-X; 978-0-399-25515-1

LC 2010014507

Nine-and-a-half-year-old Maple and her older sister, Dawn, must work together to face treacherous terrain, wild animals, and poachers as they trek through Vermont's Green Mountains seeking a miracle for their prematurely-born sister.

"Moulton describes the girls' journey—and their motivation—in vivid, heart-wrenching prose." Horn Book Guide

Mourlevat, Jean-Claude

★ The **pull** of the ocean; [by] Jean-Claude Mourlevat; translated from the French by Y. Maudet. Delacorte Press 2006 190p hardcover o.p. lib bdg $17.99; pa $6.50

Grades: 5 6 7 **Fic**

1. Size -- Fiction 2. Twins -- Fiction 3. France -- Fiction 4. Brothers -- Fiction

ISBN 978-0-385-73348-9; 0-385-73348-8; 978-0-385-90364-6 lib bdg; 0-385-90364-2 lib bdg; 978-0-385-73666-4 pa; 0-385-73666-5 pa

LC 2006001802

Loosely based on Charles Perrault's "Tom Thumb," seven brothers in modern-day France flee their poor parents' farm, led by the youngest who, although mute and unusually small, is exceptionally wise.

This "is a memorable novel that readers will find engaging and intellectually satisfying." SLJ

Mull, Brandon

Rogue Knight; by Brandon Mull. Aladdin 2014 480 p. (Five kingdoms) (hardback) $17.99

Grades: 4 5 6 7 **Fic**

1. Fantasy fiction 2. Knights and knighthood -- Fiction 3. Adventure and adventurers -- Fiction

ISBN 1442497033; 9781442497030; 9781442497047

LC 2014025800

Sequel to: Sky Raiders (2014)

In this novel, by Brandon Mull, book two of the "Five Kingdoms" series, "young Cole enters the second of five kingdoms in the otherworldly Outskirts, is exposed to a second culture and a second flavor of magic, and battles a second monster made of stolen magic as he continues the search for his fellow earthly kidnappees." (Kirkus Reviews)

"After adventuring in the Outskirts in Sky Raiders (2014), Cole Randolph is still stuck in the amazing, confusing world of the Five Kingdoms. Luckily, he is not alone--his friends Mira, Jace, Twitch, and Joe are along for the ride as they set out to rescue Mira's sister from danger in the kingdom of Elloweer. . . . Cole is a relatable and brave Everykid hero, and his friends bring different perspectives to this ongoing tale. Mull's latest series continues to be excellent, and it should easily find a home among fans of middle-grade fantasy stories." Booklist

Sky Raiders; by Brandon Mull. Aladdin 2014 432 p. (Five kingdoms) (hardback) $16.99
Grades: 4 5 6 7   **Fic**
1. Fantasy fiction 2. Adventure fiction
ISBN 1442497009; 9781442497009
LC 2013032734

"Cole Randolph was just trying to have a fun time with his friends on Halloween (and maybe get to know Jenna Hunt a little better). But when a spooky haunted house turns out to be a portal to something much creepier, Cole finds himself on an adventure on a whole different level." (Publisher's note)

"Although Mull packs quite a bit into this initial installment, he skillfully mixes the capricious logic of dreams with high stakes and constant danger. The intriguing premise, strong world-building, and numerous twists make this a real page-turner." Pub Wkly

Spirit animals; 1 wild born. Brandon Mull. Scholastic Press 2013 224 p. (Spirit animals) $12.99
Grades: 4 5 6 7   **Fic**
1. Spirits -- Fiction 2. Children and animals 3. Magic
ISBN 0545522439; 9780545522434
LC 2013932302

This book, by Brandon Mull, is set in "the world of Erdas, where every child who comes of age must discover if they have a spirit animal, a rare bond between human and beast that bestows great powers to both. A dark force has risen from distant and long-forgotten lands, and has begun an onslaught that will ravage the world. Now the fate of Erdas has fallen on the shoulders of four young strangers." (Publisher's note)

★ **A world** without heroes. Aladdin 2011 454p (Beyonders) $19.99
Grades: 4 5 6 7   **Fic**
1. Fantasy fiction 2. Magic -- Fiction 3. Space and time -- Fiction 4. Heroes and heroines -- Fiction
ISBN 978-1-4169-9792-4; 1-4169-9792-X
LC 2010-23437

Fourteen-year-old Jason Walker is transported to a strange world called Lyrian, where he joins Rachel, who was also drawn there from our world, and a few rebels, to piece together the Word that can destroy the malicious wizard emperor, Surroth.

"Mull moves his story at a brisk pace, preventing the tragedies from overwhelming the adventure, while offering

ample action and feisty dialogue to keep fantasy lovers entertained." Publ Wkly

Murphy, Jill
Dear hound. Walker Books for Young Readers 2010 175p
Grades: 2 3 4   **Fic**
1. Dogs -- Fiction 2. Foxes -- Fiction
ISBN 0-8027-2190-7; 978-0-8027-2190-7
LC 2010006833

When Alfie, a timid deerhound puppy, gets lost in the woods, he will do almost anything—including befriending a pair of foxes—to find his way home to his beloved boy, Charlie, who refuses to believe Alfie is gone for good.

"Murphy deftly conveys the dog's angst with occasional all-caps dialogue. Her charming black-and-white line illustrations appear on every spread, extending the simple text and making this an excellent choice for readers recently transitioned to chapter books." Kirkus

Murphy, Jim
Desperate journey. Scholastic Press 2006 278p il map $16.99
Grades: 5 6 7 8   **Fic**
1. Family life -- Fiction 2. Erie Canal (N.Y.) -- Fiction
ISBN 0-439-07806-7
LC 2006-02526

In the mid-1800s, with both her father and her uncle in jail on an assault charge, Maggie, her brother, and her ailing mother rush their barge along the Erie Canal to deliver their heavy cargo or lose everything.

This is a "gripping novel." Booklist

Murphy, Rita
Bird. Delacorte Press 2008 151p $15.99; lib bdg $18.99
Grades: 5 6 7 8   **Fic**
1. Kites -- Fiction 2. Flight -- Fiction 3. Houses -- Fiction 4. Vermont -- Fiction 5. Supernatural -- Fiction
ISBN 978-0-385-73018-1; 0-385-73018-7; 978-0-385-90557-2 lib bdg; 0-385-90557-2 lib bdg
LC 2008-04690

Miranda, a small, delicate girl easily carried off by the wind, lands at Bourne Manor on the coast of Lake Champlain and is raised by the dour Wysteria Barrows, but she begins to believe rumors that the Manor is cursed and, aided by a new friend and kites secreted in an attic, seeks to escape.

"This enchanting novel is well written with lyrical text and beautiful descriptions. . . . . Good for middle school students, this book will make a nice addition to school and public libraries alike." Libr Media Connect

Murphy, Sally
★ **Pearl** verses the world; [illustrations by Heather Potter] Candlewick Press 2011 73p il $14.99
Grades: 3 4 5   **Fic**
1. School stories 2. Novels in verse 3. Death -- Fiction 4. Poetry -- Fiction 5. Loneliness -- Fiction 6. Bereavement -- Fiction 7. Family life -- Fiction 8. Grandmothers -- Fiction
ISBN 978-0-7636-4821-3; 0-7636-4821-3
LC 2010040149

Pearl feels like an island in school, isolated and alone, but at home she feels loved and secure until her grandmother's illness changes the way Pearl views her world.

This is a "poignantly illustrated novella in free verse. . . . Potter's evocative pencil-and-wash drawings, with their excellent renderings of facial expressions and mood, wonderfully complement Murphy's thoughtful narrative." Kirkus

Murray, Kirsty

The **Four** Seasons of Lucy McKenzie; by Kirsty Murray. Allen & Unwin 2014 216 p. illustrations $9.99
Grades: 4 5 6 7   **Fic**
    1. Magic -- Fiction 2. Adventure fiction 3. Friendship -- Fiction
    ISBN 1743317026; 9781743317020

This book, by Kirsty Murray, is a "timeslip adventure set in a hidden valley where an 11-year-old girl travels across the river of time to fight fires, battle floodwaters, and discover the meaning of true friendship. . . . Lucy is horrified to find that she is to spend Christmas, and the summer holidays, with Great-Auntie Big in her isolated country house. . . . She discovers she can enter the magical floor-to-ceiling paintings of the four seasons that cover the dining room walls." (Publisher's note)

"Murray links past and present with sophisticated plotting and a wonderfully descriptive setting; the Australian bush comes alive in all its beauty and harshness, and the river that flows through both the past and present valley is an expressive metaphor for the flow of time." Kirkus

Musgrove, Marianne

Lucy the good; illustrated by Cheryl Orsini. Henry Holt 2010 137p il $16.99
Grades: 2 3 4   **Fic**
    1. School stories 2. Australia -- Fiction 3. Family life -- Fiction
    ISBN 978-0-8050-9051-2; 0-8050-9051-7
                  LC 2009050766

When Lucy's great-aunt Bep comes from Holland to Adelaide, Australia, to visit, she is shocked by some of Lucy's behavior, and Lucy begins to wonder about herself. Includes a glossary of Dutch words and a recipe.

"The dichotomy between what Lucy says and thinks adds ample humor to this heartfelt novel. . . . With humor of their own, Orsini's b&w spot illustrations portray Lucy's behavior." Publ Wkly

Myers, Christopher

H.O.R.S.E. a game of basketball and imagination. Christopher Myers. Egmont USA 2012 1 p. (hardback) $18.99
Grades: 1 2 3   **Fic**
    1. Games -- Fiction 2. Friendship -- Fiction 3. Basketball -- Fiction
    ISBN 1606842188; 9781606842188
                  LC 2012003793
Coretta Scott King Illustrator Honor Book (2013)

Author Christopher Myers' book presents a children's story. "One day at the basketball court, two kids, a familiar challenge--H.O.R.S.E.? But this isn't your grandmother's game of hoops. Not when a layup from the other side of the court standing on one foot with your eyes closed is just the warm-up. Around the neighborhood, around the world, off Saturn's rings, the pair goes back and forth. The game

is as much about skill as it is about imagination." (Publisher's note)

Myers, Laurie

Escape by night; a Civil War adventure. illustrated by Amy June Bates. Henry Holt 2011 120p il $14.99
Grades: 3 4 5   **Fic**
    1. Christian life -- Fiction 2. United States -- History -- 1861-1865, Civil War -- Fiction
    ISBN 978-0-8050-8825-0; 0-8050-8825-3
                  LC 2010-30117
Tommy, the son of a Presbyterian minister in Augusta, Georgia, during the Civil War, must search his conscience to decide whether he should help a Yankee soldier escape and return home. Inspired by the early life of Woodrow Wilson.

"Sporadic full-page, black-and-white illustrations by Bates bring the characters . . . to life. This quick and exciting chapter book isn't shy about advancing a moral message but does so with a light touch." Booklist

★ **Lewis** and Clark and me; a dog's tale. illustrations by Michael Dooling. Holt & Co. 2002 64p il $16.95
Grades: 3 4 5 6   **Fic**
    1. Explorers 2. Dogs -- Fiction 3. Territorial governors 4. Lewis and Clark Expedition (1804-1806) -- Fiction
    ISBN 0-8050-6368-4
                  LC 00-47298
Seaman, Meriwether Lewis's Newfoundland dog, describes Lewis and Clark's expedition, which he accompanied from St. Louis to the Pacific Ocean

"Myers is a dog lover, and that respect comes through in the dignified portrayal of Seaman. Attractive, realistic paintings illustrate the book, giving a feel for the period and, most importantly, a visual personality to Seaman." SLJ
    Includes bibliographical references

Myklusch, Matt

Jack Blank and the Imagine Nation. Aladdin 2010 480p $16.99
Grades: 4 5 6 7   **Fic**
    1. Fantasy fiction 2. Science fiction 3. Orphans -- Fiction 4. Superheroes -- Fiction
    ISBN 978-1-4169-9561-6; 1-4169-9561-7
Twelve-year-old Jack, freed from a dismal orphanage, makes his way to the elusive and impossible Imagine Nation, where a mentor saves him from dissection and trains him to use his superpower, despite the virus he carries that makes him a threat.

This creates "a richly imagined world with strong appeal to fans of comics. The island is populated by a fun cast of heroes and villains. . . . Brisk narration captures the superhero world with a mixture of fast-paced action, wry humor, and occasional heartfelt speeches about courage and friendship." SLJ
    Followed by: Jack Blank and the secret war (2011)

Myracle, Lauren

Eleven. Dutton Children's Books 2004 201p (The Winnie years) $16.99; pa $6.99
Grades: 4 5 6 7   **Fic**
    1. Friendship -- Fiction 2. Family life -- Fiction
    ISBN 0-525-47165-0; 0-14-240346-6 pa
                  LC 2003-49076

The year between turning eleven and turning twelve bring many changes for Winnie and her friends

"The inclusion of details about the everyday lives of these girls . . . will make this novel enjoyable, even for reluctant readers. However, it's the book's occasional revelation of harder truths that lifts it out of the ordinary." SLJ

Other titles in this series are:

Twelve (2007)

Thirteen (2008)

Thirteen plus one (2010)

Ten (2011)

★ **Luv** ya bunches. Amulet Books 2009 335p $15.95

Grades: 4 5 6   **Fic**

1. School stories 2. Friendship -- Fiction

ISBN 978-0-8109-4211-0; 0-8109-4211-9

LC 2009012585

Four friends—each named after a flower—navigate the ups and downs of fifth grade. Told through text messages, blog posts, screenplay, and straight narrative

Myracle "displays a shining awareness of and sensitivity to the highly textured society of tween girls. . . . This is a fun, challenging, and gently edifying story." Booklist

Another title about these characters is:

Violet in bloom (2010)

Violet in bloom; a flower power book. Amulet Books 2010 366p $15.95

Grades: 4 5 6   **Fic**

1. School stories 2. Food -- Fiction 3. California -- Fiction 4. Friendship -- Fiction

ISBN 978-0-8109-8983-2; 0-8109-8983-2

LC 2010-24319

Fifth-graders Katie-Rose, Violet, Milla, and Yasaman seem to have little in common except their flower-related names, but they nurture their new friendship through a social-networking site and a campaign to have healthier snacks served at school.

This is "a realistic, easy-to-relate-to riot of pre-adolescent exuberance. A triumph." Kirkus

Naftali, Joel

The **rendering**; [by] Joel Naftali. Egmont USA 2011 275p $15.99

Grades: 5 6 7 8   **Fic**

1. Science fiction 2. Adventure fiction 3. Weblogs -- Fiction

ISBN 978-1-60684-118-1; 1-60684-118-1

LC 2010-36640

Thirteen-year-old Doug relates in a series of blog posts the story of how he saved the world but was falsely branded a terrorist and murderer, forced to fight the evil Dr. Roach and his armored biodroid army with an electronics-destroying superpower of his own.

"Naftali balances tragedy and absurd humor with aplomb, not an easy task when dealing with horrific explosions and giant wisecracking skunks. Readers seeking a fast-paced, action-packed adventure will find this eminently suitable." Bull Cent Child Books

Nagda, Ann Whitehead

The **perfect** cat-sitter; illustrated by Stephanie Roth. Holiday House 2007 104p il $15.95

Grades: 2 3 4   **Fic**

1. School stories 2. Cats -- Fiction

ISBN 978-0-8234-2112-1; 0-8234-2112-0

LC 2007-18301

When her friend Rana goes to India, Susan volunteers to take care of her cat and her sister's fish, but the job turns out to be much more difficult than she expected.

"Humor infuses the story. . . . Classroom dynamics and school friendships are well rendered, as are all sides of Susan's perfectionism. . . . Soft black-and-white illustrations capture Susan's emotions throughout her escapades." Booklist

Naidoo, Beverley

★ **Journey** to Jo'burg; a South African story. illustrations by Eric Velasquez. Lippincott 1986 80p il hardcover o.p. pa $4.99

Grades: 5 6 7 8   **Fic**

1. South Africa -- Race relations -- Fiction

ISBN 0-06-440237-1 pa

LC 85-45508

"This touching novel graphically depicts the plight of Africans living in the horror of South Africa. Thirteen-year-old Maledi and her 9-year-old brother leave their small village, take the perilous journey to the city, and encounter, firsthand, the painful struggle for justice, freedom, and dignity in the 'City of Gold.' A provocative story with a message readers will long remember." Soc Educ

Followed by Chain of fire (1990)

Napoli, Donna Jo

Lights on the Nile. HarperCollins 2011 278p $16.99; lib bdg $17.89

Grades: 4 5 6 7   **Fic**

1. Baboons -- Fiction 2. Fairies -- Fiction 3. Kidnapping -- Fiction 4. Egypt -- History -- Fiction

ISBN 978-0-06-166793-0; 0-06-166793-5; 978-0-06-166794-7 lib bdg; 0-06-166794-3 lib bdg

LC 2011010179

Ten-year-old Kepi, a young girl in ancient Egypt, embarks on a journey to save her family when she is unexpectedly taken captive, along with the baby baboon she has rescued from a crocodile.

Napoli "crafts a mystical coming-of-age tale and a love letter of sorts to Egypt, saturated with proverbs, intriguing details of everyday life at the time, and rich descriptions of the places Kepi visits. . . . Kepi's survival skills and perspective are challenged in this absorbing adventure." Publ Wkly

The **prince** of the pond; otherwise known as De Fawg Pin. illustrated by Judy Schachner. Dutton Children's Bks. 1992 151p il hardcover o.p. pa $4.99

Grades: 4 5 6   **Fic**

1. Frogs -- Fiction

ISBN 0-525-44976-0; 0-14-037151-6 pa

LC 91-40340

"An animal fantasy that fairy tale readers will relish. . . . Schachner's numerous ink-and-wash drawings go far in supporting the characterization." Bull Cent Child Books

This story based on the frog prince motif is "told from the point of view of Jade, a female frog. . . .. Pin (as the Prince calls himself, hampered in his speech by a long, fat tongue attached at the front of his mouth) is handsome, but strangely ignorant of everything . . . so Jade must teach him the ropes. . . . Eventually, when the opportunity of kissing a princess represents itself, Pin leaps at it and disappears from Jade's life forever." Booklist

Sly the Sleuth and the pet mysteries; by Donna Jo Napoli and Robert Furrow; illustrated by Heather Maione. Dial Books for Young Readers 2005 96p il $15.99
Grades: 2 3 4   **Fic**
1. Mystery fiction 2. Pets -- Fiction
ISBN 0-8037-2993-6

LC 2003-24090

Sly the Sleuth, also known as Sylvia, solves three mysteries for her friends and neighbors, all involving pets, through her detective agency, Sleuth for Hire.

"The stories are easy to read and engaging, the pen-and-ink illustrations convey the light tone of the adventures, and Sly's first-person narration is convincing." Horn Book Guide

Other titles about Sly the Sleuth are:
Sly the Sleuth and the sports mysteries (2006)
Sly the Sleuth and the food mysteries (2007)
Sly the Sleuth and the code mysteries (2009)

Stones in water. Dutton Children's Bks. 1997 209p hardcover o.p. pa $5.99
Grades: 5 6 7 8   **Fic**
1. World War, 1939-1945 -- Fiction
ISBN 0-525-45842-5; 0-14-130600-9 pa

LC 97-14253

After being taken by German soldiers from a local movie theater along with other Italian boys including his Jewish friend, Roberto is forced to work in Germany, escapes into the Ukrainian winter, before desperately trying to make his way back home to Venice

This is a "gripping, meticulously researched story (loosely based on the life of an actual survivor)." Publ Wkly

Naylor, Phyllis Reynolds

Alice in rapture, sort of. Atheneum Pubs. 1989 166p hardcover o.p. pa $5.99
Grades: 5 6 7 8   **Fic**
1. Family life -- Fiction
ISBN 0-689-31466-3; 1-442-42362-5 pa

LC 88-8174

The summer before she enters the seventh grade becomes the summer of Alice's first boyfriend, and she discovers that love is about the most mixed-up thing that can possibly happen to you, especially since she has no mother to go to for advice

"A book that is wise, perceptive, and hilarious." SLJ

Alice in-between. Atheneum Pubs. 1994 144p pa $5.99
Grades: 4 5 6 7   **Fic**
1. Family life -- Fiction
ISBN 0-689-31890-1; 1-416-96770-2 pa

LC 93-8167

When motherless Alice turns thirteen she feels in-between, no longer a child but not yet a woman, and discovers that growing up can be both frustrating and wonderful

"This is bound to reassure the many adolescent fans who can identify with the 'in-between blues.'" SLJ

Alice the brave. Atheneum Bks. for Young Readers 1995 130p pa $7.99

Grades: 5 6 7 8   **Fic**
1. Fear -- Fiction 2. Family life -- Fiction
ISBN 0-689-80095-9; 1-416-97542-X pa

LC 94-32340

The summer before eighth grade, Alice tries to confront her fears, not the least of which is a fear of deep water.

"Alice's wry, funny, vulnerable voice expresses every girl's fears about what is 'normal' in an imperfect world." Booklist

All but Alice. Atheneum Pubs. 1992 151p hardcover o.p. pa $5.99
Grades: 5 6 7 8   **Fic**
1. School stories 2. Clubs -- Fiction
ISBN 0-689-31773-5; 1-442-42756-6 pa

LC 91-28722

Seventh grader Alice decides that the only way to stave off personal and social disasters is to be part of the crowd, especially the "in" crowd, no matter how boring and, potentially, difficult

"Naylor's light, but deft touch with important thematic concerns is most appealing." SLJ

★ **Emily's** fortune; illustrated by Ross Collins. Delacorte Press 2010 147p il $14.99
Grades: 3 4 5 6   **Fic**
1. Uncles -- Fiction 2. Orphans -- Fiction 3. West (U.S.) -- Fiction 4. Voyages and travels -- Fiction 5. Inheritance and succession -- Fiction
ISBN 978-0-385-73616-9; 0-385-73616-9

LC 2009013096

While traveling to her aunt's home in Redbud by train and stagecoach, quiet young Emily and her turtle, Rufus, team up with Jackson, fellow orphan and troublemaker extraordinaire, to outsmart mean Uncle Victor, who is after Emily's inheritance.

"The local vernacular is lively and fun and the characters are well developed. Cliff-hangers between chapters are written in large boldface to keep readers hooked. . . . Simple, black-and-white illustrations complement the unfolding story. A rip-roaring good time." SLJ

Faith, hope, and Ivy June. Delacorte Press 2009 280p $16.99; lib bdg $19.99
Grades: 5 6 7 8   **Fic**
1. School stories 2. Kentucky -- Fiction 3. Appalachian region -- Fiction
ISBN 978-0-385-73615-2; 0-385-73615-0; 978-0-385-90588-6 lib bdg; 0-385-90588-2 lib bdg

LC 2008-19625

During a student exchange program, seventh-graders Ivy June and Catherine share their lives, homes, and communities, and find that although their lifestyles are total opposites they have a lot in common.

"This finely crafted novel . . . depicts a deep friendship growing slowly through understanding. As both girls wait out tragedies at the book's end, they cling to hope—and each other—in a thoroughly real and unaffected way. Naylor depicts Appalachia with sympathetic realism." Kirkus

Outrageously Alice. Atheneum Bks. for Young Readers 1997 133p $16.99; pa $5.99

Grades: 5 6 7 8   **Fic**

1. School stories 2. Family life -- Fiction

ISBN 0-689-80354-0; 0-689-80596-9 pa

LC 96-7744

"Alice is, as always, likable, humorous, and true to life." SLJ

"As part of her campaign for a new image Alice dresses as a showgirl for Halloween, hoping to be seductive; she doesn't bargain for being French-kissed by an unknown schoolmate in a dark closet. With help from family and friends, Alice sorts out her feelings about the incident and proves she has learned something about handling herself." Horn Book Guide

★ **Roxie** and the Hooligans; with illustrations by Alexandra Boiger. Atheneum Books for Young Readers 2006 115p il $15.95; pa $4.99

Grades: 3 4 5   **Fic**

1. Adventure fiction

ISBN 1-4169-0243-0; 1-4169-0244-9 pa

LC 2004-24645

Roxie Warbler, the niece of a famous explorer, follows Uncle Dangerfoot's advice on how to survive any crisis when she becomes stranded on an island with a gang of school bullies and a pair of murderous bank robbers.

This "mixes fantasy, absurdity, and reality in a way that never diminishes or overwhelms the story's heart. Boiger's black-and-white illustrations catch the energy of Naylor's over-the-top yet sympathetically portrayed characters." Booklist

★ **Shiloh**. Atheneum Pubs. 1991 144p $16.95; pa $6.99

Grades: 4 5 6   **Fic**

1. Dogs -- Fiction 2. West Virginia -- Fiction

ISBN 0-689-31614-3; 0-689-83582-5 pa

LC 90-603

Awarded the Newbery Medal, 1992

When he finds a lost beagle in the hills behind his West Virginia home, Marty tries to hide it from his family and the dog's real owner, a mean-spirited man known to shoot deer out of season and to mistreat his dogs

"A credible plot and characters, a well-drawn setting, and nicely paced narration combine in a story that leaves the reader feeling good." Horn Book

Other titles about Shiloh are:

Shiloh season (1996)

Saving Shiloh (1997)

★ **Starting** with Alice. Atheneum Bks. for Young Readers 2002 181p hardcover o.p. pa $4.99

Grades: 3 4 5 6   **Fic**

1. School stories 2. Friendship -- Fiction 3. Family life -- Fiction

ISBN 0-689-84395-X; 0-689-84396-8 pa

LC 2001-53610

This, the first of three prequels to the series about Alice, is written for younger readers. After she, her older brother, and their father move from Chicago to Maryland, Alice has trouble fitting into her new third grade class, but with the help of some new friends and her own unique outlook, she survives

"New characters and realistic third-grade situations are explored, but young Alice's humor and earnestness are refreshingly the same." Horn Book

Other prequels to the Alice series are:

Alice in Blunderland (2003)

Lovingly Alice (2004)

Nelson, Nina

Bringing the boy home; by N.A. Nelson. HarperCollinsPublishers 2008 211p $15.99; lib bdg $16.89

Grades: 5 6 7 8   **Fic**

1. Rain forests -- Fiction 2. Amazon River valley -- Fiction 3. Senses and sensation -- Fiction 4. Extrasensory perception -- Fiction

ISBN 978-0-06-088698-1; 0-06-088698-6; 978-0-06-088699-8 lib bdg; 0-06-088699-4 lib bdg

LC 2007-31702

As two Takunami youths approach their thirteenth birthdays, Luka reaches the culmination of his mother's training for the tribe's manhood test while Tirio, raised in Miami, Florida, by his adoptive mother, feels called to begin preparations to prove himself during his upcoming visit to the Amazon rain forest where he was born.

"The vivid setting, imagined cultural particulars . . . and magical realism will captivate readers." Booklist

Nelson, S. D.

Digging a hole to heaven; a story about the coal mine boys. by S.D. Nelson. Abrams Books for Young Children 2014 64 p. color illustrations $19.95

Grades: 3 4 5 6   **Fic**

1. Child labor -- Fiction 2. Coal mines and mining -- Fiction 3. Coal mines and mining -- Accidents 4. Child labor -- United States -- History -- 19th century 5. Coal miners -- United States -- History -- 19th century 6. Coal mines and mining -- United States -- History -- 19th century

ISBN 1419707302; 9781419707308

LC 2013035246

In this book by S.D. Nelson "at 12 years old, Conall has already worked in the coal mines of West Virginia for two years. He spends his days deep underground with his faithful mule, Angel, carting loads of coal. One day a tunnel collapses, and his brother is trapped with others on the wrong side! How can Conall and Angel help to save them?" (Publisher's note)

"In this picture book for older readers, historical photographs and sidebars support a fictional tale about two brothers who work in a nineteenth-century Pennsylvania coal mine. Both elements squarely address mining's dangers but also the intense bonds that developed among the boys, men, and beasts who labored deep underground. Nelson's acrylics capture the sooty, lamp-lit atmosphere. An extensive author's note is appended. Timeline. Bib., ind." Horn Book

Includes bibliographical references

Neri, G.

Chess rumble; by G. Neri; art by Jesse Joshua Watson. Lee & Low Books 2007 64p il $18.95

Grades: 5 6 7 8   **Fic**

1. Chess -- Fiction 2. African Americans -- Fiction

ISBN 978-1-58430-279-7

LC 2007010772

Branded a troublemaker due to his anger over everything from being bullied to his sister's death a year before, Marcus begins to control himself and cope with his problems at home and at his inner-city school when an unlikely mentor teaches him to play chess

"Neri expertly captures Marcus's voice and delicately teases out his alternating vulnerability and rage. The cadence and emotion of the verse are masterfully echoed through Watson's expressive acrylic illustrations." SLJ

Ghetto cowboy; [by] G. Neri; illustrated by Jesse Joshua Watson. Candlewick Press 2011 218p il $15.99
Grades: 4 5 6 7 Fic
1. Horses -- Fiction 2. Moving -- Fiction 3. African Americans -- Fiction 4. City and town life -- Fiction 5. Philadelphia (Pa.) -- Fiction 6. Father-son relationship -- Fiction
ISBN 978-0-7636-4922-7; 0-7636-4922-8
LC 2010007565

Twelve-year-old Cole's behavior causes his mother to drive him from Detroit to Philadelphia to live with a father he has never known, but who soon has Cole involved with a group of African-American "cowboys" who rescue horses and use them to steer youths away from drugs and gangs.

"This well-written book is based on a true story of urban cowboys in Philadelphia and New York. Cole's spot-on emotional insight is conveyed through believable dialogue. . . . Watson's illustrations punctuate the intriguing aspects of the story and make the novel more appealing." SLJ

Nesbit, E.
★ The **enchanted** castle; illustrated by Paul O. Zelinsky; afterword by Peter Glassman. Morrow Junior Bks. 1992 292p il lib bdg $22.95
Grades: 4 5 6 Fic
1. Fantasy fiction 2. Great Britain -- Fiction
ISBN 0-688-05435-8
LC 91-46267
First published 1907 in the United Kingdom; first United States edition 1908 by Harper & Brothers

Four English children find a wonderful world of magic through an enchanted wishing ring

"With fine, cross-hatched lines tinted in luminous colors, Zelinsky's artwork is as lively as the story and very much of the period." Booklist

★ **Five** children and it; illustrated by H.R. Millar; with an introduction by Laurel Snyder. Random House 2010 255p il (Looking Glass library) $9.99; lib bdg $12.99
Grades: 4 5 6 Fic
1. Wishes -- Fiction 2. Fairies -- Fiction 3. Siblings -- Fiction 4. Great Britain -- Fiction
ISBN 978-0-375-86336-3; 0-375-86336-2; 978-0-375-96336-0 lib bdg; 0-375-96336-7 lib bdg
LC 2008-54569
First published 1902 in the United Kingdom; first United States edition 1905 by Dodd, Mead & Co.

When four brothers and sisters discover a Psammead, or sand-fairy, in the gravel pit near the country house where they are staying, they have no way of knowing all the adventures its wish-granting will bring them

Other titles in this series are:
The Phoenix and the carpet (1904)
The story of the amulet (1907)

Nesbo, Jo, 1960-
Doctor Proctor's fart powder; illustrated by Mike Lowery. Aladdin 2010 265p il $14.99
Grades: 4 5 6 Fic
1. Norway -- Fiction 2. Bullies -- Fiction 3. Inventors -- Fiction 4. Friendship -- Fiction 5. Eccentrics and eccentricities -- Fiction
ISBN 1-4169-7972-7; 978-1-4169-7972-2
LC 2009-27204
New friends Nilly and Lisa help eccentric professor Doctor Proctor to develop his latest invention, a powder that makes one fart, making them very popular at school, but someone is planning to steal the industrial-strength formula for evil purposes.

"Nesbo tells his fantastical story in a matter-of-fact, deadpan style, and Lowery's simple illustrations match the dry, comedic tone well." Booklist

Follwed by: Bubble in the bathtub (2011)

Neumeier, Rachel
The **Floating** Islands. Alfred A. Knopf 2011 388p map $16.99; lib bdg $19.99
Grades: 5 6 7 Fic
1. Fantasy fiction 2. Magic -- Fiction 3. Flight -- Fiction 4. Cousins -- Fiction
ISBN 0-375-84705-7; 0-375-94705-1 lib bdg; 978-0-375-84705-9; 978-0-375-94705-6 lib bdg
LC 2010-12772
The adventures of two teenaged cousins who live in a place called The Floating Islands, one of whom is studying to become a mage and the other one of the legendary island flyers.

"The author delineates complex characters, geographies and societies alike with a dab hand, deftly weaves them all— along with dragons of several sorts, mouthwatering kitchen talk, flashes of humor and a late-blooming romance—into a suspenseful plot and delivers and outstanding tale that is self-contained but full of promise for sequels." Kirkus

Neville, Emily Cheney
It's like this, Cat; [by] Emily Neville; illustrated by Emil Weiss. Harper & Row 1963 180p il $16.99; lib bdg $17.89; pa $5.99
Grades: 5 6 7 8 Fic
1. Cats -- Fiction 2. New York (N.Y.) -- Fiction
ISBN 0-06-024390-2; 0-06-024391-0 lib bdg; 0-06-440073-5 pa
Awarded the Newbery Medal, 1964

"A story told with a great amount of insight into human relationships. . . . This all provides a wonderfully real picture of a city boy's outlets and of one likable adolescent's inner feelings. An exceedingly fresh, honest, and well-rounded piece of writing." Horn Book

Newbery, Linda
Lost boy. David Fickling Books 2008 194p $15.99; lib bdg $18.99
Grades: 4 5 6 7 Fic
1. Ghost stories 2. Mystery fiction 3. Wales -- Fiction 4. Traffic accidents -- Fiction
ISBN 978-0-375-84574-1; 978-0-375-93617-3 lib bdg
LC 2007-15041
First published 2005 in the United Kingdom

After Matt moves to Hay-on-Wye in Wales, a boy his age who bears the same initials and was killed in a car accident many years earlier, appears to Matt.

"With its imaginative melding of present-day concerns, good storytelling, lush descriptions of the landscape and even a faithful dog, this novel will ensnare readers." Publ Wkly

Lucy and the green man; illustrated by Pam Smy. David Fickling Books 2010 217p il $16.99; lib bdg $19.99
Grades: 3 4 5   **Fic**
1. Gardening -- Fiction 2. Bereavement -- Fiction 3. Grandfathers -- Fiction 4. Great Britain -- Fiction 5. London (England) -- Fiction
ISBN 978-0-385-75204-6; 0-385-75204-0; 978-0-385-75207-7 lib bdg; 0-385-75207-5 lib bdg
LC 2010-13653
Lucy and her grandfather are special because only they can see Lob, the magical 'green man' who helps in the garden, but then something terrible happens and Lucy fears she will never see Lob again

"Black-and-white line spot art and occasional spreads capture the flavor of the story. . . . This gentle fantasy has an old-fashioned quality that will appeal to families and young sensitive readers." SLJ

Newbound, Andrew

Ghoul strike! Chicken House 2010 309p $16.99
Grades: 4 5 6 7   **Fic**
1. Angels -- Fiction 2. Monsters -- Fiction 3. Supernatural -- Fiction
ISBN 978-0-545-22938-8; 0-545-22938-3
LC 2010013580
When twelve-year-old, psychic ghost hunter Alannah Malarra faces demons from another dimension, rather than the treasure-hoarding ghosts she is used to, she needs the help of protectors from the Attack-ready Network of Global Evanescent Law-enforcers (A.N.G.E.L.) police force to help her quell the dangerous uprising

"Alannah is a great female hero. . . . The other main characters are also multidimensional, and descriptions of the various creatures are detailed and entertaining. Readers will enjoy the fast-paced plot and the friendship between Alannah and Wortley." SLJ

Newman, John

Mimi. Candlewick Press 2011 186p $15.99
Grades: 2 3 4 5   **Fic**
1. Bereavement -- Fiction 2. Family life -- Fiction 3. Great Britain -- Fiction
ISBN 978-0-7636-5415-3; 0-7636-5415-9
LC 2010040147
Mimi is determined not to give up on anyone or anything, but since Mammy died, her father never smiles, her sister Sally is in a bad mood, brother Conor keeps to himself, and even Sparkler the dog does not want to go for walks.

Newman "will win readers' hearts through the conversational tone and openhearted observations of . . . narrator Mimi. . . . Newman ably conveys a family hanging together by a thread; that Mimi, who is Chinese, is adopted is nearly incidental to the plot—until a climactic scene in which she stands up to a school bully." Publ Wkly

Newman, Lesléa

★ **Hachiko** waits; illustrated by Machiyo Kodaira. Henry Holt and Co. 2004 96p il $15.95; pa $6.99
Grades: 3 4 5   **Fic**
1. Dogs -- Fiction 2. Japan -- Fiction
ISBN 0-8050-7336-1; 0-312-55806-6 pa
LC 2003-68589
Professor Ueno's loyal Akita, Hachiko, waits for him at the train station every afternoon, and even after the professor has a fatal heart attack while at work, Hachiko faithfully continues to await his return until the day the dog dies. Based on a true story

"Yasuo brings a childhood focus to the poignant story . . . . and Kodaira's soft, black-and-white sketches help to break up the chapters for younger readers and add interest to the story." Booklist

Heather has two mommies; written by Lesléa Newman; illustrated by Laura Cornell. 25th anniv edition Candlewick Press 2015 32 p. color illustrations $16.99
Grades: PreK K 1   **Fic**
1. Lesbians -- Fiction 2. Homosexuality -- Fiction 3. Family -- Fiction 4. Lesbian mothers -- Fiction 5. Mothers and daughters -- Fiction
ISBN 0763666319; 9780763666316
LC 99087285
Originally published 1989
In this boo, written by Leslea Newman and illustrated by Diana Souza, "Heather's favorite number is two. She has two arms, two legs, and two pets. And she also has two mommies. When Heather goes to school for the first time, someone asks her about her daddy, but Heather doesn't have a daddy. Then something interesting happens. When Heather and her classmates all draw pictures of their families, not one drawing is the same." (Publisher's note)

"Newman's picture book about Heather and her mommies first appeared 25 years ago as the product of desktop publishing and a determination to create a story reflecting family diversity. This updated version includes new illustrations by the commercially successful Cornell, which supply humor and avoid lesbian stereotypes that dogged earlier versions." Kirkus

Nicholls, Sally

★ **Season** of secrets. Arthur A. Levine Books 2011 225p $16.99
Grades: 4 5 6   **Fic**
1. Sisters -- Fiction 2. Bereavement -- Fiction 3. Family life -- Fiction 4. Great Britain -- Fiction
ISBN 978-0-545-21825-2; 0-545-21825-X
LC 2010017070
Sent by their father to live in the country with their grandparents after the sudden death of their mother, Molly's older sister Hannah expresses her grief in a raging rebellion while imaginative Molly finds herself increasingly distracted by visions, that seemingly only she can see, of a strange hunt in the nearby forest.

"Written in gently flowing prose, the plot appropriately transitions from autumn into summer as Molly emerges from grief to acceptance and hope. A poignant story of healing tinged with mystery." Kirkus

★ **Ways** to live forever; [by] Sally Nicholls. Arthur A. Levine Books 2008 212p il $16.99

Grades: 4 5 6 7   **Fic**
1. Death -- Fiction 2. Leukemia -- Fiction 3. Authorship -- Fiction 4. Family life -- Fiction
ISBN 978-0-545-06948-9; 0-545-06948-3
     LC 2007047341
Eleven-year-old Sam McQueen, who has leukemia, writes a book during the last three months of his life, in which he tells about what he would like to accomplish, how he feels, and things that have happened to him.

This "skirts easy sentiment to confront the hard questions head-on, intelligently and realistically and with an enormous range of feeling." Publ Wkly

Nielsen, Jennifer A.
  Elliot and the goblin war; illustrated by Gideon Kendall. Sourcebooks Jabberwocky 2010 181p il (Underworld chronicles) $14.99
Grades: 4 5 6 7   **Fic**
1. Fantasy fiction 2. Boys -- Fiction 3. Goblins -- Fiction
ISBN 978-1-4022-4019-5; 1-4022-4019-8
This "begins Halloween night, when unsuspecting reluctant hero Elliot happens to save a real Brownie named Patches from a trio of real Goblins. Elliot's good deed results in his acclamation as King of the Brownies, and these spunky but weak creatures truly need a king to help them end a three-year-long war with the evil Goblins. Nielsen ably draws readers into a tale chock-full of light adventure and humor, as each chapter details the somewhat over-the-top yet entertaining dilemmas Patches and Elliot face. . . . Recommended for those who avoid dark and serious fantasies, as it's sure to evoke more giggles than gasps, despite the introductory admonitions." Kirkus

Other titles in this series are:
Elliot and the pixie plot (2011)
Elliot and the Yeti threat (2011)

The **false** prince; by Jennifer A. Nielsen. Scholastic Press 2012 342 p. (The ascendance trilogy) hbk $17.99
Grades: 4 5 6 7 8   **Fic**
1. Fantasy fiction 2. Adventure fiction 3. Impersonation -- Fiction 4. Orphans -- Fiction 5. Princes -- Fiction 6. Secrets -- Fiction 7. Courts and courtiers -- Fiction
ISBN 9780545284134
     LC 2011006692
This fantasy book depicts the adventures of Sage, a "brazen 15-year-old orphan living in the imaginary kingdom of Carthya [who] becomes embroiled in a treasonous powerplay to install a false prince on the vacant throne." He is selected with three other boys from the orphanage by Bevin Connor to compete to impersonate the missing Prince Jaron and act as Connor's pawn on the throne. "Sage's disdain, defiance and reckless arrogance mark him for failure, but his boldness, instinct and innate decency indicate there's more than meets the eye. Could Sage become Prince Jaron?" Jennifer A. Nielsen's story features "ruthless ambition, fierce action and plotting . . . and lots of sword play and hidden passages." (Kirkus)

  Mark of the thief; by Jennifer A. Nielsen. Scholastic Press 2015 352 p. (Praetor war) (jacketed hardcover) $17.99
Grades: 5 6 7 8 9   **Fic**
1. Rome -- Fiction 2. Magic -- Fiction 3. Slaves --

Fiction 4. Amulets -- Fiction 5. Slavery -- Fiction 6. Insurgency -- Fiction 7. Rome -- Antiquities -- Fiction 8. Rome -- History -- Empire, 30 B.C.-476 A.D. -- Fiction
ISBN 054556154X; 9780545561549
     LC 2014017068
In this novel by Jennifer A. Nielsen, "when Nic, a slave in the mines outside of Rome, is forced to enter a sealed cavern containing the lost treasures of Julius Caesar, he finds much more than gold and gemstones: He discovers an ancient bulla, an amulet that belonged to the great Caesar and is filled with a magic once reserved for the Gods. He finds himself at the center of a ruthless conspiracy to overthrow the emperor and spark the Praetor War." (Publisher's note)

"A fantastical alternate history set in ancient Rome. Nicolas Calva and his sister are slaves in the mines outside of Rome. When Nic is forced to retrieve treasure from Julius Caesar's cave, he assumes he is going to his death...This genre mash-up of history, fantasy, and action/adventure is fast-paced and explores themes such as class struggles, familial ties, and the immorality of slavery. Readers will have lots to digest as they quickly flip through the pages to see how Nic will escape his enemies to become a free man." SLJ

The **runaway** king; Jennifer A. Nielsen. Scholastic Press 2013 352 p. (The ascendance trilogy) (hardcover) $17.99
Grades: 4 5 6 7 8   **Fic**
1. Fantasy fiction -- Fiction 2. Kings and rulers -- Fiction 3. Princesses -- Fiction 4. Conspiracies -- Fiction 5. Courts and courtiers -- Fiction
ISBN 0545284155; 9780545284158
     LC 2012035290
"Just weeks after Jaron has taken the throne, an assassination attempt forces him into a deadly situation. Rumors of a coming war are winding their way between the castle walls, and Jaron feels the pressure quietly mounting within Carthya. Soon, it becomes clear that deserting the kingdom may be his only hope of saving it." (Publisher's note)

"Jaron has been king of Carthya for a month when an attempted assassination forces him into hiding, running away to the borders of his kingdom where he hopes to infiltrate the pirate camp and get to the bottom of things. This solid middle volume has its own arc, but still ends with a cliffhanger, an important villain on the loose, and a potential love triangle." Horn Book

The **shadow** throne; Jennifer A. Nielsen. First edition Scholastic Press 2014 336 p. (Ascendance trilogy) (hardcover) $17.99
Grades: 4 5 6 7 8   **Fic**
1. Kings and rulers 2. Adventure fiction 3. Battles -- Fiction 4. Adventure stories 5. Rescues -- Fiction 6. Adventure and adventurers -- Fiction
ISBN 9780545284172; 0545284171
     LC 2013021841
This book, by Jennifer A. Nielsen, is the "finale of the Ascendance Trilogy. . . . Jaron learns than King Vargan of Avenia and allies from Gelyn and Mendenwal have invaded Carthya and captured Jaron's friend Imogen. Determined to save Imogen, Jaron attempts a rescue and fails, leaving him a prisoner and Imogen presumed dead. As he tries to cope with

Imogen's death, captive Jaron discovers how much he loved her." (Kirkus Reviews)

"There's enough adventure, mystery, and romance in this concluding volume to please a variety of genre readers." Horn Book

Nielsen, Susin

Dear George Clooney; please marry my mom. Tundra Books 2010 229p $15.95

Grades: 5 6 7 8 **Fic**

1. Divorce -- Fiction 2. Letters -- Fiction

ISBN 978-0-88776-977-1; 0-88776-977-2

"Smarting from her parent's divorce—her director father left her mother to marry an actress—Violet is fed up with all the 'losers' her mother has since dated. . . . She pens a letter to George Clooney . . . explaining that she's trying to find a suitable suitor for her parent. . . . Nielsen skillfully balances her story's keen humor . . . with poignancy." Publ Wkly

★ **Word** nerd. Tundra Books 2008 248p $18.95; pa $12.95

Grades: 5 6 7 8 **Fic**

1. Friendship -- Fiction 2. Scrabble (Game) -- Fiction 3. Mother-son relationship -- Fiction

ISBN 978-0-88776-875-0; 0-88776-875-X; 978-0-88776-990-0 pa; 0-88776-990-X pa

"Twelve-year-old Ambrose Bukowski and his widowed, overprotective mother . . . move frequently. When he almost dies after he bites into a peanut that bullies put in his sandwich, just to see if he is really allergic, Irene . . . decides to homeschool him. . . . Ambrose gets to know 25-year-old-Cosmo, recently released from jail and the son of the Bukowskis' . . . landlords. . . . Ambrose . . . talks Cosmo into taking him to a Scrabble Club. . . . This is a tender, often funny story with some really interesting characters. It will appeal to word nerds, but even more to anyone who has ever longed for acceptance or had to fight unreasonable parental restrictions." SLJ

Nilsson, Ulf

Detective Gordon; The First Case. by Ulf Nilsson (Author), Gitte Spee (illustrator) Lerner Pub Group 2015 96 p. (hardcover) $16.99

Grades: 1 2 3 4 **Fic**

1. Toads -- Fiction 2. Mystery fiction

ISBN 1927271495; 9781927271506; 9781927271490

In this illustrated children's story, by Ulf Nilsson and illustrated by Gitte Spee, "someone's stealing nuts from the forest, and it's up to Detective Gordon to catch the thief! Unfortunately, solving this crime means standing in the snow and waiting for a long time. . . . If only he had an assistant--someone small, fast, and clever--to help solve this terrible case." (Publisher's note)

Nimmo, Jenny

Leopards' gold; Jenny Nimmo. Scholastic Press 2013 336 p. (Chronicles of the Red King) (jacketed hardcover) $16.99

Grades: 4 5 6 **Fic**

1. Magic -- Fiction 2. Castles -- Fiction 3. Brothers and sisters -- Fiction 4. Kings, queens, rulers, etc. -- Fiction

ISBN 0545251850; 9780545251853

LC 2012043508

This book, by Jenny Nimmo, is the "final installment in the . . . Red King series. . . . we now meet King Timoken's children, who, with their own magical endowments, stand divided between the forces of good and bad. Young Petrello and Tolomeo must fight to protect their siblings and their kingdom as an evil force invades the once-peaceful Red Castle." (Publisher's note)

Midnight for Charlie Bone. Orchard Bks. 2003 401p (Children of the Red King) $12.99

Grades: 5 6 7 8 **Fic**

1. School stories 2. Magic -- Fiction 3. Great Britain -- Fiction

ISBN 978-0-439-47429-0; 0-439-47429-9

LC 2002-30738

First published 2002 in the United Kingdom

Charlie Bone's life with his widowed mother and two grandmothers undergoes a dramatic change when he discovers that he can hear people in photographs talking.

"This marvelous fantasy is able to stand on its own despite inevitable comparisons to the students of Hogwarts." Voice Youth Advocates

Other titles in this series are:

Charlie Bone and the time twister (2003)

Charlie Bone and the invisible boy (2004)

Charlie Bone and the castle of mirrors (2005)

Charlie Bone and the hidden king (2006)

Charlie Bone and the beast (2007)

Charlie Bone and the shadow (2008)

Charlie Bone and the Red Knight (2010)

The **secret** kingdom. Scholastic Press 2011 207p (Chronicles of the red king) $16.99

Grades: 4 5 6 **Fic**

1. Magic -- Fiction 2. Camels -- Fiction 3. Siblings -- Fiction 4. Voyages and travels -- Fiction

ISBN 978-0-439-84673-8; 0-439-84673-0

LC 2010035710

Timoken and his sister, Zobayda, under the protection of a forest jinni but pursued by evil virideed, straddle the world of men and the world of enchantments, seeking a home while remaining young by drinking a potion called Alixir.

"The narrative voice is direct and matter-of-fact, conveying the fantastic as well as the mundane facts of Timoken's incredible life accessibly; new readers will have no difficulty making this an introduction to Nimmo's work. . . . Timoken is a highly appealing young hero, and his panoply of human and magical friends provide just the right amount of help without stealing the show." Publ Wkly

★ The **snow** spider; [by] Jenny Nimmo. Orchard Books 2006 146p (Magician trilogy) $9.99

Grades: 4 5 6 7 **Fic**

1. Magic -- Fiction 2. Wales -- Fiction 3. Father-son relationship -- Fiction

ISBN 978-0-439-84675-2; 0-439-84675-7

LC 2006009445

A reissue of the title first published 1987 by Dutton

Gifts from Gwyn's grandmother on his ninth birthday open up a whole new world to him, as he discovers he has magical powers that help him heal the breach with his father that has existed ever since his sister's mysterious disappearance four years before

"The narration is paced well and builds in excitement along with the tale." SLJ

Other titles in this series are:

Emlyn's moon (2007)

Chestnut solider (2007)

Nix, Garth, 1963-

Troubletwisters; [by] Garth Nix and Sean Williams. Scholastic Press 2011 293p $16.99

Grades: 5 6 7 8   **Fic**

1. Fantasy fiction 2. Magic -- Fiction 3. Twins -- Fiction 4. Siblings -- Fiction 5. Grandmothers -- Fiction

ISBN 978-0-545-25897-5; 0-545-25897-9

LC 2011015765

When their house mysteriously explodes and they are sent to live with an unknown relative named Grandma X, twelve-year-old twins Jaide and Jack Shield learn that they are troubletwisters, young Wardens just coming into their powers, who must protect humanity from The Evil trying to break into Earth's dimension.

"Full of adventure and the unexpected, . . . [this] is delightfully twisted. The pacing is perfect, the setting is eerily dark, the faceless Evil rings true, and the resolution is satisfying." Booklist

Noe, Katherine Schlick

Something to hold. Clarion 2011 $16.99

Grades: 4 5 6   **Fic**

1. School stories 2. Oregon -- Fiction 3. Prejudices -- Fiction 4. Native Americans -- Fiction

ISBN 978-0-547-55813-4; 0-547-55813-9

This book follows "Kitty," [who] is so used to moving with each of her father's job reassignments that making friends in each new location is usually not much of an issue. The Warm Springs Reservation in central Oregon is, however, a new experience, since she and her brothers are among the handful of white students in their new school. The brothers easily bond with Wasco, Warm Springs, and Paiute boys through common enthusiasm for baseball, but Kitty is intimidated by a pair of her classmates—dour, bullying Raymond and his snappish, aloof sister, Jewel. . . . Raymond and Jewel are often at the mercy of their abusive white stepfather, and . . . the reservation police and their municipal police are so gridlocked by jurisdictional mandates and prejudice that the children feel they have no legal recourse. . . Kitty's gradual involvement with Raymond and Jewel forms the backbone of the novel" (Bulletin of the Center for Children's Books).

"Kitty Schlick is apprehensive about starting sixth grade on Oregon's Warm Springs Indian Reservation, home to Paiute, Warm Springs and Wasco people, where her father's job has taken the family in 1962. . . . One of the school's few white students, she feels isolated until she's befriended by Pinky, a Wasco classmate whose mother, like Kitty's dad, staffs a fire lookout. As Kitty finds her footing, she's troubled by the preferential treatment teachers give white students and the casual racism of the white girls attending her church. . . . Noe . . . resists didacticism. Kitty's discoveries and ethical dilemmas are age and era-appropriate, the characters affectionately portrayed, rounded individuals." Kirkus

Noel, Alyson

Radiance. Square Fish 2010 183p pa $7.99

Grades: 5 6 7 8   **Fic**

1. Ghost stories 2. Dead -- Fiction 3. Future life -- Fiction

ISBN 978-0-312-62917-5; 0-312-62917-6

LC 2010015840

After crossing the bridge into the afterlife, a place called Here where the time is always Now, Riley's existence continues in much the same way as when she was alive until she is given the job of Soul Catcher and, together with her teacher Bodhi, returns to earth for her first assignment, a ghost called the Radiant Boy who has been haunting an English castle for centuries and resisted all previous attempts to get him across the bridge.

"Narrating in a contemporary voice with an honest and comfortable cadence, Riley is imperfect, but always likable. . . . In the midst of this wildly fanciful setting, Noël is able to capture with nail-on-the-head accuracy common worries and concerns of today's tweens." SLJ

Other titles in this series are:

Dreamland (2011)

Simmer (2011)

Nolan, Lucy A.

★ **On** the road; by Lucy Nolan; illustrated by Mike Reed. Marshall Cavendish 2005 54p il (Down Girl and Sit) $14.95

Grades: 1 2 3   **Fic**

1. Dogs -- Fiction

ISBN 0-7614-5234-6; 978-0-7614-5234-8

LC 2004-27511

A dog who thinks her name is Down Girl goes on a car ride to the beach, goes camping in the woods, and reluctantly pays a visit to the vet with her master, Rruff.

"Narrated from a dog's point of view, this easy chapter book covers the hilarious antics of two canine friends. . . . A small black-and-white illustration appears on almost every page, supporting the text's humor." SLJ

Other titles in this series are:

Smarter than squirrels (2005)

Bad to the bone (2008)

Home on the range (2010)

Nolen, Jerdine

Eliza's freedom road; an Underground Railroad diary. Simon & Schuster Books for Young Readers 2011 139p il map $14.99

Grades: 4 5 6 7   **Fic**

1. Diaries -- Fiction 2. Slavery -- Fiction 3. African Americans -- Fiction 4. Underground railroad -- Fiction

ISBN 1-4169-5814-2; 978-1-4169-5814-7

LC 2010-20931

A twelve-year-old slave girl begins writing in a journal where she documents her journey via the Underground Railroad from Alexandria, Virginia, to freedom in St. Catharines, Canada.

"Nolen reveals some of the traumas and tragedies of slavery but keeps her focus on those things that allow Eliza the power to escape: literacy, her mother's legacy, a bit of luck and a great deal of courage." Kirkus

Includes bibliographical references

Norcliffe, James

The boy who could fly. Egmont USA 2010 312p $15.99

Grades: 5 6 7 8   **Fic**
1. Fantasy fiction 2. Flight -- Fiction 3. Siblings --
Fiction 4. Abandoned children -- Fiction
ISBN 978-1-60684-084-9; 1-60684-084-3
     LC 2009-41167
First published 2009 in New Zealand with title: The
loblolly boy

Having grown up in a miserable home for abandoned
children, a young boy jumps at the chance to exchange places with the mysterious, flying "loblolly boy," but once he
takes on this new identity, he discovers what a harsh price
he must pay.

"Norcliffe has written an imaginative and richly atmospheric fantasy with sympathetic characters. . . . This is . . . a
haunting tale that will capture most readers' imaginations."
Booklist

Northrop, Michael
Plunked; Michael Northrop. Scholastic Press 2012
247 p. (jacketed hardcover) $16.99
Grades: 4 5 6 7 8   **Fic**
1. Fear -- Fiction 2. Schools -- Fiction 3. Baseball --
Fiction 4. Perseverance (Ethics) -- Fiction
ISBN 0545297141; 9780545297141
     LC 2011032737
This children's story by Michael Northrop centers on
the "Sixth grader Jack Mogens [who] has it all figured out:
He's got his batting routine down, and his outfielding earns
him a starting spot alongside his best friend Andy on their
Little League team, the Tall Pines Braves. He even manages
to have a not-totally-embarrassing conversation with Katie,
the team's killer shortstop. But in the first game of the season, a powerful stray pitch brings everything Jack's worked
so hard for crashing down around his ears. . . ," Jack then
has to face his fears and anxieties and return to the game.
(Publisher's note)

Norton, Mary
Bed-knob and broomstick; illustrated by Erik Blegvad.
Harcourt 2000 227p il hardcover o.p. pa $6
Grades: 3 4 5 6   **Fic**
1. Fantasy fiction 2. Witchcraft -- Fiction
ISBN 0-15-202450-6; 0-15-202456-5 pa
     LC 99-89153
A combined edition of The magic bed-knob (1943) and
Bonfires and broomsticks (1947); present title is a reissue of
the 1957 edition

With the powers they acquire from a spinster who is
studying to be a witch, three English children have a series
of exciting and perilous adventures traveling on a flying bed
that takes them to a London police station, a tropical island,
and back in time to the seventeenth century

Noyce, Pendred
Lost in Lexicon; an adventure in words and numbers.
by Pendred Noyce; illustrations by Joan Charles. Scarletta
Press 2011 il
Grades: 5 6 7 8   **Fic**
1. Fantasy fiction 2. Cousins -- Fiction 3. Mathematics
-- Fiction 4. English language -- Fiction
ISBN 9780983021926 pa; 0983021929 pa;
9780983021933 e-book; 0983021937 e-book
     LC 2011013583

When Aunt Adelaide sends thirteen-year-old cousins
Ivan and Daphne on a treasure hunt in the rain, they never
expect to stumble into a whole new world where words and
numbers run wild.

Nye, Naomi Shihab, 1952-
The turtle of Oman; a novel. by Naomi Shihab Nye.
Greenwillow Books, an imprint of HarperCollinsPublishers
2014 320 p. illustrations (hardback) $16.99
Grades: 4 5 6   **Fic**
1. Oman 2. Moving -- Fiction 3. Immigrants -- Fiction
4. Grandfathers -- Fiction 5. Moving, Household --
Fiction 6. Emigration and immigration -- Fiction
ISBN 0062019724; 9780062019721
     LC 2014018263
Written by Naomi Shihab Nye, this middle grades novel
"explores themes of moving, family, nature, and immigra-
tion. It tells the story of Aref Al-Amri, who must say good-
bye to everything and everyone he loves in his hometown of
Muscat, Oman, as his family prepares to move to Ann Arbor,
Michigan. . . . His mother is desperate for him to pack his
suitcase, but he refuses. . . . But rather than pack, Aref and
Siddi go on a series of adventures." (Publisher's note)

"In the last week before his family leaves Oman for a
three-year stint in Michigan, Aref has a hard time saying
good-bye to his beloved home, particularly his grandfather,
Sidi. Readers are never told Aref's exact age; he is clearly
articulate, yet excerpts from his notebook show his writing
has not transitioned to cursive...The omniscient narration
thus brings a larger context than Aref alone could share.
Simply told, yet richly rewarding." SLJ

Nylund, Eric S.
The Resisters; [by] Eric Nylund. Random House 2011
210p $16.99; lib bdg $19.99
Grades: 5 6 7 8   **Fic**
1. Science fiction 2. Brainwashing -- Fiction 3.
Extraterrestrial beings -- Fiction
ISBN 978-0-375-86856-6; 0-375-86856-9; 978-0-375-
96856-3 lib bdg; 0-375-96856-3 lib bdg
     LC 2010-19230
When twelve-year-olds Madison and Felix kidnap him,
Ethan learns that the Earth has been taken over by aliens and
that all the adults in the world are under mind control.

"Ethan, Felix, and Madison are multidimensional characters with authentic emotions and realistic attitudes and
motives. This book mixes considerable background exposition with fast-moving action. While the immediate plot issues are resolved, there are plenty of threads left dangling.
Middle school boys will enjoy the high-tech battle action
and will look forward to the next installment." SLJ

O'Brien, Annemarie
Lara's gift; by Annemarie O'Brien. Alfred A. Knopf
2013 176 p. (hardcover) $16.99; (ebook) $50.97; (library
binding) 19.99
Grades: 5 6 7 8 9   **Fic**
1. Historical fiction 2. Dogs -- Fiction 3. Borzoi --
Fiction 4. Visions -- Fiction 5. Sex role -- Fiction 6.
Family life -- Russia -- Fiction 7. Fathers and daughters
-- Fiction 8. Russia -- History -- 1904-1914 -- Fiction
ISBN 0307931749; 9780307931740; 9780307975485;
9780375971051
     LC 2012034070

In this book, on "a remote estate in 1910s Russia, Lara must prove herself capable of following in her father's footsteps as the head of a prestigious borzoi breeding kennel. There are so many things between her and the realization of her dream. That she is female is the biggest obstacle, but she must also hide the fact that she has visions of future occurrences that involve the dogs and the dangerous wolves that populate the estate." (Kirkus Reviews)

O'Brien, Robert C.

★ **Mrs.** Frisby and the rats of NIMH; [by] Robert C. O'Brien; illustrated by Zena Bernstein. Atheneum Books for Young Readers 2006 233p il $18; pa $6.99

Grades: 4 5 6 7   **Fic**

1. Mice -- Fiction 2. Rats -- Fiction

ISBN 978-0-689-20651-1; 0-689-20651-8; 978-0-689-71068-1 pa; 0-689-71068-2 pa

A reissue of the title first published 1971

Awarded the Newbery Medal, 1972

Having no one to help her with her problems, a widowed mouse visits the rats whose former imprisonment in a laboratory made them wise and long lived.

"The story is fresh and ingenious, the style witty, and the plot both hilarious and convincing." Saturday Rev

O'Connor, Barbara

★ **Fame** and glory in Freedom, Georgia. Farrar, Straus & Giroux 2003 104p $16; pa $6.95

Grades: 4 5 6 7   **Fic**

1. School stories 2. Contests -- Fiction

ISBN 0-374-32258-9; 0-374-40018-0 pa

LC 2002-190212

Unpopular sixth-grader Burdette Bird Weaver persuades the new boy at school, whom everyone thinks is mean and dumb, to be her partner for a spelling bee that might win her everything she's ever wanted

"An idiosyncratic group of characters play out this touching and well-paced story about friendship, family, and connection." Horn Books

★ **The fantastic** secret of Owen Jester. Farrar Straus Giroux 2010 168p $15.99

Grades: 3 4 5   **Fic**

1. Adventure fiction 2. Frogs -- Fiction 3. Georgia -- Fiction 4. Family life -- Fiction 5. Submersibles -- Fiction

ISBN 978-0-374-36850-0; 0-374-36850-3

After Owen captures an enormous bullfrog, names it Tooley Graham, then has to release it, he and two friends try to use a small submarine that fell from a passing train to search for Tooley in the Carter, Georgia, pond it came from, while avoiding nosy neighbor Viola.

"O'Connor has spun a lovely read that perfectly captures the schemes and plans of school-age kids in the long days of summer." Kirkus

★ **How** to steal a dog; a novel. Farrar, Straus & Giroux 2007 170p pa $6.99; $16

Grades: 4 5 6   **Fic**

1. Dogs -- Fiction 2. Siblings -- Fiction 3. Homeless persons -- Fiction

ISBN 0-312-56112-1 pa; 0-374-33497-8; 978-0-312-56112-3 pa; 978-0-374-33497-0

LC 2005-40166

Living in the family car in their small North Carolina town, Georgina persuades her younger brother to help her in an elaborate scheme to get money by stealing a dog and then claiming the reward that the owners are bound to offer

This is told "in stripped-down, unsentimental prose. . . . The myriad effects of homelessness and the realistic picture of a moral quandary will surely generate discussion." Booklist

★ **On** the road to Mr. Mineo's; Barbara O'Connor. Frances Foster Books 2012 181 p. (hardcover) $16.99

Grades: 5 6   **Fic**

1. Pigeons -- Fiction 2. Homing pigeons -- Fiction 3. South Carolina -- Fiction

ISBN 0374380023; 9780374380021

LC 2011049679

In this novel by Barbara O'Conner, "Sherman the one-legged pigeon flies into . . . Meadville, South Carolina . . . and causes a ruckus. First Stella, who's been begging for a dog, spots him on top of a garage roof and decides she wants him for a pet. Then there's Ethel and Amos, an old couple who sees the pigeon in their barn keeping company with a little brown dog that barks all night. Meanwhile, across town, Mr. Mineo has one less homing pigeon than he used to." (Publisher's note)

★ **The small** adventure of Popeye and Elvis. Frances Foster Books 2009 149p $16.99

Grades: 3 4 5 6   **Fic**

1. Adventure fiction 2. Dogs -- Fiction 3. Friendship -- Fiction 4. Grandmothers -- Fiction 5. South Carolina -- Fiction

ISBN 978-0-374-37055-8; 0-374-37055-9

LC 2008-24145

In Fayette, South Carolina, the highlight of Popeye's summer is learning vocabulary words with his grandmother until a motor home gets stuck nearby and Elvis, the oldest boy living inside, joins Popeye in finding the source of strange boats floating down the creek.

"Elvis and Popeye's journey reminds readers to look for and enjoy the small treasures in their lives. Save a spot on your shelves for this small adventure with a grand heart." SLJ

O'Connor, Sheila

★ **Sparrow** Road. G. P. Putnam's Sons 2011 247p $16.99

Grades: 5 6 7 8   **Fic**

1. Artists -- Fiction 2. Young adult literature -- Works

ISBN 978-0-399-25458-1; 0-399-25458-7

LC 2010-28290

Twelve-year-old Raine spends the summer at a mysterious artists colony and discovers a secret about her past.

This is a "beautifully written novel. . . . Readers finding themselves in this quiet world will find plenty of space to imagine and dream for themselves." Kirkus

O'Dell, Kathleen

The **aviary.** Alfred A. Knopf 2011 339p $15.99; lib bdg $18.99

Grades: 3 4 5   **Fic**

1. Birds -- Fiction 2. Magic -- Fiction 3. Maine -- Fiction 4. Friendship -- Fiction 5. Family life -- Fiction

6. Inheritance and succession -- Fiction
ISBN 978-0-375-85605-1; 0-375-85605-6; 978-0-375-95605-8 lib bdg; 0-375-95605-0 lib bdg

LC 2010045778

In late nineteenth-century Maine, isolated, eleven-year-old Clara Dooley gains a friend and uncovers a magical secret that changes her life when she learns to care for the once-feared birds in the aviary attached to the Glendoveer mansion where she lives.

"The honeycreeper's encouragement leads to discovery after discovery in a well-paced, high-tension mystery that draws not only on Burnett, but also C.S. Lewis, Zilpha Keatley Snyder, and Neil Gaiman, joining a rich heritage of stories about children with a secret 'room of their own.'" Publ Wkly

O'Dell, Scott
★ **Island** of the Blue Dolphins; illustrated by Ted Lewin. 50th anniversary ed.; Houghton Mifflin Books for Children 2010 177p il $22
Grades: 5 6 7 8   Fic
1. Native Americans -- Fiction 2. Wilderness survival -- Fiction 3. San Nicolas Island (Calif.) -- Fiction
ISBN 978-0-547-42483-5; 0-547-42483-3

A reissue of the newly illustrated edition published 1990; first published 1960

Awarded the Newbery Medal, 1961

Left alone on a beautiful but isolated island off the coast of California, a young Indian girl spends eighteen years, not only merely surviving through her enormous courage and self-reliance, but also finding a measure of happiness in her solitary life.

The edition illustrated by Ted Lewin "features twelve full-page, full-color watercolors in purple and blue hues that are appropriate to the island setting. This handsome gift-edition version includes a new introduction by Lois Lowry to commemorate the book's fiftieth anniversary." Horn Book Guide

Sing down the moon. Houghton Mifflin 1970 137p hardcover o.p. pa $6.99
Grades: 5 6 7 8   Fic
1. Navajo Indians -- Fiction
ISBN 0-395-10919-1; 978-0-547-40632-9 pa; 0-547-40632-0 pa

A Newbery Medal honor book, 1971

"There is a poetic sonority of style, a sense of identification, and a note of indomitable courage and stoicism that is touching and impressive." Saturday Rev

This story is told "through the eyes of a young Navaho girl as she sees the rich harvest in the Canyon de Chelly in 1864 destroyed by Spanish slavers and the subsequent destruction by white soldiers which forces the Navahos on a march to Fort Sumner." Publ Wkly

Streams to the river, river to the sea; a novel of Sacagawea. Houghton Mifflin 1986 191p hardcover o.p. pa $6.99
Grades: 5 6 7 8   Fic
1. Interpreters 2. Guides (Persons) 3. Native Americans -- Fiction 4. Lewis and Clark Expedition (1804-1806) -- Fiction
ISBN 0-395-40430-4; 0-618-96642-0 pa

LC 86-936

"An informative and involving choice for American history students and pioneer-adventure readers." Bull Cent Child Books

Obed, Ellen Bryan, 1944-
★ **Twelve** kinds of ice; by Ellen Bryan Obed; illustrated by Barbara McClintock. Houghton Mifflin Books for Children 2012 p. cm.
Grades: 1 2 3 4   Fic
1. Ice -- Fiction 2. Winter -- Fiction 3. Family life -- Fiction 4. Ice skating -- Fiction
ISBN 9780618891290

LC 2011046417

This book presents a "memoir of [Ellen Bryan] Obed's dreamy childhood in Maine, built around the 12 kinds of ice that served as successive signposts of the advancing season." (New York Times Book Review) "This homage to rural winter celebrates the gradual freezing of barn buckets and fields, the happy heights of ice-skating season, and the inevitable spring thaw." (Publishers Weekly)

Odyssey, Shawn Thomas
The **Wizard** of Dark Street; an Oona Crate mystery. Egmont USA 2011 352p $16.99
Grades: 5 6 7   Fic
1. Mystery fiction 2. Magic -- Fiction 3. Uncles -- Fiction 4. Orphans -- Fiction 5. Witchcraft -- Fiction 6. Apprentices -- Fiction
ISBN 978-1-60684-143-3; 1-60684-143-2

LC 2011-02496

In 1877, in an enchantment shop on the last of the Faerie roads linking New York City to the Land of the Fey, just after twelve-year-old Oona opts to relinquish her apprenticeship to her uncle, the Wizard, and become a detective, her uncle is stabbed, testing her skills.

"Upbeat in tone, this delight is an excellent blend of fantasy and mystery with a variety of suspicious characters and enough red herrings to keep the reader guessing all the way to the end." Booklist

Oertel, Andreas
The **Archaeolojesters**. Lobster Press 2010 192p pa $10.95
Grades: 4 5 6   Fic
1. Antiquities -- Fiction
ISBN 978-1-897550-83-0 pa

There is a drought in Sultana, Manitoba, and "life is getting more dismal by the minute. . . . There aren't even enough tourists to keep the local restaurant busy, and if Cody's best friend's mom loses her job there, the family will have to move away. . . . [Then] Cody, his best friend Eric, and Eric's twin sister, Rachel, concoct an elaborate hoax. . . . An 'ancient Egyptian' tablet is discovered in Sultana, and suddenly archaeologists, reporters, and tourists are rushing over. . . . The kids are convinced that their plan has succeeded ... until one suspicious stranger starts trailing every move that Cody and his friends make." (Publisher's note) "Ages nine to twelve." (Quill Quire)

Followed by: Pillars of time (2010)

Okimoto, Jean Davies
Maya and the cotton candy boy. Endicott and Hugh 2011 $16.99; pa $9.99

Grades: 4 5 6 7   **Fic**
  1. School stories 2. Siblings -- Fiction 3. Immigrants -- Fiction
  ISBN 978-0-9823167-4-0; 0-9823167-4-7; 978-0-9823167-5-7 pa; 0-9823167-5-5 pa

Newly arrived from Kazakhstan, twelve-year-old Maya Alazova resents the way her mother babies her brother, but when she leaves her English Language Learner program for mainstream classes and has to deal with a boy, a bully, and conflict at home, she finds her brother can help with their new culture in ways their parents can't.

"Maya tells her story well, and observant readers will come away with a better understanding of the sacrifices made by similar families." SLJ

Oliver, Lauren
  ★ **Liesl** & Po; illustrated by Kei Acedera. Harper 2011 307p il $16.99
Grades: 4 5 6 7   **Fic**
  1. Ghost stories 2. Fantasy fiction 3. Magic -- Fiction 4. Bereavement -- Fiction
  ISBN 978-0-06-201451-1; 0-06-201451-X

Liesl lives in a tiny attic bedroom, locked away by her cruel stepmother. Her only friends are the shadows and the mice—until one night a ghost appears from the darkness. It is Po, who comes from the Other Side. That same night, an alchemist's apprentice, Will, accidentally bungles an important delivery. He switches a box containing the most powerful magic in the world with one containing something decidedly less remarkable.

This is a "charming, insightful fantasy. . . . This original fairy tale, told by a wise and humorous omniscient narrator and peopled with broadly drawn but instantly recognizable characters, avoids sentimentality to show the magic of accepting loss without letting go and finding joy in the lives left behind." Booklist

  ★ The **spindlers**; Lauren Oliver; illustrated by Iacopo Bruno. 1st ed. Harper 2012 246 p. ill. (hardcover) $16.99
Grades: 4 5 6   **Fic**
  1. Monsters -- Fiction 2. Fantasy fiction 3. Fantasy 4. Soul -- Fiction 5. Brothers and sisters -- Fiction
  ISBN 0061978086; 9780061978081
                                        LC 2012009698

This children's fantasy novel, by Lauren Oliver, is about a young girl who travels to a fantasy realm to rescue her younger brother from monsters. "When Liza's brother, Patrick, changes overnight, Liza knows exactly what has happened: The spindlers have gotten to him and stolen his soul. . . . To rescue Patrick, Liza must go Below, armed with little more than her wits and a broom. There, she uncovers a vast world populated with . . . terrible dangers." (Publisher's note)

Oppel, Kenneth
  ★ The **Boundless**; Kenneth Oppel. First edition Simon & Schuster Books for Young Readers 2014 332 p. illustrations (hardcover: alk. paper) $16.99
Grades: 4 5 6 7 8   **Fic**
  1. Adventure fiction 2. Circus -- Fiction 3. Railroads -- Fiction 4. Canada -- History -- Fiction 5. Railroad trains -- Fiction 6. Adventure and adventurers -- Fiction 7. Canada -- History -- 1867-1914 -- Fiction
  ISBN 144247288X; 9781442472884; 9781442472891
                                        LC 2013009879

In this book, by Kenneth Oppel, "The Boundless . . . is on its maiden voyage across the country, and first-class passenger Will Everett is about to embark on the adventure of his life! When Will ends up in possession of the key to a train car containing priceless treasures, he becomes the target of sinister figures from his past. In order to survive, Will must join a traveling circus, enlisting the aid of Mr. Dorian, the ringmaster and leader of the troupe." (Publisher's note)

"Will's father is driving the Boundless, the longest train ever, on her maiden voyage. After a series of adventures (involving a sasquatch and a murder), Will finds himself stranded in the caboose, where, with the help of a cute tightrope walker, he dodges a nefarious villain. The third-person present-tense narrative creates suspense as the well-drawn characters travel through an alternate-universe Canadian wilderness." (Horn Book)

Silverwing. Simon & Schuster Bks. for Young Readers 1997 217p hardcover o.p. pa $6.99
Grades: 5 6 7 8   **Fic**
  1. Bats -- Fiction
  ISBN 0-689-81529-8; 1-4169-4998-4 pa
                                        LC 97-10977

When a newborn bat named Shade but sometimes called "Runt" becomes separated from his colony during migration, he grows in ways that prepare him for even greater journeys

"Oppel's bats are fully developed characters who, if not quite cuddly, will certainly earn readers' sympathy and respect. In Silverwing the author has created an intriguing microcosm of rival species, factions, and religions." Horn Book
Other titles in this series are:
  Sunwing (2000)
  Firewing (2003)
  Darkwing (2007)

Orlev, Uri
  The **man** from the other side; translated from the Hebrew by Hillel Halkin. Puffin Books 1995 186p pa $6.99
Grades: 5 6 7 8   **Fic**
  1. Jews -- Poland -- Fiction 2. Holocaust, 1933-1945 -- Fiction 3. World War, 1939-1945 -- Fiction
  ISBN 0-14-037088-9; 978-0-14-037088-1
                                        LC 94-30189

Living on the outskirts of the Warsaw Ghetto during World War II, fourteen-year-old Marek and his grandparents shelter a Jewish man in the days before the Jewish uprising

"This is a story of individual bravery and national shame that highlights just how hopeless was the fate of the Warsaw Jews as they fought alone and heroically against the Nazi war machine." SLJ

  ★ The **song** of the whales; translated by Hillel Halkin. Houghton Mifflin Books for Children 2010 108p $16
Grades: 5 6 7 8   **Fic**
  1. Jews -- Fiction 2. Dreams -- Fiction 3. Israel -- Fiction 4. Old age -- Fiction 5. Jerusalem -- Fiction 6. Family life -- Fiction 7. Grandfathers -- Fiction
  ISBN 978-0-547-25752-5; 0-547-25752-X
                                        LC 2009-49720

At age eight, Mikha'el knows he is different from other boys, but over the course of three years as he helps his parents care for his elderly grandfather in Jerusalem, Grandpa teaches Mikha'el to use the gift they share of making other people's dreams sweeter.

This is "the sort of story that operates on many different levels. . . . With a clean sense that less is more, Orlev has crafted a sweetly mysterious and quietly moving read." Booklist

Orr, Wendy

Lost! A dog called Bear; illustrations by Susan Boase. Henry Holt 2011 103p il (Rainbow Street Shelter) $15.99

Grades: 2 3 4 **Fic**

1. Dogs -- Fiction 2. Moving -- Fiction 3. Divorce -- Fiction 4. Lost and found possessions -- Fiction

ISBN 978-0-8050-8931-8; 0-8050-8931-4

LC 2010029886

When Logan's dog runs away as he and his mother are moving to a new home after his parents separate, a girl named Hannah, who longs for a dog of her own, finds him.

"The book is well designed for readers moving up to chapter books, with its short sentences, well-spaced lines of type, and attractive illustrations. Expressing emotions through subtle physical cues, Boase's shaded pencil drawings depict both people and dogs with grace and sensitivity." Booklist

Missing! A cat called Buster; illustrations by Susan Boase. Henry Holt and Company 2011 116p il (Rainbow Street Shelter) $15.99; pa $5.99

Grades: 2 3 4 **Fic**

1. Cats -- Fiction 2. Pets -- Fiction 3. Loss (Psychology) -- Fiction 4. Lost and found possessions -- Fiction

ISBN 978-0-8050-8932-5; 0-8050-8932-2; 978-0-8050-9382-7 pa; 0-8050-9382-6 pa

LC 2010044786

After his pet rabbit dies, Josh feels sad and does not want to own another pet until an elderly neighbor's cat goes missing.

"This effort sympathetically, if briefly, deals with some complex issues, including the responsibilities of pet ownership, death and aging, but always within the framework of an optimistic, childlike perspective appropriate for the target audience. . . . Attractive black-and-white full and half-page sketches, one or two per chapter, offer some visual interest as well. This early chapter book with plenty of heart and a bit of suspense will appeal to young pet lovers." Kirkus

Mokie & Bik; [by] Wendy Orr; illustrations by Jonathan Bean. Henry Holt 2007 72p il $15.95

Grades: 2 3 4 **Fic**

1. Twins -- Fiction 2. Siblings -- Fiction 3. Boats and boating -- Fiction

ISBN 978-0-8050-7979-1; 0-8050-7979-3

LC 2006011150

For two rambunctious twins, living on a boat means always being underfoot or overboard

"Orr's colorful use of language brings energy to the story. The many crosshatch drawings . . . are often graceful and always appealing." Booklist

Another title about Mokie & Bik is:
Mokie & Bik go to sea (2008)

Mokie & Bik go to sea; illustrations by Jonathan Bean. Henry Holt and Company 2010 75p il $16.95

Grades: 2 3 4 **Fic**

1. Twins -- Fiction 2. Siblings -- Fiction 3. Boats and

boating -- Fiction

ISBN 978-0-8050-8174-9; 0-8050-8174-7

LC 2007027590

With their father home from the sea, the rambunctious twins Mokie and Bik make the Bullfrog shipshape for a voyage out to sea, where they make friends with a scaredy-seal, save a runaway boat, and keep track of Waggles.

"Written in a whimsical style that borders on poetry. . . . Frequent black-and-white illustrations add to the zaniness of the fast-paced story." SLJ

Oswald, Nancy

Nothing here but stones; a Jewish pioneer story. [by] Nancy Oswald. Henry Holt 2004 215p $16.95

Grades: 5 6 7 8 **Fic**

1. Jews -- Fiction 2. Colorado -- Fiction 3. Immigrants -- Fiction 4. Frontier and pioneer life -- Fiction

ISBN 0-8050-7465-1

LC 2003-56969

In 1882, ten-year-old Emma and her family, along with other Russian Jewish immigrants, arrive in Cotopaxi, Colorado, where they face inhospitable conditions as they attempt to start an agricultural colony, and lonely Emma is comforted by the horse whose life she saved

"This well-paced, vivid account should capture readers' attention." SLJ

Oz, Amos, 1939-

★ **Suddenly** in the depths of the forest; translated from the Hebrew by Sondra Silverston. Harcourt 2011 134p $15.99

Grades: 4 5 6 7 **Fic**

1. Fables 2. Animals -- Fiction 3. Young adult literature -- Works

ISBN 978-0-547-55153-1; 0-547-55153-3

LC 2011-08664

In a gray and gloomy village, all of the animals—from dogs and cats to fish and snails—disappeared years before. No one talks about it and no one knows why, though everyone agrees that the village has been cursed. But when two children see a fish—a tiny one and just for a second—they become determined to unravel the mystery of where the animals have gone.

"In this swiftly moving fable . . . Oz creates palpable tension with a repetitive, almost hypnotic rhythm and lyrical language that twists a discussion-provoking morality tale into something much more enchanting." Booklist

Pakkala, Christine

Last-but-not-least lola and the wild chicken; Christine Pakkala. Boyds Mills Press 2014 216 p. illustrations (Last-but-not-least lola) (reinforced) $15.95

Grades: 2 3 4 5 **Fic**

1. Chickens -- Fiction 2. Friendship -- Fiction

ISBN 9781590789834; 1590789830

LC 2014935273

"Spirited, smart, and strong-willed Lola Zuckerman, who is always last but never least, returns for a second adventure. Still struggling with friendships, Lola doesn't want to share her on-again, off-again best friend Amanda with Jessie (who seems to be around all the time) and new girl Savannah." (Publisher's note)

" Pakkala perfectly captures the competitive jealousy that sparks among little girls as they claim best friends, as well as the supportive tone of a good teacher caring for well-intentioned but accident-causing pupils. Hoppe's smart cartoon spot illustrations suit the fast-paced, emotionally resonant, and sometimes silly story." Booklist

Palacio, R. J.
★ **Wonder**; by R.J. Palacio. Alfred A. Knopf 2012 315 p. (hardcover) $15.99
Grades: 3 4 5 6   Fic
1. Middle schools 2. Interpersonal relations 3. Birth defects -- Fiction 4. Schools -- Fiction 5. Middle schools -- Fiction 6. Self-acceptance -- Fiction 7. Abnormalities, Human -- Fiction
ISBN 9780375869020; 9780375899881; 9780375969027
LC 2011027133

In this book, "[a]fter being homeschooled for years, Auggie Pullman is about to start fifth grade, but he's worried: How will he fit into middle-school life when he looks so different from everyone else? Auggie has had 27 surgeries to correct facial anomalies he was born with, but he still has a face that has earned him such cruel nicknames as Freak, Freddy Krueger, Gross-out and Lizard face. . . . Palacio divides the novel into eight parts, interspersing Auggie's first-person narrative with the voices of family members and classmates, . . . expanding the story beyond Auggie's viewpoint and demonstrating that Auggie's arrival at school doesn't test only him, it affects everyone in the community." (Kirkus)

Palatini, Margie
Geek Chic; the Zoey zone. Katherine Tegen Books 2008 184p $10.99; lib bdg $14.89
Grades: 3 4 5   Fic
1. School stories
ISBN 978-0-06-113898-0; 0-06-113898-3; 978-0-06-113899-7 lib bdg; 0-06-113899-1 lib bdg
A contemporary Cinderella story about Zoey, 10, who desperately needs a fairy godmother to give her a makeover and teach her about style if she is ever going to make it into the cool crowd in the lunchroom.
"This amalgamation of graphic novel and chapter book cleverly integrates wrinkled-looking notes, varied typefaces, wacky line drawings, and movie countdowns with straightforward prose to tell the funny if farfetched tale." SLJ

Paley, Jane
Hooper finds a family; a Hurricane Katrina dog's survival tale. Harper 2011 137p il $15.99
Grades: 4 5 6   Fic
1. Dogs -- Fiction 2. New York (N.Y.) -- Fiction 3. Hurricane Katrina, 2005 -- Fiction
ISBN 978-0-06-201103-9; 0-06-201103-0
LC 2011002088
Jimmy, a yellow Labrador puppy, is separated from his Lake Charles, Louisiana, family and survives the horrors of Hurricane Katrina on his own before being rescued and taken to New York City, where he tries to fit in with a new family and the many neighborhood dogs, and accept his new name.
"A harsh but ultimately heartwarming story about moving forward after trauma and loss by making space for new loves ones and new possibilities." Kirkus

Papademetriou, Lisa
Chasing normal; [by] Lisa Papademetriou. Hyperion Books for Children 2008 193p $15.99; pa $5.99
Grades: 3 4 5 6   Fic
1. Cousins -- Fiction 2. Family life -- Fiction 3. Grandmothers -- Fiction 4. Houston (Tex.) -- Fiction
ISBN 978-1-4231-0340-0; 1-4231-0340-8; 978-1-4231-0341-7 pa; 1-4231-0341-6 pa
LC 2007022418
When her mean, grouchy grandmother in Texas has a heart attack and she and father go to help, twelve-year-old Mieka meets her cousins' family and wishes for their "normal" type of life.
This "is solid fare for readers looking for a family-centered story and a protagonist who is smart, funny, and instantly recognizable." Booklist

Paratore, Coleen
Sunny Holiday; [by] Coleen Murtagh Paratore. Scholastic Press 2009 160p $15.99; pa $5.99
Grades: 2 3 4   Fic
1. African Americans -- Fiction 2. Mother-daughter relationship -- Fiction
ISBN 978-0-545-07579-4; 0-545-07579-3; 978-0-545-07588-6 pa; 0-545-07588-2 pa
LC 2008009786
Spunky third-grader Sunny Holiday tries to make the best out of every situation, and even though her father is in prison, she and her mother count their blessings and manage to find joy in every day
"Difficult situations are handled gently, but realistically. . . . The text is not difficult and includes some fun images for abstract ideas." SLJ
Followed by: Sweet and sunny (2010)

Park, Barbara
Junie B. Jones and her big fat mouth; illustrated by Denise Brunkus. Random House 1993 69p il lib bdg $11.99; pa $4.99
Grades: 1 2 3   Fic
1. School stories
ISBN 0-679-94407-9 lib bdg; 0-679-84407-4 pa
LC 92-50957
When her kindergarten class has Job Day, Junie B. goes through much confusion and excitement before deciding on the "bestest" job of all
"Brunkus' energetic drawings pick up the slapstick action and the spunky comic hero." Booklist
Other titles about Junie B. Jones are:
Junie B., first grader: Aloha-ha-ha (2006)
Junie B., first grader (at last!) (2001)
Junie B., first grader: boo . . . and I mean it! (2003)
Junie B., first grader: boss of lunch (2002)
Junie B., first grader: cheater pants (2003)
Junie B., first grader: dumb bunny (2007)
Junie B., first grader: jingle bells, Batman smells! (p.s. so does May) (2005)
Junie B., first grader: one-man band (2003)
Junie B., first grader: shipwrecked (2003)
Junie B., first grader: toothless wonder (2002)
Junie B. Jones and a little monkey business (1993)
Junie B. Jones and some sneaky peeky spying (1994)
Junie B. Jones and that meanie Jim's birthday (1996)
Junie B. Jones and the mushy gushy valentine (1999)

Junie B. Jones and the stupid smelly bus (1992)
Junie B. Jones and the yucky blucky fruitcake (1995)
Junie B. Jones has a monster under her bed (1997)
Junie B. Jones has a peep in her pocket (2000)
Junie B. Jones is a beauty shop guy (1998)
Junie B. Jones is a graduation girl (2001)
Junie B. Jones is a party animal (1997)
Junie B. Jones is (almost) a flower girl (1999)
Junie B. Jones is Captain Field Day (2000)
Junie B. Jones is not a crook (1997)
Junie B. Jones loves handsome Warren (1996)
Junie B. Jones smells something fishy (1998)

Park, Linda Sue

Project Mulberry; a novel. Clarion 2005 225p $16;
pa $6.99

Grades: 5 6 7 8   **Fic**

1. Korean Americans -- Fiction
ISBN 0-618-47786-1; 0-440-42163-2 pa
                                          LC 2004-18159

While working on a project for an afterschool club, Julia,
a Korean American girl, and her friend Patrick learn not just
about silkworms, but also about tolerance, prejudice, friendship, patience, and more. Between the chapters are short
dialogues between the author and main character about the
writing of the book

"The unforgettable family and friendship story, the quiet,
almost unspoken racism, and the excitement of the science
make this a great cross-curriculum title." Booklist

★ A **single** shard. Clarion Bks. 2001 152p $15; pa
$6.99

Grades: 5 6 7 8   **Fic**

1. Korea -- Fiction 2. Pottery -- Fiction
ISBN 0-395-97827-0; 0-440-41851-8 pa
                                          LC 00-43102

Awarded the Newbery Medal, 2002

Tree-ear, a thirteen-year-old orphan in medieval Korea,
lives under a bridge in a potters' village, and longs to learn
how to throw the delicate celadon ceramics himself

"This quiet, but involving, story draws readers into a
very different time and place. . . . A well-crafted novel with
an unusual setting." Booklist

Storm warning. Scholastic 2010 190p (The 39 clues)
$12.99

Grades: 4 5 6 7   **Fic**

1. Ciphers -- Fiction
ISBN 978-0-545-06049-3; 0-545-06049-4

Sequel to: The emperor's code by Gordon Korman
(2010)

Amy and Dan hit the high seas as they follow the trail
of some infamous ancestors to track down a long lost treasure. However, the real prize isn't hidden in a chest. It's the
discovery of the Madrigals' most dangerous secret and, even
more shockingly, the true identity of the mysterious man
in black.

Followed by: Into the gauntlet by Margaret Peterson
Haddix (2010)

Trust no one; Linda Sue Park. 1st ed. Scholastic Press
2013 190 p. (reinforced) $12.99

Grades: 4 5 6 7   **Fic**

1. Spy stories 2. Mystery fiction
ISBN 0545298431; 9780545298438
                                          LC 2012939109

This is the fifth installment of Linda Sue Park's Cahills
vs. Vespers series. Here, "Amy and Dan discover that one of
their friends is a spy for the Vespers, a group of evil agents
who kidnapped seven of their family members. But which
friend is it? The shocking secrets continue when the Cahill
siblings finally figure out the Vespers' real plan, and it's
much worse than they originally thought." (Owl Magazine)

★ **When** my name was Keoko. Clarion Bks. 2002
199p $16; pa $6.99

Grades: 5 6 7 8   **Fic**

1. Korea -- Fiction 2. World War, 1939-1945 -- Fiction
ISBN 0-618-13335-6; 0-440-41944-1 pa
                                          LC 2001-32487

With national pride and occasional fear, a brother and
sister face the increasingly oppressive occupation of Korea
by Japan during World War II, which threatens to suppress
Korean culture entirely

"Park is a masterful prose stylist, and her characters
are developed beautifully. She excels at making traditional Korean culture accessible to Western readers." Voice
Youth Advocates

Includes bibliographical references

Parker, Marjorie Hodgson

David and the Mighty Eighth; a British boy and a Texas
airman in World War II. by Marjorie Hodgson Parker; illustrated by Mark Postlethwaite. Bright Sky Press 2007
176p il $17.95

Grades: 4 5 6 7   **Fic**

1. Great Britain -- Fiction 2. World War, 1939-1945
-- Fiction
ISBN 978-1-931721-93-6; 1-931721-93-9
                                          LC 2007025999

When, during the London Blitz, he and his older sister
are evacuated to go live on their grandparents' East Anglia
farm, a young English boy finds it difficult to adjust to his
new life until the arrival of the pilots and crews of the U.S.
Eight Air Force at nearby airfields brings excitement, friendship, and hope for the future.

This is an "exciting novel, based on a true story. . . . The
story is framed by extensive historical notes. . . . Spacious
type, thick paper, and an occasional black-and-white drawings make this an appealing package all around." Booklist

Parkinson, Siobhan

Blue like Friday. Roaring Brook Press 2008 160p
$16.95

Grades: 4 5 6 7   **Fic**

1. Ireland -- Fiction 2. Family life -- Fiction 3.
Synesthesia -- Fiction 4. Missing persons -- Fiction
ISBN 978-1-59643-340-3; 1-59643-340-X

When Olivia helps her quirky friend Hal, whose synesthesia causes him to experience everything in colors, with a
prank intended to get rid of Hal's potential stepfather, there
are unexpected consequences, including the disappearance
of Hal's mother.

"Parkinson creates a warm, moving story of real families
facing real problems. . . . The economy of her prose is admirable; all the characters are well drawn." Booklist

Parnell, Robyn

The **mighty** Quinn; by Robyn Parnell; illustrated by Aaron and Katie DeYoe. 1st ed. Scarletta Press 2013 263 p. ill. (paperback) $10.95

Grades: 4 5 6 7   **Fic**

1. Bullies -- Juvenile fiction 2. Friendship -- Juvenile fiction 3. School stories -- Juvenile fiction 4. Oregon -- Fiction 5. Bullies -- Fiction 6. Schools -- Fiction 7. Friendship -- Fiction

ISBN 1938063104; 9781938063107

LC 2012031518

In this story, by Robyn Parnell, "Quinn Andrews-Lee . . . faces a dismal school year. His little sister outshines him . . . , he yearns for a service award his peers disdain, and charismatic bigot Matt Barker's goal in life is to torment Quinn. . . . When Quinn reports an act of vandalism, he is accused of injuring Matt. . . . A free-spirited new kid in Quinn's class, helps Quinn deduce who hurt Matt, but Matt would probably die . . . before admitting the truth." (Publisher's note)

Parry, Rosanne

★ **Heart** of a shepherd; [by] Rosanne Parry. Random House Children's Books 2009 161p lib bdg $18.99; $15.99

Grades: 4 5 6 7   **Fic**

1. Oregon -- Fiction 2. Ranch life -- Fiction 3. Family life -- Fiction 4. Christian life -- Fiction 5. Iraq War, 2003- -- Fiction

ISBN 0-375-84802-9; 978-0-375-94802-2 lib bdg; 0-375-94802-3 lib bdg; 978-0-375-84802-5

LC 2007-48094

Ignatius 'Brother' Alderman, nearly twelve, promises to help his grandparents keep the family's Oregon ranch the same while his brothers are away and his father is deployed to Iraq, but as he comes to accept the inevitability of change, he also sees the man he is meant to be

There is "more action than introspection afoot, with sibling tensions, a wildfire, and the grandfather's death along the journey. It's refreshing . . . to find a protagonist with his eyes and heart open to positive adult examples . . . and who matches his mettle to theirs." Bull Cent Child Books

Partridge, Elizabeth

★ **Dogtag** summer. Bloomsbury Books for Young Readers 2011 226p $16.99

Grades: 4 5 6 7   **Fic**

1. Hippies -- Fiction 2. Adoption -- Fiction 3. California -- Fiction 4. Family life -- Fiction 5. Vietnamese Americans -- Fiction 6. Racially mixed people -- Fiction 7. Vietnam War, 1961-1975 -- Fiction

ISBN 978-1-59990-183-1; 1-59990-183-8

LC 2010-25515

In the summer of 1980 before she starts junior high school in Santa Rosa, California, Tracy, who was adopted from Vietnam when she was six years old, finds an old ammo box with a dog tag and picture that bring up painful memories for both her Vietnam-veteran father and her.

"This gripping yet tender coming-of-age story reveals multiple nuanced perspectives of the Vietnam War and its aftermath. . . . Powerful historical fiction." Publ Wkly

Pastis, Stephan

Timmy failure; mistakes were made. Stephan Pastis. Candlewick Press 2013 304 p. (reinforced) $14.99

Grades: 4 5 6 7   **Fic**

1. Mystery graphic novels 2. Picture books for children

ISBN 0763660507; 9780763660505

LC 2012942409

This children's graphic novel focuses on Timmy and his detective agency Total Failure Inc. Questions abound: "Who stole the Halloween candy of Timmy's classmate Gabe? Who is the mysterious girl Timmy refuses to discuss? Why is no one fazed that Timmy has a pet polar bear named Total?" (Publishers Weekly)

Timmy failure: now look what you've done; Now Look What You've Done. Stephan Pastis. Candlewick Press 2014 288 p. illustrations $14.99

Grades: 4 5 6 7   **Fic**

1. Detectives -- Fiction 2. Polar bear -- Fiction 3. Problem solving -- Fiction 4. Self-confidence -- Fiction 5. Globes 6. Schools 7. Contests 8. Humorous stories 9. Detective and mystery stories

ISBN 0763660515; 9780763660512

LC 2013944145

In this book, by Stephan Pastis, "the too-smart-for-his-own-good kid detective is back for a second zany installment, along with his 1500-pound polar/bear business partner, Total. Timmy has big dreams for his crime-solving empire, fueled by his complete self-confidence, delusions of grandeur, and his assured win in a competition to find a stolen globe worth $500. But first, shenanigans are afoot and must be thwarted." (School Library Journal)

"Timmy is back, clueless as ever, his sleuthing even clumsier than in the first installment. Timmy and his polar bear sidekick, Total, haplessly plow through the shenanigans thwarting Timmy's domination of the school detective competition. Great-aunt Coriander and her own wacky aspirations add a new layer to the winning combination of sardonically humorous text and pen-and-ink cartoons that has won Timmy many fans." Horn Book

Paterson, John

★ The **Flint** Heart; a fairy story. freely abriged from Eden Phillpott's 1910 fantasy; by Katherine and John Paterson; illustrated by John Rocco. Candlewick Press 2011 288p il $19.99

Grades: 3 4 5 6   **Fic**

1. Fairy tales

ISBN 978-0-7636-4712-4; 0-7636-4712-8

LC 2010048225

An ambitious Stone Age man demands a talisman that will harden his heart, allowing him to take control of his tribe. Against his better judgment, the tribe's magic man creates the Flint Heart, but the cruelty of it causes the destruction of the tribe. Thousands of years later, the talisman reemerges to corrupt a kindly farmer, an innocent fairy creature, and a familial badger.

"The tale will make an excellent read-aloud. . . . The Patersons have done a lovely job updating and abridging this tale for today's readers. . . . Rocco's fantastic illustrations alone make this edition worth purchasing." SLJ

Paterson, Katherine

★ **Bread** and roses, too. Clarion Books 2006 275p $16; pa $6.99

Grades: 5 6 7 8   **Fic**

1. Strikes -- Fiction 2. Immigrants -- Fiction 3.

Lawrence (Mass.) -- Fiction 4. United States -- History
-- 1898-1919 -- Fiction
  ISBN 978-0-618-65479-6; 0-618-65479-8; 978-0-547-
  07651-5 pa; 0-547-07651-7 pa

LC 2005-31702

Jake and Rosa, two children, form an unlikely friendship
as they try to survive and understand the 1912 Bread and
Roses strike of mill workers in Lawrence, Massachusetts.

"Paterson has skillfully woven true events and real historical figures into the fictional story and created vivid settings, clearly drawn characters, and a strong sense of the
hardship and injustice faced by the mostly immigrant mill
workers." SLJ

★ Bridge to Terabithia; illustrated by Donna Diamond.
Crowell 1977 128p il $15.99; lib bdg $16.89; pa $5.99
Grades: 4 5 6 7   Fic
  1. Death -- Fiction 2. Virginia -- Fiction 3. Friendship
  -- Fiction
  ISBN 0-690-01359-0; 0-690-04635-9 lib bdg; 0-06-
  440184-7 pa

LC 77-2221

Awarded the Newbery Medal, 1978

The life of Jess, a ten-year-old boy in rural Virginia
expands when he becomes friends with a newcomer who
subsequently meets an untimely death trying to reach their
hideaway, Terabithia, during a storm

"Jess and his family are magnificently characterized; the
book abounds in descriptive vignettes, humorous sidelights
on the clash of cultures, and realistic depictions of rural
school life." Horn Book

★ The great Gilly Hopkins. Crowell 1978 148p
$15.99; lib bdg $16.89; pa $5.99
Grades: 5 6 7 8   Fic
  1. Foster home care -- Fiction
  ISBN 0-690-03837-2; 0-690-03838-0 lib bdg; 0-06-
  440201-0 pa

LC 77-27075

A Newbery Medal honor book, 1979

"A well-structured story, [this] has vitality of writing
style, natural dialogue, deep insight in characterization, and
a keen sense of the fluid dynamics in human relationships."
Bull Cent Child Books

"Cool, scheming, and deliberately obstreperous, 11-year-
old Gilly is ready to be her usual obnoxious self when she
arrives at her new foster home. . . . But Gilly's old tricks
don't work against the all-encompassing love of the huge,
half-illiterate Mrs. Trotter. . . . Determined not to care she
writes a letter full of wild exaggerations to her real mother
that brings, in return, a surprising visit from an unknown
grandmother." Booklist

★ Lyddie. Lodestar Bks. 1991 182p $17.99; pa
$6.99
Grades: 5 6 7 8 9   Fic
  1. Factories -- Fiction 2. Massachusetts -- Fiction 3.
  United States -- History -- 1815-1861 -- Fiction
  ISBN 0-525-67338-5; 0-14-240254-0 pa

LC 90-42944

Impoverished Vermont farm girl Lyddie Worthen is determined to gain her independence by becoming a factory
worker in Lowell, Massachusetts, in the 1840s

"Not only does the book contain a riveting plot, engaging
characters, and a splendid setting, but the language—graceful, evocative, and rhythmic—incorporates the rural speech
patterns of Lyddie's folk, the simple Quaker expressions of
the farm neighbors, and the lilt of fellow mill girl Bridget's
Irish brogue. . . . A superb story of grit, determination, and
personal growth." Horn Book

★ Park's quest. Lodestar Bks. 1988 148p hardcover
o.p. pa $5.99
Grades: 5 6 7 8   Fic
  1. Farm life -- Fiction 2. Vietnamese Americans --
  Fiction
  ISBN 0-14-034262-1 pa

LC 87-32422

Eleven-year-old Park makes some startling discoveries
when he travels to his grandfather's farm in Virginia to learn
about his father who died in the Vietnam War and meets a
Vietnamese-American girl named Thanh

The author "confronts the complexity, the ambiguity, of
the war and the emotions of those it involved with an honesty that young readers are sure to recognize and appreciate."
N Y Times Book Rev

The same stuff as stars. Clarion Bks. 2002 242p $15
Grades: 5 6 7 8   Fic
  1. Brothers and sisters -- Fiction
  ISBN 0-618-24744-0

LC 2002-3967

When Angel's self-absorbed mother leaves her and her
younger brother Bernie with their poor great-grandmother,
the eleven-year-old girl worries not only about her mother
and brother, her imprisoned father, the frail old woman, but
also about a mysterious man who begins sharing with her the
wonder of the stars. "Intermediate." (Horn Book)

"Paterson's deft hand at characterization, her insight into
the human soul, and her glorious prose make this book one
to rejoice over." Voice Youth Advocates

Patneaude, David

A piece of the sky; [by] David Patneaude; [cover illustration by Layne Johnson] Albert Whitman 2007 178p
il $15.95
Grades: 5 6 7 8   Fic
  1. Oregon -- Fiction 2. Meteorites -- Fiction 3.
  Mountaineering -- Fiction
  ISBN 978-0-8075-6536-0

LC 2006023529

Fourteen-year-old Russell, his friend Phoebe, and her
brother Isaac must find a legendary meteor in the Oregon
mountains before it is exploited

"This old-fashioned adventure story has contemporary
appeal." Booklist

Patron, Susan

Behind the masks; the diary of Angeline Reddy. Susan
Patron. Scholastic 2012 293 p. ill., map (paper-over-
board) $12.99
Grades: 5 6 7 8 9   Fic
  1. Mystery fiction 2. Diaries -- Fiction 3. Thieves --
  Fiction 4. Gold mines and mining -- Fiction 5. Frontier
  and pioneer life -- California -- Fiction 6. Lawyers --
  Fiction 7. Mystery and detective stories 8. Robbers
  and outlaws -- Fiction 9. California -- History -- 19th

century -- Fiction
ISBN 9780545304375

LC 2011023826

"[T]his Dear America series title [is] set in Bodie, California, in 1880. Fourteen-year-old diarist and would-be dramatist Angeline Reddy does not believe her father, criminal lawyer Patrick Reddy, has been murdered. Convinced his disappearance is purposeful, Angie investigates his 'demise' and tries to bring him back to their rough-and-tumble mining community. Assisted by friends, a dashing young Wells Fargo clerk, and the members of a local theater troupe, . . . Angie offers a revealing look at frontier life "especially preoccupations with thespian entertainments, racial and social prejudices, and vigilante justice."(Booklist)

★ The **higher** power of Lucky; with illustrations by Matt Phelan. Atheneum Books for Young Readers 2006 134p il $16.95; pa $6.99
Grades: 4 5 6   Fic
1. Runaway children -- Fiction
ISBN 978-1-4169-0194-5; 1-4169-0194-9; 978-1-4169-7557-1 pa; 1-4169-7557-8 pa

LC 2005-21767

Awarded the Newbery Medal, 2007

Fearing that her legal guardian plans to abandon her to return to France, ten-year-old aspiring scientist Lucky Trimble determines to run away while also continuing to seek the Higher Power that will bring stability to her life

"Patron's plotting is as tight as her characters are endearing. Lucky is a true heroine." Booklist

Other books about Lucky are:
Lucky breaks (2009)
Lucky for good (2011)

Maybe yes, maybe no, maybe maybe; illustrated by Abigail Halpin. Aladdin Paperbacks 2009 107p il pa $5.99
Grades: 3 4 5   Fic
1. Moving -- Fiction 2. Sisters -- Fiction
ISBN 978-1-4169-6176-5 pa; 1-4169-6176-3 pa
First published 1993 by Orchard Books

When her hardworking mother decides to move, eight-year-old PK uses her imagination and storytelling to help her older and younger sisters adjust

Patt, Beverly
★ **Best** friends forever; a World War II scrapbook. with illustrations by Shula Klinger. Marshall Cavendish 2010 92p il $17.99
Grades: 5 6 7 8   Fic
1. Friendship -- Fiction 2. Washington (State) -- Fiction 3. World War, 1939-1945 -- Fiction 4. Puyallup Assembly Center (Wash.) -- Fiction 5. Japanese Americans -- Evacuation and relocation, 1942-1945 -- Fiction
ISBN 978-0-7614-5577-6; 0-7614-5577-9

LC 2008-20875

Fourteen-year-old Louise keeps a scrapbook detailing the events in her life after her best friend, Dottie, a Japanese-American girl, and her family are sent to a relocation camp during World War II.

"If the drama of the girls separation isn't enough, a romantic subplot and the antics of Dottie's goofy dog (living with Louise in her absence) will surely keep young readers

interested. This heartwarming tale of steadfast friendship makes a wonderful access point for learning more about World War II and Japanese internment." SLJ

Includes bibliographical references

Patten, E. J.
Return to Exile; illustrated by John Rocco. Simon & Schuster 2011 512p (The Hunter chronicles) $16.99
Grades: 5 6 7 8   Fic
1. Fantasy fiction 2. Uncles -- Fiction 3. Monsters -- Fiction
ISBN 978-1-4424-2032-8; 1-4424-2032-4; 978-1-4169-8259-3 e-book

LC 2010053480

"Sky's twelfth birthday is a mix. His mother's delicious homemade goulash cannot overshadow the disappearance of his beloved uncle, Phineas, or the family's return to the small town of Exile. Sky has grown up reading about the Hunters of Legend, but he never dreamed that they were real until monsters appear in Exile and make Sky their target. . . . Patten's first novel excels at world building and pacing; the monsters . . . are fully formed and vividly drawn. . . . Interspersed with humor to keep an otherwise dark story from becoming overbearing, the balance is just right." Booklist

Patterson, James, 1947-
★ **Middle** school, the worst years of my life; [by] James Patterson and Chris Tebbetts; illustrated by Laura Park. Little, Brown 2011 281p il $15.99
Grades: 4 5 6 7   Fic
1. School stories 2. Bereavement -- Fiction 3. Family life -- Fiction
ISBN 0-316-10187-7; 978-0-316-10187-5

LC 2010022852

When Rafe Kane enters middle school, he teams up with his best friend, "Leo the Silent," to create a game to make school more fun by trying to break every rule in the school's code of conduct.

"The book's ultrashort chapters, dynamic artwork, and message that 'normal is boring' should go a long way toward assuring kids who don't fit the mold that there's a place for them, too." Publ Wkly

Patterson, Nancy Ruth
Ellie ever; pictures by Patty Weise. Farrar, Straus & Giroux 2010 117p il $15.99
Grades: 3 4 5   Fic
1. School stories 2. Horses -- Fiction 3. Moving -- Fiction 4. Virginia -- Fiction 5. Bereavement -- Fiction
ISBN 978-0-374-32108-6; 0-374-32108-6

LC 2009013604

After losing her father and all their possessions in a hurricane, nine-year-old Ellie and her mother move to a small apartment on a horse farm in Virginia, where her new classmates think that she lives in a mansion and is a princess.

"Horses and animals . . . will initially attract readers, but it's the straightforward story of the little family, rebounding from terrible tragedy with bravery, honesty, and character, that is the heart of this book's appeal." Horn Book

Paulsen, Gary
The **amazing** life of birds; the twenty-day puberty journal of Duane Homer. Wendy Lamb Books 2006 84p $13.95; pa $6.50

Grades: 5 6 7 8   **Fic**
1. Boys -- Fiction 2. Birds -- Fiction 3. Puberty --
Fiction
ISBN 0-385-74660-1; 0-553-49428-7 pa;
0385746601; 0553494287 pa

As twelve-year-old Duane endures the confusing and
humiliating aspects of puberty, he watches a newborn bird
in a nest on his windowsill begin to grow and become more
independent, all of which he records in his journal.

The author "has captured a very uncomfortable time
of life amazingly well. . . . Paulsen's writing is beautiful."
Voice Youth Advocates

Crush; the theory, practice, and destructive properties
of love. Gary Paulsen. Wendy Lamb Books 2012 136 p.
Grades: 5 6 7 8   **Fic**
1. Love -- Fiction 2. Humorous fiction 3. Crushes
-- Fiction 4. High school students -- Fiction 5. Dating
(Social customs) -- Fiction 6. Humorous stories 7.
Interpersonal relations -- Fiction
ISBN 0385742304; 9780307974532; 9780375990540;
9780385742306; 9780385742313
LC 2011028915

In this book, "Tina, aka the most beautiful girl he's ever
seen, has stolen Kevin's heart, although she's blissfully
oblivious to the effect she has on him. . . . Rather than reveal his ardor outright, Kevin decides it's safer to first make
a scientific study of just how love works by setting up romantic opportunities for his victims (otherwise known as
study subjects). He starts by trying to create a candlelit dinner for his parents, although he accidentally causes a fire."
(Kirkus Reviews)

Flat broke. Wendy Lamb Books 2011 118p $12.99;
lib bdg $15.99
Grades: 4 5 6   **Fic**
1. Friendship -- Fiction 2. Family life -- Fiction 3.
Business enterprises -- Fiction 4. Money-making
projects for children -- Fiction
ISBN 978-0-385-74002-9; 0-385-74002-6; 978-0-385-
90818-4 lib bdg; 0-385-90818-0 lib bdg
LC 2010049415
Sequel to: Liar, liar (2011)

Fourteen-year-old Kevin is a hard worker, so when his
income is cut off he begins a series of businesses, from poker
games to selling snacks, earning money to take a girl to a
dance, but his partners soon tire of his methods.

"A jocular, fast-paced voyage into the sometimes simple
but never quiet mind of an ambitious eighth grader." Kirkus

★ **Lawn** Boy. Wendy Lamb Books 2007 88p $12.99;
lib bdg $15.99; pa $6.50
Grades: 4 5 6 7   **Fic**
1. Summer employment -- Fiction 2. Business
enterprises -- Fiction
ISBN 978-0-385-74686-1; 978-0-385-90923-5 lib
bdg; 978-0-553-49465-5 pa
LC 2006-39731

Things get out of hand for a twelve-year-old boy when
a neighbor convinces him to expand his summer lawn
mowing business

"This rags-to-riches success story has colorful characters, a villain, and enough tongue-in-cheek humor to make it
an enjoyable selection for the whole family." SLJ
Followed by: Lawn Boy returns (2010)

★ The **legend** of Bass Reeves; being the true and
fictional account of the most valiant marshal in the West.
Wendy Lamb Books 2006 137p $15.95; pa $6.50
Grades: 5 6 7 8   **Fic**
1. Sheriffs 2. Slavery -- Fiction 3. West (U.S.) --
Fiction 4. African Americans -- Fiction
ISBN 0-385-74661-X; 0-553-49429-5 pa
LC 2006-11492

"This engrossingly told tale fills in the unrecorded youth
of an unjustly obscure historical figure who was born a slave,
became a successful rancher, then later in his long life went
on to play an integral role in taming the rough-hewn Oklahoma Territory. . . . A stirring tale of adventure." Booklist

Liar, liar; the theory, practice, and destructive properties of deception. Wendy Lamb Books 2011 120p $12.99;
lib bdg $15.99
Grades: 4 5 6   **Fic**
1. School stories 2. Family life -- Fiction 3. Young
adult literature -- Works 4. Truthfulness and falsehood
-- Fiction
ISBN 0-385-74001-8; 0-385-90817-2 lib bdg; 978-0-
385-74001-2; 978-0-385-90817-7 lib bdg
LC 2010-28356

Fourteen-year-old Kevin is very good at lying and doing
so makes life easier, until he finds himself in big trouble with
his friends, family, and teachers. "Ages eight to twelve."
(Publisher's note)

"Kevin's grappling with family troubles adds . . . emotional dimension to Paulsen's novel." Publ Wkly
Followed by: Flat broke (2011)

Masters of disaster. Wendy Lamb Books 2010 102p
$12.95; lib bdg $15.99
Grades: 3 4 5 6   **Fic**
1. Friendship -- Fiction
ISBN 978-0-385-73997-9; 0-385-73997-4; 978-0-385-
90816-0 lib bdg; 0-385-90816-4 lib bdg
LC 2010013180

"Henry convinces his best friends, Riley and Reed, that
the three 12-year-olds should prove their manhood by undertaking a series a daring exploits. . . . Readers willing to
suspend disbelief and follow the boys' over-the-top exploits
will enjoy plenty of laughs along the way." Booklist

"Henry Mosley decides that he and his pals Riley and
Reed have got to liven things up. They need to go on some
earth-shaking adventures and make a name for themselves.
Henry is the mastermind; Riley's the cautious researcher
who's prepared for anything. And somehow fearful Reed
always ends up with the scariest, craziest assignments..."
(Publisher's note)

Mudshark. Wendy Lamb Books 2009 83p
Grades: 3 4 5 6   **Fic**
1. School stories 2. Lost and found possessions --

Fiction
ISBN 0-385-74685-7; 0-385-90922-5 lib bdg; 978-0-385-74685-4; 978-0-385-90922-8 lib bdg

LC 2008033271

Principal Wagner confidently deals with a faculty washroom crisis, a psychic parrot, and a terrorizing gerbil, but when sixty-five erasers go missing, he enlists the help of the school's best problem solver and locator of lost items, twelve-year-old Lyle Williams, aka Mudshark.

"Diversions . . . keep this compact story quick and light. Yet . . . Paulsen . . . delves deeper, shaping Mudshark as a credible and compassionate protagonist." Publ Wkly

Notes from the dog. Wendy Lamb Books 2009 133p $15.99; lib bdg $18.99
Grades: 5 6 7 8   Fic
1. Cancer -- Fiction 2. Gardening -- Fiction
ISBN 0-385-73845-5; 0-385-90730-3 lib bdg; 978-0-385-73845-3; 978-0-385-90730-9 lib bdg

LC 2009-13300

When Johanna shows up at the beginning of summer to house-sit next door to Finn, he has no idea of the profound effect she will have on his life by the time summer vacation is over.

"The plot is straightforward, but Paulsen's thoughtful characters are compelling and their interactions realistic. This emotional, coming-of-age journey about taking responsibilty for one's own happiness and making personal connections will not disappoint." Publ Wkly

Road trip; by Jim and Gary Paulsen. Wendy Lamb Books 2013 128 p. (trade) $12.99
Grades: 5 6 7 8   Fic
1. Dogs -- Fiction 2. Automobile travel -- Fiction 3. Father-child relationship -- Fiction 4. Border collie -- Fiction 5. Animal shelters -- Fiction 6. Fathers and sons -- Fiction
ISBN 038574191X; 9780307930866; 9780375988578; 9780375990311; 9780385741910

LC 2012014284

In this book, by Gary Paulsen and Jim Paulsen, "Dad and Ben haven't been getting along recently and Dad hopes a road trip to rescue a border collie will help them reconnect. But Ben is on to Dad's plan and invites Ben's thuggish buddy, Theo. The family dog, Atticus, comes along too and the story is told by Ben and Atticus. . . . Only sharp-eyed Atticus realizes that Theo is on the run--and someone is following them." (Publisher's note)

Vote; the theory, practice, and destructive properties of politics. Gary Paulsen. 1st ed. Wendy Lamb Books 2013 144 p. (hardcover) $12.99; (ebook) $38.97; (hardcover) $12.99
Grades: 5 6 7 8   Fic
1. School stories 2. Humorous fiction 3. Elections -- Fiction 4. Humorous stories 5. Schools -- Fiction 6. Middle schools -- Fiction 7. Politics, Practical -- Fiction 8. Interpersonal relations -- Fiction
ISBN 0385742282; 9780307974525; 9780375990533; 9780385742283 trade; 9780385742290

LC 2012023059

In this humorous children's novel, by Gary Paulsen, the author's lead character from previous stories is reprised when he runs for school office. "Kevin Spencer . . . has a knack for tackling big ideas and goofing up, so what's next? Politics, of course! He's running for office, and his campaign is truly unique." (Publisher's note)

"Those who started this four-book series at the beginning may sense that our protagonist is maturing a wee bit, but not so much as to dampen the humor for fans or newcomers. . . . Fast-paced action and Kevin's penchant for getting into ridiculous situations make this the perfect book bait for not-so-eager readers." BookList

★ The **winter** room. Orchard Bks. 1989 103p $16.95; pa $5.99
Grades: 5 6 7 8   Fic
1. Farm life -- Fiction 2. Minnesota -- Fiction
ISBN 0-531-05839-5; 0-545-08534-9 pa

LC 89-42541

A Newbery Medal honor book, 1990

A young boy growing up on a northern Minnesota farm describes the scenes around him and recounts his old Norwegian uncle's tales of an almost mythological logging past

"While this seems at first to be a collection of anecdotes organized around the progression of the farm calendar, Paulsen subtly builds a conflict that becomes apparent in the last brief chapters, forceful and well-prepared. . . . Lyrical and only occasionally sentimental, the prose is clean, clear, and deceptively simple." Bull Cent Child Books

Paver, Michelle
Ghost hunter. Katherine Tegen Books 2010 285p (Chronicles of ancient darkness) $16.99; pa $6.99
Grades: 5 6 7 8   Fic
1. Fantasy fiction 2. Demoniac possession -- Fiction 3. Prehistoric peoples -- Fiction
ISBN 978-0-06-072840-3; 0-06-072840-X; 978-0-06-072842-7 pa; 0-06-072842-6 pa
Sequel to: Oath breaker (2009)

To fulfill his destiny, Torak must defy demons and tokoroths, navigate through the Gorge of Hidden People, and battle the evil Eagle Owl Mage.

Wolf brother. HarperCollins 2005 295p (Chronicles of ancient darkness) $16.99; lib bdg $17.89; pa $6.99
Grades: 5 6 7 8   Fic
1. Bears -- Fiction 2. Wolves -- Fiction 3. Demoniac possession -- Fiction 4. Prehistoric peoples -- Fiction
ISBN 0-06-072825-6; 0-06-072826-4 lib bdg; 0-06-072827-2 pa

LC 2004-8857

First published 2004 in the United Kingdom

6,000 years in the past, twelve-year-old Tarak and his guide, a wolf cub, set out on a dangerous journey to fulfill an oath the boy made to his dying father—to travel to the Mountain of the World Spirit seeking a way to destroy a demon-possessed bear that threatens all the clans

"Paver's depth of research into the spiritual world of primitive peoples makes this impressive British import, slated to be the first in a six-book series, intriguing and believable." SLJ

Other titles in this series are:
Spirit walker (2006)
Soul eater (2007)
Outcast (2008)
Oath breaker (2009)

Ghost hunter (2010)

Payne, C. C.

Something to sing about; written by C. C. Payne. Eerdmans Books for Young Readers 2008 167p pa $8.50

Grades: 4 5 6   **Fic**

1. Bees -- Fiction 2. Fear -- Fiction 3. Singing -- Fiction 4. Kentucky -- Fiction 5. Family life -- Fiction 6. Choirs (Music) -- Fiction 7. Christian life -- Fiction
ISBN 978-0-8028-5344-8 pa; 0-8028-5344-7 pa
LC 2008006100

Ten-year-old Jamie Jo's fear of bees keeps her inside most of the time, but a series of events that begins when her mother is excluded from the church choir brings about many changes, including new friendships and greater trust in God

"The word wholesome sometimes gets a bad rap, but here it's leavened by gentle humor and considerable insight, and it fits this book just fine." Booklist

Peacock, Carol Antoinette

Red thread sisters; by Carol Antoinette Peacock. Viking 2012 236 p. (hardcover) $15.99

Grades: 4 5 6 7 8   **Fic**

1. Adoptees -- Fiction 2. Friendship -- Fiction 3. Chinese Americans -- Fiction 4. Adoption -- Fiction 5. Family life -- Fiction 6. Interracial adoption -- Fiction 7. Intercountry adoption -- Fiction
ISBN 0670013862; 9780670013869
LC 2012019511

This novel, by Carol Antoinette Peacock, offers a "story of friendship, family, and love. Wen has spent the first eleven years of her life at an orphanage in rural China . . . [with] her best friend, Shu Ling. When Wen is adopted by an American couple, she struggles . . . knowing that Shu Ling remains back at the orphanage, alone. Wen knows that her best friend deserves a family and a future, too. But finding a home for Shu Ling isn't easy, and time is running out." (Publisher's note)

Pearce, Emily Smith

Isabel and the miracle baby; [by] Emily Smith Pearce. Front Street 2007 125p $15.95

Grades: 2 3 4 5   **Fic**

1. Cancer -- Fiction 2. Infants -- Fiction 3. Family life -- Fiction 4. Mother-daughter relationship -- Fiction
ISBN 978-1-932425-44-4
LC 2006101750

Eight-year-old Isabel feels her mother no longer cares about her because she has no time or energy even to listen when Isa tries to share her sadness about being unpopular, her jealousy over her new baby sister, and, most importantly, her fear that her mother's cancer will come back

"Pearce gets into the mind and soul of a child. . . . [The child's] struggle is what sets this book apart from the dozens of others with the new-sibling theme." SLJ

Pearce, Philippa

A finder's magic; illustrated by Helen Craig. Candlewick Press 2009 119p il $15.99

Grades: 3 4 5   **Fic**

1. Magic -- Fiction 2. Lost and found possessions -- Fiction
ISBN 978-0-7636-4072-9; 0-7636-4072-7

After a mysterious stranger offers to help Till find his dog, they embark on a magical quest, interviewing various witnesses including a heron, a mole, a riddling cat, and Miss Mousey, whose sketch of a peaceful riverbank offers a vital clue.

"The posthumous publication by classic author Pearce envinces her usual gift for blending reality and fantasy in plain and approachable style. . . . Younger readers who crave gentle shivers without terrors will appreciate this cozy fantasy quest to find a lost pet." Bull Cent Child Books

★ **Tom's** midnight garden; illustrated by Susan Einzig. Lippincott 1959 229p il hardcover o.p. pa $5.95

Grades: 4 5 6 7   **Fic**

1. Fantasy fiction 2. Space and time -- Fiction
ISBN 0-397-30477-3; 0-06-440445-5 pa
First published 1958 in the United Kingdom

"Daytime life for Tom at his aunt's home in England is dull, but each night he participates through fantasy in the lives of the former inhabitants of the interesting old house in which he is spending an enforced vacation. The book is British in setting and atmosphere. The element of mystery is well sustained, and the reader is left to make his own interpretation of the reality of the story." Adventuring with Books

Pearsall, Shelley

All of the above; a novel. illustrations by Javaka Steptoe. Little, Brown 2006 234p il hardcover o.p. pa $5.99

Grades: 5 6 7 8   **Fic**

1. School stories 2. City and town life -- Fiction
ISBN 0-316-11524-X; 978-0-316-11524-7; 978-0-316-11526-1 pa; 0-316-11526-6 pa
LC 2005-33109

Five urban middle school students, their teacher, and other community members relate how a school project to build the world's largest tetrahedron affects the lives of everyone involved.

"Pearsall's novel, based on a real event in 2002—is a delightful story about the power of a vision and the importance of a goal. The authentic voices of the students and the well-intentioned, supportive adults surrounding them illustrate all that is good about schools, family, friendship, and community." Booklist

Peck, Richard

Fair weather; a novel. Dial Bks. 2001 130p il $16.99; pa $5.99

Grades: 5 6 7 8   **Fic**

1. Actors 2. Singers 3. Scouts 4. Hunters 5. Circus executives 6. Circus performers 7. Family life -- Fiction 8. Chicago (Ill.) -- Fiction
ISBN 0-8037-2516-7; 0-14-250034-8 pa
LC 00-55561

In 1893, thirteen-year-old Rosie and members of her family travel from their Illinois farm to Chicago to visit Aunt Euterpe and attend the World's Columbian Exposition which, along with an encounter with Buffalo Bill and Lillian Russell, turns out to be a life-changing experience for everyone

"Peck's unforgettable characters, cunning dialogue and fast-paced action will keep readers in stitches." Publ Wkly

Here lies the librarian. Dial Books 2006 145p $16.99; pa $6.99

Grades: 4 5 6   **Fic**
   1. Indiana -- Fiction 2. Librarians -- Fiction 3. Automobiles -- Fiction 4. Country life -- Fiction
   ISBN 0-8037-3080-2; 0-14-240908-1 pa
LC 2005-20279
Fourteen-year-old Eleanor "Peewee" McGrath, a tomboy and automobile enthusiast, discovers new possibilities for her future after the 1914 arrival in her small Indiana town of four young librarians.
"Another gem from Peck, with his signature combination of quirky characters, poignancy, and outrageous farce." SLJ

★ A **long** way from Chicago; a novel in stories. Dial Bks. for Young Readers 1998 148p pa $5.99; $15.99
Grades: 5 6 7 8   **Fic**
   1. Illinois -- Fiction 2. Grandmothers -- Fiction 3. Depressions -- 1929 -- Fiction 4. Country life -- Illinois -- Fiction 5. Great Depression, 1929-1939 -- Fiction
   ISBN 0-14-240110-2 pa; 0-8037-2290-7
LC 98-10953
A Newbery Medal honor book, 1999
Joe recounts his annual summer trips to rural Illinois with his sister during the Great Depression to visit their larger-than-life grandmother
"The novel reveals a strong sense of place, a depth of characterization, and a rich sense of humor." Horn Book
Followed by: A year down yonder (2000)

The **mouse** with the question mark tail; a novel. by Richard Peck; illustrated by Kelly Murphy. Dial Books for Young Readers 2013 240 p. ill. (hardcover) $16.99
Grades: 3 4 5 6   **Fic**
   1. Adventure fiction 2. Mice -- Fiction 3. Identity -- Fiction 4. Social classes -- Fiction 5. Adventure and adventurers -- Fiction 6. Kings, queens, rulers, etc. -- Fiction 7. Buckingham Palace (London, England) -- Fiction 8. Great Britain -- History -- Victoria, 1837-1901 -- Fiction
   ISBN 0803738382; 9780803738386
LC 2012027992
In this children's story, by Richard Peck, illustrated by Kelly Murphy, "the smallest mouse in London's Royal Mews is such a little mystery that he hasn't even a name. . . His Aunt Marigold, Head Needlemouse, sews him a uniform and sends him off to be educated at the Royal Mews Mouse Academy. . . Soon he's running for his life, looking high and low through the grand precincts of Buckingham Palace to find out who he is and who he might become." (Publisher's note)

★ **On** the wings of heroes. Dial Books 2007 148p $16.99; pa $6.99
Grades: 4 5 6 7   **Fic**
   1. Illinois -- Fiction 2. World War, 1939-1945 -- Fiction
   ISBN 0-8037-3081-0; 0-14-241204-X pa
LC 2006011906
A boy in Illinois remembers the homefront years of World War II, especially his two heroes, his brother in the Air Force and his father, who fought in the previous war.

"Peck's masterful, detail-rich prose describes wartime in the United States. . . . Peck's characters are memorable. . . . This book is an absolute delight." SLJ

★ A **season** of gifts. Dial Books for Young Readers 2009 156p $16.99
Grades: 5 6 7 8   **Fic**
   1. Moving -- Fiction 2. Illinois -- Fiction
   ISBN 978-0-8037-3082-3; 0-8037-3082-9
LC 2008-48050
Relates the surprising gifts bestowed on twelve-year-old Bob Barnhart and his family, who have recently moved to a small Illinois town in 1958, by their larger-than-life neighbor, Mrs. Dowdel.
"The type of down-home humor and vibrant characterizations Peck fans have come to adore re-emerge in full as Peck resurrects Mrs. Dowdel, the irrepressible, self-sufficient grandmother featured in A Year Down Yonder and A Long Way from Chicago." Publ Wkly

★ **Secrets** at sea; illustrations by Kelly Murphy. Dial Books for Young Readers 2011 238p il $16.99
Grades: 3 4 5 6   **Fic**
   1. Adventure fiction 2. Mice -- Fiction 3. Siblings -- Fiction 4. Ocean travel -- Fiction 5. Social classes -- Fiction
   ISBN 978-0-8037-3455-5; 0-8037-3455-7
LC 2011001162
In 1887, the social-climbing Cranstons voyage from New York to London, where they hope to find a husband for their awkward older daughter, secretly accompanied by Helena and her mouse siblings, for whom the journey is both terrifying and wondrous as they meet an array of titled humans despite their best efforts at remaining hidden.
This is a "rollicking comedy of manners that begs to be read aloud. . . . Peck's droll take on human and mouse society is exquisite. . . . Helena's meticulous observations . . . . [are] enhanced by hilariously upended clichés . . . . and by Murphy's dandy and detailed pencil illustrations that add just the right air of royalty." Horn Book

★ The **teacher's** funeral; a comedy in three parts. Dial Books 2004 190p $16.99; pa $6.99
Grades: 5 6 7 8   **Fic**
   1. Indiana -- Fiction 2. Teachers -- Fiction 3. Country life -- Fiction
   ISBN 0-8037-2736-4; 0-14-240507-8 pa
LC 2004-4361
In rural Indiana in 1904, fifteen-year-old Russell's dream of quitting school and joining a wheat threshing crew is disrupted when his older sister takes over the teaching at his one-room schoolhouse after mean, old Myrt Arbuckle "hauls off and dies."
"The dry wit and unpretentious tone make the story's events comical, its characters memorable, and its conclusion unexpectedly moving." Booklist

★ A **year** down yonder. Dial Bks. for Young Readers 2000 130p $16.99; pa $5.99
Grades: 5 6 7 8   **Fic**
   1. Grandmothers -- Fiction 2. Great Depression, 1929-1939 -- Fiction
   ISBN 0-8037-2518-3; 0-14-230070-5 pa
LC 99-43159

Awarded the Newbery Medal, 2001

"Peck has created a delightful, insightful tale that resounds with a storyteller's wit, humor, and vivid description." SLJ

Peet, Mal

★ **Cloud** Tea monkeys; by Mal Peet & Elspeth Graham; illustrated by Juan Wijngaard. Candlewick Press 2010 un il lib bdg $15.99

Grades: 1 2 3 4   Fic

1. Tea -- Fiction 2. Monkeys -- Fiction 3. Mother-daughter relationship -- Fiction

ISBN 978-0-7636-4453-6 lib bdg; 0-7636-4453-6 lib bdg

LC 2009-11868

When her mother becomes too ill to harvest tea on the nearby plantation, Shenaz is too small to fill in, but when she tells the monkeys she has befriended why she is sad, they bring her a basket filled with rare and valuable wild tea.

"The tale has the feel of a time-honed fable—simple, elegant, and moving—which is especially well complemented by Wijngaard's sumptuous illustrations." Booklist

Mysterious traveler; Mal Peet, Elspeth Graham, illustrated by P. J. Lynch. Candlewick Press 2013 48 p. $15.99

Grades: 3 4 5   Fic

1. Sahara Desert -- Fiction 2. Picture books for children

ISBN 0763662321; 9780763662325

LC 2012947823

This children's picture book was "inspired by the guides who navigate the Sahara in Mali." An old man named Issa rescues a baby wearing a valuable necklace and "raises the infant as his granddaughter, relying more and more on young Mariama once his eyesight begins to fail. . . . After a trio of arrogant visitors rejects Issa's guidance, he and Mariama rescue them just as a potentially deadly sandstorm swirls up." One of the boys turns out to be Mariama's brother. (School Library Journal)

Night sky dragons; Mal Peet, Elspeth Graham, illustrated by Patrick Benson. Candlewick Press 2014 64 p. color illustrations $15.99

Grades: 1 2 3 4   Fic

1. Silk Road 2. Kites -- Fiction 3. Grandfathers -- Fiction 4. Father-son relationship -- Fiction

ISBN 0763661449; 9780763661441

LC 2013955686

In this children's book, by Mal Peet, "Yazul loves making kites with his grandfather, but all he truly desires is the approval of his father. Yazul's father, lord of a han along the Silk Road, is a man made stern by loneliness, and Yazul's love of kite-making only seems to elicit disappointment. . . . But when the han is attacked by bandits, Yazul has an idea. With the help of his grandfather, he might just be able to use his kite-making skills to scare the bandits away." (Publisher's note)

"This rich, engaging story is a welcome addition to historical fiction, introducing life along the Silk Road. Yazul lives in a han, a walled town where merchants could find shelter and safety, of which his father is the lord...the uniqueness of the story and its setting make it a wonderful offering for readers looking for a far-flung, adventure-filled story." SLJ

Peirce, Lincoln

★ **Big** Nate; in a class by himself. Harper 2010 214p $12.99

Grades: 3 4 5   Fic

1. School stories

ISBN 978-0-06-194434-5; 0-06-194434-3; 978-0-06-194435-2 lib bdg; 0-06-194435-1 lib bdg

LC 2009-39668

The author "uses a mix of prose and cartoons to tell a quick story about a day in the life of an extroverted, impish kid. . . . Nate, has been the star of a long-running daily comic strip. . . . He wakes up feeling fine, sweats a bit about an upcoming test, then opens a fortune cookie at school that reads, 'Today you will surpass all others.' . . . The cartoons provide plenty of gags at the expense of various adults and classmates, and Nate's persistent good cheer and moxie make him a likable new proxy for young misfits." Booklist

Other titles in this series are:

Big Nate strikes again (2010)

Big Nate on a roll (2011)

Pennypacker, Sara, 1951-

★ **Clementine**; [illustrated by] Marla Frazee. Hyperion Books for Children 2006 144p il $14.99; pa $4.99

Grades: 2 3 4   Fic

1. School stories 2. Friendship -- Fiction 3. Family life -- Fiction

ISBN 0-7868-3882-5; 0-7868-3883-3 pa

LC 2005-50458

While sorting through difficulties in her friendship with her neighbor Margaret, eight-year-old Clementine gains several unique hairstyles while also helping her father in his efforts to banish pigeons from the front of their apartment building.

"Humorous scenarios tumble together, blending picturesque dialogue with a fresh perspective. . . . Frazee's engaging pen-and-ink drawings capture the energy and fresh-faced expressions of the irrepressible heroine." SLJ

Other titles about Clementine are:

The talented Clementine (2007)

Clementine's letter (2008)

Clementine, Friend of the Week (2010)

Clementine and the family meeting (2011)

Clementine and the spring trip; Sara Pennypacker; pictures by Marla Frazee. Disney-Hyperion Books 2013 150 p. ill. (Clementine) $14.99

Grades: 2 3 4   Fic

1. Field trips 2. School stories 3. Spring -- Fiction 4. Family life -- Massachusetts -- Fiction

ISBN 1423123573; 9781423123576

LC 2011052991

In this book by Sara Pennypacker, "changes continue for Clementine: her mother's belly is growing bigger, the fourth graders continue their reign of terror over the lunchroom (no crunching of any food!), neighbor Margaret's mother is getting married again, the third grade is going to Plimoth Plantation (and has to eat with the fourth graders!), and new girl Olive is stealing some of our heroine's thunder." (Horn Book Magazine)

"Clementine learns important life lessons about growing up, becoming independent, and making choices. She's reminiscent of Ramona, Junie B. Jones, and Judy Moody with her own style and personality that listeners will easily relate to." SLJ

★ The **summer** of the gypsy moths; Sara Pennypacker. Balzer + Bray 2012 275 p. (tr. bdg.) $15.99

Grades: 4 5 6 **Fic**

1. Siblings -- Fiction 2. Family life -- Fiction 3. Foster children -- Fiction 4. Death -- Fiction 5. Secrets -- Fiction 6. Great aunts -- Fiction 7. Cape Cod (Mass.) -- Fiction 8. Loss (Psychology) -- Fiction

ISBN 0061964204; 9780061964206

LC 2011026095

This middle reader story by Sara Pennypacker follows "Stella[, who] loves living with Great-aunt Louise in her big old house near the water on Cape Cod . . . since her mom is . . . unreliable. So while Mom 'finds herself,' Stella fantasizes that someday she'll come back to the Cape and settle down. The only obstacle to her plan? Angel, the foster kid Louise has taken in. . . . [T]he girls hardly speak to each other. But when tragedy unexpectedly strikes, Stella and Angel are forced to rely on each other to survive." (Publisher's note)

Perkins, Lynne Rae

★ **Criss** cross. Greenwillow Books 2005 337p $16.99; lib bdg $17.89; pa $6.99

Grades: 6 7 8 9 **Fic**

1. Nineteen sixties -- Fiction 2. Identity (Psychology) -- Fiction

ISBN 0-06-009272-6; 0-06-009273-4 lib bdg; 0-06-009274-2 pa

LC 2004-54023

Awarded the Newbery Medal, 2006

Teenagers in a small town in the 1960s experience new thoughts and feelings, question their identities, connect, and disconnect as they search for the meaning of life and love. "Grades five to eight." (Bull Cent Child Books)

"Debbie . . . and Hector . . . narrate most of the novel. Both are 14 years old. Hector is a fabulous character with a wry humor and an appealing sense of self-awareness. . . . The descriptive, measured writing includes poems, prose, haiku, and question-and-answer formats. There is a great deal of humor in this gentle story." SLJ

Perkins, Mitali

★ **Bamboo** people. Charlesbridge 2010 272p $16.95

Grades: 5 6 7 8 **Fic**

1. Myanmar -- Fiction 2. Wilderness survival -- Fiction

ISBN 978-1-58089-328-2; 1-58089-328-7

LC 2009005495

Two Burmese boys, one a Karenni refugee and the other the son of an imprisoned Burmese doctor, meet in the jungle and in order to survive they must learn to trust each other.

"Perkins seamlessly blends cultural, political, religious, and philosophical context into her story, which is distinguished by humor, astute insights into human nature, and memorable characters." Publ Wkly

★ **Rickshaw** girl; illustrated by Jamie Hogan. Charlesbridge 2007 91p il lib bdg $13.95

Grades: 3 4 5 **Fic**

1. Painting -- Fiction 2. Sex role -- Fiction 3. Bangladesh -- Fiction

ISBN 978-1-58089-308-4

LC 2006-09031

In her Bangladesh village, ten-year-old Naimi excels at painting designs called alpanas, but to help her impoverished family financially she would have to be a boy—or disguise herself as one

"This short chapter book tells a realistic story with surprises that continue until the end. Hogan's bold black-and-white sketches show the brave girl, the beautiful traditional alpana painting and rickshaw art, and the contemporary changes in the girl's rural home." Booklist

Tiger boy; Mitali Perkins; illustrated by Jamie Hogan. Charlesbridge 2015 144 p. (reinforced for library use) $14.95

Grades: 3 4 5 6 **Fic**

1. Tigers -- Fiction 2. Bangladesh -- Fiction 3. Family life -- Fiction 4. Animal rescue -- Fiction 5. Tiger -- Fiction 6. Wildlife rescue -- Fiction

ISBN 158089660X; 9781580896603; 9781607345435; 9781607346647

LC 2013049028

In this book, by Mitali Perkins, "[w]hen a tiger cub goes missing from the reserve, Neel is determined to find her before the greedy Gupta gets his hands on her to kill her and sell her body parts on the black market. Neel's parents, however, are counting on him to study hard and win a prestigious scholarship to study in Kolkata. Neel doesn't want to leave his family or his island home and he struggles with his familial duty." (Publisher's note)

Perl, Erica S.

Aces wild; Erica S. Perl. Alfred A. Knopf 2013 224 p. $15.99

Grades: 4 5 6 **Fic**

1. Dogs -- Fiction 2. Family life -- Fiction 3. Grandfathers -- Fiction 4. Vermont -- Fiction 5. Sleepovers -- Fiction 6. Dogs -- Training -- Fiction 7. Jews -- United States -- Fiction 8. Family life -- Vermont -- Fiction

ISBN 0307931722; 9780307931726; 9780307975478; 9780375971044

LC 2012023335

Written by Erica S. Perl, this book describes how "Zelly Fried has finally convinced her parents to let her get a dog, with the help of her grandfather Ace. Unfortunately, said dog (also named Ace) is a shoe-chewing, mud-tracking, floor-peeing kind of dog. . . . Also wild is the other Ace in Zelly's life. Grandpa Ace has decided to begin dating again and is dining and dancing every night, against his doctor's orders." (Publisher's note)

"Zelly (When Life Gives You O.J.) finally has the dog she has always wanted. Now she hopes to host a sleepover at her house in order to help her fit in at her new school. First she has to be able to control Ace, her dog--and Ace, her grandpa. Zelly tries to navigate obedience classes, school, and family in this entertaining sequel." Horn Book

When life gives you O.J. Alfred A. Knopf 2011 198p $15.99; lib bdg $18.99

Grades: 3 4 5 **Fic**

1. Dogs -- Fiction 2. Vermont -- Fiction 3. Family life -- Fiction 4. Grandfathers -- Fiction 5. Jews -- United

States -- Fiction

ISBN 978-0-375-85924-3; 0-375-85924-1; 978-0-375-95924-0 lib bdg; 0-375-95924-6 lib bdg

LC 2010023844

Zelly Fried wants a dog more than anything, so at the urging of her grandfather, during the summer before sixth grade she takes care of a "practice dog" made out of an orange juice jug to show her parents that she is ready for the responsibility, even though she is sometimes not entirely sure about the idea.

"Zelly is a sympathetic, believably flawed character. . . . [This is a] funny, often wise novel." Booklist

Perl, Lila

Isabel's War; Lila Perl. Lizzie Skurnick Books 2014 224 p. $12.95

Grades: 5 6 7 8   Fic

1. Historical fiction 2. World War, 1939-1945 -- Refugees -- Fiction 3. Refugees -- Fiction 4. Holocaust, Jewish (1939-1945) -- Fiction 5. Kindertransports (Rescue operations) -- Fiction

ISBN 1939601274; 1939601363; 9781939601278; 9781939601360

Sydney Taylor Book Awards Honor Book (2013)

In this novel, by Lila Perl, "introduces us to Isabel Brandt, . . . twelve-year-old New Yorker who's more interested in boys and bobbing her nose than the distant war across the Pacific. . . . Things change when Helga . . . comes to live with Isabel and her family. Helga is everything Isabel's not--cool, blonde, and vaguely aloof. She's also a German war refugee, with a past that gives a growing Isabel something more important to think about than boys and her own looks." (Publisher's note)

"Isabel Brandt is a typical 12-year-girl who dreams of Frank Sinatra, boys, and being popular in school. But it is 1942, and the war in Europe and the Pacific becomes very significant for this Jewish girl from the Bronx. As her family begins their summer vacation in the Catskills, Isabel meets Helga, her new roommate...As Isabel learns about the war and the treatment of Jews by Nazis, her relationship with Helga and her outlook on life radically changes. Readers will identify with the protagonist as she discovers what things are truly important." SLJ

Perro, Bryan

The **key** of Braha; Bryan Perro; translated from the French by Y. Maudet. Delacorte Press 2012 184 p. (hc) $16.99

Grades: 4 5 6 7   Fic

1. Fantasy fiction 2. Adventure fiction 3. Mythology 4. Fantasy 5. Dead -- Fiction 6. Good and evil -- Fiction 7. Adventure and adventurers -- Fiction

ISBN 0385907672; 9780375896941; 9780385739047; 9780385907675

LC 2011026173

This book is the second in Bryan Perro's "Amos Daragon" young adult fantasy series, translated from French, in which a 12-year-old sorcerer named Amos, "unwittingly takes on a hazardous mission: He's killed so he can pass into and fix a netherworld crowded with dead souls who aren't being permitted to pass on to their appointed fates. . . . Once there Amos receives aid against numerous enemies from a

varied cast of . . . characters, many of whom are figures from mythology (explained in a lexicon)." (Kirkus)

The **mask** wearer; translated from the French by Y. Maudet. Delacorte Press 2011 167p (Amos Paragon) $16.99; lib bdg $19.99

Grades: 4 5 6 7   Fic

1. Fantasy fiction 2. Adventure fiction 3. Good and evil -- Fiction

ISBN 0-385-73903-6; 0-385-90766-4 lib bdg; 978-0-385-73903-0; 978-0-385-90766-8 lib bdg

LC 2010023725

To defeat the forces of evil which threaten his world, young Amos Daragon, aided by mythical animal friends, sets out on a journey to find four masks that harness the forces of nature and sixteen powerful stones that give the masks their magic.

"Amos's journey of self-discovery and his quick thinking are sure to keep readers turning the pages to discover the truth behind the never-ending chaos." SLJ

Peterfreund, Diana

Omega City; by Diana Peterfreund. Harpercollins Childrens Books 2015 336 p. $16.99

Grades: 4 5 6 7   Fic

1. Adventure fiction 2. Cold war -- Fiction 3. Scientists -- Fiction 4. Conspiracies -- Fiction

ISBN 0062310852; 9780062310859

In this middle grades book, by Diana Peterfreund, "Gillian Seagret doesn't listen to people who say her father's a crackpot. His conspiracy theories about the lost technology of Cold War-era rocket scientist Dr. Aloysius Underberg may have cost him his job and forced them to move to the middle of nowhere, but Gillian knows he's right and plans to prove it. . . . Gillian sets off on a journey into the ruins of Omega City, a vast doomsday bunker deep inside the earth." (Publisher's note)

Petersen, P. J.

Wild river. Delacorte Press 2009 120p $14.99; lib bdg $17.99

Grades: 4 5 6 7   Fic

1. Brothers -- Fiction 2. Kayaks and kayaking -- Fiction 3. Wilderness survival -- Fiction

ISBN 978-0-385-73724-1; 0-385-73724-6; 978-0-385-90656-2 lib bdg; 0-385-90656-0 lib bdg

LC 2008-24921

Considered lazy and unathletic, twelve-year-old Ryan discovers a heroic side of himself when a kayak trip with his older brother goes horribly awry.

"The compelling first-person narration sets this apart from other adventure stories. . . . With sharp pacing, short sentences, and an unintimidating length, this is a strong, accessible choice for younger readers." Booklist

Peterson, Lois J.

The **ballad** of Knuckles McGraw; written by Lois Peterson. Orca Book Publishers 2010 105p (Orca young readers) pa $7.95

Grades: 3 4 5   Fic

1. Grandparents -- Fiction 2. Foster home care -- Fiction 3. Abandoned children -- Fiction

ISBN 978-1-55469-203-3 pa; 1-55469-203-2 pa

After Kevin's mother abandons him, he takes refuge in his fantasy of becoming a cowboy, but his reality is a foster home and grandparents he doesn't know.

"The author understands how kids think, a fact that will allow kids in your library to thoroughly enjoy this book." Libr Media Connect

Philbrick, Rodman

★ The **mostly** true adventures of Homer P. Figg; [by] Rodman Philbrick. Blue Sky Press 2009 224p $16.99
Grades: 5 6 7 8   **Fic**
1. Adventure fiction 2. Orphans -- Fiction 3. Brothers -- Fiction 4. United States -- History -- 1861-1865, Civil War -- Fiction
ISBN 978-0-439-66818-7; 0-439-66818-2
LC 2008-16925

A Newbery Medal honor book, 2010

Twelve-year-old Homer, a poor but clever orphan, has extraordinary adventures after running away from his evil uncle to rescue his brother, who has been sold into service in the Civil War

"The book wouldn't be nearly as much fun without Homer's tall tales, but there are serious moments, too, and the horror of war and injustice of slavery ring clearly above the din of playful exaggerations." Publ Wkly

★ The **young** man and the sea; [by] Rodman Philbrick. Blue Sky Press 2004 192p $16.95; pa $4.99
Grades: 5 6 7 8   **Fic**
1. Fishing -- Fiction
ISBN 0-439-36829-4; 0-439-36830-8 pa
LC 2003-050233

After his mother's death, twelve-year-old Skiff Beaman decides that it is up to him to earn money to take care of himself and his father, so he undertakes a dangerous trip alone out on the ocean off the coast of Maine to try to catch a hugh bluefin tuna

"This excellent maritime bildungsroman has all of the makings of a juvenile classic: wide-open adventure, heart-pounding suspense, and just the right amount of tear-jerking pathos, all neatly wrapped up in an ending that . . . is purely triumphant." SLJ

Zane and the hurricane; a story of Katrina. Rodman Philbrick. The Blue Sky Press, an imprint of Scholastic Inc. 2014 181 p. maps (hardback) $16.99
Grades: 5 6 7 8   **Fic**
1. Rescue work -- Fiction 2. Hurricane Katrina, 2005 -- Fiction 3. Survival -- Fiction 4. African Americans -- Fiction 5. New Orleans (La.) -- Fiction 6. Racially mixed people -- Fiction
ISBN 0545342384; 9780545342384
LC 2013025489

In this children's novel, by Rodman Philbrick, "Zane Dupree is a charismatic 12-year-old boy of mixed race visiting a relative in New Orleans when Hurricane Katrina hits. Unexpectedly separated from all family, Zane and his dog experience the terror of Katrina's wind, rain, and horrific flooding. Facing death, they are rescued from an attic air vent by a kind, elderly musician and a scrappy young girl." (Publisher's note)

"Careful attention to detail in representations of the storm, the city and local dialect give this tale a realistic feel. Zane's perspective as an outsider allows Philbrick to weave in social commentary on race, class, greed and morality, offering rich fodder for reflection and discussion." Kirkus

Pierce, Tamora

Magic steps; book one of the Circle opens quartet. Scholastic Press 2000 264p (Circle opens quartet) hardcover o.p. pa $5.99
Grades: 5 6 7 8   **Fic**
1. Fantasy fiction 2. Magic -- Fiction
ISBN 0-590-39588-2; 0-590-39605-6 pa
LC 99-31943

"Using descriptive, personable prose, Pierce combines dimensional characters, intricate details, plot twists, and alternating story lines for a gripping read. . . . There is some vivid violence." Booklist

Other titles in this series are:
Street magic (2001)
Cold fire (2002)
Shatterglass (2003)

Pierpoint, Eric

The **last** ride of Caleb O'Toole; Eric Pierpoint. Sourcebooks Jabberwocky 2013 304 p. (tp: alk. paper) $7.99
Grades: 4 5 6 7   **Fic**
1. Historical fiction 2. Orphans -- Fiction 3. Wagon trains -- Fiction 4. Bozeman Trail -- Fiction 5. Coming of age -- Fiction 6. Brothers and sisters -- Fiction 7. Adventure and adventurers -- Fiction 8. Oregon National Historic Trail -- Fiction 9. West (U.S.) -- History -- 1860-1890 -- Fiction
ISBN 1402281714; 9781402281716
LC 2013011800

In this book, it's "1877 in Great Bend, Kan., and cholera has panicked citizens and killed scores, including Caleb O'Toole's father. The story opens as 12-year-old Caleb races through town to find one of his sisters while his mother lies dying of the disease and a mob threatens to burn down their house. Caleb then witnesses a murder, and the O'Toole children escape amid an explosive gunfight, after agreeing to . . . take the Oregon Trail to their aunt's ranch in Montana Territory." (Publishers Weekly)

Pileggi, Leah

Prisoner 88; Leah Pileggi. Charlesbridge 2013 142 p. (reinforced for library use) $16.95
Grades: 4 5 6 7 8   **Fic**
1. Prisons -- Idaho Territory -- Fiction 2. Prisoners -- Idaho Territory -- Fiction
ISBN 1580895603; 9781580895606; 9781607345343; 9781607346111
LC 2012024443

In this book, by Leah Pileggi, "ten-year-old Jake Evans has just received a five-year sentence for manslaughter. . . . The warden and guards are at a bit of a loss on how to treat so young a convict, and . . . Jake's life improves considerably in the aftermath of his conviction." But "there are hardened criminals who would like to take Jake down just for the grim pleasure of it, and Jake is drawn into the turmoil of an jailbreak attempt." (Bulletin of the Center for Children's Literature)

Prisoner Eighty-eight

Pilkey, Dav, 1966-

The **Adventures** of Captain Underpants; Dav Pilkey, illustrated by Jesse Garibaldi. First color edition. Scholastic 2013 136 p. $9.99

Grades: 2 3 4   **Fic**

1. Adventure fiction 2. Superheroes -- Fiction 3. School principals -- Fiction

ISBN 0545499089; 9780545499088

LC 2013935584

This humorous children's novel, by Dav Pilkey and illustrated by Jose Garibaldi, is the first book in the author's "Captain Underpants" series. In it "George and Harold have created the greatest superhero in the history of their elementary school--and now they're going to bring him to life! Meet Captain Underpants! His true identity is so secret, even HE doesn't know who he is!" (Publisher's note)

"This edition of book one in the series now features watercolor blues, greens, yellows, purples, and reds. For the most part, the color doesn't compete for attention with the text. That said, hardly an inch of blank space remains, especially in the comics that George and Harold draw. The effect is now more splashy Sunday comics than sketchy drawn-by-kids serial." Horn Book

Part of the recommended "Captain Underpants" series.

Captain Underpants and the tyrannical retaliation of the Turbo Toilet 2000; the eleventh epic novel. by Dav Pilkey. Scholastic Inc. 2015 224 p. (hc) $9.99

Grades: 2 3 4   **Fic**

1. Adventure fiction 2. Superheroes -- Fiction 3. Humorous stories 4. Monsters -- Fiction 5. School principals -- Fiction 6. Captain Underpants (Fictitious character)

ISBN 0545504902; 9780545504904

LC 2014008919

In this middle grades adventure book by Dav Pilkey, "When the Incredible Robo-Plunger defeated the evil Turbo Toilet 2000, George and Harold thought their toilet troubles were over. Unfortunately, their porcelain problems were only beginning . . . Just when you thought it was safe to flush . . . The Turbo Toilet 2000 strikes back!" (Publisher's note)

"The famous superhero returns to fight another villain with all the trademark wit and humor the series is known for...Adults may roll their eyes here and there, but youngsters will eat this up just as quickly as they devoured every other Underpants episode. Dizzyingly silly." Kirkus

Part of the recommended "Captain Underpants" series.

Pincus, Greg

The **14** fibs of Gregory K; Greg Pincus. Arthur A. Levine Books 2013 240 p. (hardcover: alk. paper) $17.99

Grades: 4 5 6 7   **Fic**

1. Honesty -- Fiction 4. Schools -- Fiction 5. Mathematics -- Fiction 6. Middle schools -- Fiction 7. Creative writing -- Fiction 8. Fathers and sons -- Fiction 9. Brothers and sisters -- Fiction

ISBN 0439912997; 9780439912990; 9780439913003

LC 2012044117

In this book, by Greg Pincus, "Gregory K is the middle child in a family of mathematical geniuses. But if he claimed to love math? Well, he'd be fibbing. What he really wants most is to go to Author Camp. But to get his parents' permission he's going to have to pass his math class, which has

a probability of 0. THAT much he can understand!" (Publisher's note)

"Eleven-year-old Gregory doesn't love math, but everyone in his family does. He yearns to go to Author Camp with his best friend, Kelly. To please his family, he tells a series of lies and then has to fix the resulting problems. Unconvincing secondary characters weaken the plot, but the story might appeal to those who feel they just don't fit in." (Horn Book)

Pinkney, Andrea Davis

★ **Bird** in a box; illustrations by Sean Qualls. Little, Brown Books for Young Readers 2011 278p il $16.99

Grades: 4 5 6 7   **Fic**

1. Boxing -- Fiction 2. African Americans -- Fiction 3. Radio broadcasting -- Fiction 4. Young adult literature -- Works 5. Harlem (New York, N.Y.) -- Fiction 6. Great Depression, 1929-1939 -- Fiction

ISBN 978-0-316-07403-2; 0-316-07403-9

LC 2010-22851

In 1936, three children meet at the Mercy Home for Negro Orphans in New York State, and while not all three are orphans, they are all dealing with grief and loss which together, along with the help of a sympathetic staff member and the boxing matches of Joe Louis, they manage to overcome.

"Pinkney weaves quite a bit of 1930s history into her story and succeeds admirably in showing how Louis came to represent so much more than his sport. Her detailed notes make this an accessible and inspiring piece of historical fiction that belongs in most collections." SLJ

★ **The red** pencil; a novel told in poems, pictures, and possibilities. by Andrea Davis Pinkney; illustrated by Shane Evans. First edition Little, Brown & Co. 2014 336 p. illustrations, map (hardcover) $17

Grades: 4 5 6 7   **Fic**

1. Sudan -- Fiction 2. Refugees -- Fiction 3. Novels in verse 4. Blacks -- Sudan -- Fiction

ISBN 9780316247801; 0316247804

LC 2013044753

Amelia Bloomer Project (2014)

"Amira is twelve. . . . Maybe old enough to go to school in Nyala--Amira's one true dream. But life in her peaceful Sudanese village is shattered when the Janjaweed arrive. . . . After she loses nearly everything, Amira needs . . . to make the long journey . . . to safety at a refugee camp. Her days are tough at the camp, until the gift of a simple red pencil opens her mind." (Publisher's note)

"Amira's thoughts and drawings are vividly brought to life through Pinkney's lyrical verse and Evans's lucid line illustrations, which infuse the narrative with emotional intensity." SLJ

With the might of angels; the diary of Dawnie Rae Johnson. Scholastic 2011 324p il map (Dear America) $12.99

Grades: 5 6 7 8   **Fic**

1. School stories 2. Diaries -- Fiction 3. Virginia -- Fiction 4. Family life -- Fiction 5. Race relations -- Fiction 6. African Americans -- Fiction 7. School integration -- Fiction

ISBN 0-545-29705-2; 978-0-545-29705-9

LC 2011001363

In 1955 Hadley, Virginia, twelve-year-old Dawnie Rae Johnson, a tomboy who excels at baseball and at her studies, becomes the first African American student to attend the all-white Prettyman Coburn school, turning her world upside down. Includes historical notes about the period.

"Dawnie's journal is realistic, encompassing thoughts and emotions one would expect of someone so stressed. . . . The author seamlessly incorporates historical events into the child's journal. The end matter contains age-appropriate photographs, a time line, and brief biographical sketches of the people mentioned. A first purchase." SLJ

Pinkwater, Daniel Manus
Adventures of a cat-whiskered girl; illustrations by Calef Brown. Houghton Mifflin Books for Children 2010 268p il $16
Grades: 4 5 6   **Fic**
1. Science fiction 2. Cats -- Fiction 3. Extraterrestrial beings -- Fiction
ISBN 978-0-547-22324-7; 0-547-22324-2

Big Audrey, who has catlike whiskers, and her telepathic friend Molly set out on a journey to find out why flying saucers are landing behind the old stone barn in Poughkeepsie, New York, and, more importantly, to determine whether another cat-whiskered girl really exists.

"Mixing the absurd with the profound, Pinkwater's odd narration will have even the most serious readers laughing at the chaos." Booklist

The **Hoboken** chicken emergency; by Daniel Pinkwater; illustrated by Tony Auth. Atheneum Books for Young Readers 2007 101p il $16.99; pa $4.99
Grades: 3 4 5 6   **Fic**
1. Chickens -- Fiction
ISBN 978-1-4169-2809-6; 1-4169-2809-X; 978-1-4169-2810-2 pa; 1-4169-2810-3 pa
LC 2006101544

First published 1977 by Simon & Schuster

Arthur goes to pick up the turkey for Thanksgiving dinner but comes back with a 266-pound chicken.

"A contemporary tall tale that will stretch middle graders' imagination, sense of humor, and enthusiasm for reading." Booklist

Other titles about Henrietta the chicken are:
The Artsy Smartsy Club (2005)
Looking for Bobowicz (2004)

Lizard music; written and illustrated by Daniel Pinkwater. New York Review of Books 2011 157p il $15.95
Grades: 4 5 6   **Fic**
1. Science fiction 2. Lizards -- Fiction 3. Extraterrestrial beings -- Fiction
ISBN 978-1-59017-387-9; 1-59017-387-2
LC 2010026945

A reissue of the title first published 1976 by Dodd, Mead

When left to take care of himself, a young boy becomes involved with a community of intelligent lizards who tell him of a little known invasion from outer space.

"The book—part satire, part sci-fi/fantasy—is amusing the original. Occasional Escher-esque drawings reflect the story's peculiarities." Horn Book Guide

Mrs. Noodlekugel and four blind mice; by Daniel Pinkwater and illustrated by Adam Stower. 1st ed. Candlewick Press 2013 96 p. $14.99
Grades: 2 3 4   **Fic**
1. Mice -- Fiction 2. Blind -- Fiction 3. Humorous stories 4. Babysitters -- Fiction
ISBN 0763650544; 9780763650544
LC 2012947756

In author Daniel Pinkwater's book "four farsighted mice take center stage in the second installment of the Mrs. Noodlekugel series. Along with the mice, Mrs. Noodlekugel, Mr. Fuzzface (the talking cat), and children Maxine and Nick are having tea one afternoon. When the mice make a terrible mess of their tea table, Mrs. Noodlekugel declares it's their bad eyesight. So off they go to the oculist for a fitting of mice-sized glasses." (Booklist)

The **Neddiad**; how Neddie took the train, went to Hollywood, and saved civilization; by Daniel Pinkwater; illustrations by Calef Brown. Houghton Mifflin 2007 307p il $16
Grades: 5 6 7 8   **Fic**
1. Turtles -- Fiction 2. Los Angeles (Calif.) -- Fiction
ISBN 978-0-618-59444-3; 0-618-59444-2
LC 2006033944

Followed by: The Yggyssey (2009)

When shoelace heir Neddie Wentworthstein and his family take the train from Chicago to Los Angeles in the 1940s, he winds up in possession of a valuable Indian turtle artifact whose owner is supposed to be able to prevent the impending destruction of the world, but he is not sure exactly how.

"A bright and breezy adventure with a smart and funny narrator. . . . [This is a] goofy and lovingly nostalgic historical fantasy." SLJ

Pinter, Jason
Zeke Bartholomew, superspy. Sourcebooks Jabberwocky 2011 256p pa $7.99
Grades: 4 5 6 7   **Fic**
1. Adventure fiction 2. Spies -- Fiction
ISBN 978-1-4022-5755-1; 1-4022-5755-4

Zeke Bartholomew has always dreamed of being a spy. But when a case of mistaken identity goes horribly wrong, he's thrust into a world of real-life espionage beyond his wildest dreams. Soon this 7th grade nobody finds himself hunted by the lava-powered behemoth Ragnarok, aided by a mysterious butt-kicking girl who goes only by the codename 'Sparrow.'

"Zeke's first-person narration and ample one-liners provide plenty of laughs in a novel that combines espionage, wild sci-fi, and a satiric take on the ever-growing kids-save-the-world subgenre." Booklist

Pitchford, Dean
Captain Nobody. G.P. Putnam's Sons 2009 195p $16.99; pa $6.99
Grades: 3 4 5 6   **Fic**
1. Costume -- Fiction 2. Brothers -- Fiction 3. Halloween -- Fiction
ISBN 978-0-399-25034-7; 0-399-25034-4; 978-0-14-241667-9 pa; 0-14-241667-3 pa
LC 2008-27733

When ten-year-old Newton dresses up as an unusual superhero for Halloween, he decides to keep wearing the costume after the holiday to help save townspeople and eventually his injured brother.

The author "builds suspense adeptly. . . . The young narrator's earnest voice—and his raw sense of helplessness—are real and affecting." Publ Wkly

Nickel Bay Nick; Dean Pitchford. G.P. Putnam's Sons, an imprint of Penguin Group (USA) Inc. 2013 272 p. $16.99
Grades: 4 5 6   **Fic**
1. Gifts -- Fiction 2. Secrets -- Fiction 4. Behavior -- Fiction 5. Christmas -- Fiction 6. Neighbors -- Fiction 7. City and town life -- Fiction
ISBN 039925465X; 9780399254659
LC 2012048972

In this book, 11-year-old "Sam Brattle, embittered at having the lousiest Christmas ever—and with a heart transplant and extensive history of larceny behind him—is blackmailed by his mysterious neighbor into taking on the role of Nickel Bay's homegrown secret Santa, the titular Nickel Bay Nick. Wealthy Mr. Wells has stealthily been distributing $100 bills around town at Christmastime for years, boosting the spirits and fortunes of its economically discouraged citizens." (Kirkus Reviews)

Place, Francois
The **old** man mad about drawing; a tale of Hokusai. translated from the French by William Rodarmor. David R. Godine 2004 105p il $19.95
Grades: 3 4 5 6   **Fic**
1. Artists 2. Japan -- Fiction 3. Artists -- Fiction
ISBN 1-56792-260-0
LC 2003-13521

Tojiro, a young seller of rice cakes in the Japanese capital of Edo, later known as Tokyo, is amazed to discover that the grumpy and shabby old man who buys his cakes is a famous artist renowned for his sketches, prints, and paintings of flowers, animals, and landscapes.

This book "features fine reproductions of Hokusai's work, as well as . . . elegant detailed sketches of the quiet studio and crowded streets." Booklist

Platt, Chris
Astra. Peachtree 2010 144p $15.95
Grades: 5 6 7 8   **Fic**
1. Horses -- Fiction 2. Father-daughter relationship -- Fiction
ISBN 978-1-56145-541-6; 1-56145-541-5
LC 2010001654

Forbidden to ride after her mother's death in a riding accident, thirteen-year-old Lily nurses her mother's beloved horse, Astra, back to health, hoping that someday Astra will win the Tevis Cup endurance race

"Filled with information about endurance racing as well as a cast of interesting supporting characters, including the dishy new boy in town, this novel is a quick and enjoyable read." SLJ

Platt, Randall Beth
Hellie Jondoe; [by] Randall Platt. Texas Tech University Press 2009 216p pa $16.95

Grades: 5 6 7 8   **Fic**
1. Oregon -- Fiction 2. Orphans -- Fiction
ISBN 978-0-89672-663-5 pa; 0-89672-663-0 pa
LC 2009-21514

In 1918, as the Great War ends and the Spanish influenza pandemic begins, thirteen-year-old Hellie Jondoe survives on the streets of New York as a beggar and pickpocket until she boards the orphan train to Oregon, where she learns about loyalty, honesty, and the meaning of family

"This is solid historical fiction with a scrappy heroine who is genuinely tough and a true survivor. Irrepressible and irreverent." Kirkus

Poblocki, Dan
The **stone** child. Random House 2009 274p $15.99; lib bdg $18.99
Grades: 5 6 7 8   **Fic**
1. Authors -- Fiction 2. Monsters -- Fiction 3. Supernatural -- Fiction 4. Books and reading -- Fiction
ISBN 978-0-375-84254-2; 0-375-84254-3; 978-0-375-94254-9 lib bdg; 0-375-94254-8 lib bdg
LC 2008-21722

When friends Eddie, Harris, and Maggie discover that the scary adventures in their favorite author's fictional books come true, they must find a way to close the portal that allows evil creatures and witches to enter their hometown of Gatesweed.

"The creep factor is high but not graphic, and the kids act and react like real kids. . . . This briskly paced novel is sure to be popular with fans of scary stuff." SLJ

Pogue, David
Abby Carnelia's one and only magical power. Roaring Brook Press 2010 277p $15.99
Grades: 3 4 5   **Fic**
1. Camps -- Fiction 2. Magic -- Fiction 3. Connecticut -- Fiction
ISBN 978-1-59643-384-7; 1-59643-384-1
LC 2009-46619

After eleven-year-old Abby discovers that she has a completely useless magical power, she finds herself at a magic camp where her hope of finding others like herself is realized, but when a select group is taken to a different camp, a sinister plot comes to light.

"This book is a whimsical feast for children. The characters are well developed; the story is magical and reminiscent of Eva Ibbotsen's wonderful books. The chapters are short and move the plot along quickly. It is an adventure from beginning to end and a plain good story." Libr Media Connect

Polacco, Patricia
★ **January's** sparrow. Philomel Books 2009 94p il $21.99
Grades: 4 5 6   **Fic**
1. Slavery -- Fiction 2. Family life -- Fiction 3. African Americans -- Fiction 4. Underground railroad -- Fiction
ISBN 978-0-399-25077-4; 0-399-25077-8
LC 2008-52726

After a fellow slave is beaten to death, Sadie and her family flee the plantation for freedom through the Underground Railroad.

"The illustrations, which include scenes of a bloody whipping and a heavily scarred back, have an urgent, unsettled look that fully captures the sharply felt danger and terror of Sadie's experiences. . . . This moving account effectively highlights a significant instance of nonviolent community resistance to injustice." SLJ

The **junkyard** wonders. Philomel 2010 un il $17.99
Grades: 2 3 4 5   **Fic**
     1. School stories 2. Teachers -- Fiction 3. Special education -- Fiction 4. Airplanes -- Models -- Fiction
ISBN 978-0-399-25078-1; 0-399-25078-6

"Looking forward to a fresh start at a new school, Trisha is crestfallen when she is assigned to a special class with children who are different. Their teacher, Mrs. Peterson, proudly calls them the junkyard and takes them to an actual junkyard, which she describes as a place of wondrous possibilities. . . . Reclaiming and rebuilding an old model plane they intend to send to the moon, Trisha's tribe manages a triumphant launch. Illustrations, rendered in pencil and marker, portray children in saddle oxfords and poodle skirts brimming with energy and excitement, guided by a model teacher. Based on her own childhood, Polacco's inspiring story will touch children and teachers alike." Booklist

Just in time, Abraham Lincoln. G. P. Putnam's Sons 2011 un il $17.99
Grades: 2 3 4 5   **Fic**
     1. Lawyers 2. Presidents 3. State legislators 4. Brothers -- Fiction 5. Members of Congress 6. Time travel -- Fiction 7. Grandmothers -- Fiction 8. Antietam (Md.), Battle of, 1862 -- Fiction 9. United States -- History -- 1861-1865, Civil War -- Fiction
ISBN 0-399-25471-4; 978-0-399-25471-0
                      LC 2010-23200

When two brothers visit a museum in Harper's Ferry, West Virginia, with their grandmother, they find themselves in a very realistic Civil War setting where they see the Antietam battlefield and meet historical figures from the aftermath of that momentous battle. Includes author's note on the Battle of Antietam.

"Climaxed by two wordless spreads of fields covered with twisted, bloodstained victims, the illustrations convey the boys' emotional shifts from boredom to astonishment, excitement to horror. . . . Rounded off with an afterword noting where some historical details have been telescoped, the episode will take a strong grip on readers' hearts and minds both." Kirkus

Porter, Tracey
★ **Billy** Creekmore. Joanna Cotler Books 2007 305p $16.99; lib bdg $17.89; pa $6.99
Grades: 5 6 7 8   **Fic**
     1. Circus -- Fiction 2. Orphanages -- Fiction 3. West Virginia -- Fiction 4. Coal mines and mining -- Fiction
ISBN 978-0-06-077570-4; 0-06-0-77570-X; 978-0-06-077571-1 lib bdg; 0-06-077571-8 lib bdg; 978-0-06-077572-8 pa; 0-06-077572-6 pa
                      LC 2007-00001

In 1905, ten-year-old Billy is taken from an orphanage to live with an aunt and uncle he never knew he had, and he enjoys his first taste of family life until his work in a coal mine and involvement with a union brings trouble, then he joins a circus in hopes of finding his father.

"Porter's writing is strong, and the story, told in Billy's steadfast yet child-true voice, makes the shocking history

about the lives of children at the turn of the last century come alive for today's readers." Booklist

Potter, Ellen
The **humming** room; Ellen Potter. 1st ed. Feiwel & Friends 2012 184 p. $16.99
Grades: 4 5 6 7   **Fic**
     1. Children's stories 2. Family -- Fiction 3. Haunted houses -- Fiction 4. Foster children -- Fiction 5. Gardens -- Fiction 6. Islands -- Fiction 7. Orphans -- Fiction
ISBN 0312644388; 9780312644383
                      LC 2011033583

In this book by Ellen Potter, "[h]idden under the family trailer, Roo hears . . . the murder of her drug-dealing father. . . . [S]he is sent to live with her . . . reclusive uncle on Cough Rock, a spooky old house named for its former use as a sanitarium. . . . [The cast of characters includes a] personal assistant, a cheerful local servant, a mysterious wild boy, and a secluded boy cousin with a fearful temper who is not expected to live." (Bulletin of the Center for Children's Books)

★ The **Kneebone** boy. Feiwel and Friends 2010 282p $16.99
Grades: 3 4 5 6   **Fic**
     1. Adventure fiction 2. Mothers -- Fiction 3. Siblings -- Fiction 4. Great Britain -- Fiction 5. Eccentrics and eccentricities -- Fiction
ISBN 978-0-312-37772-4; 0-312-37772-X
                      LC 2010012572

Otto, Lucia, and Max Hardscrabble, whose mother has been missing for many years, have unexpected and illuminating adventures in the village of Snoring-by-the-Sea after their father, who paints portraits of deposed monarchs, goes away on a business trip.

"With a dark, witty absurdity . . . Potter . . . draws readers into this compelling mystery-adventure. . . . Potter's voice is distinguished by sharp, humorous, and poignant observations. . . . Often laugh-out-loud funny." Publ Wkly

★ **Olivia** Kidney; illustrated by Peter Reynolds. Philomel Bks. 2003 155p il $15.99; pa $5.99
Grades: 3 4 5 6   **Fic**
     1. New York (N.Y.) -- Fiction 2. Apartment houses -- Fiction
ISBN 0-399-23850-6; 0-14-240234-6 pa
                      LC 2002-3660

Twelve-year-old Olivia explores her new apartment building and finds a psychic, talking lizards, a shrunken ex-pirate, an exiled princess, ghosts, and other unusual characters

"Potter has written a first-rate novel to be enjoyed on many levels. Its plot is so tightly woven that it's difficult to separate the mystical from the fantastical. Occasional full-page illustrations add another dimension to this narrative, which is wonderful medicine for the lonely." SLJ

Other titles about Olivia Kidney are:
Olivia Kidney and the Exit Academy (2005)
Olivia Kidney and the secret beneath the city (2007)

Slob. Philomel Books 2009 199p $16.99
Grades: 5 6 7 8   **Fic**
     1. Obesity -- Fiction 2. Orphans -- Fiction 3. Siblings -- Fiction 4. Inventions -- Fiction 5. Bereavement --

Fiction 6. New York (N.Y.) -- Fiction
ISBN 978-0-399-24705-7; 0-399-24705-X
                                        LC 2008-40476

Picked on, overweight genius Owen tries to invent a television that can see the past to find out what happened the day his parents were killed.

"An intriguingly offbeat mystery, . . . at turns humorous, suspenseful and poignant." Kirkus

Poulsen, David A.

   Old Man; David A. Poulsen. Dundurn Group Ltd 2013 224 p. $12.99

Grades: 6 7 8   Fic

   1. Automobile travel -- Fiction 2. Father-son relationship -- Fiction 3. Vietnam War, 1961-1975 -- Veterans

ISBN 1459705475; 9781459705470

In this novel, by David A. Poulsen, "Nate Huffman's plans are unexpectedly shelved for the most unlikely of reasons: the reappearance of his estranged father. . . . Nate finds himself in a pickup with a man he can't stand. His father wants to reconnect, and he wants Nate to really understand him. Larry Huffman has chosen to make this happen by taking his son into his own past, which has the Vietnam War as its centrepiece." (Publisher's note)

Pratchett, Terry

   ★ Only you can save mankind. HarperCollins 2005 207p hardcover o.p. lib bdg $16.89; pa $6.99

Grades: 5 6 7 8   Fic

   1. War stories 2. Computer games -- Fiction

ISBN 0-06-054185-7; 0-06-054186-5 lib bdg; 0-06-054187-3 pa

First published 1992 in the United Kingdom

Twelve-year-old Johnny endures tensions between his parents, watches television coverage of the Gulf War, and plays a computer game called Only You Can Save Mankind, in which he is increasingly drawn into the reality of the alien ScreeWee

This is "a wild ride, full of Pratchett's trademark humor; digs at primitive, low-resolution games . . . and some not-so-subtle philosophy about war and peace." Booklist

   Other titles in this trilogy are:
   Johnny and the dead (2006)
   Johnny and the bomb (2006)

Preller, James

   Justin Fisher declares war! Scholastic Press 2010 135p $15.99

Grades: 3 4 5   Fic

   1. School stories 2. Teachers -- Fiction 3. Popularity -- Fiction

ISBN 978-0-545-03301-5; 0-545-03301-2
                                        LC 2009053641

When Justin Fisher, longtime class clown, realizes that his classmates are growing tired of his misdeeds, he declares war on their fifth-grade teacher, Mr. Tripp, in hopes of regaining his popularity.

"This quiet, universal story . . . will make a good classroom read. Preller handles sensitive issues with dignity, and kids will identify with Justin's eagerness to be liked and his snarky jokes." SLJ

   ★ Six innings; a game in the life. Feiwel and Friends 2008 147p $16.95

Grades: 4 5 6 7   Fic

   1. Cancer -- Fiction 2. Baseball -- Fiction

ISBN 978-0-312-36763-3; 0-312-36763-5
                                        LC 2007-32846

Earl Grubb's Pool Supplies plays Northeast Gas & Electric in the Little League championship game, while Sam, who has cancer and is in a wheelchair, has to call the play-by-play instead of participating in the game.

"The outcome is predictable but the journey is nailbitingly tense. Kids will be nodding in agreement at the truths laid bare." Publ Wkly

Preus, Margi

   ★ West of the moon; Margi Preus. Amulet Books 2014 224 p. (alk. paper) $16.95

Grades: 5 6 7 8   Fic

   1. Norway -- Fiction 2. Folklore -- Norway 3. Human trafficking -- Fiction 4. United States -- Immigration and emigration -- Fiction 5. Norway -- History -- 19th century -- Fiction

ISBN 1419708961; 9781419708961
                                        LC 2013023250

Author Margi Preus "weaves original fiction with myth and folktale to tell the story of Astri, a young Norwegian girl desperate to join her father in America. After being separated from her sister and sold to a cruel goat farmer, Astri makes a daring escape. She quickly retrieves her little sister, and, armed with a troll treasure, a book of spells and curses, and a possibly magic hairbrush, they set off for America." (Publisher's note)

"In the Scandinavian fairy tale "East of the Sun and West of the Moon," a young girl is taken from her home to a magnificent castle by a great bear, whom she discovers is really a prince... Like dun silk shot through with gold, Preus (Heart of a Samurai, 2010) interweaves the mesmerizing tale of Astri's treacherous and harrowing mid-nineteenth-century immigration to America with bewitching tales of magic. A fascinating author's note only adds to the wonder." Bklst

   Includes bibliographical references

Prevost, Guillaume

   The book of time; [by] Guillaume Prévost; translated by William Rodarmor. Arthur A. Levine Books 2007 213p $16.99; pa $6.99

Grades: 5 6 7 8   Fic

   1. Science fiction 2. Missing persons -- Fiction

ISBN 978-0-439-88375-7; 0-439-88375-X; 978-0-439-88379-5 pa; 0-439-88379-2 pa
                                        LC 2006-38446

Original French edition 2006

Sam Faulkner travels back in time to medieval Ireland, ancient Egypt and Renaissance Bruges in search of his missing father

"The appeal of the novel . . . comes from both well-drawn characters and a swiftly moving story." Booklist

   Other titles in this series are:
   The gate of days (2008)
   The circle of gold (2009)

Priestley, Chris

Tales of terror from the Black Ship; by Chris Priestley; illustrated by David Roberts. Bloomsbury Children's Books 2008 243p il $12.99

Grades: 5 6 7 8 **Fic**

1. Sea stories 2. Horror fiction 3. Siblings -- Fiction 4. Storytelling -- Fiction 5. Great Britain -- Fiction 6. Cornwall (England) -- Fiction

ISBN 978-1-59990-290-6; 1-59990-290-7

LC 2008-10408

One stormy night, in their family's otherwise deserted Cornwall inn, twelve-year-old Ethan and his sister Cathy shelter a mysterious guest who indulges their love of the macabre by telling horror stories of the sea

"Priestley and Roberts, whose Gorey-esque line illustrations can distill spirits from a nightmare, understand full well what kids want to read under the covers by flashlight." Bull Cent Child Books

Primavera, Elise, 1954-

Libby of High Hopes; story and pictures by Elise Primavera. Simon & Schuster Books for Young Readers 2012 185 p. (alk. paper) $14.99

Grades: 2 3 4 **Fic**

1. Horses -- Fiction 2. Sisters -- Fiction 3. Horseback riding -- Fiction 4. Horsemanship -- Fiction

ISBN 1416955429; 9781416955429

LC 2011043908

In this children's novel, Libby wants to take horseback riding lessons. "Libby's parents do indeed fork out for lessons--for Libby's older sister, Laurel. Libby does at least get the privilege of riding an old pony during Laurel's class, and she hangs around the barn and learns as much as she can, taking a special interest in a retired jumper, Princess, and getting involved in the human drama of the stable's owners." (Bulletin of the Center for Children's Books)

Prineas, Sarah

★ The **magic** thief; illustrations by Antonio Javier Caparo. HarperCollins Pubs. 2008 419p il map

Grades: 4 5 6 7 **Fic**

1. Fantasy fiction 2. Magic -- Fiction 3. Thieves -- Fiction 4. Apprentices -- Fiction

ISBN 0-06-137587-X; 0-06-137588-8 lib bdg; 0-06-137590-X pa; 978-0-06-137587-3; 978-0-06-137588-0 lib bdg; 978-0-06-137590-3 pa

LC 2007031704

Conn is a young thief who is drawn into a life of adventure after picking the pocket of the wizard Nevery Flinglas. Finglas has returned from exile to try to reverse the decline of magic in Wellmet City. "Grades five to nine." (Bull Cent Child Books)

"Conn is a thief but, through desire and inevitability, becomes a wizard . . . This evolution begins when Conn picks the pocket of the wizard Nevery. . . . What works wonderfully well here is the boy's irresistable voice." Booklist

Other titles in this series are:

Lost (2009)

Found (2010)

Pryor, Bonnie

The **iron** dragon; the courageous story of Lee Chin. Enslow Publishers 2010 160p (Historical fiction adventures) lib bdg $27.93; pa $14.95

Grades: 4 5 6 **Fic**

1. Railroads -- Fiction 2. California -- Fiction 3. Immigrants -- Fiction 4. Chinese Americans -- Fiction

ISBN 978-0-7660-3389-4 lib bdg; 0-7660-3389-9 lib bdg; 978-1-59845-215-0 pa; 1-59845-215-0 pa

LC 2009017930

In the mid-nineteenth century, teenager Lee Chin and his father leave China for California to work on the transcontinental railroad, where Lee defies his father's wishes and saves money to free his younger sister from slavery in China, then brings her to join him in beginning a new life in America. Includes historical note about the Chinese who helped build the transcontinental railroad

"Lee Chin's tale is compellingly told. . . . Historical information is accurate and honest about the period depicted." SLJ

Simon's escape; a story of the Holocaust. Enslow Publishers 2010 160p (Historical fiction adventures) lib bdg $27.93; pa $14.95

Grades: 4 5 6 **Fic**

1. Poland -- Fiction 2. Jews -- Poland -- Fiction 3. Holocaust, 1933-1945 -- Fiction 4. World War, 1939-1945 -- Fiction

ISBN 978-0-7660-3388-7 lib bdg; 0-7660-3388-0 lib bdg; 978-1-59845-216-7 pa; 1-59845-216-9 pa

LC 2009029322

Simon, a young Polish Jew, and his family are forced by Nazis to leave their home for the filth and hunger of the Warsaw ghetto then, when his family is all taken away, he escapes to fight for survival in the countryside. Includes facts about the Holocaust

This "is a compelling, informative introduction to Holocaust history." Booklist

Pullman, Philip, 1946-

★ **Clockwork**; or, All wound up. with illustrations by Leonid Gore. Levine Bks. 1998 112p il hardcover o.p. pa $4.99

Grades: 4 5 6 7 **Fic**

1. Supernatural -- Fiction

ISBN 0-590-12999-6; 0-590-12998-8 pa

LC 97-27458

First published 1996 in the United Kingdom

Long ago in Germany, a storyteller's story and an apprentice clockwork-maker's nightmare meet in a menacing, lifelike figure created by the strange Dr. Kalmenius

"Pullman laces his tale with subtle humor while maintaining the suspense until the end. Misty, moody, and atmospheric black-and-white drawings by Leonid Gore make a perfect fit for this gothic gem." Voice Youth Advocates

★ **I** was a rat! illustrated by Kevin Hawkes. Knopf 2000 164p il $15.95; pa $4.99

Grades: 4 5 6 7 **Fic**

1. Fantasy fiction

ISBN 0-375-80176-6; 0-440-41661-2 pa

LC 99-31806

First published 1999 in the United Kingdom with illustrations by Peter Bailey

"Pullman tells what happens to Cinderella's rat-turned-pageboy, who, busily sliding down banisters at the palace, misses the pumpkin-coach ride home and gets trapped in boy form. Young readers will find the story completely entertaining, whether or not they appreciate the playful spoofing of sensational news stories, mob mentality, and the royal family." Horn Book Guide

Two crafty criminals! and how they were captured by the daring detectives of the New Cut Gang; including Thunderbolt's Waxwork & the gas-fitters' ball. Philip Pullman. Alfred A. Knopf 2012 281 p. (hardback) $16.99
Grades: 5 6 7 8   **Fic**
1. Mystery fiction 2. Crime -- Fiction 3. Gangs -- Fiction 4. Humorous fiction 5. Children's stories 6. Humorous stories 7. Mystery and detective stories 8. Adventure and adventurers -- Fiction 9. London (England) -- History -- 19th century -- Fiction 10. Great Britain -- History -- Victoria, 1837-1901 -- Fiction
ISBN 9780375870293; 9780375970290; 9780375988684
           LC 2011042391

This children's book by Philip Pullman was published in 1994 as two novellas: "Thunderbolt's Waxwork" and "The Gas-Fitters' Ball," which are set in "1894 London . . . [and] star . . . the intrepid boy and girl detectives of the New Cut Gang. . . . Thunderbolt Dobney sees his own father hauled off to jail for what he thinks must be 'coining.' . . . [H]e and the New Cut Gang expose the real criminal. . . . In 'The Gas-Fitters' Ball,' . . . the Gas-Fitters' Hall is burgled." (Kirkus Reviews)

Pyron, Bobbie

  ★ A **dog's** way home. Katherine Tegen Books 2011 321p lib bdg $17.89; $16.99
Grades: 4 5 6 7   **Fic**
1. Dogs -- Fiction 2. North Carolina -- Fiction 3. Traffic accidents -- Fiction
ISBN 0-06-198673-9 lib bdg; 0-06-198674-7; 978-0-06-198673-4 lib bdg; 978-0-06-198674-1
           LC 2010006960

After a car accident strands them at opposite ends of the Blue Ridge Parkway, eleven-year-old Abby and her beloved sheltie Tam overcome months filled with physical and emotional challenges to find their way back to each other.

"A heartwarming, suspenseful tale. . . . With vibrant, sympathetic characterizations, Pyron creates an inspiring portrayal of devotion and survival against all odds." Publ Wkly

The **dogs** of winter; by Bobbie Pyron. Arthur A. Levine Books 2012 312 p. (hardcover: alk. paper) $16.99
Grades: 5 6 7 8   **Fic**
1. Wild dogs -- Fiction 2. Dogs -- Juvenile fiction 3. Abandoned children -- Fiction 4. Wilderness survival -- Fiction 5. Dogs -- Fiction 6. Gangs -- Fiction 7. Moscow (Russia) -- Fiction 8. Street children -- Fiction 9. Homeless persons -- Fiction 10. Russia (Federation) -- Fiction 11. Human-animal relationships -- Fiction
ISBN 0545399300; 9780545399302; 9780545399319; 9780545469852
           LC 2011051519

In this book by Bobbie Pyron "Ivan's mother disappears, [and] he's abandoned on the streets of Moscow, with little chance to make it through the harsh winter. But help comes in an unexpected form: Ivan is adopted by a pack of dogs, and the dogs quickly become more than just his street companions: They become his family. Soon Ivan, who used

to love reading fairytales, is practically living in one." But "when help is finally offered to him, will he be able to accept it?" (Publisher's note)

"Ivan is one of the thousands of abandoned children living on the streets of Moscow in the mid-1990s when he is adopted by a pack of feral dogs who protect him from gangs and the harsh winter. Well-crafted sentences, lively dialogue, and a remarkable plot line (based on a true story) combine for an absorbing adventure tale that young readers will find irresistible." Horn Book

Lucky strike; Bobbie Pyron. Arthur A. Levine Books; an imprint of Scholastic Inc. 2015 262 p. hbk $16.99
   Grades: 4 5 6 7   **Fic**
1. Luck -- Fiction 2. Florida -- Fiction 3. Lightning -- Fiction 4. Grandparent-grandchild relationship -- Fiction 5. Grandparent and child -- Fiction 6. Franklin County (Fla.) -- Fiction
ISBN 9780545592178; 0545592178; 0545592186; 9780545592185
           LC 2014013764

In this book, by Bobbie Pyron, "Nate Harlow has never had a lucky day in his life. . . . His best friend, Genesis Beam (aka Gen), believes in science and logic, and she doesn't think for one second that there's such a thing as luck, good or bad. But only an extremely unlucky person could be struck by lightning on his birthday... and that person is Nate Harlow. By some miracle, though, Nate survives, and the strike seems to have changed his luck." (Publisher's note)

"The quirkiness of the characters and the town never goes too far, and there is an overall cozy feeling to the book. Genesis's dad is the preacher at The Church of the One True Redeemer and Everlasting Light, but she is a scientist through and through, which adds complexity to the text, including musings on destiny, fate, probability, and weather." SLJ

Quirk, Katie

A **girl** called Problem; by Katie Quirk. Eerdmans Books for Young Readers 2013 191 p. $8
Grades: 4 5 6   **Fic**
1. Historical fiction 2. Tanzania -- Fiction 3. Healers -- Fiction 4. Villages -- Fiction 5. Moving, Household -- Fiction 6. Blessing and cursing -- Fiction 7. Farm life -- Tanzania -- Fiction 8. Mothers and daughters -- Fiction 9. Sukuma (African people) -- Fiction 10. Tanzania -- History -- 1964- -- Fiction
ISBN 0802854044; 9780802854049
           LC 2012025468

In this novel, Shida looks forward to an education when "President Nyerere asks Shida's village to become a model of ujamaa (familyhood) for the country by moving to Njia Panda and farming communally. . . . After the move, however, the cotton crop mysteriously fails overnight, the villagers' prize possessions, their cattle, escape from their pens, and Furaha dies of fever. With the help of Shida and her cousin Grace, Babu, their grandfather and the village elder, unearths the truth." (Kirkus)

Railsback, Lisa

Noonie's masterpiece; art by Sarajo Frieden. Chronicle Books 2010 208p il $18.99
Grades: 4 5 6 7   **Fic**
1. School stories 2. Artists -- Fiction 3. Family life

-- Fiction 4. Father-daughter relationship -- Fiction 5. Eccentrics and eccentricities -- Fiction

ISBN 978-0-8118-6654-5; 0-8118-6654-8

LC 2008-26831

Upon learning that her deceased mother, an artist, went through a "Purple Period," ten-year-old Noonie decides to do the same, hoping that this will bring her archaeologist father home to see her win a school art contest and that the aunt, uncle, and cousin she lives with will come to understand her just a little.

"Noonie may be an unreliable and even unlikable narrator at times, but her pain and vulnerability are as evident as her belief in herself as an artist, and by the end of the story, she'll have readers in her corner. The ink-and-watercolor illustrations, appearing throughout the book, have a 1960s-retro look." Booklist

Ransom, Candice

Rebel McKenzie; Candice Ransom. Disney Hyperion 2012 270 p. $16.99

Grades: 4 5 6 7   **Fic**

1. Country life -- Fiction 2. Beauty contests -- Fiction 3. Money-making projects for children -- Fiction 4. Nephews -- Fiction 5. Virginia -- Fiction 6. Trailer camps -- Fiction 7. Loss (Psychology) -- Fiction 8. Country life -- Virginia -- Fiction

ISBN 1423145399; 9781423145394

LC 2011032729

In this novel by Candice Ransom "Rebel McKenzie wants to spend her summer attending . . . a camp where kids discover prehistoric bones, right alongside real paleontologists. But digs cost money, and Rebel is broker than four o'clock. When she finds out her annoying neighbor Bambi Lovering won five hundred dollars by playing a ukulele behind her head in a beauty contest, Rebel decides to win the Frog Level Volunteer Fire Department's beauty pageant." (Publisher's note)

Rappaport, Doreen

Freedom ship. Hyperion Books for Children 2006 un il $15.99

Grades: 3 4 5 6   **Fic**

1. Slaves 2. State legislators 3. Slavery -- Fiction 4. Members of Congress 5. African Americans -- Fiction 6. United States -- History -- 1861-1865, Civil War -- Fiction

ISBN 0-7868-0645-1

"In 1862, Robert Smalls, 23, a black wheelman on the Confederate steamship Planter, and other members of the ship's slave crew, seized the ship and delivered it to the Union Army. Five black women and three children escaped to freedom with the crew, and Rappaport uses the fictionalized viewpoint of one of the children to tell her story. . . . Though personal narrative gives the story immediacy, and the handsome illustrations show the strong child and his proud, smiling family standing tall, Rappaport's lengthy note about Smalls is even more exciting than the fiction." Booklist

Raschka, Chris

Seriously, Norman! [by] Chris Raschka. Scholastic/di Capua 2011 342p il $17.95

Grades: 3 4 5   **Fic**

1. Teachers -- Fiction 2. Friendship -- Fiction 3.

Family life -- Fiction

ISBN 978-0-545-29877-3; 0-545-29877-6

Why are grownups so insane? That's the question Leonard, Norman, Anna and Emma (the twins) try to answer with the help of Norman's new tutor, Balthazar Birdsong (who is also fairly nuts).

"Don't expect a linear plot here but rather an ode to ten-year-old humor . . . and improbable characters and situations. . . . Emellished with Raschka's spot art, this rousing tale contains strong wordplay, a little vocabulary instruction . . . and a lot of humor." Horn Book

Raskin, Ellen

Figgs & phantoms. Dutton 2011 152p $16.99; pa $6.99

Grades: 4 5 6   **Fic**

1. Family life -- Fiction

ISBN 978-0-525-42367-6; 0-525-42367-2; 978-0-14-241169-8 pa; 0-14-241169-8 pa

A reissue of the title first published 1974

Chronicles the adventures of the unusual Figg family after they left show business and settled in the town of Pineapple.

This speaks "to both head and heart . . . a most poignant exploration of grief." Horn Book Guide

The **mysterious** disappearance of Leon (I mean Noel) Dutton 2011 149p $16.99; pa $6.99

Grades: 4 5 6   **Fic**

1. Mystery fiction

ISBN 978-0-525-42369-0; 0-525-42369-9; 978-0-14-241700-3 pa; 0-14-241700-9 pa

A reissue of the title first published 1971

The disappearance of her husband is only the first of the mysteries Mrs. Carillon must solve.

Raskin welcomes "readers in as participants in solving the story's mystery. . . . [The book speaks] to both the head and heart." Horn Book Guide

The **tattooed** potato and other clues. Dutton 2011 170p $16.99; pa $6.99

Grades: 4 5 6   **Fic**

1. Mystery fiction

ISBN 978-0-525-42368-3; 0-525-42368-0; 978-0-14-241699-0 pa; 0-14-241699-1 pa

A reissue of the title first published 1975

A Greenwich Village detective posing as an artist hires a student to act as his apprentice, spy, and eyewitness to murder.

Raskin welcomes "readers in as participants in solving the story's mystery. . . . [It speaks] to both head and heart." Horn Book Guide

★ The **Westing** game. Dutton Children's Books 2003 182p $16.99; pa $5.99

Grades: 5 6 7 8   **Fic**

1. Mystery fiction

ISBN 0-525-47137-5; 0-14-240120-X pa

LC 2004-268658

First published 1978

Awarded the Newbery Medal, 1979

"The rules of the game make eight pairs of the players; each oddly matched couple is given a ten thousand dollar check and a set of clues. The result is a fascinating medley of word games, disguises, multiple aliases and subterfuges—in a demanding but rewarding book." Horn Book

Rawlings, Marjorie Kinnan

★ The **secret** river; illustrated by Leo and Diane Dillon. Atheneum Books for Young Readers 2011 un il $19.99

Grades: K 1 2 3   **Fic**

1. Dogs -- Fiction 2. Hunger -- Fiction 3. Fishing -- Fiction 4. Florida -- Fiction 5. Forest animals -- Fiction 6. Forests and forestry -- Fiction

ISBN 978-1-4169-1179-1; 1-4169-1179-0

LC 2007-33292

A newly illustrated edition of the title first published 1955 by Scribner

Young Calpurnia takes her dog, Buggy-horse, and follows her nose to a secret river in a Florida forest, where she catches enough fresh fish to feed her hungry neighbors, even after giving some to the forest creatures she meets on the way home.

"Mesmerizing patterns and colors distinguish the Dillons' spreads, which balance large, captivating panels with smaller vignettes clustered around the text. Their acrylics are a foray into magical realism . . . and their portraits are always true to Rawlings's imaginings. Not to be missed." Publ Wkly

The **yearling**; with pictures by N. C. Wyeth. Scribner 1985 400p il hardcover o.p. pa $5.95

Grades: 5 6 7 8   **Fic**

1. Deer -- Fiction 2. Florida -- Fiction

ISBN 0-684-18461-3; 0-02-044931-3 pa

LC 85-40301

Reissue of the title first published 1938; awarded Pulitzer Prize, 1939

"With its excellent descriptions of Florida scrub landscapes, its skillful use of native vernacular, its tender relation between Jody and his pet fawn, The Yearling is a simply written, picturesque story of boyhood." Time

Rawls, Wilson

★ **Where** the red fern grows; the story of two dogs and a boy. Bantam Bks. 1996 212p $16.95; pa $5.99

Grades: 4 5 6 7   **Fic**

1. Dogs -- Fiction 2. Ozark Mountains -- Fiction

ISBN 0-385-32330-1; 0-440-41267-6 pa

First published 1961 by Doubleday

"Looking back more than 50 years to his boyhood in the Ozarks, the narrator, recalls how he achieved his heart's desire in the ownership of two redbone hounds, how he taught them all the tricks of hunting, and how they won the championship coon hunt before Old Dan was killed by a mountain lion and Little Ann died of grief. Although some readers may find this novel hackneyed and entirely too sentimental, others will enjoy the fine coonhunting episodes and appreciate the author's feelings for nature." Booklist

Ray, Delia

Ghost girl; a Blue Ridge Mountain story. Clarion Bks. 2003 216p il $15

Grades: 5 6 7 8   **Fic**

1. Presidents 2. School stories 3. Philanthropists 4. Teachers -- Fiction 5. Virginia -- Fiction 6. Spouses of

presidents 7. Secretaries of commerce

ISBN 0-618-33377-0

LC 2003-4115

Eleven-year-old April is delighted when President and Mrs. Hoover build a school near her Madison County, Virginia, home but her family's poverty, grief over the accidental death of her brother, and other problems may mean that April can never learn to read from the wonderful teacher, Miss Vest

"This excellent portrayal of four important years in a girl's life rises to the top. Based on a real school and teacher, this novel seamlessly incorporates historical facts into the narrative." SLJ

Here lies Linc. Alfred A. Knopf 2011 308p $16.99; lib bdg $19.99

Grades: 5 6 7 8   **Fic**

1. School stories 2. Iowa -- Fiction 3. Death -- Fiction 4. Cemeteries -- Fiction 5. Family life -- Fiction

ISBN 978-0-375-86757-6; 0-375-86757-0; 978-0-375-96756-6 lib bdg; 0-375-96756-7 lib bdg

LC 2010030004

While researching a rumored-to-be-haunted grave for a local history project, twelve-year-old Lincoln Crenshaw unearths some startling truths about his own family.

"Ray's tale, which centers around a real legend, strikes the perfect balance of humor, realistic chills and near-teen angst." Kirkus

Reeder, Carolyn

Across the lines. Atheneum Bks. for Young Readers 1997 220p hardcover o.p. pa $5.99

Grades: 5 6 7 8   **Fic**

1. Race relations -- Fiction 2. African Americans -- Fiction 3. United States -- History -- 1861-1865, Civil War -- Fiction

ISBN 0-689-81133-0; 0-380-73073-1 pa

LC 96-31068

Edward, the son of a white plantation owner, and his black house servant and friend Simon witness the siege of Petersburg during the Civil War

"Told in the alternating voices of Edward and Simon, this thoughtful Civil War story resonates with authenticity." Horn Book Guide

Reedy, Trent

Words in the dust. Arthur A. Levine Books 2011 266p $17.99

Grades: 5 6 7 8   **Fic**

1. Literacy -- Fiction 2. Sex role -- Fiction 3. Afghanistan -- Fiction 4. Birth defects -- Fiction

ISBN 0-545-26125-2; 978-0-545-26125-8

LC 2010-26160

Zulaikha, a thirteen-year-old girl in Afghanistan, faces a series of frightening but exhilarating changes in her life as she defies her father and secretly meets with an old woman who teaches her to read, her older sister gets married, and American troops offer her surgery to fix her disfiguring cleft lip.

"The evolution of key relationships presents a nuanced look at family dynamics and Afghan culture. Though unsentimental and fraught with tragedy, Reedy's narrative offers hope and will go a long way toward helping readers understand the people behind the headlines." Publ Wkly

Rees, Douglas

Uncle Pirate; illustrated by Tony Auth. Margaret K. McElderry Books 2008 100p il $15.99

Grades: 2 3 4 **Fic**

1. School stories 2. Uncles -- Fiction 3. Pirates -- Fiction 4. Penguins -- Fiction

ISBN 978-1-4169-4762-2; 1-4169-4762-0

LC 2006-39003

Wilson is one of the most bullied fourth-graders at the chaotic Very Elementary School until his long-lost uncle, Desperate Evil Wicked Boba pirate—and his talking penguin arrive and begin making everything shipshape, one classroom at a time

"The story's goofy humor will entertain pirate fans. Lively black-and-white pen-and-ink and watercolor spot art illustrates most pages." Horn Book Guide

Another title about Uncle Pirate is:

Uncle Pirate to the rescue (2010)

Uncle Pirate to the rescue; illustrated by Tony Auth. Margaret K. McElderry Books 2010 il pa $5.99

Grades: 2 3 4 **Fic**

1. School stories 2. Uncles -- Fiction 3. Pirates -- Fiction 4. Penguins -- Fiction

ISBN 978-1-4169-7505-2; 1-4169-7505-5

LC 2009009130

When Captain Desperate Evil Wicked Bob receives a plea from his former crew, he heads out to rescue them and is soon followed by his nephew Wilson, Commodore Purvis, Captain Jack, and others who fear that he needs to be rescued, as well.

"Auth's illustrations lend depth to the comedic elements and pirate analogies throughout the story. Avid and reluctant readers alike will be enchanted and hoping to find their own mutinous crew to rescue." SLJ

Reeve, Philip

Larklight; or, The revenge of the white spiders!, or To Saturn's rings and back!: a rousing tale of dauntless pluck in the farthest reaches of space. as chronicl'd by Art Mumby, with the aid of Philip Reeve; and decorated throughout by David Wyatt. Bloomsbury 2006 399p il $16.95; pa $7.95

Grades: 5 6 7 8 **Fic**

1. Science fiction

ISBN 1-59990-020-3; 1-59990-145-5 pa

In an alternate Victorian England, young Arthur and his sister Myrtle, residents of Larklight, a floating house in one of Her Majesty's outer space territories, uncover a spidery plot to destroy the solar system

"This wildly imaginative sci-fi pirate adventure has tongue-in-cheek humor and social commentary on accepting those who are different, among other things." SLJ

Other titles about the Mumby family are:

Starcross (2007)

Mothstorm (2008)

No such thing as dragons. Scholastic Press 2010 186p $16.99

Grades: 4 5 6 7 **Fic**

1. Fantasy fiction 2. Dragons -- Fiction

ISBN 978-0-545-22224-2; 0-545-22224-9

A young, mute boy who is apprenticed to a dragon-slayer suspects that the winged beasts do not exist, until he—and his master—learn the truth.

"This is certainly different from anything that Reeve has done previously, but is still shot through with his trademark imagination and feel for action. It will be eagerly devoured by young readers." SLJ

Oliver and the seawigs; by Philip Reeve and Sarah McIntyre. Random House Inc 2014 208 p. (hardcover library binding) $15.99

Grades: 3 4 5 **Fic**

1. Boats and boating -- Fiction 2. Parent-child relationship -- Fiction 3. Humorous stories 4. Islands -- Fiction 5. Mermaids -- Fiction 6. Explorers -- Fiction 7. Missing persons -- Fiction 8. Adventure and adventurers -- Fiction

ISBN 0385387911; 9780385387880; 9780385387910

LC 2013043653

In this children's story by Philip Reeve, illustrated by Sarah McIntyre, "When Oliver's explorer parents go missing, he sets sail on a rescue mission with some new, unexpected friends: a grumpy albatross, a nearsighted mermaid . . . even a living island! But the high seas are even more exciting, unusual, and full of mischief than Oliver could have imagined." (Publisher's note)

"Ten-year-old Oliver's parents never returned from exploring an unusual archipelago of islands. He searches for them with help from a talking bird; a mermaid in need of spectacles; and a kind, sentient wandering island, encountering an army of sea monkeys and insult-spouting seaweed along the way. A joyous, original new adventure series filled with quirky characters, buoyant illustrations, and plenty of laughs." Horn Book

Reh, Rusalka

Pizzicato; the abduction of the magic violin. translated by David Henry Wilson. AmazonCrossing 2011 124p pa $9.95

Grades: 4 5 6 7 **Fic**

1. Magic -- Fiction 2. Germany -- Fiction 3. Orphans -- Fiction 4. Violins -- Fiction

ISBN 978-1-6110-9004-8; 1-6110-9004-0

Darius is none too pleased to be paired with Archibald Archinola, a master violinmaker, for a school project, especially when he thinks about his rival—fellow orphan and constant nemesis Max—being surrounded by Porsches at Auto Frederick for the same assignment. But when Darius discovers an old violin in a glass case and strikes the chords, a cut on his hand magically disappears, and suddenly studying with the violinmaker proves to be anything but dull.

This story "has an Old World European charm, from the cast of eccentric, lovable characters to the scenes of café life. Readers will delight in watching the buffoonish villains get their comeuppance, but it's Darius' wish-fulfillment . . . that will satisfy readers most." Booklist

Reiche, Dietlof

★ I, Freddy; book one in the golden hamster saga. translated from the German by John Brownjohn; illustrated by Joe Cepeda. Scholastic Press 2003 201p il hardcover o.p. pa $4.99

Grades: 3 4 5 **Fic**

1. Hamsters -- Fiction

ISBN 0-439-28356-6; 0-439-28357-4 pa

LC 2002-6981

Freddy, a remarkably intelligent golden hamster, learns how to read and how to write on a computer and escapes captivity to become an independent and civilized creature

"Illustrated with amusing black-ink sketches, this engaging story will appeal to fans of animal fantasies." SLJ

Other titles about Freddy are:

Freddy in peril (2004)

Freddy to the rescue (2005)

The haunting of Freddy (2006)

Freddy's final quest (2007)

Reinhardt, Dana

Odessa again; Dana Reinhardt. 1st ed. Wendy Lamb Books 2013 208 p. (ebook) $47.97; (hardcover) $15.99; (library) $18.99

Grades: 4 5 6 7   **Fic**

1. Remarriage -- Fiction 4. Time travel -- Fiction

ISBN 0385739567; 9780375897887; 9780385739566; 9780385907934

LC 2012008231

In this children's novel, by Dana Reinhardt, "fourth grader Odessa Green-Light lives with her mom and her toad of a little brother, Oliver. Her dad is getting remarried. . . . Meanwhile, Odessa moves into the attic room of their new house. One day [it] . . . turns out that Odessa has gone back in time a whole day! With this new power she can fix all sorts of things--embarrassing moments, big mistakes, and even help Oliver be less of a toad. Her biggest goal: reunite Mom and Dad." (Publisher's note)

"Realistically drawn, Odessa is a believable, likable kid on the brink of growing up, struggling with family changes. . . . With humor as well as depth, this is an endearing story of a spunky girl who realizes that life gets more, not less, confusing as she grows up." Kirkus

The **summer** I learned to fly. Wendy Lamb Books 2011 216p $15.99; lib bdg $18.99; e-book $15.99

Grades: 5 6 7 8   **Fic**

1. Rats -- Fiction 2. California -- Fiction 3. Family life -- Fiction 4. Retail trade -- Fiction 5. Single parent family -- Fiction

ISBN 978-0-385-73954-2; 0-385-73954-0; 978-0-385-90792-7 lib bdg; 0-385-90792-3 lib bdg; 978-0-375-89787-0 e-book; 0-375-89787-9 e-book

LC 2010029412

Thirteen-year-old Drew starts the summer of 1986 helping in her mother's cheese shop and dreaming about co-worker Nick, but when her widowed mother begins dating, Drew's father's book of lists, her pet rat, and Emmett, a boy on a quest, help her cope.

"This quiet novel invites readers to share in its heroine's deepest yearnings, changing moods, and difficult realizations." Publ Wkly

Repka, Janice

The **clueless** girl's guide to being a genius. Dutton Children's Books 2011 218p $16.99

Grades: 4 5 6   **Fic**

1. School stories 2. Genius -- Fiction 3. Teachers -- Fiction 4. Friendship -- Fiction 5. Mathematics -- Fiction 6. Baton twirling -- Fiction

ISBN 978-0-525-42333-1; 0-525-42333-8

LC 2010038139

When Aphrodite Wigglesmith, a thirteen-year-old, Harvard-educated mathematics genius, returns home to teach remedial math to middle school students, both she and her students end up getting unexpected lessons.

"A lighthearted, funny and often bizarre saga of middle-school mayhem. . . . Equal parts silly and endearing." Kirkus

Resau, Laura

★ **Star** in the forest. Delacorte Press 2010 149p il $14.99; lib bdg $17.99

Grades: 4 5 6   **Fic**

1. Dogs -- Fiction 2. Fathers -- Fiction 3. Friendship -- Fiction 4. Illegal aliens -- Fiction 5. Mexican Americans -- Fiction

ISBN 978-0-385-73792-0; 0-385-73792-0; 978-0-385-90700-2 lib bdg; 0-385-90700-1 lib bdg

LC 2009-03898

After eleven-year-old Zitlally's father is deported to Mexico, she takes refuge in her trailer park's forest of rusted car parts, where she befriends a spunky neighbor and finds a stray dog that she nurses back to health and believes she must keep safe so that her father will return.

"Resau has woven details of immigrant life into a compelling story. . . . This is a well-told and deeply satisfying read." SLJ

★ **What** the moon saw; a novel. Delacorte Press 2006 258p $15.95; pa $5.99

Grades: 5 6 7 8   **Fic**

1. Mexico -- Fiction 2. Country life -- Fiction 3. Grandparents -- Fiction

ISBN 0-385-73343-7; 0-440-23957-5 pa

LC 2006-04571

Fourteen-year-old Clara Luna spends the summer with her grandparents in the tiny, remote village of Yucuyoo, Mexico, learning about her grandmother's life as a healer, her father's decision to leave home for the United States, and her own place in the world.

This is an "exquisitely crafted narrative. . . . The characters are well developed. . . . Resau does an exceptional job of portraying the agricultural society sympathetically and realistically." SLJ

Rex, Adam

Champions of breakfast; Adam Rex. Balzer + Bray 2014 368 p. (The cold cereal saga) (hardcover bdg.: alk. paper) $16.99

Grades: 4 5 6 7   **Fic**

1. Imaginary places 2. Magic -- Fiction 3. Fairies -- Fiction 4. Cereals, Prepared -- Fiction 5. Adventure and adventurers -- Fiction

ISBN 0062060082; 9780062060082

LC 2013021387

In this book by Adam Rex, part of the Cold Cereal Saga series, "time is quickly running out before Nimue, who has been working with the corrupt Goodco Cereal Company, finds another portal and uses it to bring the mythical dragon Saxbriton into our world--and launch the terrible fairy invasion. In the end, it's up to Scott and his companions to save the fate of two worlds." (Publisher's note)

"Scott, Polly, Emily, and Erno, together with a large supporting cast, rescue the miniaturized Queen of England and quell a fairy invasion by killing the dragon Saxbriton and healing the rift between the worlds. The superabundance of characters is hard to keep track of, but for readers following the Arthurian-reimagining trilogy, action, magic, and humor combine for a whiz-bang conclusion." (Horn Book)

★ **Cold** cereal. Balzer + Bray 2012 421p il $16.99
Grades: 4 5 6 7 **Fic**
1. Adventure fiction 2. Food -- Fiction 3. Magic -- Fiction 4. Twins -- Fiction 5. Siblings -- Fiction
ISBN 978-0-06-206002-0; 0-06-206002-3
LC 2011019538

A boy who may be part changeling, twins involved in a bizarre secret experiment, and a clurichaun in a red tracksuit try to save the world from an evil cereal company whose ultimate goal is world domination.

"The author tucks in portrait illustrations and hilariously odd TV-commercial storyboards, along with a hooded Secret Society, figures from Arthurian legend, magical spells and potions, a certain amount of violence, many wonderful throwaway lines. . . . All in all, it's a mad scramble that culminates in the revelation of a dastardly plot that will require sequels to foil." Kirkus

Smek for president! Adam Rex. Disney-Hyperion Books 2014 272 p. illustrations (hardback) $16.99
Grades: 5 6 7 8 **Fic**
1. Science fiction 2. Humorous fiction 3. Adventure and adventurers 4. Human-alien encounters -- Fiction 5. Extraterrestrial beings -- Fiction 6. Humorous stories 7. Interplanetary voyages -- Fiction 8. Adventure and adventurers -- Fiction
ISBN 1484709519; 9781484709511
LC 2014010764

Sequel to: The True Meaning of Smekday (2007)

In this book, by Adam Rex, "Tip and J.Lo are back for another hilarious intergalactic adventure. . . . After Tip and J.Lo banished the Gorg from Earth in a scheme involving the cloning of many, many cats, the pair is notorious--but not for their heroics. Instead, human Dan Landry has taken credit for conquering the Gorg, and the Boov blame J.Lo for ruining their colonization of the planet." (Publisher's note)

"After successfully banishing the Gorg and ruining the Boovs's plans to colonize planet Earth, J.Lo and Gratuity (Tip to her friends) are back in this sequel to The True Meaning of Smekday (Hyperion, 2007)... Hilarious cartoons will please graphic novel aficionados. Don't skip Appendix A: Rules for Stickyfish." SLJ

★ The **true** meaning of Smekday. Hyperion Books for Children 2007 423p il $16.99; pa $6.99
Grades: 5 6 7 8 **Fic**
1. Science fiction 2. End of the world -- Fiction 3. Extraterrestrial beings -- Fiction
ISBN 0-7868-4900-2; 978-0-7868-4900-0; 0-7868-4901-0 pa; 978-0-7868-4901-7 pa

When her mother is abducted by aliens on Christmas Eve (or "Smekday" Eve since the Boov invasion), 11 year-old Tip hops in the family car and heads south to find her and meets an alien Boov mechanic who agrees to help her and save the planet from disaster.

"Incorporating dozens of his weird and wonderful illustrations and fruitfully manipulating the narrative structure, Rex skewers any number of subjects." Publ Wkly

Unlucky charms; Adam Rex. Balzer + Bray 2013 400 p. (The cold cereal saga) (hardback) $16.99
Grades: 4 5 6 7 **Fic**
1. Fantasy fiction -- Juvenile fiction 2. Humorous fiction -- Juvenile fiction 3. Prepared cereals -- Juvenile fiction 4. Magic -- Fiction 5. Twins -- Fiction 6. Cereals, Prepared -- Fiction 7. Brothers and sisters -- Fiction
ISBN 0062060058; 9780062060051
LC 2012026714

This humorous juvenile fantasy book, by Adam Rex, is part of the "Cold Cereal Saga." "In this hectic middle volume, [Adam] Rex's notably diverse crew of human, part-human and nonhuman allies splits up in hopes of scotching the schemes of the sorceress Nimue, who is out to create a worldwide army of mind-controlled 'sugar zombies' through magically enhanced breakfast cereal." (Kirkus Reviews)

Reynolds, Peter H.

★ **Sky** color; Peter H. Reynolds. Candlewick 2012 32 p. (hardback) $14.00
Grades: PreK K 1 2 **Fic**
1. Sky -- Fiction 2. Picture books for children 3. Mural painting and decoration -- Juvenile literature 4. Color -- Fiction 5. Paint -- Fiction 6. Artists -- Fiction 7. Schools -- Fiction
ISBN 0763623458; 9780763623456
LC 2011048374

In this children's picture book, "Marisol is an artist, famous at school for her art . . . . When their teacher tells her class that they are going to paint a mural in the library, . . . Marisol volunteers to paint the sky. But to her dismay, in the box of paint there is no blue." She agonizes until she realizes that the sky isn't always blue and comes up with a solution. "On a wordless double page, her classmates admire the 'sky color' she has created." (Children's Literature)

Rhodes, Jewell Parker

★ **Ninth** Ward. Little, Brown 2010 217p $15.99
Grades: 5 6 7 8 **Fic**
1. New Orleans (La.) -- Fiction 2. Young adult literature -- Works 3. Extrasensory perception -- Fiction 4. Hurricane Katrina, 2005 -- Fiction
ISBN 978-0-316-04307-6; 0-316-04307-9
LC 2009-34423

Coretta Scott King Author Award honor book, 2011

In New Orleans' Ninth Ward, twelve-year-old Lanesha, who can see spirits, and her adopted grandmother have no choice but to stay and weather the storm as Hurricane Katrina bears down upon them.

"The dynamics of the diverse community enrich the survival story, and the contemporary struggle of one brave child humanizes the historic tragedy." Booklist

Sugar; Jewell Parker Rhodes. 1st ed. Little, Brown and Co. 2013 288 p. (hardcover) $16.99
Grades: 3 4 5 6 7 8 **Fic**
1. Historical fiction 2. Race relations -- Fiction 3. African Americans -- Fiction 4. Chinese Americans -- Fiction 5. Plantation life -- Louisiana -- Fiction 6. Louisiana -- History -- 1865-1950 -- Fiction 7. Reconstruction (U.S. history, 1865-1877) -- Fiction
ISBN 0316043052; 9780316043052
LC 2012026218

In this historical novel, by Jewell Parker Rhodes, "ten-year-old Sugar lives on the River Road sugar plantation along the banks of the Mississippi. Slavery is over, but laboring in the fields all day doesn't make her feel very free. . . . Here's another tale of a strong, spirited young girl who rises beyond her circumstances and inspires others to work toward a brighter future." (Publisher's note)

"Sugar's clipped narration is personable and engaging, strongly evoking the novel's historical setting and myriad racial tensions, making them accessible and meaningful to beginning readers." Pub Wkly

Richards, Jasmine

The **book** of wonders. HarperCollins 2012 400p $14.99

Grades: 4 5 6 7   **Fic**

1. Fantasy fiction 2. Adventure fiction 3. Friendship -- Fiction

ISBN 978-0-06-201007-0; 0-06-201007-7

LC 2011009153

In a tale loosely based on the Arabian nights, thirteen-year-old Zardi and her best friend, Ridhan, join forces with Captain Sinbad to defeat an evil sultan and restore magic to the world of Arribitha.

"This buoyant debut offers a fresh plot, brisk pacing and engaging characters. . . . Richards deftly borrows from lesser-known tales of the 1001 Arabian Nights to enrich her complex storyline while keeping style and syntax simple and direct." Kirkus

Richards, Justin

Thunder Raker; illustrated by Jim Hansen. IPG/HarperCollins 2010 139p il (Agent Alfie) pa $6.99

Grades: 3 4 5   **Fic**

1. School stories 2. Spies -- Fiction

ISBN 978-0-00-727357-7; 0-00-727357-6

"After Alfie moves to a new town, he is enrolled by mistake at Thunder Raker Manor, a top-secret school that trains children to be future British spies. At his new school, Alfie encounters a host of eccentric teachers and swashbuckling students. Although at first Alfie seems in over his head, his good sense and practical ideas help him get the best grades in the class on his first homework assignment, and by the end of the novel, he manages to thwart agents from the evil organization SPUD. . . . The bright concept, short length, and humorous, action-packed drawings that fill each chapter should keep this in demand and leave readers eager for the series' next installment." Booklist

Richter, Jutta

Beyond the station lies the sea; translated from the German by Anna Brailovsky. Milkweed Editions 2009 81p $14

Grades: 4 5 6 7   **Fic**

1. Angels -- Fiction 2. Homeless persons -- Fiction

ISBN 978-1-57131-690-5; 1-57131-690-6

LC 2009018135

Trying to get to the beach where it is warm, two homeless boys enlist the aid of a rich woman who gives them money in exchange for a guardian angel.

"Richter presents a darkly poetic, masterfully crafted view of life on the streets." Publ Wkly

Riddell, Chris

★ **Ottoline** and the yellow cat. HarperCollinsPublishers 2008 171p il $10.99; lib bdg $14.89; pa $6.99

Grades: 2 3 4 5   **Fic**

1. Mystery fiction 2. Cats -- Fiction 3. Dogs -- Fiction

ISBN 978-0-06-144879-9; 0-06-144879-6; 978-0-06-144880-5 lib bdg; 0-06-144880-X lib bdg; 978-0-06-144881-2 pa; 0-06-144881-8 pa

"While her parents are off traveling the world collecting 'interesting things,' Ottoline Brown lives in an elaborate apartment in Big City with her best friend, guardian, and accomplice in forming clever plans. He is called Mr. Monroe and is a silent creature from Norway. . . . Ottoline solves a mystery involving a cat burglar, who is actually a cat, and the missing lapdogs of well-to-do women. The story is told through the text and the detailed line drawings that appear on each page. Done in black and white with red highlighting a quirky detail or two, the illustrations add humor, depth, and momentum to the narrative. The quickly moving plot is grounded in real emotion." SLJ

Another title about Ottoline is:

Ottoline goes to school (2009)

Riel, Jorn

The **raiders**; written by Jørn Riel; illustrated by Helen Cann; translated by John Mason. Barefoot Books 2012 127 p. (alk. paper) $12.99

Grades: 4 5 6   **Fic**

1. Historical fiction 2. Inuit -- Greenland -- Fiction 3. Eskimos -- Greenland -- Fiction 4. Vikings -- Greenland -- Fiction 5. Greenland -- History -- To 1500 -- Fiction

ISBN 1846867444; 9781846867446

LC 2011044383

This book by Jorn Riel, part of the Inuk Quartet series, "continues the exciting adventures of Leiv, Apuluk and Narua established in 'The Shipwreck.' The story begins with our trio settled peacefully on Thor Gunnarrsson's farmstead in Greenland. When Viking raiders arrive at the farmstead, their quiet world is disturbed forever. Leiv, Apuluk and Narua must rely on their wits, their courage, and their friendship to protect their new home." (Publisher's note)

The **shipwreck**; translated from Danish by John Mason; illustrated by Helen Cann. Barefoot Books 2011 il (The Inuk quartet) pa $12.99

Grades: 4 5 6   **Fic**

1. Adventure fiction 2. Inuit -- Fiction 3. Vikings -- Fiction

ISBN 978-1-84686-335-6; 1-84686-335-X

"This beautifully illustrated epic adventure, set circa 1000 CE, begins with the shocking, retaliatory beheading of young Viking Leiv's father by Thorstein Gunnarsson. The playful boy becomes withdrawn and vows to take revenge. When Thorstein casts off from Iceland for Greenland to serve out his sentence of exile, Leiv stows away onboard but is swept into the sea during a storm. An Inuit brother and sister, Apuluk, 12, and Narua, 11, find him and care for him in secret. . . . The narrative is straightforward and well paced, with several engaging dramatic episodes. Riel skillfully interweaves information about the Inuit culture, language, and environment without being didactic. . . . Vocabulary may pose a challenge for less-advanced readers, and mention of beheadings and amputations may be unsuitable for others. But Cann's ethereal watercolor, graphite, and collage illustrations in cool blue tones and browns have a calmer mood that will enchant readers with the beauty of the Arctic landscape." SLJ

The **snowstorm**; written by Jørn Riel; illustrated by Helen Cann; translation by John Mason. Barefoot Books 2012 126 p. (alk. paper) $12.99

Grades: 4 5 6   **Fic**

1. Greenland -- Fiction 2. Adventure fiction 3. Inuit -- Fiction 4. Eskimos -- Fiction 5. Voyages and travels -- Fiction 6. Arctic regions -- History -- Fiction

ISBN 1846867975; 9781846867972

LC 2012009599

This book by Jørn Riel, "the third in a four-part Viking-era adventure, pits four young Greenlanders against both a howling gale and a crew of brutal pirates. . . . Leiv, his Inuit brother-and-sister companions Apuluk and Narua, and rescued serf Sølvi sled northward in search of the vanished chieftain Thorstein. . . . The explorers weather a journey highlighted by a violent . . . storm . . . [and a] battle aboard an iced-in British longship." (Kirkus Reviews)

Riley, James

Half upon a time. Aladdin 2010 385p $15.99

Grades: 5 6 7 8   **Fic**

1. Fairy tales 2. Adventure fiction

ISBN 978-1-4169-9593-7; 1-4169-9593-5

LC 2010012714

In the village of Giant's Hand Jack's grandfather has been pushing him to find a princess and get married, so when a young lady falls out of the sky wearing a shirt that says "Punk Princess," and she tells Jack that her grandmother, who looks suspiciously like the long-missing Snow White, has been kidnapped, Jack decides to help her.

"Riley does a wonderful job of combining the 21st century with the world in which fairies are alive, as well as creating characters that middle school students will relate to." Libr Media Connect

Riordan, Rick

The **blood** of Olympus; Rick Riordan. 1st edition Disney-Hyperion Books 2014 528 p. (The heroes of Olympus) (hardback) $19.99

Grades: 5 6 7 8   **Fic**

1. Adventure fiction 2. Classical mythology -- Fiction 3. Mythology, Greek -- Fiction 4. Mythology, Roman -- Fiction 5. Gaia (Greek deity) -- Fiction

ISBN 1423146735; 9781423146735

LC 2014017392

In this novel by Rick Riordan, book 5 of the "The Heroes of Olympus" series, "though the Greek and Roman crewmembers of the Argo II have made progress in their many quests, they still seem no closer to defeating the earth mother, Gaea. Her giants have risen . . . and they're stronger than ever. They must be stopped before the Feast of Spes, when Gaea plans to have two demigods sacrificed in Athens." (Publisher's note)

"Readers looking forward to the battle scenes will find plenty here, but the young heroes also rely on their wits as they dupe, charm, and negotiate their way through a series of encounters with gods, goddesses, and mythological creatures." Booklist

The **house** of Hades; Rick Riordan. Disney-Hyperion 2013 597 p. (Heroes of Olympus) (hardback) $19.99

Grades: 5 6 7 8   **Fic**

1. Hell -- Fiction 2. Gods and goddesses -- Fiction 3. Classical mythology -- Fiction 4. Camps -- Fiction 5. Giants -- Fiction 6. Mythology, Greek -- Fiction 7. Mythology, Roman -- Fiction 8. Gaia (Greek deity) -- Fiction 9. Hera (Greek deity) -- Fiction

ISBN 1423146727; 9781423146728

LC 2013015946

In this book, by Rick Riordan, "Annabeth and Percy tumble into a pit leading straight to the Underworld. The other five demigods have to put aside their grief and follow Percy's instructions to find the mortal side of the Doors of Death. If they can fight their way through the Gaea's forces, and Percy and Annabeth can survive the House of Hades, then the Seven will be able to seal the Doors from both sides and prevent the giants from raising Gaea." (Publisher's note)

"In this fourth in Riordan's series pitting Roman and Greek demigods against an awakening goddess Gaea, Percy and Annabeth trek through Tartarus to escape through the Doors of Death, while their friends fight their way to the Doors' mortal side to rescue them. The wisecracking teens reveal emotional depths while overcoming monsters and personal obstacles in this high velocity continuation of the gripping franchise." Horn Book

★ The **lightning** thief. Miramax Books/Hyperion Books for Children 2005 377p (Percy Jackson & the Olympians) pa $7.99

Grades: 5 6 7 8 9   **Fic**

1. Classical mythology -- Fiction 2. Young adult literature -- Works

ISBN 0-7868-5629-7; 1-4231-3494-X pa; 978-0-6417-2344-5; 978-1-4231-3494-7 pa

LC 2005-299400

Twelve-year-old Percy Jackson learns he is a demigod, the son of a mortal woman and Poseidon, god of the sea. His mother sends him to a summer camp for demigods where he and his new friends set out on a quest to prevent a war between the gods.

"Riordan's fast-paced adventure is fresh, dangerous, and funny." Booklist

The **Mark** of Athena; Rick Riordan. Disney Hyperion Books 2012 586 p. (The Heroes of Olympus) (hardback) $19.99

Grades: 5 6 7 8   **Fic**

1. Gods and goddesses -- Fiction 2. Classical mythology -- Fiction 3. Camps -- Fiction 4. Giants -- Fiction 5. Mythology, Greek -- Fiction 6. Mythology, Roman -- Fiction 7. Gaia (Greek deity) -- Fiction 8. Hera (Greek deity) -- Fiction

ISBN 9781423140603

LC 2012017264

In this book, by Rick Riordan, "the Greek and Roman demigods will have to cooperate in order to defeat the giants released by the Earth Mother, Gaea. Then they will have to sail together to the ancient land to find the Doors of Death. What exactly are the Doors of Death? Much of the prophecy remains a mystery." (Publisher's note)

"With Gaea awakening and pitting the Greek demigods against their Roman counterparts, Percy Jackson, Jason, and their companions travel to Rome so Annabeth can search for her mother Athena's statue, stolen by the Romans in antiquity. Its return might heal the rift between the camps. Riordan's likable, strong, distinct characters drive the narrative in this rousing continuation of the saga." Horn Book

★ The **maze** of bones. Scholastic 2008 220p il (The 39 clues) $12.99
Grades: 4 5 6 7   **Fic**
  1. Family -- Fiction 2. Ciphers -- Fiction
  ISBN 978-0-545-06039-4; 0-545-06039-7
At the reading of their grandmother's will, Dan and Amy Cahill are given the choice of receiving a million dollars or uncovering the 39 clues hidden around the world that will lead to the source of the family's power, but by taking on the clues, they end up in a dangerous race against their own family members.
"Adeptly incorporating a genuine kids' perspective, the narrative unfolds like a boulder rolling downhill and keeps readers glued to the pages. . . . The book dazzles with suspense, plot twists, and snappy humor." SLJ
  Other titles in this series are:
  One false note by Gordon Korman (2008)
  The sword thief by Peter Lerangis (2009)
  The black circle by Patrick Carman (2009)
  Beyond the grave by Jude Watson (2009)
  In too deep by Jude Watson (2010)
  The viper's nest by Peter Lerangis (2010)
  The emperor's code by Gordon Korman (2010)
  Storm warning by Linda Sue Park (2010)
  Into the gauntlet by Margaret Peterson Haddix (2010).

Percy Jackson's Greek Gods; Rick Riordan; illustrated by John Rocco. Disney-Hyperion 2014 336 p. color illustrations (hardback) $24.99
Grades: 5 6 7 8   **Fic**
  1. Greek mythology 2. Gods and goddesses -- Fiction 3. Gods, Greek -- Fiction
  ISBN 1423183649; 9781423183648
                      LC 2013034612
"Riordan takes the classic guide to Greek myths and makes it his own, with an introduction and narration by beloved character Percy Jackson. With 19 chapters, this oversize hardcover includes a variety of stories, from the early tales of Gaea and the Titans to individual tales of gods readers encounter in the 'Percy Jackson' series. . ., such as Ares, Apollo, and Dionysus." (School Library Journal)
"Combining the sarcasm and wit of Percy Jackson with the original Greek myths is a great way to hook tweens and teens on the stories without boring them. The beautiful illustrations by John Rocco enhance each story without taking away from the action and drama." VOYA
  Includes bibliographical references and index

The **Serpent's** Shadow; Rick Riordan. Disney/Hyperion Books 2012 viii, 406 p.p (hardcover) $19.99
Grades: 4 5 6 7   **Fic**
  1. Adventure fiction 2. Supernatural -- Fiction 3. Magic -- Fiction 4. Mythology, Egyptian -- Fiction 5. Voyages and travels -- Fiction 6. Brothers and sisters -- Fiction 7. Adventure and adventurers -- Fiction
  ISBN 1423140575; 9781423140573
                      LC 2012454979

This book by Rick Riordan is the third installment of the Kane Chronicles series. "Despite their best efforts, Carter and Sadie Kane can't seem to keep Apophis, the chaos snake, down. Now Apophis is threatening to plunge the world into eternal darkness, and the Kanes are faced with the impossible task of having to destroy him once and for all." (Publisher's note)

The **son** of Neptune. Disney/Hyperion Books 2011 521p (The heroes of Olympus) $19.99
Grades: 5 6 7 8   **Fic**
  1. Camps -- Fiction 2. Monsters -- Fiction 3. Prophecies -- Fiction 4. Classical mythology -- Fiction
  ISBN 978-1-4231-4059-7; 1-4231-4059-1
                      LC 2011017658
Demigod Percy Jackson, still with no memory, and his new friends from Camp Jupiter, Hazel and Frank, go on a quest to free Death, but their bigger task is to unite the Greek and Roman camps so that the Prophecy of Seven can be fulfilled.

The **throne** of fire; Rick Riordan. Disney/Hyperion Books 2011 (Kane chronicles) $18.99
Grades: 4 5 6 7   **Fic**
  ISBN 978-1-4231-4056-6; 1-4231-4056-7; 1423140567; 9781423140566
  Sequel to: The red pyramid (2010)
Carter and Sadie, offspring of the brilliant Egyptologist Dr. Julius Kane, embark on a worldwide search for the Book of Ra, but the House of Life and the gods of chaos are determined to stop them.
"Lit by flashes of humor, this fantasy adventure is an engaging addition to the Kane Chronicles series." Booklist

Vespers rising; [by] Rick Riordan, Peter Lerangis, Gordon Korman, Jude Watson. Scholastic 2011 238p (The 39 clues) $12.99
Grades: 4 5 6 7   **Fic**
  1. Ciphers -- Fiction
  ISBN 978-0-545-29059-3; 0-545-32606-0
Fourteen-year-old Amy Cahill and her younger brother Dan thought they could return to their regular lives when they found the 39 clues. But the Vespers, powerful enemies, will stop at nothing to get the clues. And with the Vespers rising, the world is in jeopardy.

Rising, Janet
The **word** on the yard. Sourcebooks 2010 189p (The pony whisperer) pa $6.99
Grades: 4 5 6   **Fic**
  1. Horses -- Fiction
  ISBN 978-1-4022-3952-6 pa; 1-4022-3952-1 pa
  First published 2009 in the United Kingdom
Pia finally starts to feel like she belongs in her new town after people begin to hear that she can communicate with horses, but her popularity is not the only thing she has to worry about when things start to go wrong.
"This combination of magic and a quick-moving, contemporary plot woven around horse and human conflicts and friendships is a light and enjoyable read for fans of this genre." SLJ

Rivers, Karen

Finding Ruby Starling; by Karen Rivers. Arthur A. Levine Books, an imprint of Scholastic Inc. 2014 288 p. (hardcover) $17.99

Grades: 5 6 7 8 **Fic**

1. Twins -- Fiction 2. Adoption -- Fiction 3. Blogs -- Fiction 4. Email -- Fiction 5. Sisters -- Fiction 6. Mothers and daughters -- Fiction

ISBN 0545534798; 9780545534796

LC 2014002269

In this middle grade book by Karen Rivers, "when Ruby Starling gets a message from a Ruth Quayle proclaiming them to be long-lost twin sisters, she doesn't know what to do with it. . . . Ruth is an extroverted American girl. Ruby is a shy English one. As they investigate the truth of their birth and the circumstances of their separation, they also share lives full of friends, family, and possible romances." (Publisher's note)

"In this epistolary, dual-narrator story, Ruth, an American twelve-year-old, e-finds her identical twin, Ruby, in England. As with any novel in letters (in this case emails, handwritten notes, and the occasional Tumblr posting), voice is everything, and Ruth and Ruby have distinctive, convincing, and entertaining writing styles. Subplots abound, including the backstory of two complicated families. Hectic, highly textured, and good-natured without being soppy." Horn Book

Roberts, Laura Peyton

Green. Delacorte Press 2010 261p $16.99; lib bdg $19.99

Grades: 5 6 7 8 **Fic**

1. Fantasy fiction 2. Leprechauns -- Fiction 3. Grandmothers -- Fiction

ISBN 978-0-385-73558-2; 0-385-73558-8; 978-0-385-90543-5 lib bdg; 0-385-90543-2 lib bdg

LC 2008-54241

Abducted by leprechauns on her thirteenth birthday, Lilybet Green learns that there is more to her family tree—and to her bond with her late grandmother—than she ever imagined.

"A fun, fresh take on leprechaun lore that pushes well past typical depictions to embrace banking transactions, lepro-human relations, and some creative problem-solving. Lily is a credible hero, by turns scared and confident, and definitely one young readers will enjoy following." Booklist

Roberts, Willo Davis

The **one** left behind; [by] Willo Davis Roberts. Atheneum Books for Young Readers 2006 139p $16.95; pa $5.99

Grades: 5 6 7 8 **Fic**

1. Twins -- Fiction 2. Sisters -- Fiction 3. Kidnapping -- Fiction 4. Bereavement -- Fiction

ISBN 978-0-689-85075-2; 0-689-85075-1; 978-0-689-85083-7 pa; 0-689-85083-2 pa

LC 2005018196

"Since losing her vivacious twin sister, Angel, nearly a year ago, . . . 11-year-old [Mandy] drifts through the days, aching for her dead sister's company. But when someone breaks into the house and steals food, Mandy snaps into action and investigates what might be going on. . . . The sus-

pense mounts to a desperate climax before all is resolved safely. An introspective page-turner." Booklist

★ The **view** from the cherry tree. Atheneum Pubs. 1975 181p hardcover o.p. pa $5.99

Grades: 5 6 7 8 **Fic**

1. Mystery fiction

ISBN 0-689-30483-8; 0-689-71784-9 pa

"Although written in a direct and unpretentious style, this is essentially a sophisticated story, solidly constructed, imbued with suspense, evenly paced, and effective in conveying the atmosphere of a household coping with the last-minute problems and pressures of a family wedding." Bull Cent Child Books

Robertson, Keith

★ **Henry** Reed, Inc. illustrated by Robert McCloskey. Viking 1958 239p il hardcover o.p. pa $4.99

Grades: 4 5 6 **Fic**

ISBN 0-14-034144-7 pa

"Henry Reed, on vacation from the American School in Naples, keeps a record of his research into the American free-enterprise system, to be used as a school report on his return. With a neighbor, Midge Glass, he starts a business in pure and applied research, which results in some very free and widely enterprising experiences, all recorded deadpan in his journal. Very funny and original escapades." Hodges. Books for Elem Sch Libr

Another title about Henry Reed is:

Henry Reed's babysitting service (1966)

Robertson, M. P.

Frank n stan; M. P. Robertson. Pgw 2012 32 p. $17.99

Grades: K 1 2 3 **Fic**

1. Robots -- Fiction 2. Siblings -- Fiction 3. Friendship -- Fiction

ISBN 1847801307; 9781847801302

In author M. P. Robertson's book, "young Franklin P. Shelley often asks his mother for a younger sibling . . . . Industrious Frank decides to take matters into his own hands and sets out to build one . . . [named Stan.] Frank charges up the battery, and the light in Stan's chest begins to glow . . . One day, Mum surprises Frank with a cute baby girl, and the boy begins to spend more time with his sister, Mary, and less with Stan. One snowy evening, Stan leaves. It doesn't take long for him to freeze or for the family to miss him. A big hug convinces the big mechanical lug to return." (Kirkus Reviews)

Robinet, Harriette Gillem

★ **Forty** acres and maybe a mule. Atheneum Bks. for Young Readers 1998 132p hardcover o.p. pa $4.99

Grades: 4 5 6 7 **Fic**

1. African Americans -- Fiction 2. Reconstruction (1865-1876) -- Fiction 3. United States -- History -- 1865-1898 -- Fiction

ISBN 0-689-82078-X; 0-689-83317-2 pa

LC 97-39169

Born with a withered leg and hand, Pascal, who is about twelve years old, joins other former slaves in a search for a farm and the freedom which it promises

"Robinet skillfully balances her in-depth historical knowledge with the feelings of her characters, creating a story that moves along rapidly and comes to a bittersweet conclusion." Booklist

Walking to the bus-rider blues. Atheneum Bks. for Young Readers 2000 146p hardcover o.p. pa $4.99
Grades: 5 6 7 8   **Fic**
1. Race relations -- Fiction 2. African Americans -- Fiction
ISBN 0-689-83191-9; 0-689-83886-7 pa
LC 99-29054
Twelve-year-old Alfa Merryfield, his older sister, and their grandmother struggle for rent money, food, and their dignity as they participate in the Montgomery, Alabama bus boycott in the summer of 1956

"Ingredients of mystery, suspense, and humor enhance and personalize this well-constructed story that offers insight into a troubled era." SLJ

Robinson, Barbara
★ The **best** Christmas pageant ever; pictures by Judith Gwyn Brown. Harper & Row 1972 80p il $15.99; lib bdg $16.89; pa $5.99
Grades: 4 5 6   **Fic**
1. Pageants -- Fiction 2. Christmas -- Fiction
ISBN 0-06-025043-7; 0-06-025044-5 lib bdg; 0-06-440275-4 pa

In this story the six Herdmans, "absolutely the worst kids in the history of the world," discover the meaning of Christmas when they bully their way into the leading roles of the local church nativity play

The story "romps through the festive preparations with comic relish, and if the Herdmans are so gauche as to seem exaggerated, they are still enjoyable, as are the not-so-subtle pokes at pageant-planning in general." Bull Cent Child Books

Other titles about the Herdmans are:
The best Halloween ever (2004)
The best school year ever (1994)

Robinson, Mabel L.
Bright Island; Mabel L. Robinson; with decorations by Lynd Ward. 75th anniversary ed. Random House Books for Young Readers 2012 276 p. ill. (hardback) $16.99
Grades: 3 4 5   **Fic**
1. Bildungsromans 2. School stories 3. Maine -- Fiction 4. Schools -- Fiction 5. Coming of age -- Fiction 6. Boarding schools -- Fiction 7. Islands -- Maine -- Fiction
ISBN 0394809866; 9780394809861
LC 2012009178
Newbery Honor Book (1938)
This book by Mabel L. Robinson follows "Thankful Curtis, [who] is more like her sea captain grandfather than any of her older brothers are. Nothing suits her better than sailing and helping her father with the farm. But when her dreaded sisters-in-law suggest that Thankful get some proper schooling on the mainland . . . Thankful finds the uncharted waters of school difficult to navigate." (Publisher's note)

Robinson, Sharon
Safe at home. Scholastic Press 2006 151p $16.99; pa $5.99
Grades: 4 5 6   **Fic**
1. Baseball -- Fiction 2. New York (N.Y.) -- Fiction 3.

African Americans -- Fiction
ISBN 0-439-67197-3; 0-439-67198-1 pa
LC 2005-50250
After the death of his father, Elijah Breeze, a ten-year-old African American boy, moves back to New York City with his mother and attends a summer baseball camp as he tries to make new friends and adapt to urban ways.

The author "has created two intriguing protagonists and a group of equally colorful secondary characters. . . . Regardless of their interest in baseball, readers will identify with these youngsters and appreciate the simple story." SLJ
Another title about Elijah Breeze is:
Slam dunk! (2007)

Slam dunk! by Sharon Robinson. 1st ed.; Scholastic Press 2007 151p $16.99
Grades: 4 5 6   **Fic**
1. Basketball -- Fiction 2. Friendship -- Fiction 3. Family life -- Fiction 4. New York (N.Y.) -- Fiction 5. African Americans -- Fiction
ISBN 978-0-439-67199-6; 0-439-67199-X
LC 2006102462
Sequel to: Safe home (2006)
At Harlem's Langston Hughes Middle School, eleven-year-old Elijah "Jumper" Breeze and his friends complete against Nia and her girlfriends on the basketball court, in a video dance tournament, and for a Student Council seat, and, meanwhile, several of the students face issues with their fathers.

"While serious issues broached in the earlier book . . . are given renewed attention, this is really an amiable story about friends who stay that way, a theme that translates well in any community." Booklist

Rockliff, Mara
The **case** of the missing moose; by Lewis B. Montgomery; illustrated by Amy Wummer. Kane Press 2011 96p il (Milo & Jazz mysteries) lib bdg $22.60; pa $6.95
Grades: 1 2 3 4   **Fic**
1. Mystery fiction 2. Camps -- Fiction 3. Lost and found possessions -- Fiction
ISBN 978-1-57565-331-0 lib bdg; 1-57565-331-1 lib bdg; 978-1-57565-322-8 pa; 1-57565-322-2 pa
LC 2010023478
While Milo and Jazz, detectives-in-training, are at summer camps on the same lake, the mascot built by Milo's team for the color wars disappears.

"The short, easy chapters are accompanied by playful pen-and-ink illustrations that enhance the story. This early chapter book mystery is engaging." Booklist

The **case** of the poisoned pig; Illustrated by Amy Wummer. Kane Press 2009 96p il (Milo & Jazz mysteries) $22.60; pa $6.95
Grades: 1 2 3 4   **Fic**
1. Mystery fiction 2. Pigs -- Fiction
ISBN 978-1-57565-289-4; 1-57565-289-7; 978-1-57565-286-3 pa; 1-57565-286-2 pa
LC 2008027537
When Jazz's pet piglet gets sick and the veterinarian suspects it was poisoned, she and Milo use their detective skills to try to figure out who did it.

The "volume ends with additional 'brain stretchers' and mini-cases. . . . The [story is] quick and satisfying, and challenges at the back of the [book contributes] to the enjoyment. Wummer's pencil and ink illustrations add a humorous touch and are perfect for the [story]." SLJ

Rocklin, Joanne

The **five** lives of our cat Zook; by Joanne Rocklin. Amulet Books 2012 218 p.

Grades: 3 4 5 6   **Fic**

1. Family life 2. Cats -- Fiction 3. Brothers and sisters -- Fiction

ISBN 1419701924; 9781419701924

LC 2011041088

"In this . . . middle-grade novel, Oona and her brother, Fred, love their cat Zook (short for Zucchini), but Zook is sick. As they conspire to break him out of the vet's office, convinced he can only get better at home with them, Oona tells Fred the story of Zook's previous lives, ranging in style from fairy tale to grand epic to slice of life. Each of Zook's lives has echoes in Oona's own family life, which is going through a transition she's not yet ready to face." (Publisher's note)

★ **One** day and one amazing morning on Orange Street. Amulet Books 2011 207p $16.95

Grades: 3 4 5   **Fic**

1. Trees -- Fiction 2. Oranges -- Fiction 3. California -- Fiction 4. Friendship -- Fiction 5. Family life -- Fiction

ISBN 0-8109-9719-3; 978-0-8109-9719-6

LC 2010-23452

The last remaining orange tree on a Southern California street brings together neighbors of all ages as they face their problems and anxieties, including the possibility that a mysterious stranger is a threat to their tree. "Grades four to six." (Bull Cent Child Books)

"Fully realized characters and setting definitely make this one morning on Orange Street amazing." Kirkus

Rockwell, Thomas

★ **How** to eat fried worms; pictures by Emily McCully. Watts 1973 115p il lib bdg $29; pa $5.99

Grades: 3 4 5 6   **Fic**

1. Worms -- Fiction

ISBN 0-531-02631-0 lib bdg; 0-440-44545-0 pa

"A hilarious story that will revolt and delight bumptious, unreachable, intermediate-grade boys and any other less particular mortals that read or listen to it." Booklist

"Billy may have bitten off more than he can chew when he is challenged by his friend Alan to eat fifteen worms in fifteen days for fifty dollars." (Publisher's Note)

Rodda, Emily

★ **The** key to Rondo. Scholastic Press 2008 342p $16.99; pa $6.99

Grades: 5 6 7 8   **Fic**

1. Fantasy fiction 2. Magic -- Fiction 3. Cousins -- Fiction

ISBN 0-545-03535-X; 978-0-545-03535-4; 0-545-03536-8 pa; 978-0-545-03536-1 pa

LC 2007-16873

Through an heirloom music box, Leo, a serious, responsible boy, and his badly-behaved cousin Mimi enter the magical world of Rondo to rescue Mimi's dog from a sorceress, who wishes to exchange him for the key that allows free travel between worlds.

"Rodda fills the cousins' quest with image-rich prose and compelling action." Bull Cent Child Books

Another title about Rondo is:
The Wizard of Rondo (2009)

Rowan of Rin. Greenwillow Books 2001 151p il hardcover o.p. pa $6.99

Grades: 4 5 6   **Fic**

1. Fantasy fiction

ISBN 0-06-029707-7; 0-06-056071-1 pa

LC 00-63619

First published 1993 in Australia

Because only he can read the magical map, young, weak and timid Rowan joins six other villagers to climb a mountain and try to restore their water supply, as fears of a dragon and other horrors threaten to drive them back

The author has created "a fully conceived fantasy world complete with its own flora and fauna, a well-developed back story, and fascinating characters." Booklist

Other titles about Rowan are:
Rowan and the travelers (2001)
Rowan and the Keeper of the Crystal (2002)
Rowan and the Zebak (2002)
Rowan and the Ice creepers (2003)

Rodgers, Mary

Freaky Friday. Harper & Row 1972 145p hardcover o.p. pa $5.99

Grades: 4 5 6 7   **Fic**

1. Mother-daughter relationship -- Fiction

ISBN 0-06-025048-8; 0-06-025049-6 lib bdg; 0-06-057010-5 pa

"A fresh, imaginative, and entertaining story." Bull Cent Child Books

"'When I woke up this morning, I found I'd turned into my mother.' So begins the most bizarre day in the life of 13-year-old Annabel Andrews, who discovers one Friday morning she has taken on her mother's physical characteristics while retaining her own personality. Readers will giggle in anticipation as Annabel plunges madly from one disaster to another trying to cope with various adult situations." Publ Wkly

Rodkey, Geoff

The **Tapper** twins go to war (with each other) Geoff Rodkey. Little, Brown & Co. 2015 240 p. illustrations ([Tapper twins) (hardcover) $13.99

Grades: 4 5 6 7   **Fic**

1. School stories 2. Twins -- Fiction 3. New York (N.Y.) -- Fiction 4. Practical jokes -- Fiction 5. Brothers and sisters -- Fiction 6. Schools -- Fiction 7. Oral history -- Fiction 8. Internet games -- Fiction 9. Family life -- New York (State) -- New York -- Fiction

ISBN 0316297798; 9780316297790

LC 2014015918

This book, by Geoff Rodkey, is a "comedy featuring twelve-year-old fraternal twins, Claudia and Reese, who couldn't be more different...except in their determination to come out on top in a vicious prank war! But when the competition escalates into an all-out battle that's fought from the cafeteria of their New York City private school all the way to the fictional universe of an online video game, the twins have to decide if their efforts to destroy each other are worth the price." (Publisher's note)

"It started with words. Or maybe with the missing toaster pastry. But when Reese Tapper called his twin sister, Claudia, "Princess Farts-a-Lot" in front of the whole sixth grade, the war was on. Through oral-history interviews, text messages, e-mails, chat-room comments, photographs, and margin notes, Claudia documents the history of the Tapper twins' war...Thanks to the inclusion of various points of view, Claudia's reasonably balanced narrative offers plenty of humorous insight, and occasional doodles and photos keep it peppy." Booklist

Rodman, Mary Ann

★ Jimmy's stars. Farrar, Straus & Giroux 2008 257p $16.95

Grades: 5 6 7 8   **Fic**

1. Siblings -- Fiction 2. Soldiers -- Fiction 3. Family life -- Fiction 4. Pittsburgh (Pa.) -- Fiction 5. World War, 1939-1945 -- Fiction

ISBN 978-0-374-33703-2; 0-374-33703-9

LC 2007-05091

In 1943, eleven-year-old Ellie is her brother Jimmy's "best girl," and when he leaves Pittsburgh just before Thanksgiving to fight in World War II, he promises he will return, asks her to leave the Christmas tree up until he does, and reminds her to "let the joy out."

Rodman "finds beauty in every emotional nuance. . . . The lively spirit of working-class Pittsburgh . . . extends Ellie's person story with a broader sense of home-front life." Booklist

Yankee girl. Farrar, Straus and Giroux 2004 219p $17; pa $7.99

Grades: 4 5 6 7   **Fic**

1. School stories 2. Mississippi -- Fiction 3. Race relations -- Fiction

ISBN 0-374-38661-7; 0-312-53576-7 pa

LC 2003-49048

When her FBI-agent father is transferred to Jackson, Mississippi, in 1964, eleven-year-old Alice wants to be popular but also wants to reach out to the one black girl in her class in a newly-integrated school.

"Rodman shows characters grappling with hard choices, sometimes courageously, sometimes willfully, sometimes inconsistently, but invariably believably." Publ Wkly

Rodowsky, Colby F.

The next-door dogs; [by] Colby Rodowsky; pictures by Amy June Bates. Farrar, Straus & Giroux 2005 103p il $15

Grades: 2 3 4   **Fic**

1. Dogs -- Fiction 2. Fear -- Fiction

ISBN 0-374-36410-9

LC 2004-43333

Although terrified of dogs, nine-year-old Sara forces herself to face a labrador retriever and a dalmatian when she must help her next-door neighbor, who has fallen and broken her leg.

"Rodowsky makes Sara's fear palpable and her eventual recovery believable. Plentiful pencil illustrations add to the book's accessibility." Horn Book Guide

Rogan, S. Jones

The **daring** adventures of Penhaligon Brush; pictures by Christian Slade. Alfred A. Knopf 2007 230p il $15.99; pa $6.50

Grades: 4 5 6   **Fic**

1. Adventure fiction 2. Foxes -- Fiction 3. Animals -- Fiction

ISBN 978-0-375-84344-0; 0-375-84344-2; 978-0-440-42208-2 pa; 0-440-42208-6 pa

LC 2006-35566

When Penhaligon Brush the fox is summoned by his stepbrother to the seaside town of Porthleven, he finds immediately upon arrival that his brother is incarcerated in the dungeon at Ferball Manor

This is a "swift-paced, large-scale adventure.... Slade's halftone art . . . [represents] these robust characters in theatrical costume and with plenty of personality." Publ Wkly

Another title about Penhaligon Brush is:

The curse of the Romany wolves (2009)

Rollins, James

Jake Ransom and the Skull King's shadow. HarperCollins 2009 399p il map $16.99; lib bdg $17.89; pa $7.99

Grades: 5 6 7 8   **Fic**

1. Adventure fiction 2. Mayas -- Fiction 3. Siblings -- Fiction 4. Archeology -- Fiction

ISBN 978-0-06-147379-1; 0-06-147379-0; 978-0-06-147380-7 lib bdg; 0-06-147380-4 lib bdg; 978-0-06-147381-4 pa; 0-06-147381-2 pa

LC 2009-14570

Connecticut middle-schooler Jake and his older sister Kady are transported by a Mayan artifact to a strange world inhabited by a mix of people from long-lost civilizations who are threatened by prehistoric creatures and an evil alchemist, the Skull King.

This is an "exciting time-travel adventure. . . . Rollins . . . presents a wide range of interesting historical information while telling a rollicking good story that should please a wide range of readers." Publ Wkly

Another title about Jake Ransom is:

Jake Ransom and the howling sphinx (2011)

Root, Phyllis

Lilly and the pirates; pictures by Rob Shepperson. Boyds Mills Press 2010 116p il $16.95

Grades: 3 4 5 6   **Fic**

1. Adventure fiction 2. Pirates -- Fiction

ISBN 978-1-59078-583-6; 1-59078-583-5

LC 2009030494

Ten-year-old Lilly, a worrier who greatly fears the sea, leaves the home of her librarian great-uncle and sets out with an old woman pirate to rescue her parents, who were shipwrecked while seeking the elusive frangipani fruit fly on an uncharted island.

"Many children will relate to this rather cozy adventure story and its lovably flawed heroine. Like the story, Shepperson's many full-page illustrations are lively, engaging, and occasionally humorous." Booklist

Rose, Caroline Starr

Blue birds; Caroline Starr Rose. G. P. Putnam's Sons, an imprint of Penguin Group (USA) 2015 400 p. map (hardcover) $16.99

Grades: 4 5 6 7 **Fic**

1. Native Americans -- Fiction 2. Roanoke Island (N.C.) -- History -- Fiction 3. Novels in verse 4. Friendship -- Fiction 5. Lumbee Indians -- Fiction 6. Roanoke Colony -- Fiction

ISBN 0399168109; 9780399168109

LC 2014012100

In this novel by Caroline Starr Rose, "it's 1587 and twelve-year-old Alis has made the long journey with her parents from England to help settle the New World. But the land, the island Roanoke, is also inhabited by the Roanoke tribe and tensions between them and the English are running high, soon turning deadly. Amid the strife, Alis meets and befriends Kimi, a Roanoke girl about her age. Though the two don't even speak the same language, these girls form a special bond." (Publisher's note)

"The use of different typefaces works well to differentiate the two voices, which occasionally appear in tandem when the girls are together. An imaginative historical novel with two sympathetic protagonists." Booklist

Includes bibliographical references

★ **May** B. a novel-in-verse. Schwartz & Wade Books 2012 $15.99; lib bdg $18.99

Grades: 4 5 6 7 **Fic**

1. Novels in verse 2. Kansas -- Fiction 3. Frontier and pioneer life -- Fiction

ISBN 978-1-58246-393-3; 1-58246-393-X; 978-1-58246-412-1 lib bdg; 1-58246-412-X lib bdg

LC 2010033222

When a failed wheat crop nearly bankrupts the Betterly family, Pa pulls twelve-year-old May from school and hires her out to a couple new to the Kansas frontier.

"If May is a brave, stubborn fighter, the short, free-verse lines are one-two punches in this Laura Ingalls Wilder-inspired ode to the human spirit." Kirkus

Rosen, Michael J.

Running with trains; a novel in poetry and two voices. Michael J. Rosen. Boyds Mills 2012 102 p. (reinforced) $15.95

Grades: 5 6 7 **Fic**

1. Locomotives 2. Novels in verse 3. Farm life -- Fiction

ISBN 159078863X; 9781590788639

Author Michael Rosen's "story begins as 13-year-old Perry makes the train trip from his grandmother's for his weekly visit with his mother. . . . He is waiting for his father, missing in action in Vietnam, to return . . . [and] for his mother to finish nursing school so they can resume the life they knew prior to his father's going to war. Watching that same train, whose tracks bisect his family's farm, is 9-year-old Steve, who feels trapped by the constancy of his doting parents and farm chores and wishes he could ride that train to exotic locales." (Kirkus Reviews)

Sailing the unknown; around the world with Captain Cook. written by Michael J. Rosen; illustrated by Maria Cristina Pritelli. Creative Editions 2012 37 p. $17.99

Grades: 3 4 5 6 7 **Fic**

1. Sea stories 2. Explorers -- Fiction 3. Voyages around the world -- Fiction 4. Diaries -- Fiction

ISBN 1568462166; 9781568462165

LC 2011040840

This children's book, by Michael J. Rosen, illustrated by Maria Cristina Pritelli, tells the story of "an 11-year-old sailor named Nicholas, . . . [who in 1768] took to the seas with British explorer James Cook on a 3-year expedition of discovery, venturing into an uncharted world filled with strange lands, mysterious peoples, and peculiar creatures." (Publisher's note)

Ross, Gary

Bartholomew Biddle and the very big wind; Gary Ross, Matthew Meyers. Candlewick Press 2012 96 p. $17.99

Grades: 1 2 3 4 5 6 **Fic**

1. Novels in verse 2. Adventure fiction 3. Voyages and travels -- Fiction

ISBN 0763649201; 9780763649203

LC 2012942303

Author Gary Ross presents an adventure story. "Bartholomew Biddle's life has always been pretty ordinary, but when a huge wind blows past his window one night, he feels the call of adventure -- and he can't resist the urge to grab his bedsheet and catch a ride. Soon he's soaring far above his little town, heading wherever the wind takes him! . . . Bart finds himself in a mysterious cove where the wind doesn't blow. Stuck, Bart is forced to face the fact that his flying days might be over. Will he ever get home again?" (Publisher's note)

Rowling, J. K.

★ **Harry** Potter and the Sorcerer's Stone; illustrations by Mary Grandpré. Arthur A. Levine Bks. 1998 309p il $22.99; pa $8.99

Grades: 4 5 6 7 8 9 10 **Fic**

1. Fantasy fiction 2. Witches -- Fiction

ISBN 0-590-35340-3; 0-590-35342-X pa

LC 97-39059

First published 1997 in the United Kingdom with title: Harry Potter and the Philosopher's Stone

Rescued from the outrageous neglect of his aunt and uncle, a young boy with a great destiny proves his worth while attending Hogwarts School for Witchcraft and Wizardry.

This "is a brilliantly imagined and beautifully written fantasy." Booklist

Other titles in this series are:

Harry Potter and the Chamber of Secrets (1999)
Harry Potter and the Deathly Hallows (2007)
Harry Potter and Goblet of Fire (2000)
Harry Potter and the Half-Blood Prince (2005)
Harry Potter and the Order of the Phoenix (2003)
Harry Potter and the prisoner of Azkaban (1999)

Roy, Carter

The **blood** guard; Carter Roy. Two Lions 2014 288 p. (trade pbk.: alk. paper) $17.99

Grades: 5 6 7 8 **Fic**

1. Fantasy fiction 2. Adventure and adventurers 3. Survival skills -- Fiction 4. Secret societies -- Fiction 5. Adventure stories 6. Kidnapping -- Fiction

ISBN 1477847251; 9781477847251

LC 2013958330

In this book, by Carter Roy, "when thirteen-year-old Ronan Truelove's . . . mom snatches him from school, then sets off on a high speed car chase, Ronan is shocked. His . . . dad has been kidnapped? And the kidnappers are after him, too? His mom, he quickly learns, is . . . a member of an ancient order of knights, the Blood Guard, a sword-wielding secret society sworn to protect the Pure—thirty-six noble souls whose safety is crucial if the world as we know it is to survive." (Publisher's note)

:Ronan thought he was just a regular kid leading a mostly normal life until his parents disappeared. He teams up with a former classmate and a two-hundred-year-old pickpocket for a life or death struggle against evil. As Ronan embarks on a hero's journey, familiar tropes of righting wrongs and self-discovery persist but nevertheless remain entertaining as mystery, mysticism, and action abound." Horn Book

Roy, James

Max Quigley; technically not a bully. written and illustrated by James Roy. Houghton Mifflin Harcourt 2009 202p il $12.95

Grades: 4 5 6   Fic

1. Bullies -- Fiction 2. Friendship -- Fiction
ISBN 978-0-547-15263-9; 0-547-15263-9
LC 2008-36110
First published 2007 in Australia

After playing a prank on one of his "geeky" classmates, sixth-grader Max Quigley's punishment is to be tutored by him.

"Straightforward chronology, believable dialogue, self-contained chapters, and plenty of humor make this accessible to reluctant readers and particularly appealing to boys who may see a bit of themselves in this realistic school story." Booklist

Roy, Jennifer

Yellow star; by Jennifer Roy. Marshall Cavendish 2006 227p $16.95

Grades: 5 6 7 8   Fic

1. Jews -- Fiction 2. Poland -- Fiction 3. Holocaust, 1933-1945 -- Fiction 4. Young adult literature -- Works
ISBN 0-7614-5277-X; 978-0-7614-5277-5
LC 2005-50788

From 1939, when Syvia is four and a half years old, to 1945 when she has just turned ten, a Jewish girl and her family struggle to survive in Poland's Lodz ghetto during the Nazi occupation.

"In a thoughtful, vividly descriptive, almost poetic prose, Roy retells the true story of her Aunt Syvia's experiences. . . . This book is a standout in the genre of Holocaust literature." SLJ

Rundell, Katherine

★ **Cartwheeling** in thunderstorms; Katherine Rundell. Simon & Schuster Books for Young Readers 2014 256 p. (hardcover) $16.99

Grades: 4 5 6 7 8   Fic

1. School stories 2. Bullies -- Fiction 3. Orphans -- Fiction 4. Boarding schools -- Fiction 5. Interpersonal relations -- Fiction 6. Zimbabweans -- England -- London -- Fiction
ISBN 1442490616; 9781442490611; 9781442490635
LC 2013021053

In this middle grades novel by Katherine Rundell, illustrated by Melissa Castrillón, "Wilhelmina Silver's world is golden. Living half-wild on an African farm with her horse, her monkey, and her best friend, every day is beautiful. But when her home is sold and Will is sent away to boarding school in England, the world becomes impossibly difficult.

Lions and hyenas are nothing compared to packs of vicious schoolgirls." (Publisher's note)

"Wilhelmina, daughter of William Silver, white foreman of the Two Tree Hill Farm in Zimbabwe, leads a "wildcat" life. Her idyll ends abruptly and tragically with her father's death from malaria, after which she's shipped off to boarding school in England. Rundell's finely drawn etchings of the people in Will's sphere and rich descriptions of African colonial farm life sprawl across the pages." Horn Book

★ **Rooftoppers**; by Katherine Rundell and illustrated by Terry Fan. Simon & Schuster Books for Young Readers 2013 288 p. (hardcover) $16.99

Grades: 4 5 6 7   Fic

1. Orphans -- Fiction 2. Mother-daughter relationship -- Fiction 3. Roofs -- Fiction 4. France -- Fiction 5. Paris (France) -- Fiction 6. Missing persons -- Fiction 7. Homeless persons -- Fiction 8. Guardian and ward -- Fiction
ISBN 1442490586; 9781442490581
LC 2012049469

In this book, by Katherine Rundell, "everyone thinks that Sophie is an orphan. . . . Her guardian tells her it is almost impossible that her mother is still alive. . . . When the Welfare Agency writes to her guardian, threatening to send Sophie to an orphanage, she takes matters into her own hands and flees to Paris to look for her mother. . . . She meets Matteo and his network of rooftoppers--urchins who live in the hidden spaces above the city. Together they scour the city in a search for Sophie's mother." (Publisher's note)

Runholt, Susan

The **mystery** of the third Lucretia. Viking Childrens Books 2008 288p $16.99; pa $6.99

Grades: 5 6 7 8   Fic

1. Mystery fiction 2. Art -- Fiction 3. Europe -- Fiction 4. Friendship -- Fiction
ISBN 978-0-670-06252-2; 0-670-06252-9; 978-0-14-241338-8 pa; 0-14-241338-0 pa
LC 2007-24009

While traveling in London, Paris, and Amsterdam, fourteen-year-old best friends Kari and Lucas solve an international art forgery mystery.

"There are enough artistic details for fans of art mysteries and enough spying and fleeing for fans of detective adventure." Bull Cent Child Books

Other titles about Kari and Lucas are:
Rescuing Seneca Crane (2009)
The adventure at Simba Hill (2011)

Rupp, Rebecca

After Eli; Rebecca Rupp. 1st ed. Candlewick 2012 245 p. (hardcover) $15.99; (ebook) $15.99

Grades: 4 5 6 7 8   Fic

1. Bildungsromans 2. Family -- Fiction 3. Brothers -- Fiction 4. Bereavement -- Fiction 5. Death -- Fiction 6. Books and reading -- Fiction 7. Interpersonal relations -- Fiction
ISBN 0763658103; 9780763658106; 9780763661946
LC 2011048344

In this book, "Daniel, a wry and thoughtful narrator, looks back on the summer when he was 14, three years after his older brother, Eli, died in Iraq at age 22." Daniel's "memories of larger-than-life Eli and his lingering anger about his death" are interwoven with "Daniel's day-to-day challenges, including his dysfunctional family . . . his frustrations with his . . . friends; his attraction to Isabelle, a . . . newcomer to town; and his nascent friendship with school outcast Walter." (Publishers Weekly)

★ **Octavia** Boone's big questions about life, the universe, and everything. Candlewick Press 2010 185p $15.99

Grades: 5 6 7 8 **Fic**

1. School stories 2. Vermont -- Fiction 3. Religion -- Fiction 4. Family life -- Fiction 5. Christian life -- Fiction

ISBN 978-0-7636-4491-8; 0-7636-4491-9

LC 2009-47408

Seventh-grader Octavia puzzles over life's biggest questions when her mother seems to find the answers in a conservative Christian church, while her artist father believes the writings of Henry David Thoreau hold the key.

"This hopeful novel highlights the resilience of children and the courage of those who seek truth in a complicated world." Publ Wkly

★ **Sarah** Simpson's Rules for Living. Candlewick Press 2008 84p $13.99

Grades: 4 5 6 **Fic**

1. School stories 2. Vermont -- Fiction 3. Remarriage -- Fiction 4. Family life -- Fiction

ISBN 978-0-7636-3220-5

LC 2007-34214

In a journal, twelve-year old Sarah Simpson records important lists and the daily events of her life at home and in school, beginning one year after her father moved from Vermont to California to divorce her mother and marry someone else.

"Although Sarah's tone ranges widely, from resentful to full-out funny, . . . her vulnerable yet take-charge personality comes through." Publ Wkly

Ruskin, John

The **king** of the Golden River; [by] John Ruskin; illustrated by Iassen Ghiuselev. Simply Read Books 2005 65p il $19.95

Grades: 3 4 5 **Fic**

1. Fairy tales

ISBN 978-1-894965-15-6; 1-894965-15-9

Written 1841

After Gluck's cruel and greedy older brothers refuse hospitality to a mysterious visitor, their prosperous farm fails and one by one each brother makes the perilous journey to find treasure in the nearby Golden River

"Exquisite drawings by Bulgarian artist Ghiuselev illustrate this . . . edition of Ruskin's classic fairy tale. . . . A well-designed and very handsome edition of the timeless tale." Booklist

Russell, Ching Yeung

★ **Tofu** quilt. Lee & Low Books 2009 125p il $16.95

Grades: 4 5 6 **Fic**

1. Novels in verse 2. Sex role -- Fiction 3. Authorship -- Fiction 4. Hong Kong (China) -- Fiction

ISBN 978-1-60060-423-2; 1-60060-423-4

LC 2009-16903

Growing up in 1960s Hong Kong, a young girl dreams of becoming a writer in spite of conventional limits placed on her by society and family.

"The story is revealed through Russell's tender poems that beautifully describe Yeung Ying's surroundings, her home life, her family, and her inner thoughts. The poems are simple, yet filled with images and language that create an atmosphere that brings the child's early years to light." SLJ

Russell, Krista

Chasing the Nightbird. Peachtree 2011 200p $15.95

Grades: 5 6 7 8 **Fic**

1. Sailors -- Fiction 2. Slavery -- Fiction 3. Abolitionists -- Fiction 4. Massachusetts -- Fiction

ISBN 1561455970; 9781561455973

LC 2011002665

In 1851 New Bedford, Massachusetts, fourteen-year-old Cape Verdean sailor Lucky Valera is kidnapped by his estranged half-brother and forced to work in a mill, but while Lucky is plotting his escape he meets a former slave and a young Quaker girl who influence his plans.

"Without slowing the story's pace, Russell gives readers plenty to think about regarding the turbulent racial dynamics of the period—Lucky, who is dark-skinned yet free, initially sees little connection between his life and the plight of slaves. Strong-willed and goodhearted, Lucky is an especially vibrant hero in this multifaceted and suspenseful historical adventure." Publ Wkly

Rutkoski, Marie

★ The **Cabinet** of Wonders; [by] Marie Rutkoski. Farrar Straus Giroux 2008 258p (The Kronos Chronicles) $16.95; pa $6.99

Grades: 5 6 7 8 **Fic**

1. Fantasy fiction 2. Magic -- Fiction 3. Gypsies -- Fiction 4. Princes -- Fiction

ISBN 978-0-374-31026-4; 0-374-31026-2; 978-0-312-60239-0 pa; 0-312-60239-1 pa

LC 2007037702

Twelve-year-old Petra, accompanied by her magical tin spider, goes to Prague hoping to retrieve the enchanted eyes the Prince of Bohemia took from her father, and is aided in her quest by a Roma boy and his sister.

"Add this heady mix of history and enchantment to the season's list of astonishingly accomplished first novels. . . . Infusions of folklore (and Rutkowski's embellishments of them) don't slow the fast plot but more deeply entrance readers." Publ Wkly

Other titles in this series are:

The Celestial Globe (2009)

The Jewel of the Kalderash (2011)

Ryan, Carrie

The **map** to everywhere; by Carrie Ryan & John Parke Davis. Little, Brown & Co. 2014 448 p. illustrations (The map to everywhere) (hardcover) $17

Grades: 4 5 6 7 **Fic**

1. Fantasy fiction 2. Pirates -- Fiction 3. Fantasy 4. Maps -- Fiction 5. Magic -- Fiction 6. Wizards -- Fiction 7. Stealing -- Fiction 8. Adventure and adventurers -- Fiction

ISBN 031624077X; 9780316240772

LC 2013044752

In this juvenile novel, by Carrie Ryan and John Parke Davis, "to Master Thief Fin, an orphan from the murky pirate world of the Khaznot Quay, the Map is the key to finding his mother. To suburban schoolgirl Marrill, it's her only way home after getting stranded on the Pirate Stream, the magical waterway that connects every world in creation. With the help of a bumbling wizard and his crew, they must scour the many worlds of the Pirate Stream to gather the pieces of the Map to Everywhere." (Publisher's note)

"Two displaced young adventurers sail streams of raw magic from world to world in this vividly cast series opener. Convergent plotlines bring together Marrill, who impulsively climbs aboard the four-master that floats into view atop a shimmering mirage in an Arizona parking lot, and Fin, another world's scruffy orphan/thief who literally passes "out of sight, out of mind" with everyone he meets. Nearly everyone, that is: To his shock, Marrill actually remembers him when he's not in view. . . . Multifaceted characters, high stakes, imaginative magic, and hints of hidden twists and complexities to come add up to a memorable start to a projected four-volume voyage." Kirkus

Ryan, Pam Munoz
★ **Becoming** Naomi Leon; [by] Pam Muñoz Ryan. Scholastic Press 2004 246p $16.95; pa $6.99
Grades: 5 6 7 8   **Fic**
1. Mexico -- Fiction 2. Family life -- Fiction 3. Mexican Americans -- Fiction
ISBN 0-439-26969-5; 0-439-26997-0 pa
LC 2004-346
When Naomi's absent mother resurfaces to claim her, Naomi runs away to Mexico with her great-grandmother and younger brother in search of her father
"Ryan has written a moving book about family dynamics. . . . All of the characters are well drawn." SLJ

★ The **dreamer**; drawings by Peter Sís. Scholastic Press 2010 372p il $17.99
Grades: 4 5 6 7   **Fic**
1. Authors 2. Diplomats 3. Novelists 4. Novelist 5. Nobel laureates for peace 6. Nobel laureates for literature 7. Father-son relationship -- Fiction
ISBN 978-0-439-26970-4; 0-439-26970-9
Boston Globe-Horn Book Award honor book: Fiction (2010)
Neftali finds beauty and wonder everywhere. He loves to collect treasures, daydream, and write—pastimes his authoritarian father thinks are for fools. Against all odds, Neftali prevails against his father's cruelty and his own crippling shyness to become one of the most widely read poets in the world, Pablo Neruda.
"Ryan loads the narrative with vivid sensory details. And although it isn't poetry, it eloquently evokes the sensation of experiencing the world as someone who savors the rhythms of words and gets lost in the intricate surprises of nature. The neat squares of Sis' meticulously stippled illustrations, richly symbolic in their own right, complement and deepen the lyrical quality of the book." Booklist

★ **Echo;** by Pam Muñoz Ryan. Scholastic Press 2015 585 p. $19.99
Grades: 4 5 6 7 8   **Fic**
1. Music -- Fiction 2. Fate and fatalism -- Fiction 3. Harmonica -- Fiction 4. Family life -- Fiction 5.

Germany -- History -- Fiction 6. California -- History -- Fiction 7. Pennsylvania -- History -- Fiction
ISBN 0439874025; 9780439874021
LC 2014021482
In this novel by Pam Muñoz Ryan, "lost and alone in a forbidden forest, Otto meets three mysterious sisters and suddenly finds himself entwined in a puzzling quest involving a prophecy, a promise, and a harmonica. Decades later, Friedrich in Germany, Mike in Pennsylvania, and Ivy in California each, in turn, become interwoven when the very same harmonica lands in their lives." (Publisher's note)
"The harmonica and the love of music serve as the unifying threads for these tales of young people who save the lives and spirits of their families and neighbors, each in a time marked by bigotry and violence. It's an ambitious device, but Ryan's storytelling prowess and vivid voice lead readers expertly through a hefty tome illuminated by layers of history, adventure, and the seemingly magical but ultimately very human spirit of music." Horn Book

★ **Esperanza** rising. Scholastic Press 2000 262p $15.95; pa $4.99
Grades: 5 6 7 8   **Fic**
1. California -- Fiction 2. Mexican Americans -- Fiction 3. Agricultural laborers -- Fiction
ISBN 0-439-12041-1; 0-439-12042-X pa
LC 00-24186
Esperanza and her mother are forced to leave their life of wealth and privilege in Mexico to go work in the labor camps of Southern California, where they must adapt to the harsh circumstances facing Mexican farm workers on the eve of the Great Depression
"Ryan writes movingly in clear, poetic language that children will sink into, and the [book] offers excellent opportunities for discussion and curriculum support." Booklist

Rylander, Chris
The **fourth** stall. Walden Pond Press 2011 314p $15.99
Grades: 4 5 6 7   **Fic**
1. School stories 2. Bullies -- Fiction 3. Friendship -- Fiction 4. Business enterprises -- Fiction
ISBN 978-0-06-199496-8; 0-06-199496-0
LC 2010016280
Sixth-graders Mac and Vince operate a business charging schoolmates for protection from bullies and for help to negotiate conflicts peacefully, with amazing challenges and results.
"Rylander mines a substantial amount of humor and heart from this combination hardboiled crime novel and middle-grade character piece. . . . A light and enjoyable caper." Publ Wkly

Rylant, Cynthia
★ A **fine** white dust. Simon & Schuster 2000 106p $25; pa $4.99
Grades: 5 6 7 8   **Fic**
1. Religion -- Fiction 2. Friendship -- Fiction 3. Family life -- Fiction
ISBN 978-0-689-84087-6; 0-689-84087-X; 978-1-4169-2769-3 pa; 1-4169-2769-7 pa
A reissue of the title first published 1986 by Bradbury Press
A Newbery Medal honor book, 1987

The visit of the traveling Preacher Man to his small North Carolina town gives new impetus to thirteen-year-old Peter's struggle to reconcile his own deeply felt religious belief with the beliefs and non-beliefs of his family and friends

"Blending humor and intense emotion with a poetic use of language, Cynthia Rylant has created a taut, finely drawn portrait of a boy's growth from seeking for belief, through seduction and betrayal, to a spiritual acceptance and a readiness 'for something whole.'" Horn Book

★ **God** got a dog; Cynthia Rylant; illustrated by Marla Frazee. 1st Beach Lane Books ed. Beach Lane Books 2013 48 p. ill. (hardcover) $17.99

Grades: 5 6 7 8   **Fic**

1. God -- Poetry 2. Picture books for children 3. Femininity of God -- Poetry 4. God -- Fiction 5. Novels in verse

ISBN 1442465182; 9781442465183

LC 2013005577

This book is an illustrated collection of poetry from Cynthia Rylant. A major theme is the multiplicity of God, which Maria Frazee's illustrations expand on, "depicting Him or Her as a black, tattooed nail artist; a middle-aged white woman eating by herself; a little dark-skinned boy on roller skates . . . a bearded, dark-skinned dude playing poker with Gabriel; a homeless black woman. An illustration appears opposite each poem." (Kirkus Reviews)

★ **Missing** May. Orchard Bks. 1992 89p hardcover o.p. pa $5.99

Grades: 5 6 7 8   **Fic**

1. Death -- Fiction 2. West Virginia -- Fiction

ISBN 0-531-05996-0; 0-439-61383-3 pa

LC 91-23303

Awarded the Newbery Medal, 1993

After the death of the beloved aunt who has raised her, twelve-year-old Summer and her uncle Ob leave their West Virginia trailer in search of the strength to go on living

"There is much to ponder here, from the meaning of life and death to the power of love. That it all succeeds is a tribute to a fine writer who brings to the task a natural grace of language, an earthly sense of humor, and a well-grounded sense of the spiritual." SLJ

Sachar, Louis

★ **Holes**; [by] Louis Sachar. 10th anniversary ed.; Farrar, Straus and Giroux 2008 265p $18

Grades: 5 6 7 8   **Fic**

1. Friendship -- Fiction 2. Buried treasure -- Fiction 3. Homeless persons -- Fiction 4. Juvenile delinquency -- Fiction

ISBN 978-0-374-33266-2; 0-374-33266-5

LC 2007045430

A reissue of the title first published 1998. Includes additional information about the author and his Newbery acceptance speech

Awarded the Newbery Medal, 1999

As further evidence of his family's bad fortune which they attribute to a curse on a distant relative, Stanley Yelnats is sent to a hellish correctional camp in the Texas desert where he finds his first real friend, a treasure, and a new sense of himself

"This delightfully clever story is well-crafted and thought-provoking, with a bit of a folklore thrown in for good measure." Voice Youth Advocates

Marvin Redpost, kidnapped at birth? illustrated by Neal Hughes. Random House 1992 68p il $11.99; pa $3.99

Grades: 1 2 3   **Fic**

1. Family life -- Fiction

ISBN 0-679-91946-5; 0-679-81946-0 pa

LC 91-51105

Red-haired Marvin is convinced that the reason he looks different from the rest of his family is that he is really the lost prince of Shampoon

"Written almost completely in dialogue, the story is fast paced, easy to read, and full of humor." SLJ

Other titles about Marvin Redpost are:

Marvin Redpost, a flying birthday cake (1999)

Marvin Redpost, a magic crystal (2000)

Marvin Redpost, alone in his teacher's house (1994)

Marvin Redpost, class president (1999)

Marvin Redpost, is he a girl? (1993)

Marvin Redpost, super fast, out of control (2000)

Marvin Redpost, why pick on me? (1993)

Sideways stories from Wayside School; illustrated by Julie Brinckloe. Morrow Junior Books 1998 124p il $15.99; pa $5.99

Grades: 3 4 5 6   **Fic**

1. School stories

ISBN 0-688-16086-7; 0-380-69871-4 pa

LC 97039420

A reissue of the title first published 1978 by Follett

Humorous episodes from the classroom on the thirtieth floor of Wayside School, which was accidentally built sideways with one classroom on each story.

Sackett, Frances

The **misadventures** of the magician's dog; by Frances Sackett. Holiday House 2013 192 p. (hardcover) $16.95

Grades: 4 5 6   **Fic**

1. Dogs -- Fiction 2. Magic -- Fiction 3. Brothers and sisters -- Fiction 4. Adventure and adventurers -- Fiction 5. Families of military personnel -- Fiction

ISBN 0823428699; 9780823428694

LC 2012041540

In this book, by Frances Sackett, "Peter Lubinsky doesn't even like dogs and can't understand why he asked for one for his birthday. But it turns out that this pet, whom Peter calls The Dog, can talk and do magic—and he needs Peter's help. In return, The Dog promises to teach Peter conjuring and to help him bring his father home from the Middle East, where he is deployed with the air force." (Publisher's note)

"Twelve-year-old Peter adopts a talking dog that needs Peter's help: his former master, a magician, has turned himself into a rock. If Peter helps return the magician to his human state, "The Dog" will teach Peter how to conjure his father, who's deployed in the Middle East. This action-packed fantasy lightly explores the impact military parents' service has on their children." (Horn Book)

Sage, Angie

★ **Magyk**; Septimus Heap, book one. illustrations by Mark Zug. Katherine Tegen Books 2005 576p il $16.99; lib bdg $17.89; pa $7.99

Grades: 5 6 7 8   **Fic**

1. Fantasy fiction 2. Magic -- Fiction
ISBN 0-06-057731-2; 0-06-057732-0 lib bdg; 0-06-057733-9 pa

LC 2003-28185

After learning that she is the Princess, Jenna is whisked from her home and carried toward safety by the Extraordinary Wizard, those she always believed were her father and brother, and a young guard known only as Boy 412, pursued by agents of those who killed her mother ten years earlier.

"Youngsters will lose themselves happily in Sage's fluent, charismatic storytelling, which enfolds supportive allies and horrific enemies, abundant quirky details, and poignant moments of self-discovery." Booklist

Other titles in this series are:
Flyte (2006)
Physik (2007)
Queste (2008)
Syren (2009)
Darke (2011)

The **Magykal** papers; illustrations by Mark Zug. Katherine Tegen Books 2009 167p il (Septimus Heap)

Grades: 5 6 7 8   **Fic**

1. Fantasy fiction 2. Magic -- Fiction 3. Princesses -- Fiction
ISBN 0-06-170416-4; 978-0-06-170416-1

LC 2008027110

Purports to be a compilation of pamphlets, journals, restaurant reviews, maps, historical information, and other never-before-published papers from the world of the apprentice alchemist, Septimus Heap.

"Fans of Sage's saga will rejoice in the little pieces if 'magyk' collected here. Beautifully rendered in full color." SLJ

My haunted house; as told to Angie Sage; illustrated by Jimmy Pickering. Katherine Tegen Books 2006 132p il (Araminta Spookie) $8.99; lib bdg $14.89; pa $4.99

Grades: 3 4 5   **Fic**

1. Ghost stories
ISBN 978-0-06-077481-3; 0-06-077481-9; 978-0-06-077482-0 lib bdg; 0-06-077482-7 lib bdg; 978-0-06-077483-7 pa; 0-06-077483-5 pa

LC 2005-23815

Araminta enlists the help of several ghosts in an attempt to stop her Aunt Tabby from selling Spook House.

This is a "humorous, fast-paced . . . caper. . . . Pickering's quirky art adds to the kooky—and in spots somewhat spooky—fun." Publ Wkly

Other titles in this series are:
The sword in the grotto (2006)
Frognapped (2007)
Vampire brat (2007)
Ghostsitters (2008)

Saint-Exupery, Antoine de

★ **The little** prince; written and illustrated by Antoine de Saint-Exupery; translated from the French by Richard Howard. Harcourt 2000 83p il $18; pa $12

Grades: 4 5 6 7 8 9 10 11 12 Adult   **Fic**

1. Fantasy fiction 2. Princes -- Fiction 3. Air pilots -- Fiction 4. Extraterrestrial beings -- Fiction
ISBN 0-15-202398-4; 0-15-601219-7 pa

LC 99-50439

A new translation of the title first published 1943 by Reynal & Hitchcock

"This many-dimensional fable of an airplane pilot who has crashed in the desert is for readers of all ages. The pilot comes upon the little prince soon after the crash. The prince tells of his adventures on different planets and on Earth as he attempts to learn about the universe in order to live peacefully on his own small planet. A spiritual quality enhances the seemingly simple observations of the little prince." Shapiro. Fic for Youth. 3d edition

The **little** prince: deluxe pop-up book; unabridged text. translated from the French by Richard Howard. Houghton Mifflin Harcourt 2009 60p il $35

Grades: 4 5 6   **Fic**

1. Fantasy fiction 2. Pop-up books 3. Princes -- Fiction 4. Air pilots -- Fiction 5. Extraterrestrial beings -- Fiction
ISBN 978-0-547-26069-3; 0-547-26069-5

An aviator whose plane is forced down in the Sahara Desert encounters a little prince from a small planet who relates his adventures in seeking the secret of what is important in life

This "volume is a beautiful piece of bookmaking that actually extends the classic story. In 3-D form, the original artwork feels new, and inventive design elements . . . add whimsy while focusing even more attention on the images." Booklist

Salisbury, Graham

Calvin Coconut: trouble magnet; illustrated by Jacqueline Rogers. Wendy Lamb Books 2009 152p il $12.99; lib bdg $15.99; pa $6.99

Grades: 3 4 5   **Fic**

1. School stories 2. Hawaii -- Fiction 3. Bullies -- Fiction 4. Family life -- Fiction
ISBN 978-0-385-73701-2; 0-385-73701-7; 978-0-385-90639-5 lib bdg; 0-385-90639-0 lib bdg; 978-0-375-84600-7 pa; 0-375-84600-X pa

LC 2008-1415

Nine-year-old Calvin catches the attention of the school bully on the day before he starts fourth grade, while at home, the unfriendly, fifteen-year-old daughter of his mother's best friend has taken over his room

"The familial relationships among Calvin and his sister, their mom and her boyfriend are touching, realistically tempered with moments of frustration. Rogers's lively ink-and-wash drawings augment the story and evoke a playful feel." Kirkus

Other titles about Calvin are:
Calvin Coconut: the zippy fix (2009)
Calvin Coconut: dog heaven (2010)
Calvin Coconut: zoo breath (2010)
Calvin Coconut: hero of Hawaii (2011)
Calvin Coconut: kung fooey (2011)

★ **Night** of the howling dogs; a novel. Wendy Lamb Books 2007 191p $16.99; lib bdg $19.99; pa $6.50

Grades: 5 6 7 8   **Fic**

1. Hawaii -- Fiction 2. Camping -- Fiction 3. Tsunamis -- Fiction 4. Earthquakes -- Fiction 5. Boy Scouts of America -- Fiction 6. Survival after airplane accidents, shipwrecks, etc. -- Fiction

ISBN 978-0-385-73122-5; 978-0-385-90146-8 lib bdg; 978-0-440-23839-3 pa

LC 2007-07054

In 1975, eleven Boy Scouts, their leaders, and some new friends camping at Halape, Hawaii, find their survival skills put to the test when a massive earthquake strikes, followed by a tsunami.

This is a "vivid adventure. . . . Salisbury weaves Hawaiian legend into the modern-day narrative to create a haunting, unusual novel." Booklist

Saller, Carol Fisher

Eddie's war; [by] Carol Fisher Saller. Namelos 2011 ix, 194p $18.95

Grades: 5 6 7 8   **Fic**

1. Novels in verse 2. Brothers -- Fiction 3. Farm life -- Fiction 4. World War, 1939-1945 -- Fiction

ISBN 1-60898-108-8; 1-60898-109-6 pa; 978-1-60898-108-3; 978-1-60898-109-0 pa

"When we meet him in 1934, Eddie is five, Tom ten. In the next ten years the brothers develop friendships, discover family secrets, . . . and ponder the causes of European conflict . . . as well as the virulent prejudice rife in their own farming community. Tom's enlisting in 1943 unveils the real nature of war that has inspired the boys' games. Narrated by Eddie, these seventy-six vignettes are beautifully phrased and vividly revealing of character." Horn Book

Salten, Felix

Bambi; a life in the woods. [by] Felix Salten; illustrated by Barbara Cooney. Pocket Books 1988 190p il pa $5.99

Grades: 4 5 6   **Fic**

1. Deer -- Fiction

ISBN 978-0-671-66607-1 pa; 0-671-66607-X pa

Original German edition 1923; first United States edition published 1928 by Simon & Schuster

Describes the life of a deer in the forest as he grows into a beautiful stag

Samworth, Kate

Aviary Wonders Inc. Spring Catalog and Instruction Manual; renewing the world's bird supply since 2031. by Kate Samworth. Clarion Books, Houghton Mifflin Harcourt 2014 31 p.

Grades: 3 4 5 6   **Fic**

1. Robots -- Fiction 2. Environmental degradation -- Fiction 3. Birds -- Fiction 4. Automata -- Fiction 5. Mechanical toys -- Fiction

ISBN 9780547978994

LC 2013020247

This book, by Kate Samworth, is "a catalog of bird parts and instructions for making your own in a . . . possible future in which living birds have nearly disappeared. Feathers, beaks, legs and feet, bodies, tails and even flight styles can be ordered from this enterprising company, whose motto is 'Renewing the World's Bird Supply Since 2031.' . . . The author also enumerates actual bird threats: insecticides, habitat loss, the exotic pet trade and cats." (Kirkus Reviews)

"Unsettling and unforgettable, this faux-catalog purports to replace extinct bird species with build-a-bird automatons. Sub-subtitled 'Renewing the World's Bird Supply Since 2031,' . . . 'We can't replace the birds that have been lost. But we can provide you with the opportunity to create an exquisite alternative.' Samworth, making her debut, marries conventional sales language to florid multimedia illustrations of disembodied bird parts 'handcrafted and made to order by world-class artisans.' . . . A closing section on assembly, with instructions for teaching the robotic birds to fly and sing, only deepens the uncanny sense of loss. This cautionary guidebook mimes ads that fetishize wildlife." Pub Wkly.

Sanderson, Brandon

★ Alcatraz versus the evil Librarians. Scholastic Press 2007 308p $16.99; pa $6.99

Grades: 4 5 6 7   **Fic**

1. Fantasy fiction 2. Librarians -- Fiction 3. Grandfathers -- Fiction

ISBN 0-439-92550-9; 978-0-439-92550-1; 0-439-92552-5 pa; 978-0-439-92552-5 pa

LC 2006-38378

On his thirteenth birthday, foster child Alcatraz Smedry receives a bag of sand which is immediately stolen by the evil Librarians who are trying to take over the world. Soon, Alcatraz is introduced to his grandfather and his own special talent, and told that he must use it to save civilization.

"Readers whose sense of humor runs toward the subversive will be instantly captivated. . . . This nutty novel isn't for everyone, but it's also sure to win passionate fans." Publ Wkly

Other titles about Alcatraz are:

Alcatraz versus the scrivener's bones (2008)

Alcatraz versus the Knights of Crystallia (2009)

Alcatraz versus the shattered lens (2010)

Saunders, Kate

★ Beswitched. Delacorte Press 2011 244p $16.99

Grades: 4 5 6 7   **Fic**

1. School stories 2. Magic -- Fiction 3. Time travel -- Fiction 4. Great Britain -- Fiction

ISBN 978-0-385-74075-3

LC 2011000747

First published 2010 in the United Kingdom

On her way, reluctantly, to a boarding school in present-day England, Flora suddenly finds herself in 1935, the new girl at St. Winifred's, having been summoned via a magic spell by her new dormitory mates.

"This absorbing novel . . . features a dimensional, delightful protagonist, whose personality and growth ring true. . . . Along with the entertaining magical elements, the universal themes of self-discovery and looking beyond appearances combine into a wholly engaging and enjoyable read." Booklist

The **Whizz** Pop Chocolate Shop; Kate Saunders. 1st ed. Delacorte Press 2013 293 p. (hardcover) $16.99

Grades: 5 6 7 8   **Fic**

1. Chocolate -- Fiction 2. Fantasy fiction 3. Cats -- Fiction 4. Magic -- Fiction 5. Twins -- Fiction 6. England -- Fiction 7. Immortality -- Fiction 8. London (England) -- Fiction 9. Brothers and sisters -- Fiction

10. Adventure and adventurers -- Fiction
ISBN 0385743017; 9780385743013

LC 2011053081

In this children's story, by Kate Saunders, "the family of eleven-year-old twins Oz and Lily have inherited [a house], together with the mysterious shop downstairs. Long ago, the shop's famous chocolate-makers . . . were clever sorcerers. Now evil villains are hunting for the secret of their greatest recipe. . . . This magic chocolate [has] the ability to destroy the world. . . . It's up to them to stop the villains and keep the magical chocolate recipe out of harm's way." (Publisher's note)

Sawyer, Ruth
★ **Roller** skates; written by Ruth Sawyer and illustrated by Valenti Angelo. Viking 1995 186p il hardcover o.p. pa $5.99
Grades: 4 5 6   Fic
1. New York (N.Y.) -- Fiction
ISBN 0-670-60310-4; 0-14-030358-8 pa

LC 85-43418

A reissue of the title first published 1936
Awarded the Newbery Medal, 1937

"For one never-to-be forgotten year Lucinda Wyman (ten years old) was free to explore New York on roller skates. She made friends with Patrick Gilligan and his hansom cab, with Policeman M'Gonegal, with the fruit vendor, Vittore Coppicco and his son Tony, and with many others. All Lucinda's adventures are true and happened to the author herself as is borne out by the occasional pages of Lucinda's diary which are a part of the story." Horn Book

Sazaklis, John
Royal rodent rescue; illustrated by Art Baltazar; Superman created by Jerry Siegel and Joe Shuster. Picture Window Books 2011 48p il (DC super-pets!) lib bdg $22.65; pa $4.95
Grades: 1 2 3   Fic
1. Cats -- Fiction 2. Superheroes -- Fiction
ISBN 978-1-4048-6307-1 lib bdg; 1-4048-6307-9 lib bdg; 978-1-4048-6622-5 pa; 1-4048-6622-1 pa

LC 2010036376

"Streaky the Super-Cat saves Queen Markela of Kardamyla's pet hamster, Prince Zouli, from the clutches of the evil cat, Rozz. . . . [The book is] full of action, including colorful graphics within the text, reminiscent of the old live-action Batman TV show. [The] title has a colorful spread in the heat of the action. [A] solid [introduction] to comic-book-style writing." SLJ

Scaletta, Kurtis
Mamba Point. Alfred A. Knopf 2010 268p il $16.99; lib bdg $19.99
Grades: 5 6 7 8   Fic
1. Fear -- Fiction 2. Snakes -- Fiction 3. Liberia -- Fiction
ISBN 978-0-375-86180-2; 0-375-86180-7; 978-0-375-96180-9 lib bdg; 0-375-96180-1 lib bdg

LC 2009-22084

After moving with his family to Liberia, twelve-year-old Linus discovers that he has a mystical connection with the black mamba, one of the deadliest snakes in Africa, which he is told will give him some of the snake's characteristics.

Includes facts about the author's experiences as a thirteen-year-old American living in Liberia in 1982

Scaletta "has created an appealing, well-written protagonist whose everyday and extraordinary experiences . . . change his life in unexpected, positive ways. . . . The engaging first-person narrative and array of diversely drawn characters further enliven the novel." Booklist

The **winter** of the robots; Kurtis Scaletta. Alfred A. Knopf 2013 272 p. (hard cover) $16.99
Grades: 5 6 7 8   Fic
1. Science fiction 2. Robots -- Fiction 3. Landfills -- Fiction 4. Science projects -- Fiction
ISBN 0307931862; 9780307931863; 9780375971105

LC 2012036376

In this book, by Kurtis Scaletta, "Jim is tired of being the sidekick to his scientific genius, robot-obsessed, best friend Oliver. So this winter, when it comes time to choose partners for the science fair, Jim dumps Oliver and teams up with a girl instead. Rocky has spotted wild otters down by the river, and her idea is to study them. But . . . they discover . . . a hidden junkyard on abandoned Half Street. And as desolate as it may seem, there's something living in the junkyard." (Publisher's note)

"The probability of his temperamental dad finding out that Jim has borrowed several high-tech security cameras for a science fair project turns out to be the least of his worries in this offbeat thriller. Set up in a seedy North Minneapolis junkyard near the river in hopes of observing otters, the cameras immediately disappear after a flash of weird footage. . . . Told in a spare, matter-of-fact narrative, this packs the space between the lines with humor, drama, romantic tension, and deftly delivered insight into the characters of a diverse, well-developed cast. . . . Scaletta amps up the voltage with suspense and excitement, but he also seamlessly integrates family issues and peer dynamics and cybernetic feats that seem only slightly futuristic." Booklist

Scanlon, Liz Garton
The **great** good summer; Liz Garton Scanlon. Beach Lane Books 2015 224 p. (hardcover) $16.99
Grades: 4 5 6 7   Fic
1. Summer -- Fiction 2. Friendship -- Fiction 3. Runaways -- Fiction 4. Bus travel -- Fiction 5. Friendship -- Fiction 6. Christian life -- Fiction 7. Mothers and daughters -- Fiction
ISBN 1481411470; 9781481411479; 9781481411486

LC 2014014988

In this children's story, by Liz Garton Scanlon, "Ivy and Paul are both having a crummy summer. . . . Ivy's mama hasn't been herself since the spring, when wildfires destroyed everything. . . . Meanwhile, Paul is sad because NASA's space shuttle program is being shut down and now he will never be able to become an astronaut. . . . The two become an unlikely pair when they hatch a plan to find Mama and say goodbye to the space shuttle." (School Library Journal)

Scattergood, Augusta
★ **Glory** be; by Augusta Scattergood. 1st ed. Scholastic Press 2012 202 p. (hardcover) $16.99; (ebook) $16.99
Grades: 4 5 6   Fic
1. Racism -- History 2. Blacks -- Civil rights 3. African Americans -- Southern States 4. Sisters -- Fiction 5. Segregation -- Fiction 6. Race relations --

Fiction 7. City and town life -- Mississippi -- Fiction 8. Mississippi -- History -- 20th century -- Fiction
ISBN 9780545331807; 9780545331814; 9780545452328

LC 2011028308

Author Augusta Scattergood tells a story of "a girl trying to make sense of the tumultuous era of the Civil Rights Movement. It's the summer of 1964 in a small Mississippi town, and [it's Glory's 12th birthday] . . . Her sister Jesslyn is entering high school and no longer has any time, and things have suddenly gotten awkward with Glory's best friend, Frankie. Plus, a new girl from the North has arrived, and everyone is riled up about what to do about the town's segregated pool. Whether she wants to or not, Glory has to make some big decisions." (Publisher's note)

Schlitz, Laura Amy

★ A **drowned** maiden's hair; a melodrama. Candlewick Press 2006 389p $15.99
Grades: 5 6 7 8   **Fic**
1. Orphans -- Fiction 2. Spiritualism -- Fiction
ISBN 978-0-7636-2930-4; 0-7636-2930-8

LC 2006-49056

At the Barbary Asylum for Female Orphans, eleven-year-old Maud is adopted by three spinster sisters moonlighting as mediums who take her home and reveal to her the role she will play in their seances.

"Filled with heavy atmosphere and suspense, this story recreates life in early-20th-century New England. . . . Maud is a charismatic, three-dimensional character." SLJ

★ The **night** fairy; illustrated by Angela Barrett. Candlewick Press 2010 117p il lib bdg $16.99; pa $6.99
Grades: 4 5 6   **Fic**
1. Adventure fiction 2. Magic -- Fiction 3. Fairies -- Fiction 4. Friendship -- Fiction
ISBN 978-0-7636-3674-6 lib bdg; 0-7636-3674-6 lib bdg; 978-07636-5295-1 pa; 0-7636-5295-4 pa

LC 2008-27659

When Flory the night fairy's wings are accidentally broken and she cannot fly, she has to learn to do everything differently.

"Schlitz writes with strength of vision and delicate precision of word choice. . . . Beautifully composed, the artwork combines subtle use of color with a keen observation of nature. . . . This finely crafted and unusually dynamic fairy story is a natural for reading aloud." Booklist

★ **Splendors** and glooms; Laura Amy Schlitz. Candlewick 2012 384 p. (reinforced trade ed.) $17.99
Grades: 4 5 6 7   **Fic**
1. Mystery fiction 2. Orphans -- Fiction 3. Kidnapping -- Fiction 4. Puppets and puppet plays -- Fiction 5. Puppets -- Fiction 6. Witches -- Fiction 7. Blessing and cursing -- Fiction 8. London (England) -- History -- 19th century -- Fiction 9. Great Britain -- History -- Victoria, 1837-1901 -- Fiction
ISBN 0763653802; 9780763653804

LC 2011048366

John Newbery Honor Book (2013)

In this book by Laura Amy Schlitz "Clara Wintermute . . . invites . . . the master puppeteer, Gaspare Grisini, . . . to entertain at her birthday party. . . . When Clara vanishes that night, suspicion of kidnapping falls upon the puppeteer and,

by association, Lizzie Rose and Parsefall. As they seek to puzzle out Clara's whereabouts, Lizzie and Parse uncover Grisini's criminal past." (Publisher's note)

Schmatz, Pat

★ **Bluefish**. Candlewick Press 2011 226p $15.99
Grades: 5 6 7 8   **Fic**
1. School stories 2. Literacy -- Fiction 3. Teachers -- Fiction
ISBN 978-0-7636-5334-7; 0-7636-5334-9

LC 2010044815

"A cast of richly developed characters peoples this work of contemporary fiction, told in the third person from Travis' point of view, with first-person vignettes from Velveeta's perspective peppered throughout. . . . A story rife with unusual honesty and hope." Kirkus

"Thirteen-year-old Travis has a secret: he can't read. But a shrewd teacher and a sassy girl are about to change everything in this witty and deeply moving novel." (Publisher's Note)

Schmidt, Gary D.

★ **Okay** for now. Clarion Books 2011 360p il $16.99
Grades: 4 5 6 7   **Fic**
1. Moving -- Fiction 2. New York (State) -- Fiction 3. City and town life -- Fiction
ISBN 978-0-547-15260-8; 0-547-15260-4

LC 2010942981

"It's 1968. The Vietnam War and Apollo 11 are in the background, and . . . Doug Swieteck starts a new life in tiny Marysville, N.Y. . . . He may have moved away, but his cruel father and abusive brothers are still with him. . . . This is Schmidt's best novel yet—darker than The Wednesday Wars and written with more restraint, but with the same expert attention to voice, character and big ideas." Kirkus

★ The **Wednesday** wars. Clarion Books 2007 264p pa $6.99; $16
Grades: 5 6 7 8   **Fic**
1. Poets 2. Authors 3. Dramatists 4. School stories
ISBN 054723760X; 0618724834; 9780547237602; 9780618724833

LC 2006-23660

A Newbery Medal honor book, 2008

During the 1967 school year, on Wednesday afternoons when all his classmates go to either Catechism or Hebrew school, seventh-grader Holling Hoodhound stays in Mrs. Baker's classroom where they read the plays of William Shakespeare and Holling learns something of value about the world he lives in. "Grades five to seven." (Bull Cent Child Books)

"The serious issues are leavened with ample humor, and the supporting cast . . . is fully dimensional. Best of all is the hero." Publ Wkly

Schneider, Josh

Tales for very picky eaters. Clarion Books 2011 47p il $14.99
Grades: K 1 2 3   **Fic**
1. Food -- Fiction 2. Father-son relationship -- Fiction
ISBN 978-0-547-14956-1; 0-547-14956-5

LC 2010-24767

"The comical illustrations are done in watercolor, ink, and colored pencil and are surrounded by plenty of white space. A perfect segue into chapter books, this easy reader is sure to be a crowd pleaser." SLJ

"An extremely picky palate forces young James' father to make rejected foods seem more appealing through kid-friendly, extra-gross yarns about such fare as pre-chewed gum and lumpy oatmeal that grows so big that it eats the dog." (Publisher's Note)

Schneider, Robyn

Knightley Academy; by Violet Haberdasher. Aladdin 2010 469p $15.99

Grades: 5 6 7 8   Fic
1. School stories 2. Orphans -- Fiction 3. Knights and knighthood -- Fiction
ISBN 978-1-4169-9143-4; 1-4169-9143-3
LC 2009-23443

In an alternate Victorian England, fourteen-year-old orphan Henry Grim, a maltreated servant at an exclusive school for the "sons of Gentry and Quality," begins a new life when he unexpectedly becomes the first commoner to be accepted at Knightley Academy, a prestigious boarding school for knights.

"Robyn Schneider . . . writing as the pseudonymous Haberdasher, delivers a cute novel that balances its simple plot with a solid lead character, witty dialogue, and a jaunty narrative voice. . . . The nebulous historical setting and focus on military training and chivalry are a welcome change of pace from fictional academies that revolve around magic." Publ Wkly

Followed by: The secret prince (2011)

The **secret** prince; [by] Violet Haberdasher. Aladdin 2011 503p $16.99

Grades: 5 6 7 8   Fic
1. School stories 2. Orphans -- Fiction 3. Secret societies -- Fiction 4. Knights and knighthood -- Fiction
ISBN 978-1-4169-9145-8; 1-4169-9145-X
LC 2010038855

Sequel to: Knightley Academy (2010)

Fourteen-year-old orphan Henry Grim's schooling at the prestigious Knightley Academy continues, as he and some friends discover an old classroom filled with forgotten weapons which lead them into a dangerous adventure.

"Though some of the past events can be gleaned from this book, it's more enjoyable for those who have read Knightley Academy. . . . The fast-moving plotline in this installment is wrapped up nicely, but enough is left hanging and the characters are interesting enough to make readers eagerly anticipate the next in the series." SLJ

Schoenberg, Jane

The **one** and only Stuey Lewis; stories from the second grade. pictures by Cambria Evans. Farrar Straus Giroux 2011 115p il $16.99

Grades: 1 2 3   Fic
1. School stories 2. Teachers -- Fiction 3. Family life -- Fiction
ISBN 978-0-374-37292-7; 0-374-37292-6
LC 2010-22312

Stuey Lewis makes his way through second grade facing reading problems, pulling off a great Halloween caper, joining a soccer team, and more with the help of family, friends, and a special teacher.

This is a "hilarious early chapter book. . . . Evans' trim-lined, stylized cartoonish illustrations play up the comedy in the text while offering occasional independent chuckles." Bull Cent Child Books

Stuey Lewis against all odds; stories from the third grade. Jane Schoenberg; pictures by Cambria Evans. Farrar Straus Giroux 2012 136 p.

Grades: 2 3   Fic
1. Boys -- Fiction 2. Field trips -- Fiction 3. School stories 4. Schools -- Fiction 5. Family life -- Fiction
ISBN 0374399018; 9780374399016
LC 2011008224

This book, by Jane Schoenberg, part of the Stuey Lewis series, "takes up just where the first left off, with Stuey and his friends comforted that their second-grade teacher, Ginger Curtis, is moving on to third grade with them. . . . With the school year as the frame, these four loosely joined stories show our hero facing new challenges while growing into a more independent, less worried young man." (Kirkus Reviews)

Schroder, Monika

Saraswati's way. Farrar Straus Giroux 2010 233p $15.99

Grades: 5 6 7 8   Fic
1. India -- Fiction 2. Education -- Fiction 3. Mathematics -- Fiction
ISBN 978-0-374-36411-3; 0-374-36411-7
LC 2009-37286

Leaving his village in rural India to find a better education, mathematically gifted, twelve-year-old Akash ends up at the New Delhi train station, where he relies on Saraswati, the Hindu goddess of knowledge, to guide him as he negotiates life on the street, resists the temptations of easy money, and learns whom he can trust.

"With skillfully integrated cultural details . . . and a fully realized child's story, Schröder presents a view, sobering and inspiring, of remarkably resilient young people surviving poverty without losing themselves." Booklist

Schroeder, Lisa

It's Raining Cupcakes. Aladdin 2010 193p $15.99

Grades: 4 5 6 7   Fic
1. Baking -- Fiction 2. Oregon -- Fiction 3. Contests -- Fiction 4. Family life -- Fiction 5. Mother-daughter relationship -- Fiction
ISBN 978-1-4169-9084-0; 1-4169-9084-4
LC 2009-14812

Twelve-year-old Isabel dreams of seeing the world but has never left Oregon, and so when her best friend, Sophie, tells her of a baking contest whose winners travel to New York City, she eagerly enters despite concerns about her mother, who is opening a cupcake bakery. Includes recipes.

Followed by: Sprinkles and secrets (2011)

Schulman, Janet

★ The **nutcracker**; [by] E.T.A. Hoffmann; adapted by Janet Schulman; illustrated by Renée Graef; audio CD narrated by Claire Bloom with music by Peter Ilyich Tchaikovsky. HarperCollins Pubs. 1999 34p il $19.95

Grades: 4 5 6 7 **Fic**
1. Fairy tales 2. Christmas -- Fiction
ISBN 0-06-027814-5

LC 97-22346

This adaptation of the Nutcracker with illustrations by Kay Chorao was published 1979 by Dutton

One Christmas after hearing how the toy nutcracker made by her godfather got his ugly face, a little girl helps break the spell and watches him change into a handsome prince

"Graef's illustrations are floridly old-fashioned, with careful attention to period detail." Booklist

Schur, Maxine
Gullible Gus; by Maxine Rose Schur; illustrated by Andrew Glass. Clarion Books 2009 45p il $16
Grades: 2 3 4 5 **Fic**
1. Tall tales 2. Texas -- Fiction 3. Cowhands -- Fiction
ISBN 978-0-618-92710-4; 0-618-92710-7

LC 2008-10477

Tired of the teasing he gets for being the most gullible man in Texas, Cowboy Gus goes to Fibrock to find the biggest liar there in hopes of hearing a tall tale that is impossible for anyone—even him—to believe.

"The stories are filled with exaggeration and alliteration. A Western twang is used to create mood. Readers will laugh out loud and share passages with friends. . . . Glass's bright oil crayon cartoons fit the exaggerated storytelling style to a tee." SLJ

Schwabach, Karen
The **storm** before Atlanta. Random House 2010 307p $16.99; lib bdg $19.99
Grades: 5 6 7 8 **Fic**
1. Freedom -- Fiction 2. Slavery -- Fiction 3. Soldiers -- Fiction 4. Runaway children -- Fiction 5. United States -- History -- 1861-1865, Civil War -- Fiction
ISBN 978-0-375-85866-6; 0-375-85866-0; 978-0-375-95866-3 lib bdg; 0-375-95866-5 lib bdg

LC 2010014514

In 1863 northwestern Georgia, an unlikely alliance forms between ten-year-old New York drummer boy Jeremy, fourteen-year-old Confederate Charlie, and runaway slave Dulcie as they learn truths about the Civil War, slavery, and freedom.

"Richly detailed and well paced, the story provides both well-developed characters and plenty of suspense and gore. For those who like to know the facts behind historical fiction, the author provides historical notes and selected sources. An appealing Civil War title for readers with strong stomachs." Kirkus

Schwartz, Ellen
★ **Stealing** home. Tundra Books 2006 217p pa $8.95
Grades: 5 6 7 8 **Fic**
1. Jews -- Fiction 2. Orphans -- Fiction 3. Family life -- Fiction 4. Racially mixed people -- Fiction
ISBN 978-0-88776-765-4 pa; 0-88776-765-6 pa

"Joey, an orphaned, mixed-race 10-year-old isn't the only one who has to make adjustments after he's taken in by Jewish relatives he never knew he had. Wondering why his mother never told him about her side of the family, Joey moves to Brooklyn—to find a warm welcome from Aunt Frieda, an instant ally in baseball-loving cousin Bobbie, and a decidedly cold shoulder from his grandfather. . . . Keenly

felt internal conflicts, lightened by some sparky banter, put this more than a cut above the average." Booklist

Schwarz, Viviane
The **Sleepwalkers**; Viviane Schwarz. Candlewick Press 2013 96 p. (paperback) $9.99
Grades: 2 3 4 5 **Fic**
1. Nightmares -- Fiction 2. Fantasy fiction
ISBN 0763662305; 9780763662301

LC 2012947253

This book by Viviane Schwarz offers a "tale of a band of intrepid dream warriors who rescue defenseless sleeping children from nightmares. Bonno (short for Bonifacius), a blanket transformed into a timid bear; Amali, an exuberant sock monkey; and Sophia, a crow made from a writing quill who communicates by writing, are the Sleepwalkers' newest recruits, learning the ropes from a trio of seasoned sheep." (Publishers Weekly)

Scieszka, Jon
Frank Einstein & the antimatter motor; by Jon Scieszka; illustrated by Brian Biggs. Amulet Books 2014 192 p. (Frank Einstein) (hardback) $13.95
Grades: 3 4 5 6 **Fic**
1. Science fiction 2. Robots -- Fiction 3. Inventors -- Fiction 4. Humorous stories
ISBN 1419712187; 9781419712180

LC 2014011918

In this middle grades novel by Jon Scieszka, illustrated by Brian Biggs, "Frank Einstein loves figuring out how the world works by creating household contraptions that are part science, part imagination, and definitely unusual. After an uneventful experiment in his garage-lab, a lightning storm and flash of electricity bring Frank's inventions--the robots Klink and Klank--to life!" (Publisher's note)

"After a freak electrical storm, boy genius Frank Einstein wakes up to find two robots--Klink (a "self-assembled artificial-intelligence entity") and Klank (a "mostly self-assembled artificial almost [intelligent]" being)--in his lab. He hopes they'll help him win a science prize and save his grandfather's repair-shop business. The book features kid-friendly humor in spades, and an impressive amount of scientific know-how." Horn Book

Other titles include:
Frank Einstein and the Electro Finger

Frank Einstein and the Electro-Finger; Jon Scieszka; illustrated by Brian Biggs. Amulet Books 2015 176 p. illustrations (Frank Einstein) (hardcover) $13.95
Grades: 3 4 5 6 **Fic**
1. Inventors -- Fiction 2. Scientists -- Fiction 3. Science fiction 4. Humorous stories 5. Robots -- Fiction 6. Power resources -- Fiction
ISBN 141971483X; 9781419714832

LC 2014029591

In this novel by Jon Scieszka, illustrated by Brian Biggs, "Frank Einstein (kid-genius scientist and inventor) and his best friend, Watson, along with [robots] Klink . . . and Klank . . . find themselves in competition with T. Edison, their classmate and archrival--this time in the quest to unlock the power behind the science of energy. Frank is working on a revamped version of one of Nikola Tesla's inventions, the 'Electro-Finger,' a device that can tap into energy anywhere." (Publisher's note)

"Kid genius Frank Einstein's back for a second shocking (and silly) science adventure. . . . There's so much actual information here that the story could pass as a textbook, but science and Scieszka fans won't likely mind." Kirkus

★ **Knights** of the kitchen table; illustrated by Lane Smith. Viking 1991 55p il (Time Warp Trio) $15.99; pa $4.99

Grades: 3 4 5   Fic

1. Fantasy fiction 2. Middle Ages -- Fiction 3. Time travel -- Fiction 4. Knights and knighthood -- Fiction

ISBN 0-670-83622-2; 0-14-240043-2 pa

LC 90-51009

"Transported to the Middle Ages, three friends save themselves from a dragon and a giant through quick thinking. The tongue-in-cheek narrative makes for laugh-out-loud enjoyment, and the easy-to-read sentences and zany dialogue perfectly suit the breathless pace." SLJ

Other titles about The Time Warp Trio are:

2095 (1995)

Da wild, da crazy, da Vinci (2004)

The good, the bad, and the goofy (1992)

Hey kid, want to buy a bridge? (2002)

It's all Greek to me (1999)

Marco? Polo! (2006)

Me oh Maya! (2003)

The not-so-jolly Roger (1991)

Oh say I can't see (2005)

Sam Samurai (2001)

See you later, gladiator (2000)

Summer reading is killing me! (1998)

Tut, tut (1996)

Viking it & liking it (2002)

Your mother was a Neanderthal (1993)

Seen Art? [by] Jon Scieszka and Lane Smith. Viking 2005 un il $16.99

Grades: 4 5 6 7   Fic

1. Art appreciation -- Fiction 2. Museum of Modern Art (New York, N.Y.) -- Fiction

ISBN 0-670-05986-2

While looking for his friend Art, a boy wanders through the Museum of Modern Art and is amazed by what he discovers there.

"The unusually long and narrow shape of the book and the stylized characters echo the modern-art theme while the muted background tones are an effective foil for the well-reproduced if sometimes diminutive artwork. . . . For anyone planning a trip to MoMA with a youngster, this is a provocative read." SLJ

★ **Spaceheadz**; [by] Jon Scieszka with Francesco Sedita; illustrated by Shane Prigmore. Simon & Schuster Books for Young Readers 2010 163p il (SPHDZ) $14.99

Grades: 3 4 5   Fic

1. School stories 2. Spies -- Fiction 3. Moving -- Fiction 4. Family life -- Fiction 5. Extraterrestrial beings -- Fiction 6. Brooklyn (New York, N.Y.) -- Fiction 7. Children's literature -- Works -- Grades two through six

ISBN 978-1-4169-7951-7; 1-4169-7951-4

LC 2010001983

On his first day at Brooklyn's P.S. 858, fifth-grader Michael K. is teamed with two very strange students, and while he gradually comes to believe they are aliens who need his help, he has trouble convincing anyone else of the truth

This is "fun enough to become the next big word-of-mouth, multiplatform attention suck." Booklist

Spaceheadz, book 2; illustrated by Shane Prigmore; sugar-free goodness by Casey Scieszka; high-fiber extras by Steven Weinberg. Simon & Schuster 2010 230p il (SPHDZ) $14.99

Grades: 3 4 5   Fic

1. School stories 2. Extraterrestrial beings -- Fiction

ISBN 978-1-4169-7953-1; 1-4169-7953-0

Sequel to: Spaceheadz (2010)

This "continues the adventures of fifth-grader Michael K. and the influx of aliens . . . who pose as students. The joke-filled, intentionally disjointed, post-modern narration eventually involves the Spaceheadz in a kindergarten play. . . . Lots of humor leads this multiplatform effort with links to websites that are sure to expand the series' fan base." Booklist

Spaceheadz, book 3; illustrated by Shane Prigmore. Simon & Schuster 2011 213p il (SPHDZ) $15.99

Grades: 3 4 5   Fic

1. School stories 2. Extraterrestrial beings -- Fiction 3. Brooklyn (New York, N.Y.) -- Fiction

ISBN 978-1-4169-7955-5; 1-4169-7955-7

"An imperiled world once more relies on rescue from Brooklyn fifth-graders Michael K. and his friends, along with aliens who are disguised as fifth-graders. . . . Meanwhile, Agent Umber of the AAA (Anti Alien Agency) is on a nonstop campaign to thwart the Spaceheadz. Finally, a tough-talking military-type Santa recruits Michael K. into a search for a stolen brain wave. . . . With plenty of twists, lots of well-timed comic noises . . . this is sure to delight fans, while recruiting new ones." Booklist

Scott, Elaine

Secrets of the Cirque Medrano. Charlesbridge 2008 216p lib bdg $15.95

Grades: 4 5 6 7   Fic

1. Artists 2. Painters 3. Circus -- Fiction 4. Orphans -- Fiction 5. Restaurants -- Fiction 6. Paris (France) -- Fiction

ISBN 978-1-57091-712-7 lib bdg; 1-57091-712-4 lib bdg

LC 2007-2329

In the Paris village of Montmartre in 1904, fourteen-year-old Brigitte works long hours in her aunt's cafe, where she serves such regular customers as the young artist Pablo Picasso, encounters Russian revolutionaries, and longs to attend the exciting circus nearby. Includes author's note on the Picasso painting "Family of Saltimbanques"

This "places an interesting historical moment within the grasp of middle-schoolers." Kirkus

Scotto, Michael

Postcards from Pismo; Michael Scotto; [edited by] Ashley Mortimer. Midlandia Press 2012 180 p. (paperback) $10.99

Grades: 4 5 6   Fic

1. Afghan War, 2001- -- Fiction 2. Filipino Americans

-- Fiction 3. Military personnel -- United States -- Correspondence -- Fiction

ISBN 0983724369; 9780983724360

LC 2011943050

In this book, a "class assignment blossoms into friendship as a fourth-grade (later fifth-) Californian showers a young soldier stationed in Afghanistan with letters, e-mail messages and postcards. [Michael] Scotto supplies only chatty Felix's side of the continuing correspondence. . . . Felix queries his pen pal about what soldiers do while detailing his own interests, teachers, town, hard-working Filipino American parents (and their reactions when his restless big brother enlists)." (Kirkus)

Seabrooke, Brenda

Wolf pie; illustrated by Liz Callen. Clarion Books 2010 46p il $16

Grades: 1 2 3 **Fic**

1. Pigs -- Fiction 2. Wolves -- Fiction 3. Friendship -- Fiction

ISBN 978-0-547-04403-3; 0-547-04403-8

LC 2009-15820

When Wilfong the wolf fails to blow down the house of the Pygg brothers, he stays outside their door all winter learning their games and listening to their jokes and stories, but although he claims to be reformed, the pigs are reluctant to offer friendship.

"Callen's humorous, vibrant multimedia art deftly matches the tone of Seabrooke's amusing tale, resulting in a winning collaboration for independent readers ready to move on to meatier texts." Kirkus

Sebestyen, Ouida

★ Words by heart. Little, Brown 1979 162p pa $5.50

Grades: 5 6 7 8 **Fic**

1. Family life -- Fiction 2. Race relations -- Fiction 3. African Americans -- Fiction

ISBN 0-440-22688-0

LC 78-27847

"It is 1910, and Lena's family is the only black family in her small Southwestern town. When Lena wins a scripture reciting contest that a white boy is supposed to win, her family is threatened. Lena's father tries to make her understand that by hating the people who did this, the problems that cause their behavior are not solved. Only more hatred and violence cause Lena and the village to understand the words of her father." ALAN

Followed by: On fire (1985)

Seegert, Scott

How to grow up and rule the world; illustrated by John Martin. Egmont USA 2010 191p il (Vordak the Incomprehensible) $13.99

Grades: 3 4 5 6 **Fic**

1. Science fiction 2. Superheroes -- Fiction

ISBN 978-1-60684-013-9; 1-60684-013-4

"Evil mastermind Vordak the Incomprehensible shares his 'evilosity' with aspiring supervillains in this hilarious spoof on superheroes. . . . Comical black-and-white cartoons on nearly every page extend the humor. . . . Vordak's distinctive voice, peppered with alliteration typical of the genre, remains fresh and funny throughout." SLJ

Seidler, Tor

★ Gully's travels; pictures by Brock Cole. Michael di Capua Books 2008 173p il $16.95

Grades: 4 5 6 **Fic**

1. Dogs -- Fiction 2. New York (N.Y.) -- Fiction 3. Voyages and travels -- Fiction

ISBN 978-0-545-02506-5; 0-545-02506-0

Gulliver leads a life of luxury with his master. But when his master falls in love with a woman who is allergic to dogs, Gulliver is sent to a new home. He finds himself with a family of raucous human beings and three mutts. But just as Gulliver begins to make a grudging peace with his new reality, he gets swept up in a harrowing new adventure.

"Gulliver is a character readers won't forget. . . . Seidler vividly evokes each setting. . . . Cole's expressive, scribbled sketches of interesting characters appear on almost every page." Booklist

Selden, George

★ The cricket in Times Square; illustrated by Garth Williams. Farrar, Straus & Giroux 1960 151p il $16; pa $6.99

Grades: 3 4 5 6 **Fic**

1. Cats -- Fiction 2. Mice -- Fiction 3. Crickets -- Fiction 4. New York (N.Y.) -- Fiction

ISBN 0-374-31650-3; 0-312-38003-8 pa

A Newbery Medal honor book, 1961

"A touch of magic comes to Times Square subway station with Chester, a cricket from rural Connecticut. He is introduced to the distinctive character of city life by three friends: Mario Bellini, whose parents operate a newsstand; Tucker, a glib Broadway mouse; and Harry, a sagacious cat. Chester saves the Bellinis' business by giving concerts from the newsstand, bringing to rushing commuters moments of beauty and repose. This modern fantasy shows that, in New York, anything can happen." Moorachian. What is a City?

Other titles about Chester and his friends are:

Chester Cricket's new home (1983)

Chester Cricket's pigeon ride (1981)

Harry Cat's pet puppy (1974)

Harry Kitten and Tucker Mouse (1986)

The old meadow (1987)

Tucker's countryside (1969)

Selfors, Suzanne

Smells like dog. Little, Brown 2010 360p $15.99

Grades: 4 5 6 7 **Fic**

1. Dogs -- Fiction 2. Uncles -- Fiction 3. Buried treasure -- Fiction

ISBN 978-0-316-04398-4; 0-316-04398-2

When farm boy Homer Pudding's explorer-uncle dies and leaves him a droopy dog with a mysterious coin hidden on its collar, it leads him to The City, where they meet Madame La Directeur, the conniving head of the Natural History Museum, who is trying to steal the coin and take Homer's place in a secret society of adventurers.

"Full of fantasy, fun, and humorous dialogue, this will attract dog lovers, mystery enthusiasts, adventure addicts, and reluctant readers. A thoroughly enjoyable read." Voice Youth Advocates

Another title about Homer Pudding is:

Smells like treasure (2011)

Selzer, Adam

I put a spell on you; from the files of Chrissie Woodward, spelling bee detective. Delacorte Press 2008 247p $15.99; lib bdg $18.99

Grades: 4 5 6 7   **Fic**
1. School stories 2. Mystery fiction 3. Spelling bees -- Fiction
ISBN 978-0-385-73504-9; 0-385-73504-9; 978-0-385-90498-8 lib bdg; 0-385-90498-3 lib bdg
           LC 2008035673

When Gordon Liddy Community School's resident tattletale-detective, Chrissie Woodward, realizes that the adults are out to fix the big spelling bee, she transfers her loyalty to her fellow students and starts collecting evidence. Told through in-class letters, administrative memos, file notes from Chrissie's investigation, and testimony from spelling bee contestants

"The wit in this school story is directed almost entirely against the grownups in a scathingly funny indictment of a shady principal and insanely competitive parents." Horn Book

Selznick, Brian

The **Houdini** box. Atheneum Books for Young Readers 2008 un il $17.99; pa $6.99

Grades: 3 4 5   **Fic**
1. Magicians 2. Nonfiction writers 3. Magicians -- Fiction
ISBN 978-1-4169-6878-8; 1-4169-6878-4; 978-0-689-84451-5 pa; 0-689-84451-4 pa
           LC 2008024693

A reissue of the title first published 1991 by Knopf

A chance encounter with Harry Houdini leaves a small boy in possession of a mysterious box—one that might hold the secrets to the greatest magic tricks ever performed.

"In this new edition, Selznick follows his intriguing tale with bonus material: a biographical note on Houdini, an illustrated magic trick, research notes on the writing of the book, and early sketches for the artwork. . . . It is sure to intrigue youngsters, particularly those interested in magic." SLJ

★ The **invention** of Hugo Cabret; a novel in words and pictures. Scholastic Press 2007 533p il $22.95

Grades: 4 5 6 7   **Fic**
1. Robots -- Fiction 2. Orphans -- Fiction 3. Motion picture directors 4. Paris (France) -- Fiction 5. Motion pictures -- Fiction
ISBN 0-439-81378-6
           LC 2006-07119

Awarded the Caldecott Medal, 2008

When twelve-year-old Hugo, an orphan living and repairing clocks within the walls of a Paris train station in 1931, meets a mysterious toyseller and his goddaughter, his undercover life and his biggest secret are jeopardized.

"With characteristic intelligence, exquisite images, and a breathtaking design, Selznick shatters conventions related to the art of bookmaking." SLJ

★ **Wonderstruck**; a novel in words and pictures. Scholastic Press 2011 637p il $29.99

Grades: 4 5 6 7   **Fic**
1. Deaf -- Fiction 2. Museums -- Fiction 3. New York (N.Y.) -- Fiction 4. Runaway children -- Fiction 5.

American Museum of Natural History -- Fiction
ISBN 978-0-545-02789-2; 0-545-02789-6
           LC 2011009113

"Readers know that the two stories will converge, but Selznick keeps them guessing, cutting back and forth with expert precision. . . . Both stories are equally immersive and impeccably paced. . . . Visually stunning, completely compelling." Kirkus

Sendak, Maurice

★ **Higglety** pigglety pop! or, There must be more to life. story and pictures by Maurice Sendak. HarperCollins Pubs. 1979 69p il $14.95; pa $8.95

Grades: 2 3 4   **Fic**
1. Dogs -- Fiction
ISBN 0-06-028479-X; 0-06-443021-9 pa

"The story has elements of tenderness and humor; it also has . . . typically macabre Sendak touches. . . . The illustrations are beautiful, amusing, and distinctive." Sutherland. The Best in Child Books

In this modern fairy tale "Jennie, the Sealyham terrier, leaves home because 'there must be more to life than having everything.' When she applies for a job as the leading lady of the World Mother Goose Theater, she discovers that what she lacks is experience. What follows are her adventures and her gaining of experience; finally Jennie becomes the leading lady of the play." Wis Libr Bull

Sensel, Joni

The **Farwalker's** quest. Bloomsbury U.S.A Children's Books 2009 372p $16.99

Grades: 5 6 7 8   **Fic**
1. Fantasy fiction
ISBN 978-1-59990-272-2; 1-59990-272-9
           LC 2008-30523

When twelve-year-old Ariel and her friend Zeke find a mysterious artifact the like of which has not been seen in a long time, it proves to be the beginning of a long and arduous journey that will untimately reveal to them their true identities.

"This is a solid and well-paced fantasy in which the journey is more important than the conclusion." SLJ

Followed by: The timekeeper's moon (2010)

Seredy, Kate

The **Good** Master; written and illustrated by Kate Seredy. Viking 1935 210p il hardcover o.p. pa $4.99

Grades: 4 5 6   **Fic**
1. Hungary -- Fiction 2. Farm life -- Fiction
ISBN 0-14-030133-X

A Newbery Medal honor book, 1936

Into this story of Jancsi, a ten-year-old Hungarian farm boy and his little hoyden of a cousin Kate from Budapest, is woven a description of Hungarian farm life, fairs, festivals, and folk tales. Under the tutelage of Jancsi's kind father, called by the neighbors The Good Master, Kate calms down and becomes a more docile young person

"The steady warm understanding of the wise father, the Good Master, is a shining quality throughout." Horn Book

Followed by The singing tree (1939)

The **white** stag; written and illustrated by Kate Seredy. Viking 1937 94p il hardcover o.p. pa $4.99

Grades: 4 5 6 **Fic**
1. Hungary -- Fiction
ISBN 0-14-031258-7 pa
Awarded the Newbery Medal, 1938
"Striking illustrations interpret this hero tale of the legendary founding of Hungary, when a white stag and a red eagle led the people to their promised land." Hodges. Books for Elem Sch Libr

Service, Pamela F.
Escape from planet Yastol; illustrated by Mike Gorman. Darby Creek 2011 102p il $15.95; pa $5.95
Grades: 4 5 6 **Fic**
1. Science fiction 2. Siblings -- Fiction 3. Authorship -- Fiction 4. Kidnapping -- Fiction 5. Books and reading -- Fiction 6. Extraterrestrial beings -- Fiction
ISBN 978-0-7613-7918-8; 0-7613-7918-5; 978-0-7613-7921-8 pa; 0-7613-7921-5 pa
LC 2010049235
Eleven-year-old Joshua Higgins' prize-winning science fiction novel draws the attention of sinister blue aliens who capture Josh and his sister Maggie and take them to the planet Yastol, the setting of his novel.
"Readers ready for longer chapter books will enjoy having some science fiction to choose from and welcome further adventures." Kirkus

Seuling, Barbara
Robert takes a stand; illustrated by Paul Brewer. Cricket Books 2004 168p il hardcover o.p. $15.95
Grades: 2 3 4 **Fic**
1. School stories 2. Endangered species -- Fiction
ISBN 0-8126-2712-1
LC 2003-18499
Political experience gained in a class election comes in handy when Robert and his friend Paul act on behalf of endangered animals.
"The simple text, short chapters, and quirky black-and-white charcoal drawings all contribute to making this a great choice for beginning independent readers. Equally important, most primary-grade children will relate to earnest, charming Robert, his world, his concerns, and his everyday adventures." Booklist
Other titles about Robert are:
Oh no, it's Robert (1999)
Robert and the snake escape (2001)
Robert and the attack of the giant tarantula (2001)
Robert and the great Pepperoni (2001)
Robert and the hairy disaster (2002)
Robert and the instant millionaire show (2002)
Robert and the scariest night (2002)
Robert and the sneaker snobs (2002)
Robert and the three wishes (2002)
Robert and the back-to-school special (2002)
Robert and the weird and wacky facts (2002)
Robert and the class president (2002)
Robert and the clickety-clackety teeth (2003)
Robert and the embarrassing secret (2003)
Robert and the troublesome tuba (2003)
Robert and the world's worst wristwatch (2003)
Robert and the lemming problem (2003)
Robert and the great escape (2003)
Robert and the chocolate-covered worms (2004)
Robert finds a way (2005)

Robert and the practical jokes (2006)
Robert and the happy endings (2007)
Robert goes to camp (2007)

Sewell, Anna
★ **Black** Beauty; the autobiography of a horse. by Anna Sewell; text illustrated by Fritz Eichenberg. Grosset & Dunlap 1995 301p il $17.99
Grades: 4 5 6 **Fic**
1. Horses -- Fiction 2. Great Britain -- Fiction
ISBN 0-448-40942-9
LC 94040990
First published 1877 in the United Kingdom; first United States edition, 1891
A horse in nineteenth-century England recounts his experiences with both good and bad masters.

Shahan, Sherry
Ice island. Delacorte Press 2012 $10.99; lib bdg $18.99; ebook $10.99
Grades: 4 5 6 7 **Fic**
1. Dogs -- Fiction 2. Alaska -- Fiction 3. Sled dog racing -- Fiction 4. Wilderness survival -- Fiction 5. Iditarod Trail Sled Dog Race, Alaska -- Fiction
ISBN 978-0-385-74154-5; 0-385-74154-5; 978-0-375-99009-0 lib bdg; 0-375-99009-7 lib bdg; 978-0-375-98575-1 ebook
LC 2011003838
Thirteen-year-old Tatum's dream of competing in the grueling 1,049-mile Iditerod Trail Sled Dog Race may be at an end when she becomes lost in a freak snowstorm during a training run on Alaska's remote Santa Ysabel Island.
"Riveting and atmospheric. . . . This survival adventure creates an almost otherworldly experience within a treacherous and bracingly beautiful landscape." Kirkus

Shang, Wendy Wan-Long
The **great** wall of Lucy Wu; [by] Wendy Wan-Long Shang. Scholastic Press 2011 312p $17.99
Grades: 4 5 6 **Fic**
1. School stories 2. Family life -- Fiction 3. Chinese Americans -- Fiction
ISBN 0-545-16215-7; 978-0-545-16215-9
LC 2010-13536
Eleven-year-old aspiring basketball star and interior designer Lucy Wu is excited about finally having her own bedroom, until she learns that her great-aunt is coming to visit and Lucy will have to share a room with her for several months, shattering her plans for a perfect sixth-grade year. "Grades four to six." (Bull Cent Child Books)
"Bolstered by frequent use of Chinese language and proverbs, this is a realistic and amusing portrait of family dynamics, heritage, and the challenge of feeling like an outsider—even in one's own family." Publ Wkly

The **way** home looks now; Wendy Wan-Long Shang. Scholastic Press 2015 272 p. $16.99
Grades: 4 5 6 7 8 **Fic**
1. Grief -- Fiction 2. Baseball -- Fiction 3. Pittsburgh (Pa.) -- Fiction 4. Chinese Americans -- Fiction 5. Traffic accidents -- Fiction 6. Bereavement 7. Baseball stories 8. Traffic accidents 9. Little League baseball -- Fiction 10. Chinese American families -- Pennsylvania

-- Pittsburgh
ISBN 0545609569; 9780545609562
LC 2014028707

This middle grades book, by Wendy Wan-Long Shang, is a "story of family and loss, healing and friendship, and the great American pastime, baseball. Twelve-year-old Peter Lee and his family are baseball lovers, who bond over back lot games and talk of the Pittsburgh Pirates. But when tragedy strikes, the family flies apart and baseball no longer seems to matter. Is that true? Peter wonders if just maybe the game they love can pull them together and bring them back." (Publisher's note)

"Twelve-year-old Peter just wants his home to be the way it was before—before his mother stopped talking, before she started sitting on the couch staring at the TV, and before his older brother died in a car accident. Peter's father is a strict Chinese immigrant who stresses homework, emphasizes respect for authority, and forbids baseball...Peter is a fully realized character, but the rest of his family and most of the players on his team fall flat. VERDICT Though the plot occasionally gets bogged down with too many side stories, this heartwarming story is still a worthy purchase." SLJ

Sharmat, Marjorie Weinman

Nate the Great and the hungry book club; by Marjorie Weinman Sharmat and Mitchell Sharmat; illustrated by Jody Wheeler. Delacorte Press 2009 62p il $12.99; lib bdg $15.99

Grades: K 1 2   **Fic**

1. Mystery fiction 2. Books and reading -- Fiction
ISBN 978-0-385-73695-4; 0-385-73695-9; 978-0-385-90637-1 lib bdg; 0-385-90637-4 lib bdg
LC 2009030319

"When Rosamond tells them about a monster who eats pages from her books, Nate the Great and his loyal companion, Sludge the dog, join the Ready Readers book club and act as undercover detectives to identify who (or what) is to blame for such mischievous deeds." (Publisher's note)

Shaw, Susan

Tunnel vision. Margaret K. McElderry Books 2011 272p $16.99

Grades: 5 6 7 8   **Fic**

1. Crime -- Fiction 2. Homicide -- Fiction 3. Witnesses -- Fiction 4. Organized crime -- Fiction
ISBN 978-1-4424-0839-5; 1-4424-0839-1
LC 2010036306

After witnessing her mother's murder, sixteen-year-old high school student Liza Wellington and her father go into the witness protection program.

"The author creates a completely believable character in Liza, who often reverts to childlike emotions only to learn the hard way that cold reality takes precedence over even dearly held wishes. Kudos for the unexpected double ending, both illusory and realistic, giving readers a choice." Kirkus

Shefelman, Janice Jordan

Anna Maria's gift; by Janice Shefelman; illustrated by Robert Papp. Random House 2010 104p il $12.99; lib bdg $15.99

Grades: 2 3 4   **Fic**

1. Composers 2. Violinists 3. School stories 4. Italy -- Fiction 5. Orphans -- Fiction 6. Violinists -- Fiction

7. Venice (Italy) -- Fiction
ISBN 978-0-375-85881-9; 0-375-85881-4; 978-0-375-95881-6 lib bdg; 0-375-95881-9 lib bdg
LC 2009004553

In 1715 Italy, eight-year-old Anna Maria Lombardini arrives at a Venice orphanage with little but the special violin her father made for her, but when her teacher, Antonio Vivaldi, favors her over a fellow student, the beloved instrument winds up in a canal

"Strong emotions . . . lie at the heart of the story. . . . [This is a] short, appealing historical novel." Booklist
Includes glossary

Sheinmel, Courtney

All the things you are. Simon & Schuster Books for Young Readers 2011 244p $15.99

Grades: 5 6 7 8   **Fic**

1. Theft -- Fiction 2. Friendship -- Fiction 3. Family life -- Fiction 4. Stepfamilies -- Fiction 5. New York (N.Y.) -- Fiction
ISBN 978-1-4169-9717-7; 1-4169-9717-2
LC 2010010090

When Carly Wheeler's mother is arrested for embezzling, Carly's perfect life begins to fall apart as friends at her prestigious private school stop talking to her, her beloved stepfather starts worrying about finances, and her image of herself and her family changes.

"Sheinmel persuasively and sensitively conveys Carly's conflicting emotions and her attempts to make sense of what's been thrust upon her." Publ Wkly

Sherlock, Patti

Letters from Wolfie. Viking 2004 232p $16.99; pa $6.99

Grades: 5 6 7 8   **Fic**

1. Dogs -- Fiction 2. Vietnam War, 1961-1975 -- Fiction
ISBN 0-670-03694-3; 0-14-240358-X pa
LC 2003-24316

Certain that he is doing the right thing by donating his dog, Wolfie, to the Army's scout program in Vietnam, thirteen-year-old Mark begins to have second thoughts when the Army refuses to say when and if Wolfie will ever return.

"In this topnotch novel, Sherlock weaves together numerous threads of emotion, information, and plot so seamlessly that readers will be surprised by how much they've learned by the time they finish this deceptively simple story." SLJ

Sherman, Deborah

The BEDMAS conspiracy. Fitzhenry & Whiteside 2011 170p pa $9.95

Grades: 4 5 6 7   **Fic**

1. School stories 2. Bands (Music) -- Fiction
ISBN 978-1-55455-181-1; 1-55455-181-1

Adam's band, Sick on a Snow Day, is challenged by more than just an unusual name: Adam is mistakenly accused of cheating on a test and must maintain a clean record and B-average if he wants to stay in the band. Then his lead singer, Daniela, gets stage fright.

"Adam's academic difficulties and Daniela's stage fright are only two of the challenges thrown their way, but both are handled imaginatively and with humor. . . . A genial read." SLJ

Sherman, Delia

Changeling. Viking 2006 292p $16.99; pa $8.99

Grades: 5 6 7 8 **Fic**

1. Fantasy fiction 2. New York (N.Y.) -- Fiction

ISBN 0-670-05967-6; 0-14-241188-4 pa

"Neef is a changeling, a human baby stolen by fairies. She lives in 'New York Between,' an invisible parallel city, and she was raised under the protection of her godmother (a white rat) and the Green Lady of Central Park. . . . After breaking Fairy Law, Neef is expelled, and she must complete a heroic quest . . . in order to regain entry to her community. . . . Silly, profound, and lightning paced all at once, this novel will please adventure fans and fantasy readers alike." Bull Cent Child Books

Another title about Neef is:

The Magic Mirror of the Mermaid Queen (2009)

Sherrard, Valerie

The **glory** wind. Fitzhenry & Whiteside 2011 222p pa $12.95

Grades: 5 6 7 8 **Fic**

1. Ontario -- Fiction 2. Prejudices -- Fiction 3. Country life -- Fiction

ISBN 978-1-55455-170-5; 1-55455-170-6

Eleven-year-old Luke must come to terms with the moral prejudices of his small town in rural 1950s Ontario when he befriends Gracie, the daughter of a young widow who moves in next door.

"Luke's first person narration is fresh and emotionally true. . . . The haunting depiction of small-mindedness will leave readers wondering, as Luke comes to, about Gracie's true nature: heavenly child—or angel?" Kirkus

★ **Tumbleweed** skies. Fitzhenry & Whiteside 2010 153p pa $11.95

Grades: 3 4 5 6 **Fic**

1. Grandmothers -- Fiction 2. Saskatchewan -- Fiction

ISBN 978-1-55455-113-2; 1-55455-113-7

"In the summer of 1954, Ellie's grandma reluctantly agrees to look after 10-year-old Ellie in Saskatchewan so that her dad can take a job as a traveling salesman. Ellie's mother died on the day that Ellie was born, and Grandma blames Ellie for her death. . . . Many kids will recognize the sorrow and difficulty of living with a hostile, bitter relative. . . . The girl next door, a spoiled, bossy brat, offers some levity, but true to Ellie's viewpoint, the spare first-person narrative tells a heartbreaking family story with no mushy reconciliation." Booklist

Sherry, Maureen

Walls within walls; illustrated by Adam Stower. Katherine Tegen Books 2010 349p il $16.99

Grades: 4 5 6 7 **Fic**

1. Mystery fiction 2. Siblings -- Fiction 3. New York (N.Y.) -- Fiction

ISBN 978-0-06-176700-5; 0-06-176700-X

LC 2010-09494

When the Smithfork family moves into a lavish Manhattan apartment building, they discover clues to a decades-old mystery hidden behind the walls of their new home.

This "packs all sorts of interesting information about topics like history and architecture into a mystery that kids can (almost) solve. . . . Readers will get a real feel for the uniqueness that is New York City." Booklist

Sheth, Kashmira

Blue jasmine; [by] Kashmira Sheth. Hyperion Books for Children 2004 186p $15.99; pa $5.99

Grades: 5 6 7 8 **Fic**

1. India -- Fiction 2. Immigrants -- Fiction 3. East Indians -- Fiction

ISBN 0-7868-1855-7; 0-7868-5565-7 pa

LC 2003-50818

When twelve-year-old Seema moves to Iowa City with her parents and younger sister, she leaves friends and family behind in her native India but gradually begins to feel at home in her new country

"Seema's story, which articulates the ache for distant home and family, will resonate with fellow immigrants and enlighten their classmates." Booklist

Boys without names. Balzer & Bray 2010 316p $15.99

Grades: 4 5 6 7 **Fic**

1. India -- Fiction 2. Slavery -- Fiction 3. Child labor -- Fiction 4. Missing persons -- Fiction

ISBN 978-0-06-185760-7; 0-06-185760-2

LC 2009-11747

Eleven-year-old Gopal and his family leave their rural Indian village for life with his uncle in Mumbai, but when they arrive his father goes missing and Gopal ends up locked in a sweatshop from which there is no escape.

"Readers quickly come to care for this clever, perceptive boy who tries hard to do the right thing. . . . The author includes more about child labor at the end of this well-told survival story with a social conscience." SLJ

Shimko, Bonnie

★ The **private** thoughts of Amelia E. Rye. Farrar, Straus Giroux 2010 234p $16.99

Grades: 5 6 7 8 **Fic**

1. Friendship -- Fiction 2. New York (State) -- Fiction 3. Mother-daughter relationship -- Fiction

ISBN 978-0-374-36131-0; 0-374-36131-2

LC 2008048092

Growing up in a small town in upstate New York during the 1960s, 13-year-old Amelia E. Ryel, unwanted by her mother, searches for love and acceptance.

"The book is peopled with believable, multilayered characters. . . . Shimko's . . . story is original, and Amelia's distinctive voice and likable nature will have readers rooting for her in times of trouble and cheering her ultimate good fortune." Publ Wkly

Shreve, Susan Richards

★ The **flunking** of Joshua T. Bates; [by] Susan Shreve; illustrated by Diane de Groat. Knopf 1984 82p il hardcover o.p. pa $4.99

Grades: 3 4 5 **Fic**

1. School stories 2. Teachers -- Fiction 3. Family life -- Fiction

ISBN 0-679-84187-3 pa

LC 83-19636

Driving home from the beach on Labor Day, Joshua receives some shocking news from his mother: he must repeat third grade.

"In addition to the warm depiction of a teacher-pupil relationship, the story has other relationships, astutely drawn: Joshua's parents, the former classmate who teases Joshua, the best friend who stoutly defends him. The dialogue is particularly good, often contributing to characterization, just as often crisply humorous." Bull Cent Child Books

Other titles about Joshua are:

Joshua T. Bates in trouble again (1997)

Joshua T. Bates takes charge (1993)

Shulman, Mark

Ann and Nan are anagrams; a mixed-up word dilemma. by Mark Shulman; illustrated by Adam McAuley. Chronicle Books 2013 36 p. (alk. paper) $16.99

Grades: 1 2 3 4   Fic

1. Word games -- Juvenile literature 2. Anagrams -- Fiction 3. Anagrams -- Juvenile fiction

ISBN 1452109141; 9781452109145

LC 2013006596

In this book, written by Mark Shulman and illustrated by Adam McCauley, "Robert (or Bert) thought he had his hands full when his mom and dad were palindromes. But now, his Grandma Reagan is in anagram danger! In fact, his sisters, Ann and Nan, and almost every other thing in his world, have become anagrams. Can Robert (or Bert) figure out the answer to his word dilemma, or is he fated to live a scrambled life?" (Publisher's note)

Treasure hunters; by James Patterson, Chris Grabenstein, and Mark Shulman and illustrated by Juliana Neufeld. Little, Brown and Company 2013 480 p. (Treasure hunters) $14.99

Grades: 3 4 5 6   Fic

1. Pirates -- Fiction 2. Siblings -- Fiction 3. Buried treasure -- Fiction 4. Twins -- Fiction 5. Seafaring life -- Fiction 6. Missing persons -- Fiction 7. New York (N.Y.) -- Fiction 8. Brothers and sisters -- Fiction 9. Adventure and adventurers -- Fiction

ISBN 031620756X; 9780316207560

LC 2012040968

In this book, by James Patterson, Chris Grabenstein and Mark Shulman, "the Kidd siblings have grown up diving down to shipwrecks and traveling the world, helping their famous parents recover everything from swords to gold doubloons from the bottom of the ocean. But after their parents disappear n the job, the kids are suddenly thrust into the biggest treasure hunt of their lives." (Publisher's note)

Shulman, Polly

★ The **Grimm** Legacy. G. P. Putnam's Sons 2010 325p $16.99

Grades: 5 6 7 8   Fic

1. Fantasy fiction 2. Magic -- Fiction 3. Libraries -- Fiction 4. New York (N.Y.) -- Fiction

ISBN 0-399-25096-4; 978-0-399-25096-5

LC 2009028919

New York high school student Elizabeth gets an after-school job as a page at the "New-York Circulating Material Repository," and when she gains coveted access to its Grimm Collection of magical objects, she and the other pages are drawn into a series of frightening adventures involving mythical creatures and stolen goods.

"This modern fantasy has intrigue, adventure, and romance, and the magical aspects of the tale are both clever and intricately woven. . . . Shulman's prose is fast paced, filled with humor, and peopled with characters who are either true to life or delightfully bizarre." SLJ

The **Wells** Bequest; by Polly Shulman. Nancy Paulsen Books, an imprint of Penguin Group (USA) Inc. 2013 272 p. (hardcover) $16.99

Grades: 5 6 7 8   Fic

1. Fantasy fiction 2. Science fiction 3. Time travel -- Fiction

ISBN 0399256466; 9780399256462

LC 2012036571

This book is a companion to Polly Shulman's "The Grimm Legacy." Here, New York Circulating Material Repository page "Leo notices an object materializing on the floor. The glittering, football-sized machine has 'gears and rods and knobs and a little saddle'—and two miniscule humans, one of whom is himself." He discovers that he and his fellow page Jaya must travel in time to prevent another page from misusing Nikola Tesla's death ray. (Kirkus Reviews)

Shurtliff, Liesl

Rump; the true story of Rumpelstiltskin. Liesl Shurtliff. 1st ed. Alfred A. Knopf 2013 272 p. (hardcover) $16.99

Grades: 3 4 5 6 7   Fic

1. Fractured fairy tales 2. Fairy tales 3. Gold -- Fiction 4. Humorous stories 5. Magic -- Fiction 6. Names, Personal -- Fiction

ISBN 0307977935; 9780307977939 trade; 9780307977946; 9780307977953; 9780307977960

LC 2012005093

In this fractured fairy tale, by Liesl Shurtliff, "12-year-old [Rumpelstiltskin] . . . finds an old spinning wheel, . . . [and] discovers he has a gift for spinning straw into gold. His best friend, Red Riding Hood, warns him that magic is dangerous, and she's right. With each thread he spins, he weaves himself deeper into a curse. To break the spell, Rump must go on a perilous quest, fighting off pixies, trolls, poison apples, and a wickedly foolish queen." (Publisher's note)

"Debut author Shurtliff upends the traditional characterization of this fairy tale's antihero, recasting Rumpelstiltskin as a sympathetic and tragically doomed protagonist. . . . [T]he picaresque-style narrative gives the maligned character a refreshingly plainspoken voice, while honoring the original story's hauntingly strange events." Pub Wkly

Silberberg, Alan

★ **Milo**; sticky notes and brain freeze. written and illustrated by Alan Silberberg. Aladdin 2010 275p il $15.99

Grades: 5 6 7 8   Fic

1. Death -- Fiction 2. Mothers -- Fiction 3. Friendship -- Fiction 4. Bereavement -- Fiction

ISBN 978-1-4169-9430-5; 1-4169-9430-0

LC 2010012708

"This is more than just another funny story about a middle school misfit who is the new kid in the neighborhood. While Milo does struggle with all the normal tween anxieties and self-consciousness about his family, there is more. Silberberg details the daily events with Wimpy Kid-like drawings and quick-witted humor that will keep the pages turning. Milo's new friendships with classmates Marshall and Hillary and elderly neighbor Sylvia Poole allow readers to glimpse at the deeper truth–Milo's mother's death–as it emerges between laugh lines. Silberberg takes on a tough topic and always stays true to the age of the character through dialogue and artwork while maintaining that wisecracking, 12-year-old humor." SLJ

Simmons, Jane

Beryl; a pig's tale. Little, Brown Books for Young Readers 2010 216p $14.99

Grades: 2 3 4 5 **Fic**

1. Adventure fiction 2. Pigs -- Fiction 3. Family -- Fiction 4. Toleration -- Fiction

ISBN 978-0-316-04410-3; 0-316-04410-5

LC 2009-3800

Tired of being mistreated and cooped up, Beryl the piglet escapes her farm and meets a group of wild pigs, whose settlement splits up over the decision of whether to let her stay, and with her new "family" she sets out to find a new home

"Simmons interjects humorous episodes through her colorful cast of animal characters, providing a rich contrast to the serious topics she explores. Before the hopeful ending is neatly resolved, Beryl and her cohorts face cruelty and despair. Vivid black-and-white drawings convey a range of emotion by varying shade and light. Expressive faces highlight a wealth of feeling." SLJ

Simon, Francesca

Horrid Henry; illustrated by Tony Ross. Sourcebooks 2009 90p il pa $4.99

Grades: 2 3 4 **Fic**

1. Brothers -- Fiction

ISBN 978-1-4022-1775-3; 1-4022-1775-7

First published 1994 in the United Kingdom

"Four short chapters follow Henry as he tries to have a perfect day (and upstages his brother, Perfect Peter), disrupts a dance recital with his imitation of a pterodactyl, meets his piratical match with neighbor Moody Margaret, and sabotages a family camping vacation. . . . Short, easy-to-read chapters will appeal to early readers, who will laugh at Henry's exaggerated antics and relate to his rambunctious personality. . . . Ross's comical illustrations perfectly complement the [text]." SLJ

Other titles in this series are:

Horrid Henry and the mega-mean time machine (2009)

Horrid Henry and the scary sitter (2009)

Horrid Henry tricks the tooth fairy (2009)

Horrid Henry's Christmas (2009)

Horrid Henry's stinkbomb (2009)

Horrid Henry rocks (2011)

Horrid Henry wakes the dead (2011)

Singh, Vandana

★ Younguncle comes to town; illustrated by B. M. Kamath. Viking 2006 153p il $14.99

Grades: 3 4 5 **Fic**

1. India -- Fiction 2. Uncles -- Fiction

ISBN 978-0-670-06051-1; 0-670-06051-8

LC 2005-14146

First published 2004 in India

In a small town in northern India, three siblings await their father's youngest brother, Younguncle, who is said to be somewhat eccentric

"Singh's prose is humorous and delightfully understated." SLJ

Skelton, Matthew

★ Endymion Spring. Delacorte Press 2006 392p il $17.95; lib bdg $19.99; pa $9.99

Grades: 5 6 7 8 **Fic**

1. Inventors 2. Printers 3. Magic -- Fiction 4. Great Britain -- Fiction 5. Books and reading -- Fiction

ISBN 0-385-73380-1; 0-385-90397-9 lib bdg; 0-385-73456-5 pa

LC 2006-46259

Having reluctantly accompanied his academic mother and pesky younger sister to Oxford, twelve-year-old Blake Winters is at loose ends until he stumbles across an ancient and magical book, secretly brought to England in 1453 by Gutenberg's mute apprentice to save it from evil forces, and which now draws Blake into a dangerous and life-threatening quest

"This book is certain to reach an audience looking for a page-turner, and it just might motivate readers to explore the . . . facts behind the fiction." SLJ

★ The story of Cirrus Flux. Delacorte Press 2010 288p il $17.99; lib bdg $20.99

Grades: 4 5 6 7 **Fic**

1. Adventure fiction 2. Orphans -- Fiction 3. Supernatural -- Fiction 4. London (England) -- Fiction 5. Great Britain -- History -- 1714-1837 -- Fiction

ISBN 978-0-385-73381-6; 0-385-73381-X; 978-0-385-90398-1 lib bdg; 0-385-90398-7 lib bdg

LC 2009-18987

In 1783 London, the destiny of an orphaned boy and girl becomes intertwined as the boy, Cirrus Flux, is pursued by a sinister woman mesmerist, a tiny man with an all-seeing eye, and a skull-collecting scoundrel, all of whom believe that he possesses an orb containing a divine power.

Skelton "neatly weaves touches of fantasy into a late-eighteenth century London setting. . . . His literary sensibility and grubby atmospherics are strong enough to carry the tale." Booklist

Skye, Obert

Wonkenstein: the creature from my closet. Henry Holt and Co. 2011 224p $13.99

Grades: 4 5 6 **Fic**

1. School stories 2. Monsters -- Fiction 3. Family life -- Fiction 4. Books and reading -- Fiction

ISBN 978-0-8050-9268-4; 0-8050-9268-4

LC 2011004870

Twelve-year-old Rob has stuffed his closet with old laboratory experiments, unread books, and more, and when a creature emerges from that chaos causing a great deal of trouble, Rob has to do such horrible things as visit a library and speak at a school assembly to set things right again.

"The writing is quite funny and has a lot of laugh-out-loud moments." SLJ

Slade, Arthur G.

Jolted; Newton Starker's rules for survival. [by] Arthur Slade. Wendy Lamb Books 2009 227p $15.99; lib bdg $18.99

Grades: 5 6 7 8 **Fic**

1. School stories 2. Lightning -- Fiction

ISBN 978-0-385-74700-4; 0-385-74700-4; 978-0-385-90944-0 lib bdg; 0-385-90944-6 lib bdg

LC 2008-8632

First published 2008 in Canada

Many of Newton Starker's ancestors, including his mother, have been killed by lightning strikes, so when he enrolls at the eccentric Jerry Potts Academy of Higher Learning and

Survival in Moose Jaw, Saskatchewan, he tries to be a model student so that he can avoid the same fate.

"The premise will snag readers immediately [and] . . . Slade's portrayal of Newton's sweep of emotions as he deals with his perceived fate–fear, fury, dogged determination–is especially convincing." Publ Wkly

Sleator, William

The **boxes**. Dutton Children's Bks. 1998 196p hardcover o.p. pa $4.99
Grades: 6 7 8 9   **Fic**
   1. Science fiction
   ISBN 0-525-46012-8; 0-14-130810-9 pa

LC 98-9285

When she opens two strange boxes left in her care by her mysterious uncle, fifteen-year-old Annie discovers a swarm of telepathic creatures and unleashes a power capable of slowing down time

"Sleator has written a page-turner. . . . His writing is crisp and clean, letting the story speak for itself." Voice Youth Advocates

Interstellar pig. Dutton 1984 197p hardcover o.p. pa $6.99
Grades: 5 6 7 8   **Fic**
   1. Science fiction
   ISBN 0-14-037595-3 pa

LC 84-4132

Barney's boring seaside vacation suddenly becomes more interesting when the cottage next door is occupied by three exotic neighbors who are addicted to a game they call "Interstellar Pig."

The author "draws the reader in with intimations of danger and horror, but the climactic battle is more slapstick than horrific, and the victor's prize could scarcely be more ironic. Problematic as straight science fiction but great fun as a spoof on human-alien contact." Booklist

   Another title about Barney is:
   Parasite Pig (2002)

Sloan, Holly Goldberg

   ★ **Counting** by 7s; by Holly Goldberg Sloan. Dial Books for Young Readers 2012 384 p. (hardcover) $16.99
Grades: 4 5 6 7   **Fic**
   1. Genius -- Fiction 2. Orphans -- Fiction 3. Alienation (Social psychology) -- Fiction 4. Schools -- Fiction 5. Gardening -- Fiction 6. High schools -- Fiction 7. Eccentrics and eccentricities -- Fiction
   ISBN 0803738552; 9780803738553

LC 2012004994

This book follows "Willow Chance . . . an extremely precocious and analytical 12-year-old 'genius'. . . . Despite Willow's social difficulties, she makes an impression on everyone around her--whether it's Dell Duke, a lonely and ineffectual school district counselor, or Jairo Hernandez, the taxi driver Willow hires to drive her to her meetings with Dell. After Willow's parents die in a car crash, her new friend Mai Nguyen persuades her mother to take Willow in." (Publishers Weekly)

Slote, Alfred

   ★ **Finding** Buck McHenry. HarperCollins Pubs. 1991 250p pa $4.95

Grades: 4 5 6   **Fic**
   1. Baseball -- Fiction 2. African Americans -- Fiction
   ISBN 0-06-440469-2 pa

LC 90-39190

Eleven-year-old Jason, believing the school custodian Mack Henry to be Buck McHenry, a famous pitcher from the old Negro League, tries to enlist him as a coach for his Little League team by revealing his identity to the world

"Slote skillfully blends comedy, suspense and baseball in a highly entertaining tale." Publ Wkly

Smiley, Jane, 1949-

   Gee Whiz; Jane Smiley; with illustrations by Elaine Clayton. Alfred A. Knopf 2013 272 p. (The horses of Oak Valley Ranch) (library binding) $19.99
Grades: 4 5 6 7   **Fic**
   1. Ranch life -- Fiction 2. Christian life -- Fiction 3. Horses -- Training -- Fiction 4. Ranch life -- California -- Fiction 5. Family life -- California -- Fiction 6. California -- History -- 1950- -- Fiction
   ISBN 0375969691; 9780375869693; 9780375969690; 9780375985331

LC 2012024370

In this book, by Jane Smiley, "Gee Whiz is a striking horse, and only part of that is because of his size. . . . When Abby is confronted with an onslaught of reminders of just how little of the world she has seen, she finds herself connecting with Gee Whiz's calm and curious nature, and his desire to know more." (Publisher's note)

   ★ The **Georges** and the Jewels; with illustrations by Elaine Clayton. Alfred A. Knopf 2009 232p il $16.99; lib bdg $19.99
Grades: 4 5 6 7   **Fic**
   1. Horses -- Fiction 2. California -- Fiction 3. Ranch life -- Fiction 4. Christian life -- Fiction
   ISBN 978-0-375-86227-4; 0-375-86227-7; 978-0-375-96227-1 lib bdg; 0-375-96227-1 lib bdg

LC 2009-06241

Seventh-grader Abby Lovitt grows up on her family's California horse ranch in the 1960s, learning to train the horses her father sells and trying to reconcile her strict religious upbringing with her own ideas about life.

"As might be expected from the skilled hands of Smiley . . . there are synchronous storylines . . . [and] many will find it difficult to say goodbye to Abby, Jack and especially to Ornery George." Publ Wkly

   Other titles in this series are:
   A good horse (2010)
   True blue (2011)

Smith, Clete Barrett

   Aliens on vacation; illustrated by Christian Slade. Hyperion 2011 251p il (The intergalactic bed & breakfast) $16.99
Grades: 4 5 6   **Fic**
   1. Vacations -- Fiction 2. Hotels and motels -- Fiction 3. Extraterrestrial beings -- Fiction
   ISBN 1-4231-3363-3; 978-1-4231-3363-6

Unhappy at being sent to stay with his grandmother at the inn she operates, The Intergalactic Bed & Breakfast, Scrub discovers that each room is actually a portal to space and the inn's visitors are aliens who are vacationing on Earth.

Smith "delivers a first novel about being a stranger in a strange land that many middle-schoolers will find funny and relatable. Slade adds a few goofy touches in the black-and-white spot art." Booklist

Smith, Cynthia Leitich
Indian shoes; illustrated by Jim Madsen, HarperCollins Pubs. 2002 66p il $15.95
Grades: 3 4 5 **Fic**
1. Grandfathers -- Fiction 2. Native Americans -- Fiction
ISBN 0-06-029531-7
LC 2001-39510
Together with Grampa, Ray Halfmoon, a Seminole-Cherokee boy, finds creative and amusing solutions to life's challenges
"The writing is warm and lively; the situations are sometimes humorous, sometimes poignant; and Ray and Grampa's loving relationship is depicted believably and without sentimentality." Horn Book Guide

Smith, Doris Buchanan
★ A **taste** of blackberries; illustrated by Charles Robinson. Crowell 1973 58p il lib bdg $14.89; pa $4.95
Grades: 4 5 6 **Fic**
1. Death -- Fiction 2. Friendship -- Fiction
ISBN 0-690-80512-8 lib bdg; 0-06-440238-4 pa
"A difficult and sensitive subject, treated with taste and honesty, is woven into a moving story about a believable little boy. The black-and-white illustrations are honest, affective, and sensitive." Horn Book

Smith, Hope Anita
★ **Keeping** the night watch; with illustrations by E.B. Lewis. Henry Holt 2008 73p il $18.95
Grades: 4 5 6 7 **Fic**
1. Novels in verse 2. Fathers -- Fiction 3. Family life -- Fiction 4. African Americans -- Fiction
ISBN 978-0-8050-7202-0; 0-8050-7202-0
LC 2007-12372
Sequel to: The way a door closes (2003)
Coretta Scott King honor book for text, 2009
A thirteen-year-old African American boy chronicles what happens to his family when his father, who temporarily left, returns home and they all must deal with their feelings of anger, hope, abandonment, and fear.
"The words are simple . . . and the beautiful watercolor pictures of the African American family have the same quiet intensity as pictures in the first book. . . . Although mainly in free verse, there's also a sonnet." Booklist

Smith, Icy
Half spoon of rice; a survival story of the Cambodian genocide. written by Icy Smith; illustrated by Sopaul Nhem. East West Discovery Press 2010 42p il
Grades: 5 6 7 8 **Fic**
1. Cambodia -- Fiction 2. Genocide -- Fiction
ISBN 0-9821675-8-X; 978-0-9821675-8-8
LC 2009002973
Nine-year-old Nat and his family are forced from their home on April 17, 1975, marched for many days, separated from each other, and forced to work in the rice fields, where Nat concentrates on survival. Includes historical notes and photographs documenting the Cambodian genocide

"Bold, impressionistic oil paintings, mainly full page but some full spreads, speak volumes, and archival photographs are appended. This powerful child's eye view of war is harsh and realistic—like its subject—though accessible and thought-provoking." SLJ

Smith, Robert Kimmel
★ **Chocolate** fever; illustrated by Gioia Fiammenghi. Putnam 1989 93p il $14.99; pa $4.99
Grades: 4 5 6 **Fic**
1. Chocolate -- Fiction
ISBN 978-0-399-24355-4; 0-399-24355-0; 978-0-14-240595-6 pa; 0-14-240595-7 pa
LC 88-23508
A reissue of the title first published 1972 by Coward-McCann
"It's all quite preposterous and lots of laughs, and so are the cartoon illustrations." Publ Wkly
"You've heard of too much of a good thing? You've never heard of it the way it happens to Henry Green. Henry's a chocolate maven, first class. No, that's too mild. Henry's absolutely freaky over chocolate, loco over cocoa. He can't get enough, until—aaarrrfh! Brown spots, brown bumps all over Henry. It's (gulp) 'Chocolate Fever.'" N Y Times Book Rev

Smith, Roland
Chupacabra; Roland Smith. Scholastic Press 2013 336 p. illustrations $16.99
Grades: 5 6 7 8 **Fic**
1. Cryptozoology 2. Kidnapping -- Fiction 3. Mythical animals -- Fiction 4. Father-daughter relationship -- Fiction 5. Chupacabras -- Fiction 6. Missing persons -- Fiction 7. Adventure and adventurers -- Fiction
ISBN 0545178177; 9780545178174
LC 2013404665
This book, part of the Cryptid Hunters series, by Roland Smith, "reunites Marty and his unusual uncle, cryptozoologist Travis Wolfe, as they search the world for Wolfe's daughter, Grace. Grace has been kidnapped by her grandfather, the ruthless and dangerous Noah Blackwood. . . . Now, with word that the mysterious creature known as Chupacabra has been sighted again, Wolfe is torn between his obsession with finding cryptids and his desperate need to rescue his daughter." (Publisher's note)
"Plunging readers in where Tentacles (Scholastic, 2009) left off, this fast-paced novel opens right after Grace discovers that her twin brother, Marty, is in fact her cousin, and that her father's unscrupulous enemy, Noah Blackwood, is actually her grandfather...Though this sequel suffers in comparison to the previous books in the series, Smith adeptly adds enough new characters, dangers, and cool science to reel in reluctant readers and keep them turning pages long after their lights should have been turned off." SLJ
Other titles in the series include:
Cryptid Hunters (2005)
Mutation (2014)
Tentacles (2009)

Mutation; Roland Smith. Scholastic Press 2014 352 p. (Cryptid hunters) (hardback) $16.99
Grades: 5 6 7 8 **Fic**
1. Brazil -- Fiction 2. Missing persons -- Fiction 3. Jungles -- Fiction 4. Animals, Mythical -- Fiction 5.

Adventure and adventurers -- Fiction

ISBN 0545081807; 9780545081801; 9780545081818

LC 2014017169

In this book by Roland Smith "Marty and his best friend, Luther, have managed to rescue Marty's cousin Grace from the clutches of the nefarious pseudo-naturalist Noah Blackwood, but . . . Marty's parents have been missing in Brazil for months. With time running out, Marty and the Cryptos Island crew race off for Brazil -- where they discover that Noah Blackwood has twisted the natural order of things beyond their wildest, most terrifying dreams." (Publisher's note)

"Marty, Grace, and friends make their way to Brazil to continue their twofold quest: find Marty's missing parents and stop the evil Noah Blackwood from continuing his unethical genetic experiments. Action, adventure, and high-tech gadgetry all combine into an exciting but over-the-top story. Stunning revelations and other dramatic turns provide additional impetus to keep readers turning the pages." Horn Book

I, Q.: book one, Independence Hall. Sleeping Bear Press 2008 302p pa $8.95

Grades: 5 6 7 8   **Fic**

1. Adventure fiction 2. Spies -- Fiction 3. Terrorism -- Fiction

ISBN 978-1-58536-325-4 pa; 1-58536-325-1 pa

In Philadelphia, Angela realizes she's being followed, and Q soon learns the secret about Angela's real mother, a former Secret Service agent

"Adventure, suspense, humor, fascinating characters, and plot twists galore will draw middle-graders to this series starter." Booklist

Followed by: I, Q.: book two, The White House (2009)

I, Q.: book two, The White House. Sleeping Bear Press 2010 pa $8.95

Grades: 5 6 7 8   **Fic**

1. Spies -- Fiction 2. Siblings -- Fiction 3. Terrorism -- Fiction 4. Remarriage -- Fiction 5. Washington (D.C.) -- Fiction 6. Philadelphia (Pa.) -- Fiction 7. White House (Washington, D.C.) -- Fiction

ISBN 978-1-58536-456-5; 1-58536-456-8

LC 2011378292

Q (Quest) and Angela make it to the White House in Washington, D.C. to find that it is even harder to determine who are the 'good' and 'bad' guys than ever before.

"This spellbinding James Bond genre espionage novel for the middle school set will leave readers breathlessly waiting for the next installment." Voice Youth Advocates

Storm runners. Scholastic Press 2011 143p $16.99

Grades: 5 6 7 8   **Fic**

1. Florida -- Fiction 2. Hurricanes -- Fiction 3. Father-son relationship -- Fiction

ISBN 978-0-545-08175-7; 0-545-08175-0

LC 2010-32720

Twelve-year-old Chase Masters travels the country with his father, a "storm runner," but he is tested in ways he never could have imagined when he and a new friend are caught in a hurricane near St. Petersburg, Florida.

"This is an exciting, quick read. . . . Readers will feel engaged with Chase and his friends in their struggles to survive." SLJ

Followed by: The surge (2011)

Sneve, Virginia Driving Hawk

Lana's Lakota moons. University of Nebraska Press 2007 116p pa $12.95

Grades: 3 4 5   **Fic**

1. Death -- Fiction 2. Cancer -- Fiction 3. Cousins -- Fiction 4. Teton Indians -- Fiction 5. Hmong (Asian people) -- Fiction

ISBN 978-0-8032-6028-3 pa; 0-8032-6028-8 pa

LC 2007-05469

Cousins Lori and Lana, Lakota Indians who have a close but competitive relationship, learn about their heritage and culture throughout the year, and when a Laotian-Hmong girl comes to their school, they make friends with her and "adopt" her as one of their own

This is an "unassuming yet potent chronicle. . . . This novel repays readers with its portraits of the sisters and their living heritage." Publ Wkly

Snicket, Lemony

The **bad** beginning; illustrations by Brett Helquist. HarperCollins Pubs. 1999 162p il (A series of unfortunate events) $11.99; pa $6.99

Grades: 4 5 6   **Fic**

1. Orphans -- Fiction

ISBN 0-06-440766-7; 0-06-114630-7 pa

LC 99-14750

After the sudden death of their parents, the three Baudelaire children must depend on each other and their wits when it turns out that the distant relative who is appointed their guardian is determined to use any means necessary to get their fortune

"While the misfortunes hover on the edge of being ridiculous, Snicket's energetic blend of humor, dramatic irony, and literary flair makes it all perfectly believable. . . . Excellent for reading aloud." SLJ

Other titles in this series are:

The reptile room (1999)
The wide window (2000)
The miserable mill (2000)
The austere academy (2000)
The ersatz elevator (2000)
The vile village (2001)
The hostile hospital (2001)
The carnivorous carnival (2003)
The slippery slope (2003)
The grim grotto (2004)
The penultimate peril (2005)
The end (2006)

File under: 13 suspicious incidents; by Lemony Snicket; art by Seth. Little Brown & Co 2014 259 p. (All the wrong questions) (hardback) $12

Grades: 4 5 6 7   **Fic**

1. Mystery fiction 2. Humorous fiction 3. Apprentices -- Fiction 4. City and town life -- Fiction 5. Humorous stories 6. Mystery and detective stories

ISBN 0316284033; 9780316284035

LC 2013037873

This book, by Lemony Snicket, presents "thirteen mini-mysteries. Paintings have been falling off of walls, a loud and loyal dog has gone missing, a specter has been seen walking the pier at midnight--strange things are happening all over the town of Stain'd-By-The-Sea. . . . Join the investigation and tackle the mysteries alongside Snicket, then turn to the back of the book to see the solution revealed." (Publisher's note)

"Kid-detective Lemony Snicket treats us to thirteen short mysteries (missing newt, ghostly appearance, series of break-ins) in which he leaves readers poised just before the reveal, with a chance to solve the mystery themselves before they flip to the back of the book. (It's Encyclopedia Brown for Snicket-Hipsters.) The actual puzzles are dandy, and the format is ideal for the author's comic avalanche." Horn Book

Other titles in the series include:
Who Could That be at This Hour
When Did You See Her Last
Shouldn't You Be in School

Lemony Snicket: the unauthorized autobiography. HarperCollins Pubs. 2002 212p il $11.99; pa $6.99
Grades: 4 5 6 7   **Fic**
1. Humorous fiction
ISBN 0-06-000719-2; 0-06-056225-0 pa
LC 2001-51745

"The story of the fictitious Lemony Snicket and how he has dedicated his life to the case of the orphaned Baudelaire children. . . . Snicket tells you what he cannot tell you and then tells you, but what he tells you makes no sense. . . . [A] hilarious and clever book. . . . Lemony Snicket fans will love it, and new readers will laugh so much that they will want to read the series." Voice Youth Advocates

Shouldn't you be in school? Lemony Snicket. Little, Brown & Co. 2014 325 p. illustrations (some color) (All the wrong questions) (hardcover) $16
Grades: 4 5 6 7   **Fic**
1. School stories 2. Mystery fiction 3. Arson -- Fiction 4. Humorous stories 5. Apprentices -- Fiction 6. Detective and mystery stories 7. Arson investigation -- Fiction
ISBN 0316123064; 9780316123068; 9780316225045; 9780316279703; 9780316409681
LC 2014933203

In this children's book by Lemony Snicket "Lemony Snicket must work together with his incompetent chaperone to figure out who is burning down all of the buildings in the quaint town of Stain'd-by-the-Sea. Snicket is part of a special program, the V.F.D., and spends his days sleuthing with his chaperone, Theodora, in an attempt to catch the elusive and mysterious Hangfire, who is supposedly to blame for all of the mysterious happenings." (School Library Journal)

"In his third adventure, twelve-year-old Lemony Snicket, apprentice investigator, tackles a series of arsons in the economically depressed and highly mysterious town of Stain'd-by-the-Sea. Readers already hooked by this series will be pleased to check in with heroic librarian Qwerty, investigative journalist Moxie Mallahan, and the bickering Officers Mitchum and their bullying son, Stewart...As to the actual story, clues of the gray-matter sort (such as anagrams) combine with escapes, attacks, cliffhangers, and

looming bad guys, keeping the whole crazy plot buoyant. Just." Horn Book
Other titles in the series include:
Who Could That Be at this Hour (2012)
When Did You See Her Last (2013)

★ **Who** could that be at this hour? by Lemony Snicket; art by Seth. Little, Brown 2012 272 p. $15.99
Grades: 4 5 6 7   **Fic**
1. Bildungsromans 2. Mystery fiction 3. Humorous fiction 4. Statues -- Fiction 5. Stealing -- Fiction 6. Apprentices -- Fiction
ISBN 0316123080; 9780316123082
LC 2012012657

This children's adventure mystery, by Lemony Snicket, begins in "Stain'd-by-the-Sea, the mostly deserted town where 12-year-old Lemony Snicket takes his first case as apprentice to chaperone S. Theodora Markson. They have been hired by Mrs. Murphy Sallis to retrieve a vastly valuable statue of the local legend, the Bombinating Beast. . . . With the help and/or hindrance of girls Moxie and Ellington, can Snicket keep his promises and come close to solving a mystery?" (Kirkus Reviews)

Sniegoski, Tom
Billy Hooten, Owlboy; by Thomas E. Sniegoski; illustrated by Eric Powell. Yearling 2007 242p il lib bdg $11.99; pa $5.99
Grades: 3 4 5 6   **Fic**
1. Superheroes -- Fiction 2. Cartoons and comics -- Fiction
ISBN 978-0-385-90402-5 lib bdg; 978-0-440-42180-1 pa
LC 2007001552

Unassuming twelve-year-old Billy Hooten, who loves reading superhero comic books, suddenly learns that he has been chosen to become the next Owlboy, whose destiny it is to save the inhabitants of Monstros, a city underneath the cemetery next to Billy's house

"This lively tale should be a hit, especially with reluctant readers. A few black-and-white sketches appear throughout." SLJ
Others title about Owlboy are:
Billy Hooten, Owlboy: the girl with the destructo touch (2007)
Billy Hooten, Owlboy: the flock of fury (2008)
Billy Hooten, Owlboy: tremble at the terror of Zis-boom-bah (2008)

Quest for the Spark; Book 2 written by Tom Sniegoski; illustrated by Jeff Smith; color by Steve Hamaker. Graphix 2012 234 p. (hardcover: alk. paper) $22.99
Grades: 4 5 6 7   **Fic**
1. Fantasy fiction 2. Magic -- Fiction 3. Adventure fiction 4. Dreams -- Fiction 5. Dragons -- Fiction 6. Fantasy 7. Humorous stories 8. Heroes -- Fiction 9. Adventure and adventurers -- Fiction
ISBN 9780545141031; 9780545141048
LC 2011020281

This book is set in the world of illustrator Jeff Smith's "Bone" graphic novels. Here, author Tom Sniegoski tells the story of "Tom, a Valley turnip farmer" who "receives a vision that the peaceful otherworld of the Dreaming is under attack. The evil Nacht, a renegade Dragon, seeks to control the dreamland, and through it, the Waking World as well. A mysterious forest woman tells Tom that he has been chosen to lead a quest to find the scattered pieces of the Spark--the light of creation that can drive back the dark power. When his family falls under the Nacht's corrupted sleep spell, Tom realizes that he has no choice and sets out with his best friend, a talking raccoon." (School Libr J)

Quest for the spark; book one. written by Tom Sniegoski; illustrated by Jeff Smith; color by Steve Hamaker. Graphix 2011 218p il (Bone) $22.99; pa $10.99
Grades: 4 5 6 7   **Fic**
1. Fantasy fiction 2. Adventure fiction 3. Magic -- Fiction 4. Dreams -- Fiction 5. Heroes and heroines -- Fiction
ISBN 978-0-545-14101-7; 0-545-14101-X; 978-0-545-14102-4 pa; 0-545-14102-8 pa
LC 2010017002
Twelve-year-old Tom Elm, his raccoon friend Roderick, Percival, Abbey, and Barclay Bone, warrior-priest Randolf, and forest-woman Lorimar join in a quest to find the pieces of the Spark that can save Dreaming—and the Waking World—from a Darkness created by the Nacht.

"At long last . . . we return to the Valley that was the setting for Smith's comics-landscape-changing Bone, though this adventure takes place in prose rather than panels. . . . As long as fans are not expecting a repeat of the old magic and not too disappointed that there isn't nearly enough of Smith's always excellent full-color, full-page artwork helping out, it looks as if they're in for a cheery jaunt back through a beloved world." Booklist

Snow, Maya
Sisters of the sword. HarperCollins 2008 275p (Sisters of the sword) $16.99; lib bdg $17.89; pa $6.99
Grades: 5 6 7 8   **Fic**
1. Japan -- Fiction 2. Samurai -- Fiction 3. Sisters -- Fiction 4. Sex role -- Fiction
ISBN 978-0-06-124387-5; 0-06-124387-6; 978-0-06-124388-2 lib bdg; 0-06-124388-4 lib bdg; 978-0-06-124389-9 pa; 0-06-124389-2 pa
LC 2007-029610
Two aristocratic sisters in ancient Japan disguise themselves as samurai warriors to take revenge on the uncle who betrayed their family.

"This rousing new series . . . starts off with a bang, or more accurately, the silent thrust of a sword." Booklist
Other titles in this series are:
Chasing the secret (2009)
Journey through fire (2009)

Snyder, Laurel
Any which wall; drawings by LeUyen Pham. Random House 2009 242p il $16.99; lib bdg $19.99
Grades: 4 5 6 7   **Fic**
1. Iowa -- Fiction 2. Magic -- Fiction 3. Wishes -- Fiction 4. Siblings -- Fiction 5. Space and time -- Fiction
ISBN 978-0-375-85560-3; 0-375-85560-2; 978-0-375-95560-0 lib bdg; 0-375-95560-7 lib bdg
LC 2008-22605
In the middle of an Iowa cornfield, four children find a magic wall that enables them to travel through time and space.

"Snyder's fresh, down-to-earth voice is complemented by Pham's energetic illustrations, which seem at once retro and modern. Fantasy fans will enjoy this novel, but so will readers who like stories about ordinary kids." SLJ

Bigger than a bread box. Random House 2011 226p $16.99
Grades: 4 5 6   **Fic**
1. Magic -- Fiction 2. Family life -- Fiction
ISBN 978-0-375-86916-7; 0-375-86916-6
Twelve-year-old Rebecca is struggling with her parents' separation, as well as a sudden move to her Gran's house in another state. For a while, a magic bread box, discovered in the attic, makes life away from home a little easier. Then suddenly it starts to make things much, much more difficult, and Rebecca is forced to decide not just where, but who she really wants to be.

"Introspective and rich with delicate imagery. . . . The insightful, memorable, and complex characters that Snyder creates result in a story with the same qualities." Publ Wkly

★ **Penny** Dreadful; drawings by Abigail Halpin. Random House 2010 304p il $16.99; lib bdg $19.99
Grades: 3 4 5   **Fic**
1. Tennessee -- Fiction 2. Family life -- Fiction 3. Country life -- Fiction
ISBN 978-0-375-86199-4; 0-375-86199-8; 978-0-375-96199-1 lib bdg; 0-375-96199-2 lib bdg
LC 2009-32104
When her father suddenly quits his job, the almost-ten-year-old, friendless Penny and her neglectful parents leave their privileged life in the city for a ramshackle property in the eccentric town of Thrush Junction, Tennessee.

"Snyder's characters are well-developed and endearing, and the author strikes an excellent balance between the reality of the Greys' financial straits and the quiet magic that everyday life has to offer." Publ Wkly

Snyder, Zilpha Keatley
★ The **Egypt** game; drawings by Alton Raible. Atheneum Books for Young Readers 2007 215p il $16.99; pa $6.99
Grades: 5 6 7 8   **Fic**
1. Egypt -- Fiction 2. Games -- Fiction 3. Imagination -- Fiction
ISBN 978-1-4169-6065-2; 1-4169-6065-1; 978-1-4169-9051-2 pa; 1-4169-9051-8 pa
First published 1967
A Newbery Medal honor book, 1968
A group of children, entranced with the study of Egypt, play their own Egypt game, are visited by a secret oracle, become involved in a murder, and befriend the Professor before they move on to new interests, such as Gypsies.

★ The **headless** cupid; illustrated by Alton Raible. Atheneum Books for Young Readers 2009 219p il $16.99; pa $6.99
Grades: 5 6 7 8   **Fic**
1. Occultism -- Fiction
ISBN 978-1-4169-9532-6; 1-4169-9532-3; 978-1-4169-9052-9 pa; 1-4169-9052-6 pa
A reissue of the title first published 1971
A Newbery Medal honor book, 1972

Life is never quite the same again for eleven-year-old David after the arrival of his new stepsister, a student of the occult.

"The author portrays children with acute understanding, evident both in her delineation of Amanda and David and of the distinctively different younger children. Good style, good characterization, good dialogue, good story." Sutherland. The Best in Child Books

William S. and the great escape. Atheneum Books for Young Readers 2009 214p $16.99

Grades: 5 6 7 8　　　　　　　　　　　　　　　**Fic**

1. Acting -- Fiction 2. Siblings -- Fiction

ISBN 978-1-4169-6763-7; 1-4169-6763-X

　　　　　　　　　　　　　　LC 2008-10377

In 1938, twelve-year-old William has already decided to leave home when his younger sister informs him that she and their brother and sister are going too, and right away, but complications arise when an acquaintance decides to "help" them.

"Wit and pluck are rewarded in this quick-paced, high-drama adventure, which may also whet young appetites for Shakespeare." Publ Wkly

Followed by: William's midsummer dreams (2011)

William's midsummer dreams. Atheneum Books for Young Readers 2011 209p $16.99

Grades: 5 6 7 8　　　　　　　　　　　　　　　**Fic**

1. Aunts -- Fiction 2. Acting -- Fiction 3. Theater -- Fiction 4. Adoption -- Fiction 5. Siblings -- Fiction

ISBN 978-1-4424-1997-1; 9781442419995 e-book

　　　　　　　　　　　　　　LC 2010036958

Sequel to: William S. and the great escape (2009)

Now permanently settled with Aunt Fiona, who has adopted him and his siblings, thirteen-year-old William gets the chance to play Puck in a professional production of A Midsummer Night's Dream.

"An adventure story with a lot to say about identity, ambition and character." Kirkus

The **witches** of Worm; illustrated by Alton Raible. Atheneum Books for Young Readers 2009 183p il $16.99; pa $6.99

Grades: 5 6 7 8　　　　　　　　　　　　　　　**Fic**

1. Cats -- Fiction 2. Witchcraft -- Fiction

ISBN 978-1-4169-9531-9; 1-4169-9531-5; 978-1-4169-9053-6 pa; 1-4169-9053-4 pa

A reissue of the title first published 1972

A Newbery Medal honor book, 1973

Lonely, twelve-year-old Jessica is convinced that the cat she finds is possessed by a witch and is responsible for her own strange behavior.

"This is a haunting story of the power of mind and ritual, as well as of misunderstanding, anger, loneliness and friendship. It is written with humor, pace, a sure feeling for conversation and a warm understanding of human nature." Commonweal

Sobol, Donald J.

Encyclopedia Brown, boy detective; illustrated by Leonard Shortall. Dutton Children's Bks. 1963 88p il hardcover o.p. pa $4.99

Grades: 3 4 5　　　　　　　　　　　　　　　**Fic**

1. Mystery fiction

ISBN 978-0-14-240888-9; 0-14-240888-3

First published by Thomas Nelson

"The answers are logical; some are tricky, but there are no trick questions, and readers who like puzzles should enjoy the . . . challenge. The episodes are lightly humorous, brief, and simply written." Bull Cent Child Books

Other titles about Encyclopedia Brown are:

Encyclopedia Brown and the case of the carnival crime (2011)

Encyclopedia Brown and the case of the dead eagles (1975)

Encyclopedia Brown and the case of the disgusting sneakers (1990)

Encyclopedia Brown and the case of the jumping frogs (2003)

Encyclopedia Brown and the case of the midnight visitor (1977)

Encyclopedia Brown and the case of the mysterious handprints (1985)

Encyclopedia Brown and the case of Pablo's nose (1996)

Encyclopedia Brown and the case of the secret pitch (1965)

Encyclopedia Brown and the case of the secret UFO (2010)

Encyclopedia Brown and the case of the sleeping dog (1998)

Encyclopedia Brown and the case of the slippery salamander (1999)

Encyclopedia Brown and the case of the treasure hunt (1988)

Encyclopedia Brown and the case of the two spies (1994)

Encyclopedia Brown cracks the case (2007)

Encyclopedia Brown finds the clues (1966)

Encyclopedia Brown gets his man (1967)

Encyclopedia Brown keeps the peace (1969)

Encyclopedia Brown lends a hand (1974)

Encyclopedia Brown saves the day (1970)

Encyclopedia Brown sets the pace (1982)

Encyclopedia Brown shows the way (1972)

Encyclopedia Brown solves them all (1968)

Encyclopedia Brown: super sleuth (2009)

Encyclopedia Brown takes the cake! (1983)

Encyclopedia Brown takes the case (1973)

Encyclopedia Brown tracks them down (1971)

Sonneborn, Scott

Shell shocker; written by Scott Sonneborn; illustrated by Dan Schoening, Mike DeCarlo, and Lee Loughridge. Stone Arch Books 2011 48p il (DC super heroes: The Flash) lib bdg $25.32; pa $5.95

Grades: 2 3 4　　　　　　　　　　　　　　　**Fic**

1. Superheroes -- Fiction

ISBN 978-1-4342-2615-0 lib bdg; 1-4342-2615-8 lib bdg; 978-1-4342-3092-8 pa; 1-4342-3092-9 pa

　　　　　　　　　　　　　　LC 2010025350

While deactivating an explosive for the bomb squad, the police scientist receives a call, tipping him off about a robbery across town. Luckily, Barry is secretly the fastest man alive, the Flash!

This "chapter-book [adaptation] of [a] popular comic [superhero has] great, full-page illustrations and . . . onomatopoeia. . . . [The cover is a] 3D [hologram] that will attract kids. . . . [This is] action-packed." SLJ

Includes glossary and bibliographical references

Sonnenblick, Jordan

★ **After** ever after. Scholastic Press 2010 260p $16.99

Grades: 5 6 7 8   **Fic**

1. School stories 2. Cancer -- Fiction 3. Friendship -- Fiction 4. Family life -- Fiction

ISBN 978-0-439-83706-4; 0-439-83706-5

Jeffery's cancer is in remission but the chemotherapy and radiation treatments have left him with concentration problems, and he worries about school work, his friends, his family, and a girl who likes him

"Sonnenblick imbues Jeffrey with a smooth, likable, and unaffected voice. . . . As hilarious as it is tragic, and as honest as it is hopeful . . . [this book is] irresistable reading." Booklist

Zen and the art of faking it. Scholastic Press 2007 264p $16.99; pa $7.99

Grades: 5 6 7 8   **Fic**

1. School stories 2. Pennsylvania -- Fiction 3. Zen Buddhism -- Fiction 4. Asian Americans -- Fiction

ISBN 978-0-439-83707-1; 0-439-83707-3; 978-0-439-83709-5 pa; 0-439-83709-X pa

LC 2006-28841

When thirteen-year-old San Lee moves to a new town and school for the umpteenth time, he is looking for a way to stand out when his knowledge of Zen Buddhism, gained in his previous school, provides the answer—and the need to quickly become a convincing Zen master.

The author gives readers "plenty to laugh at. . . . Mixed with more serious scenes, . . . lighter moments take a basic message about the importance of honesty and forgiveness and treat it with panache." Publ Wkly

Sonnichsen, A. L.

Red butterfly; A. L. Sonnichsen, illustrated by Amy June Bates. Simon & Schuster Books for Young Readers 2015 392 p. hardcover $16.99

Grades: 4 5 6 7   **Fic**

1. Novels in verse 2. China -- Fiction 3. Adoption -- Fiction 4. Families -- Fiction 5. Foundlings -- Fiction 6. Abnormalities, Human -- Fiction 7. Intercountry adoption -- Fiction

ISBN 1481411098; 9781481411097

LC 2013050300

"Kara never met her birth mother. Abandoned as an infant, she was taken in by an American woman living in China. Now eleven, Kara spends most of her time in their apartment, wondering why she and Mama cannot leave the city of Tianjin and go live with Daddy in Montana. Mama tells Kara to be content with what she has but what if Kara secretly wants more? Told in lyrical, moving verse, Red Butterfly is the story of a girl learning to trust her own voice, discovering that love and family are limitless, and finding the wings she needs to reach new heights." (Publisher's Note)

"An innocent victim of China's adoption system, Kara was left in a basket and rescued by an American woman. An unwanted female baby with a deformed hand set Kara apart from birth, but Mama, her savior, was a 60-year-old Montana woman living on an expired visa...Sympathetic readers will appreciate that Kara learns to build trust with

those who demonstrate their compassion in constructive attempts to right some of the wrongs of her difficult beginnings." Booklist

Soto, Gary

The **skirt**; illustrated by Eric Velasquez. Delacorte Press 2008 74p il $14.99; lib bdg $17.99; pa $5.99

Grades: 1 2 3   **Fic**

1. Mexican Americans -- Fiction 2. Clothing and dress -- Fiction 3. Lost and found possessions -- Fiction

ISBN 978-0-385-30665-2; 0-385-30665-2; 978-0-385-90534-3 lib bdg; 0-385-90534-3 lib bdg; 978-0-440-40924-3 pa; 0-440-40924-1 pa

A reissue of the title first published 1992

When Miata leaves on the school bus the skirt that she is to wear in a dance performance, she needs all her wits to get it back without her parents' finding out that she has lost something yet again.

"This is a light, engaging narrative that successfully combines information on Hispanic culture with familiar and recognizable childhood themes. . . . A fine read-aloud and discussion starter, this story blends cultural differences with human similarities to create both interest and understanding." SLJ

★ **Taking** sides. Harcourt Brace Jovanovich 1991 138p hardcover o.p. pa $5.95

Grades: 5 6 7 8   **Fic**

1. Basketball -- Fiction 2. Hispanic Americans -- Fiction

ISBN 0-15-284076-1; 0-15-204694-1 pa

LC 91-11082

Fourteen-year-old Lincoln Mendoza, an aspiring basketball player, must come to terms with his divided loyalties when he moves from the Hispanic inner city to a white suburban neighborhood

This is a "light but appealing story. . . . Because of its subject matter and its clear, straightforward prose, it will be especially good for reluctant readers." SLJ

Includes glossary

Soup, Cuthbert

A **whole** nother story; illustrations by Jeffrey Stewart Timmins. Bloomsbury 2010 264p il $16.99

Grades: 3 4 5 6   **Fic**

1. Spies -- Fiction 2. Moving -- Fiction 3. Inventions -- Fiction 4. Family life -- Fiction 5. Automobile travel -- Fiction

ISBN 978-1-59990-435-1; 1-59990-435-7

LC 2009-21998

Ethan Cheeseman and his children, ages eight, twelve, and fourteen, hope to settle in a nice small town, at least long enough to complete work on a time machine, but spies and government agents have been pursuing them for two years and are about to catch up

"The storytelling, which merges deadpan narration with an absurdist sense of humor, is the real star of this fast-paced adventure." Publ Wkly

Followed by: Another whole nother story (2011)

Severn, Megan Jean

★ The **meaning** of Maggie; by Megan Jean Severn. Chronicle Books 2014 224 p. (alk. paper) $16.99

Grades: 4 5 6 7 **Fic**
1. Family life -- Fiction 2. Middle schools -- Fiction 3. Multiple sclerosis -- Fiction 4. Father-daughter relationship -- Fiction 5. Fathers and daughters -- Fiction
ISBN 1452110212; 9781452110219
LC 2013029644

In this book, by Megan Jean Sovern, "Maggie Mayfield has decided to write a memoir of the past year of her life. And what a banner year it's been! During this period she's Student of the Month on a regular basis, an official shareholder of Coca-Cola stock, and defending Science Fair champion. Most importantly, though, this is the year Maggie has to pull up her bootstraps (the family motto) and finally learn why her cool-dude dad is in a wheelchair, no matter how scary that is." (Publisher's note)

"In her debut novel, Sovern introduces readers to determined eleven-year-old Maggie Mayfield. Thinking there's nothing she can't conquer, Maggie is stymied by her dad's mysterious illness--slowly revealed as multiple sclerosis. Maggie's self-realizations come quickly, but her distinct voice, with a snarky superiority that often masks her true vulnerability, creates a character who's not easy to love but tough to forget." Horn Book

Speare, Elizabeth George

The **bronze** bow. Houghton Mifflin 1961 255p $16; pa $6.95
Grades: 6 7 8 9 **Fic**
1. Palestine -- Fiction 2. Christianity -- Fiction
ISBN 0-395-07113-5; 0-395-13719-5 pa
Awarded the Newbery Medal, 1962

"Daniel had sworn vengence against the Romans who had killed his parents, and he had become one of a band of outlaws. . . . Each time he saw the Rabbi Jesus, the youth was drawn to his cause; at last he resolved his own conflict by giving up his hatred and, as a follower of the Master, accepting his enemies. The story has drama and pace, fine characterization, and colorful background detail." Bull Cent Child Books

The **sign** of the beaver. Houghton Mifflin 1983 135p $16
Grades: 5 6 7 8 **Fic**
1. Friendship -- Fiction 2. Native Americans -- Fiction 3. Frontier and pioneer life -- Fiction
ISBN 0-395-33890-5
LC 83-118
A Newbery Medal honor book, 1984

Left alone to guard the family's wilderness home in eighteenth-century Maine, Matt is hard-pressed to survive until local Indians teach him their skills

Matt "begins to understand the Indians' ingenuity and respect for nature and the devastating impact of the encroachment of the white man. In a quiet but not unsuspenseful story . . . the author articulates historical facts along with the adventures and the thoughts, emotions, and developing insights of a young adolescent." Horn Book

★ The **witch** of Blackbird Pond. Houghton Mifflin 1958 249p $17
Grades: 6 7 8 9 **Fic**
1. Puritans -- Fiction 2. Witchcraft -- Fiction 3. Connecticut -- History -- 1600-1775, Colonial period -- Fiction
ISBN 0-395-07114-3
LC 58-11063
Awarded the Newbery Medal, 1959

"Headstrong and undisciplined, Barbados-bred Kit Tyler is an embarrassment to her Puritan relatives, and her sincere attempts to aid a reputed witch soon bring her to trial as a suspect." Child Books Too Good to Miss

Speck, Katie

Maybelle goes to tea; [by] Katie Speck; illustrations by Paul Ratz de Tagyos. 1st ed.; Henry Holt 2008 60p il $15.95
Grades: 2 3 4 **Fic**
1. Insects -- Fiction 2. Cockroaches -- Fiction
ISBN 978-0-8050-8093-3; 0-8050-8093-7
LC 2007040937

Maybelle the cockroach follows the advice of her new fly friend Maurice and tumbles into a terrifying but tasty adventure during Mrs. Peabody's Ladies' Spring Tea.

"Easy-reader graduates will delight in Maybelle's antics and enjoy her housefly pal, Maurice. . . . With humorous illustrations on nearly every spread, this is a sweet offering." SLJ

Sperry, Armstrong

Call it courage. Simon & Schuster Books for Young Readers 1968 95p il $17.99; pa $5.99
Grades: 5 6 7 8 **Fic**
1. Courage -- Fiction 2. Polynesia -- Fiction 3. Wilderness survival -- Fiction
ISBN 978-0-02-786030-6; 0-02-786030-2; 978-1-4169-5368-5 pa; 1-4169-5368-X pa
First published 1940 by Macmillan
Awarded the Newbery Medal, 1941

"Because he fears the ocean, a Polynesian boy is scorned by his people and must redeem himself by an act of courage. His lone journey to a sacred island and the dangers he faces there earn him the name Mafatu, 'Stout Heart.' Dramatic illustrations add atmosphere and mystery." Hodges. Books for Elem Sch Libr

Spinelli, Eileen

The **Dancing** Pancake; illustrated by Joanne Lew-Vriethoff. Alfred A. Knopf 2010 248p il $12.99; lib bdg $15.99
Grades: 3 4 5 **Fic**
1. Novels in verse 2. Divorce -- Fiction 3. Restaurants -- Fiction
ISBN 978-0-375-85870-3; 0-375-85870-9; 978-0-375-95870-0 lib bdg; 0-375-95870-3 lib bdg
LC 2009-22645

"Bindi's life is pretty normal. She loves to read and has good friends and a loving extended family. This normalcy ends when her parents announce that they are separating and that her father is moving to another city to look for a job. Told entirely in verse, the story relates the sixth grader's experiences, her feelings, and snippets of her daily life. . . . The poetic structure of this novel succeeds in capturing the child's voice and deepest feelings. The verse also provides sound development of secondary characters. Lew-Vriethoff's lively pen-and-ink illustrations add texture to the story and offer touches of humor." SLJ

★ **Where** I live; illustrated by Matt Phelan. Dial
Books 2007 un il $16.99

Grades: 1 2 3 4   **Fic**

1. Novels in verse 2. Moving -- Fiction 3. Family life
-- Fiction

ISBN 978-0-8037-3122-6; 0-8037-3122-1

LC 2006-30971

In a series of poems, Diana writes about her life, both
before and after her father loses his job and she and her family move far away to live with Grandpa Joe.

"Spinelli crafts a reassuring and engaging story in verse.
. . . Phelan's charming pencil drawings are a perfect complement to this heartfelt tale." SLJ

Spinelli, Jerry

Hokey Pokey; by Jerry Spinelli. Alfred A. Knopf
Books for Young Readers 2013 304 p. (hard cover) $15.99

Grades: 5 6 7 8   **Fic**

1. Bildungsromans 2. Fantasy fiction 3. Imaginary
places 4. Play -- Fiction 5. Growth -- Fiction

ISBN 0375831983; 9780307975706; 9780375831980;
9780375832017; 9780375931987

LC 2012004177

In this book, Jerry Spinelli "creates a surreal landscape."
There are no adults in "Hokey Pokey, where boys and girls
dine on flavored ice and spend their days watching cartoons,
playing cowboy games, and using their bicycles as trusty
steeds. Jack's bike, Scramjet, is . . . stolen by his archenemy,
Jubilee. This marks the first of a series of unsettling events
that give Jack, a boy on the brink of adolescence, the eerie
impression that 'things have shifted.'" (Publishers Weekly)

Jake and Lily; Jerry Spinelli. 1st ed. Balzer + Bray
2012 335 p. (hardback) $15.99

Grades: 3 4 5 6 7   **Fic**

1. Twins -- Fiction 2. Bullies -- Fiction 3. Children's
stories 4. Friendship -- Fiction 5. Individuality --
Fiction 6. Brothers and sisters -- Fiction

ISBN 9780060281359; 9780060281366

LC 2011053362

This book offers a "story about a pair of twins growing
apart. For almost as long as they can remember, Jake and
Lily have shared a 'special sense,' which they call 'goombla.' . . . Lily tries to find out who she is without her brother,
but it's hard work, and most of her attempts are unsuccessful. . . . Though the twins eventually rediscover their
'goombla,' . . . [author Jerry] Spinelli doesn't suggest that
the two will go back to being the people they once were."
(Publishers Weekly)

Loser. HarperCollins Pubs. 2002 218p $15.99; lib
bdg $16.89; pa $5.99

Grades: 4 5 6 7   **Fic**

1. School stories 2. Family life -- Fiction

ISBN 0-06-000193-3; 0-06-000483-5 lib bdg; 0-06-
054074-5 pa

LC 2001-47484

Even though his classmates from first grade on have considered him strange and a loser, Daniel Zinkoff's optimism
and exuberance and the support of his loving family do not
allow him to feel that way about himself

"This novel is an offbeat, affectionate, colorful, and melancholy work." Voice Youth Advocates

★ **Maniac** Magee; a novel. Little, Brown 1990 184p
$16.99; pa $6.99

Grades: 5 6 7 8   **Fic**

1. Orphans -- Fiction 2. Race relations -- Fiction 3.
Homeless persons -- Fiction

ISBN 0-316-80722-2; 0-316-80906-3 pa

LC 89-27144

Awarded the Newbery Medal, 1991

"Orphaned at three, Jeffery Lionel Magee, after eight
unhappy years with relatives, one day takes off running. A
year later, he ends up 200 miles away in Two Mills, a highly
segregated community. Part tall tale and part contemporary
realistic fiction, this unusual novel magically weaves timely
issues of homelessness, racial prejudice, and illiteracy into
an energetic story that bursts with creativity, enthusiasm,
and hope for the future. In short, it's a celebration of life."
Booklist

Wringer. HarperCollins Pubs. 1997 228p $16.99; lib
bdg $16.89; pa $6.50

Grades: 4 5 6 7   **Fic**

1. Courage -- Fiction 2. Pigeons -- Fiction 3. Violence
-- Fiction

ISBN 0-06-024913-7; 0-06-024914-5 lib bdg; 0-06-
440578-8 pa

LC 96-37897

A Newbery Medal honor book, 1998

"During the annual pigeon shoot, it is a town tradition
for 10-year-old boys to break the necks of wounded birds.
In this riveting story told with verve and suspense, Palmer
rebels." SLJ

"Palmer LaRue is running out of birthdays. For as long
as he can remember, he's dreaded the day he turns ten --
the day he'll take his place beside all the other ten-year-old
boys in town, the day he'll be a wringer. But Palmer doesn't
want to be a wringer...Palmer can't stop himself from being a wringer just like he can't stop himself from growing
one year older, just like he can't stand up to a whole town
-- right?" (Publisher's note)

Spratt, R. A.

★ The **adventures** of Nanny Piggins; illustrated by
Dan Santat. Little, Brown 2010 239p il $15.99

Grades: 3 4 5 6   **Fic**

1. Pigs -- Fiction 2. Nannies -- Fiction 3. Siblings
-- Fiction

ISBN 978-0-316-06819-2; 0-316-06819-5

LC 2009045047

When Mr. Green, a stingy widower with three children
he cannot be bothered with, decides to find a nanny for his
children, he winds up hiring a glamorous ex-circus pig who
knows nothing about children but a lot about chocolate.

"This is smart, sly, funny, and marvelously illustrated
with drawings that capture Nanny's sheer pigginess." Booklist

Springer, Nancy

★ The **case** of the missing marquess; an Enola Holmes
mystery. Philomel Books 2006 216p pa $6.99; $10.99

Grades: 5 6 7 8   **Fic**

1. Mystery fiction 2. Missing persons -- Fiction 3.

London (England) -- Fiction

ISBN 0-14-240933-2 pa; 0-399-24304-6

Enola Holmes, much younger sister of detective Sherlock Holmes, must travel to London in disguise to unravel the disappearance of her missing mother. "Grades four to eight." (Bull Cent Child Books)

"Enola's loneliness, intelligence, sense of humor, and sheer pluck make her an extremely appealing heroine." SLJ

Other titles about Enola Holmes are:

The case of the left-handed lady (2007)

The case of the bizarre bouquets (2008)

The case of the peculiar pink fan (2008)

The case of the cryptic crinoline (2009)

The case of the gypsy good-bye (2010)

★ **Rowan** Hood, outlaw girl of Sherwood Forest. Philomel Bks. 2001 170p hardcover o.p. pa $5.99

Grades: 4 5 6 7   **Fic**

1. Adventure fiction 2. Middle Ages -- Fiction 3. Robin Hood (Legendary character) -- Fiction

ISBN 0-399-23368-7; 0-698-11972-X pa

LC 00-63694

In her quest to connect with Robin Hood, the father she has never met, thirteen-year-old Rosemary disguises herself as a boy, befriends a half-wolf, half-dog, a runaway princess, and an overgrown boy whose singing is hypnotic, and makes peace with her elfin heritage

"This tale is a charmer, filled with exciting action, plenty of humor, engaging characters, and a nice fantasy twist." Booklist

Other titles about Rowan Hood are:

Lionclaw (2002)

Outlaw princess of Sherwood (2003)

Wild boy (2004)

Rowan Hood returns (2005)

Springstubb, Tricia

Mo Wren, lost and found. Balzer + Bray 2011 248p $15.99

Grades: 3 4 5 6   **Fic**

1. Moving -- Fiction 2. Family life -- Fiction 3. Restaurants -- Fiction

ISBN 978-0-06-199039-7; 0-06-199039-6

LC 2011001896

Sequel to: What happened on Fox Street (2010)

When eleven-year-old Mo's mother dies in an accident and Mo's devastated father deals with the loss by moving the family to a new town and starting a new life as the owner of a sports bar, Mo must leave her much loved neighborhood on Fox Street to live in an apartment above the 'cursed' Corky's Tavern.

"Readers will feel both inspired and comforted by these indefatigable sisters, whose humanity brings out the very same qualities in others." Booklist

Moonpenny Island; Tricia Springstubb; illustrated by Gilbert Ford. Balzer + Bray, an imprint of HarperCollins Publishers 2015 292 p. map (hardcover) $16.99

Grades: 4 5 6 7   **Fic**

1. Change -- Fiction 2. Islands -- Fiction 3. Friendship -- Fiction 4. Best friends -- Fiction

ISBN 9780062112958; 0062112937; 9780062112934

LC 2014006062

In this book, by Patricia Springstubb, "Flor and her best friend Sylvie are the only eleven year-old girls on Moonpenny Island, a rocky little bit of land in the middle of one of the Great Lakes. . . . At the beginning of sixth grade Sylvie is shipped off to a boarding school on the mainland while Flor must deal with both Sylvie's absence and her own mother's, who has left the island to care for Flor's ailing grandmother." (Bulletin of the Center for Children's Books)

"While exploring familiar themes of the unavoidable changes of adolescence, the novel weaves complex layers of fresh, relatable imagery and charming characterization across education levels, cultures, and generations, beautifully teaching that our shared humanity is one thing that doesn't change." Pub Wkly

Includes bibliographical references

★ **What** happened on Fox Street. Balzer + Bray 2010 218p $15.99

Grades: 3 4 5 6   **Fic**

1. Ohio -- Fiction 2. Friendship -- Fiction 3. Family life -- Fiction 4. Father-daughter relationship -- Fiction

ISBN 978-0-06-198635-2; 0-06-198635-6

LC 2009053563

Fox Street means everything to Mo Wren, who is nearly eleven, and so she is very upset when a land developer offers to buy her father's house, especially since she has not yet found the fox she is sure lives in the nearby ravine.

"Springstubb creates a richly human and believable story of the conflicts of growing up and a well-paced, interesting plot with plenty of surprises that readers should find pleasurable and satisfying." SLJ

Followed by: Mo Wren, lost and found (2011)

Spyri, Johanna

★ **Heidi**; by Johanna Spyri; illustrated by Jessie Willcox Smith. Morrow/Books of Wonder 1996 383p il $24.99

Grades: 4 5 6   **Fic**

1. Alps -- Fiction 2. Orphans -- Fiction 3. Switzerland -- Fiction

ISBN 0-688-14519-1

First published 1880

A Swiss orphan is heartbroken when she must leave her beloved grandfather and their happy home in the mountains to go to school and to care for an invalid girl in the city.

St. Antoine, Sara

Three bird summer; Sara St. Antoine. Candlewick Press 2014 256 p. $16.99

Grades: 5 6 7   **Fic**

1. Mystery fiction 2. Lakes -- Fiction 3. Summer -- Fiction 4. Neighbors -- Fiction 5. Grandmothers -- Fiction 6. Vacations -- Fiction 7. Summer resorts -- Fiction

ISBN 0763665649; 9780763665647

LC 2013946623

In this book, by Sara St. Antoine, "[f]or as long as he can remember, Adam and his parents have spent their summers at his grandmother's rustic cabin on Three Bird Lake. But this year will be different. There will be no rowdy cousins running around tormenting Adam. There will be no Uncle John or Aunt Jean. And there'll be no Dad to fight with Mom. This year, the lake will belong just to Adam. But then Adam meets Alice, the girl next door, who seems to want to become friends." (Publisher's note)

"Summertime for twelve-year-old Adam has always meant traveling to Grandma's rustic cabin in Minnesota. This summer is different: his parents have divorced, and Grandma's showing signs of dementia. St. Antoine's setting is remarkably palpable and lyrically described: pine trees are "spindly giants in pointy hats." And her characters are well realized, with Grandma both strong-willed and fragile and loner Adam experiencing true friendship." Horn Book

St. John, Lauren

The white giraffe; illustrated by David Dean. Dial Books for Young Readers 2007 180p il $16.99; pa $6.99

Grades: 4 5 6 7   **Fic**

1. Orphans -- Fiction 2. Giraffes -- Fiction 3. South Africa -- Fiction 4. Mythical animals -- Fiction
ISBN 978-0-8037-3211-7; 0-8037-3211-2; 978-0-14-241152-0 pa; 0-14-241152-3 pa

LC 2006-21323

After a fire kills her parents, eleven-year-old Martine must leave England to live with her grandmother on a wild-life game reserve in South Africa, where she befriends a mythical white giraffe

"The story is captivating and well spun." SLJ

Other titles in this series are:
Dolphin song (2008)
Last leopard (2009)
The elephant's tale (2010)

Stadler, Alexander

★ Julian Rodriguez: episode one, Trash crisis on earth. Scholastic Press 2008 123p $15.99; pa $5.99

Grades: 2 3 4   **Fic**

1. Science fiction 2. Extraterrestrial beings -- Fiction
ISBN 978-0-439-91966-1; 0-439-91966-5; 978-0-439-91970-8 pa; 0-439-91970-3 pa

"This hybrid of fiction and graphic novel dusts off a favorite conceit with a slick swipe of edgy visuals and tart commentary. . . . It's impossible to read this without laughing." Publ Wkly

Another title in this series is:
Julian Rodriguez: episode two, Invasion of the relatives (2009)

Julian Rodriguez: episode two, Invasion of the relatives. Scholastic Press 131p $16.99

Grades: 2 3 4   **Fic**

1. Science fiction 2. Extraterrestrial beings -- Fiction
ISBN 978-0-439-91967-8; 0-439-91967-3

First Officer Julian Rodriguez, imaginary space warrior, must endure the odious and unhygienic festivities of geneti-cally linked minibrains when members of his extended fam-ily visit over the holidays.

"This entry in the Julian Rodriguez series is even sharper and funnier than the first." Booklist

Staib, Walter

A feast of freedom; tasty tidbits from the City Tavern. by Walter Staib and Jennifer Fox; illustrated by Fernando Juarez. RP Kids 2010 un il map $15.95

Grades: 3 4 5 6   **Fic**

1. Mice -- Fiction 2. City Tavern (Philadelphia, Pa.) -- Fiction 3. United States -- History -- 1775-1783, Revolution -- Fiction
ISBN 978-0-7624-3598-2; 0-7624-3598-4

"The City Tavern, a pedigreed Philadelphia institution, bore witness to much of the behind-the-scenes wrangling and politicking of a country on the verge of independence. . . . This book's initial, chronological spreads cover the build-ing's conception, the basic floor plans, the importance of its location to both trade and politics, and how people ate, partied, did business, and kept up with the news in the late 1700s. Later spreads describe the building's historical con-nections. . . . Closing pages include a recipe for corn bread, a time line, and an update on the City Tavern as it now stands. A Disneyesque mouse in a tricornered hat leads readers through the pages, adding a touch of humor with brief quips in speech bubbles. . . . Add this title for a fresh look at a requisite time in U.S. history." SLJ

Standiford, Natalie

The secret tree; Natalie Standiford. Scholastic Press 2012 245 p. $16.99

Grades: 4 5 6 7   **Fic**

1. Bildungsromans 2. Mystery fiction 3. Children's stories 4. Friendship -- Fiction
ISBN 0545334799; 9780545334792

This coming of age story combines "[m]iddle-school dy-namics, pesky sibling relations, a rumored haunted house, . . . and a mystery. . . . When 10-year-old Minty discovers a hollow tree in the woods . . . [and] find[s] a secret written on a scrap of paper stashed inside, it sets the stage for a . . . mys-tery. . . . [W]hile Minty tries to figure out what's going on, she . . . befriend[s] an apparently parentless kid, Raymond, who seems to live in an abandoned spec house." (Kirkus)

Switched at birthday; Natalie Standiford. Scholastic Press 2014 240 p. (jacketed hardcover) $16.99

Grades: 4 5 6 7   **Fic**

1. Change -- Fiction 2. Birthdays -- Fiction 3. Friendship -- Fiction 4. Identity (Psychology) -- Fiction 5. Magic -- Fiction 6. Schools -- Fiction 7. Identity -- Fiction 8. Middle schools -- Fiction 9. Change (Psychology) -- Fiction
ISBN 0545346509; 9780545346504

LC 2013018598

In this book, by Natalie Standiford, "Lavender and Scar-let are nothing alike. . . . There's only one thing Lavender and Scarlet know for sure they have in common: the same birthday. . . . They've never swapped presents. But this year, because of two wishes that turned all too true, they are about to swap something much bigger than presents. Because the morning after their birthdays, Lavender is going to wake up in Scarlet's body . . . and Scarlet is going to make up in Lav-ender's." (Publisher's note)

"Shortly before she turns 13, Lavender sums up her situation mathematically: 'Short hairy cavegirl + glasses = loser.' Her few friends are outnumbered by the group of cool girls who, routinely, publicly put her down. When popular Scarlet magically and inadvertently switches bodies with Lavender on their thirteenth birthdays, each girl is thrown into a new family and a new set of friends, as well as sud-den, unforeseen challenges. . . . This well-paced novel will appeal to readers who loved Wendy Mass' popular 11 Birth-days (2009), which it resembles both in tone and in its use of a magical element." Booklist

Staniszewski, Anna

My sort of fairy tale ending; Anna Staniszewski. Sourcebooks Jabberwocky 2013 224 p. (tp: alk. paper) $6.99

Grades: 4 5 6 7   **Fic**

1. Magic -- Fiction 2. Fairies -- Fiction 3. Rescues -- Fiction 4. Families -- Fiction 5. Adventure and adventurers -- Fiction

ISBN 1402279337; 9781402279331

LC 2013017896

Sequel to: My epic fairy tale fail

In this book, by Anna Staniszewski, "Jenny only wants to rescue her parents . . . She's certain that the Queen Fairy has captured them, but when the queen captures Jenny too, the plot becomes complex. It turns out that the Queen Fairy is more than a bit insane. . . . When Jenny actually finds her parents, she must concoct a plan to rescue them, but with no power and her friends disappearing, she faces difficulties. . . . Of course Jenny will prevail, but how?" (Kirkus Reviews)

My very unfairy tale life. Sourcebooks Jabberwocky 2011 198p pa $6.99

Grades: 4 5 6 7   **Fic**

1. Fairy tales 2. Magic -- Fiction

ISBN 978-1-4022-5946-3; 1-4022-5946-8

Jenny, a professional adventurer, would prefer spending time with her friends over helping magical kingdoms around the universe, but soon she is given the choice to return to her normal life or go into a battle she doesn't think she can win.

"An eye for imaginative detail mixes with these likable characters and a theme of empathy for others to keep the story appropriate to a younger audience, who easily will identify with Jenny. Charming." Kirkus

Stanley, Diane

★ **Bella** at midnight; illustrated by Bagram Ibatoulline. HarperCollins Pubs. 2006 278p il $15.99; lib bdg $16.89; pa $6.99

Grades: 5 6 7 8   **Fic**

1. Fairy tales 2. Knights and knighthood -- Fiction

ISBN 978-0-06-077573-5; 0-06-077573-4; 978-0-06-077574-2 lib bdg; 0-06-077574-2 lib bdg; 978-0-06-077575-9 pa; 0-06-077575-0 pa

LC 2005-05906

Raised by peasants, Bella discovers that she is actually the daughter of a knight and finds herself caught up in a terrible plot that will change her life and the kingdom forever

"What raises this above other recreated fairy tales is the quality of the writing, dotted with jeweled description and anchored by the strong values—loyalty, truth, honor." Booklist

The **chosen** prince; Diane Stanley. Harper, an imprint of HarperCollinsPublishers 2015 368 p. illustration, map $16.99

Grades: 5 6 7 8   **Fic**

1. Magic -- Fiction 2. Princes -- Fiction 3. Shipwrecks -- Fiction 4. Fate and fatalism -- Fiction

ISBN 0062248979; 9780062248978

LC 2014022042

This children's book by Diane Stanley is "based on [William] Shakespeare's 'The Tempest.' On the day of his birth, Prince Alexos is revealed to be the long-awaited champion of Athene. He grows up lonely, conscious of all that is expected of him. Alexos follows the course of his destiny through war and loss and a deadly confrontation with his enemy to its end: shipwreck on a magical, fog-shrouded island. There he meets the unforgettable Aria and faces the greatest challenge of his life." (Publisher's note)

"Stanley's newest fantasy, set in ancient Greece, is a bittersweet delight. Prince Alexos learns early that being the champion of a goddess does not make for an easy life. Alexos is destined to bring about reconciliation between battling gods, Athene and Zeus, if he can survive a childhood filled with near-impossible challenge and little joy, except for his love of running and his little brother Teo... Other characters—especially the court physician Suliman and Teo's new sister Aria—are equally well done. The language is lyrical and accessible, and the end is satisfying in the extreme." SLJ

The **cup** and the crown; Diane Stanley. Harper 2012 344 p. (hardback) $16.99

Grades: 5 6 7 8   **Fic**

1. Fantasy fiction 2. Magic -- Fiction 3. Fantasy 4. Identity -- Fiction 5. Clairvoyance -- Fiction 6. Drinking cups -- Fiction

ISBN 0061963216; 9780061963216

LC 2012025280

In this fantasy novel by Diane Stanley "Molly has visions of a beautiful goblet: one of her grandfather's loving cups, which he filled with magic that bound people together. So it hardly surprises Molly when handsome King Alaric asks her to find a loving cup to help him win the heart of the beautiful Princess of Cortova. As Molly and her friends Winifred and Tobias journey far beyond the safe borders of Westria, a mysterious raven appears to guide their quest." (Publisher's note)

The **mysterious** matter of I.M. Fine. HarperCollins Pubs. 2001 201p hardcover o.p. pa $5.99

Grades: 4 5 6 7   **Fic**

1. Mystery fiction 2. Magic -- Fiction 3. Books and reading -- Fiction

ISBN 0-688-17546-5; 0-380-73327-7 pa

LC 00-54040

Noticing that a popular series of horror novels is having a bizarre effect on the behavior of its readers, Franny and Beamer set out to find the mysterious author

"The solidly constructed mystery, well-rounded characters, and playful jab at wildly successful horror writers go down a treat." Horn Book Guide

Another title about Franny and her friends is:

The mysterious case of the Allbright Academy (2008)

★ The **princess** of Cortova; Diane Stanley. Harper, an imprint of HarperCollinsPublishers 2013 320 p. (hardback) $16.99

Grades: 5 6 7 8   **Fic**

1. Betrothal -- Fiction 2. Occult fiction 3. Alternative histories 4. Fantasy 5. Magic -- Fiction 6. Princesses -- Fiction 7. Clairvoyance -- Fiction 8. Courts and courtiers -- Fiction 9. Kings, queens, rulers, etc. -- Fiction

ISBN 0062047302; 9780062047304; 9780062047311

LC 2013021824

Sequel to: The cup and the crown

This book is the final one in Diane Stanley's trilogy about prescient Molly and her friends. Here, Molly and "young Kind Alaric and .... Tobias journey from Westria to the Kingdom of Cortova in search of an alliance that will include Alaric's betrothal to Princess Elizabetta. To complicate matters, however, Alaric's cousin, the foxy Reynard, King of Austlind, has arrived with a similar goal. Who will win the hand of the fair Elizabetta?" (Booklist)

Roughing it on the Oregon Trail; illustrated by Holly Berry. HarperCollins Pubs. 2000 un il (Time-traveling twins) hardcover o.p. pa $7.99
Grades: 2 3 4   **Fic**
1. Oregon Trail -- Fiction 2. Frontier and pioneer life -- Fiction 3. Overland journeys to the Pacific -- Fiction
ISBN 0-06-027065-9; 0-06-449006-8 pa
                                        LC 98-41711
Twins Liz and Lenny, along with their time-traveling grandmother, join a group of pioneers journeying west on the Oregon Trail in 1843
"An engaging trip and a painless history lesson." SLJ
Other titles in this series are:
Joining the Boston Tea Party (2001)
Thanksgiving on Plymouth Plantation (2004)

★ **Saving** Sky. Harper 2010 199p $15.99
Grades: 5 6 7 8   **Fic**
1. Terrorism -- Fiction 2. Immigrants -- Fiction 3. New Mexico -- Fiction 4. Prejudices -- Fiction 5. Ranch life -- Fiction 6. Family life -- Fiction
ISBN 978-0-06-123905-2; 0-06-123905-4
                                        LC 2010-09393
In an America that has suffered continual terrorist attacks since 9/11, seventh-grader Sky stands up for what is right and helps a classmate of Middle Eastern descent, although doing so places her and her family at great risk.
"Readers will have much to discuss after finishing this beautifully written, disturbing book." Booklist

★ The **silver** bowl. Harper 2011 307p $16.99
Grades: 5 6 7 8   **Fic**
1. Fantasy fiction 2. Clairvoyance -- Fiction
ISBN 978-0-06-157543-3; 0-06-157543-7
"Molly is a young scullery maid in the castle of King Edmund, and like her mother before her, she sees visions and hears voices that offer glimpses of the future. But is this a blessing or a curse?.... The girl's choice of silence . . . is challenged when she learns that a rumored curse on the royal family is true and only by sharing her visions might they be saved. Combining carefully chosen details of setting with a richly realized fantasy premise, Stanley succeeds in creating a believable world large enough to accommodate not only menace and evil but also loyalty, enduring friendship, and love." Booklist

Starke, Ruth
Noodle pie. Kane Miller 2010 187p il $15.99
Grades: 4 5 6 7   **Fic**
1. Vietnam -- Fiction 2. Vietnamese -- Fiction
ISBN 978-1-935279-25-9; 1-935279-25-4
"Eleven-year-old Andy's first trip to Vietnam with his father, a 'Viet Kieu' (someone born in Vietnam who now lives overseas), exposes him to internalized prejudices about his heritage. . . . Andy distinguishes himself from his pushy

relatives by emphasizing his Australian citizenship and criticizing customs that seem unfair. . . . This humorous, touching novel is a delicious cross-cultural treat, and includes an appendix of Vietnamese recipes." Publ Wkly

Starmer, Aaron
The **only** ones. Delacorte Press 2011 321p $17.99; lib bdg $20.99; e-book $17.99
Grades: 4 5 6 7   **Fic**
1. Supernatural -- Fiction
ISBN 978-0-385-74043-2; 0-385-74043-3; 978-0-385-90839-9 lib bdg; 0-385-90839-3 lib bdg; 978-0-375-89919-5 e-book
                                        LC 2010040383
After setting off from the island where he has been leading a solitary existence, thirteen-year-old Martin discovers a village with other children who have been living similarly without any adults, since the grown-ups have all been spirited away.
"Both literary and engaging, this is the kind of book readers will want to return to for new discoveries." Kirkus

Stauffacher, Sue
★ **Gator** on the loose! illustrated by Priscilla Lamont. Alfred A. Knopf 2010 149p il (Animal rescue team) $12.99; lib bdg $15.99
Grades: 4 5 6   **Fic**
1. Alligators -- Fiction 2. Family life -- Fiction 3. Racially mixed people -- Fiction
ISBN 978-0-375-85847-5; 0-375-85847-4; 978-0-375-95847-2 lib bdg; 0-375-95847-9 lib bdg
                                        LC 2009018340
Chaos ensues when Keisha's father brings an escaped alligator home to Carter's Urban Rescue, but it gets out of the bathroom while Grandma is guarding it.
"Situational comedy, appealing spot art, and a personable protagonist will give this series broad appeal." Booklist
Other titles about Keisha and the Carter family are:
Hide and seek (2010)
Show time (2011)
Special delivery (2010)

★ **Harry** Sue. Knopf 2005 288p hardcover o.p. lib bdg $17.99; pa $6.50
Grades: 5 6 7 8   **Fic**
1. Prisoners -- Fiction 2. People with disabilities -- Fiction 3. Mother-daughter relationship -- Fiction
ISBN 0-375-83274-2; 0-375-93274-7 lib bdg; 0-440-42064-4 pa
                                        LC 2004-16945
Although tough-talking Harry Sue would like to start a life of crime in order to be "sent up" and find her incarcerated mother, she must first protect the children at her neglectful grandmother's home day care center and befriend a paralyzed boy.
"This is a riveting story, dramatically and well told, with characters whom readers won't soon forget." SLJ

Stead, Rebecca
Liar & spy; by Rebecca Stead. Wendy Lamb Books 2012 180 p. (hardback) $15.99
Grades: 4 5 6 7 8   **Fic**
1. Spy stories 2. Boys -- Fiction 3. Neighbors -- Fiction 4. Friendship -- Fiction 5. Spies -- Fiction

6. Schools -- Fiction 7. Middle schools -- Fiction 8. Apartment houses -- Fiction 9. Brooklyn (New York, N.Y.) -- Fiction 10. Family life -- New York (State) -- New York -- Fiction

ISBN 0385737432; 9780375899539; 9780385737432; 9780385906654

LC 2011042674

In this book, protagonist "Georges has a lot going on. Dad was laid off so Mom has started working extra shifts at the hospital, and they had to sell their house in Brooklyn and move into an apartment. One good thing about the new building is Safer, an unusual boy who lives on the top floor. He's determined to teach Georges how to be a spy. Their main case: spy on the mysterious Mr. X in the apartment above Georges. As Georges and Safer go deeper into their Mr. X plan, the line between games, lies, and reality begin to blur." (Barnes and Noble)

★ When you reach me. Wendy Lamb Books 2009 199p $15.99; lib bdg $18.99

Grades: 5 6 7 8   Fic

1. Space and time -- Fiction 2. New York (N.Y.) -- Fiction

ISBN 0-385-73742-4; 0-385-90664-1 lib bdg; 978-0-385-73742-5; 978-0-385-90664-7 lib bdg

LC 2008-24998

Awarded the Newbery Medal, 2010

As her mother prepares to be a contestant on the 1980s television game show, The 20,000 Pyramid, a twelve-year-old New York City girl tries to make sense of a series of mysterious notes received from an anonymous source. "Ages nine to fourteen." (Publisher's note)

"The '70s New York setting is an honest reverberation of the era; the mental gymnastics required of readers are invigorating; and the characters . . . are honest bits of humanity." Booklist

Steele, William Owen

The perilous road; [by] William O. Steele; with an introduction by Jean Fritz. Harcourt 2004 156p $17; pa $5.95

Grades: 5 6 7 8   Fic

1. Tennessee -- Fiction 2. United States -- History -- 1861-1865, Civil War -- Fiction

ISBN 0-15-205203-8; 0-15-205204-6 pa

A reissue of the title first published 1958

A Newbery Medal honor book, 1959

Fourteen-year-old Chris, bitterly hating the Yankees for invading his Tennessee mountain home, learns a difficult lesson about the waste of war and the meaning of tolerance and courage when he reports the approach of a Yankee supply troop to the Confederates, only to learn that his brother is probably part of that troop.

"Mr. Steele makes the tensions and excitements of the Brother's War very real, and customs of the mountain people, the speech and setting are well integrated into the narrative." NY Times Book Rev

Steer, Dugald

The dragon diary; [by] Dugald A. Steer; illustrated by Douglas Carrel. Candlewick Press 2009 248p il (Dragonology chronicles) $16.99

Grades: 5 6 7 8   Fic

1. Fantasy fiction 2. Dragons -- Fiction 3. Siblings -- Fiction

ISBN 978-0-7636-3425-4; 0-7636-3425-5

LC 2009005795

Apprentice dragonologists Daniel and Beatrice Cook's mentor is called away at a crucial time, leaving the brother and sister alone to search for an ancient diary that could cure some gravely ill dragons

"This fast-paced fantasy features sibling rivalry, multitudes of dragons, and mid-air heroics." Horn Book Guide

Steig, William

★ Abel's island. Farrar, Straus & Giroux 1976 117p il $15; pa $5.99

Grades: 3 4 5   Fic

1. Mice -- Fiction 2. Survival after airplane accidents, shipwrecks, etc. -- Fiction

ISBN 0-374-30010-0; 0-312-37143-8 pa

A Newbery Medal honor book, 1977

Castaway on an uninhabited island, Abel, a very civilized mouse, finds his resourcefulness and endurance tested to the limit as he struggles to survive and return to his home.

"The line drawings washed with gray faithfully and delightfully record not only the rigors of Abel's experiences but the refinement of his domestic existence." Horn Book

Dominic; story and pictures by William Steig. Farrar, Straus & Giroux 1972 145p il hardcover o.p. pa $5.99

Grades: 3 4 5   Fic

1. Dogs -- Fiction

ISBN 0-312-37144-6 pa

Dominic, a gregarious dog, sets out on the high road one day, going no place in particular, but moving along to find whatever he can. And that turns out to be plenty, including an invalid pig who leaves Dominic his fortune; a variety of friends and adventures; and even—in the end—his life's companion

"A singular blend of naiveté and sophistication, comic commentary and philosophizing, the narrative handles situation clichés with humor and flair—perhaps because of the author's felicitous turn of phrase, his verbal cartooning, and his integration of text and illustrations. A chivalrous and optimistic tribute to gallantry and romance." Horn Book

★ The real thief; story and pictures by William Steig. Farrar, Straus & Giroux 1973 58p il hardcover o.p. pa $5.99

Grades: 3 4 5   Fic

1. Animals -- Fiction 2. Thieves -- Fiction

ISBN 0-312-37145-4 pa

"Steig's gray line-and-wash drawings provide a charming accompaniment to a wholly winning story." SLJ

"Proud of his job as guard to the Royal Treasury, loyal to his king (Basil the bear) Gawain the goose is baffled by the repeated theft of gold and jewels from the massive building to which only Gawain and Basil have keys. He is heartsick when the king dismisses him publicly and calls him a disgrace to the kingdom. Sentenced to prison, the goose flies off to isolation. The true thief, a mouse, is penitent and decides that he will go on stealing so that the king will know Gawain is innocent." Bull Cent Child Books

Steinhofel, Andreas

An **elk** dropped in; [by] Andreas Steinhofel; pictures by Kerstin Meyer; translated by Alissa Jaffa. Front Street 2006 78p il $16.95

Grades: 2 3 4   **Fic**

1. Elk -- Fiction 2. Christmas -- Fiction 3. Santa Claus -- Fiction

ISBN 1-932425-80-2; 978-1-932425-80-2

LC 2006-00804

While on a pre-Christmas trial run for the famous man in red, an elk named Mr. Moose crashes through the roof of a house and, while recuperating from a sprain, regales Billy Wagner and his family with stories.

"Winsome watercolor illustrations, droll details, and a young narrator who relates both wild and everyday details in the same matter-of-fact tone combine to create a charming, if offbeat, Christmas fantasy." SLJ

Stephens, John

The **black** reckoning; John Stephens. Alfred A. Knopf 2015 432 p. (Books of beginning) (hardback) $17.99

Grades: 4 5 6 7   **Fic**

1. Magic -- Fiction 2. Identity -- Fiction 3. Monsters -- Fiction 4. Prophecies -- Fiction 5. Space and time -- Fiction 6. Brothers and sisters -- Fiction 7. Books and reading -- Fiction

ISBN 0375868720; 9780375868726; 9780375968723

LC 2014023538

In this novel, by John Stephens, part of the Books of Beginning series, "the adventures of siblings Kate, Michael, and Emma come to a stunning conclusion when they must find the last Book of Beginning--the Book of Death--before the Dire Magnus does, for when all three books are united, their combined power will be unstoppable." (Publisher's note)

"Heartbreaking sacrifices, joyous reunions, and poignant partings round out this rousing old-school fantasy adventure." Horn Book

Other titles in the trilogy are:

The Emerald Atlas (2011)

The Fire Chronicle (2012)

★ The **emerald** atlas. Alfred A. Knopf 2011 417p (The books of beginning) $17.99; lib bdg $20.99

Grades: 4 5 6   **Fic**

1. Magic -- Fiction 2. Monsters -- Fiction 3. Siblings -- Fiction 4. Prophecies -- Fiction 5. Space and time -- Fiction 6. Books and reading -- Fiction

ISBN 978-0-375-86870-2; 0-375-86870-4; 978-0-375-96870-9 lib bdg; 0-375-96870-9 lib bdg

LC 2010029100

Kate, Michael, and Emma have passed from one orphanage to another in the ten years since their parents disappeared to protect them, but now they learn that they have special powers, a prophesied quest to find a magical book, and a fearsome enemy.

"This fast-paced, fully imagined fantasy is by turns frightening and funny, and the siblings are well-crafted and empathetic heroes. Highly enjoyable, it should find many readers." Publ Wkly

★ The **fire** chronicle; John Stephens. Alfred A. Knopf 2012 437 p. (hardback) $17.99

Grades: 4 5 6   **Fic**

1. Fantasy Fiction 2. Adventure Fiction 3. Time travel Fiction 4. Magic -- Fiction 5. Identity -- Fiction 6. Monsters -- Fiction 7. Prophecies -- Fiction 8. Space and time -- Fiction 9. Books and reading -- Fiction 10. Brothers and sisters -- Fiction 11. New York (N.Y.) -- History -- 1898-1951 -- Fiction

ISBN 0375868712; 9780375868719; 9780375899560; 9780375968716

LC 2012016139

In this novel by John Stephens, part of the Books of Beginning series, "Kate, Michael, and Emma long to continue the hunt for their missing parents. . . . A frantic chase sends Kate a hundred years into the past, to a perilous, enchanted New York City. . . . Meanwhile, Michael and Emma have set off to find the second of the Books of Beginning. A series of clues leads them into a hidden world where they must brave harsh polar storms, track down an ancient order of warriors, and confront terrible monsters." (Publisher's note)

Sternberg, Julie

Like pickle juice on a cookie; illustrations by Matthew Cordell. Amulet Books 2011 122p il $14.95

Grades: 3 4 5   **Fic**

1. Novels in verse 2. Babysitters -- Fiction 3. Loss (Psychology) -- Fiction

ISBN 0-8109-8424-5; 978-0-8109-8424-0

LC 2009-15975

When nine-year-old Eleanor's beloved babysitter Bibi moves away to take care of her ailing father, Eleanor must spend the summer adjusting to a new babysitter while mourning the loss of her old one. "Grades two to three." (Bull Cent Child Books)

"Eleanor's gradual warming to her new sitter is affectingly narrated, and Cordell's halftone cartoons convey the story's pathos and humor, as well as Eleanor's changeable moods." Publ Wkly

The **top**-secret diary of Celie Valentine; friendship over. Julie Sternberg. Boyds Mills Press, an imprint of Highlights 2014 160 p. illustrations (The top-secret diary of celie valentine) $15.95

Grades: 3 4 5 6   **Fic**

1. Diaries -- Fiction 2. Sisters -- Fiction 3. Emotions -- Fiction 4. Friendship -- Fiction 5. Humorous stories

ISBN 1590789938; 9781590789933

LC 2014939248

In this book, by Julie Sternberg, "ten-year-old Celie's father gives her a journal and a punching bag for her birthday [and] tells her they'll help her work through her feelings. . . . Her best friend Lula isn't speaking to her, her sister Jo locks her out of their room to hang out with her new, cooler friend, and her Granny is suddenly behaving in the most perplexing manner. Good thing Celie's armed with a grape-flavored pen and a solid sense of humor." (Publisher's note)

"Ten-year-old Celie confides her worries about her ex-best friend, her maddening older sister, and her ailing grandmother in her journal. Humor and an accessible epistolary format lighten the story's heavy issues of bullying, age-related illness, and parental discord...This title has both wide appeal and substance and begins what will likely be a popular series."

Stevens, Robin

Murder is bad manners; Robin Stevens. Simon & Schuster Books for Young Readers 2015 320 p. (hardcover) $16.99

Grades: 4 5 6 7   **Fic**

1. School stories 2. Mystery fiction 3. Murder -- Fiction 4. Friendship -- Fiction 5. Boarding schools -- Fiction 6. Chinese -- England -- Fiction 7. Mystery and detective stories

ISBN 148142212X; 9781481422123; 9781481422130

LC 2014003939

In this middle grades book, by Robin Stevens, "Daisy Wells and Hazel Wong are best friends at Deepdean School for Girls, and they both have a penchant for solving mysteries. . . . [T]hey form their own (secret!) detective agency. The only problem? They have nothing to investigate. But that changes once Hazel discovers the body of their science teacher, Miss Bell - and the body subsequently disappears." (Publisher's note)

"Here's a mystery import, set in the 1930s, that does justice to its British roots. Hazel Wong has come from Hong Kong to attend Deepdean boarding school. An outcast until she is accepted by upper-crust Daisy Wells, Hazel is happy to be half of a two-girl detective agency...Hazel makes a good narrator, and while the mystery plods a bit and has too many teachers—though a cast list helps—not every reader will guess the ending. Nancy Drew, meet Wells and Wong." Booklist

Stevenson, Robert Louis

Treasure Island; Robert Louis Stevenson; illustrated by John Lawrence. 1st U.S. ed. Candlewick Press 2009 269 p. col. ill. (reinforced) $24.99

Grades: 5 6 7 8 9 10 11 12 Adult   **Fic**

1. Adventure fiction 2. Pirates -- Fiction 3. Buried treasure -- Fiction

ISBN 0763644455; 9780763644451

LC 2009007338

First published in 1883.

While going through the possessions of a deceased guest who owed them money, the mistress of the inn and her son find a treasure map that leads them to a notorious pirate's fortune

"Lawrence evokes the essence of classic adventure stories with his vinyl-cut illustrations, as thick black shapes are tempered by muted tones of blue, gold and green. . . . Readers will feel they've discovered a true relic with this edition." Publ Wkly

Stevenson, Steve

The curse of the pharaoh; by Sir Steve Stevenson; illustrated by Stefano Turconi; translated by Siobhan Kelly; translation adapted by Maya Gold. Grosset & Dunlap, an imprint of Penguin Group (USA) Inc. 2013 144 p. (Agatha Mistery) (pbk: alk. paper) $5.99

Grades: 3 4 5   **Fic**

1. Mystery fiction 2. Adventure fiction 3. Memory -- Fiction 4. Mystery and detective stories 5. Egypt -- Antiquities -- Fiction 6. Adventure and adventurers -- Fiction 7. Eccentrics and eccentricities -- Fiction

ISBN 0448462176; 9780448462172

LC 2012031484

This children's novel, by Steve Stevenson, illustrated by Stefano Turconi, is first in the "Agatha: Girl of Mystery"

series. It features "a headstrong girl detective who jets off on exotic . . . adventures with the help of her hulking bodyguard and loyal cat named . . . Watson. . . . Rumors of a mysterious tablet unearthed in the Valley of the Kings may be just the clue that Agatha needs to unlock the secret curse of an ancient Pharaoh." (Publisher's note)

"A well-plotted mystery full of quirky details... and carefully constructed clues." Booklist

Stevermer, Caroline

Magic below stairs. Dial Books for Young Readers 2010 199p $16.99

Grades: 4 5 6 7   **Fic**

1. Magic -- Fiction 2. Orphans -- Fiction 3. Household employees -- Fiction 4. Great Britain -- History -- 19th century -- Fiction

ISBN 978-0-8037-3467-8; 0-8037-3467-0

LC 2009-25100

Ten-year-old Frederick, who is surreptitiously watched over by a household elf, is plucked from a London orphanage to be a servant to a wealthy wizard, and eventually his uncanny abilities lead him to become the wizard's apprentice.

"A well-developed fictional world and the many concrete details of belowstairs life make the magical events in this engaging chapter book more believable." Booklist

Stewart, Paul

★ Beyond the Deepwoods; [by] Paul Stewart, Chris Riddell. David Fickling Bks. 2004 276p il (Edge chronicles) $12.95; lib bdg $14.99; pa $6.99

Grades: 4 5 6   **Fic**

1. Fantasy fiction

ISBN 0-385-75068-4; 0-385-75069-2 lib bdg; 0-440-42087-3 pa

First published 1998 in the United Kingdom

Thirteen-year-old Twig, having always looked and felt different from his woodtroll family, learns that he is adopted and travels out of his Deepwoods home to find the place where he belongs

"Those with hearty appetites for adventure (and strong stomachs) will find this a tremendously exciting fantasy. Riddell's wonderfully detailed ink drawings, on nearly every page, create a strong sense of the believable, well-imagined otherworld and bring its strange creatures to life." Booklist

Other titles in The Edge Chronicles series are:

Stormchaser (2004)
Midnight over Sanctaphrax (2004)
The curse of the Gloamglozer (2005)
The last of the sky pirates (2005)
Vox (2005)
Freeglader (2006)
The winter knights (2007)
Clash of the sky galleons (2007)
Immortals (2010)

The curse of the night wolf; [by] Paul Stewart and Chris Riddell; illustrated by Chris Riddell. David Fickling Books 2008 204p il (Barnaby Grimes) $15.99; lib bdg $18.99

Grades: 4 5 6 7   **Fic**

1. Mystery fiction 2. Physicians -- Fiction 3. Werewolves -- Fiction 4. London (England) -- Fiction

5. Great Britain -- History -- 19th century -- Fiction
ISBN 978-0-385-75125-4; 0-385-75125-7; 978-0-385-75126-1 lib bdg; 0-385-75126-5 lib bdg

LC 2008-01697

Soon after Victorian messenger Barnaby Grimes is attacked by a huge beast while crossing London's rooftops, he becomes entangled in a mystery involving patent medicine, impoverished patients, and very expensive furs.

"Moody, highly detailed pen-and-ink drawings provide ornamentation throughout, lending a classic Victorian feel to help punctuate the drama. . . . Possessing an easy confidence and quick wit . . . Barnaby is an appealing character." Booklist

Other titles in this series are:
Return of the emerald skull (2009)
Legion of the Dead (2010)

★ **Fergus** Crane; [by] Paul Stewart & Chris Riddell. David Fickling Books 2006 214p (Far-flung adventures) $14.95

Grades: 3 4 5   **Fic**
1. Adventure fiction
ISBN 0-385-75088-9

LC 2005018478

Nine-year-old Fergus Crane's life is filled with classes on the school ship Betty Jeanne, interesting neighbors, and helping with his mother's work until a mysterious box flies into his window and leads him toward adventure

"With a simple plot, a few hints of mystery, and many intriguing details, this story will quickly hook readers. Riddell's expressive ink drawings make the fantastic elements more believable and add enormously to the book's appeal." Booklist

Other titles in this series are:
Corby Flood (2006)
Hugo Pepper (2007)

Phantom of Blood Alley; [by] Paul Stewart & Chris Riddell; illustrated by Chris Riddell. David Fickling Books 2010 201p il (Barnaby Grimes) $16.99

Grades: 4 5 6 7   **Fic**
1. Mystery fiction 2. Photography -- Fiction 3. Supernatural -- Fiction 4. Great Britain -- History -- 19th century -- Fiction
ISBN 978-0-385-75134-6; 0-385-75134-6

First published 2009 in the United Kingdom

Barnaby finds himself in the fiercely competitive world of early photography, where the rewards are immense but so are the risks. After an experiment goes disastrously wrong, Barnaby is on the trail of a mad chemist with a talent for disappearing into thin air.

Stewart, Trenton Lee

The **extraordinary** education of Nicholas Benedict; by Trenton Lee Stewart; illustrated by Diana Sudyka. Little, Brown 2012 470 p. $17.99

Grades: 4 5 6 7 8   **Fic**
1. Bullies -- Fiction 2. Orphans -- Fiction 3. Friendship -- Fiction 4. Narcolepsy -- Fiction 5. Orphanages -- Fiction 6. Genius -- Fiction 7. Mystery and detective stories 8. Adventure and adventurers -- Fiction
ISBN 9780316176194

LC 2011031690

This book tells the story of Nicholas Benedict who "is just 9 years. . . . Small in physical stature but intellectually gifted, he has an 'unfortunate' nose . . . and a medical condition that prompts 'unpredictable sleeping episodes' that drop 'him from consciousness like a trapdoor into a black dungeon' at the least opportune of times. . . . What has long made him a nuisance to less intelligent adults and target practice for bullies also makes him a curiosity for a slightly older boy who befriends him at his new home -- the ominously named Rothschild's End. The orphanage is housed in a two-story mansion. . . . [The book] revolves around . . . the . . . themes . . . [of] orphans, friendship and the sorts of surrogate families that form as a result." (LA Times)

★ The **mysterious** Benedict Society; illustrated by Carson Ellis. Little, Brown 2007 485p il $16.99; pa $6.99

Grades: 5 6 7 8   **Fic**
1. Science fiction 2. Adventure fiction
ISBN 978-0-316-05777-6; 0-316-05777-0; 978-0-316-00395-7 pa; 0-316-00395-6 pa

LC 2006-09925

After passing a series of mind-bending tests, four children are selected for a secret mission that requires them to go undercover at the Learning Institute for the Very Enlightened, where the only rule is that there are no rules

"Stewart's unusual characters, threatening villains, and dramatic plot twists will grab and hold readers' attention." SLJ

Other titles about the Benedict Society are:
The mysterious Benedict Society and the perilous journey (2008)
The mysterious Benedict Society and the prisoner's dilemma (2009)

Stiefvater, Maggie

Hunted; Maggie Stiefvater. Scholastic Inc. 2014 192 p. map (Spirit animals) (paper-over-board) $12.99

Grades: 4 5 6 7   **Fic**
1. Fantasy fiction 2. Wolves -- Fiction 3. Human-animal relationship -- Fiction
ISBN 0545522447; 9780545522441; 9780545522564; 9780545599726

LC 2013947126

This fantasy novel by Maggie Stiefvater, part of the Spirit Animals series, describes how its "four young heroes have barely had time to come together as a team, and their own spirit animal bonds are still greatly untested. But now they face a brutal confrontation against an enemy who will break any rule to defeat them." (Publisher's note)

"Stiefvater blends Mull's brilliant world building with her talent of writing memorable villains." Booklist

Stier, Catherine

The **terrible** secrets of the Tell-All Club. Albert Whitman & Co. 2009 125p $14.99

Grades: 4 5 6   **Fic**
1. School stories 2. Clubs -- Fiction 3. Friendship -- Fiction
ISBN 978-0-8075-7798-1; 0-8075-7798-7

LC 2008055704

When four fifth-grade friends complete a "tell-all" survey, tensions arise and come to a head during an overnight class trip

"Told in the four voices of the club members, the story shows the characters' insecurities and the family issues they face. Reluctant readers will find it fast paced, easy to follow, and populated with likable personalities." SLJ

Stine, R. L., 1943-

★ It's the first day of school--forever! Feiwel and Friends 2011 183p $15.99

Grades: 3 4 5   **Fic**

1. Horror fiction 2. School stories 3. Monsters -- Fiction

ISBN 978-0-312-64954-8; 0-312-64954-1

LC 2010050896

Everything goes wrong for eleven-year-old Artie on his first day at Ardmore Middle School, from the moment his alarm goes off until the next morning, when everything is repeated exactly the same way.

"Stine delivers the hilarity and horror that readers love, and his mastery of sustaining mood will not disappoint." SLJ

StJohn, Amanda, 1982-

Bridget and Bo build a blog; by Amanda St John; illustrated by Katie McDee. Norwood House Press 2012 32 p.

Grades: K 1 2 3   **Fic**

1. Weblogs -- Fiction 2. Internet and children 3. Child authors -- Fiction 4. Online authorship 5. Language arts (Elementary)

ISBN 1599535076; 9781599535074

LC 2011039361

This children's book presents "introductions to a number of tasks young writers will eventually tackle. . . . This volume introduces nine-year-old Bo, whose recent experience blogging from a family stay in England gives him the expertise to show his friend, Bridget, how it's done. . . . Bridget's concerns are understandable: "Well, does my blog have to be as long as yours?" Bo's answers are a little my-way-or-the-highway, but nonetheless bring up good things to consider: a design template, the intended audience, and using correct terminology such as posting. They read other blogs for inspiration, which is where they learn never to gossip or use full names or personal info. The wisecracks never intrude upon the learning, and the advice can easily extend to other kinds of writing." (Booklist)

Includes bibliographical references (p. 32)

Stockton, Frank

The bee-man of Orn; [by] Frank R. Stockton; illustrated by P.J. Lynch. Candlewick Press 2003 un il $17.99

Grades: 2 3 4   **Fic**

1. Fairy tales

ISBN 0-7636-2239-7

LC 2003-48454

Story first published in St. Nicholas magazine 1883

When a Sorcerer tells him that he has been transformed from another sort of being, the Beeman sets out to discover what he was in his earlier incarnation. Story is accompanied by a DVD which provides a behind-the-scenes look at the illustrator at work.

"Lynch's spirited artwork, richly detailed and darkly atmospheric, provides a series of imaginative settings and creates a romantic and broadly appealing vision of this original fairy tale. . . . This edition is a read-aloud treasure for good listeners." Booklist

Stone, Phoebe

The boy on Cinnamon Street; by Phoebe Stone. Arthur A. Levine Books 2012 234 p. (alk. paper) $16.99

Grades: 3 4 5 6 7 8   **Fic**

1. Girls -- Psychology 2. Friendship -- Fiction 3. Grandparent-grandchild relationship 4. Memory -- Fiction 5. Schools -- Fiction 6. Best friends -- Fiction 7. Grandparents -- Fiction 8. Massachusetts -- Fiction

ISBN 0545215129; 9780545215121

LC 2011017862

This book tells the story of "seventh-grader [Louise who] lives with her grandparents in their condo and she's quit [gymnastics], . . . instead spending her time with friends Reni and her brother Henderson Elliot, whose warm and embracing family she adores. When a cute ninth-grader turns up on her doorstep delivering pizza, and she then finds a note under the mat confessing interest in Louise, she's transported into her first serious crush." (Bulletin of the Center for Children's Books)

Deep down popular; a novel. by Phoebe Stone. Arthur A. Levine Books 2008 280p $16.99; pa $4.99

Grades: 4 5 6 7   **Fic**

1. School stories 2. Virginia -- Fiction 3. Friendship -- Fiction 4. Family life -- Fiction 5. Country life -- Fiction

ISBN 978-0-439-80245-1; 0-439-80245-8; 978-0-439-80244-4 pa; 0-439-80244-X pa

LC 2007017198

In a small Virginia town, sixth-grader Jessie Lou Ferguson has a crush on the hugely popular Conrad Parker Smith, and when he suddenly develops a medical problem and the teacher asks Jessie Lou to help him, they become friends, to her surprise

"Jessie Lou tells her tale with the strong, rough-edged purity of a young poet, which she is; equally strong are the story's underpinnings, longing and laughter, and a willingness to believe in something despite the facts." Booklist

★ The Romeo and Juliet code. Arthur A. Levine Books 2011 300p $16.99

Grades: 4 5 6 7   **Fic**

1. Maine -- Fiction 2. Ciphers -- Fiction 3. Family life -- Fiction 4. World War, 1939-1945 -- United States -- Fiction 5. World War, 1939-1945 -- Evacuation of civilians -- Fiction

ISBN 978-0-545-21511-4; 0-545-21511-0

LC 2010-30005

During World War II, eleven-year-old Felicity is sent from London to Bottlebay, Maine, to live with her grandmother, aunt, uncle, and a reclusive boy who helps her decode mysterious letters that contain the truth about her missing parents.

Felicity "is endearingly portrayed, and the back story, so gradually revealed, provides a peek into the depths of the souls of some of the adults. The pacing is deliberately slow, yet Felicity's growing awareness of how she can help heal the troubled adults makes this an eminently satisfying read." Kirkus

Romeo blue; by Phoebe Stone. 1st ed. Arthur A. Levine Books 2013 352 p. (hardcover) $16.99

Grades: 4 5 6 7   **Fic**
1. Espionage -- Fiction 2. World War, 1939-1945
-- Children -- Fiction 3. World War, 1939-1945 --
Evacuation of civilians -- Fiction 4. Identity -- Fiction
5. Foster children -- Fiction 6. Family life -- Maine
-- Fiction
ISBN 0545443601; 9780545443609
        LC 2012038060
Parents' Choice: Silver Medal Fiction (2013)
"In this sequel to the WWII historical mystery 'The Romeo and Juliet Code,' . . . twelve-year old . . . Flissy now knows her Uncle Gideon is actually her biological father. . . . And she knows her whole family are some kind of spies, but she does not know . . . if they are still alive. And she has no idea why the creepy neighbor, Mr. Fitzwilliam, has invited her and adopted cousin Derek for tea, how he seems to know about her parents' secret activities." (Children's Literature)

Stout, Shawn K.
Fiona Finkelstein meets her match!! illustrated by Angela Martini. Aladdin 2010 146p il $14.99; pa $4.99
Grades: 2 3 4   **Fic**
1. School stories 2. Clubs -- Fiction 3. Maryland --
Fiction 4. Family life -- Fiction
ISBN 978-1-4169-7928-9; 1-4169-7928-X; 978-1-
4169-7110-8 pa; 1-4169-7110-6 pa
        LC 2010026829
Fiona Finkelstein does not get along with Milo, a new student in her Ordinary, Maryland, fourth-grade class, and when he starts a meteorology club she responds by trying to start a matchmaking club.
"Stout continues to develop her protagonist in this entertaining installment." Horn Book Guide

Fiona Finkelstein, big-time ballerina! illustrated by Angela Martini. Aladdin 2009 166p il $14.99; pa $4.99
Grades: 2 3 4   **Fic**
1. Worry -- Fiction 2. Ballet -- Fiction 3. Maryland --
Fiction 4. Family life -- Fiction 5. Weather forecasting
-- Fiction
ISBN 978-1-4169-7927-2; 1-4169-7927-1; 978-1-
4169-7109-2 pa; 1-4169-7109-2 pa
        LC 2009022593
Nine-year-old Marylander Fiona Finkelstein tries to deal with stage-fright, missing her mother who is an actress in California, and hoping that her father, a television meteorologist, does not get in trouble when she antagonizes the anchorman.
"This novel is light and fun, with just enough wit and sass to keep young readers entertained. . . . The story maintains a fast pace throughout, and the illustrations give Fiona and company a sweet look that is simple and charming." SLJ
Another title about Fiona Finkelstein is:
Fiona Finkelstein meets her match (2010)

Streatfeild, Noel
Ballet shoes. Yearling 1999 281p il pbk 6.99
Grades: 2 3 4 5   **Fic**
1. Ballet -- Fiction 2. Orphans -- Fiction 3. Sisters
-- Fiction 4. Acting -- Fiction
ISBN 9780679847595
"In the tradition of Frances Hodgson Burnett's The Little Princess come Noel Streatfeild's tales of triumph. In this story, three orphan girls vow to make a name for themselves

and find their own special talents. With hard work, fame just may be in the stars! Originally published in 1937." (Publisher's Note)
Companion titles include:
Circus Shoes (2015)
Theater Shoes (1994)
White Boots (2014)

Strickland, Brad
The **sign** of the sinister sorcerer; [by] Brad Strickland.
Dial Books for Young Readers 2008 168p $16.99
Grades: 4 5 6 7   **Fic**
1. Mystery fiction 2. Magic -- Fiction 3. Uncles --
Fiction 4. Orphans -- Fiction 5. Witches -- Fiction 6.
Michigan -- Fiction 7. Supernatural -- Fiction
ISBN 978-0-8037-3151-6; 0-8037-3151-5
        LC 2008007698
In Michigan in the mid-1950s, Lewis Barnavelt is convinced that the series of accidents he and his uncle are experiencing are the result of a curse by a mysterious, hooded figure that may be part of his uncle's past.
"For readers who enjoy trying to solve the mystery as they read, there are abundant clues including an anagram. A quick, exciting read." SLJ
Other titles about Lewis Barnavelt by Brad Strickland are:
The beast under the wizard's bridge (2000)
The house where nobody lived (2006)
The spector from the magician's museum (1998)
The tower at the end of the world (2001)
The whistle, the grave, and the ghost (2003)

Stringer, Helen
★ **Spellbinder**. Feiwel and Friends 2009 372p $17.99
Grades: 5 6 7 8   **Fic**
1. Ghost stories 2. Dead -- Fiction 3. Great Britain
-- Fiction
ISBN 978-0-312-38763-1; 0-312-38763-6
        LC 2008-28552
Twelve-year-old Belladonna Johnson, who lives with the ghosts of her parents in the north of England, teams up with an always-in-trouble classmate to investigate why all of the ghosts in the world have suddenly disappeared.
"Magical creatures, amulets, and verses are all a part of this delightful tale. . . . Stringer maintains the humor and logic of preteens who are awkwardly coming into their magical destinies." SLJ
Followed by: The midnight gate (2011)

Stroud, Jonathan, 1970-
★ The **screaming** staircase; by Jonathan Stroud. Disney-Hyperion 2013 400 p. (Lockwood & Co.) hbk $16.99
Grades: 4 5 6 7   **Fic**
1. Adventure fiction 2. Ghosts -- Fiction 3. Supernatural
-- Fiction 4. Haunted houses -- Fiction 5. Psychic
ability -- Fiction
ISBN 1423164911; 9781423164913
        LC 2013000352
This is the first book in Jonathan Stroud's Lockwood & Co. series. Lucy Carlyle has joined the Lockwood & Co. firm to help with England's ghost problem. "As its third member, she teams with glib, ambitious Anthony Lockwood and slovenly-but-capable scholar George Cubbins to entrap malign spirits for hire. The work is fraught with peril, not

only because a ghost's merest touch is generally fatal, but also, as it turns out, as none of the three is particularly good at careful planning." (Kirkus Reviews)

The **whispering** skull; by Jonathan Stroud. Disney-Hyperion 2014 448 p. illustrations (Lockwood & Co.) (hardback) $17.99
Grades: 4 5 6 7   **Fic**
   1. Occult fiction 2. Mystery fiction 3. Ghosts -- Fiction 4. England -- Fiction 5. Supernatural -- Fiction 6. Psychic ability -- Fiction 7. London (England) -- Fiction 8. Mystery and detective stories
   ISBN 142316492X; 9781423164920
                        LC 2014014683

This novel, by Jonathan Stroud, is book 2 in the "Lockwood & Co." supernatural mystery series. "In the six months since Anthony, Lucy, and George survived a night in the most haunted house in England, Lockwood & Co. hasn't made much progress. . . . A new client, Mr. Saunders, hires Lockwood & Co. to be present at the excavation of Edmund Bickerstaff. . . . Saunders needs the coffin sealed with silver to prevent any supernatural trouble. All goes well-until George's curiosity attracts a horrible phantom." (Publisher's note)

"In this sequel to The Screaming Staircase (2013), Stroud delivers another riveting narrative in which the three young psychic investigators deal with malevolent supernatural forces in an alternate London. Narrator Lucy Carlyle, the newest member of Lockwood & Company, develops the rare ability to converse with a mysterious skull kept in a sealed jar. Though this captive spirit has the firsthand knowledge the group needs to solve its latest case, Lucy suspects that beyond his entreaties and wisecracks, the tortured skull is manipulating them with misleading information. Physically and psychologically taxing, the case strains the bond that Anthony Lockwood, Lucy, and their colleague, George, share. Stroud writes with a fine ear for dialogue, a wry sense of humor, and a knack for describing haunted places. Creating tension that ebbs and flows, he slowly builds the dramatic narrative to a resounding crescendo, and he makes the quieter scenes that follow just as compelling. The second entry in the Lockwood & Company series, this imaginative adventure features one of the most hair-raising chase scenes in children's fiction. At the book's end, when the enigmatic Lockwood reveals a chilling secret, readers can only hope that more sequels are in the offing. High-Demand Backstory: Stroud, of Bartimaeus fame, is no stranger to the New York Times best-seller list, and this second installment of his new series looks primed to keep him there." Booklist

Stuchner, Joan Betty
Honey cake; illustrated by Cynthia Nugent. Random House 2008 101p il $11.99; lib bdg $14.99; pa $4.99
Grades: 3 4 5   **Fic**
   1. Jews -- Fiction 2. Denmark -- Fiction 3. Holocaust, 1933-1945 -- Fiction
   ISBN 978-0-375-85189-6; 0-375-85189-5; 978-0-375-95189-3 lib bdg; 0-375-95189-X lib bdg; 978-0-375-85190-2 pa; 0-375-85190-9 pa
                        LC 2007-11501

First published 2007 in the United Kingdom and Canada

David and his family live in Denmark during the Nazi occupation, until September 1943 when their neighbors help smuggle them to Sweden to escape Hitler's orders to send the Danish Jews to concentration camps. Includes a recipe for honey cake, typically made to celebrate the Jewish New Year.

"The simply told story and black-and-white illustrations convey tension, fear, and hope." Horn Book Guide

Sullivan, Laura L.
Under the green hill. Henry Holt and Company 2010 308p $16.99
Grades: 5 6 7 8   **Fic**
   1. Fantasy fiction 2. Fairies -- Fiction 3. Siblings -- Fiction 4. Supernatural -- Fiction
   ISBN 978-0-8050-8984-4; 0-8050-8984-5
                        LC 2009-50772

While staying with distant relatives in England, Americans Rowan, Meg, Silly, and James Morgan, with their neighbors Dickie Rhys and Finn Fachan, learn that one of them must fight to the death in the Midsummer War required by the local fairies

"Sullivan draws heavily on her knowledge of Middle English folklore and creates a story rich with memorable characters and evocative language." SLJ

Followed by: Guardian of the green hill (2011)

Summers, Susan
The greatest gift; the story of the other Wise Man. retold by Susan Summers; illustrated by Jackie Morris. Barefoot Books 2011 il $16.99
Grades: K 1 2 3   **Fic**
   1. Magi -- Fiction 2. Christmas stories 3. Middle East -- Fiction 4. Voyages and travels -- Fiction
   ISBN 978-1-84686-578-7; 1-84686-578-6
                        LC 2011015507

Artaban, a fourth Wise Man, delays journeying with the other Magi to see the newborn Jesus, but after thirty-three years of helping others he has an unusual opportunity to meet his Savior.

"This intriguing story unfolds in flowing prose with the feeling of a folktale, conveying a subtle message in Artaban's kindness toward the needy of any religion. Morris provides handsome watercolor illustrations in a smoky palette of earth tones, with a soft focus that complements the ancient setting." Kirkus

Swinburne, Stephen R.
Wiff and Dirty George: the Z.E.B.R.A. Incident. Boyds Mills Press 2010 167p il $17.95
Grades: 4 5 6 7   **Fic**
   1. Nineteen sixties -- Fiction 2. Great Britain -- Fiction
   ISBN 978-1-59078-755-7; 1-59078-755-2

Witt and Dirty George give chase to the notorious Basil King, a criminal genius who is best on taking over Great Britain. "Grades four to seven." (Bull Cent Child Books)

"London in 1969 was a trippy place, no doubt, but it's made even more psychodelic with the adventures of Wiff and Dirty George, two twelve-year-olds who follow their noses into a world of trouble. While on a morning train, the boys are slightly horrified when everyone's pants fall down, but instead of worrying overmuch about their own embarrassment, they take off after the large white rabbit who seems to be the instigator of the mass humiliation. . . . The humor is more situational than verbal; the characters are all comedic straight men in a twisted, absurd world. . . . Delightfully daft 'clues' precede each chapter, and a glossary

of Britishisms will help young Yanks navigate the dialect."
Bull Cent Child Books

Taback, Simms
Postcards from camp. Nancy Paulsen Books 2011 un
il $17.99
Grades: 1 2 3   **Fic**
1. Camps -- Fiction 2. Letters -- Fiction
ISBN 978-0-399-23973-1; 0-399-23973-1

"Taback's signature illustrative style is perfect for this
brief tale. Michael's scrawl and his father's cursive share
space with collaged stamps and photographs as well as illustrations that suit the correspondents' ages." Kirkus

"Using postcards and removable letters, Taback depicts
a boy's first time at sleep-away camp through correspondence with his father, Harry." Publ Wkly

Tacang, Brian
Bully-be-gone; [by] Brian Tacang. HarperCollins 2006
216p (Misadventures of Millicent Madding) $15.99
Grades: 3 4 5 6   **Fic**
1. Bullies -- Fiction 2. Friendship -- Fiction 3.
Inventions -- Fiction
ISBN 0-06-073911-8

LC 2005-07777

Budding-inventor Millicent Madding launches her latest
invention to disastrous results, and she has only days to create an antidote before the local bullies wreak havoc and her
dearest friendships are destroyed forever

"The book has zippy dialogue and brilliant use of alliteration. . . . The eccentric characters are fun, and the silly
but substantive plot will surely appeal to children." SLJ

Tak, Bibi Dumon
Soldier bear; written by Bibi Dumon Tak; illustrated by
Philip Hopman; translated by Laura Watkinson. Eerdmans
Books for Young Readers 2011 145p il $13
Grades: 4 5 6 7   **Fic**
1. Iran -- Fiction 2. Bears -- Fiction 3. Italy -- Fiction
4. Poland -- Fiction 5. Soldiers -- Fiction 6. World
War, 1939-1945 -- Fiction
ISBN 978-0-8028-5375-2; 0-8028-5375-7

LC 2011013963

An orphaned Syrian brown bear cub is adopted by Polish soldiers during World War II and serves for five years
as their mischievous mascot in Iran and Italy. Based on a
true story.

"This is smoothly translated and engagingly illustrated
with sketches and helpful maps. Funny, fresh and heartwarming." Kirkus

Tanner, Lian
Museum of thieves. Delacorte Press 2010 312p (The
Keepers Trilogy) $16.99; lib bdg $19.99
Grades: 5 6 7 8   **Fic**
1. Fantasy fiction 2. Adventure fiction 3. Museums
-- Fiction 4. Thieves -- Fiction
ISBN 978-0-385-73905-4; 0-385-73905-2; 978-0-385-
90768-2 lib bdg; 0-385-90768-0 lib bdg

LC 2009053655

Goldie, an impulsive and bold twelve-year-old, escapes
the oppressive city of Jewel, where children are required to
wear guardchains for their protection, and finds refuge in
the extraordinary Museum of Dunt, an ever-shifting world

where she discovers a useful talent for thievery and mysterious secrets that threaten her city and everyone she loves.

"Readers will be quickly caught up in the highly dramatic chases, the intriguing museum that shifts layout at will,
and the nifty otherworld elements. There's depth beneath
that, though. . . . [The book] may set young readers thinking
about their own world's choices." Bull Cent Child Books

Followed by: City of lies (2011)

Tarshis, Lauren
★ **Emma**-Jean Lazarus fell out of a tree. Dial Books for
Young Readers 2007 199p $16.99
Grades: 5 6 7   **Fic**
1. School stories 2. Friendship -- Fiction
ISBN 978-0-8037-3164-6; 0-8037-3164-7

LC 2006-18428

A quirky and utterly logical seventh-grade girl named
Emma-Jean Lazarus discovers some interesting results
when she gets involved in the messy everyday problems of
her peers.

"Readers will be fascinated by Emma-Jean's emotion-
less observations and her adult-level vocabulary. Tarshis
pulls off a balancing act, showing the child's detachment yet
making her a sympathetic character. Exceptionally fleshed-
out secondary characters add warmth to the story." SLJ

Followed by: Emma-Jean Lazarus fell in love (2009)

I survived the shark attacks of 1916; illustrated by Scott
Dawson. Scholastic 2010 87p il (I survived) $16.99; pa
$4.99
Grades: 3 4 5 6   **Fic**
1. Sharks -- Fiction 2. New Jersey -- Fiction
ISBN 978-0-545-20688-4; 0-545-20688-4; 978-0-545-
20695-2 pa; 0-545-20695-2 pa

In the summer of 1916, ten year-old Chet Roscow is
captivated by the local news: A great white shark has been
attacking and killing people up and down the Atlantic coast,
not far from Chet's hometown of Springfield, New Jersey.

"An absorbing story. . . . Black-and-white illustrations
that resemble old photographs enhance the events of the
story. Tarshis incorporates information about the real attacks
and fictionalizes it, then follows the story with facts about
the attacks and sharks. This is a gripping story that will hold
the interest of reluctant readers." SLJ

Other titles in this series are:
I survived the sinking of the Titanic, 1912 (2010)
I survived Hurricane Katrina, 2005 (2011)
I survived the bombing of Pearl Harbor, 1941 (2011)

Tashjian, Janet
★ **My** life as a book; with cartoons by Jake Tashjian.
Henry Holt 2010 211p il $16.99; pa $6.99
Grades: 4 5 6 7   **Fic**
1. Summer -- Fiction 2. Animals -- Fiction 3. Family
life -- Fiction 4. Books and reading -- Fiction
ISBN 978-0-8050-8903-5; 0-8050-8903-9; 978-0-312-
67289-8 pa; 0-312-67289-6 pa

LC 2009-18909

Dubbed a "reluctant reader" by his teacher, twelve-
year-old Derek spends summer vacation learning important lessons even though he does not complete his summer
reading list.

"The protagonist is by turns likable and irritating, but
always interesting. He is sure to engage fans of Jeff Kinney's

'Diary of a Wimpy Kid' books . . . as well as those looking for a spunky, contemporary boy with a mystery to solve. Reluctant readers will appreciate the book's large print and quick-paced story." SLJ

"Another title about Derek is:
My life as a stuntboy (2011)

My life as a joke; Janet Tashjian; with cartoons by Jake Tashjian. Henry Holt and Company 2014 252 p. illustrations (hardback) $13.99
Grades: 4 5 6 7   **Fic**
1. School stories 2. Middle schools -- Fiction 3. Friendship -- Fiction 4. Maturation (Psychology) -- Fiction 5. Family life -- California -- Los Angeles -- Fiction
ISBN 080509850X; 9780805098501
LC 2013046395
In this middle grade book by Janet Tashjian, illustrated by Jake Tashjian, "Derek Fallon discovers all the angst that comes with being twelve--he just wants to feel grown up, but life gets in the way with a series of mishaps that make him look like a baby. . . . Why isn't being in middle school as great as Derek imagined?" (Publisher's note)

"In his fourth appearance, twelve-year-old Derek resolves to appear more mature, but he's constantly a laughingstock. . . . Fans will enjoy the fast plot, Derek's supportive friends, and cartoon marginalia representing Derek's ever-expanding collection of vocabulary words." Horn Book

Tate, Eleanora E.
Celeste's Harlem Renaissance. Little, Brown 2007 279p $15.99; pa $5.99
Grades: 4 5 6 7   **Fic**
1. Aunts -- Fiction 2. African Americans -- Fiction 3. Harlem Renaissance -- Fiction 4. Harlem (New York, N.Y.) -- Fiction
ISBN 978-0-316-52394-3; 978-0-316-11362-5 pa
In 1921, thirteen-year-old Celeste leaves North Carolina to stay with her glamorous Aunt Valentina in Harlem, New York, where she discovers the vibrant Harlem Renaissance in full swing, even though her aunt's life is not exactly what she was led to believe.

"Both sobering and inspiring, Tate's novel is a moving portrait of growing up black and female in 1920s America." Booklist

Tate, Lindsey
Kate Larkin, bone expert; [by] Lindsey Tate; illustrated by Diane Palmisciano. Henry Holt 2008 72p il $16.95
Grades: 1 2 3 4   **Fic**
1. Bones -- Fiction 2. Family life -- Fiction
ISBN 978-0-8050-7901-2; 0-8050-7901-7
LC 2007027588
When Kate breaks her arm, she learns all about bones, from how x-rays work to how bones heal, and by the time she gets her cast removed at the end of the summer, she is an expert. Includes related activities and glossary

"The format is appealing: large type, short chapters, and black-and-white illustrations generously dispersed throughout. . . . This is a solid choice for newly independent readers or for science-minded children looking for some fiction." SLJ

Taylor, Chloe
Ready to wear; Chloe Taylor. 1st ed. Simon Spotlight 2013 176 p. (Sew Zoey) (paperback) $5.99; (hardcover) $15.99
Grades: 3 4 5 6 7   **Fic**
1. Fashion 2. Middle schools 3. School stories
ISBN 1442479345; 9781442479333; 9781442479340
LC 2013935204
In this children's novel, by Chloe Taylor, illustrated by Nancy Zhang, "fashion-loving Zoey Webber gets the best news ever: Her middle school is getting rid of uniforms! . . . Zoey has sketchbooks full of fashion designs, but nothing to wear! So with a little help from her best friends Kate and Priti, she learns to make her own clothes. She even begins to post her fashion design sketches online in a blog. That's how the Sew Zoey blog begins, and soon it becomes much more." (Publisher's note)

Taylor, Mildred D.
★ **The friendship**; pictures by Max Ginsburg. Dial Bks. for Young Readers 1987 53p il $15.99; pa $4.99
Grades: 4 5 6 7   **Fic**
1. Mississippi -- Fiction 2. Race relations -- Fiction 3. African Americans -- Fiction
ISBN 0-8037-0417-8; 0-14-038964-4 pa
LC 86-29309
Coretta Scott King Award for text
This "story about race relations in rural Mississippi during the Depression focuses on an incident between an old Black man, Mr. Tom Bee, and a white storekeeper, Mr. John Wallace. Indebted to Tom for saving his life as a young man, John had promised they would always be friends. But now, years later, John insists that Tom call him 'Mister' and shoots the old man for defiantly—and publicly—calling him by his first name. Narrator Cassie Logan and her brothers . . . are verbally abused by Wallace's villainous sons before witnessing the encounter." Bull Cent Child Books

★ **The gold** Cadillac; pictures by Michael Hays. Dial Bks. for Young Readers 1987 43p il $16.99; pa $4.99
Grades: 4 5 6 7   **Fic**
1. Prejudices -- Fiction 2. Race relations -- Fiction 3. African Americans -- Fiction
ISBN 0-8037-0342-2; 0-14-038963-6 pa
LC 86-11526
"Full-page sepia paintings effectively portray the characters, setting, and mood of the story events as Hays ably demonstrates his understanding of the social and emotional environments which existed for blacks during this period." SLJ

"The shiny gold Cadillac that Daddy brings home one summer evening marks a stepping stone in the lives of Wilma and [Lois,] two black sisters growing up in Ohio during the fifties. At first neighbors and relatives shower them with attention. But when the family begins the long journey to the South to show off the car to their Mississippi relatives, the girls, for the first time, encounter the undisguised ugliness of racial prejudice." Horn Book

★ **Let** the circle be unbroken. Dial Bks. for Young Readers 1981 394p $17.99; pa $7.99
Grades: 4 5 6 7   **Fic**
1. Mississippi -- Fiction 2. African Americans -- Fiction

3. Great Depression, 1929-1939 -- Fiction
ISBN 0-8037-4748-9; 0-14-034892-1 pa

LC 81-65854

Sequel to: Roll of thunder, hear my cry

The author "provides her readers with a literal sense of witnessing important American history. . . . Moreover, [she] never neglects the details of her volatile 9-year-old heroine's interior life. The daydreams, the jealousy, the incredible ardor of that age come alive." N Y Times Book Rev

This novel featuring the Logans covers "a series of tangential events so that it is a family record, a picture of the depression years in rural Mississippi, and an indictment of black-white relations in the Deep South. A young friend is convicted of a murder of which he is innocent, a pretty cousin is insulted by some white boys and her father taunted because he married a white woman, an elderly neighbor tries to vote, the government pays farmers to plow their crops under, etc." Bull Cent Child Books

★ **Mississippi** bridge; by Mildred Taylor; pictures by Max Ginsburg. Dial Bks. for Young Readers 1990 62p il hardcover o.p. pa $4.99
Grades: 4 5 6 7 **Fic**
1. Prejudices -- Fiction 2. Mississippi -- Fiction 3. Race relations -- Fiction 4. African Americans -- Fiction
ISBN 0-14-130817-6 pa

LC 89-27898

"Taylor has shaped this episode into a haunting meditation that will leave readers vividly informed about segregation practices and the unequal rights that prevailed in that era. . . . The incident and its context constitute a telling piece of social history." Booklist

In this story featuring the children of Mississippi's Logan family, "Jeremy Simms, a 10-year-old white neighbor, describes a harrowing incident after the Logans and other blacks are ordered off the weekly bus in a foggy rainstorm." N Y Times Book Rev

★ The **road** to Memphis; by Mildred Taylor. Dial Bks. 1989 290p pa $6.99; $18.99
Grades: 4 5 6 7 **Fic**
1. Mississippi -- Fiction 2. Race relations -- Fiction 3. African Americans -- Fiction
ISBN 0-14-036077-8 pa; 0-8037-0340-6

LC 88-33654

Coretta Scott King Award for text

This is a sequel to Let the Circle Be Unbroken. "The time is 1941, with the U.S. on the verge of war; Cassie {Logan} . . . is sure that nothing will stop her from college and career. When her friend Moe is humiliated and ridiculed by local bigots, he loses control and attacks three men with a crowbar. Cassie and her brothers and friends (including one white friend, Jeremy Simms) help Moe escape. . . . Grades seven to twelve." (Booklist)

"Taylor's continued smooth, easy language provides readability for all ages, with a focus on universal human pride, worthy values, and individual responsibility. This action-packed drama is highly recommended." Voice Youth Advocates

★ **Roll** of thunder, hear my cry; 25th anniversary ed; Phyllis Fogelman Books 2001 276p $17.99; pa $7.99

Grades: 4 5 6 7 8 9 **Fic**
1. Mississippi -- Fiction 2. African Americans -- Fiction
ISBN 0-8037-2647-3; 0-14-240112-9 pa

LC 00-39378

First published 1976 by Dial Press
Awarded the Newbery Medal, 1977

"The time is 1933. The place is Spokane, Mississippi where the Logans, the only black family who own their own land, wage a courageous struggle to remain independent, displeasing a white plantation owner bent on taking their land. But this suspenseful tale is also about the story's young narrator, Cassie, and her three brothers who decide to wage their own personal battles to maintain the self-dignity and pride with which they were raised. . . . Ms. Taylor's richly textured novel shows a strong, proud black family . . . resisting rather than succumbing to oppression." Child Book Rev Serv

Song of the trees; pictures by Jerry Pinkney. Dial Bks. for Young Readers 1975 48p il hardcover o.p. pa $5.99
Grades: 4 5 6 7 **Fic**
1. Mississippi -- Fiction 2. African Americans -- Fiction 3. Great Depression, 1929-1939 -- Fiction
ISBN 0-8037-5452-3; 0-14-250075-5 pa

Eight-year-old Cassie Logan tells how her family "leaving Mississippi during the Depression was cheated into selling for practically nothing valuable and beautiful giant old pines and hickories, beeches and walnuts in the forest surrounding their house." Adventuring with Books

★ The **well**; David's story. Dial Bks. for Young Readers 1995 92p hardcover o.p. pa $5.99
Grades: 4 5 6 7 **Fic**
1. Mississippi -- Fiction 2. Race relations -- Fiction 3. African Americans -- Fiction
ISBN 0-8037-1802-0; 0-14-038642-4 pa

LC 94-25360

This story "delivers an emotional wallop in a concentrated span of time and action. . . . This story reverberates in the heart long after the final paragraph is read." Horn Book

"David Logan (Cassie's father) tells this story from his childhood. . . . There's a drought, and the Logans possess the only well in the area that has not gone dry. Black and white alike come for water freely given by the family, but the Simms boys can't seem to stand the necessary charity, and their resentment explodes when David's big brother Hammer beats Charlie Simms after Charlie hits David." Bull Cent Child Books

Taylor, S. S.
The **Expeditioners** and the Treasure of Drowned Man's Canyon; by S. S. Taylor; illustrated by Katherine Roy. Pgw 2012 320 p. $22
Grades: 5 6 7 8 **Fic**
1. Adventure fiction 2. Maps -- Fiction 3. Exploration -- Fiction
ISBN 1938073061; 9781938073069

In this book by S. S. Taylor, illustrated by Katherine Roy, "computers have failed, electricity is extinct, and the race to discover new lands is underway! Brilliant explorer Alexander West has just died under mysterious circumstances, but not before smuggling half of a strange map to his intrepid children--Kit the brain, M.K. the tinkerer, and Zander the brave. Why are so many government agents trying to steal the half-map? (And where is the other half?)" (Publisher's note)

"A wonderful example of steampunk done well, this thoroughly satisfying adventure contains enough danger and suspense to keep even reluctant readers turning the pages." SLJ

Taylor, Sydney

★ All-of-a-kind family; illustrations by Helen John. Delacorte Press 2005 188p il hardcover o.p. pa $5.99

Grades: 4 5 6　　　　　　　　　　　　　　　　　Fic

1. Jews -- Fiction 2. New York (N.Y.) -- Fiction

ISBN 0-385-73295-3; 0-440-40059-7 pa

First published 1951 by Follett

"A genuine and delightful picture of a Jewish family . . . with an understanding mother and father, rich in kindness and fun though poor in money. The important part the public library played in the lives of these children is happily evident; and the Jewish holiday celebrations are particularly well described." Horn Book

Other titles about this family are:

All-of-a-kind family downtown (1957)

All-of-a-kind family uptown (1957)

Ella of all-of-a-kind family (1978)

More all-of-a-kind family (1954)

Taylor, Theodore

★ The cay. Delacorte Press 1987 137p $16.95; pa $5.50

Grades: 5 6 7 8　　　　　　　　　　　　　　　　Fic

1. Blind -- Fiction 2. Race relations -- Fiction 3. Caribbean region -- Fiction 4. Survival after airplane accidents, shipwrecks, etc. -- Fiction

ISBN 0-385-07906-0; 0-440-22912-X pa

A reissue of the title first published 1969

When the freighter on which they are traveling is torpedoed by a German submarine during World War II, Phillip, an adolescent white boy blinded by a blow on the head, and Timothy, an old black man, are stranded on a tiny Caribbean island where the boy acquires a new kind of vision, courage, and love from his old companion

"Starkly dramatic, believable and compelling." Saturday Rev

Followed by: Timothy of the cay

Ice drift; [by] Theodore Taylor. Harcourt 2005 224p $16; pa $5.95

Grades: 4 5 6 7　　　　　　　　　　　　　　　　Fic

1. Inuit -- Fiction 2. Brothers -- Fiction 3. Arctic regions -- Fiction

ISBN 0-15-205081-7; 0-15-205550-9 pa

LC 2003-27783

Two Inuit brothers must fend for themselves while stranded on an ice floe that is adrift in the Greenland Strait.

This is "a masterful and detailed look into a culture unfamiliar to most Americans, a gripping adventure, and a moving depiction of brotherly love." SLJ

★ Teetoncey. Harcourt 2004 208p hardcover o.p. pa $5.95

Grades: 5 6 7 8　　　　　　　　　　　　　　　　Fic

1. Amnesia -- Fiction 2. North Carolina -- Fiction

ISBN 0-15-205298-4; 0-15-205294-1 pa

LC 2003-67745

A reissue of the title first published 1974 by Doubleday

In this first novel of the Cape Hatteras trilogy, eleven-year-old Ben rescues an English girl from a shipwreck off the Outer Banks of North Carolina; and, though she becomes part of his family, she never speaks.

"The novel is rich with details of of local geography, history, and folklore." Horn Book

Other titles in the Cape Hatteras trilogy are:

The odyssey of Ben O'Neal (2004 c1977)

Teetoncey and Ben O'Neal (2004 c1975)

The trouble with Tuck. Doubleday 1981 110p hardcover o.p. pa $4.50

Grades: 5 6 7 8　　　　　　　　　　　　　　　　Fic

1. Dogs -- Fiction 2. Blind -- Fiction

ISBN 0-385-17774-7; 0-440-41696-5 pa

LC 81-43139

Helen trains her blind dog Tuck to follow and trust a seeing-eye companion dog

This is "a touching dog story, written with good flow, pace, and structure." Bull Cent Child Books

Another title about Helen and Tuck is:

Tuck triumphant (1991)

Teague, David

★ Saving Lucas Biggs; by Marisa de los Santos and David Teague. Harper, an imprint of HarperCollinsPublishers 2014 288 p. (hardback) $16.99

Grades: 5 6 7 8　　　　　　　　　　　　　　　　Fic

1. Girls -- Fiction 2. Time travel -- Fiction 3. Detective and mystery stories

ISBN 0062274627; 9780062274625

LC 2013043189

This "time-travel story from husband-and-wife team Marisa de los Santos and David Teague follows one girl's race to change the past in order to save her father's future. Thirteen-year-old Margaret knows her father is innocent, but that doesn't stop the cruel Judge Biggs from sentencing him to death. Margaret is determined to save her dad, even if it means using her family's secret--and forbidden--ability to time travel." (Publisher's note)

"...The authors weave a tale of justice and family bonds with threads of historical fiction accented with the fantastical physics of time travel. The heroine begins to realize that the very stuff that makes people who they are—that combination of all their life experiences—can sometimes shift the very fabric of history. At least that's what Margaret is hoping, because the only way to save her father is to first save corrupt Lucas Biggs from himself." SLJ

Teague, Mark

★ The doom machine; a novel. Blue Sky Press 2009 376p $17.99

Grades: 4 5 6 7　　　　　　　　　　　　　　　　Fic

1. Science fiction 2. Space and time -- Fiction 3. Extraterrestrial beings -- Fiction

ISBN 978-0-545-15142-9; 0-545-15142-2

LC 2009-14262

When a spaceship lands in the small town of Vern Hollow in 1956, juvenile delinquent Jack Creedle and prim, studious Isadora Shumway form an unexpected alliance as they try to keep a group of extraterrestrials from stealing eccentric Uncle Bud's space travel machine.

"This book is filled with humor and dramatic figurative language that makes the setting completely approachable. It is a great fit for science fiction, humor, and adventure genre fans." Voice Youth Advocates

Tellegen, Toon

Letters to anyone and everyone; stories by Toon Tellegen; illustrated by Jessica Ahlberg; translated by Martin Cleaver. Boxer Books 2010 154p il lib bdg $12.95
Grades: 2 3 4 5   **Fic**
1. Animals -- Fiction 2. Letters -- Fiction
ISBN 978-1-906250-95-9 lib bdg; 1-906250-95-2 lib bdg

"In this novel, snails, elephants, bears, and ants write letters to one another, to the Sun, and to other letter writers. . . . Every brief missive is written in a distinct voice, and the complete collection reveals Tellegen's richly imagined world in which the creatures reside. The book was originally published in Holland, and Cleaver's smooth English translation retains humor and charm." SLJ

TenNapel, Doug

Cardboard; Doug TenNapel. Graphix / Scholastic 2012 288 p. $24.99
Grades: 5 6 7 8   **Fic**
1. Boxes -- Fiction 2. Gifts -- Graphic novels 3. Magic -- Graphic novels 4. Bullies -- Graphic novels 5. Father-son relationship -- Graphic novels
ISBN 0545418720; 9780545418720; 9780545418737
LC 2011934533

In this graphic novel, "Cam Howerton's out-of-work father is so broke, the best he can do for Cam's birthday is an empty cardboard box purchased from a toy seller with two mysterious rules: return every unused scrap of cardboard and don't ask for any more. . . . [T]he box becomes a project. What should father and son make out of the box? 'A boxer,' Cam suggests. . . . 'Boxer Bill,' created from inanimate material, comes alive. Unfortunately, Marcus, the neighborhood bully . . . steals the scrap materials, and begins turning out a whole evil empire of cardboard monsters. . . . [A]fter losing control of them he must unite with Cam and his father to defeat the massive cardboard army. . . . [Q]uestions are raised about what it means to be a man, what makes a good man, and what forms people's character." (Horn Book)

Teplin, Scott

The **clock** without a face; a Gus Twintig mystery. [by Scott Teplin, Mac Barnett & Eli Horowitz; plus faces by Adam Rex & numbers by Anna Sheffield] McSweeney's 2010 un il $19.95
Grades: 4 5 6 7   **Fic**
1. Mystery fiction 2. Picture puzzles 3. Theft -- Fiction 4. Apartment houses -- Fiction 5. Clocks and watches -- Fiction
ISBN 978-1-934781-71-5; 1-934781-71-1

Narrator Gus Twintig and Roy Dodge "are summoned to a 13-story apartment building to investigate a string of robberies: the emerald-encrusted numbers have been stolen from a clock belonging to owner Bevel Ternky, and his 12 tenants have also been burgled. . . . The right side of each spread is an overhead cutaway view of each apartment, ostensibly drawn by Twintig. Given the potential of discovering clues to where the actual bejeweled numbers . . . have

been hidden, kids should be plenty motivated to pore over each scene." Publ Wkly

Testa, Maria

Almost forever. Candlewick Press 2003 69p $14.99; pa $5.99
Grades: 3 4 5   **Fic**
1. Vietnam War, 1961-1975 -- Fiction
ISBN 0-7636-1996-5; 0-7636-3366-6 pa
LC 2002-34757

In free verse, a young girl describes what she, her brother, and their mother do during the year that her doctor father is serving in the Army in Vietnam

This is "sensitive and moving. . . . Testa's poems give her young speaker a believable, sympathetic voice." Publ Wkly

Thomason, Mark

Moonrunner. Kane/Miller 2009 217p $15.95
Grades: 4 5 6 7   **Fic**
1. Horses -- Fiction 2. Australia -- Fiction
ISBN 978-1-935279-03-7; 1-935279-03-3
First published 2008 in Australia

"In the 1890s, Casey and his parents immigrate to Australia, to a homestead that they inherited from his grandfather. The 12-year-old finds the change difficult. He is bullied at school, and he misses his baseball team in Montana and his horse. Then he happens upon a magnificent wild stallion, and he is determined to befriend the brumby, whom he names Moonrunner. . . . This well-paced story effectively portrays the family's struggles. Casey is a strong, engaging protagonist whose interactions with the other characters are believable and interesting." SLJ

Thompson, Colin

Good neighbors; by Colin Thompson; illustrated by Crab Scrambly. HarperCollinsPublishers 2008 214p il (The Floods) lib bdg $16.89; pa $5.99
Grades: 3 4 5 6   **Fic**
1. Magic -- Fiction 2. Witches -- Fiction
ISBN 978-0-06-113199-8 lib bdg; 0-06-113196-2 lib bdg; 978-0-06-113197-4 pa; 0-06-113197-0 pa

A family of wizards and witches living in an ordinary neighborhood in an ordinary town decides that they have had enough of the noisy family living next-door and makes them disappear.

The author "careens wildly from one extreme scenario to the next, letting the Floods get away with everything— despite their appearances, they're the good guys. Kids can enjoy the prankishness; adults can rest easy given the conventional underpinnings." Publ Wkly

Another title in this series is:
School plot (2008)

Thompson, J. E.

The **girl** from Felony Bay; John Thompson. Walden Pond Press, an imprint of HarperCollinsPublishers 2013 384 p. (hardcover bdg.) $16.99
Grades: 4 5 6 7   **Fic**
1. Theft -- Fiction 2. Mystery fiction -- Fiction 3. Coma -- Fiction 4. Fathers -- Fiction 5. Families -- Fiction 6. Charleston (S.C.) -- Fiction 7. Mystery and detective stories
ISBN 0062104462; 9780062104465
LC 2012025338

In this book, 12-year-old Abbey Force's "father has suffered an accident and now lies in the hospital in a coma. Meanwhile, he has been accused of stealing from a client named Miss Lydia Jenkins, and his law firm . . . has sold the Force family home, Reward Plantation, in order to repay her." Abbey makes friends with the new owners' daughter Bee and the girls "stumble upon a mystery--someone is digging holes at Felony Bay, perhaps in search of buried treasure." (Kirkus Reviews)

Thompson, Kate

Highway robbery; illustrated by Jonny Duddle and Robert Dress. Greenwillow Books 2009 118p il $15.99

Grades: 3 4 5 6   **Fic**

1. Thieves 2. Adventure fiction 3. Horses -- Fiction 4. Thieves -- Fiction 5. Great Britain -- History -- 1714-1837 -- Fiction
ISBN 978-0-06-173034-4; 0-06-173034-3

                LC 2008-27720

On a cold day in eighteenth-century England, a poor young boy agrees to watch a stranger's fine horse for a golden guinea but soon finds himself in a difficult situation when the king's guard appears and wants to use him as bait in their pursuit of a notorious highwayman

"It's a suspenseful and tautly written story as is, and Thompson's sly twist makes it all the richer." Publ Wkly

Most wanted; illustrated by Jonny Duddle. Greenwillow Books 2010 136p il $15.99

Grades: 3 4 5   **Fic**

1. Emperors 2. Horses -- Fiction 3. Slavery -- Fiction 4. Rome -- History -- Fiction
ISBN 978-0-06-173037-5; 0-06-173037-8; 978-0-06-173038-2 lib bdg; 0-06-173038-6 lib bdg

In first century Rome, in the turmoil after a rumor circulates that mad Emperor "Littleboots" is dead, young Marcus brings home a horse that the emperor had proclaimed a consul and his family decides they must treat it as an honored guest.

"This brief chapter book is nicely suited for reading aloud or for those independent readers who enjoy their adventure and history touched with humor. Marcus's voice is engaging and credible. . . . A cleverly told tale of an odd and interesting piece of history that will intrigue young readers." Publ Wkly

Thompson, Paul B.

The **devil's** door; a Salem witchcraft story. Enslow Publishers 2010 160p (Historical fiction adventures) lib bdg $27.93; pa $14.95

Grades: 4 5 6   **Fic**

1. Trials -- Fiction 2. Witchcraft -- Fiction 3. Salem (Mass.) -- Fiction
ISBN 978-0-7660-3387-0 lib bdg; 0-7660-3387-2 lib bdg; 978-1-59845-214-3 pa; 1-59845-214-2 pa

Sarah Wright and her father Ephraim move to Salem Village, Massachusetts, in 1692, where they witness the Salem witchcraft hysteria, during which Ephraim is arrested and Sarah must try to help him escape from jail.

"Factual material is incorporated into the narrative, creating a fast-paced, fascinating read." SLJ

Thomson, Melissa

Keena Ford and the second-grade mixup; pictures by Frank Morrison. Dial Books for Young Readers 2008 102p il $14.99; pa $5.99

Grades: 1 2 3   **Fic**

1. School stories 2. Diaries -- Fiction 3. African Americans -- Fiction
ISBN 978-0-8037-3263-6; 0-8037-3263-5; 978-0-14-241396-8 pa; 0-14-241396-8 pa

                LC 2007-43749

Keena Ford chronicles her many mishaps as she begins second grade

"Thomson, a former teacher, skillfully zeroes in on an eight-year-old's anxieties and creates a vivid sense of Keena's world, both at school and at home. . . . Morrison's full-page pencil sketches extend both the comedy and the emotions, particularly Keena's sense that she is accepted and loved, even as she clears up mistakes with family and friends." Booklist

Other titles about Keena Ford are:

Keena Ford and the field trip mix-up (2009)

Keena Ford and the secret journal mix-up (2010)

Thor, Annika

★ A **faraway** island; translated from the Swedish by Linda Schenck. Delacorte Press 2009 247p map $16.99; lib bdg $19.99

Grades: 4 5 6 7   **Fic**

1. Jews -- Fiction 2. Sweden -- Fiction 3. Islands -- Fiction 4. Sisters -- Fiction 5. Refugees -- Fiction 6. World War, 1939-1945 -- Fiction
ISBN 978-0-385-73617-6; 0-385-73617-7; 978-0-385-90590-9 lib bdg; 0-385-90590-4 lib bdg

                LC 2009-15420

ALA ALSC Batchelder Award (2010)

In 1939 Sweden, two Jewish sisters wait for their parents to flee the Nazis in Austria, but while eight-year-old Nellie settles in quickly, twelve-year-old Stephie feels stranded at the end of the world, with a foster mother who is as cold and unforgiving as the island on which they live.

"Children will readily empathize with Stephie's courage. Both sisters are well-drawn, likable characters. This is the first of four books Thor has written about the two girls." SLJ

Followed by: The lily pond (2011)

Timberlake, Amy

★ **One** came home; Amy Timberlake. Alfred A. Knopf 2012 272 p. (hard cover) $16.99

Grades: 4 5 6   **Fic**

1. Historical fiction 2. Sharpshooters -- Fiction 3. Missing persons -- Fiction 4. Counterfeits and counterfeiting -- Fiction 5. Wisconsin -- History -- 19th century -- Fiction 6. Frontier and pioneer life -- Wisconsin -- Fiction
ISBN 0375869255; 9780375869259; 9780375969256; 9780375989346

                LC 2011037095

Newberry Honor Book (2014)

This novel, by Amy Timberlake, is set "in the town of Placid, Wisconsin, in 1871, . . . when Georgie blurts out something she shouldn't, her older sister Agatha flees. . . . And when the sheriff returns to town with an unidentifiable body--wearing Agatha's blue-green ball gown--everyone assumes the worst. Except Georgie. Refusing to believe the facts that are laid down (and coffined) before her, Georgie sets out on a journey to find her sister." (Publisher's note)

Tingle, Tim

★ **Crossing** Bok Chitto; a Choctaw tale of friendship & freedom. illustrated by Jeanne Rorex Bridges. Cinco Puntos Press 2006 un il $17.95; pa $8.95

Grades: 2 3 4 5   **Fic**

1. Slavery -- Fiction 2. Friendship -- Fiction 3. Mississippi -- Fiction 4. Choctaw Indians -- Fiction 5. African Americans -- Fiction

ISBN 978-0-938317-77-7; 0-938317-77-6; 978-1-933693-20-0 pa; 1-933693-20-7 pa

LC 2005-23612

In the 1800s, a Choctaw girl becomes friends with a slave boy from a plantation across the great river, and when she learns that his family is in trouble, she helps them cross to freedom

The "text has the rhythm and grace of . . . oral tradition. It will be easily and effectively read aloud. The paintings are dark and solemn, and the artist has done a wonderful job of depicting all of the characters as individuals." Booklist

How I became a ghost; a Choctaw trail of tears story. by Tim Tingle. RoadRunner Press 2013 160 p. (The how I became a ghost series) (hardcover: alk. paper) $18.95

Grades: 4 5 6 7   **Fic**

1. Ghost stories 2. Choctaw Indians -- Fiction

ISBN 1937054535; 9781937054533; 9781937054540; 9781937054557

LC 2013935579

American Indian Youth Literature Award Winner (2014)

In this book, "a 10-year-old Choctaw boy recounts the beginnings of the forced resettlement of his people from their Mississippi-area homelands in 1830. . . . Even as the Choctaw prepare to leave their homes, Isaac begins to have unsettling visions. . . [The] visions begin to come true, as some are burned to death by the Nahullos and others perish due to smallpox-infested blankets. . . . But the Choctaw barrier between life and death is a fluid one, and ghosts follow Isaac, providing reassurance." (Kirkus Reviews)

Tocher, Timothy

Bill Pennant, Babe Ruth, and me. Cricket Books 2009 178p $16.95

Grades: 5 6 7 8   **Fic**

1. Baseball players 2. Baseball managers 3. Baseball -- Fiction 4. New York Giants (Baseball team) -- Fiction 5. New York Yankees (Baseball team) -- Fiction.

ISBN 978-0-8126-2755-8; 0-8126-2755-5

LC 2008026829

In 1920, sixteen-year-old Hank finds his loyalties divided when he is assigned to care for the Giants' mascot, a wildcat named Bill Pennant, as well as keep an eye on Babe Ruth in Ruth's first season with the New York Yankees.

The author "seamlessly blends fact and fiction. He recreates the era with scrupulous attention to its syntax and slang, as well as details of daily life. Ruth, McGraw and the other historical figures come alive for readers, and the fictional Hank is a sympathetic, fully developed character." Kirkus

Toft, Di

Wolven. Scholastic 2010 322p $16.99; pa $7.99

Grades: 5 6 7 8   **Fic**

1. Werewolves -- Fiction 2. Supernatural -- Fiction 3. Great Britain -- Fiction

ISBN 978-0-545-17109-0; 0-545-17109-1; 978-0-545-17110-6 pa; 0-545-17110-5 pa

Twelve-year-old Nat, with help from his friends, and his "pet" Woody, a wolf that turns into a boy, must face werewolves that have been altered as part of a dastardly plan.

"Toft spins an incredible tale full of action, mystery, and suspense. This hair-raising adventure with its fresh perspective on werewolf lore is perfect for audiences not ready for some of the edgier material out there. A satisfying read with a fly-off-the-shelves cover." SLJ

Another title in this series is:
The twilight circus (2011)

Toksvig, Sandi

★ **Hitler's** canary. Roaring Brook Press 2007 191p $16.95

Grades: 5 6 7 8   **Fic**

1. Jews -- Fiction 2. Denmark -- Fiction 3. World War, 1939-1945 -- Fiction

ISBN 978-1-59643-247-5; 1-59643-247-0

LC 2006-16607

Ten-year-old Bamse and his Jewish friend Anton participate in the Danish Resistance during World War II.

"Though . . . suspenseful episodes will thrill readers, it is Bamse's growing courage and deepening understanding that drive the story." Booklist

Tolan, Stephanie S.

Surviving the Applewhites. HarperCollins Pubs. 2002 216p $15.99; lib bdg $17.89; pa $5.99

Grades: 5 6 7 8   **Fic**

1. Theater -- Fiction 2. Family life -- Fiction 3. Eccentrics and eccentricities -- Fiction

ISBN 0-06-623602-9; 0-06-623603-7 lib bdg; 0-06-441044-7 pa

LC 2002-1474

A Newbery Medal honor book, 2003

Jake, a budding juvenile delinquent, is sent for home schooling to the arty and eccentric Applewhite family's Creative Academy, where he discovers talents and interests he never knew he had

This is a "thoroughly enjoyable book with humor, well-drawn characters, and a super cover." Voice Youth Advocates

Wishworks, Inc. illustrated by Amy June Bates. Arthur A. Levine Books 2009 146p il $15.99

Grades: 3 4 5   **Fic**

1. Dogs -- Fiction 2. Moving -- Fiction 3. Wishes -- Fiction 4. Divorce -- Fiction 5. Friendship -- Fiction 6. Imagination -- Fiction

ISBN 978-0-545-03154-7; 0-545-03154-0

LC 2008-42694

When he is granted his wish for a dog from Wishworks, Inc., third-grader Max is disappointed to find that his new pet is nothing like the dog of his imagination.

"Tolan's vivid, clean writing is deceptively uncomplicated and the many issues touched upon are handled well." SLJ

Tolkien, J. R. R. (John Ronald Reuel), 1892-1973

★ The **hobbit,** or, There and back again. Houghton Mifflin 2001 330p il $18; pa $10

Grades: 5 6 7 8 9 10 11 12 Adult **Fic**
1. Magic 2. Satire 3. Allegories 4. Fantasy fiction 5. Fantasies 6. Imaginary kingdoms
ISBN 0-618-16221-6; 0-618-26030-7 pa
LC 2001276594

First published 1937 in the United Kingdom; first United States edition 1938

Bilbo Baggins, a respectable, well-to-do hobbit, lives comfortably in his hobbit-hole until the day the wandering wizard Gandalf chooses him to share in an adventure from which he may never return. "Grades four to eight." (Bull Cent Child Books)

"It must be understood that this is a children's book only in the sense that the first of many readings can be undertaken in the nursery. . . . [The hobbit] will be funniest to its youngest readers, and only years later, at a tenth or twentieth reading, will they begin to realize what deft scholarship and profound reflection have gone to make everything in it so ripe, so friendly, and in its own way so true." Times Lit Suppl

Tooke, Wes
King of the mound; my summer with Satchel Paige. Simon & Schuster Books for Young Readers 2012 155p $15.99
Grades: 4 5 6 **Fic**
1. Baseball players 2. Baseball -- Fiction 3. Disabled persons -- Fiction 4. Poliomyelitis -- Fiction 5. African Americans -- Fiction 6. Father-son relationship -- Fiction
ISBN 978-1-4424-3346-5; 1-4424-3346-9
LC 2011012740

Twelve-year-old Nick loves baseball so after a year in the hospital fighting polio and with a brace on one leg, Nick takes a job with the minor league team for which his father is catcher and gets to see the great pitcher, Satchel Paige, play during the 1935 season. Includes historical notes.

"Tooke sticks closely to historical records, with the addition of a few extra Paige exploits and aphorisms, and . . . the fictional overlay offers a comfortably predictable 'hard work brings just rewards' arc. Nourishing fare for Matt Christopher graduates." Kirkus

Towell, Ann
Grease town. Tundra Books 2010 232p $19.99
Grades: 5 6 7 8 **Fic**
1. Canada -- Fiction 2. Race relations -- Fiction
ISBN 0-88776-983-7; 978-0-88776-983-2

"When twelve-year-old Titus Sullivan decides to run away to join his Uncle Amos and older brother, Lem, he finds an alien and exciting world in Oil Springs, the first Canadian oil boomtown of the 19th century. The Enniskillen swamp is slick with oil, and it takes enterprising folk to plumb its depths. The adventurers who work there are a tough lot of individuals. In this hard world, Titus becomes friends with a young black boy, the child of slaves who came to Canada on the Underground Railroad. When tragedy strikes in the form of a race riot, Titus's loyalties are tested." (Publisher's note) "Ages ten to fourteen." (Quill Quire)

"In 1863, oil has recently been discovered in Oil Springs, Ontario, and a variety of people, black and white, and from many different walks of life, are settling there. Orphans Lem and Titus Sullivan live in their aunt's stuffy and regimented house. When 19-year-old Lem sets out for Oil Springs, 13-year-old Titus stows away in his brother's wagon. . . .

Towell skillfully creates the setting of this mucky little town and its colorful inhabitants. Titus, who narrates, has a voice that is believable and uncontrived. . . . Supporting characters are equally strong and well developed. . . . Towell has created a strong narrator and a compelling plot." SLJ

Towell, Katy
Skary childrin and the carousel of sorrow. Alfred A. Knopf 2011 265p $16.99; lib bdg $19.99; ebook $16.99
Grades: 4 5 6 7 **Fic**
1. Ghost stories 2. School stories 3. Supernatural -- Fiction
ISBN 978-0-375-86859-7; 0-375-86859-3; 978-0-375-96860-0 lib bdg; 0-375-96860-1 lib bdg; 978-0-375-89931-7 e-book; 0-375-89931-6 e-book
LC 2010-38830

In Widowsbury, an isolated village where people believe "known is good, new is bad," three outcasts from the girls' school join forces with a home-schooled boy to uncover and combat the evil that is making people disappear.

"Towell tucks violent tempests, maggoty slime, hideous transformations, nightmares, sudden terrors and like atmosphere-building elements into a rousingly melodramatic literary debut." Kirkus

Townley, Rod
The blue shoe; a tale of thievery, villainy, sorcery, and shoes. by Roderick Townley; illustrated by Mary GrandPré. Alfred A. Knopf 2009 254p il $16.99; lib bdg $19.99
Grades: 4 5 6 7 **Fic**
1. Fables 2. Fairy tales
ISBN 978-0-375-85600-6; 0-375-85600-5; 978-0-375-95600-3 lib bdg; 0-375-95600-X lib bdg
LC 2008-43851

A mysterious stranger commissions a single, valuable shoe from a humble cobbler, changing the cobbler's life and the life of his young apprentice forever.

This is a "fun, whimsical fairy tale. . . . The good-versus-evil plotline, dynamic cast of characters, . . . light romance between Hap and Sophia, and copious amounts of magic and intrigue will be a hit with a wide range of readers." Booklist

The door in the forest; [by] Roderick Townley. Alfred A. Knopf 2011 245p $16.99; lib bdg $19.99
Grades: 4 5 6 **Fic**
1. Magic -- Fiction 2. Honesty -- Fiction 3. Soldiers -- Fiction 4. Space and time -- Fiction
ISBN 0-375-85601-3; 0-375-95601-8 lib bdg; 978-0-375-85601-3; 978-0-375-95601-0 lib bdg
LC 2010034710

While trying to outwit the soldiers who are occupying their small town, fourteen-year-old Daniel, who cannot lie, and Emily, who discovers she has magical powers, are inexplicably drawn to a mysterious island in the heart of the forest where townsfolk have been warned never to go. "Intermediate." (Horn Book)

"Townley's fanciful story swings like a pendulum from Wild West tall tale to a vague mysticism that is enlivened by colorful imagery. . . . At its considerable best, it is quirky and engaging; sentences hurry purposefully along, deepening atmosphere, theme, and plot." Horn Book

Townsend, Wendy
★ The sundown rule. Namelos 2011 128p $18.95

Grades: 5 6 7 8   **Fic**
1. Aunts -- Fiction 2. Uncles -- Fiction 3. Wildlife conservation -- Fiction 4. Father-daughter relationship -- Fiction
  ISBN 1-60898-099-5; 978-1-60898-099-4

Louise and her dad live an idyllic life surrounded by nature. When he gets an assignment to go to Brazil to write an article for a magazine, Louise has to go live in a suburb with her aunt and uncle, leaving her cat, Cash, behind, since Aunt Kay is allergic to animals. Her dad says that it will be for only six weeks, and that everything will be okay. But it isn't, especially when Cash gets hit by a car and dies. And when a new friend's dad shoots a crow for no reason. And when her own dad gets sick, really sick, and might not be coming home.

"Townsend builds a rich, moving story that is refreshing for its subject matter and lyrical realism." Publ Wkly

Tracy, Kristen
  Bessica Lefter bites back; by Kristen Tracy. Delacorte Press 2012 263 p. $16.99
Grades: 4 5 6 7   **Fic**
1. Gifts -- Fiction 2. Mascots -- Fiction 3. Middle schools -- Fiction 4. School children -- Fiction 5. Friendship -- Fiction 6. Schools -- Fiction
  ISBN 9780385740692; 0385740697
                    LC 2011045677

In this children's book, "[s]ixth-grader Bessica's new middle-school persona meets a host of problems, including mending a friendship damaged by mean text messages, facing a bully in her first outing as team mascot and coming to terms with her grandmother's boyfriend. . . . Rumor has it the opposing mascot in the first game will facebomb her. Neither Bessica nor readers learn what facebombing actually is in this context until after the disastrous event." (Kirkus Reviews)

  ★ **Camille** McPhee fell under the bus. Delacorte Press 2009 293p $16.99; lib bdg $19.99
Grades: 3 4 5   **Fic**
1. School stories 2. Idaho -- Fiction 3. Friendship -- Fiction 4. Family life -- Fiction
  ISBN 978-0-385-73687-9; 0-385-73687-8; 978-0-385-90633-3 lib bdg; 0-385-90633-1 lib bdg
                    LC 2008-24903

Ten-year-old Camille McPhee relates the ups and downs of her fourth-grade year at her Idaho elementary school as she tries to adjust to the absence of her best friend, maintain control of her low-blood sugar, cope with the intensifying conflict between her parents, and understand the importance of honesty and fairness.

"The lively, first-person narrative moves readers through possibly banal or overly traumatic episodes with a gentleness and humor that has them rooting for Camille." SLJ

  The **reinvention** of Bessica Lefter. Delacorte Press 2011 305p $15.99
Grades: 4 5 6 7   **Fic**
1. School stories 2. Idaho -- Fiction 3. Friendship -- Fiction
  ISBN 978-0-385-90634-0; 0-385-90634-X
                    LC 2010-04844

Eleven-year-old Bessica's plans to begin North Teton Middle School as a new person begin to fall apart even before school begins.

Tracy "offers a positive and comforting message about learning to make adjustments, ending the book on a happy note, with Bessica finding her niche as school mascot." Publ Wkly

Trafton, Jennifer
  ★ The **rise** and fall of Mount Majestic; illustrations by Brett Helquist. Dial Books for Young Readers 2010 338p il $16.99
Grades: 4 5 6 7   **Fic**
1. Fairy tales 2. Adventure fiction 3. Giants -- Fiction
  ISBN 978-0-8037-3375-6; 0-8037-3375-5
                    LC 2009-51659

Ten-year-old Persimmony Smudge, who longs for heroic adventures, overhears a secret that thrusts her into the middle of a dangerous mission that could destroy the island on which she lives.

"Trafton imbues her tale with a delightful sense of fun and fascinating, well-rounded characters-playful wordsmithing and flowing dialogue make this an excellent choice for bedtime read-aloud." Publ Wkly

Travers, P. L.
  ★ **Mary** Poppins; illustrated by Mary Shepard. rev ed; Harcourt Brace & Co. 1997 202p il $12.95; pa $6
Grades: 4 5 6   **Fic**
1. Fantasy fiction
  ISBN 0-15-205810-9; 0-15-201717-8 pa
                    LC 97-223987

First published 1934; this is a reissue of the 1981 revised edition

An extraordinary English nanny blows in on the East Wind with her parrot-headed umbrella and magic carpetbag and introduces her charges, Jane and Michael Banks, to some delightful people and experiences

"The chapter 'Bad Tuesday,' in which Mary and the Banks children travel to the four corners of the earth and meet the inhabitants, has been criticized for portraying minorities in an unfavorable light. . . . [In] the revised edition . . . the entourage meet up with a polar bear, macaw, panda, and dolphin instead of Eskimos, Africans, Chinese, and American Indians." Booklist

  Other titles about Mary Poppins are:
  Mary Poppins comes back (1935)
  Mary Poppins in the kitchen (1975)
  Mary Poppins in the park (1952)
  Mary Poppins opens the door (1943)

Trevino, Elizabeth Borton de
  I, Juan de Pareja. Farrar, Straus & Giroux 1965 180p $17; pa $6.99
Grades: 6 7 8 9   **Fic**
1. Slaves 2. Artists 3. Painters 4. Spain -- Fiction 5. Artists -- Fiction 6. Slavery -- Fiction
  ISBN 0-374-33531-1; 0-312-38005-4 pa
                    LC 65-19330

Awarded the Newbery Medal, 1966

The black slave boy, Juan de Pareja, "began a new life when he was taken into the household of the Spanish painter, Velázquez. As he worked beside the great artist learning how to grind and mix colors and prepare canvases, there grew between them a warm friendship based on mutual respect and love of art. Created from meager but authentic facts, the story, told by Juan, depicts the life and character of Velázquez and the loyalty of the talented seventeenth-century slave who eventually won his freedom and the right to be an artist." Booklist

Tripp, Jenny

Pete & Fremont; [by] Jenny Tripp; with illustrations by John Manders. Harcourt 2007 180p il $16; pa $5.95

Grades: 2 3 4   **Fic**

1. Dogs -- Fiction 2. Bears -- Fiction 3. Circus -- Fiction

ISBN 978-0-15-205629-2; 0-15-205629-7; 978-0-15-206238-5 pa; 0-15-206238-6 pa

LC 2006008757

When circus owner Mike decides Pete the poodle has grown too old to continue as the starring act, Pete forms an unlikely alliance with a young grizzly bear, who only wants to go home to the woods

"Manders's busy, freewheeling illustrations add an appropriate and enticing touch to this entertaining chapter book." SLJ

Another title about Pete is:

Pete's disappearing act (2009)

Trivas, Tracy

The wish stealers. Aladdin 2010 283p $16.99

Grades: 4 5 6 7   **Fic**

1. Wishes -- Fiction

ISBN 978-1-4169-8725-3; 1-4169-8725-8

LC 2009-42742

"Wish-obsessed sixth-grader Griffin Penshine's life changes dramatically following a chance encounter with an evil old woman, who curses her with a gift of 11 Indian Head pennies. Each penny represents a wish stolen from a wishing fountain, and the curse says that the person holding the stolen wishes will never have a good wish come true (bad ones will, though)." Publ Wkly

Trueit, Trudi Strain

No girls allowed (dogs okay) [illustrated by Jim Paillot] Aladdin Paperbacks 2009 128p il (Secrets of a lab rat) $14.99; pa $4.99

Grades: 2 3 4   **Fic**

1. School stories 2. Twins -- Fiction 3. Siblings -- Fiction

ISBN 978-1-4169-7592-2; 1-4169-7592-6; 978-1-4169-6111-6 pa; 1-4169-6111-9 pa

LC 2008-22329

Fearless nine-year-old 'Scab' McNally tries to get his twin sister's help in convincing their parents to let them get a dog, but when he embarrasses her in school with a particularly obnoxious invention, it looks like he has lost her cooperation forever.

"Scab is a likable, freethinking boy who is full of charm and humor. . . . His many tips, diagrams, and facts scattered throughout are entertaining, as are the numerous comical black-and-white illustrations." SLJ

Other titles in this series are:

Mom, there's a dinosaur in Beeson's Lake (2010)

Scab for president? (2011)

Trueman, Terry

Hurricane; a novel. HarperCollins 2008 137p $15.99; lib bdg $16.89

Grades: 5 6 7   **Fic**

1. Honduras -- Fiction 2. Hurricanes -- Fiction 3. Survival after airplane accidents, shipwrecks, etc. -- Fiction

ISBN 978-0-06-000018-9; 0-06-000018-X; 978-0-06-000019-6 lib bdg; 0-06-000019-8 lib bdg

LC 2007-02990

A revised edition of Swallowing the sun, published 2004 in the United Kingdom

"Thirteen-year-old Jose lives with his family in Honduras. A hurricane hits, causing the recently clear-cut hillside adjacent to his village to become a mudslide that smothers and kills most of its fifty inhabitants. . . . Jose quickly takes charge and becomes a resourceful member of his ailing community. This survival tale is concise but engaging. Trueman's descriptions of the village buried in mud and of the difficulties it creates for the survivors are vivid." Voice Youth Advocates

Tuck, Pamela M.

As fast as words could fly; by Pamela M. Tuck; illustrations by Eric Velasquez. Lee & Low Books 2013 40 p. (hardcover) $18.95

Grades: K 1 2 3   **Fic**

1. Picture books for children 2. Segregation in education -- Fiction 3. Racism -- Fiction 4. Typewriting -- Fiction 5. African Americans -- Fiction 6. School integration -- Fiction 7. Civil rights movements -- Fiction 8. Family life -- North Carolina -- Fiction 9. Greenville (N.C.) -- History -- 20th century -- Fiction

ISBN 1600603483; 9781600603488

LC 2012030983

This book by Pamela M. Tuck, which won Lee & Low's New Voices award in 2007, is based on Tuck's "father's personal experiences with school segregation in 1960s North Carolina. . . . Mason Steele helps his father's civil rights efforts by writing letters for him; when the Steeles get a manual typewriter, Mason shows a gift for typing quickly and accurately. . . . Mason's typing skills earn him the chance to represent the school at a typing competition, but his record-setting victory there is tinged by prejudice." (Publishers Weekly)

Tunis, John R.

The kid from Tomkinsville; with an introduction by Bruce Brooks. Odyssey Classic/Harcourt 2006 278p pa $5.95

Grades: 4 5 6 7   **Fic**

1. Baseball -- Fiction 2. Brooklyn Dodgers (Baseball team) -- Fiction

ISBN 0-15-205641-6

LC 2006277855

A reissue of the title first published 1940

As the newest addition to the Brooklyn Dodgers, young Roy Tucker's pitching helps pull the team out of a slump; but, when a freak accident ends his career as a pitcher, he must try to find another place for himself on the team.

Other titles about Roy Tucker and the Brooklyn Dodgers are:

World series (1941)

Keystone kids (1943)

Rookie of the year (1944)

The kid comes back (1946)

Turnage, Sheila

★ The **ghosts** of Tupelo Landing; by Sheila Turnage. Kathy Dawson Books 2014 368 p. (hardcover) $16.99

Grades: 5 6 7 8   Fic

1. Ghost stories 2. Hotels and motels 3. City and town life -- Fiction 4. Ghosts -- Fiction 5. Hotels -- Fiction 6. Identity -- Fiction 7. Foundlings -- Fiction 8. Haunted places -- Fiction 9. North Carolina -- Fiction 10. Mystery and detective stories 11. Community life -- North Carolina -- Fiction

ISBN 0803736711; 9780803736719

LC 2013019376

In this book, by Sheila Turnage, "when Miss Lana makes an Accidental Bid at the Tupelo auction and winds up the mortified owner of an old inn, she doesn't realize there's a ghost in the fine print. Naturally, Desperado Detective Agency (aka Mo and Dale) opens a paranormal division to solve the mystery of the ghost's identity. But Mo and Dale start to realize . . . [p]eople can also be haunted by their own past." (Publisher's note)

★ **Three** times lucky; by Sheila Turnage. Dial Books for Young Readers 2012 256 p. (hardcover) $16.99

Grades: 5 6 7 8   Fic

1. Absent mothers -- Fiction 2. Adopted children -- Fiction 3. Abandoned children -- Fiction 4. Murder -- Fiction 5. Identity -- Fiction 6. Foundlings -- Fiction 7. Restaurants -- Fiction 8. North Carolina -- Fiction 9. Mystery and detective stories 10. Community life -- North Carolina -- Fiction

ISBN 0803736703; 9780803736702

LC 2011035027

John Newbery Honor Book (2013)

This is the story of Mo LoBeau, who washed downstream as an infant 11 years ago and who has since been in the care of the Colonel, "a stranger who can't remember anything about his own past," and "Miss Lana, owner of the Tupelo Cafe. Mo . . . loves the Colonel and Lana, but" wonders about her origins. She "send[s] messages in bottles to her 'Upstream Mother.'" Also featured are "an out-of-town detective, a dead body . . . , a long-forgotten bank robbery, and a kidnapping." (Publishers Weekly)

Twain, Mark, 1835-1910

★ The **adventures** of Tom Sawyer; illustrated by Barry Moser; afterword by Peter Glassman. Books of Wonder 1989 261p il $24.99

Grades: 5 6 7 8   Fic

1. Missouri -- Fiction 2. Mississippi River -- Fiction

ISBN 0-688-07510-X

First published 1876

The adventures and pranks of a mischievous boy growing up in a Mississippi River town on the early nineteenth century.

Uchida, Yoshiko

★ A **jar** of dreams. Atheneum Pubs. 1981 131p hardcover o.p. pa $4.99

Grades: 5 6 7 8   Fic

1. California -- Fiction 2. Prejudices -- Fiction 3.

Family life -- Fiction 4. Japanese Americans -- Fiction

ISBN 0-689-50210-9; 0-689-71672-9 pa

LC 81-3480

"Rinko in her guilelessness is genuine and refreshing, and her worries and concerns seem wholly natural, honest, and convincing." Horn Book

Other titles about Rinko Tsujimura and her family are:

The best bad thing (1983)

The happiest ending (1985)

★ **Journey** to Topaz; a story of the Japanese-American evacuation. illustrated by Donald Carrick. Heyday Books 2005 149p il pa $9.95

Grades: 5 6 7 8   Fic

1. World War, 1939-1945 -- Fiction 2. Japanese Americans -- Evacuation and relocation, 1942-1945 -- Fiction

ISBN 978-1-890771-91-1 pa; 1-890771-91-0 pa

LC 2004-16537

First published 1971 by Scribner

After the Pearl Harbor attack an eleven-year-old Japanese-American girl and her family are forced to go to an aliens camp in Utah

Followed by: Journey home (1978)

Umansky, Kaye

Clover Twig and the magical cottage; illustrated by Johanna Wright. Roaring Brook 2009 297p il $16.99

Grades: 4 5 6   Fic

1. Magic -- Fiction 2. Witches -- Fiction

ISBN 978-1-59643-507-0; 1-59643-507-0

"British author Umansky's giggle-worthy characterizations and dialogue make this winsome read-aloud stand out from the pack." Kirkus

Solomon Snow and the stolen jewel. Candlewick Press 2007 245p $12.99

Grades: 5 6 7 8   Fic

1. Orphans -- Fiction

ISBN 978-0-7636-2793-5; 0-7636-2793-3

LC 2006-47331

Sequel to: The silver spoon of Solomon Snow (2005)

While trying to rescue Prudence's father from prison, Solomon, Prudence, the Infant Prodigy, and Mr. Skippy the rabbit find themselves caught up in the mad plans of the villainous Dr. Calimari to steal a fabulous and cursed ruby.

"Fans of Lemony Snicket will enjoy this fast-paced read. . . . Reluctant readers might find the short chapters, silly comedy, and simple characters attractive." SLJ

Updale, Eleanor

Johnny Swanson. David Fickling Books 2011 383p $16.99; lib bdg $19.99

Grades: 4 5 6   Fic

1. Mystery fiction 2. Fraud -- Fiction 3. Honesty -- Fiction 4. Homicide -- Fiction 5. Great Britain -- Fiction 6. Single parent family -- Fiction 7. Mother-son relationship -- Fiction

ISBN 0-385-75198-2; 0-385-75199-0 lib bdg; 978-0-385-75198-8; 978-0-385-75199-5 lib bdg

LC 2010-11762

In 1929 England, eleven-year-old Johnny Swanson helps his widowed mother by starting a newspaper advertising scam, which leads him to a real-life murder mystery. "Grades five to eight." (Bull Cent Child Books)

This is "a compelling tale. . . . Updale spins an enjoyable tale, seamlessly mixing the humor of Johnny's fraudulent ads . . . with the seriousness of medical fraud and murder, as well as painting a fascinating picture of an England that is just starting to forget the sacrifices made by WWI soldiers." Publ Wkly

Upjohn, Rebecca

The **secret** of the village fool; by Rebecca Upjohn; illustrated by Renne Benoit. Second Story Press 2012 32 p. $18.95

Grades: 5 6 7 8   **Fic**
1. World War, 1939-1945 -- Jews -- Fiction 2. World War, 1939-1945 -- Poland -- Fiction 3. World War, 1939-1945 -- Children -- Fiction
ISBN 1926920759; 9781926920757

In this children's book by Rebecca Upjohn, illustrated by Renne Benoit, "Milek and his brother Munio live in a sleepy village in Poland. . . . They reluctantly do as their mother asks when she asks them to visit their neighbor Anton, knowing that the rest of the village laughs at him because of his strange habits of speaking to animals and only eating vegetables. Things change quickly when war comes to their town in the form of Nazi soldiers searching for Jewish families like that of Milek and Munio." (Publisher's note)

Urban, Linda

★ The **center** of everything; by Linda Urban. Houghton Mifflin Harcourt 2013 208 p. $15.99

Grades: 4 5 6 7   **Fic**
1. Wishes -- Fiction 2. Bereavement -- Fiction
ISBN 0547763484; 9780547763484

LC 2012954515

In this book, "months after her grandmother's death, 12-year-old Ruby Pepperdine composes a winning essay honoring her New Hampshire town's namesake" and will get to read it to the community. But she's more concerned that "she didn't listen to her grandmother's final words before she died. Ruby thinks that maybe if she wishes hard enough, 'everything will be back to how it is supposed to be,' but making a wish the right way is a tricky business." (Publishers Weekly)

★ A **crooked** kind of perfect. Harcourt 2007 213p $16; pa $5.95

Grades: 4 5 6   **Fic**
1. School stories 2. Musicians -- Fiction 3. Family life -- Fiction 4. Organ (Musical instrument) -- Fiction
ISBN 978-0-15-206007-7; 0-15-206007-3; 978-0-15-206608-6 pa; 0-15-206608-X pa

LC 2006-100622

Ten-year-old Zoe Elias, who longs to play the piano but must resign herself to learning the organ, instead, finds that her musicianship has a positive impact on her workaholic mother, her jittery father, and her school social life.

"An impressive and poignant debut novel. . . . The refreshing writing is full of pearls of wisdom, and readers will relate to this fully developed character. The sensitive story is filled with hope and humor." SLJ

★ **Hound** dog true. Harcourt 2011 152p $15.99

Grades: 3 4 5   **Fic**
1. School stories 2. Moving -- Fiction 3. Shyness -- Fiction 4. Janitors -- Fiction 5. Friendship -- Fiction 6. Family life -- Fiction
ISBN 978-0-547-55869-1; 0-547-55869-4

LC 2011009599

Mattie, a shy fifth-grader, wants to hide out at her new school by acting as apprentice to her Uncle Potluck, the custodian, but her plan falls apart when she summons the courage to speak about what matters most and finds a true friend.

"Combining Mattie's poignant writing and interior monologue, exquisite character development and a slow, deliberate pace, Urban spins a story that rings true." Kirkus

Ursu, Anne

★ **Breadcrumbs**; drawings by Erin McGuire. Walden Pond Press 2011 313p il $16.99

Grades: 4 5 6 7   **Fic**
1. Fairy tales 2. Magic -- Fiction 3. Friendship -- Fiction
ISBN 978-0-06-201505-1; 0-06-201505-2

LC 2010045666

"Fifth-grader Hazel embarks on a memorable journey into the Minnesota woods to find her best friend Jack, who vanishes after a shard of glass pierces his eye. . . . Hazel enters the woods to find 'an entirely different place,' populated by creatures from the pages of Hans Christian Andersen. . . . [This is a] multi-layered, artfully crafted, transforming testament to the power of friendship." Kirkus

The **Real** Boy. Harpercollins Childrens Books 2013 288 p. (hardcover) $16.99

Grades: 3 4 5 6 7   **Fic**
1. Occult fiction 2. Fantasy fiction
ISBN 0062015079; 9780062015075

LC 2013021861

In this book, "an isolated, insecure orphan living in magical Aletheia becomes a 'real boy' when his ordered world crumbles and he must rely on himself." Oscar works for the magician Caleb. "When urgent business takes Caleb away, his apprentice is murdered, and Oscar must run Caleb's shop. Lacking social skills, Oscar longs to fold 'up, like an envelope,' but he manages the shop with help from a kindhearted girl who befriends him." More things go wrong, and Oscar must help. (Kirkus Reviews)

Usher, Mark David

The **golden** ass of Lucius Apuleius; adapted from the Latin original by M.D. Usher; illustrations by T. Motley. David R. Godine 2011 85p il $17.95

Grades: 4 5 6 7   **Fic**
1. Magic -- Fiction 2. Social classes -- Fiction 3. Classical mythology -- Fiction
ISBN 978-1-56792-418-3; 1-56792-418-2

LC 2010032978

Lucius Apuleius, a young nobleman fascinated by magic, accidentally turns himself into an ass and then sets out on a journey that reveals to him the conditions of peasants and slaves in and around Thessaly and leads him to find redemption as a follower of Isis and Osiris.

"A faithful (if relatively clean) version of the world's oldest surviving complete novel. . . . Though all of the sex and most of the dissolute behavior has been excised, the lad's first transformation is milked throughout for double entendres . . . and there are plenty of silly incidents and names . . . to lighten the overall tone. Motley's elaborate illustrated initials and pen-and-ink drawings add satiric bite. . . . An entertaining romp." Kirkus

Vail, Rachel

★ **Justin** Case; school, drool, and other daily disasters. illustrated by Matthew Cordell. Feiwel and Friends 2010 245p il $16.99

Grades: 3 4 5   **Fic**

1. School stories 2. Family life -- Fiction

ISBN 978-0-312-53290-1; 0-312-53290-3

"Honest and full of heart, Justin Case is a story for an oft-ignored segment of kids: the sensitive, introverted, and observant." SLJ

Valente, Catherynne M.

The **boy** who lost Fairyland; Catherynne M. Valente; illustrated by Ana Juan. Feiwel & Friends 2015 240 p. (Fairyland) (hardback) $16.99

Grades: 5 6 7 8   **Fic**

1. Fantasy fiction 2. Trolls -- Fiction 3. Fantasy 4. Changelings -- Fiction

ISBN 1250023491; 9781250023490; 9781250073327
                                                          LC 2014042417

In this novel, by Catherynne M. Valente, illustrated by Ana Juan, "when a young troll named Hawthorn is stolen from Fairyland by the Golden Wind, he becomes a changeling--a human boy--in the strange city of Chicago. . . . Left with a human family, Hawthorn struggles with his troll nature and his changeling fate. But when he turns twelve, he stumbles upon a way back home, to a Fairyland much changed from the one he remembers." (Publisher's note)

"In this fourth book in the fantastical series, a young troll named Hawthorn is stolen away by the Golden Wind and brought to live in Chicago as a changeling. When he turns 12, he finds a way back to Fairyland, a place now much changed from the magical realm he left...While readers unfamiliar with the series can certainly jump in with this novel, most will want to start at the beginning. A phenomenal fantasy series worthy of a spot in every library collection." SLJ

Other titles in the series include:

The Girl who Soared Over Fairyland and Cut the Moon in Two (2013)

The Girl who Circumnavigated Fairyland in a Ship of her Own Making (2011)

The Girl who Fell Beneath Fairyland and Led the Revels There (2012)

★ The **girl** who circumnavigated Fairyland in a ship of her own making; [by] Catherynne M. Valente; with illustrations by Ana Juan. Feiwel and Friends 2011 247p il $16.99

Grades: 4 5 6 7 8   **Fic**

1. Fantasy fiction

ISBN 978-0-312-64961-6; 0-312-64961-4
                                                          LC 2010050895

"The book's appeal is crystal clear from the outset: this is a kind of The Wonderful Wizard of Oz by way of Alice's Adventures in Wonderland, made vivid by Juan's Tenniel-inflected illustrations. . . . Those who thrill to lovingly wrought tales of fantasy and adventure . . . will be enchanted." Publ Wkly

The **girl** who fell beneath Fairyland and led the revels there; by Catherynne M. Valente; with illustrations by Ana Juan. Feiwel and Friends 2012 258 p. $16.99

Grades: 4 5 6 7 8   **Fic**

1. Fantasy fiction 2. Magic -- Fiction 3. Fairies -- Fiction

ISBN 0312649622; 9780312649623

In this book by Catherynne M. Valente, illustrated by Ana Juan, "September has longed to return to Fairyland after her first adventure there. And when she finally does, she learns that its inhabitants have been losing their shadows--and their magic--to the world of Fairyland Below. This underworld has a new ruler: Halloween, the Hollow Queen, who is September's shadow. And Halloween does not want to give Fairyland's shadows back." (Publisher's note)

The **Girl** Who Soared over Fairyland and Cut the Moon in Two; by Catherynne M. Valente; illustrated by Ana Juan. Feiwel & Friends 2013 256 p. $16.99

Grades: 4 5 6 7 8   **Fic**

1. Moon -- Fiction 2. Fairies -- Fiction 3. Female friendship -- Fiction

ISBN 1250023505; 9781250023506

In this book, by Catherynne M. Valente, September is "tasked with delivering a package to the moon, which has begun to shudder and shake with moonquakes because a . . . yeti is trying to break it to pieces. September and her friends traverse the moon, meet their fates, encounter older and younger versions of themselves, and wonder what, exactly, makes them who they are--all while trying to find the speedy yeti and stop him from his destructive plans." (Booklist)

"In this third volume, following The Girl Who Fell Beneath Fairyland and Led the Revels There, September returns to Fairyland and finds herself on a mission to stop a vengeful yeti from destroying his Fairy abusers--and everyone else on the moon. September is now wiser and sadder, and longs for autonomy; likewise, Fairyland and its inhabitants have become darker and more adult." (Horn Book)

Van Cleve, Kathleen

★ **Drizzle**. Dial Books for Young Readers 2010 358p il $16.99

Grades: 4 5 6   **Fic**

1. Rain -- Fiction 2. Farms -- Fiction 3. Magic -- Fiction 4. Droughts -- Fiction

ISBN 978-0-8037-3362-6; 0-8037-3362-3
                                                          LC 2009-23819

When a drought threatens her family's magical rhubarb farm, eleven-year-old Polly tries to find a way to make it rain again

"Van Cleve's debut is emotionally subtle and action packed with a highly memorable setting." Publ Wkly

Van Draanen, Wendelin, 1965-

Flipped. Knopf 2001 212p $14.95

Grades: 6 7 8 9   **Fic**

1. Family life 2. Conduct of life 3. Self-perception 4. Interpersonal relations

ISBN 9780375811746; 0-375-81174-5; 0-375-82544-4 pa
                                                          LC 2001-29238

In alternating chapters, two teenagers describe how their feelings about themselves, each other, and their families have changed over the years. "Grades six to nine." (Bull Cent Child Books)

"There's lots of laugh-out-loud egg puns and humor in this novel. There's also, however, a substantial amount of serious social commentary woven in, as well as an exploration of the importance of perspective in relationships." SLJ

★ **Sammy** Keyes and the hotel thief. Knopf 1998 163p il hardcover o.p. pa $6.50

Grades: 4 5 6 7   **Fic**
 1. Mystery fiction
 ISBN 978-0-679-88839-0; 0-679-89264-8 pa
            LC 97-40776

Thirteen-year-old Sammy's penchant for speaking her mind gets her in trouble when she involves herself in the investigation of a robbery at the "seedy" hotel across the street from the seniors' building where she is living with her grandmother

"This is a breezy novel with vivid characters." Bull Cent Child Books

Other titles about Sammy Keyes are:
Sammy Keyes and the art of deception (2003)
Sammy Keyes and the cold hard cash (2008)
Sammy Keyes and the curse of Moustache Mary (2000)
Sammy Keyes and the dead giveaway (2005)
Sammy Keyes and the Hollywood mummy (2001)
Sammy Keyes and the night of skulls (2011)
Sammy Keyes and the psycho Kitty Queen (2004)
Sammy Keyes and the runaway elf (1999)
Sammy Keyes and the search for snake eyes (2002)
Sammy Keyes and the Sisters of Mercy (1999)
Sammy Keyes and the skeleton man (1998)
Sammy Keyes and the wedding crasher (2010)
Sammy Keyes and the wild things (2007)

Sammy Keyes and the killer cruise; by Wendelin Van Draanen. Alfred A. Knopf 2013 336 p. (trade) $16.99; (lib. bdg.) $19.99

Grades: 4 5 6 7   **Fic**
 1. Missing persons -- Fiction 2. Mystery fiction -- Fiction 3. Father-daughter relationship -- Fiction 4. Wealth -- Fiction 5. Friendship -- Fiction 6. Cruise ships -- Fiction 7. Family problems -- Fiction 8. Mystery and detective stories 9. Fathers and daughters -- Fiction
 ISBN 0375870547; 0375970541; 9780307930620; 9780375870545; 9780375970542
          LC 2012045296

In this book by Wendelin Van Draanen "Sammy knew that getting to know her new rockstar dad on a cruise would be a little uncomfortable. . . . But when the heiress to a perfume empire disappears from the ship, it turns out everyone's in for a rocky ride. In this penultimate book in the Sammy Keyes mystery series, Wendelin Van Draanen pays homage to the mystery genre." (Publisher's note)

Sammy Keyes and the night of skulls. Alfred A. Knopf 2011 304p $15.99; lib bdg $18.99

Grades: 4 5 6 7   **Fic**
 1. School stories 2. Mystery fiction 3. Skeleton -- Fiction 4. Halloween -- Fiction 5. Missing persons -- Fiction
 ISBN 978-0-375-86108-6; 0-375-86108-4; 978-0-375-96108-3 lib bdg; 0-375-96108-9 lib bdg
          LC 2011027485

Junior high detective Sammy Keyes and her friends take a detour through a graveyard on Halloween night and find themselves in the middle of a mystery involving missing people, human skulls, and a ghoulish embalmer, while school presents its own set of tricks and treats.

"Van Draanen has created a sometimes scary and sometimes funny story that realistically depicts young teen personalities, peer pressure, crushes, and some serious concepts." Voice Youth Advocates

Sammy Keyes and the showdown in Sin City; Wendelin Van Draanen. Alfred A. Knopf 2013 288 p. (trade) $16.99

Grades: 4 5 6 7   **Fic**
 1. Las Vegas (Nev.) -- Fiction 2. Mystery fiction -- Juvenile fiction 3. Mother-daughter relationship -- Fiction 4. Fathers -- Fiction 5. Identity -- Fiction 6. Mystery and detective stories 7. Mothers and daughters -- Fiction
 ISBN 0375870539; 9780307930613; 9780307974082; 9780375870538; 9780375970535
          LC 2012013474

This book, by Wendelin Van Draanen, is part of the "Sammy Keyes" series. In it "Sammy tackles the persistent mysteries of her own life. Mysteries like: Who is her father? . . . How long can she manage to hide out in Grams' seniors-only building before someone catches on? Is her mother really planning to marry her boyfriend's father? . . . During one crazy weekend in Las Vegas, with the help of an entire army of Elvis impersonators, Sammy finally gets some answers." (Publisher's note)

Van Eekhout, Greg
 The **boy** at the end of the world. Bloomsbury Children's Books 2011 212p $16.99

Grades: 4 5 6 7   **Fic**
 1. Science fiction 2. Robots -- Fiction
 ISBN 978-1-59990-524-2; 1-59990-524-8
          LC 2010035741

Born half-grown in a world that is being destroyed, Fisher has instinctive knowledge of many things, including that he must avoid the robot that knows his name.

"A pleaser for readers who prefer their sf livened up with unpredictable elements and emotional complexity." Booklist

Van Leeuwen, Jean
 ★ **Bound** for Oregon; pictures by James Watling. Dial Bks. for Young Readers 1994 167p il map hardcover o.p. pa $5.99

Grades: 4 5 6   **Fic**
 1. Oregon Trail -- Fiction 2. Overland journeys to the Pacific -- Fiction
 ISBN 0-14-038319-0 pa
          LC 93-26709

A fictionalized account of the journey made by nine-year-old Mary Ellen Todd and her family from their home in Arkansas westward over the Oregon Trail in 1852

"The appealing narrator, the forthright telling, and the concrete details of life along the Oregon Trail will draw readers into the story." Booklist

Cabin on Trouble Creek. Dial Books for Young Readers 2004 119p $16.99; pa $6.99

Grades: 4 5 6 7   **Fic**

1. Ohio -- Fiction 2. Brothers -- Fiction 3. Frontier and pioneer life -- Fiction

ISBN 0-8037-2548-5; 0-14-241164-7 pa

LC 2003-14151

In 1803 in Ohio, two young brothers are left to finish the log cabin and guard the land while their father goes back to Pennsylvania to fetch their mother and younger siblings.

"Excellent pacing is what makes this novel work so well. . . . The suspense builds consistently. The boys' struggle is portrayed realistically, without sugarcoating nature's harshness." SLJ

Van Leeuwen, Joke

Eep! Joke van Leeuwen; translated by Bill Nagelkerke. Gecko Press 2012 149 p. ill.

Grades: 3 4 5   **Fic**

1. Fantasy fiction 2. Birds -- Fiction 3. Girls -- Fiction 4. Friendship -- Juvenile fiction

ISBN 1877579076; 9781877579073

In this children's book by Dutch children's author Joke van Leeuwen, "avid bird watcher Warren finds a strange creature under a bush. 'This was a bird in the shape of a little girl. Or a little girl in the shape of a bird.' . . . He takes the bird-girl home to his reclusive wife, Tina. . . . When Beedy flies away one day without a good-bye, Warren and Tina . . . begin to search for their bird-girl. On their quest, they meet a host of equally downtrodden individuals." (Kirkus Reviews)

"This original and creative work is compelling from the opening drawing right to the end of the book." SLJ

Van Vleet, Carmella

Eliza Bing is (not) a big, fat quitter; by Carmella Van Vleet; illustrated by Karen Donnelly. Holiday House 2014 165 p. (hardcover) $16.95

Grades: 3 4 5 6 7   **Fic**

1. Family life -- Fiction 2. Tae kwon do -- Fiction 3. Attention deficit disorder -- Fiction 4. Martial arts -- Fiction 5. Determination (Personality trait) -- Fiction 6. Attention-deficit hyperactivity disorder -- Fiction

ISBN 082342944X; 9780823429448

LC 2013015279

This novel, written by Carmella Van Vleet and illustrated by Karen Donnelly, is "about determination and the rewards of hard work[.] A preteen girl struggling with ADHD must stick with a summer taekwondo class to prove that she s dedicated enough to pursue her true passion: cake decorating." (Publisher's note)

"Eliza Bing, 11, is not a big, fat quitter, or is she? Her track record isn't great. She has a history of not following through with activities—Junior Scouts, gymnastics, tap, piano . So, when she wants to sign up for a cake-decorating class with her bakery loving friend, her parents flat-out say no. Eliza strikes a nearly impossible deal with her parents: if she can finish a tae kwon do class over the summer, she can take cake decorating in the fall...Fast moving and humorous with chapter titles such as "Sticky Note to Self: Wear White Underwear on Wednesdays and Saturdays," feisty Eliza will

have readers, especially those with ADHD, rooting for her." SLJ

Vande Velde, Vivian

8 class pets + one squirrel one dog; illustrated by Steve Björkman. Holiday House 2011 68p il $15.95

Grades: 2 3 4   **Fic**

1. School stories 2. Animals -- Fiction

ISBN 978-0-8234-2364-4; 0-8234-2364-6

LC 2010048153

A dog chases a squirrel into an elementary school one night, creating monumental chaos.

This is a "fast-paced romp. . . . The action is predictably frenetic, but the changes in voice from chapter to chapter provide a refreshing and humorous diversion from most chapter-book fare. . . . Occasional pen-and-ink spot illustrations add energy to an already high-octane story." Kirkus

Frogged; Vivian Vande Velde. Houghton Mifflin Harcourt 2013 208 p. $16.99

Grades: 5 6 7 8   **Fic**

1. Fantasy fiction 2. Fractured fairy tales 3. Fairy tales 4. Frogs -- Fiction 5. Humorous stories 6. Princesses -- Fiction 7. Self-perception -- Fiction

ISBN 054794215X; 9780547942155

LC 2013003905

In this alternate version of "The Frog Prince," "Princess Imogene, who is 12 and 'gawky,' is tired of falling short in her family's eyes. The real trouble begins when a . . . . frog, who tells Imogene he's a prince beset by a witch's spell, tricks her into kissing him. He returns to his human form, but she is transformed into a frog as a result; worse, he was just the lowly son of a wagon maker. Too kind to use that sort of deceit on someone else, Imogene searches for another solution." (Publishers Weekly)

Three good deeds. Harcourt 2005 147p $16; pa $5.95

Grades: 3 4 5   **Fic**

1. Geese -- Fiction 2. Witches -- Fiction

ISBN 0-15-205382-4; 0-15-205455-3 pa

LC 2004-29578

Caught stealing some goose eggs from a witch, Howard is cursed for his heartlessness and turned into a goose himself, and he can only become human again by performing three good deeds.

"With well-spaced print, plenty of dialogue, a strong dose of humor, and more invention than many books written at this level, this goose tale is a nicely accomplished, entertaining read." Booklist

Wizard at work; a novel in stories. Harcourt 2003 134p $16; pa $5.95

Grades: 3 4 5 6   **Fic**

1. Magic -- Fiction 2. Princesses -- Fiction

ISBN 0-15-204559-7; 0-15-205309-3 pa

LC 2002-68665

A young wizard, who runs a school to teach wizards, looks forward to a quiet summer off but is drawn into adventures with princesses, unicorns, and ghosts instead

"A lot of fairy-tale conventions are turned on their heads. . . . The language sparkles with sunny good humor. . . . Lighthearted and sly." Booklist

Vanderpool, Clare

★ **Moon** over Manifest. Delacorte Press 2010 351p $16.99; lib bdg $19.99

Grades: 5 6 7 8 **Fic**

1. Kansas -- Fiction 2. Fathers -- Fiction 3. Great Depression, 1929-1939 -- Fiction

ISBN 978-0-385-73883-5; 0-385-73883-8; 978-0-385-90750-7 lib bdg; 0-385-90750-8 lib bdg

LC 2009-40042

Awarded the Newbery Medal, 2011

Twelve-year-old Abilene Tucker is the daughter of a drifter who, in the summer of 1936, sends her to stay with an old friend in Manifest, Kansas, where he grew up, and where she hopes to find out some things about his past.

"The absolute necessity of story as a way to redemption and healing past wounds is at the heart of this beautiful debut, and readers will cherish every word up to the heartbreaking yet hopeful and deeply gratifying ending." Kirkus

★ **Navigating** Early; Clare Vanderpool. Delacorte Press 2013 320 p. $16.99

Grades: 5 6 7 8 **Fic**

1. Adventure fiction 2. Appalachian Trail 3. Eccentrics and eccentricities 4. Maine -- Fiction 5. Schools -- Fiction 6. Boarding schools -- Fiction

ISBN 0385742096; 9780307974129; 9780375990403; 9780385742092

LC 2012014973

Printz Honor Book (2014)

In this children's novel, by Clare Vanderpool, "Jack Baker, . . . after his mother's death, . . . [is] placed in a boy's boarding school in Maine. There, Jack encounters Early Auden. . . . Newcomer Jack feels lost yet can't help being drawn to Early. . . . When the boys find themselves unexpectedly alone at school, they embark on a quest on the Appalachian Trail in search of the great black bear. But what they are searching for is sometimes different from what they find." (Publisher's note)

Vaupel, Robin

The **rules** of the universe by Austin W. Hale. Holiday House 2007 265p $16.95

Grades: 4 5 6 7 **Fic**

1. Science fiction 2. Death -- Fiction 3. Grandfathers -- Fiction

ISBN 978-0-8234-1811-4; 0-8234-1811-1

LC 2003-56751

Thirteen-year-old Austin Hale, an aspiring scientist and disciple of his grandfather, a Nobel Prize-winning molecular physicist, finds himself in control of a powerful energy force that can turn back time and turn his orbit upside down

"The captivating blend of scientific research and magic is effectively balanced against the stark realism of a boy facing his first significant losses; the overall tone is one of cautious optimism." Bull Cent Child Books

Vawter, Vince

★ **Paperboy**; Vince Vawter. 1st ed. Delacorte Press 2013 240 p. (library) $19.99; (hardcover) $16.99

Grades: 5 6 7 8 **Fic**

1. Stuttering -- Fiction 2. Race relations -- Fiction 3. Newspaper carriers -- Fiction 4. Self-esteem -- Fiction 5. Interpersonal relations -- Fiction 6. Family life -- Tennessee -- Fiction 7. Memphis (Tenn.) -- History --

20th century -- Fiction

ISBN 0385742444; 9780307975058; 9780375990588; 9780385742443

LC 2012030546

Newberry Honor Book (2014)

In this book by Vince Vawter, "[a]fter an overthrown baseball busts his best friend's lip, 11-year-old Victor Vollmer takes over the boy's paper route. This is a particularly daunting task for the able-armed Victor, as he has a prominent stutter that embarrasses him. . . .Through the paper route he meets a number of people, gains a much-needed sense of self and community, and has a life-threatening showdown with a local cart man." (School Library Journal)

"Carefully crafted language, authenticity of setting and quirky characters that ring fully true all combine to make this a worthwhile read. Although Little Man's stutter holds up dialogue, that annoyance also powerfully reflects its stultifying impact on his life. An engaging and heartfelt presentation that never whitewashes the difficult time and situation as Little Man comes of age." Kirkus

Venable, Colleen A. F.

Raining cats and detectives; Colleen A.F. Venable; illustrated by Stephanie Yue. Graphic Universe 2012 46 p. col. ill. (lib. bdg.: alk. paper) $27.93

Grades: 2 3 4 **Fic**

1. Cats -- Fiction 2. Detectives -- Fiction 3. Missing persons -- Fiction 4. Graphic novels 5. Humorous stories 6. Animals -- Fiction 7. Hamsters -- Fiction 8. Pet shops -- Fiction 9. Guinea pigs -- Fiction 10. Mystery and detective stories

ISBN 0761360085; 9780761360087

LC 2011021626

In author Colleen AF Venable's book, "[g]uinea pig Sasspants, her faithful, exuberantly enthusiastic sidekick, Hamisher the hamster, and all the denizens of Mr. Venezi's Pets & Stuff are still in the store . . . Then (human) Detective Pickles arrives and adopts Sasspants, so when Tummytickles, the bookstore cat next door, vanishes, there's no one to find him. Suddenly, everyone from the goldfish . . . . to the snooty chinchillas are donning detective hats and well, calling themselves detectives. Will Sasspants return to save the day, or can Hamisher detect on his own?" (Kirkus)

Venkatraman, Padma

★ **Island's** end. G.P. Putnam's Sons 2011 240p $16.99

Grades: 5 6 7 8 9 **Fic**

1. India -- Fiction 2. Islands -- Fiction 3. Apprentices -- Fiction

ISBN 978-0-399-25099-6; 0-399-25099-9

LC 2010036298

"Uido's clear, intelligent, present-tense voice consistently engrosses as she pushes through doubt and loss to find the right path. The beach, jungle and cliff settings are palpable. . . . There is very little information known about Andaman Islanders, making it hard to gauge the authenticity of this portrayal; the author's note indicates a respectful and diligent approach to her subject. . . . Refreshingly hopeful and beautifully written." Kirkus

Venuti, Kristin Clark

Leaving the Bellweathers. Egmont USA 2009 242p $15.99; lib bdg $18.99

Grades: 4 5 6 **Fic**

1. Authorship -- Fiction 2. Family life -- Fiction 3. Lighthouses -- Fiction 4. Household employees -- Fiction 5. Eccentrics and eccentricities -- Fiction
ISBN 978-1-60684-006-1; 1-60684-006-1; 978-1-60684-050-4 lib bdg; 1-60684-050-9 lib bdg
LC 2009016244

In Eel-Smack-by-the-Bay, put-upon butler Tristan Benway writes a memoir of his years spent working for the chaotic and eccentric Bellweather family in their lighthouse, as he prepares for his long-awaited departure from indentured servitude

"Venuti's entertaining and humorous debut features an eccentric cast, absurdities, and droll details. . . . Readers will find much amusement in the quirky characters and scenarios touched with heart." Booklist

Another title about the Bellweathers is:

The butler gets a break (2010)

Verne, Jules

★ **20,000** leagues under the sea; illustrated by the Dillons; translated by Anthony Bonner. Books of Wonder 2000 394p il $21.95
Grades: 5 6 7 8 9 10 11 12 Adult **Fic**

1. Science fiction 2. Submarines -- Fiction
ISBN 0-688-10535-1
LC 00-24336

Original French edition, 1870

Retells the adventures of a French professor and his two companions as they sail above and below the world's oceans as prisoners on the fabulous electric submarine of the deranged Captain Nemo

Vernick, Audrey

★ **Water** balloon. Clarion Books 2011 312p $16.99
Grades: 4 5 6 7 **Fic**

1. Dogs -- Fiction 2. Divorce -- Fiction 3. Friendship -- Fiction 4. Babysitters -- Fiction 5. Father-daughter relationship -- Fiction
ISBN 978-0-547-59554-2; 0-547-59554-9
LC 2011009847

With her best friends pulling away from her, her newly-separated parents deciding she should spend the summer at her father's new home, and a babysitting job she does not want, Marley's life is already as precarious as an overfull water balloon when a cute boy enters the picture.

"The book moves along at a pace that will keep tweens interested, and the dialogue among the characters feels real. Marley's relationships with her friends and family are complex, and even the most reluctant readers will relate to her and the choices that she makes." SLJ

Vernick, Shirley Reva

The **blood** lie; a novel. Cinco Puntos Press 2011 141p $15.95
Grades: 5 6 7 8 **Fic**

1. Love -- Fiction 2. Prejudices -- Fiction 3. Antisemitism -- Fiction 4. New York (State) -- Fiction 5. Jews -- United States -- Fiction
ISBN 978-1-933693-84-2; 1-933693-84-3
LC 2011011429

"Based on an actual incident in Massena in 1928, the slim novel effectively mines layers of ignorance, fear, intolerance and manipulation, and it connects the incident to Henry Ford's anti-Semitic writing and to the lynching of Jewish businessman Leo Frank in 1915." Kirkus

"September 22, 1928, Massena, New York. Jack Pool's sixteenth birthday. He's been restless lately, especially during this season of more-times-at-the-synagogue than you can shake a stick at...But temple's good for some things. It gives him lots of time to daydream about a beautiful but inaccessible Gentile girl named Emaline...music is definitely his ticket out of this remote whistle-stop town•he doesn't want to be stuck here one more minute. But he doesn't realize exactly how stuck he is until Emaline's little sister Daisy goes missing and he and his family are accused of killing her for a blood sacrifice." (Publisher's note)

Vernon, Ursula

Castle Hangnail; by Ursula Vernon. Dial Books for Young Readers, an imprint of Penguin Group (USA) Inc. 2015 384 p. (hardback) $16.99
Grades: 5 6 7 8 9 **Fic**

1. Humorous fiction 2. Magic -- Fiction 3. Witches -- Fiction 4. Haunted houses -- Fiction 5. Humorous stories
ISBN 0803741294; 9780803741294
LC 2014017106

In this book, by Ursula Vernon, "Molly shows up on Castle Hangnail's doorstep to fill the vacancy for a wicked witch [and] the castle's minions are understandably dubious. After all, she is twelve years old, barely five feet tall, and quite polite. . . . But the castle desperately needs a master or else the Board of Magic will decommission it, leaving all the minions without the home they love." (Publisher's note)

"Molly, a 12-year-old witch, arrives as the new master of Castle Hangnail, despite some misgivings on the part of Majordomo, the Igor-like guardian responsible for the management of its legacy and various minion occupants.. An appealing fantasy for upper middle grade readers." SLJ

★ **Dragonbreath**: attack of the ninja frogs. Dial Books for Young Readers 2010 203p il $16
Grades: 3 4 5 **Fic**

1. Japan -- Fiction 2. Ninja -- Fiction 3. Dragons -- Fiction 4. Reptiles -- Fiction 5. Amphibians -- Fiction 6. Friendship -- Fiction
ISBN 978-0-8037-3365-7; 0-8037-3365-8
LC 2009012273

When Suki the salamander—the new foreign exchange student—is being stalked by ninja frogs, Danny, Wendell the iguana, and Suki travel to Great-grandfather Dragonbreath's home in mythical Japan to find a solution for the problem.

"The spirited illustrations, done in green and black with touches of red, capture the humor of the characters' adventures. This delightful easy chapter book could tempt reluctant readers into turning another page." SLJ

Other titles in this series are:
Dragonbreath (2009)
Dragonbreath: curse of the were-wiener (2010)
Dragonbreath: lair of the bat monster (2011)
Dragonbreath: no such thing as ghosts (2011)

Vigilante, Danette

Trouble with half a moon. G. P. Putnam's Sons 2011 181p $16.99
Grades: 5 6 7 8 **Fic**

1. Faith -- Fiction 2. Friendship -- Fiction 3.

Bereavement -- Fiction 4. Child abuse -- Fiction 5. Puerto Ricans -- Fiction 6. City and town life -- Fiction 7. Jamaican Americans -- Fiction

ISBN 978-0-399-25159-7; 0-399-25159-6

LC 2010-07377

Overwhelmed by grief and guilt over her brother's death and its impact on her mother, and at odds with her best friend, thirteen-year-old Dellie reaches out to a neglected boy in her building in the projects and learns from a new neighbor to have faith in herself and others.

"The story is told with considerable appeal and accessibility, and kids won't have to lead the same life as Dellie to recognize her travails." Bull Cent Child Books

Vining, Elizabeth Gray

Adam of the road; illustrated by Robert Lawson. Viking 1942 317p il $19.99; pa $6.99

Grades: 5 6 7 8   Fic

1. Minstrels -- Fiction 2. Middle Ages -- Fiction 3. Great Britain -- Fiction

ISBN 0-670-10435-3; 0-14-240659-7 pa

Awarded the Newbery Medal, 1943

Tale of a minstrel and his son Adam, who wandered through southeastern England in the thirteenth century. Adam's adventures in search of his lost dog and his beloved father led him from St. Alban's Abbey to London, and thence to Winchester, back to London, and then to Oxford where the three were at last reunited

Viorst, Judith, 1931-

Lulu's mysterious mission; Judith Viorst; illustrated by Kevin Cornell; jacket by Lane Smith. Atheneum Books for Young Readers 2014 192 p. (hardcover) $15.99

Grades: 2 3 4 5   Fic

1. Spies -- Fiction 2. Secrets -- Fiction 3. Babysitters -- Fiction 4. Behavior -- Fiction

ISBN 1442497467; 9781442497467; 9781442497474

LC 2013004350

In this book, by Judith Viorst, "Lulu has put her tantrum-throwing days behind her. That is, until her parents announce that they are going on vacation—WITHOUT LULU. Not only that, but they are leaving her with the formidable Ms. Sonia Sofia Solinsky. . . . The second her parents are out of the house, Lulu tries out several elaborate schemes to bring them straight back. But just when she seems to finally be making some headway, her babysitter reveals an astonishing secret." (Publisher's note)

"Spoiled little Lulu is back in a third book to tackle a new challenge: a babysitter. Despite Lulu's objection that 'babysitters sit babies, and I'm no baby,' her parents head off on vacation, leaving her in the care of the intimidating Ms. Solinsky...Lulu now looks a little more like a regular girl, with a rounder nose and sneakers, but in the wide variety of diabolical facial expressions she wears, readers will recognize the same troublemaker they have come to know and love. Lulu's fans will be happy to read her next (mis) adventure." SLJ

Other titles include:

Lulu and the Brontosaurus

Lulu Walks the Dogs

Voake, Steve

Daisy Dawson is on her way! illustrated by Jessica Meserve. Candlewick Press 2008 98p il $14.99; pa $5.99

Grades: 2 3 4   Fic

1. Dogs -- Fiction 2. Animals -- Fiction

ISBN 978-0-7636-3740-8; 0-7636-3740-8; 978-0-7636-4294-5 pa; 0-7636-4294-0 pa

LC 2007-23150

One day when Daisy is late for school, an encounter with a butterfly leaves her suddenly able to communicate with animals, and when Boom, a stray dog, is caught by the pound, she enlists the help of a host of other animals to rescue him.

"Sprightly illustrations in a variety of shapes appear throughout. First in a series, this charmer, long on whimsy and adventure, is sure to appeal to newly independent and reluctant readers." SLJ

Other titles about Daisy Dawson are:

Daisy Dawson and the secret pond (2009)

Daisy Dawson and the big freeze (2010)

Daisy Dawson at the beach (2011)

Daisy Dawson on the farm (2012)

Voelkel, Jon

The end of the world club; [by] J&P Voelkel. Egmont USA 2011 384p (The Jaguar stones) $16.99

Grades: 4 5 6 7   Fic

1. Adventure fiction 2. Mayas -- Fiction 3. Supernatural -- Fiction 4. Central America -- Fiction

ISBN 978-1-60684-072-6; 1-60684-072-X

LC 2010036641

Sequel to: Middleworld (2007)

With the end of the Mayan calendar fast approaching, fourteen-year-old Max Murphy and his friend Lola, the Maya girl who saved his life in the perilous jungle, race against time to outwit the twelve villainous Lords of Death, following the trail of the conquistadors into a forgotten land steeped in legend and superstition.

"The authors use Maya mythology and terms and add interesting facts about Spain and Spanish culture. This is a fast-paced book, and the action starts right away." SLJ

Middleworld; [by] J & P Voelkel [i.e., Jon Voelkel, Pamela Craik Voelkel] Smith and Kraus Publishers 2007 397p il (The Jaguar stones) $17.95; pa $8.99

Grades: 4 5 6 7   Fic

1. Adventure fiction 2. Mayas -- Fiction 3. Central America -- Fiction

ISBN 978-1-57525-561-3; 1-57525-561-8; 978-1-60684-071-9 pa; 1-60684-071-1 pa

"Suspense and intrigue, human sacrifice, smuggling, and secret doors and escape routes through pyramids ensure that the novel, the first in a projected trilogy, is likely to win legions of fans." SLJ

Followed by: The end of the world club (2010)

The river of no return; J&P Voelkel. Egmont USA 2012 348 p. ill., maps (hardcover) $16.99; (ebook) $16.99

Grades: 5 6 7 8   Fic

1. Mayas -- Fiction 2. Fantasy fiction -- Juvenile fiction 3. Supernatural -- Fiction 4. Adventure and adventurers -- Fiction 5. Indians of Central America -- Fiction

ISBN 1606840738; 9781606840733; 9781606842706

LC 2012007093

This is the third book in the Jaguar Stones series from J. and P. Voelkel. Here, "after spending the previous two books evading the disgusting and power-hungry machinations of the Death Lords of the Mayan Underworld, Max and Lola are back together again, trying to stop the same bad guys from taking over the world yet again." (School Library Journal)

Voigt, Cynthia
Dicey's song. Atheneum Pubs. 1982 196p $17.95; pa $6.99
Grades: 5 6 7 8 **Fic**
1. Siblings -- Fiction 2. Grandmothers -- Fiction
ISBN 0-689-30944-9; 0-689-86362-4 pa
LC 82-3882
Sequel to Homecoming
Awarded the Newbery Medal, 1983
"The vividness of Dicey is striking; Voigt has plumbed and probed her character inside out to fashion a memorable protagonist." Booklist
Dicey "had brought her siblings to the grandmother they'd never seen when their mother (now in a mental institution) had been unable to cope. This is the story of the children's adjustment to Gram (and hers to them) and to a new school and a new life—but with some of the old problems." Bull Cent Child Books

Mister Max; the book of lost things. by Cynthia Voigt; illustrated by Iacopo Bruno. Alfred A. Knopf 2013 384 p. (hardcover) $16.99; (library) $19.99
Grades: 5 6 7 8 **Fic**
1. Abandoned children -- Fiction 2. Historical fiction 3. Self-reliance -- Fiction 4. Problem solving -- Fiction
ISBN 0307976815; 9780307976819; 9780307976826; 9780375971235
LC 2012033823
In this book, Max "is left at the dock when he misses a boat to India, where his [actor] parents supposedly have been invited by a maharajah to start a theater. . . . Although his wise yet bossy librarian grandmother lives next door, 12-year-old Max wants to earn his keep and be independent. Cleverly donning the costumes and different roles performed by his missing parents, Max discovers an aptitude for finding lost things. . . . He is a 'solutioneer,' solving people's problems." (Kirkus Reviews)

★ **Young** Fredle. Alfred A. Knopf 2011 227p il $16.99; lib bdg $19.99
Grades: 3 4 5 6 **Fic**
1. Adventure fiction 2. Cats -- Fiction 3. Dogs -- Fiction 4. Mice -- Fiction 5. Freedom -- Fiction
ISBN 978-0-375-86457-5; 0-375-86457-1; 978-0-375-96457-2 lib bdg; 0-375-96457-6 lib bdg
LC 2010-11430
"Readers will identify with the universal conflict at the heart of Fredle's journey—even as he longs for home, he enjoys the newfound freedom and experiences that contrast with the restrictive regulations of his clan. Yates's expressive cartoon spot art counters the book's darker, sadder moments with cheeriness." Publ Wkly

Vrabel, Beth
Pack of dorks; Beth Vrabel. Skyhorse Publishing, Inc. 2014 240 p. (hardback) $15.95
Grades: 4 5 6 **Fic**
1. School stories 2. Bullies -- Fiction 3. Friendship -- Fiction 4. Interpersonal relations -- Fiction 5. Popularity 6. Schools -- Fiction 7. Bullying -- Fiction

8. Cliques (Sociology)
ISBN 1629146234; 9781629146232
LC 2014021035
In this book, by Beth Vrabel, "Lucy knows that kissing Tom Lemmings behind the ball shed will make her a legend. But she doesn't count on [it] propelling her from coolest to lamest fourth grader overnight. Suddenly Lucy finds herself trapped in Dorkdom, where a diamond ring turns your finger green, where the boy you kiss hates you three days later, where your best friend laughs as you cry, where parents seem to stop liking you, and where baby sisters are born different." (Publisher's note)
"Debut author Vrabel takes three knotty, seemingly disparate problems—bullying, the plight of wolves and coping with disability—and with tact and grace knits them into an engrossing whole of despair and redemption. Popular fourth-grader Lucy and her best friend, Becky, kiss Tom and Henry behind the shed during recess as their class looks on, Lucy's brief, reluctant peck paling against Becky's smoldering "suction cup" smooch. When Lucy gets home, her mother's in labor; Molly is born later that day with Down syndrome. . . . Simultaneously, Lucy and her parents slowly, believably come to grips with Molly's uncertain future. Useful tips for dealing with bullying are neatly incorporated into the tale but with a refreshing lack of didacticism. Lucy's perfectly feisty narration, the emotionally resonant situations and the importance of the topic all elevate this effort well above the pack." Kirkus

Wagner, Hilary
Lords of Trillium; by Hilary Wagner; illustrated by Omar Rayyan. Holiday House 2014 224 p. (Nightshade chronicles) (hardcover) $17.95
Grades: 5 6 7 8 **Fic**
1. Fantasy fiction 2. Rats -- Fiction 3. Animal experimentation -- Fiction 4. Fantasy
ISBN 0823424138; 9780823424139
LC 2013031299
In this book, by Hilary Wagner, "when the albino rat Billycan left Trillium at the end of The White Assassin, he fled to the island of Tosca. There, here learns that a former ally, working undercover in Nightshade City, is plotting to free Killdeer's imprisoned evil generals and seize power. . . . But something even more sinister is afoot in Trillium City. . . . They discover that Prince Pharmaceuticals, the insidious corporation that tortured so many rats, is back in business." (Publisher's note)
"Wagner reveals lingering secrets, along with intrigue, rivalries, revenge, and redemption in the satisfying third book in this complex animal fantasy series." Booklist

Nightshade City; [illustrations by Omar Rayyan] Holiday House 2010 262p il $17.95
Grades: 5 6 7 8 **Fic**
1. Fantasy fiction 2. Rats -- Fiction
ISBN 978-0-8234-2285-2; 0-8234-2285-2
LC 2010-02474
Eleven years after the cruel Killdeer took over the Catacombs far beneath the human's Trillium City, Juniper Belancourt, assisted by Vincent and Victor Nightshade, leads a maverick band of rats to escape and establish their own city.
"The themes of love, loss and loyalty resonate through the novel, and the moments of darkness and violence are ul-

timately overpowered by hope and redemption. A good story well-told." Kirkus

Followed by: The white assassin (2011)

Waite, Michael P.

The **witches** of Dredmoore Hollow; by Riford McKenzie; with illustrations by Peter Ferguson. Marshall Cavendish Children 2008 264p il $16.99

Grades: 4 5 6 7 **Fic**

1. Aunts -- Fiction 2. Witches -- Fiction 3. New England -- Fiction

ISBN 978-0-7614-5458-8; 0-7614-5458-6

LC 2007-29781

Strange things begin happening at Elijah's New England home just before his twelfth birthday in 1927, especially after two aunts he had never met whisk him away to Moaning Marsh, where he realizes that they are witches who need something from him in order to remove a curse.

"The book has continuous action and piles of demonic atmosphere." SLJ

Walden, Mark

H.I.V.E; The Higher Institute of Villainous Education. Simon & Schuster Books for Young Readers 2007 309p $15.99; pa $6.99

Grades: 5 6 7 8 **Fic**

1. Criminals -- Fiction

ISBN 1-4169-3571-1; 978-1-4169-3571-1; 978-1-4169-3572-8 pa; 1-4169-3572-X pa

LC 2007-16205

"H.I.V.E. is operated on a volcanic island in a distant ocean by G.L.O.V.E., a shadowy organization of worldwide wickedness. And, as 13-year-old master of mischief Otto Malpense soon discovers, here the slickest of young tricksters, thieves, and hackers have been brought against their will to be trained as the next generation of supervillains. . . . [This] novel is a real page-turner; those who love superhero stories will eat it up." SLJ

Another title about H.I.V.E. is:

H.I.V.E.: The Overlord protocol (2008)
H.I.V.E.: Escape velocity (2011)
H.I.V.E.: Dreadnought (2011)

Walker, Kate

I hate books! [by] Kate Walker; illustrated by David Cox. Cricket Books 2007 78p il $16.95

Grades: 2 3 4 5 **Fic**

1. School stories 2. Brothers -- Fiction 3. Books and reading -- Fiction

ISBN 978-0-8126-2745-9; 0-8126-2745-8

LC 2006-36492

Although he is a great storyteller and good at art, Hamish cannot read, even with remedial classes, but his brother Nathan finally comes up with a way to teach him

"This is a warm and fast-paced story. . . . Witty black-and-white line drawings enhance the narrative." SLJ

Wallace, Bill

★ **Skinny**-dipping at Monster Lake. Simon & Schuster Bks. for Young Readers 2003 212p hardcover o.p. pa $5.99

Grades: 4 5 6 7 **Fic**

ISBN 0-689-85150-2; 0-689-85151-0 pa

LC 2002-152820

When twelve-year-old Kent helps his father in a daring underwater rescue, he wins the respect he has always craved.

"This old-fashioned adventure has wide appeal, and the youngsters' games and camaraderie will hook even reluctant readers." SLJ

Wallace, Rich

The **ball** hogs; illustrated by Jimmy Holder. Alfred A. Knopf 2010 119p il (Kickers) $12.99

Grades: 2 3 4 **Fic**

1. Soccer -- Fiction

ISBN 978-0-375-85754-6; 0-375-85754-0

Nine-year-old Ben, a natural athlete and member of the Bobcats coed soccer team, wants to overcome his inexperience and prove himself on the field, but his obnoxious teammate, Mark, keeps hogging the ball.

"A good sports story for younger readers, this beginning chapter book balances bits of information about playing the game with realistic scenes on the field, at home, and at school. . . . Lively black-and-white drawings illustrate the story." Booklist

Other titles in this series are:

Fake out (2010)
Benched (2010)
Game-day jitters (2011)

Sports camp. Alfred A. Knopf 2010 149p $15.99; lib bdg $18.99

Grades: 4 5 6 **Fic**

1. Camps -- Fiction 2. Sports -- Fiction

ISBN 978-0-375-84059-3; 0-375-84059-1; 978-0-375-94059-0 lib bdg; 0-375-94059-6 lib bdg

LC 2009-04278

Eleven-year-old Riley Liston tries to fit in at Camp Olympia, a summer sports camp where he is one of the youngest boys.

Wicked cruel; Rich Wallace. Knopf Books for Young Readers 2013 208 p. (hardback) $16.99

Grades: 5 6 7 8 **Fic**

1. Ghost stories 2. Horror fiction 3. Schools -- Fiction 4. Halloween -- Fiction 5. Supernatural -- Fiction 6. New Hampshire -- Fiction 7. Folklore -- New Hampshire -- Fiction

ISBN 0375867481; 9780375865145; 9780375867484; 9780375967481

LC 2012042504

This book of three "ghostly stories explore urban legends--actually rural New England legends--and how they changed lives. A bullied boy moves away and dies from a brain injury, yet he is seen in a music video after his death. A team of horses drowns in a flooded brickyard, but on certain rainy nights, they run free. Five farm children die young, but one mysteriously communicates with a young boy who may be as afraid of girls as of ghosts." (Kirkus Reviews)

Wallace, Sandra Neil

Little Joe; illustrated by Mark Elliott. Alfred A. Knopf 2010 192p il $15.99; lib bdg $18.99

Grades: 3 4 5 6 **Fic**

1. Bulls -- Fiction 2. Farm life -- Fiction 3. Family life -- Fiction 4. Grandfathers -- Fiction 5. Father-son

relationship -- Fiction

ISBN 978-0-375-86097-3; 0-375-86097-5; 978-0-375-96097-0 lib bdg; 0-375-96097-X lib bdg

"This is a sweet book about the relationships among three generations of farmers—Eli Stegner, his father, and his grandfather. It is also about Eli's connection to the first calf he gets to call his own. Little Joe is destined to be a winner at the county fair cattle show, but that blue ribbon will pretty much insure that he goes to the highest bidder and then to the butcher. . . . This thoughtful, tender book will appeal to those readers who are familiar with the Stegners' world, and many more will be able to identify with the highs and lows of familial love." SLJ

Walliams, David

★ The **boy** in the dress; illustrated by Quentin Blake. Razorbill 2009 231p il $15.99

Grades: 4 5 6 7   **Fic**

1. School stories 2. Soccer -- Fiction 3. Great Britain -- Fiction 4. Transvestites -- Fiction

ISBN 978-1-59514-299-3; 1-59514-299-1

"Dennis is a bit surprised—but not terribly nonplussed—to discover that he enjoys wearing dresses. The 12-year-old does, however, realize this is not the kind of revelation he wants to share with his truck-driving dad, his older brother, or his mates on the school football team, where he is the star player. . . . Walliams . . . has written a witty, high-spirited, and, well, sensible story about cross-dressing and other real-life issues." Booklist

★ **Mr.** Stink; illustrated by Quentin Blake. Razorbill 2010 265p il pa $9.99

Grades: 4 5 6   **Fic**

1. School stories 2. Family life -- Fiction 3. Homeless persons -- Fiction

ISBN 978-1-59514-332-7 pa; 1-59514-332-7 pa

Walliams "has a gift for crafting memorable scenes and, in the person of Mr. Stink, has created a delightfully offbeat character. . . . Readers of all ages will be thrilled with the in-a-word perfect illustrations of the great Quentin Blake." Booklist

Walsh, Pat

★ The **Crowfield** curse. Chicken House 2010 326p il $16.99

Grades: 5 6 7 8   **Fic**

1. Magic -- Fiction 2. Orphans -- Fiction 3. Monasteries -- Fiction 4. Great Britain -- History -- 1154-1399, Plantagenets -- Fiction

ISBN 0-545-22922-7; 978-0-545-22922-7

LC 2009-51483

In 1347, when fourteen-year-old orphan William Paynel, an impoverished servant at Crowfield Abbey, goes into the forest to gather wood and finds a magical creature caught in a trap, he discovers he has the ability to see fays and becomes embroiled in a strange mystery involving Old Magic, a bitter feud, and ancient secrets.

"This suspenseful and spooky story will thrill readers. . . . With fascinating attention to detail and an edgy battle between evil and good, Walsh sweeps readers almost effortlessly into another time and place." SLJ

The **Crowfield** demon; Pat Walsh. Scholastic 2012 360 p. $16.99

Grades: 5 6 7 8   **Fic**

1. Fantasy fiction 2. Adventure fiction 3. Children's stories 4. Demonology -- Fiction 5. Magic -- Fiction 6. Orphans -- Fiction 7. Identity -- Fiction 8. Monasteries -- Fiction 9. Blessing and cursing -- Fiction 10. Great Britain -- History -- 14th century -- Fiction

ISBN 054531769X; 9780545317696; 9780545373500

LC 2011029246

Sequel to: The Crowfield curse

This juvenile historical fantasy novel by Pat Walsh is the sequel to his earlier story "The Crowfield Curse." "In "The Crowfield Curse," young monks' apprentice Will learned he was gifted with the Sight: able to see beyond this mortal coil into the spirit realms of Old Magic. Protected by the warrior fay Shadlok -- and befriended by the wry, wary hobgoblin called Brother Walter -- the boy is just coming into his strange powers. But now, from its very foundations, Crowfield Abbey has begun to crumble. As Will slaves to salvage the chapel, he discovers something truly terrifying. A heathen creature from a pagan past is creeping up through the rubble -- avowed to unleash havoc on holy ground!" (Publisher's note)

Walter, Mildred Pitts, 1922-

★ **Justin** and the best biscuits in the world; with illustrations by Catherine Stock. Lothrop, Lee & Shepard Bks. 1986 122p il pa $7.99; $16

Grades: 3 4 5 6   **Fic**

1. Sex role -- Fiction 2. Family life -- Fiction 3. Grandfathers -- Fiction 4. African Americans -- Fiction

ISBN 0-06-195891-3 pa; 0-688-06645-3

LC 86-7148

Coretta Scott King Award for text

Ten-year-old Justin feels that cleaning and keeping house is women's work until he spends time on his beloved grandfather's ranch." Grades three to six." (SLJ)

"The strong, well-developed characters and humorous situations in this warm family story will appeal to intermediate readers; the large print will draw slow or reluctant readers." SLJ

Walters, Eric

Catboy. Orca Book Publishers 2011 229p pa $9.95

Grades: 4 5 6 7   **Fic**

1. Boys -- Fiction 2. Cats -- Fiction 3. Canada -- Fiction

ISBN 978-1-55469-953-7 pa; 1-55469-953-3 pa

The wild cat colony Taylor has been caring for is at risk of being destroyed, and in order to save it, Taylor will need the help of all his friends.

"Walters' story . . . moves fast and is plenty appealing. . . . Solid writing, strong kid characters, caring adults, and cute animals could make this a popular choice." Booklist

The **money** pit mystery. Fitzhenry & Whiteside 2011 289p pa $9.95

Grades: 4 5 6 7   **Fic**

1. Mystery fiction 2. Islands -- Fiction 3. Family life -- Fiction 4. Buried treasure -- Fiction

ISBN 978-1-55455-123-1; 1-55455-123-4

"Sam's grandfather and mother had a fight years ago, and now Sam, his sister, and their mother are visiting him for the first time in years. When they arrive on tiny Oak Island, they are shocked to discover how rundown the man's once-immaculate house has become. To make matters worse, he isn't even there. When Sam, Beth, and their friend, Buzz, do some exploring, they are surprised by some security guards at the town's 'money pit.' Some folks believe that Captain Kidd buried treasure here. . . . This is a well-thought-out mystery with lots of suspense and a fully realized picture of a struggling family." SLJ

Ward, David

Between two ends. Amulet Books 2011 288p $16.95
Grades: 4 5 6   **Fic**
1. Fantasy fiction 2. Adventure fiction 3. Pirates -- Fiction 4. Arabian nights -- Fiction 5. Books and reading -- Fiction
ISBN 978-0-8109-9714-1; 0-8109-9714-2
         LC 2010-23696

Trying to help his father deal with his long-standing depression, Yeats and his parents visit his grandmother's old and eerie house, where he discovers a pair of pirate bookends that unlock a thirty-year-old secret that Yeats must try to resolve by entering the exotic world of The Arabian Nights.

"Quickly sketching credible characters in both worlds, Ward plunges Yeats into a series of adventures. . . . Unexpected moments of humor lighten the gloomy prospect of failure and offer hope that the ending will resolve the family crisis so vividly portrayed in the opening chapters. A satisfying chapter-book fantasy." Booklist

Warner, Penny

The secret of the skeleton key. Egmont USA 2011 209p (The Code Busters Club) $15.99; e-book $15.99
Grades: 3 4 5 6   **Fic**
1. Mystery fiction 2. Ciphers -- Fiction 3. Cousins -- Fiction
ISBN 978-1-60684-162-4; 1-60684-162-9; 978-1-6068-4281-2 e-book
         LC 2011003240

"Cody and Quinn notice their neighbor Mr. Skelton signaling from his window; later his house burns and cousins Jasper and Jezabel appear, searching for Mr. Skelton's will. By solving Mr. Skelton's coded clues, the club members manage to unearth the authentic document before his cousins can force him to sign a new one. . . . This well-crafted mystery reads smoothly; characters are well developed, clues . . . skillfully dropped, and the solution feels plausible." Booklist

Warner, Sally

EllRay Jakes is not a chicken! illustrated by Jamie Harper. Viking Children's Books 2011 108p il $14.99
Grades: 1 2 3   **Fic**
1. School stories 2. Bullies -- Fiction 3. California -- Fiction 4. Family life -- Fiction
ISBN 978-0-670-06243-0; 0-670-06243-X
         LC 2010-25106

Eight-year-old EllRay's father has promised a family trip to Disneyland if EllRay can stay out of trouble for a week, but not defending himself against Jared, the class bully, proves to be a real challenge.

"Warner's clever plotting brings an unexpected and rewarding ending. EllRay's ingenuous narration and the well-observed classroom dynamics are the main draw, and Harper's cartoons, incorporated throughout, further enliven the story." Publ Wkly

Another title about EllRay is:
EllRay Jakes is a rock star! (2011)

EllRay Jakes Rocks the Holidays! by Sally Warner; illustrated by Brian Biggs. Viking, published by Penguin Group 2014 143 p. illustrations (hardcover) $14.99
Grades: 1 2 3   **Fic**
1. School stories 2. Christmas -- Fiction 3. African Americans -- Fiction 4. African American children -- Fiction 5. Schools -- Fiction 6. California -- Fiction 7. Family life -- California -- Fiction
ISBN 0451469097; 9780451469090
         LC 2013048390

In this children's book, by Sally Warner, illustrated by Brian Biggs, "[i]t's almost Christmas and school is going great for EllRay. He's 'blending in' just the way he likes. So when his father tells him he should be proud to be part of the African-American 'community,' EllRay isn't so sure he wants to call attention to his differences. After all, he's only one of two boys in his class with brown skin. And then, totally by accident, he insults the other boy." (Publisher's note)

"In a holiday-themed episode, EllRay finds himself the emcee of his school's Winter Wonderland show. When he accidentally hurts a friend's feelings, it results in an exploration of friendship, values, and race perfectly pitched for middle graders. EllRay must ultimately make a difficult choice and stand up for what he knows is right. Biggs's black-and-white illustrations capture all the emotional nuances." Horn Book

Other titles in the series include:
Ellray Jakes is not a Chicken (2011)
Ellray Jakes is a Rock Star (2011)
Ellray Jakes Walks the Plank (2012)
Ellray Jakes the Dragon Slayer (2013)
Ellray Jakes and the Beanstalk (2013)
Ellray Jakes is Magic (2014)

It's only temporary; written and illustrated by Sally Warner. Viking Childrens Books 2008 182p il $15.99
Grades: 4 5 6 7   **Fic**
1. Bullies -- Fiction 2. Siblings -- Fiction 3. Grandmothers -- Fiction 4. Brain -- Wounds and injuries -- Fiction
ISBN 978-0-670-06111-2; 0-670-06111-5
         LC 2007-038220

When Skye's older brother comes home after a devastating accident, she moves from Albuquerque, New Mexico, to California to live with her grandmother and attend middle school, where she somewhat reluctantly makes new friends, learns to stand up for herself and those she cares about, and begins to craft a new relationship with her changed brother.

"Warner deftly handles Skye's anger toward her brain-injured brother, also infusing her with a convincingly developed sense of compassion. Witty line art decorates some pages." Horn Book Guide

Only Emma; illustrated by Jamie Harper. Viking 2004 115p il $14.99; pa $5.99
Grades: 2 3 4   **Fic**
ISBN 0-670-05979-X; 0-14-240711-9 pa
         LC 2004-12478

Third-grader Emma's peaceful life as an only child is disrupted when she has to temporarily share her tidy bedroom with four-year-old Anthony Scarpetto.

"The black-and-white illustrations are charming, and thumbnail sidebars present fun scientific facts about animals mentioned in the story. . . . Emma is a likable character whose feelings and behaviors are common to many children." SLJ

Other titles about Emma are:
Not-so-weird Emma (2005)
Super Emma (2006)
Best friend Emma (2007)
Excellent Emma (2009)
Happily ever Emma (2010)

Waters, Zack C.

Blood moon rider; [by] Zack C. Waters. Pineapple Press 2006 126p $13.95

Grades: 5 6 7 8 **Fic**

1. Florida -- Fiction 2. Ranch life -- Fiction 3. Grandfathers -- Fiction 4. World War, 1939-1945 -- Fiction

ISBN 978-1-56164-350-9; 1-56164-350-5

LC 2005030749

After his father's death in World War II, fourteen-year-old Harley Wallace tries to join the Marines but is, instead, sent to live with his grandfather in Peru Landing, Florida, where he soon joins a covert effort to stop Nazis from destroying a secret airbase on Tampa Bay

This is "an adventure filled with unexpected kindnesses and the irrepressibility of family ties, as well as a brush with espionage and a couple of suspenseful shoot'em-up scenes. A colorful cast of characters and a nod to teenage romance help make this a good choice for middle school boys." SLJ

Watkins, Yoko Kawashima

My brother, my sister, and I. Bradbury Press 1994 275p hardcover o.p. pa $5.99

Grades: 6 7 8 9 **Fic**

1. Japan -- Fiction 2. Korea -- Fiction 3. World War, 1939-1945 -- Fiction

ISBN 0-02-792526-9; 0-689-80656-6 pa

LC 93-23535

"Watkins's first-person narrative is beautifully direct and emotionally honest." Publ Wkly

"The author continues her autobiographical account begun in So Far from the Bamboo Grove with the story of how the two sisters, Ko and Yoko, now reunited with their brother Hideyo, try to survive in postwar Japan." Horn Book

★ So far from the bamboo grove. Lothrop, Lee & Shepard Bks. 1986 183p map hardcover o.p. pa $5.99

Grades: 6 7 8 9 **Fic**

1. Japan -- Fiction 2. Korea -- Fiction 3. World War, 1939-1945 -- Fiction

ISBN 0-688-13115-8 pa

LC 85-15939

A fictionalized autobiography in which eight-year-old Yoko escapes from Korea to Japan with her mother and sister at the end of World War II

"An admirably told and absorbing novel." Horn Book

Followed by: My brother, my sister and I

Watson, Geoff

Edison's gold. Egmont USA 2010 312p $15.99; lib bdg $18.99

Grades: 4 5 6 7 **Fic**

1. Inventors 2. Mystery fiction 3. Adventure fiction 4. Electrical engineers 5. Inventors -- Fiction 6. Secret societies -- Fiction

ISBN 978-1-60684-094-8; 1-60684-094-0; 978-1-60684-095-5 lib bdg; 1-60684-095-9 lib bdg

LC 2010-11312

Tom Edison and his friends become embroiled in a mystery involving his 'double-great' grandfather's inventions, a secret society, and a vendetta being carried out by a descendant of inventor Nikola Tesla.

This "is a fast-paced adventure filled mystery that middle schoolers will like." SLJ

Watson, Jude

The **39** clues; unstoppable: nowhere to run. Jude Watson. Scholastic 2013 272 p. (The 39 clues: unstoppable) (paper over board) $12.99

Grades: 4 5 6 7 **Fic**

1. Supernatural 2. Brothers and sisters 3. Adventure and adventurers

ISBN 9780545521376; 0545521378

LC 2013934701

In this book, by Jude Watson, "the Cahill family has a secret. For five hundred years, they have guarded the 39 Clues–thirty-nine ingredients in a serum that transforms whomever takes it into the most powerful person on earth. . . . Certain Cahills have always made it their mission to keep the serum safe. . . . Thirteen-year-old Dan Cahill and his older sister, Amy, are the latest guardians of the Clues. They think they've done everything right, but a tiny mistake leads to catastrophe." (Publisher's note)

"Six months after sixteen-year-old Amy and thirteen-year-old Dan defeated the Vespers, the Cahill siblings set out on another quest to stop the serum their family has protected for centuries from wreaking havoc on the world. This first entry in a new spinoff series is formulaic, but the suspense and high stakes that 39 Clues fans love are front and center." (Horn Book)

Beyond the grave. Scholastic 2009 190p (The 39 clues) $12.99

Grades: 4 5 6 7 **Fic**

1. Ciphers -- Fiction 2. Orphans -- Fiction 3. Siblings -- Fiction

ISBN 978-0-545-06044-8; 0-545-06044-3

Sequel to: The sword thief by Peter Lerangis (2009)

A clue sends Amy and Dan jetting off to find out just what's behind the fierce rivalry between the Tomas and Ekaterina branches of the Cahill family. Was a Clue stolen from the Tomas branch? Where is it now? And most important, can Amy and Dan get their hands on it before their rivals do?

"Like the previous books, historical information is woven into the fast-paced adventure." SLJ

Followed by: The black circle by Patrick Carman (2009)

In too deep. Scholastic 2009 206p (The 39 clues) $12.99

Grades: 4 5 6 7 **Fic**

1. Adventure fiction 2. Ciphers -- Fiction 3. Orphans

-- Fiction 4. Siblings -- Fiction
ISBN 978-0-545-09064-3; 0-545-09064-4

Sequel to: Beyond the grave by Jude Watson (2009)

"Amy and Dan fly to Australia. Attemping to trace their late parents' journey eight years earlier, they link Amelia Earhart's last flight to their own family quest. . . . The spy-versus-spy mentality will keep readers guessing. . . . The series' fans will devour the breathless action scenes in this fast-paced adventure." Booklist

Followed by: The viper's nest by Peter Lerangis (2010)

Loot; how to steal a fortune. Jude Watson. Scholastic Press 2014 272 p. (alk. paper) $16.99
Grades: 4 5 6 7   **Fic**
1. Twins -- Fiction 2. Adventure fiction 3. Jewelry -- Fiction 4. Orphans -- Fiction 5. Robbers and outlaws -- Fiction 6. Brothers and sisters -- Fiction 7. Adventure and adventurers -- Fiction
ISBN 0545468027; 9780545468022

LC 2014001218

"When master jewel thief Alfie McQuinn dies, his stashed set of clues and cryptic last words to March, his 12-year-old son and apprentice, mark the beginning of a race against time. The first clue leads March to discover his twin sister, Jules, a traveling circus acrobat. Tossed into a group home, they meet Darius, a juvenile delinquent with a soft spot for Izzy, a code-cracking hacker." (Booklist)

"Pitch-perfect characters, from scheming criminals to a twisted former cop to the twins' father, move in and out of the narrative, but it's the four young teens that drive the tale forward with enviable schemes and ingenious plans.Taut, engrossing and unstoppable." Kirkus

Watson, Renee
What Momma left me. Bloomsbury 2010 224p $15.99
Grades: 5 6 7 8   **Fic**
1. Orphans -- Fiction 2. Bereavement -- Fiction 3. Family life -- Fiction 4. Grandparents -- Fiction 5. Christian life -- Fiction 6. African Americans -- Fiction
ISBN 978-1-59990-446-7; 1-59990-446-2

LC 2009-18263

After the death of their mother, thirteen-year-old Serenity Evans and her younger brother go to live with their grandparents, who try to keep them safe from bad influences and help them come to terms with what has happened to their family.

"Serenity's struggles and insights, as she wrestles with her parents' legacy and an uncertain future, are inspiring, authentic, and told in a straighforward yet poetic style. The first-person narration is consistent, and the mystery of the painful circumstances of her mother's death—as well as additional tragedies—propels the story." Publ Wkly

Watson, Stephanie Elaine
Elvis & Olive; by Stephanie Watson. Scholastic Press 2008 230p $15.99
Grades: 3 4 5   **Fic**
1. Friendship -- Fiction
ISBN 978-0-545-03183-7; 0-545-03183-4

LC 2007023924

In spite of their differences, Natalie Wallis and Annie Beckett become friends and decide to spend their summer spying on their neighbors

This is an "accomplished first novel." Publ Wkly

Another title about Elvis & Olive is:
Elvis & Olive: super detectives (2010)

Watts, Frances
Extraordinary Ernie and Marvelous Maud; illustrated by Judy Watson. Eerdmans Books for Young Readers 2010 66p il (Ernie & Maude) pa $5.99
Grades: 2 3 4   **Fic**
1. Sheep -- Fiction 2. Superheroes -- Fiction
ISBN 978-0-8028-5363-9; 0-8028-5363-3

Ten-year-old Ernie is thrilled when he wins a contest to be trained as a superhero, and although he is disappointed that his sidekick is a talking sheep, just looking at his costume makes him feel heroic

"The action is tame . . . but the slapstick premise and banter between superhero and sidekick save the day. The brevity, spry pace, and humorous line art make Watts's . . . story a good choice for kids." Publ Wkly

Other titles about Ernie and Maud are:
The middle sheep (2010)
The greatest sheep in history (2011)

Weatherford, Carole Boston
Dear Mr. Rosenwald; by Carole Boston Weatherford; illustrated by Gregory Christie. Scholastic Press 2006 un il $16.99
Grades: 2 3 4   **Fic**
1. School stories 2. Philanthropists 3. Retail executives 4. African Americans -- Fiction 5. Segregation in education -- Fiction
ISBN 0-439-49522-9

LC 2005-27971

Young Ovella rejoices as her community comes together to raise money and build a much-needed school in the 1920s, with matching funds from Julius Rosenwald, the president of Sears, Roebuck, and Company

"Christie's gouache and colored-pencil illustrations have the variegated look and stylized layout of collage art— a good complement to the child's rough-around-the-edges narration. An afterword explains Rosenwald's impact on thousands of poor black communities. An uplifting and inspiring story." SLJ

Webb, Holly
The **case** of the stolen sixpence; written by Holly Webb; illustrated by Marion Lindsay. Houghton Mifflin Harcourt 2014 108 p. illustrations (The mysteries of Maisie Hitchins) (hardback) $14.99
Grades: 2 3 4 5   **Fic**
1. Mystery fiction 2. Detectives -- Fiction 3. London (England) -- Fiction 4. Boardinghouses -- Fiction 5. Mystery and detective stories 6. London (England) -- History -- 19th century -- Fiction 7. Great Britain -- History -- Victoria, 1837-1901 -- Fiction
ISBN 0544339282; 9780544339286

LC 2014007446

Written by Holly Webb, illustrated by Marion Lindsay, and part of The Mysteries of Maisie Hitchins series, this is a middle grades mystery story. "In 'The Case of the Stolen Sixpence,' Maisie's big chance to prove herself finally arrives when crime strikes her Victorian London neighborhood. While the grown-ups turn a blind eye to the whodunit and justice goes un-served, Maisie and her canine sidekick,

Eddie, search the streets for clues to crack the case." (Publisher's note)

"Twelve-year-old Maisie Hitchins, who helps her grandmother run a Victorian boarding house, idolizes dashing detective Gilbert Carrington and hopes one day to solve cases of her own. When her friend George is accused of stealing money from the butcher shop where he works, Maisie and her faithful canine assistant, Eddie, are on the case, ready to right this terrible wrong...Lindsay's black-line drawings add to the appeal and break up the text for younger readers. This makes a perfect choice for graduates of David A. Adler's Cam Jansen series who are not quite ready for Nancy Springer's Enola Holmes Mysteries." Booklist

Other titles include:

The Case of the Vanishing Emerald (2015)

Webb, Philip

Six days. Chicken House 2011 336p $17.99

Grades: 5 6 7 8   Fic

1. Science fiction 2. Siblings -- Fiction 3. Space and time -- Fiction 4. London (England) -- Fiction

ISBN 978-0-545-31767-2; 0-545-31767-3

LC 2010054233

Cass and her brother Wilbur scavenge in the ruins of a future London seeking an artifact for their Russian masters, but the search takes on a new urgency after the arrival of Erin and Peyto, strangers from afar who claim to hold the key to locating the mysterious object.

Webb "has created a complex and intriguing dystopia filled with devastation, clever devices . . . and lots of local color. . . . The novel's rapid pacing will hook readers and keep them turning pages." Booklist

Weber, Elka

★ The Yankee at the seder; illustrated by Adam Gustavson. Tricycle Press 2009 un il $16.99

Grades: 2 3 4 5   Fic

1. Jews -- Fiction 2. Passover -- Fiction 3. Soldiers -- Fiction 4. United States -- History -- 1861-1865, Civil War -- Fiction

ISBN 978-1-58246-256-1; 1-58246-256-9

LC 2008-11229

As a Confederate family prepares for Passover the day after the Civil War has ended, a Yankee arrives on their Virginia doorstep and is invited to share their meal, to the dismay of ten-year-old Jacob. Includes historical notes about Corporal Myer Levy, on whom the story is based, and his prominent Philadelphia family.

"With a cinematic flair and rich, realist oils, Gustavson . . . depicts how a détente between North and South is forged—albeit tenuously—by the timeless values of faith, civility and chicken soup. Basing her writing on a historical incident, Weber makes an impressive debut. . . . Sensitively written and beautifully illustrated." Publ Wkly

Wedekind, Annie

A horse of her own; by Annie Wedekind. Feiwel and Friends 2008 275p $16.95; pa $7.99

Grades: 5 6 7 8   Fic

1. Camps -- Fiction 2. Horses -- Fiction 3. Kentucky -- Fiction 4. Horsemanship -- Fiction

ISBN 978-0-312-36927-9; 0-312-36927-1; 978-0-312-58146-6 pa; 0-312-58146-7 pa

LC 2007032769

At summer camp Jane feels like an outsider among the cliquish rich girls who board their horses at Sunny Acres farm, and when the horse she has been riding is sold to another camper, she feels even worse until her teacher asks her to help train a beautiful but skittish new horse, and the experience brings out the best in her.

"Tenacious and thoughtful, Jane is an appealing protagonist who gradually recognizes that being accepted no longer matters to her. The plot . . . has enough twists, including a hint of romance, to sustain readers' interest." SLJ

Wild Blue; the story of a mustang Appaloosa. Feiwel and Friends 2009 124p (Breyer horse collection) $16.99; pa $5.99

Grades: 3 4 5   Fic

1. Horses -- Fiction

ISBN 978-0-312-38424-1; 0-312-38424-6; 978-0-312-59917-1 pa; 0-312-59917-X pa

LC 2008-34742

After being captured by men, Blue the Appaloosa grabs a chance at freedom and tries to find her way home.

"A modern-day adventure that reads like an exuberant nature journal, this novel will grip readers from start to finish." SLJ

Weeks, Sarah

As simple as it seems. Laura Geringer Books 2010 181p $15.99; lib bdg $16.89

Grades: 4 5 6   Fic

1. Ghost stories 2. Adoption -- Fiction 3. Friendship -- Fiction 4. Catskill Mountains (N.Y.) -- Fiction

ISBN 978-0-06-084663-3; 0-06-084663-1; 978-0-06-084664-0 lib bdg; 0-06-084664-X lib bdg

Eleven-year-old Verbena Polter gets through a difficult summer of turbulent emotions and the revelation of a disturbing family secret with an odd new friend who believes she is the ghost of a girl who drowned many years before.

"Weeks's characters are well rounded and her story line is engaging." Horn Book Guide

Jumping the scratch; a novel. Laura Geringer Books 2006 167p il $15.99; pa $5.99

Grades: 5 6 7 8   Fic

1. Aunts -- Fiction 2. Memory -- Fiction 3. Child sexual abuse -- Fiction

ISBN 978-0-06-054109-5; 0-06-054109-1; 978-0-06-054110-1 pa; 0-06-054111-3 pa

LC 2005-17776

After moving with his mother to a trailer park to care for an injured aunt, eleven-year-old Jamie Reardon struggles to cope with a deeply buried secret

"Weeks alludes to sexual abuse, but with a broad brush and no graphic details. . . . Weeks perfectly captures not only the guilt, shame, and pain of the abused boy but also the tenor of a fifth-grade classroom from the point of view of a new student who is friendless, targeted, and belittled by an insensitive teacher. Touches of humor ameliorate the pain and poignancy." SLJ

Oggie Cooder. Levithan/Scholastic Press 2008 172p il $16.99; pa $5.99

Grades: 3 4 5   Fic

1. School stories 2. Friendship -- Fiction 3. Eccentrics

and eccentricities -- Fiction
ISBN 978-0-439-92791-8; 0-439-92791-9; 978-0-439-92794-9 pa; 0-439-92794-3 pa

LC 2007-18645

Quirky fourth-grader Oggie Cooder goes from being shunned to everyone's best friend when his uncanny ability to chew slices of cheese into the shapes of states wins him a slot on a popular television talent show, but he soon learns the perils of being a celebrity—and having a neighbor girl as his manager.

The author "delivers a funny, fast-paced story, with the likable Oggie at its center." Booklist

Followed by: Oggie Cooder, party animal (2009)

Oggie Cooder, party animal; illustrations by Doug Holgate. Scholastic Press 2009 165p il $16.99

Grades: 3 4 5   Fic
1. School stories 2. Parties -- Fiction 3. Birthdays -- Fiction 4. Friendship -- Fiction 5. Eccentrics and eccentricities -- Fiction
ISBN 978-0-439-92792-5; 0-439-92792-7

LC 2009024909

Neither a long list of rules, nor the inability to find the perfect gift—Cheddar Jam—nor being locked in a bathroom with a juggling bear will keep quirky fourth-grader Oggie Cooder from attending neighbor Donnica Perfecto's birthday pool party.

"A fast-paced chapter book with cheerful cartoon illustrations provided by Holgate, this can easily be read on its own and will certainly win Oggie new fans." Kirkus

★ **Pie**. Scholastic Press 2011 183p $16.99

Grades: 4 5 6 7   Fic
1. Cats -- Fiction 2. Pies -- Fiction 3. Aunts -- Fiction
ISBN 978-0-545-27011-3; 0-545-27011-1

In the 1950s in the small town of Ipswitch, PA, Polly Portman dies and leaves the recipe for her prize-winning piecrust to her cat Lardo, in the care of her niece Alice, but then the cat is kidnapped and the bakery is trashed.

"Weeks deftly leavens moments of hilarity with the process of grieving in this sweet coming-of-age story in which Alice learns from Aunt Polly to follow her heart and to open it as well. Readers will close the book with a satisfied sigh and may seek out an adult to help them bake a pie. Recipes included." SLJ

★ **So** B. it; a novel. Laura Geringer Books 2004 245p $15.99; pa $6.99

Grades: 5 6 7 8   Fic
1. Mental illness -- Fiction 2. People with mental disabilities -- Fiction
ISBN 0-06-623622-3; 0-06-441047-1 pa

LC 2003-15643

After spending her life with her mentally disabled mother and agoraphobic neighbor, twelve-year-old Heidi sets out from Reno, Nevada, to New York to find out who she is.

"This is lovely writing—real, touching, and pared cleanly down to the essentials." Booklist

Weissman, Elissa Brent
Nerd camp. Atheneum Books for Young Readers 2011 261p $15.99

Grades: 4 5 6   Fic
1. Camps -- Fiction
ISBN 1-4424-1703-X; 978-1-4424-1703-8

LC 2010-42913

For ten-year-old Gabe, the Summer Center for Gifted Enrichment is all that he dreamed it would be, but he must work hard to write about the fun in letters to Zach, his cool future stepbrother, without revealing that it is a camp for "nerds."

This "novel features an appealing 10-year-old.... Weissman depicts a camp whose academic classes sound almost as fun as kayaking and color war." Booklist

The **short** seller; Elissa Brent Weissman. 1st ed. Atheneum Books for Young Readers 2013 256 p. (hardcover) $15.99

Grades: 3 4 5 6   Fic
1. Girls -- Fiction 2. Stocks -- Fiction 3. Friendship -- Fiction 4. Best friends -- Fiction 5. Mononucleosis -- Fiction 6. Electronic trading of securities -- Fiction
ISBN 1442452552; 9781442452558

LC 2012018632

In this middle-grade novel, by Elissa Brent Weissman, "a twelve-year-old takes on the stock market.... It all starts when seventh grader Lindy Sachs is granted $100 and access to her father's online trading account.... With trading talent and access to her parents' savings, the opportunity to make some real dough is too tempting to pass up. In fact, given how well Lindy's stocks are doing, it would be a disservice to not invest it all.... Right?" (Publisher's note)

The **trouble** with Mark Hopper. Dutton Children's Books 2009 227p $16.99

Grades: 5 6 7 8   Fic
1. School stories 2. Contests -- Fiction 3. Maryland -- Fiction 4. Identity (Psychology) -- Fiction
ISBN 978-0-525-42067-5; 0-525-42067-3

LC 2008-34211

When two eleven-year-olds with the same name, similar looks, and very different personalities go to the same Maryland middle school, confusion and bad feelings ensue, but things improve after a teacher insists that they become study partners.

"Realistic school interactions give Weissman's novel a lot of kid appeal with substance." Horn Book Guide

Welch, Sheila Kelly
Waiting to forget. Namelos 2011 170p $18.95

Grades: 5 6 7 8   Fic
1. Siblings -- Fiction 2. Foster home care -- Fiction
ISBN 978-1-60898-114-4; 1-60898-114-2

T.J. and his sister, Angela, learn how to move forward and be happy while in foster care.

"T.J.'s authentic voice and the multilayered presentation of his memories, shifting between the waiting room and his past, make for a poignant, realistic tale of child-survivors." Kirkus

Wells, Ken
Rascal; a dog and his boy. illustrations by Christian Slade. Alfred A. Knopf 2010 201p il $16.99; lib bdg $19.99

Grades: 4 5 6 7 **Fic**

1. Dogs -- Fiction 2. Louisiana -- Fiction

ISBN 978-0-375-86652-4; 0-375-86652-3; 978-0-375-96652-1 lib bdg; 0-375-96652-8 lib bdg

LC 2009-37606

Rascal may be the happiest beagle ever to live. He used to live on Voclain's Farm, but now he lives with his very own boy, Meely. Together they explore the Louisiana bayou. But when Meely gets stuck on a rotting bridge deep in the bayou, it's up to Rascal to save his boy from danger.

"This is a cracking good animal story of classic pedigree. . . . Characterizations of both humans and animals are sharp and distinct. . . . [The] narration sings with the same lively Cajun-flavored spice as the dialogue, and it's an easy dialect to get the hang of." Bull Cent Child Books

Wells, Kitty

Paw power; illustrated by Joanna Harrison. David Fickling Books 2011 199p il (Pocket cats) $13.99; lib bdg $16.99

Grades: 2 3 4 **Fic**

1. School stories 2. Cats -- Fiction 3. Magic -- Fiction 4. Bullies -- Fiction

ISBN 978-0-385-75201-5; 0-385-75201-6; 978-0-385-75202-2 lib bdg; 0-385-75202-4 lib bdg

LC 2010011892

"Nine-year-old Maddy Lloyd is desperate for a kitten, but younger brother Jack is allergic, so she settles for three small ceramic cats purchased at a flea market. Later, Maddy is surprised when one of the figurines, Greykin, comes to life, explaining that he has been sent to help her do a job— eventually revealed to be dealing with school-bully Sherry. . . . Newly independent readers will identify with Maddy's concerns about friendship and self-assertiveness (as well as her desire for a cat), and the inclusion of large type and frequent illustrations . . . will support those readers through the book's lengthy chapters." Booklist

Followed by: Shadow magic (2011)

Wells, Rosemary

★ **Ivy** takes care; Rosemary Wells, illustrated by Jim LaMarche. Candlewick Press 2013 208 p. $15.99

Grades: 2 3 4 **Fic**

1. Pets 2. Historical fiction

ISBN 0763653527; 9780763653521

LC 2012942383

This book is "set in 1949 on a ranch near Reno, Nev., where almost-sixth-grader Ivy's parents work. Ivy's deep compassion for animals spurs her to offer herself as caretaker for pets and farm animals while their owners are away; her experiences inspire her aspirations to become a veterinarian." (Publishers Weekly)

Lincoln and his boys; illustrated by P.J. Lynch. Candlewick Press 2009 96p il $16.99

Grades: 3 4 5 6 **Fic**

1. Lawyers 2. Presidents 3. State legislators 4. Members of Congress 5. Presidents -- Fiction 6. Children of presidents 7. Father-son relationship -- Fiction

ISBN 978-0-7636-3723-1; 0-7636-3723-8

LC 2008-21418

"Inspired by a 200-word essay by Willie Lincoln, Wells offers a fictional account of Lincoln and his boys. Written first from Willie's point of view, then Tad's after Willie dies, it's a touching account of Lincoln as a patient and loving father. . . . Lynch captures the people and the warmth of their interactions in carefully researched oil paintings that reflect his mastery with light, perspective, and portraiture." SLJ

My Havana; [by] Rosemary Wells with Secundino Fernandez; illustrated by Peter Ferguson. Candlewick Press 2010 65p il $17.99

Grades: 4 5 6 7 **Fic**

1. Architects 2. Cuba -- Fiction 3. Dictators -- Fiction 4. Family life -- Fiction

ISBN 978-0-7636-4305-8; 0-7636-4305-X

LC 2009-12053

Relates events in the childhood of architect Secundino Fernandez, who left his beloved Havana, Cuba, with his parents, first to spend a year in Spain, and later to move to New York City.

"Wells has chosen anecdotes wisely, and Ferguson's illustrations are atmospheric, capturing Dino's childlike enthusiasm and longing." Kirkus

★ **On** the Blue Comet; illustrated by Bagram Ibatoulline. Candlewick Press 2010 329p il $16.99

Grades: 5 6 7 8 **Fic**

1. Adventure fiction 2. Railroads -- Fiction 3. California -- Fiction 4. Space and time -- Fiction

ISBN 978-0-7636-3722-4; 0-7636-3722-X

LC 2009051358

During the Great Depression, Oscar's dad must sell their home and head west in search of work. Oscar meets a mysterious drifter and witnesses a crime so stunning it catapults Oscar on a train journey from coast to coast, from one decade to another.

"Ibatoulline's full-color, atmospheric Norman Rockwell-like vignettes enhance the nostalgic feel of this warm, cleverly crafted adventure." Kirkus

Welsh, M. L.

Heart of stone; a Verity Gallant tale. M.L. Welsh. David Fickling Books 2012 409 p. (hard cover) $16.99

Grades: 5 6 7 8 **Fic**

1. Love stories 2. Occult fiction 3. Witches -- Fiction 4. Fantasy 5. Sailing -- Fiction 6. Betrayal -- Fiction 7. Friendship -- Fiction 8. Family life -- Fiction 9. Books and reading -- Fiction

ISBN 0385752431; 9780375899164; 9780385752428; 9780385752435

LC 2011023878

Sequel to: Mistress of the Storm

This book is a "companion novel to 'Mistress Of The Storm' . . . tell[ing] the story of heroine Verity Gallant's fight against an evil force determined to put an end to all happily-ever-after stories. . . . The evil force appears to be trying to destroy Verity's cliffside hometown of Wellow, which is rapidly being eroded by white sand gathering as if it had a single motive—to erase all the 'Original Stories' with happy endings." (Voice of Youth Advocates)

★ **Mistress** of the Storm; a Verity Gallant tale. David Fickling Books 2011 318p $16.99; lib bdg $19.99

Grades: 5 6 7 8 **Fic**

1. Fantasy fiction 2. Sailing -- Fiction 3. Witches -- Fiction 4. Friendship -- Fiction 5. Family life -- Fiction

6. Books and reading -- Fiction
ISBN 978-0-385-75244-2; 0-385-75244-X; 978-0-385-75245-9 lib bdg; 0-385-75245-8 lib bdg

LC 2010018721

First published in the United Kingdom

After a stranger gives an ancient book to unpopular, twelve-year-old Verity Gallant, she and her new-found friends, Henry and Martha, uncover secrets stirring in the harbor town of Wellow and use them to face a powerful, vengeful witch.

"Welsh's prose is lovely, her characters are well-drawn, and the atmosphere of the town is palpable. In creating a place in the world where a story read aloud can become true, Welsh offers a benediction of sorts to readers, that 'every child who is alone or out of place will find the friends they need, and the love they deserve.'" Publ Wkly

West, Jacqueline

Still life; by Jacqueline West; illustrated by Poly Bernatene. Dial Books for Young Readers, an imprint of Penguin Group (USA) Inc. 2014 330 p. (The books of Elsewhere) (hardback) $16.99
Grades: 4 5 6   Fic
1. Fantasy fiction 2. Magic -- Fiction 3. Dwellings -- Fiction 4. Space and time -- Fiction
ISBN 0803736916; 9780803736917

LC 2013041383

In this middle grades book by Jacqueline West, illustrated by Poly Bernatene, part of The Books of Elsewhere series, "Annabelle McMartin is gone for good, but something worse lurks just out of sight--watching, waiting, preparing to strike. Then a field trip to the local art museum reveals a shock. What Olive discovers will create a chain of events that propel her to discoveries she may not wish to uncover." (Publisher's note)

"In this series-ending fifth installment, Olive learns further secrets behind the paintings-as-portals magic of Elsewhere, its origins, and the world's creator. The magic's ability to preserve life indefinitely gets creepy, but characters with silly quirks keep the tone from becoming too dark. Illustrations are shadowy but still manage to make the heroes appear friendly." Horn Book

Other titles in the series include:
The Shadows (2010)
Spellbound (2011)
The Second Spy (2012)
The Strangers (2013)

Westera, Marleen

★ Sheep and Goat; by Marleen Westera; illustrations by Sylvia van Ommen; translation by Nancy Forest-Flier. Front Street 2006 99p il $16.95
Grades: 1 2 3   Fic
1. Goats -- Fiction 2. Sheep -- Fiction 3. Friendship -- Fiction
ISBN 978-1-932425-81-9

LC 2006000793

Follows the daily activities of Sheep and Goat who, despite often being grouchy or grumpy, are always there for one another when it counts

"Told with a subtle and consistent undercurrent of wit, these 18 short stories are pleasant bedtime reading. . . . The occasional pen-and-ink drawings are pitch perfect and more

than a little extraordinary. They convey the low-key humor exquisitely." SLJ

Weston, Carol

The diary of Melanie Martin; or, How I survived Matt the Brat, Michelangelo, and the Leaning Tower of Pizza. Knopf 2000 144p hardcover o.p. pa $5.50
Grades: 3 4 5 6   Fic
1. Italy -- Fiction 2. Family life -- Fiction 3. Voyages and travels -- Fiction
ISBN 0-375-80509-5; 0-440-41667-1 pa

LC 99-53384

Fourth-grader Melanie Martin writes in her diary, describing her family's trip to Italy and all that she learned

"Sections of the book are laugh-out-loud funny and Weston's descriptions will have readers wanting to see the country for themselves. An enjoyable read." SLJ

Other titles about Melanie Martin are:
Melanie in Manhattan (2005)
Melanie Martin goes Dutch (2002)
With love from Spain, Melanie Martin (2005)

Weston, Robert Paul

Prince Puggly of Spud and the Kingdom of Spiff; Robert Paul Weston. Penguin Group USA 2013 256 p. $15.99
Grades: 2 3 4 5   Fic
1. Fashion 2. Humorous fiction
ISBN 1595145672; 9781595145673

In this "middle-grade rhyming novel . . . [by Robert Paul Weston] Prince Puggly of the . . . Kingdom of Spud . . . receives an invitation to a lavish ball in the far more chic Kingdom of Spiff. Puggly is sure that the Spiffs will take one look at him and laugh him out of their kingdom. . . . But then Puggly meets Francesca, the bookish Princess of Spiff, and together the two set out to teach Francesca's Spiffian countrymen an absurd lesson in style." (Publisher's note)

"Plot, theme, and writing style make this a terrific read-aloud." SLJ

★ Zorgamazoo. Razorbill 2008 281p il $15.99
Grades: 4 5 6 7   Fic
1. Novels in verse 2. Adventure fiction 3. Imagination -- Fiction
ISBN 978-1-59514-199-6; 1-59514-199-5

LC 2007-51682

Imaginative and adventurous Katrina eludes her maniacal guardian to help Morty, a member of a vanishing breed of zorgles, with his quest to uncover the fate of the fabled zorgles of Zorgmazoo as well as of other creatures that seem to have disappeared from the earth.

"This book is a natural descendant to the works of Dr. Seuss and Roald Dahl." Booklist

Westrick, A. B.

Brotherhood; Anne Westrick. Viking Juvenile 2013 368 p. (hardback) $17.99
Grades: 5 6 7 8 9   Fic
1. Historical fiction 2. Ku Klux Klan -- Fiction 3. Prejudices -- Fiction 4. Race relations -- Fiction 5. Family life -- Virginia -- Fiction 6. Ku Klux Klan (19th cent.) -- Fiction
ISBN 0670014397; 9780670014392

LC 2013008272

In this historical novel, 14-year-old Shad Weaver's "life is full of secrets. Desperate to learn to read, he begins attending a school for African-Americans. . . . He is very careful not to be seen, especially by any members of the other secret group to which he belongs, the Klan. Shad is deeply ambivalent about the brotherhood, appreciating it for the camaraderie it fosters but becoming increasingly uncomfortable with the violence it perpetuates." He must make a stand when his teacher is murdered. (Kirkus Reviews)

Wharton, Thomas

The **shadow** of Malabron. Candlewick Press 2009 382p (The perilous realm) $16.99

Grades: 5 6 7 8   **Fic**

1. Fantasy fiction

ISBN 978-0-7636-3911-2; 0-7636-3911-7

LC 2009-7768

When Will, a rebellious teen, stumbles from the present into the realm where stories come from, he learns he has a mission concerning the evil Malabron and, aided by some of the story folk, he faces a host of perils while seeking the gateless gate that will take him home.

"Lush descriptive prose, cleverly sustained suspense, a sprinkling of humor and an exciting climax will keep readers riveted to the story, while those who know their folklore will be delighted by Wharton's twisting of the tropes and tales of myth and legend." Kirkus

Whelan, Gloria

★ **Homeless** bird. HarperCollins Pubs. 2000 216p hardcover o.p. pa $5.99

Grades: 6 7 8 9 10   **Fic**

1. India -- Fiction 2. Women -- India -- Fiction

ISBN 0-06-028454-4; 0-06-440819-1 pa

LC 99-33241

When thirteen-year-old Koly enters into an ill-fated arranged marriage, she must either suffer a destiny dictated by India's tradition or find the courage to oppose it.

"This beautifully told, inspiring story takes readers on a fascinating journey through modern India and the universal intricacies of a young woman's heart." Booklist

In Andal's house; written by Gloria Whelan; illustrated by Amanda Hall. Sleeping Bear Press 2013 40 p. $17.95

Grades: 2 3 4   **Fic**

1. Religious holidays 2. India -- Social conditions -- Fiction 3. India -- Fiction 4. Prejudices -- Fiction 5. Social classes -- Fiction

ISBN 158536603X; 9781585366033

LC 2012033684

In this book by Gloria Whelan, "as part of the annual Diwali celebration, Kumar is invited to the house of his classmate Andal. Andal is from a high-caste Brahmin family so Kumar is especially pleased to be included. But there in Andal's house, Kumar's two worlds collide. Instead of being welcomed as a guest, Kumar is sent away, forbidden to join the festivities. Angry and hurt, Kumar is left questioning his place in Indian society. Where does he fit in?" (Publisher's note)

★ **Listening** for lions. HarperCollins 2005 194p $15.99; lib bdg $16.89; pa $5.99

Grades: 5 6 7 8   **Fic**

1. Orphans -- Fiction 2. Physicians -- Fiction 3. East

Africa -- Fiction 4. Great Britain -- Fiction

ISBN 0-06-058174-3; 0-06-058175-1 lib bdg; 0-06-058176-X pa

Left an orphan after the influenza epidemic in British East Africa in 1918, thirteen-year-old Rachel is tricked into assuming a deceased neighbor's identity to travel to England, where her only dream is to return to Africa and rebuild her parents' mission hospital.

"In a straightforward, sympathetic voice, Rachel tells an involving, episodic story." Booklist

★ The **locked** garden. HarperCollins Children's Books 2009 168p $15.99

Grades: 4 5 6 7   **Fic**

1. Michigan -- Fiction 2. Family life -- Fiction 3. Mental illness -- Fiction 4. Psychiatric hospitals -- Fiction

ISBN 978-0-06-079094-3; 0-06-079094-6

LC 2008-24637

After their mother dies of typhoid, Verna and her younger sister Carlie move with their father, a psychiatrist, and stern Aunt Maude to an asylum for the mentally ill in early-twentieth-century Michigan, where new ideas in the treatment of mental illness are being proposed, but old prejudices still hold sway.

"Whelan establishes a strong sense of time, unusual setting and characters. . . . This convincing melodrama portrays an atypical attitude toward treating mental illness." Kirkus

White, E. B.

★ **Charlotte's** web; pictures by Garth Williams. Harper & Row 1952 184p il $16.95; lib bdg $16.89; pa $5.95

Grades: 3 4 5 6   **Fic**

1. Pigs -- Fiction 2. Spiders -- Fiction

ISBN 0-06-026385-7; 0-06-026386-5 lib bdg; 0-06-440055-7 pa

A Newbery Medal honor book, 1953

The story of a little girl who could talk to animals, but especially the story of the pig, Wilbur, and his friendship with Charlotte, the spider, who could not only talk but write as well

"Illustrated with amusing sketches . . . [this] story is a fable for adults as well as children and can be recommended to older children and parents as an amusing story and a gentle essay on friendship." Libr J

★ **Stuart** Little; pictures by Garth Williams. Harper & Row 1945 131p il $16.95; lib bdg $16.89; pa $5.95

Grades: 3 4 5 6   **Fic**

1. Mice -- Fiction

ISBN 0-06-026395-4; 0-06-026396-2 lib bdg; 0-06-440056-5 pa

This is "the story of a 'Tom Thumb'-like child born to a New York couple who is to all intents and purposes a mouse. . . . The first part of the book explores, with deadpan humour, the advantages and disadvantages of having a mouse in one's family circle. Then Stuart sets out on a quest in search of his inamorata, a bird named Margalo, and the story ends in mid-air. The book is outstandingly funny and sometimes touching." Oxford Companion to Child Lit

★ The **trumpet** of the swan; illustrated by Fred Marcellino. HarperCollins Pubs. 2000 251p il $16.95; pa $5.95

Grades: 3 4 5 6 **Fic**
1. Swans -- Fiction
ISBN 0-06-028935-X; 0-06-440867-1 pa
LC 99-44250

A newly illustrated edition of the title first published 1970

Louis, a voiceless Trumpeter swan, finds himself far from his wilderness home when he determines to communicate by learning to play a stolen trumpet

The author "deftly blends true birdlore with fanciful adventures in a witty, captivating fantasy." Booklist

White, J. A.

The **Thickety**; a path begins. J.A. White. Katherine Tegen Books, an imprint of HarperCollinsPublishers 2014 496 p. (hardcover bdg.) $16.99
Grades: 5 6 7 8 **Fic**
1. Fantasy fiction 2. Magic -- Fiction 3. Witches -- Fiction
ISBN 0062257242; 9780062257246
LC 2013021509

This book, by J.A. White, "is the thrilling start of a new middle-grade fantasy series about a girl, a mysterious forest, and a book of untold magical powers. Kara and her brother, Taff, are shunned by their village because their mother was a witch. The villagers believe nothing is more evil than magic, except for what lurks in the nearby Thickety. But when Kara enters the forbidden forest, she discovers a strange book, a grimoire that might have belonged to her mother." (Publisher's note)

"When Kara was just a child, she was accused of witchcraft and forced to watch her mother executed for the same crime. Ever after, she and her family have lived in their isolated theocratic community as pariahs...White's persistent dark imagery, along with Offermann's eerie silhouette spot illustrations, adds to the overall dark atmosphere." Booklist

Path begins

The **whispering** trees; J.A. White; illustrations by Andrea Offermann. Katherine Tegen Books, an imprint of HarperCollinsPublishers 2015 528 p. illustrations (The thickety) $16.99
Grades: 5 6 7 8 **Fic**
1. Fantasy fiction 2. Magic -- Fiction 3. Brothers and sisters -- Fiction 4. Human-animal communication -- Fiction 5. Fantasy
ISBN 0062257293; 9780062257291
LC 2014022226

In this book, by J.A. White, "[a]fter Kara Westfall's village turns on her for practicing witchcraft, she and her brother, Taff, flee to the one place they know they won't be followed: the Thickety. Only this time the Forest Demon, Sordyr, is intent on keeping them there. Sordyr is not the Thickety's only danger: unknown magic lurks behind every twist and shadow of the path." (Publisher's note)

"The menacing Thickety is forbidden, but it's safer for Kara and her little brother, Taff, than staying in the village, now that it's being controlled by a vicious witch. . . . He's created a vivid, unsettling environment of rich magic and terrifying horrors: monsters composed of bones and teeth, tentacled creatures that feed on feelings, shadows that consume bodies, and more. Kara still seems much older than her 12 years, but that's a minor complaint that doesn't distract from the lush descriptions of a spine-tingling, captivating place." Booklist

White, Ruth

★ **Belle** Prater's boy. Farrar, Straus & Giroux 1996 196p $17
Grades: 5 6 7 8 **Fic**
1. Cousins -- Fiction 2. Virginia -- Fiction 3. Appalachian region -- Fiction
ISBN 0-374-30668-0
LC 94-43625

A Newbery Medal honor book, 1997

"Gypsy and her cousin Woodrow become close friends after Woodrow's mother disappears. Both sixth-graders feel deserted by their parents—Gypsy discovers that her father committed suicide—and need to define themselves apart from these tragedies. White's prose evokes the coal mining region of Virginia and the emotional quality of her characters' transformations." Horn Book Guide

Another title about Belle Prater is:

The search for Belle Prater (2005)

★ **Little** Audrey. Farrar, Straus & Giroux 2008 145p $16
Grades: 5 6 7 8 **Fic**
1. Death -- Fiction 2. Virginia -- Fiction 3. Coal miners -- Fiction 4. Country life -- Fiction
ISBN 978-0-374-34580-8; 0-374-34580-5
LC 2007-29310

In 1948, eleven-year-old Audrey lives with her father, mother, and three younger sisters in Jewell Valley, a coal mining camp in Southwest Virginia, where her mother still mourns the death of a baby, her father goes on drinking binges on paydays, and Audrey tries to recover from the scarlet fever that has left her skinny and needing to wear glasses.

"The setting is perfectly portrayed and the characterizations ring true." Voice Youth Advocates

The **treasure** of Way Down Deep; Ruth White. Margaret Ferguson Books 2013 176 p. (hardcover) $16.99
Grades: 5 6 7 8 **Fic**
1. Halloween -- Fiction 2. Buried treasure -- Fiction 3. Dogs -- Fiction 4. Orphans -- Fiction 5. Foundlings -- Fiction 6. Boardinghouses -- Fiction 7. Community life -- West Virginia -- Fiction 8. West Virginia -- History -- 1951- -- Fiction
ISBN 0374380678; 9780374377472; 9780374380670
LC 2012021665

Sequel to: Way Down Deep

Parents' Choice: Silver Medal Fiction (2013)

In this book by Ruth White, "Ruby loves her life, but things start turning when her pet goat dies and Miss Arbutus feels an ill wind blowing into town. Then the local mines start closing, and everyone in Way Down Deep feels the pinch. Can Ruby help save the town? Will the special button Rita gave her as a gift be part of the solution? And can the town come together when a treasure appears?" (Booklist)

★ **Way** Down Deep. Farrar, Straus and Giroux 2007 197p $16
Grades: 5 6 7 8 **Fic**
1. Orphans -- Fiction 2. West Virginia -- Fiction
ISBN 0-374-38251-4; 978-0-374-38251-3
LC 2006-46324

In the West Virginia town of Way Down Deep in the 1950s, a foundling called Ruby June is happily living with

Miss Arbutus at the local boarding house when suddenly, after the arrival of a family of outsiders, the mystery of Ruby's past begins to unravel.

This is "a story as tender as a breeze and as sharp as a tack. . . . At the heart of the story are profound questions that readers will enjoy puzzling out." Booklist

You'll like it here (everybody does) Delacorte Press 2011 272p $16.99; lib bdg $19.99
Grades: 4 5 6 7 **Fic**
1. Science fiction 2. Family life -- Fiction 3. Interplanetary voyages -- Fiction 4. Extraterrestrial beings -- Fiction
ISBN 978-0-385-73998-6; 0-385-73998-2; 978-0-385-90813-9 lib bdg; 0-385-90813-X lib bdg
LC 2010-32153
Although Meggie Blue seems to be an average sixth-grader she is abnormally frightened when residents of her small, North Carolina town become fixated on aliens, and soon she and her family are forced to flee, making it clear that all is not as it seems.

White's "considerable writing skills elevate a story with many familiar elements, including the importance of individuality, the pitfalls of conformity, and the tyranny of a dictatorship. Kids will like this, but it's also a fun jumping off point for serious discussion." Booklist

White, T. H.
★ The **sword** in the stone; with illustrations by Dennis Nolan. Putnam 1993 256p il $24.99
Grades: 4 5 6 7 **Fic**
1. Kings 2. Merlin (Legendary character) -- Fiction
ISBN 0-399-22502-1
LC 92-24808
A newly illustrated edition of the title first published 1938 in the United Kingdom; first United States edition 1939 by G.P Putnam's Sons

"In White's classic story about the boyhood of King Arthur, Wart—unaware of his true identity—is tutored by Merlyn, who occasionally transform the young boy into various animals as part of his schooling. Contemporary children will still enjoy the text, which is both fantastical and down-to-earth." Horn Book Guide

Whittemore, Jo
Odd girl in. Simon & Schuster 2011 234p pa $6.99
Grades: 4 5 6 **Fic**
1. School stories 2. Siblings -- Fiction
ISBN 978-1-4424-1284-2; 1-4424-1284-4
"Spunky 12-year-old Alex doesn't really want friends or a social life. . . . She hates girly giggling parties and doesn't see any other girls in her middle school that she'd want to have as a friend, so she just concentrates on following in the footsteps of her prankster older twin brothers. . . . Alex's absent mother provides an element of drama in this otherwise witty, laugh-out-loud romp. Whittemore handles not only the comedy but deftly portrays Alex's and her brothers' advancement into a more mature state of mind. It should keep middle-schoolers laughing from start to finish." Kirkus

Whittenberg, Allison
Sweet Thang. Delacorte Press 2006 149p $15.95
Grades: 5 6 7 8 **Fic**
1. School stories 2. Family life -- Fiction 3. African

Americans -- Fiction
ISBN 0-385-73292-9
LC 2005-03809
In 1975, life is not fair for fourteen-year-old Charmaine Upshaw, who shares a room with her brother, tries to impress a handsome classmate, and acts as caretaker for a rambunctious six-year-old cousin who has taken over the family.

"Whittenberg has created a refreshing cast and a good read." SLJ
Another title about the Upshaw family is:
Hollywood & Maine (2009)

Wildavsky, Rachel
The **secret** of Rover. Amulet Books 2011 351p $16.95
Grades: 5 6 7 8 **Fic**
1. Twins -- Fiction 2. Uncles -- Fiction 3. Siblings -- Fiction 4. Inventions -- Fiction 5. Kidnapping -- Fiction 6. Washington (D.C.) -- Fiction 7. Voyages and travels -- Fiction
ISBN 0-8109-9710-X; 978-0-8109-9710-3
LC 2010-23450
Twelve-year-old twins Katie and David Bowen evade foreign militants and make their way from Washington, D.C. to their uncle's Vermont home, hoping he can help rescue their parents, who were kidnapped because of their secret invention, Rover.

"Kids making the transition from series mysteries to more sophisticated thrillers will do well by this suspenseful and age-appropriate drama." Bull Cent Child Books

Wilder, Laura Ingalls
★ **Little** house in the big woods; illustrated by Garth Williams. newly illustrated, uniform ed; Harper & Row 1953 237p il (Little house) $16.95; lib bdg $16.89; pa $6.99
Grades: 4 5 6 **Fic**
1. Wisconsin -- Fiction 2. Family life -- Fiction 3. Frontier and pioneer life -- Fiction
ISBN 0-06-026430-6; 0-06-026431-4 lib bdg; 0-06-440001-8 pa
First published 1932
A year in the life of two young girls growing up on the Wisconsin frontier, as they help their mother with the daily chores, enjoy their father's stories and singing, and share special occasions when they get together with relatives or neighbors.

Other titles in the Little House series are:
Farmer boy (1933)
Little house on the prairie (1935)
On the banks of Plum Creek (1937)
By the shores of Silver Lake (1939)
The long winter (1940)
Little town on the prairie (1941)
These happy golden years (1943)
The first four years (1971)

Wiles, Deborah
★ The **Aurora** County All-Stars. Harcourt 2007 242p il $16; pa $5.99
Grades: 4 5 6 **Fic**
1. Death -- Fiction 2. Baseball -- Fiction 3. Mississippi

-- Fiction 4. Race relations -- Fiction

ISBN 978-0-15-206068-8; 0-15-206068-5; 978-0-15-206626-0 pa; 0-15-206626-8 pa

LC 2006-102551

In a small Mississippi town, after the death of the old man to whom twelve-year-old star pitcher House Jackson has been secretly reading for a year, House uncovers secrets about the man and the history of baseball in Aurora County.

"Quotations from Walt Whitman's poetry, baseball players and Aurora County news dispatches pepper the story and add color. . . . A home run for Wiles." Publ Wkly

★ **Countdown**. Scholastic 2010 377p il (The sixties trilogy) $17.99

Grades: 5 6 7 8   **Fic**

1. Cold war -- Fiction 2. Family life -- Fiction 3. Cuban Missile Crisis, 1962 -- Fiction

ISBN 978-0-545-10605-4; 0-545-10605-2

It's 1962, and it seems everyone is living in fear. Twelve-year-old Franny Chapman lives with her family in Washington, DC, during the days surrounding the Cuban Missile Crisis. Amidst the pervasive threat of nuclear war, Franny must face the tension between herself and her younger brother, figure out where she fits in with her family, and look beyond outward appearances.

"Wiles skillfully keeps many balls in the air, giving readers a story that appeals across the decades as well as offering enticing paths into the history." Booklist

Love, Ruby Lavender. Harcourt 2001 188p il $16; pa $5.95

Grades: 4 5 6   **Fic**

1. Mississippi -- Fiction 2. Grandparents -- Fiction

ISBN 0-15-202314-3; 0-15-205478-2 pa

LC 00-11159

When her quirky grandmother goes to Hawaii for the summer, nine-year-old Ruby learns to survive on her own in Mississippi by writing letters, befriending chickens as well as the new girl in town, and finally coping with her grandfather's death

"The engaging narrative . . . is witty and fast paced and the quirky, diverse cast of human and poultry characters is colorful and spirited, if not totally realistic." SLJ

★ **Revolution**; Deborah Wiles. First edition Scholastic 2014 495 p. illustrations, map (The sixties trilogy) $19.99

Grades: 5 6 7 8   **Fic**

1. Family life -- Fiction 2. Nineteen sixties -- Fiction 3. United States -- History -- Fiction 4. African Americans -- Civil rights -- Fiction

ISBN 0545106079; 9780545106078

LC 2014935954

National Book Award Shortlist: Young People's Literature (2014)

In this book, by Deborah Wiles, "it's 1964, and Sunny's town is being invaded. Or at least that's what the adults of Greenwood, Mississippi are saying. All Sunny knows is that people from up north are coming to help people register to vote. They're calling it Freedom Summer. Meanwhile, Sunny can't help but feel like her house is being invaded, too. She has a new stepmother, a new brother, and a new

sister crowding her life, giving her little room to breathe." (Publisher's note)

"Wiles does an excellent job of entwining the two plot strands and seamlessly integrating her exhaustive research, which is detailed at the book's conclusion. . . . As in Countdown, the outstanding period artwork, photographs, snippets of sayings, and songs interspersed throughout bring a troubled time close." Booklist

Williams, Alex

The **talent** thief; an extraordinary tale of an ordinary boy. Philomel Books 2010 300p $16.99

Grades: 5 6 7 8   **Fic**

1. Adventure fiction 2. Orphans -- Fiction

ISBN 978-0-399-25278-5; 0-399-25278-9

Orphaned Cressida, a magnificent singer, and her twelve-year-old brother Adam attend the by-invitation-only Festival of Youthful Genius, where they join forces with a former race car driver to try to stop a bizarre creature from stealing the talents of the young prodigies.

"This is a story that fantasy and adventure fans will enjoy, and the well-paced action will propel them to the end." SLJ

Williams, Laura E.

Slant; [by] Laura E. Williams. Milkweed Editions 2008 149p $16.95; pa $6.95

Grades: 5 6 7 8 9   **Fic**

1. Mothers -- Fiction 2. Adoption -- Fiction 3. Friendship -- Fiction 4. Prejudices -- Fiction 5. Plastic surgery -- Fiction 6. Korean Americans -- Fiction

ISBN 978-1-57131-681-3; 1-57131-681-7; 978-1-57131-682-0 pa; 1-57131-682-5 pa

LC 2008007093

Thirteen-year-old Lauren, a Korean-American adoptee, is tired of being called "slant" and "gook," and longs to have plastic surgery on her eyes, but when her father finds out about her wish—and a long-kept secret about her mother's death is revealed—Lauren starts to question some of her own assumptions

"The characters are exceptionally well drawn, and the friendship between Julie and Lauren is not only believable, featuring humor, conflict, and true wit, but also captures both girls' gains in maturity." SLJ

Williams, Maiya

The **Fizzy** Whiz kid. Amulet Books 2010 273p $16.95

Grades: 5 6 7 8   **Fic**

1. Moving -- Fiction 2. Advertising -- Fiction 3. Hollywood (Calif.) -- Fiction

ISBN 978-0-8109-8347-2; 0-8109-8347-8

Moving to Hollywood with his academic parents, eleven-year-old Mitch feels like an outsider in his school where everyone has connections to the powerful and famous in the entertainment industry, until he is cast in a soda commercial that launches a popular catchphrase.

"Williams' breezy tale is as addictive and bubbly as a Fizzy Whiz itself, and her experience in the entertainment industry packs real value into her descriptions of auditions, movie sets, and agent negotiations. . . . Mitchell's realization that he is a product being assembled is both goofy and poignant." Booklist

Williams, Marcia, 1945-

Archie's war; my scrapbook of the First World War, 1914-1918. Candlewick Press 2007 45p il $17.99

Grades: 3 4 5 6   **Fic**

1. Great Britain -- Fiction 2. World War, 1914-1918 -- Fiction

ISBN 0-7636-3532-4; 978-0-7636-3532-9

LC 2007-23012

When Archie is given a scrapbook for his tenth birthday in 1914, he chronicles the next four years of his life using documents, artifacts, and comic strips

"The large-format pages, jam-packed with tiny colored-pencil drawings with extensive captions, detailed sidebars, and pasted-in letters and postcards, flesh out the story and characters. . . . This imaginative presentation of historical fiction puts them in context and provides a highly visual experience that readers will pore over again and again." SLJ

My secret war diary, by Flossie Albright; my history of the Second World War, 1939-1945. Candlewick Press 2008 141p il lib bdg $21.99

Grades: 3 4 5 6   **Fic**

1. Diaries -- Fiction 2. World War, 1939-1945 -- Fiction

ISBN 978-0-7636-4111-5 lib bdg; 0-7636-4111-1 lib bdg

Marcia Williams uses her own childhood momentos to create a diary of a nine-year-old girl in Britain during World War II

"Children will quickly come to enjoy Flossie's energetic delivery and endless doodling. They will love poring over the extras-asides, sidebars, and letters found under flaps and in envelopes, that Williams has compiled to give the book the feel that one has stumbled into a real girl's private keepsake. . . . Children who enjoy history will be fascinated by Flossie and will undoubtedly be inspired to learn more about the events she describes." SLJ

Williams, Mary

Brothers in hope; the story of the Lost Boys of Sudan. illustrated by R. Gregory Christie. Lee & Low Books 2005 un il $17.95

Grades: 3 4 5   **Fic**

1. War stories 2. Sudan -- Fiction 3. Refugees -- Fiction

ISBN 1-58430-232-1

LC 2004-20965

Eight-year-old Garang, orphaned by a civil war in Sudan, finds the inner strength to help lead other boys as they trek hundreds of miles seeking safety in Ethiopia, then Kenya, and finally in the United States.

"Christie's distinctive acrylic illustrations, done in broad strokes of predominantly green, yellow, and burnt orange, are arresting in their combination of realism and the abstract. . . . This important profile in courage is one that belongs in most collections." SLJ

Williams, Michael

★ Now is the time for running. Little, Brown 2011 233p $17.99

Grades: 6 7 8 9 10   **Fic**

1. Soccer -- Fiction 2. Brothers -- Fiction 3. Refugees -- Fiction 4. Zimbabwe -- Fiction 5. Homeless persons

-- Fiction 6. People with mental disabilities -- Fiction

ISBN 978-0-316-07790-3; 0-316-07790-9

LC 2010043460

"There is plenty of material to captivate readers: fast-paced soccer matches every bit as tough as the players; the determination of Deo and his fellow refugees to survive unthinkably harsh conditions; and raw depictions of violence. . . . But it's the tender relationship between Deo and Innocent, along with some heartbreaking twists of fate, that will endure in readers' minds." Publ Wkly

"Just down the road from their families, Deo and his friends play soccer in the dusty fields of Zimbabwe, cheered on by Deo's older brother, Innocent. It is a day like any other . . . until the soldiers arrive and Deo and Innocent are forced to run for their lives, fleeing the wreckage of their village for the distant promise of safe haven." (Publisher's note)

Williams, Tad

The dragons of Ordinary Farm; by Tad Williams and Deborah Beale; pictures by Greg Swearingen. Harper 2009 412p il $16.99

Grades: 4 5 6 7   **Fic**

1. Farms -- Fiction 2. Uncles -- Fiction 3. Siblings -- Fiction 4. Supernatural -- Fiction 5. Mythical animals -- Fiction

ISBN 978-0-06-154345-6; 0-06-154345-4

LC 2008035298

When their great-uncle Gideon invites Tyler and Lucinda to his farm for the summer, they discover his animals are extremely unusual.

"Williams and Beale have created a gripping fantasy with realistic but appealing characters as well as scientific magic that explains the appearance of legendary creatures." SLJ

Williams-Garcia, Rita

★ Gone Crazy in Alabama; by Rita Williams-Garcia. Harpercollins Childrens Books 2015 304 p. $16.99

Grades: 4 5 6 7 8   **Fic**

1. Sisters -- Fiction 2. Family secrets -- Fiction 3. African American children -- Fiction 4. Mothers -- Fiction

ISBN 0062215876; 9780062215871

This novel by Rita Williams-Garcia "tells the story of the Gaither sisters, who are about to learn what it's like to be fish out of water as they travel from the streets of Brooklyn to the rural South for the summer of a lifetime. . . . As Delphine hears about her family history, she uncovers the surprising truth that's been keeping the sisters apart. But when tragedy strikes, Delphine discovers that the bonds of family run deeper than she ever knew possible." (Publisher's note)

"This well-crafted depiction of a close-knit community in rural Alabama works beautifully, with language that captures its humor, sorrow and resilience. Rich in all areas, Delphine and her sisters' third outing will fully satisfy the many fans of their first two." Kirkus

Previous books in the trilogy are:

One Crazy Summer (2010)

P.S. Be Eleven (2013)

★ One crazy summer. Amistad 2010 218p $15.99; lib bdg $16.89

Grades: 4 5 6 7 8   **Fic**

1. Poets -- Fiction 2. Mothers -- Fiction 3. Sisters

-- Fiction 4. Black Panther Party -- Fiction. 5. Young adult literature -- Works 6. African Americans -- Civil rights -- Fiction

ISBN 978-0-06-076088-5; 0-06-076088-5; 978-0-06-076089-2 lib bdg; 0-06-076089-3 lib bdg

LC 2009-09293

A Newbery Medal honor book, 2011

In the summer of 1968, after travelling from Brooklyn to Oakland, California, to spend a month with the mother they barely know, eleven-year-old Delphine and her two younger sisters arrive to a cold welcome as they discover that their mother, a dedicated poet and printer, is resentful of the intrusion of their visit and wants them to attend a nearby Black Panther summer camp.

"Delphine's growing awareness of injustice on a personal and universal level is smoothly woven into the story in poetic language that will stimulate and move readers." Publ Wkly

★ **P.S.** Be Eleven; Rita Williams-Garcia. Harpercollins Childrens Books 2013 288 p. $16.99

Grades: 4 5 6 7 8   Fic

1. Historical fiction 2. African American children

ISBN 0061938629; 9780061938627

Sequel to: One crazy summer.

Coretta Scott King Book Award Author Winner (2014)

This book is a follow-up to Rita Williams-Garcia's Newbery Honor-winning "One Crazy Summer." Here, "Delphine and her sisters return to Brooklyn from visiting their estranged mother, Cecile, a poet .... Change and conflict have the Gaither household in upheaval: Pa has a new girlfriend, Uncle Darnell returns from Vietnam a damaged young man, and the sixth-grade teacher Delphine hoped to get has been replaced by a man from Zambia." (Publishers Weekly)

"...Soars as a finely drawn portrait of a family in flux and as a memorable slice of a specific time in our nation's history." Booklist

Willingham, Bill

★ **Down** the Mysterly River; illustrations by Mark Buckingham. Tor/Starscape 2011 333p il $15.99

Grades: 4 5 6 7   Fic

1. Fantasy fiction 2. Memory -- Fiction 3. Animals -- Fiction 4. Forests and forestry -- Fiction

ISBN 978-0-7653-2792-5; 0-7653-2792-9

LC 2011018958

Top notch Boy Scout Max "the Wolf" cannot remember how he came to be in a strange forest, but soon he and three talking animals are on the run from the Blue Cutters, hunters who will alter the foursome's very essence if they can catch them.

"Willingham rolls out his themes slowly, only fully spelling them out in the final scene, but they don't interfere with the rollicking story, nasty (but fully realized) villains, and heroic camaraderie. . . . [This] is a stellar example of a novel working both as an adventure tale and as metafiction." Publ Wkly

Willner-Pardo, Gina

The **hard** kind of promise. Clarion Books/Houghton Mifflin Harcourt 2010 200p $16

Grades: 4 5 6 7   Fic

1. School stories 2. California -- Fiction 3. Friendship

-- Fiction 4. Popularity -- Fiction

ISBN 978-0-547-24395-5; 0-547-24395-2

California seventh-graders Sarah and Marjorie made a promise in kindergarten to always be friends, but Marjorie is weird and Sarah, wanting to be at least somewhat popular, makes friends with a fellow choir member.

"Willner-Pardo's avoidance of overblown crises and dramatic climaxes creates a steadily paced, authentic story" Publ Wkly

Willocks, Tim

Doglands. Random House 2011 308p $16.99; lib bdg $19.99; ebook $16.99

Grades: 5 6 7 8   Fic

1. Adventure fiction 2. Dogs -- Fiction 3. Supernatural -- Fiction 4. Animal welfare -- Fiction

ISBN 978-0-375-86571-8; 0-375-86571-3; 978-0-375-96571-5 lib bdg; 0-375-96571-8 lib bdg; 978-0-375-89604-0 ebook; 0-375-89604-X ebook

LC 2009033328

Furgal, a half-greyhound puppy, escapes a cruel dog-track owner and sets out in the hope of finding his father and the fabled Doglands, later returning to try to free his mother, sisters, and the other abused dogs.

"The dogs each have distinct personalities, and the mystic lore of the Doglands adds a secondary fantasy layer to the narrative. Humans are only sketched in, which is fitting, since the tale is told from the dog point of view. A riveting dog tale with a healthy serving of savagery, not all on the part of the four-legged characters." Kirkus

Wilson, Daniel H.

A **boy** and his bot. Bloomsbury 2011 180p $16.99

Grades: 4 5 6 7   Fic

1. Science fiction 2. Robots -- Fiction

ISBN 978-1-59990-280-7; 1-59990-280-X

LC 2010-10635

When timid young Code falls down a hole into Mekhos, where everything is made of metal and circuitry, he must obtain the legendary Robonomicon from evil Immortalis in order to save the robots of this subterranean world and return home.

"Wilson ably balances Code's grief about his grandfather's fate with his astonishment and excitement about the quest upon which he embarks; both sets of emotions feel authentic. . . . Readers who are curious about the ways robots work or about electronics in general will find the level of detail throughout particularly interesting." Bull Cent Child Books

Wilson, Jacqueline

Cookie; illustrated by Nick Sharratt. Roaring Brook Press 2009 320p il $16.99

Grades: 4 5 6 7   Fic

1. Friendship -- Fiction 2. Father-daughter relationship -- Fiction

ISBN 978-1-59643-534-6; 1-59643-534-8

Cookie is plain and shy, not the confident, popular girl her father wanted when he named her Beauty Cookson. Her mother helps her cook up a clever scheme to change her image—but, as usual, Dad doesn't approve, and this time his anger reaches frightening new heights

"Wilson's talent shows again in this novel with strong, compelling characters and a plot that makes the book hard to put down." SLJ

The **illustrated** Mum; [by] Jacqueline Wilson. Delacorte Press 2005 282p hardcover o.p. pa $5.50
Grades: 5 6 7 8   **Fic**
1. Sisters -- Fiction 2. Tattooing -- Fiction 3. Manic-depressive illness -- Fiction 4. Mother-daughter relationship -- Fiction
ISBN 0-385-73237-6; 0-440-42043-1 pa
                                        LC 2003-70123
First published 1999 in the United Kingdom
Ten-year-old Dolphin is determined to stay with her family, no matter what, but when her sister goes to live with her newly-discovered father, sending their mother further into manic-depression, Dolphin's life takes a turn for the better.
"Dolphin is a sympathetic character and the relationship between the sisters is realistically portrayed, as is Marigold's mental illness." SLJ

Wilson, N. D.
★ The **dragon's** tooth; [by] N. D. Wilson. Random House 2011 485p (Ashtown burials) $16.99; lib bdg $19.99; e-book $16.99
Grades: 5 6 7 8   **Fic**
1. Fantasy fiction 2. Magic -- Fiction 3. Siblings -- Fiction 4. Secret societies -- Fiction
ISBN 978-0-375-86439-1; 0-375-86439-3; 978-0-375-96439-8 lib bdg; 0-375-96439-8 lib bdg; 978-0-375-89572-2 e-book
                                        LC 2009038651
"This fast-paced fantasy quickly draws readers in to its alternate reality. . . . Allusions to mythology and complex character development . . . make Wilson's first in a proposed series a gem." Booklist
"Cyrus and Antigone, siblings ages 12 and 13 1/2, respectively, are thrown into adventure when they must leave the ancient motel in Wisconsin that has been their home in ashes and are driven by a lawyer with very strange speech patterns in a limo to Ashtown, where an alternate world awaits. Might their parents, thought dead, actually be alive?" Kirkus

The **drowned** vault; N.D. Wilson. Random House 2012 449 p. (Ashtown burials) (lib. bdg.) $19.99
Grades: 5 6 7 8   **Fic**
1. Occult fiction 2. Fantasy fiction 3. Magic -- Fiction 4. Apprentices -- Fiction
ISBN 0375964401; 9780375864407; 9780375895739; 9780375964404
                                        LC 2011051618
This book is N.D. Wilson's sequel to "The Dragon's Tooth." "Thanks to Cyrus and Antigone Smith, Dr. Phoenix now possesses the Dragon's Tooth—and he's been using it to hunt and kill immortals worldwide. Phoenix has a dark agenda, but an evil alliance of immortals, Ordo Draconis, also seeks the tooth's power. Worse, the Ordos have a centuries-old vendetta against the Smith family." (School Library Journal)

Wilson, Nancy Hope
Mountain pose. Farrar, Straus & Giroux 2001 233p $17

Grades: 5 6 7 8   **Fic**
1. Diaries -- Fiction 2. Vermont -- Fiction 3. Grandmothers -- Fiction
ISBN 0-374-35078-7
                                        LC 00-57269
When twelve-year-old Ellie inherits an old Vermont farm from her cruel and heartless grandmother Aurelia, she reads a set of diaries written by an ancestor and discovers secrets from the past
"Beautifully written and suspenseful, this novel explores the many emotions associated with the tragedy of spousal and child abuse." Voice Youth Advocates

Wilson, Nathan D.
100 cupboards; [by] N. D. Wilson. Random House 2007 289p $16.99; lib bdg $19.99; pa $6.99
Grades: 5 6 7 8   **Fic**
1. Magic -- Fiction 2. Kansas -- Fiction 3. Cousins -- Fiction
ISBN 978-0-375-83881-1; 978-0-375-93881-8 lib bdg; 978-0-375-83882-8 pa
                                        LC 2007-00164
After his parents are kidnapped, timid twelve-year-old Henry York leaves his sheltered Boston life and moves to small-town Kansas, where he and his cousin Henrietta discover and explore hidden doors in his attic room that seem to open onto other worlds
"There's an appealing blend of genuine creepiness and kindly domesticity here." Bull Cent Child Books
Other titles in this series are:
Dandelion Fire (2008)
The Chestnut King (2010)

★ **Leepike** Ridge; [by] N. D. Wilson. Random House 2007 224p $15.99; lib bdg $18.99; pa $6.99
Grades: 4 5 6 7   **Fic**
1. Adventure fiction 2. Caves -- Fiction 3. Missing persons -- Fiction 4. Mother-son relationship -- Fiction
ISBN 978-0-375-83873-6; 0-375-83873-2; 978-0-375-93873-3 lib bdg; 0-375-93873-7 lib bdg; 978-0-375-83874-3 pa; 0-375-83874-0 pa
                                        LC 2006-13352
While his widowed mother continues to search for him, eleven-year-old Tom, presumed dead after drifting away down a river, finds himself trapped in a series of underground caves with another survivor and a dog, and pursued by murderous treasure-hunters
"While Leepike Ridge is primarily an adventure story involving murder, treachery, and betrayal, Wilson's rich imagination and his quirky characters are a true delight." SLJ

Winerip, Michael
Adam Canfield of the Slash. Candlewick Press 2005 326p $15.99; pa $6.99
Grades: 5 6 7 8   **Fic**
1. School stories 2. Journalism -- Fiction
ISBN 0-7636-2340-7; 0-7636-2794-1 pa
While serving as co-editors of their school newspaper, middle-schoolers Adam and Jennifer uncover fraud and corruption in their school and in the city's government.
"This is a deceptively fun read that somehow manages to present kids with some of the most subtle social and ethical questions currently shaping their futures." SLJ
Other titles about Adam Canfield are:

Adam Canfield, watch you back! (2007)

Adam Canfield, the last reporter (2009)

Winston, Sherri

President of the whole fifth grade. Little, Brown 2010 273p $15.99

Grades: 3 4 5   **Fic**

1. School stories 2. Baking -- Fiction 3. Elections -- Fiction 4. Friendship -- Fiction

ISBN 0-316-11432-4; 978-0-316-11432-5

LC 2010-06366

To gain leadership skills needed to run a cupcake-baking empire when she grows up, Brianna runs for president of the fifth grade—expecting little competition—until a new girl enters the race.

"The story will resonate with preteens navigating the ups, downs, and drama that come with the territory of many young girls' friendships." SLJ

Winters, Ben H.

The **mystery** of the missing everything. Harper 2011 263p $16.99

Grades: 4 5 6 7   **Fic**

1. School stories 2. Mystery fiction

ISBN 978-0-06-196544-9; 0-06-196544-8

LC 2011010167

Sequel to: The secret life of Ms. Finkleman (2010)

When a treasured trophy disappears from the display case at Mary Todd Lincoln Middle School and the principal cancels the eagerly anticipated eighth grade class trip, Bethesda Fielding has no choice but to solve the mystery.

"Featuring the same cast of eccentric teachers and eclectic students, this zany sequel offers another fast-moving middle-school puzzler, lots of pre and early teen humor and one relentless sleuth who's willing to admit when she's wrong. Fans will cheer more mystery and mayhem at Mary Todd Lincoln Middle School." Kirkus

The **secret** life of Ms. Finkleman. Harper 2010 247p $16.99

Grades: 4 5 6 7   **Fic**

1. School stories 2. Teachers -- Fiction 3. Musicians -- Fiction 4. Rock music -- Fiction

ISBN 978-0-06-196541-8; 0-06-196541-3

LC 2010-04601

Spurred by a special project from her social studies teacher, seventh-grader Bethesda Fielding uncovers the secret identity of her music teacher, which leads to a most unusual concert performance and a tutoring assignment.

"Liberally laced with humor and featuring an upbeat heroine, unexpected friendship and rock-music trivia, this witty middle-school drama offers a lighthearted lesson in the importance of getting the facts straight." Kirkus

Another title about Bethesda Fielding is:

The mystery of missing everything (2011)

Winterson, Jeanette

Tanglewreck. Bloomsbury Children's Books 2006 414p $16.95; pa $6.95

Grades: 5 6 7 8   **Fic**

1. Science fiction 2. Space and time -- Fiction 3.

Clocks and watches -- Fiction

ISBN 978-1-58234-919-0; 1-58234-919-3; 978-1-59990-081-0 pa; 1-59990-081-5 pa

LC 2005-30630

Eleven-year-old Silver sets out to find the Timekeeper—a clock that controls time—and to protect it from falling into the hands of two people who want to use the device for their own nefarious ends

"Winterson seamlessly combines rousing adventure with time warps, quantum physics, and a few wonderfully hapless flunkies." Booklist

Winthrop, Elizabeth

Counting on Grace. Wendy Lamb Books 2006 232p $15.95; lib bdg $17.99; pa $6.99

Grades: 5 6 7 8   **Fic**

1. Photographers 2. Vermont -- Fiction 3. Factories -- Fiction 4. Child labor -- Fiction 5. Photographers -- Fiction

ISBN 0-385-74644-X; 0-385-90878-4 lib bdg; 0-553-48783-3 pa

It's 1910 in Pownal, Vermont. At 12 Grace and her best friend Arthur must go to work in the mill, helping their mothers work the looms. Together Grace and Arthur write a secret letter to the Child Labor Board about underage children working in the mill. A few weeks later, Lewis Hine, a famous reformer, arrives undercover to gather evidence. Grace meets him and appears in some of his photographs, changing her life forever.

"Much information on early photography and the workings of the textile mills is conveyed, and history and fiction are woven seamlessly together in this beautifully written novel." SLJ

Wise, William

Christopher Mouse; the tale of a small traveler. illustrations by Patrick Benson. Bloomsbury Children's Books 2004 152p il $15.95; pa $5.95

Grades: 3 4 5   **Fic**

1. Mice -- Fiction

ISBN 1-58234-878-2; 1-58234-708-5 pa

LC 2003-56393

After being sold to an unscrupulous pet store owner, a young mouse lives with several owners and has many adventures, before ending up with an appreciative family.

"The writing is nicely mannered but very accessible, making the book not only a winner for reading aloud but also a delightful offering for children moving past beginning readers. The ink illustrations and the enticing cover will help them along." Booklist

Wiseman, David

Jeremy Visick. Houghton Mifflin 1981 170p hardcover o.p. pa $5.95

Grades: 5 6 7 8   **Fic**

1. Miners -- Fiction 2. Supernatural -- Fiction 3. Great Britain -- Fiction 4. Space and time -- Fiction

ISBN 0-618-34514-0 pa

LC 80-28116

Twelve-year-old Matthew is drawn almost against his will to help a boy his own age who was lost in a mining disaster a century before.

"This story blends the mystery and awe of the supernatural with the real terror and peril of descending the shaft of an 1850 Cornish copper mine." SLJ

Wissinger, Tamera Will

Gone fishing; a novel. by Tamera Will Wissinger. Houghton Mifflin Books for Children 2013 128 p. (hardcover) $15.99

Grades: 1 2 3 4   **Fic**

1. Novels in verse 2. Fishing -- Poetry 3. Fishing -- Fiction 4. Brothers and sisters -- Fiction
ISBN 0547820119; 9780547820118

LC 2012032796

This book from Tamera Will Wissinger "offers a collection of more than 40 poems, which join to form a novel in verse about a family's fishing trip. Sam is initially distraught when his sister, Lucy, worms her way into his fishing trip with his father; as the day progresses, though, sibling rivalry turns to appreciation, especially after Sam catches a giant catfish." (Publishers Weekly)

Wittlinger, Ellen

This means war! Simon & Schuster Books for Young Readers 2010 224p $16.99

Grades: 5 6 7 8   **Fic**

1. Fear -- Fiction 2. Contests -- Fiction 3. Friendship -- Fiction
ISBN 978-1-4169-97101-6; 1-4169-7101-7

LC 2008-32586

In 1962, when her best friend Lowell begins to hang around new friends who think girls are losers, Juliet, a fearful fifth-grader, teams up with bold, brave Patsy who challenges the boys to a series of increasingly dangerous contests

"Wittlinger latches on to a poignant metaphor for war in the lively and readable tale set against the backdrop of the 1962 Cuban missile crisis." Booklist

Woelfle, Gretchen

All the world's a stage; a novel in five acts. illustrated by Thomas Cox. Holiday House 2011 163p il $16.95

Grades: 4 5 6 7   **Fic**

1. Actors -- Fiction 2. Orphans -- Fiction 3. Theater -- Fiction 4. Apprentices -- Fiction 5. Globe Theatre (London, England) -- Fiction 6. Chamberlain's Men (Theater company) -- Fiction 7. Great Britain -- History -- 1485-1603, Tudors -- Fiction
ISBN 978-0-8234-2281-4; 0-8234-2281-X

LC 2010023474

Twelve-year-old orphan Christopher "Kit" Buckles becomes a stage boy in a London theater in 1598, tries his hand at acting, and later helps build the Globe Theater for playwright William Shakespeare and the Chamberlain's Men acting troupe.

"The most compelling drama is Kit's universal search for his calling and his shifting friendships. . . . Frequent charming drawings enhance the sense of time and place." Booklist

Includes glossary and bibliographical references

Wojciechowska, Maia

Shadow of a bull; drawings by Alvin Smith. Atheneum Pubs. 1964 165p il $16; pa $5.99

Grades: 6 7 8 9   **Fic**

1. Spain -- Fiction 2. Bullfights -- Fiction
ISBN 0-689-30042-5; 1-4169-3395-6 pa

Awarded the Newbery Medal, 1965

"In spare, economical prose [the author] makes one feel, see, smell the heat, endure the hot Andalusian sun and shows one the sand and glare of the bullring. Above all, she lifts the veil and gives glimpses of the terrible loneliness in the soul of a boy. . . . Superbly illustrated." N Y Times Book Rev

Wolf, Joan M.

★ **Someone** named Eva. Clarion Books 2007 200p $16; pa $6.99

Grades: 5 6 7 8   **Fic**

1. School stories 2. National socialism -- Fiction 3. World War, 1939-1945 -- Fiction
ISBN 0-618-53579-9; 0-547-23766-9 pa

LC 2006-26070

From her home in Lidice, Czechoslovakia, in 1942, eleven-year-old Milada is taken with other blond, blue-eyed children to a school in Poland to be trained as "proper Germans" for adoption by German families, but all the while she remembers her true name and history.

"This amazing, eye-opening story, masterfully written, is an essential part of World War II literature and belongs on the shelves of every library." SLJ

Wolf-Morgenlander, Karl

Ragtag. Clarion Books 2009 225p il $16

Grades: 3 4 5 6   **Fic**

1. War stories 2. Fantasy fiction 3. Birds -- Fiction 4. Boston (Mass.) -- Fiction
ISBN 978-0-547-07424-5; 0-547-07424-7

LC 2008025319

A young swallow leads a band of birds against an empire of raptors that has invaded Boston

"This novel opens up the world of these lively feathered creatures and their way of life. The story line moves quickly." SLJ

Wolfson, Jill

Home, and other big, fat lies. Henry Holt 2006 281p $16.95

Grades: 5 6 7 8   **Fic**

1. Nature -- Fiction 2. Foster home care -- Fiction 3. Environmental protection -- Fiction
ISBN 978-0-8050-7670-7; 0-8050-7670-0

LC 200035843

Eleven-year-old Termite, a foster child with an eye for the beauty of nature and a talent for getting into trouble, takes on the loggers in her new home town when she tries to save the biggest tree in the forest.

"Written with humor and sensitivity." Voice Youth Advocates

What I call life. Holt & Co. 2005 270p $16.95; pa $6.99

Grades: 5 6 7 8   **Fic**

1. Foster home care -- Fiction
ISBN 0-8050-7669-7; 0-312-37752-5 pa

Placed in a group foster home, eleven-year-old Cal Lavender learns how to cope with life from the four other girls who live there and from their storytelling guardian, the Knitting Lady.

"Wolfson paints her characters with delightful authenticity. Her debut novel is a treasure of quiet good humor and skillful storytelling that conveys subtle messages about kindness, compassion, and the gift of family regardless of its configuration." Booklist

Wolitzer, Meg

The **fingertips** of Duncan Dorfman. Dutton Childrens Books 2011 294p $16.99

Grades: 4 5 6 7   Fic

1. Contests -- Fiction 2. Individualism -- Fiction 3. Scrabble (Game) -- Fiction

ISBN 978-0-525-42304-1; 0-525-42304-4

LC 2011005228

"The novel is shot through with Scrabble words and rules in a way that is reminiscent of Louis Sachar's The Cardturner (2010). Readers will identify with and root for the characters as their tales intertwine to a satisfying if slightly too cheery close. Word wizards aren't the only ones who will enjoy this readable rumination on ethics, competition and identity." Kirkus

Wong, Janet S.

Me and Rolly Maloo; illustrated by Elizabeth Buttler. Charlesbridge 2010 121p il $15.95

Grades: 3 4 5   Fic

1. School stories 2. Honesty -- Fiction 3. Popularity -- Fiction 4. Mathematics -- Fiction

ISBN 978-1-58089-158-5; 1-58089-158-6

"The characterizations are spot-on, and Buttler's frequent graphic-novel-style artwork and dialogue balloons emphsize reactions and emotions . . . The story is one worth telling." SLJ

"Rolly is the most popular girl in fourth grade. So why does she suddenly invite Jenna over? Is it because Jenna gets perfect scores on math tests? Should Jenna help Rolly cheat?" Booklist

Minn and Jake; [by] Janet Wong; pictures by Geneviève Côté. Farrar, Straus & Giroux 2003 146p il $16; pa $6.95

Grades: 3 4 5   Fic

1. School stories 2. Novels in verse 3. Friendship -- Fiction

ISBN 0-374-34987-8; 978-0-374-34987-5; 978-0-374-40021-7 pa; 0-374-40021-0 pa

LC 2002-35421

Fifth-grader Minn, the tallest girl in school, begins a rocky friendship with Jake, a new student who is not only very short, but is also afraid of the worms and lizards that Minn likes to collect

"This breezy free-verse novel introduces memorable characters in recognizable situations. . . [Côté's] b&w illustrations achieve unusual dimension. Incorporating what seem to be collage elements, her strikingly graphic compositions mirror the deceptive ease of the verse narration." Publ Wkly

Another title about Minn and Jake is:

Minn and Jake's almost terrible summer (2008)

Wood, Maryrose

The **hidden** gallery; illustrated by Jon Klassen. Balzer + Bray 2011 313p il (Incorrigible children of Ashton Place) $15.99

Grades: 4 5 6   Fic

1. Orphans -- Fiction 2. Great Britain -- Fiction 3. Wild children -- Fiction 4. London (England) -- Fiction

ISBN 978-0-06-179112-3; 0-06-179112-1

LC 2010-32737

Sequel to: The mysterious howling (2010)

Fifteen-year-old Miss Penelope Lumley, a governess trained at the Swanburne Academy for Poor Bright Females, takes the three Incorrigible Children of Ashton Place to London, England, and learns they are under a curse.

"Humorous antics and a climactic cliffhanger ending will keep children turning pages and clamoring for the next volume, while more sophisticated readers will take away much more. Frequent plate-sized illustrations add wit and period flair." SLJ

★ The **mysterious** howling; illustrated by Jon Klassen. Balzer & Bray 2010 267p il (The incorrigible children of Ashton Place) $15.99

Grades: 4 5 6   Fic

1. Orphans -- Fiction 2. Christmas -- Fiction 3. Wild children -- Fiction

ISBN 978-0-06-179105-5; 0-06-179105-9

Fifteen-year-old Miss Penelope Lumley, a recent graduate of the Swanburne Academy for Poor Bright Females, is hired as governess to three young children who have been raised by wolves and must teach them to behave in a civilized manner quickly, in preparation for a Christmas ball.

"Smartly written with a middle-grade audience in mind, this is both fun and funny and sprinkled with dollops of wisdom." Booklist

Another title in this series is:

The hidden gallery (2011)

The **unseen** guest; by Maryrose Wood; illustrated by Jon Klassen. Balzer + Bray 2012 340 p. (hardback) $15.99

Grades: 4 5 6   Fic

1. Mystery fiction 2. Wolves -- Fiction 3. Nannies -- Fiction 4. Wild children -- Fiction 5. Great Britain -- History -- 19th century -- Fiction 6. England -- Fiction 7. Orphans -- Fiction 8. Secrets -- Fiction 9. Governesses -- Fiction 10. Feral children -- Fiction 11. London (England) -- Fiction

ISBN 9780061791185

LC 2011053315

This young adult novel offers a "Victorian mystery [story about] teenage governess Penelope Lumley [who] takes on threats to her wolfish young charges that include a hustler after the Ashton fortune. . . . Once he meets the three feral children Penelope is charged with training up to be human, Faucet's scheme to finance the introduction of ostrich racing to the British Isles by marrying the Dowager Lady Ashton is transformed into visions of wolf racing and sideshow exhibitions. . . . Along with . . . pitching her plucky protagonist into one crisis after another . . . the author slips in a few more seemingly significant Clues to the Ashtons' curious history and Penelope's apparent involvement in it." (Kirkus)

Woodruff, Elvira

Fearless. Scholastic Press 2008 224p il $16.99; pa $6.99

Grades: 5 6 7 8   Fic

1. Artists 2. Engravers 3. Inventors 4. Architects 5. Adventure fiction 6. Orphans -- Fiction 7. Lighthouses

-- Fiction 8. Great Britain -- History -- 1603-1714, Stuarts -- Fiction

ISBN 978-0-439-67703-5; 0-439-67703-3; 978-0-439-67704-2 pa; 0-439-67704-1 pa

LC 2006-10137

In late seventeenth-century England, eleven-year-old Digory, forced to leave his hometown after his father is lost at sea, becomes an apprentice to the architect Henry Winstanley, who built a lighthouse on the treacherous Eddystone Reef—the very rocks that sank Digory's grandfather's ship years before.

"This fascinating, well-written story is closely based on the life of the real Henry Winstanley. . . . The characters are finely drawn and the action is nonstop." SLJ

George Washington's spy; a time travel adventure. Scholastic Press 2010 229p $16.99

Grades: 4 5 6 **Fic**

1. Authors 2. Diplomats 3. Inventors 4. Statesmen 5. Scientists 6. Writers on science 7. Members of Congress 8. Time travel -- Fiction 9. Boston (Mass.) -- Fiction 10. United States -- History -- 1775-1783, Revolution -- Fiction

ISBN 978-0-545-10487-6; 0-545-10487-4

LC 2009032700

Sequel to: George Washington's socks (1991)

Ten-year-old Matt and six other children travel to 1776 Boston, living out American history as they meet Benjamin Franklin, learn about colonial medicine, and become part of a rebel spy ring.

"Woodruff does an excellent job of conveying the complexities of war. . . . This is a great introduction to the Revolutionary period. . . . The story is fast paced, exciting, and informative." SLJ

The **Ravenmaster's** secret. Scholastic Press 2003 225p $15.95; pa $5.99

Grades: 5 6 7 8 **Fic**

1. Ravens -- Fiction 2. London (England) -- Fiction 3. Tower of London (England) -- Fiction 4. Great Britain -- History -- 1714-1837 -- Fiction

ISBN 0-439-28133-4; 0-439-28134-2 pa

LC 2002-15963

The eleven-year-old son of the Ravenmaster at the Tower of London befriends a Jacobite rebel being held prisoner there.

"An absorbing historical adventure with a unique and colorful setting. . . . The novel can be read for its exciting plot and sympathetic characters, but readers will also sense its underlying theme of courage." Booklist

Woods, Brenda

My name is Sally Little Song. G.P. Putnam's Sons 2006 182p $15.99; pa $5.99

Grades: 4 5 6 7 **Fic**

1. Florida -- Fiction 2. Georgia -- Fiction 3. Slavery -- Fiction 4. Seminole Indians -- Fiction 5. African Americans -- Fiction

ISBN 0-399-24312-7; 0-14-240943-X pa

LC 2005-32651

When their owner plans to sell one of them in 1802, twelve-year-old Sally and her family run away from their Georgia plantation to look for both freedom from slavery and a home in Florida with the Seminole Indians.

"Based on historical accounts, this novel provides readers with an alternative view of the realities of slavery—an escape to the South rather than North. . . . This accessible tale will prove a rich resource for study and discussion." SLJ

The **red** rose box. Putnam 2002 136p $16.99; pa $5.99

Grades: 5 6 7 8 **Fic**

1. Louisiana -- Fiction 2. African Americans -- Fiction 3. Los Angeles (Calif.) -- Fiction

ISBN 0-399-23702-X; 0-14-250151-4 pa

LC 2001-18354

In 1953, Leah Hopper dreams of leaving the poverty and segregation of her home in Sulphur, Louisiana, and when Aunt Olivia sends train tickets to Los Angeles as part of her tenth birthday present, Leah gets a first taste of freedom

"In language made musical with southern phrases, this . . . novel shapes the era and characters with both well-chosen particulars and universal emotions." Booklist

★ **Saint** Louis Armstrong Beach. Nancy Paulsen Books 2011 137p $16.99

Grades: 4 5 6 **Fic**

1. Dogs -- Fiction 2. Musicians -- Fiction 3. New Orleans (La.) -- Fiction 4. Hurricane Katrina, 2005 -- Fiction

ISBN 978-0-399-25507-6; 0-399-25507-9

Saint Louis Armstrong Beach is enjoying life in New Orleans, playing clarinet for the tourists in his spare time, accompanied by Shadow, a local stray dog. When Hurricane Katrina approaches, Saint faces unexpected challenges in trying to rescue Shadow.

This is a "gripping addition to the growing body of fiction portraying Katrina's profound effect on children and families. . . . Woods' marvelous characterizations of Saint and Miz Moran more than stand up to the vivid backdrop of the flooded, chaotic city. Shadow's credulity-straining heroics will please kids." Kirkus

Woodson, Jacqueline

★ **Feathers**. G.P. Putnam's Sons 2007 118p $15.99; pa $6.99

Grades: 4 5 6 7 **Fic**

1. Religion -- Fiction 2. Race relations -- Fiction 3. African Americans -- Fiction

ISBN 978-0-399-23989-2; 0-399-23989-8; 978-0-14-241198-8 pa; 0-14-241198-1 pa

LC 2006-24713

A Newbery Medal honor book, 2008

When a new, white student nicknamed "The Jesus Boy" joins her sixth grade class in the winter of 1971, Frannie's growing friendship with him makes her start to see some things in a new light.

"Woodson creates in Frannie a strong protagonist who thinks for herself and recognizes the value and meaning of family. The story ends with hope and thoughtfulness while speaking to those adolescents who struggle with race, faith, and prejudice." SLJ

★ **Locomotion**. Putnam 2003 100p $17.99; pa $5.99

Grades: 4 5 6 7 **Fic**

1. Novels in verse 2. Foster home care -- Fiction 3.

African Americans -- Fiction

ISBN 978-0-399-23115-5; 0-399-23115-3; 978-0-14-241552-8 pa; 0-14-241552-9 pa

LC 2002-69779

In a series of poems, eleven-year-old Lonnie writes about his life, after the death of his parents, separated from his younger sister, living in a foster home, and finding his poetic voice at school

"In a masterful use of voice, Woodson allows Lonnie's poems to tell a complex story of loss and grief and to create a gritty, urban environment. Despite the spare text, Lonnie's foster mother and the other minor characters are three-dimensional, making the boy's world a convincingly real one." SLJ

★ **Peace,** Locomotion. G.P. Putnam's Sons 2009 134p $15.99; pa $7.99

Grades: 4 5 6 7 **Fic**

1. Letters -- Fiction 2. Orphans -- Fiction 3. Siblings -- Fiction 4. Foster home care -- Fiction 5. African Americans -- Fiction

ISBN 978-0-399-24655-5; 0-399-24655-X; 978-0-14-241512-2 pa; 0-14-241512-X pa

LC 2008-18583

Through letters to his little sister, who is living in a different foster home, sixth-grader Lonnie, also known as "Locomotion," keeps a record of their lives while they are apart, describing his own foster family, including his foster brother who returns home after losing a leg in the Iraq War

"Woodson creates a full-bodied character in kind, sensitive Lonnie. Readers will understand his quest for peace, and appreciate the hard work he does to find it." Publ Wkly

Worley, Rob M.

Scratch 9; created and written by Rob M. Worley; illustrated by Jason T. Kruse. Ape Entertainment 2011 100p. 1

Grades: 3 4 5 **Fic**

1. Cats -- Fiction 2. Pets -- Fiction 3. Comic books, strips, etc.

ISBN 9781936340538

In this collection of comics, named one of the Best Comics for Kids 2010 by School Library Journal, "mad science gives an ordinary cat named Scratch the ability to summon any of his nine lives. He must use his powers to save his pet friends from the CRUEL corporation." (Publisher's note) The protagonist "can summon any of his previous or future lives and fight side-by-side with them, a handy skill when you were a saber-toothed tiger, a ninja, and a minor Egyptian deity in your previous lives!" (School Libr J)

Wrede, Patricia C.

Dealing with dragons. Harcourt Brace Jovanovich 1990 212p (The Enchanted Forest Chronicles) hardcover o.p. pa $6.99

Grades: 5 6 7 8 **Fic**

1. Fairy tales 2. Magic -- Fiction 3. Dragons -- Fiction

ISBN 0-15-222900-0; 0-15-204566-X pa

LC 89-24599

Bored with traditional palace life, a princess goes off to live with a group of dragons and soon becomes involved with fighting against some disreputable wizards who want to steal away the dragons' kingdom

"A decidedly diverting novel with plenty of action and many slightly skewed fairy-tale conventions that add to the

laugh-out-loud reading pleasure and give the story a wide appeal." Booklist

Other titles in this series are:

Searching for dragons (1991)
Calling on dragons (1993)
Talking to dragons (1993)

Wright, Barbara

★ **Crow.** Random House 2012 $16.99; lib bdg $19.99; ebook $10.99

Grades: 4 5 6 **Fic**

1. Friendship -- Fiction 2. Family life -- Fiction 3. North Carolina -- Fiction 4. Race relations -- Fiction 5. African Americans -- Fiction

ISBN 978-0-375-86928-0; 0-375-86928-X; 978-0-375-96928-7 lib bdg; 0-375-96928-4; 978-0-375-98270-5 ebook

LC 2011014892

In 1898, Moses Thomas's summer vacation does not go exactly as planned as he contends with family problems and the ever-changing alliances among his friends at the same time as he is exposed to the escalating tension between the African-American and white communities of Wilmington, North Carolina.

"An intensely moving, first-person narrative of a disturbing historical footnote told from the perspective of a very likable, credible young hero." Kirkus

Wright, Betty Ren

The **dollhouse** murders. Holiday House 1983 149p $17.95; pa $7.95

Grades: 4 5 6 7 **Fic**

1. Mystery fiction

ISBN 0-8234-0497-8; 0-8234-2172-4 pa

LC 83-6147

A dollhouse filled with a ghostly light in the middle of the night and dolls that have moved from where she last left them lead Amy and her mentally disabled sister to unravel the mystery surrounding grisly murders that took place years ago

"More than just a mystery, this offers keen insight into the relationship between handicapped and nonhandicapped siblings and glimpses into the darker adult emotions of guilt and anger. A successful, full-bodied work." Booklist

Princess for a week; illustrated by Jacqueline Rogers. Holiday House 2006 105p il $16.95; pa $6.95

Grades: 2 3 4 **Fic**

1. Ghost stories 2. Mystery fiction

ISBN 0-8234-1945-2; 0-8234-2111-2 pa

LC 2005-50288

When a confident girl named Princess arrives to spend a week at Roddy's house, she encourages him to help her investigate the suspicious activities happening at a supposedly haunted house.

"The story moves quickly and is excellently paced. . . . The full-page illustrations add realism and depth to the story." SLJ

Wynne-Jones, Tim

★ **Rex** Zero and the end of the world. Farrar, Straus & Giroux 2007 86p $16

Grades: 4 5 6 **Fic**

1. Canada -- Fiction 2. Moving -- Fiction 3. Cold war

-- Fiction 4. Family life -- Fiction
ISBN 0-374-33467-6; 978-0-374-33467-3

LC 2006-45172

In the summer of 1962 with everyone nervous about a possible nuclear war, ten-nearly-eleven-year-old Rex, having just moved to Ottawa from Vancouver with his parents and five siblings, faces his own personal challenges as he discovers new friends and a new understanding of the world around him.

"Despite the weighty themes, Wynne-Jones writes with a light, often humorous touch and maintains a perspective true to an 11-year-old's perspective." Publ Wkly

Other titles about Rex Zero are:
Rex Zero, king of nothing (2008)
Rex Zero, the great pretender (2010)

Wyss, Johann David
The **Swiss** family Robinson; by Johann Wyss; edited by William H. G. Kingston; illustrated by Lynd Ward. Grosset & Dunlap 1999 388p il $18.99
Grades: 5 6 7 8   Fic
1. Survival after airplane accidents, shipwrecks, etc. -- Fiction
ISBN 0-448-06022-1
Originally published 1812-1813 in Switzerland
When a Swiss couple and their four sons are shipwrecked on an isolated island, they adapt to their "New Switzerland" using many imaginative methods of farming and animal taming.

Wyss, Thelma Hatch
Bear dancer; the story of a Ute girl. Margaret K. McElderry Books 2005 181p il $15.95
Grades: 5 6 7 8   Fic
1. Ute Indians -- Fiction
ISBN 1-4169-0285-6

LC 2005-40620

In late nineteenth-century Colorado, Elk Girl, sister of Ute chief Ouray, is captured by Cheyenne and Arapaho warriors, rescued by the white "enemy," and finally returned to her home. Includes historical notes.

"This fascinating story is based on a real person. . . . An excellent addition to historical-fiction collections." SLJ

Yee, Lisa
Aloha, Kanani; illustrations by Sarah Davis. American Girl 2011 116p il (American girl) $12.95; pa $6.95
Grades: 3 4 5   Fic
1. Hawaii -- Fiction 2. Cousins -- Fiction 3. Racially mixed people -- Fiction
ISBN 978-1-59369-840-9; 1-59369-840-2; 978-1-59369-839-3 pa; 1-59369-839-9 pa

LC 2010046870

When the tropical paradise of Kauai, Hawaii, fails to impress her cousin from New York City, ten-year-old Kanani wonders why nothing seems to make her happy.

"In this story with an animal-rescue sub-plot, beautiful full-color illustrations and a Hawaiian glossary are included, along with several ending pages about real-life girls who have helped animals." Booklist

Another title about Kanani is:
Good job, Kanani (2011)

Bobby vs. girls (accidentally) illustrated by Dan Santat. Arthur A. Levine Books 2009 170p il $15.99; pa $5.99
Grades: 3 4 5   Fic
1. School stories 2. Friendship -- Fiction
ISBN 978-0-545-05592-5; 0-545-05592-X; 978-0-545-05593-2 pa; 0-545-05593-8 pa
When Bobby inadvertently gets into a fight with his best friend Holly, their disagreement develops into a boys versus girls war involving their whole fourth-grade class.

"Yee really understands children's thought processes and presents them with tact and good humor. . . . Santat's drawings manage the fine line between cartoon and realism and add dimension to the events. Readers will recognize themselves and learn some gentle lessons about relationships while they are laughing at the antics." Kirkus

Another title about Bobby is:
Bobby the brave (sometimes) (2010)

Millicent Min, girl genius. Arthur A. Levine Books 2003 248p $16.95; pa $4.99
Grades: 5 6 7   Fic
1. School stories 2. Gifted children -- Fiction 3. Chinese Americans -- Fiction
ISBN 0-439-42519-0; 0-439-42520-4 pa

LC 2003-3747

"At the tender age of eleven, Millicent Min has completed her junior year of high school. Summer school is Millie's idea of fun, so she is excited that her parents are allowing her to take a college poetry course. . . . The tension between Millie's formal, overly intellectual way of expressing herself and her emotional immaturity makes her a very funny narrator. . . . Readers considerably older than Millicent's eleven years will enjoy this strong debut novel." Voice Youth Advocates

Other titles about Millicent Min and her friends are:
Stanford Wong flunks big-time (2005)
So totally Emily Ebers (2007)

Warp speed. Arthur A. Levine Books 2011 310p $16.99
Grades: 5 6 7 8   Fic
1. School stories 2. Bullies -- Fiction 3. California -- Fiction 4. Popularity -- Fiction 5. Family life -- Fiction
ISBN 978-0-545-12276-4; 0-545-12276-7

LC 2010-24228

"Yee's combination of humor and sympathy works a charm here, giving Marley a life of his own and a chance at success in this solid addition to her prismatic look at middle school." Kirkus

Yelchin, Eugene
★ **Breaking** Stalin's nose; written and illustrated by Eugene Yelchin. Henry Holt and Company 2011 140p il $15.99
Grades: 4 5 6 7   Fic
1. Communism -- Fiction 2. Soviet Union -- Fiction 3. Father-son relationship -- Fiction
ISBN 0-8050-9216-1; 978-0-8050-9216-5

LC 2011005792

In the Stalinist era of the Soviet Union, ten-year-old Sasha idolizes his father, a devoted Communist, but when police take his father away and leave Sasha homeless, he is forced to examine his own perceptions, values, and beliefs.

"Readers will quickly pick up on the dichotomy between Sasha's ardent beliefs and the reality of life under Stalinism, and be glad for his ultimate disillusion, even as they worry for his future. An author's note concisely presents the chilling historical background and personal connection that underlie the story." Publ Wkly

Yep, Laurence, 1948-

City of fire. Tom Doherty Associates 2009 320p $15.99

Grades: 5 6 7 8   **Fic**

1. Fantasy fiction 2. Magic -- Fiction 3. Hawaii -- Fiction 4. Dragons -- Fiction

ISBN 978-0-7653-1924-1; 0-7653-1924-1

LC 2009016737

Twelve-year-old Scirye and her companions travel to Houlani, a new Hawaiian island created by magic, where they enlist the help of volcano goddess Pele in an attempt to stop an evil dragon and a mysterious man from altering the universe.

"Readers will be on tenterhooks awaiting the next episode of this exhilarating chase." Booklist

Followed by: City of ice (2011)

★ The **dragon's** child; a story of Angel Island. [by] Laurence Yep, with Kathleen S. Yep. HarperCollinsPublishers 2008 133p $15.99; lib bdg $16.89

Grades: 3 4 5 6   **Fic**

1. China -- Fiction 2. California -- Fiction 3. Immigrants -- Fiction 4. Chinese Americans -- Fiction

ISBN 978-0-06-027692-8; 0-06-027692-4; 978-0-06-027693-5 lib bdg; 0-06-027693-2 lib bdg

LC 2007-18373

"In a dramatic blend of fact and fiction, Laurence Yep and his niece draw on family stories, immigration records, and memories of Laurence's own conversations to tell his dad's story of coming to America at age 10 with his Chinese American dad. . . . With family photos, a historical note, and a long bibliography, this stirring narrative will spark readers' own search for roots." Booklist

A **dragon's** guide to the care and feeding of humans; Laurence Yep & Joanne Ryder; Illustrations by Mary Grand-Pré. Crown Books for Young Readers 2015 160 p. illustrations (hc) $15.99

Grades: 4 5 6 7   **Fic**

1. Pets -- Fiction 2. Dragons -- Fiction 3. Magic -- Fiction 4. Artists -- Fiction 5. Friendship -- Fiction 6. Imaginary creatures -- Fiction

ISBN 0385392281; 9780385392280; 9780385392297

LC 2014017803

In this novel by Laurence Yep and Joanne Ryder, "crusty dragon Miss Drake has a new pet human, precocious Winnie. Oddly enough, Winnie seems to think Miss Drake is her pet. . . . Unknown to most . . . , the City by the Bay is home to many . . . fantastic creatures. . . . And Winnie wants to draw every new creature she encounters. . . . But Winnie's sketchbook is not what it seems. Somehow, her sketchlings have been set loose on the city streets!" (Publisher's note)

"With a black-and-white spot illustration opening most chapters, an engaging narrator, and a consistently fluid writing style, this title makes a fine dragon choice for readers not yet ready for more weighty fantasy novels." SLJ

The **magic** paintbrush; drawings by Suling Wang. HarperCollins Pubs. 2000 89p il hardcover o.p. pa $5.99

Grades: 3 4 5   **Fic**

1. Magic -- Fiction 2. Chinese Americans -- Fiction

ISBN 0-06-028199-5; 0-06-440852-3 pa

LC 99-34959

A magic paintbrush transports Steve and his elderly caretakers from their drab apartment in Chinatown to a world of adventures

"Yep's crisp style keeps the pages turning, and he leavens his story with snappy dialogue, realistic characters and plenty of wise humor." Publ Wkly

★ The **star** maker. Harper 2010 100p $15.99; lib bdg $16.89

Grades: 5 6 7 8   **Fic**

1. Uncles -- Fiction 2. Family life -- Fiction 3. Chinese New Year -- Fiction 4. Chinese Americans -- Fiction 5. San Francisco (Calif.) -- Fiction

ISBN 978-0-06-025315-8; 0-06-025315-0; 978-0-06-025316-5 lib bdg; 0-06-025316-9 lib bdg

LC 2010-07856

With the help of his popular Uncle Chester, a young Chinese American boy tries hard to fulfill a promise to have firecrackers for everyone on the Chinese New Year in 1954. Includes an afterword with information about the Chinese customs portrayed in the story.

"Yep skillfully portrays the significance and emotional nature of common childhood dramas, from fears of going back on one's word to worries of losing a favorite uncle to a new girlfriend. . . . Yep has crafted other memorable characters, including Chinatown itself, which sparkle with energy and camaraderie." Publ Wkly

Includes bibliographical references

★ The **traitor**; Golden Mountain chronicles, 1885. HarperCollins Pubs. 2003 310p hardcover o.p. pa $6.99

Grades: 5 6 7 8   **Fic**

1. Friendship -- Fiction 2. Prejudices -- Fiction 3. Chinese Americans -- Fiction

ISBN 0-06-027522-7; 0-06-000831-8 pa

LC 2002-22534

Sequel to: Dragon's gate

In 1885, a lonely illegitimate American boy and a lonely Chinese American boy develop an unlikely friendship in the midst of prejudices and racial tension in their coal mining town of Rock Springs, Wyoming

"The short chapters read quickly, and readers will become involved through the first-person voices that capture each boy's feelings of being an outsider and a traitor." Booklist

When the circus came to town; drawings by Suling Wang. HarperCollins Pubs. 2002 113p il hardcover o.p. pa $5.99

Grades: 3 4 5   **Fic**

1. Circus -- Fiction 2. Chinese New Year -- Fiction 3. Chinese Americans -- Fiction 4. Frontier and pioneer life -- Fiction

ISBN 0-06-029325-X; 0-06-440965-1 pa

LC 2001-39290

An Asian cook and a Chinese New Year celebration help ten-year-old Ursula at a Montana stage coach station to regain her confidence after smallpox scars her face

"Yep has based his novel on a true story, and his writing is, by turns, direct, humorous, and poignant." Booklist

Ylvisaker, Anne

The **luck** of the Buttons. Candlewick Press 2011 224p $15.99

Grades: 4 5 6   **Fic**

1. Mystery fiction 2. Iowa -- Fiction 3. Chance -- Fiction 4. Friendship -- Fiction 5. Family life -- Fiction 6. Photography -- Fiction 7. Great Depression, 1929-1939 -- Fiction

ISBN 978-0-7636-5066-7; 0-7636-5066-8

LC 2010039169

In Iowa circa 1929, spunky twelve-year-old Tugs vows to turn her family's luck around, with the help of a Brownie camera and a small-town mystery that only she can solve.

"The tale has a whiff of nostalgia, . . . but the good old days are balanced by the strongly realized, immediate characters and the delicacy and originality of the writing." Horn Book

Yohalem, Eve

★ **Escape** under the forever sky; a novel. Chronicle Books 2009 220p $16.99

Grades: 4 5 6 7   **Fic**

1. Ethiopia -- Fiction 2. Kidnapping -- Fiction 3. Wilderness survival -- Fiction 4. Mother-daughter relationship -- Fiction

ISBN 978-0-8118-6653-8; 0-8118-6653-X

LC 2008-19565

As a future conservation zoologist whose mother is the United States Ambassador to Ethiopia, thirteen-year-old Lucy uses her knowledge for survival when she is kidnapped and subsequently escapes.

"Lucy's past and present are gracefully woven together, through well-integrated flashbacks, into a powerful picture of the life of a foreigner in Ethiopia. The story should appeal to all with a sense of adventure." Publ Wkly

Yolen, Jane

B.U.G. (Big Ugly Guy) by Jane Yolen and Adam Stemple. Dutton Children's Books 2013 344 p.

Grades: 4 5 6 7 8   **Fic**

1. Golem -- Fiction 2. Magic -- Fiction 3. Bullies -- Fiction 4. Friendship -- Fiction 5. Bands (Music) -- Fiction 6. Klezmer music -- Fiction 7. Jews -- United States -- Fiction

ISBN 9780525422389

LC 2012018217

A constant target for bullies, Sammy Greenburg is glad to make friends with a boy named Skink, who even agrees to "start up a Klezmer fusion garage band after Sammy introduces Skink to the unique combination of jazz and Jewish folk music. When the bullies beat up Skink, however, Sammy decides enough is enough, and, using a formula he finds in his rabbi's study, he creates a golem to take vengeance on his enemies—and fill the missing drummer spot in his new band." (Bulletin of the Center for Children's Books)

Snow in Summer. Philomel Books 2011 243p $16.99

Grades: 4 5 6 7   **Fic**

1. Fairy tales 2. Magic -- Fiction 3. Stepmothers -- Fiction 4. West Virginia -- Fiction

ISBN 0-399-25663-6; 978-0-399-25663-9

LC 2010044242

Recasts the tale of Snow White, setting it in West Virginia in the 1940s with a stepmother who is a snake-handler.

"This story is beautifully written and deliciously scary, with just enough differences from familiar versions to keep readers guessing." Publ Wkly

Yoo, David

The **detention** club. Balzer + Bray 2011 299p $16.99

Grades: 5 6 7 8   **Fic**

1. School stories 2. Siblings -- Fiction 3. Popularity -- Fiction 4. Korean Americans -- Fiction

ISBN 978-0-06-178378-4; 0-06-178378-1

LC 2010-46211

Sixth-grader Peter Lee, in a desperate attempt to regain the popularity he had in elementary school, discovers that serving detention can win him important friends, much to the dismay of his over-achieving eighth-grade sister, Sunny.

"Even readers who guess the thief's identity early on will be entertained by the boys' hijinks and empathize with their desire to fit in." Publ Wkly

Young, Judy

A **book** for black-eyed Susan; written by Judy Young; illustrated by Doris Ettlinger. Sleeping Bear Press 2011 un il $16.95

Grades: 2 3 4   **Fic**

1. Oregon -- Fiction 2. Sewing -- Fiction 3. Sisters -- Fiction 4. Books and reading -- Fiction 5. Frontier and pioneer life -- Fiction 6. Overland journeys to the Pacific -- Fiction

ISBN 978-1-58536-463-3; 1-58536-463-0

LC 2010028422

While traveling along the Oregon Trail, ten-year-old Cora and her newborn baby sister suffer the loss of their mother and are separated, but Cora stitches a book to tell the dark-eyed baby of their journey and family.

"The surprise ending, however unlikely, will warm readers' hearts. Realistic watercolor images reveal the intricacies of pioneer life and the emotional turmoil of the characters. An engaging introduction to life during the Westward expansion." SLJ

Minnow and Rose; an Oregon trail story. written by Judy Young; illustrated by Bill Farnsworth. Sleeping Bear Press 2009 un il (Tales of young Americans) $17.95

Grades: 3 4 5   **Fic**

1. Friendship -- Fiction 2. Native Americans -- Fiction 3. Frontier and pioneer life -- Fiction

ISBN 978-1-58536-421-3; 1-58536-421-5

LC 2008024768

Traveling west with her pioneer family in a wagon train, Rose meets Minnow, who lives in a native American village along the banks of a river.

"Beautiful oil paintings . . . lend additional action and understanding to the story." SLJ

Young, Karen Romano

Doodlebug; a novel in doodles. Feiwel and Friends 2010 un il $14.99

Grades: 4 5 6 7 **Fic**
1. School stories 2. Moving -- Fiction 3. California
-- Fiction 4. Family life -- Fiction 5. Racially mixed
people -- Fiction
ISBN 978-0-312-56156-7; 0-312-56156-3

Doreen Bussey, aka Dodo, takes the nickname Doodle-bug when her family moves from Los Angeles to San Francisco and she records her experiences in a notebook with words, scribbles, and drawings.

This offers "an engaging, originial heroine, a satisfying story and lots of great pictures. . . . Some details, like the fact that the family is interracial, are shown but not stated, rewarding careful examination of the artwork. . . . Charming and thoughtful." Kirkus

Zahler, Diane
The **thirteenth** princess. Harper 2009 243p
Grades: 4 5 6 7 **Fic**
1. Fairy tales 2. Magic -- Fiction 3. Sisters -- Fiction
4. Princesses -- Fiction 5. Household employees --
Fiction 6. Father-daughter relationship -- Fiction 7.
Folklore -- Germany
ISBN 0-06-182498-4; 0-06-182499-2 lib bdg; 978-0-06-182498-2; 978-0-06-182499-9 lib bdg
LC 2009-14575

Zita, cast aside by her father and raised as a kitchen maid, learns when she is nearly twelve that she is a princess and that her twelve sisters love her, and so when she discovers they are victims of an evil enchantment, she desperately tries to save them. Inspired by the Grimm fairy tale, "The twelve dancing princesses."

Zahler "deftly and thoughtfully embellishes the tale's classic elements. . . . Zahler takes a light story and gives it gratifying depth, rounding out the characters and their motivations without betraying the source material and wrapping it all together in a graceful and cohesive romantic drama." Publ Wkly

A **true** princess. Harper 2011 182p $15.99
Grades: 4 5 6 **Fic**
1. Fairy tales 2. Friendship -- Fiction 3. Princesses
-- Fiction 4. Voyages and travels -- Fiction
ISBN 978-0-06-182501-9; 0-06-182501-8
LC 2010017846

Twelve-year-old Lilia goes north to seek the family she has never known, accompanied by her friends Kai and Karina and their dog Ove, on an adventure fraught with peril, especially when they become lost in Bitra Forest, the Elf King's domain. Inspired by the Hans Christian Andersen tale, The princess and the pea.

"Readers who enjoyed . . . Zahler's The Thirteenth Princess . . . will also relish this tale." SLJ

Zalben, Jane Breskin
Brenda Berman, wedding expert; illustrated by Victoria Chess. Clarion Books 2009 48p il lib bdg $16
Grades: 2 3 4 **Fic**
1. Uncles -- Fiction 2. Weddings -- Fiction 3. Friendship -- Fiction
ISBN 978-0-618-31321-1 lib bdg; 0-618-31321-4 lib bdg
LC 2006-34851

When Brenda's favorite uncle decides to marry, Brenda sees visions of a gold lame flower-girl's outfit, until Uncle

Harry and his bride-to-be show up with her niece. Includes cake recipe.

"Brenda's robust personality drives the narrative as well as the art, as Chess's folksy watercolors capture the girl's expressions, which vacillate wildly between outrage and exhilaration." Publ Wkly

Zimmer, Tracie Vaughn
42 miles; illustrated by Elaine Clayton. Clarion Books 2008 73p il $16
Grades: 4 5 6 **Fic**
1. Novels in verse 2. Divorce -- Fiction 3. Farm life
-- Fiction 4. Family life -- Fiction 5. City and town life -- Fiction
ISBN 978-0-618-61867-5; 0-618-61867-8
LC 2007-31032

As her thirteenth birthday approaches, JoEllen decides to bring together her two separate lives—one as Joey, who enjoys weekends with her father and other relatives on a farm, and another as Ellen, who lives with her mother in an apartment near her school and friends.

"Using free verse, Zimmer shows the richness in both places, while black-and-white composit illustrations bright the bits and pieces together." Booklist

The **floating** circus; by Tracie Vaughn Zimmer. Bloomsbury Children's Books 2008 198p $15.99
Grades: 4 5 6 **Fic**
1. Circus -- Fiction 2. Boats and boating -- Fiction 3. Abandoned children -- Fiction
ISBN 978-1-59990-185-5; 1-59990-185-4
LC 2007038998

In 1850s Pittsburgh, thirteen-year-old Owen leaves his younger brother and sneaks aboard a circus housed in a riverboat, where he befriends a freed slave, learns to work with elephants, and finally comes to terms with the choices he has made in his difficult life

This is a "lively historical novel. Readers will be hooked from the start by the voice of the narrator. . . . Bittersweet and satisfying." Publ Wkly

Sketches from a spy tree; poems by Tracie Vaughn Zimmer; illustrated by Andrew Glass. Clarion Books 2005 63p il $16
Grades: 3 4 5 6 **Fic**
1. Twins -- Fiction 2. Divorce -- Fiction 3. Sisters
-- Fiction 4. Stepfamilies -- Fiction
ISBN 0-618-23479-9
LC 2003-27768

In a series of poems, narrator Anne Marie paints pictures of family life from grief to hope after her father abandons his "four girls" Anne Marie and her mother and twin and baby sister.

"The writing is lyrical yet fresh. . . . Glass's remarkable watercolors, sketches, photographs, and collages bring Anne Marie's experiences to life." SLJ

Zoehfeld, Kathleen Weidner
★ **Secrets** of the garden; food chains and the food web in our backyard. illustrated by Priscilla Lamont. Alfred A. Knopf 2012 il $16.99; lib bdg $19.99
Grades: K 1 2 3 **Fic**
1. Gardens -- Fiction 2. Gardening -- Fiction 3. Food

chains (Ecology) -- Fiction
ISBN 978-0-517-70990-0; 0-517-70990-2; 978-0-517-70991-7 lib bdg; 0-517-70991-0 lib bdg; 978-0-375-98730-4 ebook

LC 2011032059

This "is a wonderfully informative and enjoyable journey through one family's backyard garden, from spring planting to fall harvest. Covering a dazzling array of topics, the author still manages to hold onto a story line that will draw readers in and allow them to experience both the good and the bad right along with narrator Alice. . . . The text comes alive through Lamont's pen-and-watercolor illustrations, which reinforce the learning while entertaining at the same time." Kirkus

Zucker, Naomi Flink

★ **Callie's** rules; by Naomi Zucker. Egmont USA 2009 240p $15.99; lib bdg $18.99
Grades: 4 5 6 7   **Fic**
1. School stories 2. Halloween -- Fiction 3. New Jersey -- Fiction 4. Family life -- Fiction
ISBN 978-1-60684-027-6; 1-60684-027-4; 978-1-60684-052-8 lib bdg; 1-60684-052-5 lib bdg

LC 2009-15419

Eleven-year-old Callie Jones tries to keep track of all the rules for fitting in that other middle schoolers seem to know, but when the town decides to replace Halloween with an Autumn Festival, Callie leads her large family in an unusual protest.

"Callie herself is both funny and resourceful. Worthwhile and entertaining." Kirkus

Followed by: Write on, Callie Jones (2010)

S C   STORY COLLECTIONS

Aiken, Joan

Shadows and moonshine; stories. illustrations by Pamela Johnson. Godine 2001 171p il hardcover o.p. pa $10.95
Grades: 4 5 6 7   **S C**
1. Short stories 2. Fantasy fiction
ISBN 1-56792-167-1; 1-56792-346-1 pa

LC 2001-23830

This is a collection 13 stories about such things as witches, enchanted pigs, mermaids, and dragons, selected from the author's earlier anthologies

"Whether scary, satiric, or poetic, Aiken's tales have strong settings, memorable characters, insight, and humor." SLJ

Alexander, Lloyd

★ The **foundling** and other tales of Prydain; rev & expanded ed; Holt & Co. 1999 98p hardcover o.p. pa $5.99
Grades: 5 6 7 8   **S C**
1. Short stories 2. Fantasy fiction
ISBN 0-8050-6130-4; 0-8050-8053-8 pa

LC 98-42807

First published 1973; this revised and expanded edition includes two additional stories Coll and his white pig and The truthful harp, first published separately 1965 and 1967 respectively

Eight short stories dealing with events that preceded the birth of Taran, the Assistant Pig-Keeper and key figure in the author's five works on the Kingdom of Prydain which began with The book of three

"The stories are written with vivid grace and humor." Chicago. Children's Book Center [review of 1973 edition]

Andersen, Hans Christian

★ **Hans** Christian Andersen's Fairy Tales; selected and illustrated by Lisbeth Zwerger; translated by Anthea Bell. Minedition 2006 104p il $19.99
Grades: 4 5 6 7   **S C**
1. Fairy tales 2. Short stories
ISBN 0-698-40035-6

A reissue of the edition first published 1991

"This collection of . . . tales includes relatively unknown stories, such as 'The Rose Tree Regiment,' along with such familiar favorites as 'The Princess & the Pea.' Bell's finesse in writing is well matched by Zwerger's delicate, understated approach in the illustrations, which are introspective rather than dramatic. Sophisticated in design, the book features fluid watercolors and wide-bordered text on tall, white pages." Booklist

Arato, Rona

On a medieval day; story voyages around the world. illustrated by Peter Ferguson. Maple Tree Press 2010 96p il $24.95; pa $15.95
Grades: 4 5 6   **S C**
1. Short stories 2. Middle Ages -- Fiction
ISBN 978-1-897349-94-6; 1-897349-94-7; 978-1-897349-95-3 pa; 1-897349-95-5 pa

"Alternating between male and female narrators, this book presents stories about nine fictional youth of the medieval period. From the Mayan Civilization in 720 to the Kingdom of Castile in 1395, with stops in Vinland in 1002, Japan in 1205, and other places and years, their tales provide readers with a worldview of the era. Each chapter follows one child or teen through a day in which a conflict or crisis for the protagonist brings in some cultural and social context of the period. . . . The fast-paced stories make for entertaining reading. Each chapter ends with a brief history of the period and includes a simple map. . . . The book is a wonderful attempt to expand the usual concept of the medieval world beyond Europe." SLJ

Avi

Strange happenings; five tales of transformation. Harcourt 2006 147p $15; pa $5.95
Grades: 5 6 7 8   **S C**
1. Short stories 2. Supernatural -- Fiction
ISBN 0-15-205790-0; 0-15-206461-3 pa

LC 2004-29579

"In this short story collection, Avi offers five fantastical tales, set in both contemporary and fairy-tale lands, that explore the notion of transformation. . . . The pieces are vividly imagined and shot through with a captivating, edgy spookiness, which, along with their brevity and some droll, crackling dialogue, makes them great choices for sharing aloud in class or as inspiration in creative-writing units." Booklist

What do fish have to do with anything? and other stories; illustrated by Tracy Mitchell. Candlewick Press 1997 202p il hardcover o.p. pa $6.99

Grades: 4 5 6 7   **S C**
1. Short stories
ISBN 0-7636-0329-5; 0-7636-2319-9 pa
LC 97-1354

"While Avi's endings are not tidy, they are effective: each story brings its protagonist beyond childhood self-absorption to the realization that one is an integral part of a bigger picture." Horn Book

Babbitt, Natalie

The **Devil's** storybook; stories and pictures by Natalie Babbitt. Farrar, Straus & Giroux 1974 101p il hardcover o.p. pa $3.95
Grades: 4 5 6   **S C**
1. Short stories 2. Devil -- Fiction
ISBN 0-374-41708-3 pa

"Twists of plot within traditional themes and a briskly witty style distinguish this book, illustrated amusingly with black-and-white line drawings." Booklist

Ten "stories about the machinations of the Devil to increase the population of his realm. He is not always successful and, despite his clever ruses, meets frustration as often as his intended victims do." Horn Book

Bachmann, Stefan

The **Cabinet** of Curiosities; 36 Tales Brief & Sinister. by Stefan Bachmann, Katherine Catmull, Claire Legrand and Emma Trevayne; illustrated by Alexander Jansson. Harpercollins Childrens Books 2014 496 p. illustrations $16.99
Grades: 3 4 5 6 7   **S C**
1. Short stories 2. Horror fiction 3. Mystery fiction
ISBN 0062331051; 9780062331052
LC 2013362532

This book, by Stefan Bachmann, Katherine Catmull, Claire Legrand and Emma Trevayne, is "a collection of thirty-six forty eerie, mysterious, intriguing, and very short stories. . . . The book features an introduction and commentary by the authors and black-and-white illustrations throughout." (Publisher's note)

"Many of these are moral tales in which nasty children or adults die horribly; others, though, feature perfectly nice people who meet similarly gruesome ends. Readers who enjoy their Halloween chills all year round will find this anthology a delight." Pub Wkly

★ **Baseball** crazy: ten short stories that cover all the bases; edited by Nancy E. Mercado. Dial Books for Young Readers 2008 191p $16.99; pa $6.99
Grades: 4 5 6 7   **S C**
1. Short stories 2. Baseball -- Fiction
ISBN 978-0-8037-3162-2; 0-8037-3162-0; 978-0-14-241371-5 pa; 0-14-241371-2 pa
LC 2007-26649

"There's no shortage of great writing in this collection of 10 stories. Baseball unifies the entries, but there the similarities end. . . . Readers will be drawn in by the masterful storytelling." Publ Wkly

The **big** book of pirates; text abridged and adapted by Alissa Heyman; illustrated by Xose Tomas; [original Spanish

text by by Joan and Albert Vinyoli] Sterling Pub. Co. 2011 103p il $12.95
Grades: 3 4 5 6   **S C**
1. Short stories 2. Adventure fiction 3. Pirates -- Fiction
ISBN 978-1-4027-8056-1; 1-4027-8056-7
LC 2010015049

This "is a treasure trove of abridged yarns by the likes of Sir Arthur Conan Doyle, Joseph Conrad, Daniel Defoe, and others. Of course the stories deal with pillaging, treachery, and all-around bad behavior on the open seas. The artwork is a dark, graphic-novel-like spin on N.C. Wyeth's illustrations for classics such as Treasure Island and Robinson Crusoe. Tomás uses a bold color palette and has given many of his characters angular faces and staring eyes, all to an appropriately menacing effect. This entertaining package will not make port on the shelves for long." SLJ

Brown, Dustin

The **sports** pages; edited and with an introduction by Jon Scieszka; stories by Dustin Brown, ... [et al.]; with illustrations by Dan Santat. Walden Pond Press 2012 245 p ill (Guys read) (paberback bdg.) $6.99; (hardcover bdg.) $16.99
Grades: 4 5 6 7 8   **S C**
1. Short stories 2. Sports -- Fiction
ISBN 9780061963773; 9780061963780
LC 2012012716

This book, edited and with an introduction by Jon Scieszka, "offers a smorgasbord of sportswriting--fiction and non-fiction--to appeal to every sports enthusiast. From baseball to football, ice hockey to track and mixed martial arts, there is plenty here for sports-minded readers to like, with lively action, humor and even a dose of mysticism in the form of magical grapefruit and a witch doctor." (Kirkus Reviews)

"In the third volume of his Guys Read series (the first focused on humor, and the second on thrillers), editor Scieszka turns his attention to sports, serving up 10 stories. . . . In his introduction, Scieszka wisely notes that good stories and good games are alike: Both reveal character and truths bigger than the game or the story." Booklist

Byars, Betsy Cromer

Cat diaries; secret writings of the MEOW Society. [by] Betsy Byars, Betsy Duffey, Laurie Myers; illustrated by Erik Brooks. Henry Holt and Company 2010 80p il $15.99
Grades: 2 3 4   **S C**
1. Short stories 2. Cats -- Fiction
ISBN 978-0-8050-8717-8; 0-8050-8717-6
LC 2009-18877

On one night every year, cats in the MEOW Society, which stands for "Memories Expressed In Our Writing," gather to read from their diaries, hearing stories of a gypsy cat, a Caribbean pirate cat, a library cat, and many others.

"This is a solid collection of stories that young readers will enjoy." Libr Media Connect

Dog diaries; secret writings of the WOOF Society. [by] Betsy Byars, Betsy Duffey, Laurie Myers; illustrated by Erik Brooks. Henry Holt 2007 72p il $15.95
Grades: 2 3 4   **S C**
1. Short stories 2. Dogs -- Fiction 3. Storytelling

-- Fiction
ISBN 978-0-8050-7957-9; 0-8050-7957-2

LC 2006011634

At the first annual meeting of WOOF—Words of Our Friends—assorted dogs preserve their heritage by sharing tales of canines throughout history, including Abu, who ruled all of Egypt except for one pesky cat, and Zippy, who simply must find the squeaky toy

"This collection of short stories combines the bedrocks of mass appeal: dogs, humor, and short chapters brimming with illustrations. . . . Expressive, energetic pencil illustrations adorn nearly every page." Booklist

★ The **chronicles** of Harris Burdick; 14 amazing authors tell the tales. Houghton Mifflin Harcourt 2011 un il $24.99
Grades: 5 6 7 8 9   **S C**
1. Short stories
ISBN 978-0-547-54810-4; 0-547-54810-9; 0547548109; 9780547548104

LC 2011006564

"Van Allsburg's The Mysteries of Harris Burdick, published in 1984, paired foreboding sentences with cryptic, highly detailed charcoal-pencil illustrations. With mostly stimulating, sometimes conventional results, seasoned authors (and Van Allsburg himself) play the game children have for decades, incorporating the sentences and visual cues into new stories . . . that expand on the original's enigmas. The liveliest entries pick up on Van Allsburg's haunting ambiguity; Jon Scieszka ends with a cliffhanger, Gregory Maguire weaves a complex tale of magic, and M.T. Anderson concocts a chilling Halloween offering. For a lakeside picture of two children, Sherman Alexie writes a sinister narrative about exasperating twins who pretend to have a third sibling, until their creepy prank backfires. . . . This star-studded exercise in creative writing tests the wits of favorite authors and shows readers how even the big shots hone their craft." Publ Wkly

Del Negro, Janice
★ **Passion** and poison; tales of shape-shifters, ghosts, and spirited women. Marshall Cavendish 2007 64p il $16.99
Grades: 5 6 7 8   **S C**
1. Ghost stories 2. Short stories 3. Supernatural -- Fiction
ISBN 978-0-7614-5361-1; 0-7614-5361-X

LC 2007-07237

"Including both original tales and retellings, this collection of seven stories . . . features diverse female protagonists facing challenges and perils—from human bullies to ghosts. More eerie than scary, the tales of bravery, revenge, grief, and redemption share a gothic sensibility. . . . The black-and-white illustrations . . . evoke bygone times." Booklist

Delacre, Lulu
★ **Salsa** stories; stories and linocuts by Lulu Delacre. Scholastic Press 2000 105p il hardcover o.p. $16.99
Grades: 4 5 6   **S C**
1. Short stories 2. Latin America 3. Family life -- Fiction 4. Latin America -- Fiction
ISBN 0-590-63118-7; 0-590-63121-7 pa

LC 99-25534

A collection of stories within the story of a family celebration where the guests relate their memories of growing up in various Latin American countries. Also contains recipes

"Kids will respond to both the warmth and the anxiety of the family life described in the vivid writing, and in Delacre's nicely composed linocuts." Booklist

Delaney, Joseph
The **Spook's** tale and other horrors; illustrations by Patrick Arrasmith. Greenwillow Books 2009 166p il (The last apprentice) $10.95; lib bdg $14.89
Grades: 5 6 7 8   **S C**
1. Short stories 2. Witches -- Fiction 3. Supernatural -- Fiction
ISBN 978-0-06-173028-3; 0-06-173028-9; 978-0-06-173030-6 lib bdg; 0-06-173030-0 lib bdg

LC 2008042235

As sixty-year-old John Gregory reflects on the past, he reveals how the world of ghosts, ghasts, witches, and boggarts was exposed to him and he later became the Spook, even though his first intention had been to join the priesthood.

"These short stories are narrated by secondary characters from the popular series, giving insight into some of Tom Ward's well-known companions. A 'Gallery of Villains' section identifies additional characters and gives a citation to the novels. . . . This book would be perfect for pulling reluctant readers into the series. The occasional black-and-white illustrations add a creepy, atmospheric touch." SLJ

Explorer; the mystery boxes. Kazu Kibuishi. Abrams Books 2012 126 p. (Explorer) (pbk.) $10.95; (hardcover with jacket) $19.95
Grades: 4 5 6 7 8   **S C**
1. Short stories 2. Graphic novels 3. Boxes -- Fiction 4. Mystery graphic novels 5. Boxes
ISBN 1419700103; 9781419700095; 9781419700101

LC 2011025343

This collection of short stories offers "[s]even . . . stories [which] answer one simple question: what's in the box? . . . [E]ach of these . . . illustrated short graphic works revolves around a central theme: a mysterious box and the marvels--or mayhem--inside. Artists include . . . Kazu Kibuishi, Raina Telgemeier ('Smile'), and Dave Roman ('Astronaut Academy'), as well as Jason Caffoe, Stuart Livingston, Johane Matte, Rad Sechrist (all contributors to the . . . comics anthology series 'Flight'), and . . . artist Emily Carroll." (Publisher's note)

Flanagan, John
The **lost** stories. Philomel 2011 422p (Ranger's apprentice) $17.99
Grades: 5 6 7 8   **S C**
1. Short stories 2. Fantasy fiction
ISBN 978-0-399-25618-9; 0-399-25618-0

This is "a collection of nine stories showing events not recorded in the books [of the Ranger's Apprentice series] and following the familiar characters during certain unrecorded times. In the framework story, set in 1896, an archaeologist discovers the fabled lost stories of the medieval Kingdom of Araluen. . . . Inspired by questions from readers, these short stories retain the adventure and the camaraderis of the novels." Booklist

Fleischman, Paul

Graven images; three stories. by Paul Fleischman; illustrations by Bagram Ibatoulline. Candlewick Press 2006 116p il $16.99; pa $5.99

Grades: 5 6 7 8   S C

1. Short stories 2. Supernatural -- Fiction

ISBN 0-7636-2775-5; 0-7636-2984-7 pa

LC 2005054283

A newly illustrated edition with a new afterword of the title first published 1982 by Harper & Row

A Newbery Medal honor book, 1983

A collection of three stories about a child who reads the lips of those who whisper secrets into a statue's ear; a daydreaming shoemaker's apprentice who must find ways to make the girl he loves notice him; and a stone carver who creates a statue of a ghost.

"Readers will be delighted with the return to print of [this title] with haunting new acrylic gouache illustrations . . . evoking the spinetingling aspects of this trio of tales. . . . Via a new afterword, the author explains the stories' inspiration and describes this book's significance early in his career." Publ Wkly

Girl meets boy; edited by Kelly Milner Halls. Chronicle Books 2012 v. cm. S C

1. Short stories 2. Teenagers -- Fiction 3. Interpersonal relations -- Fiction 4. Short stories, American 5. Perspective (Philosophy) -- Fiction 6. Interpersonal relations -- Fiction 7. Perspective (Philosophy) -- Fiction

ISBN 9781452102641

LC 2011025405

In this book "[t]welve writers answer [editor Kelly Milner] Halls's question: 'What if a group of authors took on the challenge of perception—boys versus girls?' Together, they create a thoughtful collection of paired short stories (and one joint offering) that give two distinct perspectives on the same events. While romantically themed, the stories do not all end in love connections. In James Howe and Ellen Wittlinger's stories, a gay teen learns the person he has been chatting with online is actually a girl; meanwhile, in Sarah Ryan and Randy Powell's joint story, 'Launchpad to Neptune,' a teen reunites with his first crush, only to find Stephanie has transitioned to Stephen." (Publishers Weekly)

★ The **Great** War; an anthology of stories inspired by objects from the first World War. illustrated by Jim Kay. Candlewick Press 2014 304 p. illustrations

Grades: 3 4 5 6 7 8   S C

1. World War, 1914-1918 2. War stories 3. Historical fiction

ISBN 9780763675547

LC 2013955699

In this book, illustrated by Jim Kay, "eleven internationally acclaimed writers draw on personal objects to bring the First World War to life. . . . Each author was invited to choose an object that had a connection to the war . . . and use it as the inspiration for an original short story." (Publisher's note)

"Each of the 11 original short stories in this superlative collection about WWI has been inspired by an object evoking the conflict. Thus, the catalyst for contributor Almond is a soldier's writing case; for Timothée de Fombelle, it's a Victoria Cross; for Adèle Geras, a wartime butter dish; for John Boyne, a recruitment poster; and so forth...Haunting

black-and-white illustrations by Kate Greenaway Medal-winning illustrator Kay reinforce the stories' somber mood and cumulative power. This book is both beautifully designed and beautifully written." Booklist

★ **Guys** read: funny business; edited and with an introduction by Jon Scieszka; stories by Mac Barnett [et al.]; with illustrations by Adam Rex. Walden Pond Press 2010 268p il $16.99; pa $5.99

Grades: 4 5 6 7   S C

1. Short stories 2. Humorous fiction 3. Boys -- Fiction

ISBN 978-0-06-196374-2; 0-06-196374-7; 978-0-06-196373-5 pa; 0-06-196373-9 pa

LC 2010-08122

A collection of humorous stories featuring a teenaged mummy, a homicidal turkey, and the world's largest pool of chocolate milk.

"A must-have collection for the boys in your library—and while you're at it, get a copy for the girls too!" Booklist

★ **Guys** read: thriller. Walden Pond Press 2011 viii, 272p $16.99; pa $6.99

Grades: 5 6 7 8   S C

1. Short stories 2. Adventure fiction

ISBN 978-0-06-196376-6; 0-06-196376-3; 978-0-06-196375-9 pa; 0-06-196375-5 pa

"Scieszka has gathered 10 thrilling stories from stellar writers. There are ghost stories, a deeply touching tale of a wish-granting machine and one about monsters that live in storm drains. . . . This anthology is brimming with choice stuff for guys who appreciate the uncanny, the uncouth and the unput-down-able." Kirkus

★ **Half**-minute horrors; edited by Susan Rich. HarperCollinsPublishers 2009 141p il $12.99

Grades: 5 6 7 8   S C

1. Short stories 2. Horror fiction

ISBN 978-0-06-183379-3; 0-06-183379-7

LC 2009-18293

An anthology of very short, scary stories by an assortment of authors and illustrators including Chris Raschka, Joyce Carol Oates, Neil Gaiman, Jack Gantos, and Lane Smith.

"This collection of more than 70 chilling snippets is ideal for campfires and car trips. The stories—some a couple sentences, some a few pages—range from darkly humorous . . . to outright creepy. . . . These are inherently quick reads, but with enough plot and detail to encourage further imagining." Publ Wkly

Hawes, Louise

Black pearls; a faerie strand. by Louise Hawes; illustrations by Rebecca Guay. Houghton Mifflin Company 2008 211p il $16

Grades: 5 6 7 8 9 10 11 12   S C

1. Fairy tales 2. Short stories

ISBN 978-0-618-74797-9; 0-618-74797-4

LC 2007-41166

"Seven gems based on traditional fairy tales make up this collection of unique short stories. . . . Each contains enough clues to guide teens back to the familiar and sometimes innuendo-laden classic fairy tales of their childhoods, and Guay's fantastical pencil drawings . . . enhance the sense of character and magic. Twisted, clever, and artfully written." Booklist

Hearne, Betsy Gould

The **canine** connection: stories about dogs and people; [by] Betsy Hearne. Margaret K. McElderry Bks. 2003 113p hardcover o.p. pa $8.95

Grades: 5 6 7 8   S C

1. Short stories 2. Dogs -- Fiction

ISBN 0-689-85258-4; 1-4169-6817-2 pa

LC 2001-58991

Twelve short stories that reflect the varied ways that dogs and humans relate

"The emotions and dialogue are pitch perfect. . . . A rewarding collection that will stay with readers." Booklist

Horse tales; collected by June Crebbin; illustrated by Inga Moore. Candlewick Press 2005 148p il $18.99

Grades: 4 5 6 7   S C

1. Short stories 2. Horses -- Fiction

ISBN 0-7636-2657-0

LC 2004-51897

In these "short stories, the remarkable nature of the horse is revealed. . . . The offerings excerpted from novels work well as short stories here and may inspire readers to look for the full-length books. . . . This is an excellently conceived and executed collection with wonderful art." SLJ

I fooled you; ten stories of tricks, jokes, and switcheroos. collected and edited by Johanna Hurwitz. Candlewick Press 2010 174p il $16.99; pa $6.99

Grades: 4 5 6   S C

1. Short stories

ISBN 978-0-7636-3789-7; 0-7636-3789-0; 978-0-7636-4877-0 pa; 0-7636-4877-9 pa

LC 2009-26017

"Hurwitz asked 10 authors to write a piece with the tagline of the title. . . . Megan McDonald uses her familiar characters, Judy Moody and Stink. . . . Douglas Florian's poem is distinctively in his style, but contains unexpected elements, nonetheless. . . . Michelle Knudsen's 'The Bridge to Highlandsville' is absolutely logical yet lacks the ending most would expect. Matthew Holm's almost wordless 'Sam and Pam' . . . adds a nice graphic-novel-style component to the package. Most readers will likely find something that they appreciate and something that they don't—which may be the best indication of the range of depth and complexity in this collection." SLJ

Ionesco, Eugène, 1912-1994

Stories 1,2,3,4; Eugene Ionesco; illustrated by Etienne Delessert. Pgw 2012 112 p. $19.95

Grades: K 1 2 3   S C

1. Children's stories 2. Picture books for children

ISBN 1936365510; 9781936365517

In this collection of stories by Eugene Ionesco, illustrated by Etienne Delessert, provides "snippets of playful conversation between Papa, Mama, their daughter Josette, and Jacqueline the maid. . . . In Story 3, the father tells Josette about an airplane journey they'll take together . . . over the Paris rooftops, and on to the moon. . . . Visual quotes (including plenty of Ionesco rhinoceri) pop up everywhere." (Publishers Weekly)

Juster, Norton

Alberic the Wise and other journeys; illustrated by Domenico Gnoli. 2010 88p il pa $5.99

Grades: 3 4 5 6   S C

1. Short stories

ISBN 978-0-375-86699-9; 0-375-86699-X

A reissue of the title first published 1965 by Pantheon

"Three stories leave readers wondering: What happened next? The first tells of Alberic, who spent his life searching without knowing what for. In the second a modern boy steps into a Renaissance painting. The third tells of two kings who briefly exchange kingdoms. Juster's smooth storytelling weaves together action and characterization. Gnoli's striking illustrations have a medieval feeling and are in perfect harmony." Horn Book Guide

Kipling, Rudyard, 1865-1936

★ A **collection** of Rudyard Kipling's Just so stories. Candlewick Press 2004 127p il $22.99

Grades: 3 4 5 6   S C

1. Short stories 2. India -- Fiction 3. Animals -- Fiction

ISBN 0-7636-2629-5

LC 2004-45858

"This colorful collection of eight tales distinguishes itself with its range of artwork. Well-known children's book artists, including Peter Sis, Jane Ray, and Satoshi Kitamura, contributed the art, each one illustrating a different story. The vibrant mix of styles and materials adds new dimension to favorite stories. . . . A lively, accessible edition." Booklist

Lay-ups and long shots; an anthology of short stories. by Joseph Bruchac . . . [et al.] Darby Creek Pub. 2008 112p il $15.95

Grades: 4 5 6   S C

1. Short stories 2. Sports -- Fiction

ISBN 978-1-58196-078-5; 1-58196-078-6

"These nine new short stories feature tweens or teens who, despite lack of skill or other obstacles, engage in athletic pursuits. Some . . . have autobiographical elements. . . . Consistently readable and engaging, the collection should have as much appeal for geeks as it does for jocks." Booklist

Marcantonio, Patricia Santos

Red ridin' in the hood; and other cuentos. pictures by Renato Alarcão. Farrar, Straus & Giroux 2005 181p il $16

Grades: 3 4 5   S C

1. Fairy tales 2. Short stories 3. Hispanic Americans -- Fiction

ISBN 0-374-36241-6

"The fractured fairy tale gets cool Latino flavor in this lively collection of 11 fresh retellings, with witty reversals of class and gender roles and powerful, full-page pictures that set the drama in venues ranging from the desert and the barrio to a skyscraper." Booklist

Marshall, James

Rats on the roof, and other stories. Dial Bks. for Young Readers 1991 79p il hardcover o.p. pa $4.99

Grades: 2 3 4   S C

1. Short stories 2. Animals -- Fiction

ISBN 0-8037-0835-1; 0-14-038646-7 pa

LC 90-44084

An illustrated collection of seven stories about various animals, including a frog with magnificent legs, a hungry brontosaurus, and a mouse who gets married

"Marshall's fertile imagination gets lots of exercise here as does his sardonic wit, and he's included plenty of expressive illustrations, all done in his signature style." Booklist

McKissack, Patricia C.

★ The **dark**-thirty; Southern tales of the supernatural. illustrated by Brian Pinkney. Knopf 1992 122p il $18.95; lib bdg $20.99; pa $6.50

Grades: 4 5 6 7   S C

1. Ghost stories 2. Short stories 3. African Americans -- Fiction

ISBN 0-679-81863-4; 0-679-91853-9 lib bdg; 0-679-89006-8 pa

LC 92-3021

Coretta Scott King Award for text, 1993; A Newbery honor book, 1993

A collection of ghost stories with African American themes, designed to be told during the Dark Thirty—the half hour before sunset—when ghosts seem all too believable

"Strong characterizations are superbly drawn in a few words. The atmosphere of each selection is skillfully developed and sustained to the very end. Pinkney's stark scratchboard illustrations evoke an eerie mood, which heightens the suspense of each tale." SLJ

★ **Porch** lies; tales of slicksters, tricksters, and other wily characters. [by] Patricia C. McKissack; illustrated by André Carrilho. Schwartz & Wade Books 2006 146p il $18.95; lib bdg $22.99

Grades: 4 5 6 7   S C

1. Short stories 2. African Americans -- Fiction

ISBN 0-375-83619-5; 0-375-93619-X lib bdg

LC 2005-22048

The "original tales in this uproarious collection draw on African American oral tradition and blend history and legend with sly humor, creepy horror, villainous characters, and wild farce. McKissack based the stories on those she heard as a child while sitting on her grandparents' porch. . . . Carrilho's full-page illustrations—part cartoon, part portrait in silhouette—combine realistic characters with scary monsters." Booklist

Naidoo, Beverley

Out of bounds: seven stories of conflict and hope. HarperCollins Pubs. 2003 175p $16.99; pa $5.99

Grades: 5 6 7 8   S C

1. Short stories 2. South Africa -- Race relations -- Fiction

ISBN 0-06-050799-3; 0-06-050801-9 pa

LC 2002-68901

First published 2001 in the United Kingdom

Seven stories, spanning the time period from 1948 to 2000, chronicle the experiences of young people from different races and ethnic groups as they try to cope with the restrictions placed on their lives by South Africa's apartheid laws

"Naidoo's book reveals our humanity and inhumanity with starkness and precision. . . . She honors her country's past, present, and future with these brave tales." Horn Book

Other worlds; edited by Jon Scieszka, illustrated by Greg Ruth. Walden Pond Press 2013 352 p. (Guys read) (hardback) $16.99

Grades: 4 5 6 7 8   S C

1. Short stories 2. Science fiction 3. Fantasy fiction

ISBN 0061963801; 9780061963797; 9780061963803

LC 2013021863

This book, edited by Jon Scieszka, is the fourth Guys Read collection of science fiction short stories. It "is anchored by Ray Bradbury's 1946 'Frost and Fire,' about colonists stranded for generations on a planet so harsh that the average life span is less than two weeks." Other topics include "unsuccessful alien invasions of Earth to Tom Angleberger's tale of smart clothes in rebellion, an eerie ghost story from Kenneth Oppel and . . . a 'girl in armor' episode from Shannon Hale." (Kirkus Reviews)

"Though most of the tales here are entertaining and 'mind-expandingly fun,' Shusterman's and Bradbury's especially stand out as intriguing, suspenseful, and thought-provoking." Horn Book

Paulsen, Gary

Paintings from the cave; three novellas. Wendy Lamb Books 2011 161p $15.99; lib bdg $18.99

Grades: 4 5 6 7   S C

1. Short stories 2. Art -- Fiction 3. Dogs -- Fiction 4. Violence -- Fiction 5. Homeless persons -- Fiction

ISBN 978-0-385-74684-7; 978-0-385-90921-1 lib bdg; 978-0-375-89743-6 e-book

LC 2011016287

"These novellas portray an unflinching look at children who have endured neglectful and abusive homes and are surviving on their own. The atmospheric first tale, 'Man of the Iron Heads,' is narrated by Jake, a boy of about 11, who hides from the local gang until he finds the courage to outsmart its violent leader. 'Jo-Jo the Dog-Faced Girl' presents a lonely girl with three adopted dogs who finds acceptance in befriending a girl with leukemia. Finally, 'Erik's Rules' celebrates the power of art and is told by Jamie, the younger of two homeless brothers, whose unstable existence changes after a chance encounter with a friendly volunteer at the animal shelter. By incorporating the solace found in dogs, art, libraries, and new friends into these tales of heartache and redemption, Paulsen provides his readers with hope of a better life." SLJ

Pratchett, Terry

Dragons at Crumbling Castle; and other tales. Terry Pratchett; illustrated by Mark Beech. Clarion Books, Houghton Mifflin Harcourt 2015 336 p. illustrations (hardback) $16.99

Grades: 3 4 5 6   S C

1. Short stories 2. Fantasy fiction 3. Humorous fiction 4. Humorous stories 5. Youths' writings 6. Teenagers' writings

ISBN 0544466594; 9780544466593

LC 2014024233

This book, by Terry Pratchett, illustrated by Mark Beech, is a "never-before-published collection of fourteen funny and inventive tales by acclaimed author Sir Terry Pratchett features a memorable cast of inept wizards, sensible heroes, and unusually adventuresome tortoises. Including more than one hundred black-and-white illustrations, the . . . book celebrates Pratchett's inimitable wordplay and irreverent approach to the conventions of storytelling." (Publisher's note)

"Though these stories lack the perfectly timed wordplay of Pratchett's later work, they are a charming and funny sample of his early fictional imaginings. Accompanied by Beech's wiry Quentin Blake–like illustrations, as well as numerous typographical flourishes, this volume will please both its intended audience and older Pratchett completists." Pub Wkly

Priestley, Chris

Uncle Montague's tales of terror; [by] Chris Priestley; illustrations by David Roberts. Bloomsbury Children's Books 2007 238p il $12.95

Grades: 5 6 7 8 9   **S C**

1. Short stories 2. Horror fiction 3. Uncles -- Fiction 4. Storytelling -- Fiction

ISBN 978-1-59990-118-3; 1-59990-118-8

"Ghosts, demons, jinns, and deadly trees populate these 10 chilly short stories set in the late 19th century, with the language and black-and-white illustrations capturing the feel of Victorian times. Young Edgar hears these tales while visiting his eccentric Uncle Montague, and each one is connected to a strange object in his uncle's study.... An enjoyable collection with enough creepy atmosphere (and some gruesome action) to hold readers' attention." SLJ

Reichenstetter, Friederun

Andersen's fairy tales; retold by Friederun Reichenstetter; illustrated by Silke Leffler. North-South 2007 92p il $19.95

Grades: 4 5 6   **S C**

1. Authors 2. Novelists 3. Dramatists 4. Fairy tales 5. Children's authors 6. Short story writers

ISBN 0-7358-2141-0

"Thirteen tales ... are adapted from excellent translations by Anthea Bell and H. P. Paul.... Leffler's often-humorous painted folk-art illustrations show cute little people with chubby line-drawn faces dressed in clothing of 18th-century style.... The volume ... is quite handsome." SLJ

Root, Phyllis

Aunt Nancy and the bothersome visitors; illustrated by David Parkins. Candlewick Press 2007 57p il $16.99

Grades: 1 2 3 4   **S C**

1. Aunts -- Fiction 2. Cousins -- Fiction

ISBN 978-0-7636-3074-4; 0-7636-3074-8

LC 2007-60856

Includes two stories previously published separately in picture book format: Aunt Nancy and Old Man Trouble (1996) and Aunt Nancy and Cousin Lazybones (1998)

Clever Aunt Nancy manages to foil all those who try to get the better of her.

"Root's folksy style shines in every sentence.... Parkins provides full-color paintings to introduce each story, but his wit really shows itself in the droll silhouettes that milk body language for all it's worth." Horn Book

Rowling, J. K.

The tales of Beedle the Bard; translated from the ancient runes by Hermione Granger; commentary by Albus Dumbledore; introduction, notes, and illustrations by J.K. Rowling. Arthur A. Levine 2008 111p il $12.99

Grades: 5 6 7 8 9 10 11 12   **S C**

1. Fairy tales 2. Short stories 3. Magic -- Fiction

ISBN 978-0-545-12828-5; 0-545-12828-5

A collection of tales from the world of Harry Potter.

"The introduction is captivating ... [and] the tales themselves are entertaining.... Rowling is at the top of her game as a superb storyteller, providing her legions of fans with an enchanting collection of wizard folklore." Voice Youth Advocates

San Souci, Robert

Dare to be scared 4; thirteen more tales of terror. [by] Robert D. San Souci; illustrations by David Ouimet. Cricket Books 2009 275p il $17.95

Grades: 4 5 6 7   **S C**

1. Short stories 2. Horror fiction

ISBN 978-0-8126-2754-1; 0-8126-2754-7

LC 2009018490

"These deliciously shivery tales are perfect for campfire spookiness or as Halloween read-alouds. As in the previous books in the series, San Souci relies heavily on folklore and urban legends, giving the stories an even more chilling impact.... Strong themes such as death and murder are prevalent throughout. Ouimet's dark illustrations are paired perfectly with this creepy collection." SLJ

Double-dare to be scared: another thirteen chilling tales; [by] Robert D. San Souci; illustrated by David Ouimet. Cricket Books 2004 170p il $15.95

Grades: 4 5 6 7   **S C**

1. Short stories 2. Horror fiction

ISBN 0-8126-2716-4

LC 2003-26610

Companion volume to Dare to be scared (2003)

"San Souci uses elements of urban legend and folklore to weave powerful and suspenseful yet age-appropriate stories that youngsters will revisit, finding new meaning with each reading." SLJ

Haunted houses; [by] Robert D. San Souci; illustrated by Kelly Murphy and Antoine Revoy. Henry Holt 2010 276p il (Are you scared yet?) $16.99

Grades: 4 5 6 7   **S C**

1. Ghost stories 2. Short stories 3. Horror fiction

ISBN 978-0-8050-8750-5; 0-8050-8750-8

LC 2009-50763

"These 10 spooky stories include a classic Halloween scare: visitors get their admission fee of $25 back if they make it to the top floor of a haunted house—but can they? In another, the primary occupant of a dollhouse is a ghost of a child who needs help moving from one consciousness to another.... The stories are well paced and satisfyingly startling.... This book won't stay on the shelves for long. Murphy and Revoy's black-and-white illustrations heighten the fright factor, making San Souci's collection even more riveting." SLJ

Sandburg, Carl

★ Rootabaga stories; illustrated by Maud and Miska Petersham. Harcourt 2003 176p il hardcover o.p. pa $5.95 **S C**

1. Fairy tales 2. Short stories

ISBN 0-15-204709-3; 0-15-204714-X pa

LC 2002-191949

First published 1922; previously published as: Rootabaga stories, part one

A selection of tales from Rootabaga Country peopled with such characters as the Potato Face Blind Man, the Blue Wind Boy, and many others

★ **Shelf** life: stories by the book; edited by Gary Paulsen. Simon & Schuster Bks. for Young Readers 2003 173p $16.95

Grades: 5 6 7 8   S C

  1. Short stories 2. Books and reading -- Fiction

ISBN 0-689-84180-9

LC 2002-66901

Ten short stories in which the lives of young people in different circumstances are changed by their encounters with books

"Covering almost every genre of fiction, including mystery, SF, fantasy and realism, these well-crafted stories by familiar authors offer sharply drawn characterizations and intriguing premises." Publ Wkly

Shusterman, Neal

Darkness creeping; twenty twisted tales. Puffin Books 2007 291p pa $7.99

Grades: 5 6 7 8   S C

  1. Short stories 2. Horror fiction

ISBN 0-14-240721-6

"The author takes a walk on the dark side in this collection of spooky stories, some old, some new, all delightfully creepy. He knows his audience, providing enough horrific touches to appeal to the most challenging readers—those hard-to-reach middle school boys. Each story is introduced with a brief statement describing where he got the idea." Voice Youth Advocates

Singer, Isaac Bashevis

Stories for children. Farrar, Straus & Giroux 1984 337p hardcover o.p. pa $14

Grades: 4 5 6 7   S C

  1. Short stories 2. Jews -- Fiction

ISBN 0-374-37266-7; 0-374-46489-8 pa

LC 84-13612

This collection of thirty-six stories includes "parables, beast fables, allegories and reminiscences. Some stories are silly and charming, while others are wildly fantastic, dealing with savagery and miracles in mythical, medieval Poland. Frequently they are about scary situations, but all tend to end happily, with an edifying idea. Most appealing is the Nobel Prize winner's sheer story-telling power. In this respect, he has no equal among contemporaries." N Y Times Book Rev

Soto, Gary

★ **Baseball** in April, and other stories; 10th anniversary ed; Harcourt Brace Jovanovich 2000 111p $16; pa $6

Grades: 5 6 7 8   S C

  1. Short stories 2. California -- Fiction 3. Mexican Americans -- Fiction

ISBN 0-15-202573-1; 0-15-202567-7 pa

A reissue of the title first published 1990

A collection of eleven short stories focusing on the everyday adventures of Hispanic young people growing up in Fresno, California

Each story "gets at the heart of some aspect of growing up. The insecurities, the embarrassments, the triumphs, the inequities of it all are chronicled with wit and charm. Soto's characters ring true and his knowledge of, and affection for, their shared Mexican-American heritage is obvious and infectious." Voice Youth Advocates

Facts of life; stories. Harcourt 2008 176p $16

Grades: 5 6 7 8   S C

  1. Short stories 2. California -- Fiction 3. Mexican Americans -- Fiction

ISBN 978-0-15-206181-4; 0-15-206181-9

LC 2007-35765

"Pivitol moments in the lives of California Latino teens and tweens provide the starting points for Soto's collection of 10 . . . stories. For Letty, it's the realization that her boyfriend loves her money more than he does her; for Hector, it's the announcement of his parents' plan to divorce. . . . Soto's affection and concern for his characters is evident throughout." Booklist

Local news. Harcourt Brace Jovanovich 1993 148p hardcover o.p. pa $5.95

Grades: 5 6 7 8   S C

  1. Short stories 2. California -- Fiction 3. Mexican Americans -- Fiction

ISBN 0-15-248117-6; 0-15-204695-X pa

LC 92-37905

A collection of thirteen short stories about the everyday lives of Mexican American young people in California's Central Valley

"These stories resonate with integrity, verve, and compassion." Horn Book

Petty crimes. Harcourt Brace & Co. 1998 157p $16; pa $6.99

Grades: 5 6 7 8   S C

  1. Short stories 2. Mexican Americans -- Fiction

ISBN 0-15-201658-9; 0-15-205437-5 pa

LC 97-37114

A collection of short stories about Mexican American youth growing up in California's Central Valley

"A sense of family strength relieves the under-current of sadness in these raw stories." Horn Book Guide

Spinelli, Jerry

The **library** card. Scholastic 1997 148p pa $4.99

Grades: 4 5 6 7   S C

  1. Short stories 2. Books and reading -- Fiction

ISBN 0-590-38633-6

LC 96-18412

"A library card is the magical object common to each of these four stories in which a budding street thug, a television addict, a homeless orphan, and a lonely girl are all transformed by the power and the possibilities that await them within the walls of the public library. Spinelli's characters . . . are unusual and memorable; his writing both humorous and convincing." Horn Book Guide

Stine, R. L.

The **haunting** hour. HarperCollins Pubs. 2001 153p il $11.95; pa $5.99

Grades: 4 5 6 7   S C

  1. Short stories 2. Horror fiction

ISBN 0-06-623604-5; 0-06-441045-5 pa

LC 2001-39142

A collection of ten short horror stories featuring a ghoulish Halloween party, a long, mysterious car trip, and a very dangerous imaginary friend. Each story includes drawings by a different illustrator

"The predictability of the stories and the unsophisticated storytelling won't keep Stine fans old and new from swallowing this down in one big gulp." Bull Cent Child Books

Tan, Shaun

★ **Lost** & found; 3 by Shaun Tan. Arthur A. Levine Books 2011 un il $21.99

Grades: 5 6 7 8   **S C**

1. Short stories

ISBN 978-0-545-22924-1; 0-545-22924-3

          LC 2010030936

This book comprises three previously published stories by the Australian author-illustrator "In 'The Red Tree,' a young girl moves listlessly through her day with a sense of dreadful ennui that escalates with each page turn . . . until finally finding some hope at the end. In 'The Lost Thing,' a young boy discovers a most peculiar object and dutifully tries to find a proper home for it. . . . Finally, 'The Rabbits' (with a text by John Marsden) is a colonization fable, as rabbits invade and populate a new land, overwhelming the native animal population and severely altering the landscape. . . . Intermediate, middle school." (Horn Book)

"'The Red Tree' follows a solitary girl through a single, not very good day, exploring her feelings as they shift from disappointment and confusion to alienation and despair. The spare, lyrical text provides an anchor for Tan's large, moody, beautiful paintings. 'The Lost Thing' is a more upbeat tale of a boy who discovers an unusual object and then must decide what to do with it. Freedom and imagination are the themes in this story, and here the art includes fascinating and sometimes humorous bits of technical drawings. The prose of John Marsden's 'The Rabbits,' an allegory about imperialism, is so simple and melodic that it verges on poetry. The artist emphasizes the invasive foreignness of the rabbits by dressing them in baroque uniforms, drawing mystifying, gigantic machines and buildings for them to build and deploy in their inexorable drive to dominate." SLJ

★ **Troll's** eye view; a book of villainous tales. Viking 2009 200p $16.99; pa $7.99

Grades: 5 6 7 8   **S C**

1. Fairy tales 2. Short stories

ISBN 978-0-670-06141-9; 0-670-06141-7; 978-0-14-241673-0 pa; 0-14-241673-8 pa

Everyone thinks they know the real story behind the villains in fairy tales—evil, no two ways about it. But the villains themselves beg to differ. In this anthology for younger readers, you'll hear from the Giant's wife (from Jack and the Beanstalk), Rumpelstiltskin, the oldest of the Twelve Dancing Princesses, and more.

"A mixed bag of funny, quirky, and downright creepy entries. . . . The collection is largely accessible and very enjoyable." Booklist

Under my hat; tales from the cauldron. edited by Jonathan Strahan. Random House 2012 415 p. (trade) $16.99

Grades: 5 6 7 8   **S C**

1. Short stories 2. Witches -- Fiction

ISBN 0375868305; 9780375868047; 9780375868306; 9780375898815; 9780375968303

          LC 2011031253

This book presents "eighteen short tales about witches. . . . Garth Nix's 'A Handful of Ashes' features a library and librarian. Delia Sherman's 'The Witch in the Woods' . . . [features] deer and bear shape-shifters and no small darkness. . . . Jane Yolen makes Hans Christian Andersen's life a tale itself." (Kirkus Reviews)

Under the weather; stories about climate change. edited by Tony Bradman. Frances Lincoln Children's 2009 215p pbk. $8.99; $16.95

Grades: 5 6 7 8   **S C**

1. Short stories 2. Greenhouse effect -- Fiction

ISBN 9781845079444; 1-84507-930-2; 978-1-84507-930-7

"Eight stories by a variety of authors attempt to make the facts about climate change and its global ramifications relevant to today's children. The majority of the selections are about youngsters enacting change and working toward solutions in tangible ways. For example, 'How to Build the Perfect Sandcastle' is about a Philippino boy who works to rebuild the coral reefs, which are dying due to the rise in ocean temperature. . . . Overall . . . this is a worthwhile effort that will appeal to children wanting to make a difference in their world as well as to teachers trying to make the scientific reality of climate change real to their students." SLJ

AUTHOR, TITLE, AND SUBJECT INDEX

This index to the books in the Classified Collection includes author, title, and subject entries; added entries for publishers' series, illustrators, joint authors, and editors of works entered under title; and name and subject cross-references; all arranged in one alphabet.

The number or symbol in bold face type at the end of each entry refers to the Dewey Decimal Classification or to the Fiction (Fic) or Story Collection (S C), or Easy Books (E) section where the main entry for the book will be found. Works classed in 92 will be found under the headings for the biographies' subject.

ADVENT

See also Church year; Religious holidays

The **Advent** Craft and Activity Book. Dhom, C. **745**

Adventure according to Humphrey. Birney, B. G. **Fic**

ADVENTURE AND ADVENTURERS

Almond, D. Heaven Eyes **Fic**

Belanger, J. What it's like **179**

Black, P. J. Urban outlaws **Fic**

Branzei, S. Adventurers **920.72**

Catalanotto, P. More of Monkey & Robot **E**

Horowitz, A. Eagle Strike **Fic**

The imaginary **Fic**

Mister Max **Fic**

Quest **E**

Roy, C. The blood guard **Fic**

Splat! **E**

Springer, N. Rowan Hood, outlaw girl of Sherwood Forest **Fic**

ADVENTURE AND ADVENTURERS -- BIOG-RAPHY

Branzei, S. Adventurers **920.72**

ADVENTURE AND ADVENTURERS -- FIC-TION

Abbott, T. The forbidden stone **Fic**

Abbott, T. Wade and the scorpion's claw **Fic**

Anderson, J. D. Sidekicked **Fic**

Anderson, M. T. He laughed with his other mouths **Fic**

Armstrong, A. Racing the moon **Fic**

Barnett, M. Sam and Dave dig a hole **E**

Black, H. Doll bones **Fic**

Black, P. J. Urban outlaws **Fic**

Brawer, M. Archie takes flight **Fic**

Brawer, M. Water planet rescue **Fic**

Brodien-Jones, C. The glass puzzle **Fic**

Cameron, A. The lightning catcher **Fic**

Carman, P. The field of wacky inventions **Fic**

Carroll, M. Stronger **Fic**

Catmull, K. Summer and Bird **Fic**

Chad, J. Leo Geo and the cosmic crisis **741.5**

Colfer, E. Artemis Fowl **Fic**

Columbus, C. House of secrets **Fic**

The curse of the pharaoh **Fic**

De Lint, C. Seven wild sisters **Fic**

Duck & Goose go to the beach **E**

Durham, P. The luck uglies **Fic**

Finding Serendipity **Fic**

Flanagan, J. The hunters **Fic**

Flanagan, J. The invaders **Fic**

Flanagan, J. The royal ranger **Fic**

Fork-tongue charmers **Fic**

Gabriel Finley and the raven's riddle **Fic**

Gaiman, N. Fortunately, the milk **Fic**

Gidwitz, A. In a glass Grimmly **Fic**

Grant, M. The call **Fic**

Gratz, A. The League of Seven **Fic**

The green bath **E**

The Grimm conclusion **Fic**

Grounded **Fic**

Hobbs, W. Never say die **Fic**

The imaginary **Fic**

Johnson, J. The mark of the dragonfly **Fic**

Johnson-Shelton, N. The seven swords **Fic**

The key of Braha **Fic**

King, C. Seven sorcerers **Fic**

Kraegel, K. King Arthur's very great grandson **E**

Kurtz, C. The adventures of a South Pole pig **Fic**

Lacey, J. Island of Thieves **Fic**

Lane, A. J. B. Stop thief! **E**

Larson, M. A. Pennyroyal Academy **Fic**

Lawrence, I. The smugglers **Fic**

Lawson, J. The actual & truthful adventures of Becky Thatcher **Fic**

Lerangis, P. The colossus rises **Fic**

Light, S. Zephyr takes flight **E**

Mackey, H. Dreamwood **Fic**

Marr, M. Loki's wolves **Fic**

Marr, M. Odin's ravens **Fic**

McQuerry, M. D. Beyond the door **Fic**

Mister Max **Fic**

The mouse with the question mark tail **Fic**

Nielsen, J. A. The shadow throne **Fic**

Oliver and the seawigs **Fic**

Oppel, K. The Boundless **Fic**

Pearson, S. We're going on a ghost hunt **E**

Peggy **E**

Pierpoint, E. The last ride of Caleb O'Toole **Fic**

Pullman, P. Two crafty criminals! **Fic**

Quest for the Spark **Fic**

Rex, A. Champions of breakfast **Fic**

Rex, A. Smek for president! **Fic**

Rex, A. Unlucky charms **Fic**

Riordan, R. The Serpent's Shadow **Fic**

Rogue Knight **Fic**

Ryan, C. The map to everywhere **Fic**

Sackett, F. The misadventures of the magician's dog **Fic**

Saunders, K. The Whizz Pop Chocolate Shop **Fic**

Smith, R. C. Mutation **Fic**

Smith, R. Chupacabra **Fic**

Soman, D. Three bears in a boat **E**

Staniszewski, A. My sort of fairy tale ending **Fic**

Stewart, T. L. The extraordinary education of Nicholas Benedict **Fic**

Treasure hunters **Fic**

Vanderpool, C. Navigating Early **Fic**

Villeneuve, A. Loula is leaving for Africa **E**

Voelkel, J. The river of no return **Fic**

Watson, J. The 39 clues **Fic**

Watson, J. Loot **Fic**

ADVENTURE AND ADVENTURERS -- FIC- TION *See* Adventure fiction

Adventure Annie goes to work. Buzzeo, T. **E**

Adventure at Simba Hill. Runholt, S. **Fic**

Adventure beneath the sea. Mallory, K. **551.46**

ADVENTURE FICTION

Boyne, J. The Terrible Thing That Happened to Barnaby Brocket **Fic**

Cody, M. Super **Fic**

Garza, X. Maximilian and the mystery of the Guardian Angel **Fic**

Holub, J. Little Red Writing **E**

Lerangis, P. Lost in babylon **Fic**

MacHale, D. J. SYLO **Fic**

The man from the land of Fandango **E**

Rosenthal, E. I'll save you Bobo! **E**

Seagulls don't eat pickles **Fic**

The snowstorm **Fic**

ADVENTURE FILMS

See also Motion pictures

ADVENTURE GRAPHIC NOVELS

Aguirre, J. Giants beware! **741.5**

Chantler, S. Tower of treasure **741.5**

City of spies **741.5**

Colfer, E. Artemis Fowl: the graphic novel **741.5**

Davis, E. The secret science alliance and the copy- cat crook **741.5**

Farshtey, G. Bionicle #1: rise of the Toa Nuva **741.5**

Flight explorer **741.5**

Ford, C. Stickman Odyssey **741.5**

Herge The adventures of Tintin, vol. 1 **741.5**

Ita, S. The Odyssey **741.5**

Kibuishi, K. Amulet, book one: The Stonekeep- er **741.5**

Kibuishi, K. Copper **741.5**

McCranie, S. Mal and Chad **741.5**

McGuiness, D. Pilot & Huxley: the first adven- ture **741.5**

McGuiness, D. Pilot & Huxley: the next adven- ture **741.5**

Parker, J. Missile Mouse: rescue on Tanki- um3 **741.5**

Parker, J. Missile Mouse: the star crusher **741.5**

Phelan, M. The storm in the barn **741.5**

Renier, A. The Unsinkable Walker Bean **741.5**

Sava, S. C. Hyperactive **741.5**

Slavin, B. Big city Otto: elephants never for- get **741.5**

Smith, J. Bone: out from Boneville **741.5**

Smith, J. Bone: Rose **741.5**

Smith, J. Bone: tall tales **741.5**

Weigel, J. Thunder from the sea **741.5**

Wetterer, M. K. The snowshoeing adventure of Milton Daub, blizzard trekker **741.5**

See also Graphic novels

Adventure sports [series]

Wurdinger, S. D. Kayaking **797.1**

ADVENTURE STORIES

Abbott, T. The serpent's curse **Fic**

Carman, P. The field of wacky inventions **Fic**

Erskine, K. The badger knight **Fic**

Hirsch, J. The 39 clues: Breakaway **Fic**

Hunters of the great forest **E**

Lerangis, P. Tomb of shadows **Fic**

Nielsen, J. A. The shadow throne **Fic**

Roy, C. The blood guard **Fic**

Stephens, H. The big adventure of the Smalls **E**

The stowaways **Fic**

Viminy Crowe's comic book **Fic**

See also Adventure fiction

ADVENTURE TELEVISION PROGRAMS

See also Television programs

ADVENTURE TRAVEL

See also Travel; Voyages and travels

Adventurers. Branzei, S. **920.72**

Adventures in cartooning. Sturm, J. **741.5**

Adventures in memory [series]

Cleary, B. P. Mrs. Riley Bought Five Itchy Aard- varks and other painless tricks for memorizing sci- ence facts **500**

Adventures of a cat-whiskered girl. Pinkwater, D. M. **Fic**

The **adventures** of a South Pole pig. Kurtz, C. **Fic**

The **adventures** of Ali Baba Bernstein. Hurwitz, J. **Fic**

The **adventures** of Beanboy. Harkrader, L. **Fic**

The **adventures** of Beekle. Santat, D. **E**

The **Adventures** of Captain Underpants. **Fic**

Adventures of Daniel Boom AKA Loud Boy [se- ries]

Steinberg, D. Sound off! **741.5**

The **adventures** of Granny Clearwater & Little Crit- ter. Holt, K. W. **E**

The **adventures** of High John the Conqueror. San- field, S. **398.2**

The **adventures** of Jack Lime. Leck, J. **Fic**

The **adventures** of Mark Twain by Huckleberry Finn. **92**

The adventures of Max and Pinky [series]

Eaton, M. Best buds **E**

The **adventures** of Medical Man. Evans, M. **616**

The **adventures** of Molly Whuppie and other Ap- palachian folktales. Shelby, A. **398.2**

The **adventures** of Nanny Piggins. Spratt, R. A. **Fic**

The **adventures** of Odysseus. Lupton, H. **292**

The **adventures** of Ook and Gluk. Pilkey, D. **741.5**

The **adventures** of Pinocchio. Collodi, C. **Fic**

The **adventures** of Polo. Faller, R. **E**

Adventures of Riley [series]

Lumry, A. Safari in South Africa **E**

The **adventures** of Sir Lancelot the Great. Morris, G. **Fic**

Morpurgo, M. The McElderry book of Aesop's fables **398.2**

Mouse & Lion **E**

Naidoo, B. Aesop's fables **398.2**

Palatini, M. Lousy rotten stinkin' grapes **398.2**

Pinkney, J. The lion & the mouse **E**

Waters, F. Aesop's fables **398.2**

Wormell, C. Mice, morals, & monkey business **398.2**

Aesop's fables. Waters, F. **398.2**

Aesop's fables. Naidoo, B. **398.2**

Aesop's fables: a pop-up book of classic tales. Moerbeek, K. **398.2**

AESTHETICS
See also Philosophy

AESTHETICS -- FICTION
Reibstein, M. Wabi Sabi **E**

AFFECTION *See* Friendship; Love

AFFLUENT PEOPLE *See* Rich

Afghan dreams. O'Brien, T. **958.1**

AFGHAN WAR, 2001-
Biden, J. Don't forget, God bless our troops **355.1**

Souter, J. War in Afghanistan and Iraq **355**

AFGHAN WAR, 2001- -- FICTION
Postcards from Pismo **Fic**

Afghanistan. Fordyce, D. **958.1**

Afghanistan. Bjorklund, R. **958.1**

AFGHANISTAN
Ali, S. E. Afghanistan **958.1**

Bjorklund, R. Afghanistan **958.1**

Ellis, D. Off to war **303.6**

Fordyce, D. Afghanistan **958.1**

O'Brien, T. Afghan dreams **958.1**

Whitfield, S. Afghanistan **958.1**

Afghanistan. Whitfield, S. **958.1**

Afghanistan. Ali, S. E. **958.1**

AFGHANISTAN -- FICTION
Clements, A. Extra credit **Fic**

King, D. I see the sun in Afghanistan **E**

Reedy, T. Words in the dust **Fic**

Whelan, G. Waiting for the owl's call **E**

Williams, K. L. Four feet, two sandals **E**

AFGHANISTAN -- SOCIAL CONDITIONS
Winter, J. Nasreen's secret school **371.82**

Africa. Solway, A. **780.9**

AFRICA
Bowden, R. Modern Africa **960**

Isadora, R. 12 days of Christmas **782.42**

Mooney, C. Amazing Africa **960**

Stojic, M. Rain **E**

Africa. Murray, J. **960**

AFRICA -- ANTIQUITIES
Sherrow, V. Ancient Africa **939**

AFRICA -- CIVILIZATION
Bowden, R. African culture **960**

Lee, R. B. Africans thought of it! **609**

Murray, J. Africa **960**

Sherrow, V. Ancient Africa **939**

AFRICA -- ECONOMIC CONDITIONS
Bowden, R. Changing Africa **960**

AFRICA -- EXPLORATION
Bodden, V. To the heart of Africa **916**

AFRICA -- FICTION
Atinuke (Author) Anna Hibiscus **Fic**

Atinuke (Author) Anna Hibiscus' song **Fic**

Atinuke (Author) Good luck, Anna Hibiscus! **Fic**

Atinuke (Author) The no. 1 car spotter **Fic**

Atinuke Hooray for Anna Hibiscus! **Fic**

Beard, A. The jungle grapevine **E**

Beard, A. Monkey see monkey draw **E**

Blessing, C. New old shoes **E**

Brett, J. Honey . . . honey . . . lion! **E**

Broach, E. Gumption! **E**

Bynum, E. Jamari's drum **E**

Daly, J. Sivu's six wishes **E**

Daly, N. Welcome to Zanzibar Road **E**

Don't spill the milk **E**

A gift from childhood **92**

Gravett, E. Meerkat mail **E**

Greenfield, E. Africa dream **E**

Heap, S. Danny's drawing book **E**

Joosse, B. M. Papa, do you love me? **E**

Landstrom, L. A hippo's tale **E**

MacLachlan, P. Your moon, my moon **E**

Marino, G. Meet me at the moon **E**

McGrory, A. Quick, slow, mango! **E**

Mouse & Lion **E**

Naidoo, B. Aesop's fables **398.2**

Stojic, M. Rain **E**

Villeneuve, A. Loula is leaving for Africa **E**

Vries, A. d. Raf **E**

We're going on a lion hunt **E**

AFRICA -- HISTORY
Bowden, R. Ancient Africa **960**

Murray, J. Africa **960**

AFRICA -- HISTORY -- TO 1498 -- FICTION
Leeds, C. The unfortunate son **Fic**

AFRICA -- POETRY
Cendrars, B. Shadow **841**

AFRICA -- SOCIAL CONDITIONS
Bowden, R. Changing Africa **960**

AFRICA -- SOCIAL LIFE AND CUSTOMS
Bowden, R. African culture **960**

Musgrove, M. Ashanti to Zulu: African traditions **960**

Africa dream. Greenfield, E. **E**

Africa focus [series]
Bowden, R. African culture **960**

Bowden, R. Ancient Africa **960**

Bowden, R. Changing Africa **960**

Bowden, R. Modern Africa **960**

Stone, T. L. Courage has no color, the true story of the Triple Nickles **940.54**

AFRICAN AMERICAN SOLDIERS -- FICTION
Garland, S. The buffalo soldier **E**
Hopkinson, D. From slave to soldier **E**
Myers, W. D. Patrol **E**
Polacco, P. Pink and Say **E**

AFRICAN AMERICAN SONGS *See* African American music

The **African** American story. Masoff, J. **305.8**

AFRICAN AMERICAN WOMEN
Adler, D. A. A picture book of Harriet Tubman **305.5**
Adler, D. A. A picture book of Sojourner Truth **305.5**
Bolden, T. Maritcha **92**
Bolden, T. Searching for Sarah Rector **92**
Freedman, R. The voice that challenged a nation **92**
Jemison, M. C. Find where the wind goes **92**
Lasky, K. Vision of beauty: the story of Sarah Breedlove Walker **B**
Let it shine **920**
Lowery, L. Aunt Clara Brown **978.8**
McKissack, F. Mary McLeod Bethune **370.92**
My Name Is Truth **92**
Parks, R. Rosa Parks: my story **976.1**
Pinkney, A. D. Ella Fitzgerald **92**
Rockwell, A. F. Only passing through: the story of Sojourner Truth **92**
Rosa **92**
Ryan, P. M. When Marian sang: the true recital of Marian Anderson, the voice of a century **92**
Stompin' at the Savoy **92**
Turner, G. T. An apple for Harriet Tubman **92**
Washburn, K. Heart of a champion **796.440**
Weatherford, C. B. Moses **92**
See also Black women; Women

AFRICAN AMERICAN WOMEN -- BIOGRAPHY
Adler, D. A. Harriet Tubman and the Underground Railroad **973.7**
Fradin, D. B. Zora! **813**
Horn, G. M. Sojourner Truth **305.5**
Woodson, J. Brown girl dreaming **92**

AFRICAN AMERICAN WOMEN -- MASSACHUSETTS -- BIOGRAPHY
Mumbet's Declaration of Independence **92**

AFRICAN AMERICAN WOMEN -- OKLAHOMA -- CREEK COUNTY -- BIOGRAPHY
Bolden, T. Searching for Sarah Rector **92**

AFRICAN AMERICAN WOMEN ATHLETES -- UNITED STATES
Malaspina, A. Touch the sky **796.42**

AFRICAN AMERICAN WOMEN AUTHORS -- BIOGRAPHY -- POETRY
Woodson, J. Brown girl dreaming **92**

AFRICAN AMERICAN WOMEN CIVIL RIGHTS WORKERS -- BIOGRAPHY
Let it shine **920**
Wishinsky, F. Freedom heroines **920**

AFRICAN AMERICAN WOMEN EDUCATORS -- BIOGRAPHY
McKissack, F. Mary McLeod Bethune **370.92**

AFRICAN AMERICAN YOUTH
See also Youth

AFRICAN AMERICANS
28 days **973.04**
Barbour, K. Mr. Williams **92**
Bolden, T. Tell all the children our story **305.8**
Cameron, A. Gloria's way **Fic**
Cooke, T. Full, full, full of love **E**
Coy, J. Strong to the hoop **E**
Curtis, G. The bat boy & his violin **E**
Dillon, L. Rap a tap tap **792.7**
English, K. Francie **Fic**
Green, M. Y. A strong right arm: the story of Mamie Peanut Johnson **92**
Gutman, D. Jackie & me **Fic**
Hartfield, C. Me and Uncle Romie **E**
Hesse, K. Come on, rain! **E**
Howard, E. F. Virgie goes to school with us boys **E**
Hudson, W. Powerful words **081**
In the hollow of your hand **782.42**
Keats, E. J. Hi, cat! **E**
Lester, J. Black cowboy, wild horses **E**
Lindsey, K. Sweet potato pie **E**
McKissack, P. C. Black hands, white sails **639.2**
Mead, A. Junebug in trouble **Fic**
Pinkney, S. L. Shades of black **305.23**
Powell, P. H. Josephine **92**
Rodman, M. A. Yankee girl **Fic**
Tarpley, N. Bippity Bop barbershop **E**
Wahl, J. Candy shop **E**
Walter, M. P. Alec's primer **E**
Wiles, D. Freedom Summer **E**
Woods, B. The red rose box **Fic**

AFRICAN AMERICANS
Hughes, L. Lullaby (for a Black mother) **811**

AFRICAN AMERICANS -- BIOGRAPHY
The amazing age of John Roy Lynch **92**
Capital days **92**
Pinkney, A. D. Hand in hand **973**
See also Blacks -- Biography

AFRICAN AMERICANS -- CIVIL RIGHTS
Gordon Parks **92**
Kanefield, T. The girl from the tar paper school **92**
Rubin, S. G. Freedom Summer **323.11**
Seeds of freedom **323.1**
Sheinkin, S. The Port Chicago 50 **940.54**
Wishinsky, F. Freedom heroines **920**

AFRICAN AMERICANS -- CIVIL RIGHTS
See also Blacks -- Civil rights; Civil rights

ing African American children's and young adult literature **028.5**

Casement, R. Black history in the pages of children's literature **028.5**

Wilkin, B. T. African and African American images in Newbery Award winning titles **810**

AFRICAN AMERICANS IN MOTION PICTURES

See also Blacks in motion pictures; Minorities in motion pictures; Motion pictures

African and African American images in Newbery Award winning titles. Wilkin, B. T. **810**

African animal alphabet. Joubert, B. **E**

AFRICAN ART

Garner, L. African crafts **745.5**

AFRICAN ART

See also Art

AFRICAN COOKING

Sheen, B. Foods of Kenya **641.5**

African crafts. Garner, L. **745.5**

African culture. Bowden, R. **960**

AFRICAN DIASPORA

See also Human geography

AFRICAN ELEPHANT -- INFANCY -- NAMIBIA

A baby elephant in the wild **599.67**

AFRICAN ELEPHANT -- PICTORIAL WORKS

A baby elephant in the wild **599.67**

AFRICAN GRAY PARROT

Alex the parrot **636.6**

African legends, myths, and folktales for readers theatre. Fredericks, A. D. **812**

AFRICAN LITERATURE

See also Literature

AFRICAN LITERATURE (ENGLISH)

See also Literature

AFRICAN MUSIC

Solway, A. Africa **780.9**

See also Music

AFRICAN MYTHOLOGY

See also Mythology

AFRICAN SONGS

See also Songs

African tales. **398.2**

African-American Collective Biographies [series]

Aretha, D. Awesome African-American rock and soul musicians **781.644**

African-American heroes [series]

Feinstein, S. Barack Obama **92**

AFRICANS -- FICTION

Applegate, K. Home of the brave **Fic**

Atinuke Have fun, Anna Hibiscus! **Fic**

Runholt, S. Adventure at Simba Hill **Fic**

AFRICANS -- UNITED STATES -- FICTION

Foggo, C. Dear baobab **E**

McQuinn, A. My friend Jamal **E**

Africans thought of it! Lee, R. B. **609**

AFRO-AMERICAN ART *See* African American art

AFRO-AMERICAN ARTISTS *See* African American artists

AFRO-AMERICAN ATHLETES *See* African American athletes

AFRO-AMERICAN AUTHORS *See* African American authors

AFRO-AMERICAN BUSINESSPEOPLE *See* African American businesspeople

AFRO-AMERICAN CHILDREN *See* African American children

AFRO-AMERICAN MUSICIANS *See* African American musicians

AFRO-AMERICAN WOMEN *See* African American women

AFRO-AMERICANS *See* African Americans

AFRO-AMERICANS -- MUSIC *See* African American music

AFRO-AMERICANS IN ART *See* African Americans in art

AFRO-AMERICANS IN LITERATURE *See* African Americans in literature

AFTER DINNER SPEECHES

See also Speeches

After Eli. Rupp, R. **Fic**

After ever after. Sonnenblick, J. **Fic**

After Iris. Farrant, N. **Fic**

After the dinosaurs. Brown, C. L. **569**

After the kill. Lunde, D. **591.5**

Afternoon of the elves. Lisle, J. T. **Fic**

AFTERNOON TEAS

See also Cooking

Idle, M. Tea Rex **E**

Tea party rules **E**

Again! Gravett, E. **E**

Against the odds. Hof, M. **Fic**

Agatha Mistery [series]

The curse of the pharaoh **Fic**

Age of dinosaurs [series]

Peterson, S. Pterodactyl **567.9**

Age of the Dinosaur. Parker, S. **567.9**

Agee, Jon

Jon Agee's palindromania! **428**

Little Santa **E**

Milo's hat trick **E**

Mr. Putney's quacking dog **E**

My rhinoceros **E**

Nothing **E**

The retired kid **E**

Smart feller fart smeller & other Spoonerisms **793.73**

Terrific **E**

Why did the chicken cross the road? **E**

Z goes home **411**

ALBINOS AND ALBINISM -- FICTION
Erskine, K. The badger knight   **Fic**
Alborough, Jez
Duck in the truck   **E**
Some dogs do   **E**
Tall   **E**
Where's my teddy?   **E**
Albrecht, Jeff
(il) Presidential pets   **973**
ALCATRAZ ISLAND (CALIF.) -- FICTION
Choldenko, G. Al Capone does my homework **Fic**
Choldenko, G. Al Capone does my shirts   **Fic**
Choldenko, G. Al Capone shines my shoes   **Fic**
Alcatraz versus the evil Librarians. Sanderson, B.   **Fic**
ALCHEMY
   See also Chemistry; Occultism
ALCHEMY -- FICTION
Cushman, K. Alchemy and Meggy Swann   **Fic**
Alchemy and Meggy Swann. Cushman, K.   **Fic**
Alcohol. Gottfried, T.   **362.292**
ALCOHOL
Bjornlund, L. D. Alcohol   **362.292**
ALCOHOL -- PHYSIOLOGICAL EFFECT
Gottfried, T. Alcohol   **362.292**
ALCOHOL AS FUEL
Benduhn, T. Ethanol and other new fuels   **662**
ALCOHOL CONSUMPTION *See* Drinking of alcoholic beverages
ALCOHOL FUELS
   See also Alcohol; Fuel
ALCOHOL USE *See* Alcohol; Alcoholism; Drinking of alcoholic beverages
ALCOHOLIC BEVERAGE CONSUMPTION
See Drinking of alcoholic beverages
ALCOHOLIC BEVERAGES
   See also Alcohol; Beverages
ALCOHOLISM
Bjornlund, L. D. Alcohol   **362.292**
Gantos, J. Joey Pigza loses control   **Fic**
Gottfried, T. Alcohol   **362.292**
   See also Social problems
ALCOHOLISM -- FICTION
Bredsdorff, B. Tink   **Fic**
Conly, J. L. Crazy lady!   **Fic**
Mason, S. Moon pie   **Fic**
Alcorn, Stephen
A gift of days   **808.88**
Odetta, the queen of folk   **92**
(il) America at war   **811**
(il) Dray, P. Yours for justice, Ida B. Wells   **92**
(il) Hopkins, L. B. Days to celebrate   **051**
(il) Hopkinson, D. Keep on!   **92**
(il) I, too, sing America   **811**
(il) Let it shine   **920**
(il) My America   **811**

Alcott, Louisa May
Little women   **Fic**
            About
Ellis, S. From reader to writer   **372.62**
Lives of the writers   **809**
McDonald, M. The rule of three   **Fic**
McDonough, Y. Z. Louisa   **92**
Alda, Arlene
Did you say pears?   **E**
Hello, good-bye   **E**
Aldana, Patricia
(ed) Under the spell of the moon   **741.6**
Alderfer, Jonathan
National Geographic kids bird guide of North America   **598**
Alderson, Brian
Thumbelina   **E**
Aldridge, Eve
(il) Seskin, S. Sing my song   **782.42**
Aldrin, Buzz
Aldrin, B. Reaching for the moon   **92**
Look to the stars   **629.4**
Alec's primer. Walter, M. P.   **E**
Alekseĭ Nikolaevich, Czarevitch, son of Nicholas II, Emperor of Russia, 1904-1918
            About
Haddix, M. P. Risked   **Fic**
Alex and Lulu: two of a kind. Siminovich, L.   **E**
Alex Rider [series]
Horowitz, A. Ark angel   **Fic**
Horowitz, A. Crocodile tears   **Fic**
Horowitz, A. Eagle Strike   **Fic**
Horowitz, A. Point blank   **Fic**
Horowitz, A. Scorpia   **Fic**
Horowitz, A. Scorpia rising   **Fic**
Horowitz, A. Skeleton Key   **Fic**
Horowitz, A. Stormbreaker   **Fic**
Horowitz, A. Stormbreaker: the graphic novel   **741.5**
Alex Rodriguez. Rappoport, K.   **796.357**
Alex the parrot.   **636.6**
Alexander. Adams, S.   **92**
Alexander and the terrible, horrible, no good, very bad day. Viorst, J.   **E**
Alexander and the wind-up mouse. Lionni, L.   **E**
Alexander Graham Bell invents. Garmon, A.   **92**
Alexander Hamilton. Fritz, J.   **92**
Alexander the Great. Demi   **92**
Alexander, Cecil Frances
All things bright and beautiful   **264**
Alexander, Chris
Difficult origami   **736**
Sort-of-difficult origami   **736**
Alexander, Claire
Lucy and the bully   **E**
Alexander, Goldie

Players in pigtails **E**
Rappaport, D. Dirt on their skirts **796.357**
The **all-I'll-ever-want** Christmas doll. McKissack, P. **E**
All-of-a-kind family. Taylor, S. **Fic**
Allan, June
(il) Robinson, A. Hamzat's journey **947**
Allard, Harry
Miss Nelson is missing! **E**
ALLEGORIES
Achebe, C. How the leopard got his claws **Fic**
Adams, R. Watership Down **Fic**
Babbitt, N. Kneeknock Rise **Fic**
The hobbit **Fic**
Saint-Exupery, A. d. The little prince **Fic**
Tonatiuh, D. Pancho Rabbit and the coyote **E**
ALLEGORY
    See also Arts; Fiction
Allegra, Mike
Sarah gives thanks **E**
Allen, Debbie
Dancing in the wings **E**
Allen, Elanna
(il) Violet Mackerel's brilliant plot **Fic**
(il) Violet Mackerel's natural habitat **Fic**
(il) Violet Mackerel's personal space **Fic**
(il) Violet Mackerel's pocket protest **Fic**
(il) Violet Mackerel's possible friend **Fic**
(il) Violet Mackerel's remarkable recovery **Fic**
Itsy Mitsy runs away **E**
Allen, Jonathan
I'm not Santa! **E**
I'm not scared! **E**
The little rabbit who liked to say moo **E**
Allen, Joy
(il) Adler, D. A. Cam Jansen and the Sports Day mysteries **Fic**
(il) Adler, D. A. Cam Jansen and the summer camp mysteries **Fic**
(il) Adler, D. A. Cam Jansen and the wedding cake mystery **Fic**
(il) Cora, C. A suitcase surprise for Mommy **E**
(il) Glatt, L. Abigail Iris: the one and only **Fic**
(il) Glatt, L. Abigail Iris: the pet project **Fic**
Allen, Judy
Unexplained **001.9**
Allen, Kathy
Deformed frogs **597.8**
Elephants under pressure **599.67**
The first American flag **929.9**
The human head **611**
President George Washington **92**
Sea turtles' race to the sea **597.92**
Allen, Patrick
Europe **780.94**
Allén, Raúl

(il) Come see the Earth turn: the story of Leon Foucault **92**
Allen, Rick
(il) Dark Emperor and other poems of the night **811**
(il) Winter Bees & Other Poems of the Cold **811.54**
Allen, Thomas
            About
Bildner, P. The Hallelujah Flight **E**
Allen, Thomas B.
Remember Pearl Harbor **940.54**
Remember Valley Forge **973.3**
(il) Bulla, C. R. The chalk box kid **E**
Allergies. Royston, A. **616.97**
ALLERGIES, FOOD *See* Food allergy
ALLERGY
Royston, A. Allergies **616.97**
Siy, A. Sneeze! **612.2**
Thomas, P. I think I am going to sneeze **616.97**
ALLERGY -- FICTION
Koster, G. The Peanut-Free Cafe **E**
ALLERGY, FOOD *See* Food allergy
Alley, R. W.
(il) Alley, Z. B. There's a princess in the palace **398.2**
(il) Alley, Z. B. There's a wolf at the door **398.2**
(il) Bradley, K. B. Ballerino Nate **E**
(il) Cheshire, S. The curse of the ancient mask and other case files **Fic**
(il) Cheshire, S. The pirate's blood and other case files **Fic**
(il) Cheshire, S. The treasure of Dead Man's Lane and other case files **Fic**
(il) Demas, C. Valentine surprise **E**
(il) Fore, S. J. Read to Tiger **E**
(il) Grandits, J. The travel game **E**
(il) Hamilton, K. R. Police officers on patrol **E**
(il) McMullan, K. Pearl and Wagner: four eyes **E**
(il) McMullan, K. Pearl and Wagner: one funny day **E**
(il) Mills, C. Being Teddy Roosevelt **Fic**
(il) Pearl and Wagner **E**
(il) Saturday is Dadurday **E**
(il) Skofield, J. Detective Dinosaur **E**
(il) Skofield, J. Detective Dinosaur undercover **E**
(il) Skofield, J. Detective Dinosaur: lost and found **E**
Alley, Zoe B.
There's a princess in the palace **398.2**
There's a wolf at the door **398.2**
Allgor, Marie
Endangered desert animals **591.68**
Allie Finkle's rules for girls [series]
Cabot, M. Best friends and drama queens **Fic**
Cabot, M. Blast from the past **Fic**
Cabot, M. Glitter girls and the great fake out **Fic**
Cabot, M. Moving day **Fic**

ural disasters. **Fic**

Alvin Ho: allergic to dead bodies, funerals, and other fatal circumstances. Look, L. **Fic**

Alvin Ho: allergic to girls, school, and other scary things. Look, L. **Fic**

Always. McGhee, A. **E**

Always. Stott, A. **E**

Always in trouble. Demas, C. **E**

Always listen to your mother. Heide, F. P. **E**

The **always** prayer shawl. Oberman, S. **E**

Always remember me. Russo, M. **940.53**

Always room for one more. Leodhas, S. N. **782.42**

Always with you. **E**

ALZHEIMER'S DISEASE -- FICTION

Gerdner, L. Grandfather's story cloth **E**

Knowlton, L. L. A young man's dance **E**

Amadi's snowman. Saint-Lot, K. N. **E**

Amado, Elisa

What are you doing? **E**

(tr) Jimmy the greatest! **E**

(tr) My tattooed dad **E**

(tr) What a party! **E**

Tricycle **E**

What are you doing? **E**

Amahl and the night visitors. Menotti, G. C. **232.9**

Amanda Pig and the awful, scary monster. Van Leeuwen, J. **E**

Amandina. Ruzzier, S. **E**

AMATEUR FILMS

See also Motion pictures

AMATEUR THEATER

See also Amusements; Theater

Amato, Mary

The chicken of the family **E**

Edgar Allan's official crime investigation notebook **Fic**

Snarf attack, underfoodle, and the secret of life **Fic**

Amaze [series]

Stewart, D. E. How your body works **612**

Amazement park. Munro, R. **793.73**

The **amazing** adventures of Bumblebee Boy. Soman, D. **E**

The **amazing** adventures of John Smith, Jr., aka Houdini. Johnson, P. **Fic**

Amazing Africa. Mooney, C. **960**

The **amazing** age of John Roy Lynch. **92**

Amazing Americans [series]

Wade, M. D. Amazing Cherokee writer Sequoyah **92**

Wade, M. D. Amazing civil war nurse Clara Barton **92**

Wade, M. D. Amazing Olympic athlete Wilma Rudolph **92**

Wade, M. D. Amazing president Theodore Roosevelt **92**

Amazing animal defenses [series]

Mitchell, S. K. Animal body-part regenerators **571.8**

Mitchell, S. K. Animal chemical combat **591.47**

Mitchell, S. K. Animal mimics **591.47**

Mitchell, S. K. Animals with awesome armor **591.47**

Mitchell, S. K. Animals with crafty camouflage **591.47**

Mitchell, S. K. Animals with wicked weapons **591.47**

Amazing animal journeys. Marsh, L. **591.56**

Amazing animals. **591.5**

Amazing animals [series]

Bodden, V. Crocodiles **597.98**

Bodden, V. Lions **599.75**

Bodden, V. Monkeys **599.8**

Bodden, V. Owls **598.9**

Bodden, V. Parrots **598**

Bodden, V. Penguins **598**

Bodden, V. Polar bears **599.78**

Bodden, V. Sharks **597**

Bodden, V. Snakes **597.96**

Mitton, T. Ocean odyssey **591.7**

Mitton, T. Rainforest romp **591.7**

Riggs, K. Alligators **597.98**

Riggs, K. Dolphins **599.5**

Riggs, K. Elephants **599.67**

Riggs, K. Killer whales **599.53**

Riggs, K. Sea lions **599.79**

Riggs, K. Wolves **599.77**

Amazing armor. Pryor, K. J. **591.47**

Amazing biome projects you can build yourself. Latham, D. **577**

The **amazing** bone. Steig, W. **E**

Amazing Cherokee writer Sequoyah. Wade, M. D. **92**

Amazing civil war nurse Clara Barton. Wade, M. D. **92**

Amazing cows. Boynton, S. **636.2**

Amazing crime scene science [series]

Townsend, J. Famous forensic cases **363.2**

Amazing decades in photos [series]

Corrigan, J. The 1900s decade in photos **973.91**

Corrigan, J. The 1910s decade in photos **973.91**

Corrigan, J. The 1920s decade in photos **973.91**

Corrigan, J. The 1930s decade in photos **973.917**

Corrigan, J. The 1940s decade in photos **973.917**

Corrigan, J. The 1950s decade in photos **973.921**

Corrigan, J. The 1960s decade in photos **973.923**

Corrigan, J. The 1970s decade in photos **973.924**

Corrigan, J. The 1980s decade in photos **973.927**

Corrigan, J. The 1990s decade in photos **973.92**

Corrigan, J. The 2000s decade in photos **973.93**

Amazing DNA. Johnson, R. L. **572.8**

Amazing eggs. Hodgkins, F. **591.4**

Amazing faces. **811**

Amazing giant dinosaurs. Greenwood, M.   **567.9**

Amazing giant sea creatures.   **591.77**

Amazing Grace. Hoffman, M.   **E**

AMAZING GRACE (HYMN)

   Granfield, L. Out of slavery   **264**

The **amazing** Harry Kellar. Jarrow, G.   **793.809**

The **amazing** impossible Erie Canal. Harness, C.   **386**

The **amazing** International Space Station.   **629**

The **amazing** life of birds. Paulsen, G.   **Fic**

Amazing magic tricks: a beginner level. Barnhart, N.   **793.8**

Amazing magic tricks: apprentice level. Barnhart, N.   **793.8**

Amazing magic tricks: expert level. Barnhart, N.   **793.8**

Amazing magic tricks: master level. Barnhart, N.   **793.8**

Amazing Olympic athlete Wilma Rudolph. Wade, M. D.   **92**

Amazing peace. Angelou, M.   **811**

Amazing planet earth [series]

   Green, J. Mighty rivers   **551.48**

   Green, J. The world's oceans   **551.46**

   Jennings, T. Earthquakes and tsunamis   **551.2**

   Jennings, T. Massive mountains   **551.4**

   Jennings, T. Violent volcanoes   **551.2**

Amazing pop-up trucks. Crowther, R.   **E**

Amazing president Theodore Roosevelt. Wade, M. D.   **92**

Amazing rubber band cars. Rigsby, M.   **745.592**

Amazing science. Animal classification [series]

   Salas, L. P. Amphibians   **597.8**

Amazing ships [series]

   Sutherland, J. Aircraft carriers   **623.82**

   Sutherland, J. Container ships and oil tankers   **623.82**

   Sutherland, J. Cruise ships   **623.82**

   Sutherland, J. Submarines   **623.82**

Amazing stadiums. Graham, I.   **725**

The **amazing** trail of Seymour Snail. Hazen, L. E.   **Fic**

Amazing water frogs. Goldish, M.   **597.8**

Amazing whales! Thomson, S. L.   **599.5**

Amazing working dogs with American Humane [series]

   Bozzo, L. Fire dog heroes   **636.7**

   Bozzo, L. Guide dog heroes   **362.4**

   Bozzo, L. Police dog heroes   **363.2**

   Bozzo, L. Search and rescue dog heroes   **636.7**

   Bozzo, L. Service dog heroes   **362.4**

   Bozzo, L. Therapy dog heroes   **615.8**

Amazing you. Saltz, G.   **612.6**

AMAZON RIVER REGION -- DESCRIPTION AND TRAVEL

   Cobb, V. This place is wet   **574.5**

AMAZON RIVER VALLEY

   Berkenkamp, L. Discover the Amazon   **981**

AMAZON RIVER VALLEY -- FICTION

   London, C. A. We dine with cannibals   **Fic**

   Nelson, N. Bringing the boy home   **Fic**

AMAZON RIVER VALLEY -- FOLKLORE

   McDermott, G. Jabuti the tortoise   **398.2**

Amazons! Clayton, S. P.   **398.2**

Ambassador. Alexander, W.   **Fic**

AMBASSADORS

   See also Diplomats

AMBASSADORS -- FICTION

   Alexander, W. Ambassador   **Fic**

Amber Brown goes fourth. Danziger, P.   **Fic**

Amber Brown is feeling blue. Danziger, P.   **Fic**

Amber Brown is green with envy. Danziger, P.   **Fic**

Amber Brown is not a crayon. Danziger, P.   **Fic**

Amber Brown is tickled pink. Coville, B.   **Fic**

Amber Brown sees red. Danziger, P.   **Fic**

Amber Brown wants extra credit. Danziger, P.   **Fic**

Amber was brave, Essie was smart. Williams, V. B.   **811**

AMBITION -- PICTORIAL WORKS

   Baker-Smith, G. Farther   **Fic**

Ambrose, Stephen E.

   The good fight   **940.53**

An **ambush** of tigers.   **372.61**

Ambushed by a cougar. Hamilton, S. L.   **599.75**

AMEBAS -- FICTION

   Holm, J. L. Brave new pond   **741.5**

   Holm, J. L. Squish, Super Amoeba   **741.5**

Amelia Bedelia. Parish, P.   **E**

Amelia Bedelia bakes off. Parish, H.   **E**

An **Amelia** Bedelia celebration. Parish, P.   **E**

Amelia Bedelia's first apple pie. Parish, H.   **E**

Amelia Bedelia's first field trip. Parish, H.   **E**

Amelia Bedelia's first Valentine. Parish, H.   **E**

Amelia Earhart. Tanaka, S.   **92**

Amelia lost: the life and disappearance of Amelia Earhart. Fleming, C.   **92**

Amelia rules!: the whole world's crazy! Gownley, J.   **741.5**

Amelia writes again. Moss, M.   **Fic**

Amelia's 6th-grade notebook. Moss, M.   **Fic**

Amelia's notebook. Moss, M.   **Fic**

Amendola, Dana

   A day at the New Amsterdam Theatre   **792.6**

Amenta, Charles A.

   Russell's world   **616.85**

AMERICA -- ANTIQUITIES

   Huey, L. M. American archaeology uncovers the Dutch colonies   **974.7**

   Huey, L. M. American archaeology uncovers the earliest English colonies   **973.2**

   Huey, L. M. American archaeology uncovers the Vikings   **970.01**

ANDROIDS

See also Robots

Andronik, Catherine M.

Copernicus **92**

Andy and the lion. Daugherty, J. H. **E**

Andy Shane and the barn sale mystery. Jacobson, J. **Fic**

Andy Shane and the pumpkin trick. Jacobson, J. **Fic**

Andy Shane and the Queen of Egypt. Jacobson, J. **Fic**

Andy Shane and the very bossy Dolores Starbuckle. Jacobson, J. **Fic**

Andy Shane is NOT in love. Jacobson, J. **Fic**

Andy Shane, hero at last. **Fic**

Andy Warhol. Rubin, S. G. **92**

ANECDOTES

Belanger, J. What it's like **179**

ANEMONES

Rustad, M. E. H. Clown fish and sea anemones work together **597**

Ang, Joy

(il) Mustache baby **E**

Angaramo, Roberta

(il) Gormley, G. Dog in boots **E**

(il) Perry, A. The Bicklebys' birdbath **E**

ANGEL ISLAND (CALIF.) -- HISTORY

Angel Island **979.4**

ANGEL ISLAND (CALIF.) -- HISTORY -- 20TH CENTURY -- FICTION

James, H. F. Paper son **Fic**

Angel, Carl

(il) Moss, M. Sky high: the true story of Maggie Gee **92**

Angela and the baby Jesus. McCourt, F. **E**

Angelina Ballerina. Holabird, K. **E**

Angelo, Valenti

(il) Sawyer, R. Roller skates **Fic**

Angelou, Maya

Amazing peace **811**

ANGELS -- FICTION

Arrigan, M. Mario's Angels **E**

Chaikin, M. Angels sweep the desert floor **296.1**

Creech, S. The unfinished angel **Fic**

DePaola, T. Pascual and the kitchen angels **E**

Durango, J. Angels watching over me **E**

Kleven, E. The friendship wish **E**

Morpurgo, M. On angel wings **Fic**

Newbound, A. Ghoul strike! **Fic**

Richter, J. Beyond the station lies the sea **Fic**

Angels sweep the desert floor. Chaikin, M. **296.1**

Angels watching over me. Durango, J. **E**

ANGER

Vail, R. Sometimes I'm Bombaloo **E**

ANGER

See also Emotions

ANGER -- FICTION

Applesauce **E**

Bang, M. When Sophie gets angry--really, really angry **E**

Berger, S. Crankenstein **E**

Eaton, M. Two dumb ducks **E**

Elliott, D. Finn throws a fit **E**

Graves, S. I hate everything! **152.4**

Harris, R. H. The day Leo said I hate you **E**

Sakai, K. Mad at Mommy **E**

Urban, L. Mouse was mad **E**

Vail, R. Sometimes I'm Bombaloo **E**

Yolen, J. How do dinosaurs act when they're mad? **E**

ANGER IN CHILDREN

Graves, S. I hate everything! **152.4**

ANGER IN CHILDREN -- FICTION

McDonnell, P. A perfectly messed-up story **E**

ANGINA PECTORIS

See also Heart diseases

ANGKOR WAT (ANGKOR: ANCIENT CITY)

Sobol, R. The mysteries of Angkor Wat **959.6**

Angleberger, Tom

Crankee Doodle **E**

Darth Paper strikes back **Fic**

Emperor Pickletine rides the bus **Fic**

Fake mustache **Fic**

Hemphill, M. Stonewall Hinkleman and the Battle of Bull Run **Fic**

Horton Halfpott **Fic**

Princess Labelmaker to the rescue! **Fic**

The strange case of Origami Yoda **Fic**

The surprise attack of Jabba the Puppett **Fic**

ANGLES

Murphy, S. J. Hamster champs **516**

ANGLING See Fishing

Angliss, Sarah

Gold **546**

ANGLO-SAXONS

See also Great Britain -- History -- 0-1066; Teutonic peoples

Angola. Sheehan, S. **967.3**

ANGOLA

Sheehan, S. Angola **967.3**

Angus, Jennifer

In search of Goliathus hercules **Fic**

Anholt, Laurence

Cezanne and the apple boy **E**

Matisse **92**

ANIMAL ABUSE See Animal welfare

Animal aha! Swanson, D. **590**

Animal architects [series]

George, L. Prairie dogs **599.3**

Animal attack and defense [series]

Pryor, K. J. Amazing armor **591.47**

Pryor, K. J. Clever camouflage **591.47**

Pryor, K. J. Mimicry and relationships **591.47**

Pryor, K. J. Tricky behavior **591.47**

Pryor, K. J. Venom, poison, and electricity **591.6**

Pryor, K. J. Warning colors **591.47**

ANIMAL ATTACKS

Claybourne, A. 100 deadliest things on the planet **591.6**

Hamilton, S. L. Ambushed by a cougar **599.75**

Hamilton, S. L. Attacked by a crocodile **597.98**

Hamilton, S. L. Bitten by a rattlesnake **597.96**

Hamilton, S. L. Eaten by a shark **597**

Hamilton, S. L. Mauled by a bear **599.78**

Hamilton, S. L. Swarmed by bees **595.7**

ANIMAL BABIES

See also Animals

ANIMAL BABIES -- FICTION

Chicks! **E**

I hatched! **E**

Il Sung Na A book of babies **E**

Judge, L. Born in the wild **591.3**

Kalman, B. Baby rodents **599.35**

Lucky Ducklings **E**

My first day **591.3**

Nascimbeni, B. Animals and their families **E**

Shea, B. Cheetah can't lose **E**

Wild about you! **E**

Wolfie the bunny **E**

Animal baths. Fielding, B. **591.5**

Animal baths. Barner, B. **591.5**

ANIMAL BEHAVIOR

125 true stories of amazing animals **590**

Amazing animals **591.5**

Animals upside down **591.5**

Antle, B. Suryia swims! : the true story of how an orangutan learned to swim **E**

Asper-Smith, S. I would tuck you in **E**

Bancroft, H. Animals in winter **591.56**

Barner, B. Animal baths **591.5**

Batten, M. Please don't wake the animals **591.5**

Benbow, A. Awesome animal science projects **590.7**

Beneath the sun **591.5**

Buckley, C. Tarra & Bella **599.67**

Burnie, D. How animals work **591.4**

Claybourne, A. 100 deadliest things on the planet **591.6**

Collard, S. B. Animal dads **591.56**

Fielding, B. Animal baths **591.5**

Gardner, R. Ace your animal science project **590.7**

Heppermann, C. City chickens **636.5**

Hile, L. Animal survival **591.5**

Himmelman, J. Who's at the seashore? **591.7**

Jenkins, S. How many ways can you catch a fly? **591.5**

Jenkins, S. Sisters & brothers **591.56**

Jenkins, S. Time for a bath **591.56**

Jenkins, S. Time to sleep **591.5**

Johnson, J. Insects and creepy-crawlies **595.7**

Katz, J. Lenore finds a friend **636.73**

Kehret, P. Animals welcome **636.08**

Kvatum, L. Saving Yasha **599.78**

Markle, S. Jumping spiders **595.4**

Markle, S. Snow school **E**

My first day **591.3**

Nascimbeni, B. Animals and their families **E**

Pattison, D. Desert baths **591.754**

Pipe, J. Swarms **591.5**

Racanelli, M. Animal mimics **591.5**

Riggs, K. Gorillas **599.884**

Riggs, K. Kangaroos **599.2**

Riggs, K. Leopards **599.75**

Riggs, K. Moose **599.65**

Rissman, R. Ants **595.79**

Rustad, M. E. H. Animals in fall **578.4**

Rutherford, C. A dog is a dog **636.7**

Schuette, S. L. Let's look at fall **508.2**

Schuette, S. L. Let's look at spring **508.2**

Schuette, S. L. Let's look at summer **508.2**

Schuette, S. L. Let's look at winter **508.2**

Silverstein, A. Dung beetles, slugs, leeches, and more **590**

Stewart, M. Under the snow **591.7**

Stewart, M. When rain falls **591.7**

Stockdale, S. Carry me! **591.56**

Thimmesh, C. True Stories of Extraordinary Friendship **591.5**

Track that scat! **591.47**

Wild ideas **153.4**

Zelch, P. R. Ready, set . . . wait! **591.5**

ANIMAL BEHAVIOR

See also Animals; Zoology

ANIMAL BEHAVIOR -- FICTION

Derrick, D. G. Animals don't, so I won't! **E**

Foreman, M. Friends **E**

What happens next? **E**

Animal body-part regenerators. Mitchell, S. K. **571.8**

The **Animal** Book. Jenkins, S. **590**

ANIMAL CAMOUFLAGE *See* Camouflage (Biology)

Animal chemical combat. Mitchell, S. K. **591.47**

Animal colors. Fielding, B. **591.47**

ANIMAL COMMUNICATION

Baines, R. What did one elephant say to the other **591.59**

Davies, N. Talk talk squawk **591.59**

Downer, A. Elephant talk **599.67**

Jenkins, S. How to clean a hippopotamus **591.7**

Judge, L. Bird talk **598**

Katz, J. Lenore finds a friend **636.73**

Martin, B. Polar bear, polar bear, what do you hear? **813**

Weitzman, G. How to Speak Dog **636.7**

Nardo, D. The Blue marble **525.022**

APOLLO PROJECT

    See also Life support systems (Space environment); Orbital rendezvous (Space flight); Space flight to the moon

APOLLO PROJECT -- GRAPHIC NOVELS

  Ottaviani, J. T-Minus: the race to the moon **629.45**

APOLOGIZING -- JUVENILE POETRY.

  Sidman, J. This is just to say **811**

APOSTLES

    See also Christian saints; Church history -- 30-600, Early church

The **apothecary.** Petersen, C. **615**

Appalachia. Rylant, C. **974**

APPALACHIAN REGION

  Houston, G. My great-aunt Arizona **371.1**

  Rylant, C. Appalachia **974**

APPALACHIAN REGION -- FICTION

  Hamilton, V. M.C. Higgins, the great **Fic**

  Henson, H. That Book Woman **E**

  Houston, G. The year of the perfect Christmas tree **E**

  Naylor, P. R. Faith, hope, and Ivy June **Fic**

  Rylant, C. When I was young in the mountains **E**

  White, R. Belle Prater's boy **Fic**

APPALACHIAN TRAIL -- FICTION

  Vanderpool, C. Navigating Early **Fic**

APPARATUS, ELECTRIC *See* Electric apparatus and appliances

APPARITIONS

  Matthews, R. Ghosts and spirits **133.1**

    See also Parapsychology; Spirits

APPEARANCE, PERSONAL *See* Personal appearance

Appelhans, Chris

  (il) Sparky **E**

Appelt, Kathi

  Bats around the clock **E**

  Brand-new baby blues **E**

  Counting crows **E**

  Keeper **Fic**

  Mogie **E**

  Oh my baby, little one **E**

  The true blue scouts of Sugarman Swamp **Fic**

  The underneath **Fic**

  When Otis courted Mama **E**

APPERCEPTION

    See also Educational psychology; Psychology

APPETIZERS

    See also Cooking

Apple. McClure, N. **E**

APPLE *See* Apples

Apple cider making days. Purmell, A. **E**

APPLE COMPUTER INC.

  Goldsworthy, S. Steve Jobs **92**

Apple countdown. Holub, J. **E**

The **apple** doll. Kleven, E. **E**

Apple farmer Annie. Wellington, M. **E**

An **apple** for Harriet Tubman. Turner, G. T. **92**

Apple for the teacher. Yolen, J. **782.42**

APPLE GROWERS -- UNITED STATES -- BIOGRAPHY

  Codell, R. E. Seed by seed **634.11**

  Moses, W. Johnny Appleseed **634**

The **apple** orchard riddle. **E**

Apple pie 4th of July. Wong, J. S. **E**

Apple pie ABC. Murray, A. **E**

An **apple** pie for dinner. VanHecke, S. **E**

The **apple** pie that Papa baked. Thompson, L. **E**

The **apple** pie tree. **583**

An **apple's** life. Dickmann, N. **634**

Apple, Margot

  (il) The name quilt **E**

  (il) Shaw, N. Sheep in a jeep **E**

The **apple-pip** princess. Ray, J. **E**

Applegate, Katherine

  The buffalo storm **E**

  Home of the brave **Fic**

  Ivan **599.884**

  The one and only Ivan **Fic**

Apples. Gibbons, G. **634**

APPLES

    See also Fruit

Apples. Farmer, J. **634**

APPLES

  The apple pie tree **583**

  Bulla, C. R. A tree is a plant **582.16**

  Dickmann, N. An apple's life **634**

  Esbaum, J. Apples for everyone **634**

  Farmer, J. Apples **634**

  Gibbons, G. Apples **634**

  Hutchins, P. Ten red apples **E**

  Maestro, B. How do apples grow? **634**

  McClure, N. Apple **E**

  Purmell, A. Apple cider making days **E**

  Rustad, M. E. H. Fall apples **634**

  Smucker, A. E. Golden delicious **634**

  Turner, G. T. An apple for Harriet Tubman **92**

  Wellington, M. Apple farmer Annie **E**

  Worth, R. Johnny Appleseed **92**

  Yolen, J. Johnny Appleseed **92**

  Ziefert, H. One red apple **634**

APPLES -- FICTION

  The apple orchard riddle **E**

  Apples and pumpkins. Rockwell, A. F. **E**

  Apples for everyone. Esbaum, J. **634**

  Apples to Oregon. Hopkinson, D. **E**

  Apples, cherries, red raspberries. Cleary, B. P. **641.3**

Applesauce. **E**

Applesauce season. Lipson, E. R. **E**

Appleseed, Johnny, 1774-1845

      About

Archers, alchemists, and 98 other medieval jobs you might have loved or loathed. Galloway, P. **940.1**

ARCHERY

See also Martial arts; Shooting

ARCHERY -- FICTION

Lloyd, A. Year of the tiger **Fic**

Archie. Gordon, D. M. **E**

Archie and the pirates. Rosenthal, M. **E**

Archie takes flight. Brawer, M. **Fic**

Archie's vacation. Gordon, D. M. **E**

Archie's war. **Fic**

Archimedes, ca. 287-212 B.C.

About

Hightower, P. The greatest mathematician **92**

ARCHITECTS

Adler, D. A. A picture book of Thomas Jefferson **973.4**

Arrigan, M. Mario's Angels **E**

Balliett, B. The Wright 3 **Fic**

Bodden, V. Frank Gehry **92**

Bradley, K. B. Jefferson's sons **Fic**

Fern, T. E. Pippo the Fool **E**

Fleming, C. The hatmaker's sign **E**

Jurmain, S. The worst of friends **973.4**

Juster, N. The annotated Phantom tollbooth **813**

Mannis, C. D. Julia Morgan built a castle **92**

Pericoli, M. The true story of Stellina **E**

Rodriguez, R. Building on nature **92**

Stanley, D. Michelangelo **92**

Wells, R. My Havana **Fic**

Woodruff, E. Fearless **Fic**

ARCHITECTS

See also Artists

ARCHITECTURAL ACOUSTICS

See also Sound

ARCHITECTURAL DECORATION AND ORNAMENT

Hill, I. (. T. Urban animals **729**

ARCHITECTURAL DECORATION AND ORNAMENT

See also Architecture; Decoration and ornament

ARCHITECTURAL DESIGN

See also Architecture; Design

ARCHITECTURAL DRAWING

See also Drawing

ARCHITECTURAL ENGINEERING *See* Building; Structural analysis (Engineering); Structural engineering

ARCHITECTURE

From mud huts to skyscrapers **720**

Hosack, K. Buildings **720**

Kirk, D. Library mouse **E**

Macaulay, D. Building big **720**

Macaulay, D. Built to last **729**

Roeder, A. 13 buildings children should know **720**

The Story of buildings **690**

Tomecek, S. Art & architecture **701**

ARCHITECTURE

See also Art

ARCHITECTURE -- COMPOSITION, PROPORTION, ETC.

See also Composition (Art)

ARCHITECTURE -- DECORATION AND ORNAMENT *See* Architectural decoration and ornament

ARCHITECTURE -- HISTORY

The Story of buildings **690**

ARCHITECTURE AND PEOPLE WITH DISABILITIES

See also People with disabilities

ARCHITECTURE, GOTHIC *See* Gothic architecture

ARCHITECTURE, ROMAN *See* Roman architecture

ARCHIVISTS

Penrose, A. The boy who bit Picasso **92**

Archvillain. Lyga, B. **Fic**

Arctic adventures. Rivera, R. **920**

Arctic fox. Person, S. **599.77**

Arctic lights, arctic nights. Miller, D. S. **591.4**

ARCTIC REGIONS

Goodman, S. Life on the ice **998**

Markle, S. Waiting for ice **599.786**

ARCTIC REGIONS

See also Earth; Polar regions

ARCTIC REGIONS -- EXPLORATION

See also Exploration; Scientific expeditions

ARCTIC REGIONS -- FICTION

Blown away **E**

Cub's big world **E**

Evert, L. The Christmas wish **E**

George, J. C. Nutik, the wolf pup **E**

Lester, A. Sophie Scott goes south **E**

Murphy, Y. Baby Polar **E**

Pelletier, M. Avati **577.09**

Taylor, T. Ice drift **Fic**

ARCTIC REGIONS -- HISTORY -- FICTION

The snowstorm **Fic**

Arctic thaw. Lourie, P. **998**

Arctic tundra and polar deserts. Woodford, C. **577**

Ardley, Neil

Macaulay, D. The new way things work **600**

Are the dinosaurs dead, Dad? **E**

Are the drums for you? Landau, E. **786.9**

Are there other Earths? Portman, M. **523.2**

Are we alone? Skurzynski, G. **576.8**

Are we there yet, Daddy? Walters, V. **E**

Are you afraid yet? the science behind scary stuff. O'Meara, S. J. **500**

Are you awake? Blackall, S. **E**

Are you my mother? Eastman, P. D. **E**

Are you ready for fall? Anderson, S. **508.2**
Are you ready for spring? Anderson, S. **508.2**
Are you scared yet? [series]
  San Souci, R. Haunted houses **S**
Are you there God?, it's me, Margaret. Blume, J. **Fic**
Area 51. Karst, K. **001.9**
AREA 51 (NEV.)
  Karst, K. Area 51 **001.9**
ARENA THEATER
  See also Theater
Arena, Jill
  (il) Playing loteria **E**
Aretha, David
  Awesome African-American rock and soul musi-
    cians **781.644**
  Sit-ins and freedom rides **323.1**
  The story of the civil rights march on Washington
    for jobs and freedom in photographs **975.3**
Argent, Kerry
  (il) Fox, M. Sleepy bears **E**
ARGENTINA -- HISTORY
  Favor, L. J. Eva Peron **92**
ARGONAUTS (LEGENDARY CHARACTERS)
  See also Legendary characters
Argueta, Jorge
  A movie in my pillow **861**
  Talking with Mother Earth **811**
ARGUMENTATION *See* Debates and debating;
  Logic
Argus. Knudsen, M. **E**
ARID REGIONS
  See also Earth
Arihara, Shino
  (il) Franco, B. Zero is the leaves on the tree **513**
  (il) Hudes, Q. A. Welcome to my neighborhood! **E**
  (il) Lord, M. A song for Cambodia **92**
Ariol. **741.5**
ARISTOCRACY
  See also Political science; Upper class
Arithme-tickle. Lewis, J. P. **513**
ARITHMETIC
  Fisher, V. How high can a dinosaur count? **513**
  Lewis, J. P. Arithme-tickle **513**
  Markel, M. Tyrannosaurus math **513**
  Marsico, K. Football **796.332**
  Marsico, K. Running **796.42**
  Marsico, K. Speed skating **796.91**
  Marsico, K. Tennis **796.342**
  Minden, C. Swimming **797.2**
  Murphy, S. J. Betcha! **519.5**
  Murphy, S. J. Less than zero **513**
  Murphy, S. J. More or less **513**
ARITHMETIC
  See also Mathematics; Set theory
ARITHMETIC -- ESTIMATION *See* Approxi-
  mate computation

ARITHMETIC -- FICTION
  Max's math **E**
Arizona. Somervill, B. A. **979.1**
Arizona. Brezina, C. **979.1**
Arizona. McDaniel, M. **979.1**
ARIZONA
  Brezina, C. Arizona **979.1**
  McDaniel, M. Arizona **979.1**
  Somervill, B. A. Arizona **979.1**
ARIZONA -- FICTION
  Broach, E. Revenge of Superstition Mountain **Fic**
Ark angel. Horowitz, A. **Fic**
Arkansas. Prentzas, G. S. **976.7**
Arkansas. Levy, J. **976.7**
ARKANSAS
  Altman, L. J. Arkansas **976.7**
  Levy, J. Arkansas **976.7**
  Prentzas, G. S. Arkansas **976.7**
  Arkansas. Altman, L. J. **976.7**
ARKANSAS -- FICTION
  Greene, B. Philip Hall likes me, I reckon maybe **Fic**
  Hilmo, T. With a name like Love **Fic**
  Manley, C. Skeeter's dream **Fic**
  McCrite, K. D. In front of God and everybody **Fic**
ARKANSAS -- RACE RELATIONS
  Walker, P. R. Remember Little Rock **379**
Arlington. Demarest, C. L. **975.5**
ARLINGTON NATIONAL CEMETERY (VA.)
  Demarest, C. L. Arlington **975.5**
Arlon, Penelope
  Emergency vehicles **629.04**
  Puppies and kittens **636.7**
ARMADILLOS
  Swinburne, S. R. Armadillo trail **599.3**
ARMADILLOS -- FICTION
  Brimner, L. D. Trick or treat, Old Armadillo **E**
  Fearnley, J. Milo Armadillo **E**
Armand, Glenda
  Love twelve miles long **E**
Armando and the blue tarp school. Fine, E. H. **E**
ARMED FORCES
  See also Military art and science
Armenia. Dhilawala, S. **947.5**
ARMENIA
  Dhilawala, S. Armenia **947.5**
ARMIES -- MEDICAL CARE
  See also Medical care; Military medicine
ARMOR
  Byam, M. Arms & armor **355.8**
  Kent, P. Peter Kent's big book of armor **687**
ARMOR
  See also Art metalwork; Costume; Military
    art and science
Arms & armor. Byam, M. **355.8**
ARMS AND ARMOR *See* Armor; Weapons
ARMS CONTROL

AROMATHERAPY

See also Therapeutics

AROMATIC PLANTS

See also Plants

Aron, Bill

(il) Hoffman, L. A. What you will see inside a synagogue   **296.4**

Aronica-Buck, Barbara

Over the moon   **811**

Aronin, Miriam

The ant's nest   **595.7**

Aye-aye   **599.8**

Earthquake in Haiti   **972.94**

Mangled by a hurricane!   **551.55**

The prairie dog's town   **599.3**

Slammed by a tsunami!   **551.46**

Tuberculosis   **616.9**

Aronson, Billy

The chicken problem   **E**

Richard M. Nixon   **92**

Aronson, Marc

(jt. auth) Mayor, A. The Griffin and the Dinosaur   **398.245**

For boys only   **031.02**

If stones could speak   **936**

The skull in the rock   **569.9**

Trapped   **363.1**

The world made new   **910.4**

Nelson, S. R. Ain't nothing but a man   **92**

Aronson, Sarah

Beyond lucky   **Fic**

Around our way on neighbors' day. Brown, T. F.   **E**

Around the world. Phelan, M.   **741.5**

Around the world cookbook. Dodge, A. J.   **641.5**

Around the world in a hundred years. Fritz, J. **910.92**

Around the world in one Shabbat. Bernhard, D. Y.   **296.4**

Around the world on eighty legs. Gibson, A.   **811**

Around-the-house history [series]

Lauber, P. What you never knew about beds, bedrooms, and pajamas   **392**

Lauber, P. What you never knew about fingers, forks, & chopsticks   **394.1**

Around-the-world art & activities. Press, J.   **372.5**

Arrasmith, Patrick

(il) Delaney, J. Attack of the Fiend   **Fic**

(il) Delaney, J. Clash of the demons   **Fic**

(il) Delaney, J. Curse of the bane   **Fic**

(il) Delaney, J. Night of the soul-stealer   **Fic**

(il) Delaney, J. Rage of the fallen   **Fic**

(il) Delaney, J. Revenge of the witch   **Fic**

(il) Delaney, J. The Spook's tale and other horrors   **S**

(il) Delaney, J. Wrath of the Bloodeye   **Fic**

(il) Rise of the huntress   **Fic**

Arree Chung

Ninja!   **E**

Arrigan, Mary

Mario's Angels   **E**

Arrorro mi nino.   **398.8**

ARROW *See* Bow and arrow

The **arrow** finds its mark.   **811**

The **arrow** over the door. Bruchac, J.   **Fic**

Arrow to the sun. McDermott, G.   **398.2**

Arroyo, Sheri L.

How chefs use math   **641.5**

How crime fighters use math   **363.2**

How deep sea divers use math   **797.2**

How race car drivers use math   **796.72**

Arsenault, Isabelle

(il) Jane, the fox & me   **Fic**

(il) Maclear, K. Spork   **E**

(il) Migrant   **E**

(il) Virginia Wolf   **Fic**

ARSON

Bozzo, L. Fire dog heroes   **636.7**

DeFelice, C. C. The ghost and Mrs. Hobbs   **Fic**

ARSON -- FICTION

Shouldn't you be in school?   **Fic**

ART

The art treasure hunt   **701**

Balliett, B. Chasing Vermeer   **Fic**

Brooks, S. Get into Art!   **E**

Colón, R. Draw!   **E**

Enz, T. Repurpose it   **600**

An eye for art   **708**

Henry, S. Making amazing art   **745.5**

Hensley, L. Art for all   **701**

Luxbacher, I. The jumbo book of outdoor art **704.9**

Linnea in Monet's garden   **Fic**

McArthur, M. An ABC of what art can be   **700**

Mix it up!   **E**

Museum of Modern Art (New York, N. Y. Make art mistakes   **701**

My art book   **745.5**

Rissman, R. Shapes in art   **516**

Speaking of art   **700**

Vry, S. 13 art illusions children should know **702.8**

Wenzel, A. 13 art mysteries children should know   **759.2**

ART

See also Arts

Art & architecture. Tomecek, S.   **701**

Art & Max. Wiesner, D.   **E**

ART -- 20TH CENTURY

Heart to heart   **811**

ART -- ANALYSIS, INTERPRETATION, APPRECIATION *See* Art -- Study and teaching; Art appreciation; Art criticism

ART -- COLLECTORS AND COLLECTING

Fillion, S. Miss Etta and Dr. Claribel   **92**

ART -- COMPOSITION *See* Composition (Art)

Knight, J. Charlotte in Paris **Fic**
Krull, K. Leonardo da Vinci **92**
Krull, K. Lives of the artists **709.2**
Kushner, T. The art of Maurice Sendak **741.6**
Lewis, J. P. Self-portrait with seven fingers **811**
Linnea in Monet's garden **Fic**
Lisle, J. T. The art of keeping cool **Fic**
MacLachlan, P. Painting the wind **E**
Maestro, B. The story of the Statue of Liberty **974.7**
Magic trash **92**
Maguire, G. Making mischief **741.6**
Maltbie, P. I. Claude Monet **92**
Mann, E. Statue of Liberty **974.7**
Marsden, C. Silk umbrellas **Fic**
McCloskey, J. Robert McCloskey **92**
McKay, H. Saffy's angel **Fic**
Me, Frida **E**
Morales, Y. Viva Frida! **E**
Nahson, C. J. The snowy day and the art of Ezra Jack Keats **741.6**
Niepold, M. Oooh! Picasso **730.9**
Nikola-Lisa, W. Setting the turkeys free **E**
Nivola, C. A. Orani **945**
Nobleman, M. T. Boys of steel **92**
Parker-Rock, M. Bruce Hale **92**
Peet, B. Bill Peet: an autobiography **813**
Penrose, A. The boy who bit Picasso **92**
Pericoli, M. The true story of Stellina **E**
Phillips, J. Leonardo da Vinci **92**
Place, F. The old man mad about drawing **Fic**
Raczka, B. Before they were famous **704**
Raczka, B. Here's looking at me **757**
Raczka, B. The Vermeer interviews **759.9**
Ray, D. K. Hokusai **769.92**
Ray, D. K. Wanda Gag **92**
Rivera, R. Arctic adventures **920**
Robbins, T. Lily Renée, escape artist **940.53**
Rodriguez, R. Through Georgia's eyes **92**
Rubin, S. G. Andy Warhol **92**
Rubin, S. G. Edward Hopper **92**
Rubin, S. G. Whaam!: the art & life of Roy Lichtenstein **92**
Russo, M. Always remember me **940.53**
Sabbeth, C. Van Gogh and the Post-Impressionists for kids **759.05**
Say, A. Drawing from memory **741.6**
Schroeder, A. In her hands **92**
Scott, E. Secrets of the Cirque Medrano **Fic**
Sellier, M. Renoir's colors **759.05**
Serres, A. And Picasso painted Guernica **759**
Shea, P. D. Liberty rising **974.7**
Shea, P. D. Patience Wright **92**
Sis, P. The wall **92**
Somervill, B. A. Pierre-Auguste Renoir **92**
Stanley, D. Leonardo da Vinci **709.2**
Stanley, D. Michelangelo **92**

Steig, W. When everybody wore a hat **E**
Stone, T. L. Sandy's circus **92**
Sweet, M. Balloons over Broadway **92**
Tejubehan (Singer) Drawing from the City **745**
Thomas, P. For the birds: the life of Roger Tory Peterson **92**
Tonatiuh, D. Diego Rivera **92**
Trevino, E. B. d. I, Juan de Pareja **Fic**
Venezia, M. Diego Velazquez **92**
Venezia, M. Faith Ringgold **92**
Venezia, M. Horace Pippin **92**
Waldman, N. Out of the shadows **92**
Warhola, J. Uncle Andy's **E**
Welton, J. Henri Matisse **92**
Wenzel, A. 13 art mysteries children should know **759.2**
Wenzel, A. 13 artists children should know **709**
Wing, N. An eye for color: the story of Josef Albers **92**
Winter, J. My name is Georgia **92**
Winter, J. Frida **759.9**
Woodruff, E. Fearless **Fic**
Yaccarino, D. All the way to America **92**
Yolen, J. Naming Liberty **E**
Yolleck, J. Paris in the spring with Picasso **E**
Youme Mali under the night sky **92**
Young, E. The house Baba built **92**
ARTISTS -- BIOGRAPHY
Invitation to ballet **792.8**
ARTISTS -- FICTION
Alexander, M. G. Max and the dumb flower picture **E**
Anholt, L. Cezanne and the apple boy **E**
Arrigan, M. Mario's Angels **E**
Becker, B. Holbrook **Fic**
Brewster, H. Carnation, Lily, Lily, Rose **Fic**
Broach, E. Masterpiece **Fic**
Browning, D. Signed, Abiah Rose **E**
Carle, E. The artist who painted a blue horse **E**
Carmichael, C. Wild things **Fic**
Catalanotto, P. Emily's art **E**
Cole, H. A nest for Celeste **Fic**
Cuevas, M. The masterwork of a painting elephant **Fic**
Demi The boy who painted dragons **E**
A dragon's guide to the care and feeding of humans **Fic**
Georgia in Hawaii **E**
Giff, P. R. Pictures of Hollis Woods **Fic**
Hartfield, C. Me and Uncle Romie **E**
Harvey, J. My hands sing the blues **E**
Haseley, D. Twenty heartbeats **E**
Hazen, L. E. The amazing trail of Seymour Snail **Fic**
Hector, J. The Little Matador **E**
Hillenbrand, W. Louie! **E**

ARTISTS, INUIT
Rivera, R. Arctic adventures   920
ARTISTS, ITALIAN
Krull, K. Leonardo da Vinci   92
Phillips, J. Leonardo da Vinci   92
Stanley, D. Leonardo da Vinci   709.2
Stanley, D. Michelangelo   92
ARTISTS, JAPANESE
Ray, D. K. Hokusai   769.92
ARTISTS, MEXICAN
Frith, M. Frida Kahlo   92
Tonatiuh, D. Diego Rivera   92
Winter, J. Frida   759.9
ARTISTS, RUSSIAN
The noisy paint box   92
ARTISTS, SPANISH
Venezia, M. Diego Velazquez   92
ARTS
Ajmera, M. To be an artist   700
ARTS -- FICTION
Hattemer, K. The vigilante poets of Selwyn Academy   Fic
ARTS AND CRAFTS *See* Handicraft
ARTS AND CRAFTS MOVEMENT
     See also Art; Decoration and ornament; Decorative arts; Industrial arts
Arts and culture in the early Islamic world. Flatt, L.   700.9
ARTS, DECORATIVE *See* Decorative arts
Aruego, Jose
The last laugh   E
(il) Beaumont, K. Duck, duck, goose!   E
(il) Bruchac, J. How Chipmunk got his stripes 398.2
(il) Bruchac, J. Turtle's race with Beaver   398.2
Dewey, A. Splash!   E
(il) Five little ducks   782.42
(il) Ginsburg, M. The chick and the duckling   E
(il) Kraus, R. Whose mouse are you?   E
(il) Sharmat, M. Gregory, the terrible eater   E
Arzoumanian, Alik
(il) MacDonald, M. R. Tunjur! Tunjur! Tunjur!   398.2
As fast as words could fly. Tuck, P. M.   Fic
As good as anybody: Martin Luther King Jr. and Abraham Joshua Heschel's amazing march toward freedom. Michelson, R.   92
As luck would have it. San Souci, R.   398.2
As simple as it seems. Weeks, S.   Fic
ASBESTOS
     See also Minerals
Ascendance trilogy [series]
Nielsen, J. A. The false prince   Fic
Nielsen, J. A. The runaway king   Fic
Nielsen, J. A. The shadow throne   Fic
ASCETICISM
     See also Ethics; Religious life

Asch, Devin
(il) Asch, F. The Daily Comet   E
Asch, F. Like a windy day   E
Asch, Frank
The Daily Comet   E
Gravity buster   Fic
Happy birthday, Moon   E
Like a windy day   E
Star jumper   Fic
The sun is my favorite star   E
Time twister   Fic
ASHANTI (AFRICAN PEOPLE) -- FOLKLORE
McDermott, G. Anansi the spider   398.2
Ashanti to Zulu: African traditions. Musgrove, M.   960
McPhail, D. M. Drawing lessons
Ashburn, Boni
I had a favorite dress   E
Over at the castle   E
Ashby, Ruth
Young Charles Darwin and the voyage of the Beagle   92
Ashe, Arthur, 1943-1993
           About
Hubbard, C. Game, set, match, champion Arthur Ashe   92
Krull, K. Lives of the athletes   796
Ashley Bryan. Bryan, A.   92
Ashley Bryan's ABC of African-American poetry.   811
Ashley Bryan's African tales, uh-huh. Bryan, A.   398.2
Ashley Bryan's Puppets. Bryan, A.   811
Ashley, Bernard
Ronnie's war   Fic
Ashley, Carol
(il) Swaim, J. Scarum fair   811
Ashman, Linda
M is for mischief   E
Rain!   E
Ashtown burials [series]
Wilson, N. D. The dragon's tooth   Fic
Wilson, N. D. The drowned vault   Fic
ASIA
Law, F. Atlas of Southwest and Central Asia   950
Law, F. Atlas of the Far East and Southeast Asia 950
ASIA -- DESCRIPTION
Rumford, J. Traveling man: the journey of Ibn Battuta, 1325-1354   910
ASIA -- DESCRIPTION AND TRAVEL
Markle, S. Animals Marco Polo saw   92
ASIA -- EMIGRATION AND IMMIGRATION -- HISTORY
Angel Island   979.4
ASIA -- POLITICS AND GOVERNMENT
     See also Politics
ASIAN AMERICANS

Atlas of North America. Foster, K. **970**

Atlas of South America. Foster, K. **980**

Atlas of Southwest and Central Asia. Law, F. **950**

Atlas of the Far East and Southeast Asia. Law, F. **950**

Atlas of the Poles and Oceans. Foster, K. **998**

ATLASES

Beginner's United States atlas **912**

Boyer, C. National Geographic kids ultimate U.S. road trip atlas **912**

Crane, N. Barefoot Books world atlas **912**

Johnson, J. Animal Planet atlas of animals **591.4**

National Geographic atlas of the world **912**

National Geographic Kids beginner's world atlas **912**

National Geographic United States atlas for young explorers **912**

National Geographic world atlas for young explorers **912**

Rand McNally Goodes World Atlas **912**

Student atlas **912**

Waldron, M. How to read a map **912.01**

Wojtanik, A. The National Geographic Bee ultimate fact book **910**

ATLASES

See also Geography; Maps

Atmosphere. Gallant, R. A. **551.51**

ATMOSPHERE

See also Air; Earth

Cosgrove, B. Weather **551.5**

Gallant, R. A. Atmosphere **551.51**

ATMOSPHERE -- POLLUTION *See* Air pollution

ATMOSPHERIC DUST *See* Dust

ATMOSPHERIC GREENHOUSE EFFECT *See* Global warming

ATMOSPHERIC HUMIDITY *See* Humidity

ATOLLS *See* Coral reefs and islands

The atom. Cregan, E. R. **539.7**

ATOMIC BOMB

Lawton, C. Hiroshima **940.54**

ATOMIC BOMB

See also Bombs; Nuclear weapons

ATOMIC BOMB -- FICTION

Klages, E. The green glass sea **Fic**

Klages, E. White sands, red menace **Fic**

ATOMIC BOMB -- GERMANY -- HISTORY

Sheinkin, S. Bomb **623.4**

ATOMIC BOMB -- HISTORY

Sheinkin, S. Bomb **623.4**

ATOMIC BOMB -- PHYSIOLOGICAL EFFECT

Coerr, E. Sadako **92**

Coerr, E. Sadako and the thousand paper cranes **92**

ATOMIC ENERGY *See* Nuclear energy

ATOMIC NUCLEI *See* Nuclear physics

ATOMIC POWER *See* Nuclear energy

ATOMIC POWER PLANTS *See* Nuclear power plants

ATOMIC THEORY

Cregan, E. R. The atom **539.7**

McLean, A. What is atomic theory? **539.7**

Atomic universe. Jerome, K. B. **539.7**

ATOMIC WARFARE *See* Nuclear warfare

ATOMIC WEAPONS *See* Nuclear weapons

ATOMS

Baxter, R. The particle model of matter **530**

Campbell, M. C. Discovering atoms **539.7**

Cregan, E. R. The atom **539.7**

Lepora, N. Atoms and molecules **539.7**

McLean, A. What is atomic theory? **539.7**

Older than the stars **523.1**

Atoms and molecules. Lepora, N. **539.7**

ATONEMENT -- CHRISTIANITY

See also Christianity; Sacrifice; Salvation

ATONEMENT -- JUDAISM

See also Judaism

ATONEMENT, DAY OF *See* Yom Kippur

ATROCITIES

See also Crime; Cruelty

Attack of the Fiend. Delaney, J. **Fic**

Attack of the fluffy bunnies. Beaty, A. **Fic**

The attack of the frozen woodchucks. Elish, D. **Fic**

Attacked by a crocodile. Hamilton, S. L. **597.98**

ATTACKS BY ANIMALS *See* Animal attacks

Atteberry, Kevan

(il) Schaefer, L. M. Frankie Stein **E**

(il) Schaefer, L. M. Frankie Stein starts school **E**

ATTENTION

See also Apperception; Educational psychology; Memory; Psychology; Thought and thinking

ATTENTION DEFICIT DISORDER

Capaccio, G. ADD and ADHD **616.85**

Chilman-Blair, K. Medikidz explain ADHD **616.85**

Kraus, J. Annie's plan **371.3**

Quinn, P. O. Attention, girls! **616.85**

Robbins, L. How to deal with ADHD **616.85**

Silverstein, A. The ADHD update **616.85**

Taylor, J. F. The survival guide for kids with ADD or ADHD **616.85**

Wood, D. Miss Little's gift **E**

ATTENTION DEFICIT DISORDER -- FICTION

Egan, K. The Vanishing Coin **Fic**

Eliza Bing is (not) a big, fat quitter **Fic**

Attention, girls! Quinn, P. O. **616.85**

ATTENTION-DEFICIT HYPERACTIVITY DISORDER -- FICTION

Gantos, J. Joey Pigza swallowed the key **Fic**

Gantos, J. The key that swallowed Joey Pigza **Fic**

Attica. Kilworth, G. **Fic**

ATTITUDE (PSYCHOLOGY)

See also Emotions; Psychology

want to survive the school bus E
Australia. Rau, D. M. 994
AUSTRALIA
Bancroft, B. Kangaroo and crocodile E
Australia. Turner, K. 994
AUSTRALIA -- FICTION
Baker, J. Mirror E
Baker, J. Where the forest meets the sea E
Baker, J. Window E
Bateson, C. Being Bee Fic
Bateson, C. Magenta McPhee Fic
Chatterton, M. The Brain finds a leg Fic
Edgar, E. The Visconti house Fic
Fox, M. Hunwick's egg E
Giles, S. M. The body thief Fic
Herrick, S. Naked bunyip dancing Fic
Millard, G. Layla, Queen of hearts Fic
Morgan, S. Sam's bush journey E
Musgrove, M. Lucy the good Fic
The naming of Tishkin Silk Fic
Ormerod, J. Lizzie nonsense E
Shields, C. D. Wombat walkabout E
Thomason, M. Moonrunner Fic
AUSTRALIA -- SOCIAL LIFE AND CUSTOMS
Sheen, B. Foods of Australia 641.59
Australia, Hawaii, and the Pacific. Underwood, D. 780.9
AUSTRALIAN ABORIGINES *See* Aboriginal Australians
AUSTRALIAN COOKING
Sheen, B. Foods of Australia 641.59
An **Australian** outback food chain. Wojahn, R. H. 577.5
Australian spotted jellyfish. Gray, S. H. 593.5
AUSTRALIANS
See also Australia
Austria. Indovino, S. C. 943.6
Austria. Grahame, D. A. 943.6
AUSTRIA
Grahame, D. A. Austria 943.6
AUSTRIA -- FICTION
Lester, A. Running with the horses E
AUSTRIA -- HISTORY
Indovino, S. C. Austria 943.6
AUSTRIA -- HISTORY -- 1867-1918 -- FICTION
A gift for Mama Fic
AUSTRIAN COOKING
Hughes, H. Cooking the Austrian way 641.5
Auth, Tony
(il) Gannij, J. Topsy-turvy bedtime E
(il) Pinkwater, D. M. The Hoboken chicken emergency Fic
(il) Rees, D. Uncle Pirate Fic
(il) Rees, D. Uncle Pirate to the rescue Fic
Author. Lester, H. 813
AUTHORITY

See also Political science
AUTHORS
Abrams, D. Gary Soto 92
Ada, A. F. Under the royal palms 813
Adler, D. A. B. Franklin, printer 973.3
Adler, D. A. A picture book of Harriet Beecher Stowe 92
The adventures of Mark Twain by Huckleberry Finn 92
Aliki William Shakespeare & the Globe 792.09
Amoroso, C. Helen Keller 92
Andersen, H. C. The nightingale E
Anderson, W. T. Pioneer girl: the story of Laura Ingalls Wilder 92
Armand, G. Love twelve miles long E
Armstrong, A. Raleigh's page Fic
Barretta, G. Now & Ben 609
Berne, E. C. Laura Ingalls Wilder 92
Berne, J. Manfish: a story of Jacques Cousteau 92
Blackwood, G. L. The Shakespeare stealer Fic
Blackwood, G. L. Shakespeare's scribe Fic
Bogacki, T. The champion of children 92
Bond, V. Zora and me Fic
Borden, L. The journey that saved Curious George 92
A boy called Dickens Fic
The boy on Fairfield Street: how Ted Geisel grew up to become Dr. Seuss 92
The boy, the bear, the baron, the bard E
Bradby, M. More than anything else E
Brimner, L. D. Booker T. Washington 92
Brown, D. Far beyond the garden gate: Alexandra David-Neel's journey to Lhasa 92
Brown, M. Pablo Neruda 92
Bryan, A. Ashley Bryan 92
Bryant, J. A river of words: the story of William Carlos Williams 92
Bryant, J. The right word 92
Burningham, J. John Burningham 92
Chrisp, P. Welcome to the Globe 792
Christelow, E. What do authors do? 808
The Christmas coat 92
Clinton, C. Phillis's big test 92
Cohen, C. D. The Seuss, the whole Seuss, and nothing but the Seuss 92
Colbert, D. The magical worlds of Harry Potter 823
Conlan, K. Under the ice 578.7
Cooney, B. Chanticleer and the fox E
Cooper, F. Coming home 818
Cooper, S. King of shadows Fic
Cotter, C. Born to write 920
Coville, B. William Shakespeare's A midsummer night's dream 822.3
Coville, B. William Shakespeare's Twelfth night 822.3
Cox, C. Shakespeare kids 792.9

B

B is for blue planet. **550**
B. Franklin, printer. Adler, D. A. **973.3**
B.U.G. Yolen, J. **Fic**
Baasansuren, Bolormaa
  My little round house **E**
Baba Yaga and Vasilisa the brave. Mayer, M. **398.2**
Babbitt, Natalie
  The Devil's storybook **S**
  The eyes of the Amaryllis **Fic**
  Jack Plank tells tales **Fic**
  Kneeknock Rise **Fic**
  The moon over High Street **Fic**
  The search for delicious **Fic**
  Tuck everlasting **Fic**
  (il) Worth, V. All the small poems and fourteen more **811**
Babe. King-Smith, D. **Fic**
The **Babe** & I. Adler, D. A. **E**
Babe & me. Gutman, D. **Fic**
Babe conquers the world. Wallace, R. **92**
Babe Didrikson Zaharias. Freedman, R. **92**
BABIES See Infants
BABIES -- FICTION
  The baby swap **E**
  Blackall, S. The baby tree **E**
  Gantos, J. The key that swallowed Joey Pigza **Fic**
  Howatt, S. J. Sleepyheads **E**
  Hyewon Yum The twins' little sister **E**
  Katz, K. Now I'm big **E**
  Leo loves baby time **E**
  Look, L. Henry's first-moon birthday **E**
  Maple **E**
  Mustache baby **E**
  One special day **E**
  Palatini, M. No nap! yes nap! **E**
  Paschkis, J. Mooshka **E**
  Use your words, Sophie **E**
  The year of the baby **Fic**
Babies can't eat kimchee! Patz, N. **E**
Babies don't eat pizza. Danzig, D. **649**
Babies in the bayou. Arnosky, J. **E**
Babies in the library! Marino, J. **027.62**
The **babies** on the bus. Katz, K. **782.42**
Babies on the go. **E**
Baboon. Banks, K. **E**
BABOONS
  See also Apes
BABOONS -- FICTION
  Banks, K. Baboon **E**
  Napoli, D. J. Lights on the Nile **Fic**
Baboushka and the three kings. Robbins, R. **398.2**
Babushka's doll. Polacco, P. **E**
Babushka's Mother Goose. Polacco, P. **398.8**
Baby animal pop! **590**
BABY ANIMALS See Animal babies
Baby animals of lakes and ponds. Bredeson, C. **591.7**

Baby animals of the frozen tundra. Bredeson, C. **591.7**
Baby animals of the grasslands. Bredeson, C. **591.7**
Baby animals of the mountains. Bredeson, C. **591.7**
Baby animals of the ocean. Bredeson, C. **591.7**
Baby animals of the seashore. Bredeson, C. **591.7**
Baby animals of the wetlands. Bredeson, C. **591.7**
Baby Australian animals [series]
  Doudna, K. It's a baby kangaroo! **599.2**
  Hengel, K. It's a baby Australian fur seal! **599.79**
Baby baby baby! Janovitz, M. **E**
Baby Bear. Nelson, K. **E**
Baby Bear sees blue. Wolff, A. **E**
Baby Bear's books. Yolen, J. **E**
Baby Bear, Baby Bear, what do you see? Martin, B. **E**
Baby Beluga. Raffi **782.42**
Baby blessings. Jordan, D. **242**
Baby board books [series]
  Kubler, A. Humpty Dumpty **E**
BABY BOOM GENERATION
  See also Population
Baby Brains. James, S. **E**
Baby can. Bunting, E. **E**
Baby carnivores. Kalman, B. **599.7**
Baby danced the polka. Beaumont, K. **E**
Baby Dragon. Ehrlich, A. **E**
A **baby** elephant in the wild. **599.67**
Baby Flo. **782.421**
The **baby** goes beep. O'Connell, R. **E**
The **baby** in the hat. Ahlberg, A. **E**
Baby knows best. Granstrom, B. **E**
Baby mammals. Kalman, B. **591.3**
Baby mammoth mummy. Sloan, C. **569**
The **baby** on the way. English, K. **E**
Baby Pig Pig talks. McPhail, D. **E**
Baby Pig Pig walks. **E**
Baby Polar. Murphy, Y. **E**
Baby primates. Kalman, B. **599.813**
Baby rhyming time. Ernst, L. L. **027.62**
Baby rodents. Kalman, B. **599.35**
Baby Ruby bawled. Stanley, M. R. **E**
Baby says moo! Macken, J. E. **E**
Baby Seasons [series]
  Broach, E. Barnyard baby **E**
Baby shoes. Slater, D. **E**
Baby shower. Zalben, J. B. **E**
The **baby** sister. DePaola, T. **E**
BABY SITTING See Babysitting
The **baby** swap. **E**
Baby talk. Hindley, J. **E**
The **baby** tree. Blackall, S. **E**
Baby whale's journey. London, J. **E**
Baby whales drink milk. Esbensen, B. J. **599.5**
Baby's got the blues. Shields, C. D. **E**
Baby, come away. Adler, V. **E**

See also Dolls

Barbour, Karen
  (il) African American Poetry   **811**
  (il) Bunting, E. You were loved before you were born   **E**
  (il) Herrera, J. F. Laughing out loud, I fly   **811**
  (il) Lester, J. Let's talk about race   **305.8**
  (il) Marvelous math   **811**
  Mr. Williams   **92**

Barchers, Suzanne I.
  Revolution in space   **629.4**

Barclay, Jane
  Proud as a peacock, brave as a lion   **E**

Bard of Avon: the story of William Shakespeare. Stanley, D.   **822.3**

Barden, Stephanie
  Cinderella Smith   **Fic**
  The super secret mystery   **Fic**

Bardhan-Quallen, Sudipta
  Ballots for Belva   **92**
  Chicks run wild   **E**
  Duck, Duck, Moose!   **E**
  Nature science experiments   **508**
  Tyrannosaurus wrecks!   **E**

Bardoe, Cheryl
  Gregor Mendel   **92**
  Mammoths and mastodons   **569**
  The ugly dinosaur   **E**

Bardos, Magali
  (il) 100 Bears   **E**

Bardsley, John, d. 1999
About
  Gerstein, M. Sparrow Jack   **E**

The **Barefoot** book of Earth tales.   **398.2**

Barefoot Books world atlas. Crane, N.   **912**

Barg, Soosoonam
  Bowler, A. M. All about Korea   **951.9**

Barger, Jan
  (il) Ross, K. Crafts for kids who are learning about dinosaurs   **745.5**

Bark, George. Feiffer, J.   **E**

Barker, Dan
  Maybe right, maybe wrong   **370.1**

Barker, David
  Compost it   **631.8**
  Top 50 reasons to care about great apes   **599.8**

Barker, David M.
  Archaea   **579.3**

Barker, M. P.
  A difficult boy   **Fic**
  Mending horses   **Fic**

Barkley, James
  (il) Armstrong, W. H. Sounder   **Fic**

Barlas, Robert
  Latvia   **947.96**
  Uganda   **967.61**

Barn boot blues. Friend, C.   **Fic**
Barn dance! Martin, B.   **E**
Barn storm. Ghigna, C.   **E**

Barnaby Grimes [series]
  Stewart, P. The curse of the night wolf   **Fic**
  Stewart, P. Phantom of Blood Alley   **Fic**

Barnard, Alan
  (il) Brewster, H. Dinosaurs in your backyard   **567.9**
  (il) Tanaka, S. New dinos   **567.9**

Barnard, Bryn
  The genius of Islam   **297**
  Outbreak   **614.4**
  (il) Discovery in the cave   **944**
  (il) Redmond Tentacles!   **594**

Barneda, David
  (il) Reynolds, A. Snowbots   **E**

Barner, Bob
  Animal baths   **591.5**
  Bears! bears! bears!   **599.78**
  Bug safari   **E**
  Dem bones   **612.7**
  Dinosaurs roar, butterflies soar!   **560**
  Penguins, penguins, everywhere!   **598**
  (il) Lewis, J. P. Big is big (and little, little)   **E**

Barnes, Julia
  Camels and llamas at work   **636.2**
  Elephants at work   **636.9**
  Horses at work   **636.1**
  Pet cats   **636.8**
  Pet dogs   **636.7**
  Pet guinea pigs   **636.9**
  Pet rabbits   **636.9**

Barnes, Trevor
  The Kingfisher children's illustrated Bible   **220.9**

Barnes-Murphy, Rowan
  (il) Banking   **332.1**
  (il) Managing money   **332.02**
  (il) Payment methods   **332.4**

Barnett, Mac
  Battle Bunny   **E**
  Billy Twitters and his big blue whale problem   **E**
  The case of the case of mistaken identity   **Fic**
  Extra yarn   **E**
  The ghostwriter secret   **Fic**
  Guess again!   **E**
  It happened on a train   **Fic**
  Oh no! Not again!   **E**
  Oh no!, or, How my science project destroyed the world   **E**
  President taft is stuck in the bath   **E**
  Mustache!   **E**
  Sam and Dave dig a hole   **E**
  Teplin, S. The clock without a face   **Fic**
  The terrible two   **Fic**

Barnett, Moneta
  (il) Greenfield, E. Sister   **Fic**

Peter and the starcatchers **Fic**

Peter and the Sword of Mercy **Fic**

Barry, Frances

Let's save the animals **591.68**

Barshaw, Ruth McNally

Ellie McDoodle: best friends fur-ever **Fic**

Ellie McDoodle: have pen, will travel **Fic**

Ellie McDoodle: new kid in school **Fic**

Barsony, Piotr

The stories of the Mona Lisa **759.06**

Bart's king-sized book of fun. King, B. **793**

BARTER

See also Commerce; Economics; Money; Subsistence economy; Underground economy

A gift for Mama **Fic**

VanHecke, S. An apple pie for dinner **E**

Bartholdi, Frédéric Auguste, 1834-1904

About

Maestro, B. The story of the Statue of Liberty **974.7**

Mann, E. Statue of Liberty **974.7**

Shea, P. D. Liberty rising **974.7**

Yolen, J. Naming Liberty **E**

Bartholomew and the oobleck. Seuss **E**

Bartholomew Biddle and the very big wind. **Fic**

Bartholomew, Alan

Electric mischief **621.31**

Bartholomew, Lynn

(il) Bartholomew, A. Electric mischief **621.31**

Bartleby speaks! Cruise, R. **E**

Bartlett, Alison

(il) French, V. T. Rex **567.9**

Bartlett, T. C.

Tuba lessons **E**

Bartoletti, Susan Campbell

The boy who dared **Fic**

Growing up in coal country **331.3**

Kids on strike! **331.892**

Naamah and the ark at night **E**

Barton, Byron

Airplanes **387.7**

Airport **387.7**

Boats **387.2**

Bones, bones, dinosaur bones **567.9**

Building a house **690**

Dinosaurs, dinosaurs **E**

The little red hen **398.2**

Machines at work **690**

My bike **E**

My car **E**

The three bears **398.2**

Trains **625.1**

Trucks **629.224**

(il) Ginsburg, M. Good morning, chick **E**

(il) Kalan, R. Jump, frog, jump! **E**

(il) My bus **E**

(il) The paper airplane book **629**

(il) Sharmat, M. W. Gila monsters meet you at the airport **E**

Barton, Chris

The amazing age of John Roy Lynch **92**

The Day-Glo brothers **535.6**

Shark vs. train **E**

Barton, Clara, 1821-1912

About

Krensky, S. Clara Barton **92**

Rosenberg, A. The Civil War **920**

Somervill, B. A. Clara Barton **92**

Wade, M. D. Amazing civil war nurse Clara Barton **92**

Barton, Hazel

About

Jackson, D. M. Extreme scientists **509**

Barton, Jill

(il) Hest, A. Guess who, Baby Duck! **E**

(il) Two little monkeys **E**

(il) Waddell, M. It's quacking time! **E**

Barton, Michael

(il) It's raining cats and dogs **616.85**

Barton, Patrice

(il) I like old clothes **E**

(il) The invisible boy **E**

(il) Millard, G. Layla, Queen of hearts **Fic**

(il) Mine! **E**

(il) The naming of Tishkin Silk **Fic**

(il) Wortche, A. Rosie Sprout's time to shine **E**

(il) The year of the baby **Fic**

(il) The year of the fortune cookie **Fic**

Bartone, Elisa

Peppe the lamplighter **E**

Bartram, Simon

Bob's best ever friend **E**

(il) Lewis, J. P. Once upon a tomb **811**

Baruzzi, Agnese

The true story of Little Red Riding Hood **E**

BASANT FESTIVAL -- FICTION

Khan, R. King for a day **E**

Base, Graeme

Animalia **E**

Enigma **Fic**

The Jewel Fish of Karnak **E**

The water hole **E**

Baseball. McClellan, R. **796.357**

BASEBALL

See also Ball games; Sports

Bertoletti, J. C. How baseball managers use math **796.357**

Bildner, P. The unforgettable season **796.357**

Bonnet, R. L. Home run! **530**

Borden, L. Baseball is... **E**

Bow, J. Baseball science **796.357**

Buckley, J. Ultimate guide to baseball **796.357**

Burleigh, R. Home run **811**

Bash, Barbara
Desert giant **583**
Urban roosts: where birds nest in the city **598**
(il) Sayre, A. P. Dig, wait, listen **E**
(il) Schaefer, L. M. What's up, what's down? **E**
Basher basics [series]
Budzik, M. Punctuation: the write stuff! **428**
Basher science [series]
Green, D. Algebra & geometry **516.2**
Basher, Simon
ABC Kids **E**
Dingle, A. The periodic table **546**
Gilpin, D. Planet Earth **550**
Go! go! Bobo: colors **E**
Green, D. Chemistry **540**
Green, D. Math **510**
Human body **612**
Oceans **551.46**
(il) Budzik, M. Punctuation: the write stuff! **428**
(il) Dinosaurs **567.9**
(il) Extreme biology **570**
(il) Green, D. Algebra & geometry **516.2**
(il) Green, D. Astronomy **520**
(il) Green, D. Physics **530**
(il) Green, D. Rocks and minerals **552**
BASHFULNESS -- FICTION
Kirk, D. A friend's tale **E**
Levine, K. The lions of Little Rock **Fic**
Srinivasan, D. Octopus alone **E**
Basho and the river stones. Myers, T. **E**
Basic biographies [series]
Amoroso, C. Charles Schulz **92**
Amoroso, C. Helen Keller **92**
Amoroso, C. Jackie Robinson **92**
Amoroso, C. Rosa Parks **92**
Kesselring, S. Albert Einstein **92**
Kesselring, S. Barack Obama **92**
Kesselring, S. Michelle Obama **92**
Kesselring, S. Thomas Edison **92**
BASIC LIFE SKILLS See Life skills
BASIC RIGHTS See Civil rights; Human rights
Basil's birds. Reed, L. R. **E**
BASKET MAKING
See also Weaving
La Valley, J. The Vine basket **Fic**
Basketball. Labrecque, E. **796.323**
Basketball. Robinson, T. **796.323**
Basketball. Yancey, D. **796.323**
Basketball. Slade, S. **796.323**
BASKETBALL
See also Ball games; Sports
Basketball. Gifford, C. **796.323**
Basketball. McClellan, R. **796.323**
BASKETBALL -- BIOGRAPHY
Basketball belles **796.323**
Gatto, K. Lebron James **92**

Wilner, B. Kevin Garnett **92**
Yasuda, A. Lebron James **92**
BASKETBALL -- FICTION
Abdul-Jabbar, K. Sasquatch in the paint **Fic**
Lupica, M. Play Makers **Fic**
Stealing the game **Fic**
BASKETBALL -- HISTORY
Wyckoff, E. B. The man who invented basketball **92**
BASKETBALL -- POETRY
Burleigh, R. Hoops **811**
BASKETBALL -- UNITED STATES -- HISTORY
Coy, J. Hoop genius **E**
Basketball Bats. Hicks, B. **Fic**
Basketball belles. **796.323**
BASKETBALL COACHES
Wyckoff, E. B. The man who invented basketball: James Naismith and his amazing game **92**
Basketball disasters. Mills, C. **Fic**
BASKETBALL PLAYERS
Basketball belles **796.323**
Cooper, F. Jump! **92**
Gatto, K. Lebron James **92**
Jordan, D. Salt in his shoes **E**
Krull, K. Lives of the athletes **796**
Thornley, S. Kobe Bryant **796.323**
Thornley, S. Tim Duncan **796.323**
Wilner, B. Kevin Garnett **92**
Yasuda, A. Lebron James **92**
Basketball step-by-step. Burns, B. **796.323**
BASKETBALL TEAMS
See also Basketball; Sports teams
Basketballs. Blaxland, W. **688.7**
BASKETS -- FICTION
Raven, M. Circle unbroken **E**
Baskin, Nora Raleigh
Baskin, N. R. Anything but typical **Fic**
The truth about my Bat Mitzvah **Fic**
Baskin, Nora Raleigh, 1961-
Anything but typical **Fic**
Runt **Fic**
Basman, Michael
Chess for kids **794.1**
Bass, Hester
The secret world of Walter Anderson **92**
Seeds of freedom **323.1**
Bass, L. G.
Boom boom go away! **E**
Bass, Scott
Kayaking **797.1**
Bassis, Volodymyr
Ukraine **947.7**
Bastedo, Jamie
Free as the wind **E**
Bastianich, Lidia
Nonna's birthday surprise **E**

Keister, D. To grandmother's house **951**

Beil, Karen Magnuson
Jack's house **E**

Beil, Michael D.
The Red Blazer Girls: the ring of Rocamadour **Fic**
The Red Blazer Girls: The vanishing violin **Fic**
Beil, M. The Red Blazer Girls: the mistaken masterpiece **Fic**

Being Bee. Bateson, C. **Fic**
Being caribou. Heuer, K. **599.65**
Being me. Moss, W. **158**
Being Teddy Roosevelt. Mills, C. **Fic**

Beingessner, Laura
(il) Sail away with me **808.81**
(il) Schwartz, J. Our corner grocery store **E**

Bekkering, Annalise
Bats **599.4**
Frogs **597.8**
NCAA Basketball **796.323**

Bekoff, Marc
Jasper's story **599.78**

Belanger, Jeff
What it's like **179**

BELFAST (NORTHERN IRELAND) -- FICTION
Bunting, E. Walking to school **E**

Belford, Kevin
(il) Hubbard, C. Game, set, match, champion Arthur Ashe **92**

Belgium. Indovino, S. C. **949.304**

BELGIUM
Indovino, S. C. Belgium **949.304**

BELGIUM -- FICTION
Barnett, M. Oh no! Not again! **E**

BELIEF AND DOUBT
See also Philosophy; Theory of knowledge
Belinda, the ballerina. Young, A. **E**
Belize. Jermyn, L. **972.82**

BELIZE
Jermyn, L. Belize **972.82**

The **bell** bandit. Davies, J. **Fic**
Bell Hoot fables [series]
Berkeley, J. The hidden boy **Fic**

Bell, Alexander Graham, 1847-1922
About
Garmon, A. Alexander Graham Bell invents **92**

Bell, Cathleen Davitt
Little blog on the prairie **Fic**

Bell, Cece
(il) Angleberger, T. Crankee Doodle **E**
(il) Bug patrol **E**
El deafo **741.5**
Itty bitty **E**
Rabbit and Robot **E**

Bell, Gertrude Margaret Lowthian, 1868-1926
About
Krull, K. Lives of extraordinary women **920**

Bell, Jennifer
(il) Bauer, M. D. Little dog, lost **Fic**
(il) When a dad says "I love you" **E**
(il) When a grandpa says "I love you" **E**

Bell, Krista
If the shoe fits **Fic**

Bell-Rehwoldt, Sheri
The kids' guide to building cool stuff **745.5**
The kids' guide to classic games **790.1**
The kids' guide to jumping rope **796.2**
Science experiments that surprise and delight **507.8**
Speaking secret codes **652**

Bella and Stella come home. Denise, A. **E**
Bella at midnight. Stanley, D. **Fic**
Bella loves Bunny. McPhail, D. **E**

Bellairs, John
The house with a clock in its walls **Fic**
Strickland, B. The sign of the sinister sorcerer **Fic**
Belle Prater's boy. White, R. **Fic**
Belle Teal. Martin, A. M. **Fic**
Belle, the last mule at Gee's Bend. **E**

Beller, Susan Provost
Billy Yank and Johnny Reb **973.7**
The doughboys over there **940.4**
Roman legions on the march **937**

BELLES LETTRES *See* Literature
The **Bellmaker.** Jacques, B. **Fic**

Belloc, Hilaire
Jim who ran away from his nurse and was eaten by a lion **E**

BELLS
See also Musical instruments

BELLS -- FICTION
Preus, M. The Peace Bell **E**
The **belly** book. Harris, J. **E**
The **belly** book. Manushkin, F. **E**

BELLY DANCING
See also Dance
Belly up. Gibbs, S. **Fic**
Below. Crews, N. **E**
Below. McKinlay, M. **Fic**

Belton, Robyn
Herbert **E**

BELTS AND BELTING
See also Machinery

Beltz, Ellin
Frogs: inside their remarkable world **597.8**
Beluga whales. Landau, E. **599.5**

Bemelmans, Ludwig
Madeline **E**
Madeline and the bad hat **E**
Madeline's rescue **E**
Ben and me. Lawson, R. **Fic**
Ben and the Emancipation Proclamation. Sherman, P. **E**
Ben draws trouble. **E**

(il) How Mama brought the spring **E**

(il) Stanley, D. Roughing it on the Oregon Trail **Fic**

(il) Weeks, S. Woof **E**

Berry, Lynne

Duck skates **E**

What floats in a moat? **E**

Berry, Matt

Up on Daddy's shoulders **E**

Berry, Minta

What comes in sets? **511.3**

Bersani, Shennen

(il) Harvey, J. Astro the Steller sea lion **599.79**

(il) Pallotta, J. Ocean counting **E**

Berthod, Anne

Ali, R. Slumgirl dreaming **92**

Bertholf, Bret

Long gone lonesome history of country music **781.642**

Bertoletti, John C.

How baseball managers use math **796.357**

How fashion designers use math **746.9**

Bertrand, Diane Gonzales

Adelita and the veggie cousins **E**

Bertrand, Lynne

Granite baby **E**

Beryl. Simmons, J. **Fic**

Besel, Jennifer

(ed) Gaming safely **794.8**

Beshore, George W.

Science in ancient China **509**

Beskow, Elsa

Princess Sylvie **E**

Bessica Lefter bites back. Tracy, K. **Fic**

The **best** bad luck I ever had. Levine, K. **Fic**

The **best** beekeeper of Lalibela. Kessler, C. **E**

Best best friends. Chodos-Irvine, M. **E**

The **best** bike ride ever. Proimos, J. **E**

The **best** birthday parties ever! **793.2**

The **best** birthday party ever. Huget, J. L. **E**

BEST BOOKS

Freeman, J. Books kids will sit still for 3 **011.6**

Garcha, R. The world of Islam in literature for youth **016**

Gates, P. Cultural Journeys **372**

Keane, N. J. 101 great, ready-to-use book lists for children **028.5**

Matthew, K. I. Neal-Schuman guide to recommended children's books and media for use with every elementary subject **011.6**

Zbaracki, M. D. Best books for boys **028.5**

BEST BOOKS

See also Books

BEST BOOKS -- UNITED STATES

Barr, C. Best books for children **011.62**

Silvey, A. Children's book-a-day almanac **011.62**

Zvirin, S. Read with me **028.5**

Best books for boys. Zbaracki, M. D. **028.5**

Best books for children. Barr, C. **011.62**

Best buds. Eaton, M. **E**

The **best** cat in the world. Newman, L. **E**

The **best** children's books of the year. Child Study Children's Book Committee at Bank Street **016**

The **best** Christmas pageant ever. Robinson, B. **Fic**

The **best** Eid ever. Mobin-Uddin, A. **E**

The **best** family in the world. Lopez, S. **E**

Best friend on wheels. Shirley, D. **E**

Best friends. Kellogg, S. **E**

BEST FRIENDS -- FICTION

Ain, B. Starring Jules (in drama-rama) **Fic**

Baker, B. Digby and Kate and the beautiful day **E**

Berk, J. Strike three, you're dead **Fic**

Carnesi, M. Sleepover with Beatrice and Bear **E**

Cat & Bunny **E**

Catalanotto, P. More of Monkey & Robot **E**

Cerra, K. O. Just a drop of water **Fic**

Cheng, A. The year of the book **Fic**

Cotler, S. Cheesie Mack is running like crazy! **Fic**

Dowell, F. O. R. The sound of your voice, only really far away **Fic**

English, K. Nikki & Deja **FIC**

Federle, T. Five, six, seven, Nate! **Fic**

Fort **Fic**

Green, T. Force out **Fic**

Harper, C. M. Just Grace gets crafty **Fic**

The imaginary **Fic**

Johnson, V. The great Greene heist **Fic**

Kinard, K. The boy prediction **Fic**

Kirk, D. Ten thank-yous **E**

Magaziner, L. The only thing worse than witches **Fic**

Mass, W. The last present **Fic**

Moonpenny Island **Fic**

Nyeu, T. Squid and Octopus **E**

Spooky friends **E**

Stick and Stone **E**

Stone, P. The boy on Cinnamon Street **Fic**

Weissman, E. B. The short seller **Fic**

Wish girl **Fic**

The year of the baby **Fic**

Yee, W. H. Mouse and Mole, secret valentine **E**

Best friends and drama queens. Cabot, M. **Fic**

Best friends forever. Patt, B. **Fic**

The **best** gift of all. Emmett, J. **E**

Best holiday books [series]

MacMillan, D. M. Diwali--Hindu festival of lights **394.26**

MacMillan, D. M. Ramadan and Id al-Fitr **297.3**

The **best** horse ever. DeLaCroix, A. **Fic**

The **best** nest. Mueller, D. L. **398.2**

Best of the best. Green, T. **Fic**

The **best** of times. Tang, G. **513**

The **best** place. Meddaugh, S. **E**

Big red barn. Brown, M. W.　　　　　　　　E

The big red horse. Scanlan, L.　　　　　798.4

Big red kangaroo.　　　　　　　　　　599.2

Big red lollipop. Khan, R.　　　　　　　E

Big rig. Swenson, J. A.　　　　　　　　E

Big rig bugs. Cyrus, K.　　　　　　　　E

Big rigs on the move. Ransom, C. F.　　629.224

Big scary monster. Docherty, T.　　　　E

Big sister now. Sheldon, A.　　　　　306.8

Big Smelly Bear. Teckentrup, B.　　　　E

The big snow. Hader, B.　　　　　　　E

The big snuggle-up.　　　　　　　　　E

The big splash. Ferraiolo, J. D.　　　　Fic

The big storm. Tafuri, N.　　　　　　　E

The big swim. Fagan, C.　　　　　　　Fic

Big talk. Fleischman, P.　　　　　　　811

The big test. Danneberg, J.　　　　　　E

The big time. Green, T.　　　　　　　Fic

Big Top Otto. Slavin, B.　　　　　　741.5

Big tracks, little tracks. Selsam, M. E.　590

The big wet balloon. Liniers　　　　　741.5

Big wheels. Rockwell, A. F.　　　　　　E

Big wig. Krull, K.　　　　　　　　　391

The big wish. Conahan, C.　　　　　　E

Big Wolf & Little Wolf. Brun-Cosme, N.　E

Big words for little people. Curtis, J. L.　E

Bigda, Diane

(il) Park, L. S. Mung-mung!　　　　413

BIGFOOT See Sasquatch

Bigfoot Boy [series]

Into the woods　　　　　　　　　　741.5

The Sound of Thunder　　　　　　　741.5

The unkindness of ravens　　　　　　741.5

Bigger isn't always better. Simons, R.　613.2

Bigger than a bread box. Snyder, L.　　Fic

Bigger, Better, BEST! Murphy, S. J.　　516

The biggest bear. Ward, L. K.　　　　E

Biggest bugs life-size. Beccaloni, G.　595.7

The biggest kiss. Walsh, J.　　　　　E

The biggest test in the universe. Poydar, N.　E

Biggest, strongest, fastest. Jenkins, S.　590

Biggs, Brian

(il) Brownie & Pearl go for a spin　　E

(il) By sea　　　　　　　　　　　　E

Everything goes in the air　　　　　　E

Everything goes: On land　　　　　　629

EllRay Jakes Rocks the Holidays!　　Fic

(il) Frank Einstein & the antimatter motor　Fic

Frank Einstein and the Electro-Finger　Fic

(il) Rylant, C. Brownie & Pearl grab a bite　E

(il) Rylant, C. Brownie & Pearl hit the hay　E

(il) Rylant, C. Brownie & Pearl see the sights　E

(il) Rylant, C. Brownie & Pearl step out　E

(il) Rylant, C. Brownie & Pearl take a dip　E

Bigmama's. Crews, D.　　　　　　　92

BIGOTRY See Prejudices; Toleration

BIGOTRY-MOTIVATED CRIMES　See　Hate
crimes

BIKES See Bicycles

Bikes on the move. Clark, W.　　　629.227

BIKING See Cycling

Bildner, Phil

The greatest game ever played　　　　E

The Hallelujah Flight　　　　　　　　E

Shoeless Joe & Black Betsy　　　　　E

The soccer fence　　　　　　　　　　E

Turkey Bowl　　　　　　　　　　　E

The unforgettable season　　　　　796.357

BILDUNGSROMANS

Hayles, M. Breathing room　　　　　Fic

Leeds, C. The unfortunate son　　　　Fic

Robinson, M. L. Bright Island　　　　Fic

Rupp, R. After Eli　　　　　　　　　Fic

Spinelli, J. Hokey Pokey　　　　　　Fic

Standiford, N. The secret tree　　　　Fic

Who could that be at this hour?　　　Fic

Bileck, Marvin

Scheer, J. Rain makes applesauce　　　E

BILINGUAL BOOKS

See also Books; Editions

BILINGUAL BOOKS -- ENGLISH-ARABIC

Addasi, M. Time to pray　　　　　　　E

BILINGUAL BOOKS -- ENGLISH-CHINESE

Keister, D. To grandmother's house　951

BILINGUAL BOOKS -- ENGLISH-CREE

Wild berries　　　　　　　　　　　E

BILINGUAL BOOKS -- ENGLISH-DARI

King, D. I see the sun in Afghanistan　E

BILINGUAL BOOKS -- ENGLISH-HMONG

Gerdner, L. Grandfather's story cloth　E

BILINGUAL BOOKS -- ENGLISH-JAPANESE

Art and life in rural Japan　　　　　952

Carle, E. Where are you going? To see my friend!　E

BILINGUAL BOOKS -- ENGLISH-SPANISH

Call me tree　　　　　　　　　　　E

Colato Laínez, R. Señor Pancho had a rancho　E

BILINGUAL BOOKS -- SPANISH-ENGLISH

See Bilingual books -- English-Spanish

BILINGUAL EDUCATION

Diamant-Cohen, B. Early literacy programming en
Espanol　　　　　　　　　　　　027.6

BILINGUAL EDUCATION

See also Bilingualism; Multicultural education

BILINGUALISM

See also Language and languages

BILINGUALISM -- FICTION

Colato Laínez, R. Señor Pancho had a rancho　E

Harris, T. Say something, Perico　　　E

The Bill Martin Jr. Big book of poetry.　811

The Bill of Rights. Baxter, R.　　　342.73

The Bill of Rights in translation. Leavitt, A. J.　342

The Penderwicks on Gardam Street   **Fic**

Birdseye, Tom

Storm Mountain   **Fic**

Birdsong. Sandall, E.   **E**

BIRDSONGS

Judge, L. Bird talk   **598**

BIRDSONGS

See also Animal sounds

BIRDSONGS -- FICTION

Portis, A. Froodle   **E**

Birkemoe, Karen

Strike a pose   **613.7**

BIRMINGHAM (ALA.) -- RACE RELATIONS

Brimner, L. D. Birmingham Sunday   **323.1**

BIRMINGHAM (ALA.) -- RACE RELATIONS -- POETRY

Weatherford, C. B. Birmingham, 1963   **811**

Birmingham Sunday. Brimner, L. D.   **323.1**

Birmingham, 1963. Weatherford, C. B.   **811**

Birmingham, Christian

(il) Haddon, M. Footprints on the Moon   **E**

Birmingham, Maria

Weird zone   **796.1**

Birney, Betty G.

Adventure according to Humphrey   **Fic**

Friendship according to Humphrey   **Fic**

The seven wonders of Sassafras Springs   **Fic**

Summer according to Humphrey   **Fic**

Surprises according to Humphrey   **Fic**

Trouble according to Humphrey   **Fic**

The world according to Humphrey   **Fic**

BIRTH *See* Childbirth

BIRTH -- FICTION

Il Sung Na A book of babies   **E**

BIRTH ATTENDANTS *See* Midwives

BIRTH CONTROL

See also Population; Sexual hygiene

BIRTH CONTROL -- ETHICAL ASPECTS

See also Ethics

BIRTH CUSTOMS *See* Childbirth

BIRTH DEFECTS -- FICTION

Palacio, R. J. Wonder   **Fic**

BIRTH ORDER

See also Children; Family

BIRTH ORDER -- FICTION

Crow, K. The middle-child blues   **E**

Birtha, Becky

Grandmama's pride   **E**

Lucky beans   **E**

The **birthday** ball. Lowry, L.   **Fic**

BIRTHDAY BOOKS

See also Birthdays; Calendars

The **birthday** box. Patricelli, L.   **E**

A **birthday** cake is no ordinary cake. Frasier, D.   **E**

BIRTHDAY PARTIES -- FICTION

Browne, A. What if...?   **E**

Mann, J. K. Two speckled eggs   **E**

The **birthday** pet. Javernick, E.   **E**

The **birthday** room. Henkes, K.   **Fic**

The **birthday** storm. Draper, S. M.   **Fic**

Birthday suit.   **E**

The **birthday** tree. Fleischman, P.   **E**

Birthday zoo. Rose, D. L.   **E**

BIRTHDAYS

The best birthday parties ever!   **793.2**

Danziger, P. It's Justin Time, Amber Brown   **E**

Elya, S. M. F is for fiesta   **E**

Horse, H. Little Rabbit lost   **E**

Rose, D. L. Birthday zoo   **E**

BIRTHDAYS -- FICTION

Bastianich, L. Nonna's birthday surprise   **E**

Beaty, A. Happy Birthday, Madame Chapeau   **E**

Brown, M. Marisol McDonald and the clash bash

Jessica Finch in Pig Trouble   **E**

Lester, H. Happy birdday, Tacky!   **E**

Mann, J. K. Two speckled eggs   **E**

Mass, W. The last present   **Fic**

Otto's backwards day   **741.5**

The Penderwicks in spring   **Fic**

Princess pistachio   **E**

Schneider, J. The meanest birthday girl   **E**

The seven silly eaters   **E**

Standiford, N. Switched at birthday   **Fic**

Bisaillon, Josee

Salas, L. P. Bookspeak!   **811**

Tibo, G. My diary   **E**

Wiviott, M. Benno and the Night of Broken Glass   **E**

Biscuit. Capucilli, A.   **E**

Biscuit's new trick. Capucilli, A.   **E**

Bishop, Gavin

(il) Cowley, J. Snake and Lizard   **Fic**

(il) Mister Whistler   **Fic**

Bishop, Kay

The collection program in schools   **027.8**

Connecting libraries with classrooms   **375**

Bishop, Nic

Butterflies   **595.7**

(il) Chasing cheetahs   **599.75**

(il) Cowley, J. Chameleon chameleon   **597.95**

(il) Cowley, J. Red-eyed tree frog   **597.8**

Digging for bird-dinosaurs   **567.9**

Jackson, E. B. The mysterious universe   **523.8**

Lizards   **597.95**

(il) Montgomery, S. Kakapo rescue   **639.9**

(il) Montgomery, S. Quest for the tree kangaroo   **599.2**

(il) Montgomery, S. Saving the ghost of the mountain   **599.75**

(il) Montgomery, S. The snake scientist   **597.96**

(il) Montgomery, S. The tarantula scientist   **595.4**

Nic Bishop butterflies and moths   **595.7**

Nic Bishop frogs   **597.8**

See also Children

Black cowboy, wild horses. Lester, J. **E**
The **Black** Death. Ollhoff, J. **616.9**
BLACK DEATH *See* Plague
Black dog. Pinfold, L. **E**
Black Elk, 1863-1950
About
Nelson, S. D. Black Elk's vision **92**
Black hands, white sails. McKissack, P. C. **639.2**
The black heart crypt. Grabenstein, C. **Fic**
Black history in the pages of children's literature. Casement, R. **028.5**
A black hole is not a hole. **523.8**
Black holes. Rau, D. M. **523.8**
BLACK HOLES (ASTRONOMY)
A black hole is not a hole **523.8**
Jackson, E. B. The mysterious universe **523.8**
Rau, D. M. Black holes **523.8**
Venezia, M. Stephen Hawking **92**
Waxman, L. H. Exploring black holes **523.8**
BLACK HOLES (ASTRONOMY)
See also Astronomy; Astrophysics; Stars
BLACK HUMOR (LITERATURE)
See also Fiction; Literature; Wit and humor
Black ice. Lane, A. **Fic**
Black is brown is tan. Adoff, A. **E**
Black Jack: the ballad of Jack Johnson. Smith, C. R. **92**
BLACK LIBRARIANS
See also Librarians
Black magic. Johnson, D. **E**
BLACK MAGIC (WITCHCRAFT) *See* Magic; Witchcraft
BLACK MARKET
See also Commerce
BLACK MUSIC
See also Music
BLACK MUSICIANS
See also Musicians
BLACK MUSLIM LEADERS
Gunderson, J. X: the biography of Malcolm X **92**
Malcolm X **92**
Black on white. Hoban, T. **E**
BLACK PANTHER PARTY -- FICTION.
Williams-Garcia, R. One crazy summer **Fic**
Black pearls. Hawes, L. **S**
Black pioneers [series]
Hansen, J. Home is with our family **Fic**
BLACK POETRY (AMERICAN) *See* American poetry -- African American authors
The **Black** rabbit. Leathers, P. **E**
Black radishes. Meyer, S. **Fic**
The black reckoning. **Fic**
Black spiny-tailed iguana. Lunis, N. **597.95**
The **Black** Stallion. Farley, W. **Fic**
Black widows. Markle, S. **595.4**

BLACK WOMEN
See also Women
Black, Angela
Sheehan, S. Jamaica **972.92**
Black, Ann N.
Readers theatre for middle school boys **812**
Black, Holly, 1971-
Doll bones **Fic**
The iron trial **Fic**
Black, Jess
A year in the life of Bindi **333.72**
Black, Michael Ian
Chicken cheeks **E**
A pig parade is a terrible idea **E**
Black, Peter Jay
Urban outlaws **Fic**
Black? white! day? night! Seeger, L. V. **E**
Blackaby, Susan
Brownie Groundhog and the February fox **E**
Cleopatra **92**
Nest, nook & cranny **811**
Blackall, Sophie
(il) The 9 lives of Alexander Baddenfield **Fic**
(il) And two boys booed **E**
Are you awake? **E**
The baby tree **E**
(il) Barrows, A. Ivy + Bean **Fic**
(il) Barrows, A. Ivy + Bean and the ghost that had to go **Fic**
(il) Barrows, A. Ivy + Bean bound to be bad **Fic**
(il) Barrows, A. Ivy + Bean break the fossil record **Fic**
(il) Barrows, A. Ivy + Bean take care of the babysitter **Fic**
(il) Barrows, A. Ivy + Bean: doomed to dance **Fic**
(il) Barrows, A. Ivy + Bean: what's the big idea? **Fic**
(il) Best, C. What's so bad about being an only child? **E**
(il) Bridges, S. Y. Ruby's wish **E**
(il) Edwin speaks up **E**
(il) Khan, R. Big red lollipop **E**
(il) Lord and Lady Bunny -- almost royalty! **Fic**
(il) Manners mash-up: a goofy guide to good behavior **395**
(il) The mighty Lalouche **E**
(il) Mr. and Mrs. Bunny-- detectives extraordinaire! **FIC**
(il) Noyes, D. Red butterfly **E**
(il) Pecan pie baby **E**
(il) Rosoff, M. Jumpy Jack and Googily **E**
(il) Rosoff, M. Meet wild boars **E**
(il) Shields, C. D. Wombat walkabout **E**
Spinster Goose **811**
Blackbeard, 1680?-1718
About

Blessing, Charlotte
New old shoes **E**
Blexbolex
People **E**
Seasons **E**
Bley, Anette
And what comes after a thousand? **E**
Blia Xiong
Nine-in-one, Grr! Grr! **398.2**
BLIMPS *See* Airships
BLIND
Adler, D. A. A picture book of Louis Braille **686.2**
Alexander, S. H. She touched the world: Laura Bridgman, deaf-blind pioneer **92**
Amoroso, C. Helen Keller **92**
Bender, L. Explaining blindness **617.7**
Delano, M. F. Helen's eyes **92**
Freedman, R. Out of darkness: the story of Louis Braille **92**
Lawlor, L. Helen Keller: rebellious spirit **92**
Markle, S. Lost sight **617.7**
My three best friends and me, Zulay **E**
Saltypie **92**
Sullivan, G. Helen Keller **92**
BLIND -- BOOKS AND READING
Adler, D. A. A picture book of Louis Braille **686.2**
Freedman, R. Out of darkness: the story of Louis Braille **92**
Jeffrey, L. S. All about Braille **411**
BLIND -- BOOKS AND READING
See also Books and reading
BLIND -- FICTION
Pinkwater, D. M. Mrs. Noodlekugel and four blind mice **Fic**
Yuko-chan and the Daruma doll **E**
BLINDNESS
See also Vision disorders
Blink of an eye. Superfast animals! [series]
Lunis, N. Black spiny-tailed iguana **597.95**
Lunis, N. California sea lion **599.7**
Lunis, N. Cheetah **599.75**
Lunis, N. Greyhound **636.7**
Lunis, N. Peregrine falcon **598**
Lunis, N. Pronghorn **599.6**
Bliss, Harry
Bailey **E**
Luke on the loose **741.5**
(il) Cronin, D. Diary of a fly **E**
(il) Cronin, D. Diary of a spider **E**
(il) Diary of a worm **E**
(il) DiCamillo, K. Louise **E**
(il) Invisible Inkling **Fic**
(il) McGhee, A. Mrs. Watson wants your teeth **E**
(il) McGhee, A. A very brave witch **E**
Bliss, John
Art that moves **791.43**

Preening, painting, and piercing **391**
Blitt, Barry
(il) The adventures of Mark Twain by Huckleberry Finn **92**
The Founding Fathers **920**
Kloske, G. Once upon a time, the end **E**
(il) While you were napping **E**
(il) Wilson, K. What's the weather inside? **811**
Blitzed by a blizzard! Markovics, J. L. **551.55**
Blizzard. Rocco, J. **E**
Blizzard of glass. Walker, S. M. **971**
BLIZZARDS
Fleisher, P. Lightning, hurricanes, and blizzards **551.55**
Markovics, J. L. Blitzed by a blizzard! **551.55**
Stewart, M. Blizzards and winter storms **551.55**
BLIZZARDS
See also Storms
BLIZZARDS -- FICTION
Rocco, J. Blizzard **E**
BLIZZARDS -- GRAPHIC NOVELS
Wetterer, M. K. The snowshoeing adventure of Milton Daub, blizzard trekker **741.5**
Blizzards and winter storms. Stewart, M. **551.55**
Blobaum, Cindy
Awesome snake science **597.96**
Explore money! **332.4**
Geology rocks! **551**
Insectigation! **595.7**
Bloch, Serge
Butterflies in my stomach and other school hazards **E**
(il) Cali, D. The enemy **E**
(il) I dare you not to yawn **E**
(il) I scream ice cream! **E**
(il) Lewis, J. P. The underwear salesman **811**
(il) Morgenstern, S. H. A book of coupons **Fic**
(il) My snake Blake **E**
Snowed under and other Christmas confusions **E**
Block city. Stevenson, R. L. **E**
Block, Francesca Lia
House of dolls **Fic**
Block, Ira
(il) Lange, K. E. 1607 **975.5**
Blockhead. D'Agnese, J. **92**
BLOGS *See* Weblogs
BLOGS -- FICTION
Rivers, K. Finding Ruby Starling **Fic**
Blogs, wikis, podcasts, and other powerful Web tools for classrooms. Richardson, W. **371.3**
Blom, Jen K.
Possum summer **Fic**
Blomgren, Jennifer
Where do I sleep? **E**
BLOOD
Kyi, T. L. Seeing red **612.1**

Newquist, H. The book of blood 612.1
Showers, P. A drop of blood 612.1
Venezia, M. Charles Drew 92

BLOOD
See also Physiology

BLOOD -- CIRCULATION
Corcoran, M. K. The circulatory story 612.1
Yount, L. William Harvey 92

BLOOD -- DISEASES
See also Diseases

BLOOD GROUPS
See also Blood

The **blood** guard. Roy, C. Fic
The **blood** lie. Vernick, S. R. Fic
Blood moon rider. Waters, Z. C. Fic
The **blood** of Olympus. Riordan, R. Fic
Blood on the river. Carbone, E. L. Fic

BLOOD PRESSURE
See also Blood

BLOODSUCKING ANIMALS
Knapp, R. Bloodsucking creatures 591.5
Bloodsucking creatures. Knapp, R. 591.5
Bloom! Lieshout, M. v. E

Bloom, Suzanne
(il) Alone together E
(il) Bunting, E. Girls A to Z E
(il) Bunting, E. My special day at Third Street
School E
Feeding friendsies E
A splendid friend, indeed E

Bloom, Tom
(il) While You Were Sleeping 031.02
Bloomability. Creech, S. Fic

Bloomfield, Alan
Jennings, M. Baseball step-by-step 796.357

Bloomfield, Jill
Jewish holidays cookbook 641.5

Blos, Joan W.
A gathering of days: a New England girl's journal,
1830-32 Fic
Letters from the corrugated castle Fic

Blount, Marcellus
(ed) African American Poetry 811
Blown away. E
Blue 2. Carter, D. A. E
Blue birds. Fic
The **blue** book on information age inquiry, instruc-
tion and literacy. Callison, D. 028.7
Blue chameleon. Gravett, E. E
Blue chicken. Freedman, D. E
BLUE COLLAR WORKERS *See* Labor; Work-
ing class
The **Blue** fairy book. 398.2
Blue fire. Hardy, J. Fic
The **blue** ghost. Bauer, M. D. Fic
Blue Goose. Tafuri, N. E

The **blue** house dog. Blumenthal, D. E
Blue jasmine. Sheth, K. Fic

BLUE JAY -- FICTION
The Chicken Squad E

BLUE JAYS
Berendt, J. My baby blue jays 598
Blue like Friday. Parkinson, S. Fic
Blue lipstick. Grandits, J. 811
The **Blue** marble. Nardo, D. 525.022
Blue Moo. Boynton, S. 782.42
Blue on blue. E
Blue potatoes, orange tomatoes. Creasy, R. 635

**BLUE RIDGE MOUNTAINS REGION -- FIC-
TION**
McDowell, M. T. Carolina Harmony Fic
The **blue** shoe. Townley, R. Fic
Blue sky. Wood, A. E
Blue whales up close. Rake, J. S. 599.5
Blue willow. Gates, D. Fic

Blue, Rose
Ron's big mission E
Naden, C. J. James Monroe 92
Blue-ribbon dad. Glass, B. R. E
Blueberries for Sal. McCloskey, R. E
Bluebird. Staake, B. E

BLUEBIRDS
Kirby, P. F. What bluebirds do 598

BLUEBIRDS -- FICTION
Staake, B. Bluebird E
Bluefish. Schmatz, P. Fic

BLUEGRASS MUSIC
See also Music

Bluemel Oldfield, Dawn
Leaping ground frogs 597.8

Bluemle, Elizabeth
How do you wokka-wokka? E
Tap tap boom boom E
Blues. Handyside, C. 781.643
Blues journey. Myers, W. D. 811

BLUES MUSIC
Handyside, C. Blues 781.643

BLUES MUSIC
See also African American music; Folk music
-- United States; Popular music

BLUES MUSIC -- FICTION
Crow, K. The middle-child blues E
Harvey, J. My hands sing the blues E
Myers, W. D. The blues of Flats Brown E
Staub, L. Everybody gets the blues E

BLUES (MUSIC) -- HISTORY AND CRITICISM
Adoff, A. Roots and blues 811

BLUES MUSIC -- POETRY
Adoff, A. Roots and blues 811
Myers, W. D. Blues journey 811

BLUES MUSICIANS
Boynton, S. Sandra Boynton's One shoe

blues **782.42**

The **blues** of Flats Brown. Myers, W. D. **E**

BLUES SONGS *See* Blues music

Bluffton. **741.5**

Bluhm, Joe

(il) The fantastic flying books of Mr. Morris Lessmore **E**

Blumberg, Rhoda

Commodore Perry in the land of the Shogun **952**

Shipwrecked!: the true adventures of a Japanese boy **92**

Blume, Judy

Are you there God?, it's me, Margaret **Fic**

Cool zone with the Pain and the Great One **Fic**

Double Fudge **Fic**

Freckle juice **Fic**

Friend or fiend? with the Pain & the Great One **Fic**

Fudge-a-mania **Fic**

Going, going, gone! with the Pain and the Great One **Fic**

Otherwise known as Sheila the Great **Fic**

The Pain and the Great One **E**

Soupy Saturdays with The Pain and The Great One **Fic**

Superfudge **Fic**

Tales of a fourth grade nothing **Fic**

Blume, Lesley M. M.

Cornelia and the audacious escapades of the Somerset sisters **Fic**

The rising star of Rusty Nail **Fic**

Blumenthal, Deborah

The blue house dog **E**

Blumenthal, Karen

Let me play **796**

Mr. Sam **92**

Blundell, Judy

A city tossed and broken **Fic**

Bluthenthal, Diana Cain

(il) Edwards, P. D. The neat line **E**

(il) Viorst, J. Just in case **E**

Bly, Nellie, 1864-1922

About

Macy, S. Bylines: a photobiography of Nellie Bly **92**

Blythe, Gary

(il) Davies, N. Ice bear **599.78**

(il) De Quidt, J. The toymaker **Fic**

(il) Ehrlich, A. A treasury of princess stories **398.2**

Bo at Ballard Creek. Hill, K. **Fic**

Boake, Kathy

(il) Swanson, D. You are weird **612**

BOARD BOOKS FOR CHILDREN

Baby Pig Pig walks **E**

Balouch, K. Feelings **E**

Bancroft, B. W is for wombat **E**

Basher, S. Go! go! Bobo: colors **E**

Boynton, S. Happy Hippo, angry Duck **E**

Brown, H. The robot book **E**

Caterpillar Inc. My big book of trucks & diggers **621.8**

Dahl, M. Nap time for Kitty **E**

Doodler, T. H. What color is Bear's underwear? **E**

Dowdy, L. C. All kinds of kisses **E**

DwellStudio (Firm) Good morning, toucan **E**

DwellStudio (Firm) Goodnight, owl **E**

Emberley, E. Where's my sweetie pie? **E**

Endle, K. Bunny Rabbit in the sunlight **E**

Franceschelli, C. (oliver) **E**

Gershator, P. Who's in the forest? **E**

Global baby girls **E**

Global Fund for Children (Organization) American babies **E**

Global Fund for Children (Organization) Global babies **E**

Henkes, K. A good day **E**

Hills, T. Duck & Goose, it's time for Christmas! **E**

Hoban, T. Black on white **E**

Hoban, T. White on black **E**

Horacek, P. Choo choo **E**

Hubbell, P. Firefighters! speeding! spraying! saving! **E**

Isol It's useful to have a duck **E**

Janovitz, M. Baby baby baby! **E**

Katz, S. ABC, baby me! **E**

Katz, K. How Does Baby Feel? **E**

Kim, S. How does a seed grow? **581.4**

Klinting, L. What do you want? **E**

Kubler, A. Hop a little, jump a little! **398.8**

Kubler, A. Humpty Dumpty **E**

Kubler, A. Pat-a-cake **398.8**

Laden, N. Peek-a-who? **E**

Laval, T. Colors **E**

Lester, J. D. Daddy calls me doodlebug **E**

Lester, J. D. Grandma calls me gigglepie **E**

Lester, J. D. Mommy calls me monkeypants **E**

Light, S. Trains go **E**

Martin, D. Christmas tree **E**

Martin, D. Hanukkah lights **E**

McBratney, S. When I'm big **E**

McPhail, D. Baby Pig Pig talks **E**

Moore, C. C. The night before Christmas **811**

Newman, L. Daddy, papa, and me **E**

Newman, L. Mommy, mama, and me **E**

Night owl **E**

O'Connell, R. The baby goes beep **E**

Patricelli, L. Potty **E**

Patricelli, L. Tubby **E**

Penn, A. A bedtime kiss for Chester Raccoon **E**

Perrin, M. Look who's there! **E**

Perrin, M. What do you see? **E**

Quay, E. Good night, sleep tight **E**

Quay, E. Let's play house **E**

Goodnight Lulu **E**

Bogart, Jo Ellen

Big and small, room for all **E**

The **Boggart**. Cooper, S. **Fic**

The **Boggart** and the monster. Cooper, S. **Fic**

BOGS

See also Wetlands

Boie, Kirsten

The princess plot **Fic**

The princess trap **Fic**

Boiger, Alexandra

(il) Huget, J. L. Thanks a LOT, Emily Post! **E**

(il) MacHale, D. J. The monster princess **E**

(il) Naylor, P. R. Roxie and the Hooligans **Fic**

(il) Orgel, D. Doctor All-Knowing **398.2**

(il) Poor Doreen **E**

(il) Quattlebaum, M. Pirate vs. pirate **E**

(il) Singer, M. Tallulah's tutu **E**

(il) Tallulah's Nutcracker **E**

(il) Tallulah's solo **E**

(il) Tallulah's toe shoes **E**

Boisrobert, Anouck

Popville **E**

Bolam, Emily

(il) Ehrlich, F. Does an elephant take a bath? **E**

(il) Ehrlich, H. M. Louie's goose **E**

(il) Piper, S. I can say a prayer **242**

(il) Ziefert, H. Little Red Riding Hood **398.2**

Bolden, Tonya

Beautiful moon **E**

Capital days **92**

The champ! **92**

Finding family **Fic**

George Washington Carver **92**

Maritcha **92**

Portraits of African-American heroes **920**

Searching for Sarah Rector **92**

Tell all the children our story **305.8**

Boldt, Mike

123 versus ABC **E**

Boles, Philana Marie

Little divas **Fic**

Boling, Katharine

January 1905 **Fic**

Bolivia. Pateman, R. **984**

BOLIVIA

Pateman, R. Bolivia **984**

BOLIVIA -- FICTION

Ellis, D. I am a taxi **Fic**

Ellis, D. Sacred leaf **Fic**

Bollard, John K.

Scholastic children's thesaurus **423**

Bolognese, Don

(il) Brenner, B. Wagon wheels **E**

Bolton, Anne

Pyramids and mummies **932**

Bomb. Sheinkin, S. **623.4**

BOMB ATTACKS *See* Bombings

BOMBERS

See also Airplanes; Military airplanes

BOMBINGS

Brimner, L. D. Birmingham Sunday **323.1**

BOMBINGS

See also Offenses against public safety; Political crimes and offenses; Terrorism

BOMBINGS -- ALABAMA -- BIRMINGHAM

Brimner, L. D. Birmingham Sunday **323.1**

Weatherford, C. B. Birmingham, 1963 **811**

BOMBINGS -- POETRY

Weatherford, C. B. Birmingham, 1963 **811**

Bon appetit! Hartland, J. **641.509**

Bond, Felicia

Big hugs, little hugs **E**

(il) Brown, M. W. Big red barn **E**

(il) Kramer, S. How to think like a scientist **507**

(il) Numeroff, L. J. If you give a dog a donut **E**

(il) Numeroff, L. J. If you give a mouse a cookie **E**

Bond, Higgins

(il) A place for bats **599.4**

(il) Batten, M. Please don't wake the animals **591.5**

(il) Stewart, M. A place for birds **598**

(il) Stewart, M. A place for fish **597**

(il) Stewart, M. A place for frogs **597.8**

Bond, Michael

A bear called Paddington **Fic**

Bond, Nancy

A string in the harp **Fic**

Bond, Rebecca

(il) The house that George built **975.3**

In the belly of an ox: the unexpected photographic adventures of Richard and Cherry Kearton **92**

Bond, Victoria

Zora and me **Fic**

Bondoux, Anne-Laure

A time of miracles **Fic**

BONDS

See also Finance; Investments; Negotiable instruments; Securities; Stock exchanges

Bone [series]

Sniegoski, T. Quest for the spark **Fic**

Bone dog. Rohmann, E. **E**

The **bone** magician. Higgins, F. E. **Fic**

Bone soup. Evans, C. **E**

Bone: out from Boneville. Smith, J. **741.5**

Bone: Rose. Smith, J. **741.5**

Bone: tall tales. Smith, J. **741.5**

Bones. Jenkins, S. **612.7**

Bones. Simon, S. **612.7**

BONES

See also Musculoskeletal system

Baines, R. The bones you own **612.7**

Barner, B. Dem bones **612.7**

(il) Heiligman, D. Cool dog, school dog **E**
(il) Palatini, M. Gorgonzola **E**
Bowers, Vivien
Hey Canada! **971**
Bowhunting. Adamson, T. K. **799.2**
BOWHUNTING
See also Hunting
Bowler, Ann Martin
All about Korea **951.9**
BOWLING -- FICTION
Durand, H. Mitchell goes bowling **E**
BOWLING ALLEYS -- FICTION
Durand, H. Mitchell goes bowling **E**
Box Turtle at Long Pond. George, W. T. **E**
BOXERS (PERSONS)
Adler, D. A. Joe Louis **92**
Bolden, T. The champ! **92**
De la Peña, M. A nation's hope **92**
Myers, W. D. Muhammad Ali **92**
Smith, C. R. Black Jack: the ballad of Jack Johnson **92**
Smith, C. R. Twelve rounds to glory: the story of Muhammad Ali **92**
The **boxes.** Sleator, W. **Fic**
BOXES
Russo, M. The big brown box **E**
Walsh, D. The cardboard box book **745.54**
BOXES -- COLLECTORS AND COLLECTING
See also Collectors and collecting
BOXES -- FICTION
Explorer **S**
TenNapel, D. Cardboard **Fic**
Boxes for Katje. Fleming, C. **E**
Boxing. Mason, P. **796.8**
BOXING
See also Athletics; Self-defense
Lewin, T. At Gleason's gym **796.8**
Mason, P. Boxing **796.8**
BOXING -- BIOGRAPHY
Adler, D. A. Joe Louis **92**
Bolden, T. The champ! **92**
De la Peña, M. A nation's hope **92**
Myers, W. D. Muhammad Ali **92**
Smith, C. R. Black Jack: the ballad of Jack Johnson **92**
Smith, C. R. Twelve rounds to glory: the story of Muhammad Ali **92**
BOXING -- FICTION
Jimmy the greatest! **E**
The mighty Lalouche **E**
The **boy** & the book. **E**
A **boy** and a jaguar. **E**
Boy and Bot. Dyckman, A. **E**
A **boy** and his bot. Wilson, D. H. **Fic**
The **boy** at the end of the world. Van Eekhout, G. **Fic**

A **boy** called Dickens. **Fic**
A **boy** called Slow: the true story of Sitting Bull. Bruchac, J. **92**
Boy dumplings. Compestine, Y. C. **E**
The **boy** from the dragon palace. MacDonald, M. R. **398.2**
A **boy** had a mother who bought him a hat. Kuskin, K. **E**
The **boy** in the dress. Walliams, D. **Fic**
Boy in the garden. Say, A. **E**
The **boy** in the oak. Albarn, J. **Fic**
Boy meets dog. **E**
A **boy** named Beckoning: the true story of Dr. Carlos Montezuma, Native American hero. Capaldi, G. **92**
A **boy** named FDR. Krull, K. **92**
The **boy** of the three-year nap. Snyder, D. **398.2**
The **boy** on Cinnamon Street. Stone, P. **Fic**
The **boy** on Fairfield Street: how Ted Geisel grew up to become Dr. Seuss. **92**
Boy on the lion throne. Kimmel, E. C. **92**
The **boy** prediction. Kinard, K. **Fic**
BOY SCOUTS
See also Boys' clubs; Scouts and scouting
BOY SCOUTS OF AMERICA -- FICTION
Salisbury, G. Night of the howling dogs **Fic**
Boy talk. **612.6**
Boy were we wrong about the solar system! Kudlinski, K. V. **523.2**
The **boy** who bit Picasso. Penrose, A. **92**
The **boy** who climbed into the moon. Almond, D. **Fic**
The **boy** who could fly. Norcliffe, J. **Fic**
The **boy** who cried Bigfoot! Magoon, S. **E**
The **boy** who cried ninja. Latimer, A. **E**
The **boy** who cried wolf. Hennessy, B. G. **398.2**
The **boy** who dared. Bartoletti, S. C. **Fic**
The **boy** who drew birds: a story of John James Audubon. Davies, J. **92**
The **boy** who harnessed the wind. Kamkwamba, W. **92**
The **boy** who invented TV. **92**
The **boy** who lost Fairyland. **Fic**
The **boy** who loved math. Heiligman, D. **510.92**
The **boy** who loved to draw: Benjamin West. Brenner, B. **92**
The **boy** who loved words. Schotter, R. **E**
The **boy** who painted dragons. Demi **E**
The **boy** who saved Cleveland. Giblin, J. **Fic**
The **Boy** who swam with piranhas. Almond, D. **Fic**
Boy wonders. Brown, C. **E**
A **boy,** a dog, and a frog. Mayer, M. **E**
Boy, Bird, and Dog. McPhail, D. M. **E**
The **boy,** the bear, the baron, the bard. **E**
Boy, were we wrong about dinosaurs! Kudlinski, K. V. **567.9**
Boyce, Natalie Pope

Bradbury, Judy
The read-aloud scaffold **372.47**
Bradby, Marie
Momma, where are you from? **E**
More than anything else **E**
Bradford, Chris
Young samurai: the way of the sword **Fic**
Young samurai: the way of the warrior **Fic**
Bradford, June
(il) MacLeod, E. Bake and make amazing cookies **641.8**
(il) MacLeod, E. Chock full of chocolate **641.6**
(il) Sadler, J. A. Embroidery **746.44**
(il) Sadler, J. A. Hemp jewelry **746.42**
Bradford, Wade
Why do I have to make my bed? **E**
Bradley, Kimberly Brubaker
Ballerino Nate **E**
Energy makes things happen **531**
Forces make things move **531**
Jefferson's sons **Fic**
The perfect pony **E**
Pop! **530.4**
The war that saved my life **Fic**
Bradley, Timothy J.
Paleo bugs **560**
Bradman, Tony
(ed) Under the weather **S**
Bradshaw, Carrie Anne, 1976-
(il) Track that scat! **591.47**
Brady, Hana
About
Levine, K. Hana's suitcase **940.53**
Levine, K. Hana's suitcase on stage **812**
Brady, Mathew B., ca. 1823-1896
About
Rosenberg, A. The Civil War **920**
Brady, Tom
About
Wilner, B. Tom Brady **92**
Bragg, Georgia
How they choked **920**
How they croaked **920**
BRAHMANISM
See also Religions
Brahms, Johannes, 1833-1897
About
Krull, K. Lives of the musicians **920**
A **Braid** of lives. **970.004**
BRAIDS (HAIRSTYLING)
See also Hair
BRAILLE
See also Writing
BRAILLE BOOKS
See also Books
Braille, Louis, 1809-1852

About
Adler, D. A. A picture book of Louis Braille **686.2**
Freedman, R. Out of darkness: the story of Louis Braille **92**
The **brain.** Simon, S. **612.8**
BRAIN
Funston, S. It's all in your head **612.8**
Guillain, C. Our brains **612.8**
Halvorson, K. Inside the brain **612.8**
Korb, R. My brain **612.8**
Simon, S. The brain **612.8**
Simpson, K. The human brain **612.8**
Winston, R. M. L. What goes on in my head? **612.8**
BRAIN
See also Head; Nervous system
BRAIN -- DISEASES
See also Diseases
BRAIN -- PHYSIOLOGY
Halvorson, K. Inside the brain **612.8**
BRAIN -- WOUNDS AND INJURIES
Fleischman, J. Phineas Gage: a gruesome but true story about brain science **362.1**
Markle, S. Wounded brains **617**
BRAIN -- WOUNDS AND INJURIES -- FICTION
Hartry, N. Watching Jimmy **Fic**
Warner, S. It's only temporary **Fic**
BRAIN DEATH
See also Death
The **Brain** finds a leg. Chatterton, M. **Fic**
The **Brain** full of holes. Chatterton, M. **Fic**
BRAINWASHING -- FICTION
Nylund, E. S. The Resisters **Fic**
Robbins, T. The drained brains caper **741.5**
Brake, Mark
Alien Hunter's Handbook **576.8**
Braley, Shawn
(il) Reilly, K. M. The human body **612**
Brallier, Jess M.
Tess's tree **E**
Bramble and Maggie. [series]
Bramble and Maggie. Haas, J. **Fic**
Bramble and Maggie give and take. **Fic**
Bramble and maggie spooky season. **Fic**
Branching out. **582.16**
BRAND NAME PRODUCTS
See also Commercial products; Manufactures
Brand new readers [series]
Friend, C. Eddie the raccoon **E**
Brand-new baby blues. Appelt, K. **E**
Brand-new pencils, brand-new books. **E**
Brandeis, Gayle
My life with the Lincolns **Fic**
Brandenburg, Jim
Face to face with wolves **599.77**
Brandenburg, Judith Berman
Brandenburg, J. Face to face with wolves **599.77**

Annie Shapiro and the clothing workers' strike **331.8**

Down syndrome **616.85**

Marshall Major Taylor **92**

Michigan **977.4**

Minnesota **977.6**

Schuman, M. Delaware **975.1**

Brilliant! Mulder, M. **339.79**

Brimberg, Sisse

(il) Grace, C. O. 1621 **394.264**

Brimner, Larry Dane

Brimner, L. D. Birmingham Sunday **323.1**

Booker T. Washington **92**

Chief Crazy Horse **92**

Pocahontas **92**

Trick or treat, Old Armadillo **E**

We are one: the story of Bayard Rustin **92**

Brimsby's hats. **E**

Brinckloe, Julie

(il) Sachar, L. Sideways stories from Wayside School **Fic**

Bring me some apples and I'll make you a pie. Gourley, R. **E**

Bring on the birds. Stockdale, S. **598**

Bringing dinosaur bones to life. Farlow, J. O. **567.9**

Bringing Ezra back. DeFelice, C. C. **Fic**

Bringing in the New Year. Lin, G. **E**

Bringing mysteries alive for children and young adults. Larson, J. C. **028.5**

Bringing the boy home. Nelson, N. **Fic**

Bringing the rain to Kapiti Plain. Aardema, V. **398.2**

Bringle, Jennifer

Nebraska **978.2**

Brink, Carol Ryrie

Caddie Woodlawn **Fic**

Brisson, Pat

I remember Miss Perry **E**

Tap-dance fever **E**

Bristow, David

Sky sailors **910.4**

Bristow, M. J.

(ed) National anthems of the world **782.42**

BRITISH COLUMBIA -- FICTION

Baker, D. F. Becca at sea **Fic**

Horvath, P. Everything on a waffle **Fic**

Britt, Fanny

Jane, the fox & me **Fic**

Britt, Stephan

(il) Dickinson, R. Over in the hollow **E**

Brittain, Bill

The wish giver **Fic**

The **Brixen** Witch. DeKeyser, S. **Fic**

The **Brixton Brothers** [series]

Barnett, M. The case of the case of mistaken identity **Fic**

Barnett, M. The ghostwriter secret **Fic**

Barnett, M. It happened on a train **Fic**

Broach, Elise

Barnyard baby **E**

Gumption! **E**

Masterpiece **Fic**

The miniature world of Marvin & James **Fic**

Missing on Superstition Mountain **Fic**

Revenge of Superstition Mountain **Fic**

Shakespeare's secret **Fic**

Treasure on Superstition Mountain **Fic**

BROADBAND INTERNET

See also Internet; Internet access

BROADCASTING

See also Telecommunication

BROADWAY (NEW YORK, N.Y.) -- FICTION

Federle, T. Better Nate than ever **Fic**

Federle, T. Five, six, seven, Nate! **Fic**

Broadway, Hannah

(il) Hayes, S. Dog day **E**

Brocket, Jane

Circles, stars, and squares **516**

Ruby, violet, lime **535.6**

Spiky, slimy, smooth **612.8**

(il) Spotty, stripy, swirly **152.14**

Brodie, Carolyn S.

Latrobe, K. H. The children's literature dictionary **028.5**

Brodien-Jones, Christine

The glass puzzle **Fic**

Broeck, Fabricio Vanden

(il) Under the mambo moon **811**

Brogger, Lilian

Varmer, H. Hans Christian Andersen **92**

The **broken** bike boy and the Queen of 33rd Street. Flake, S. G. **Fic**

Broken bones. Landau, E. **617.1**

The **Broken** Lands. Milford, K. **Fic**

Bromann, Jennifer

More storytime action! **027.62**

Bromine. West, K. **546**

BROMINE

West, K. Bromine **546**

Bromley, Anne C.

The lunch thief **Fic**

BRONCHIAL ASTHMA *See* Asthma

Bronte, Charlotte

About

Lives of the writers **809**

Bronte, Emily

About

Lives of the writers **809**

Brontorina. Howe, J. **E**

BRONX (NEW YORK, N.Y.) -- FICTION

Colon, E. Good-bye, Havana! Hola, New York! **E**

BRONX (NEW YORK, N.Y.) -- GRAPHIC NOVELS

Wetterer, M. K. The snowshoeing adventure of

Marisol McDonald and the clash bash
Pablo Neruda **92**
Tito Puente, Mambo King **784.4**
Waiting for the BiblioBurro **E**

Brown, Peter, 1979-
(il) Creepy carrots! **E**
Mr. Tiger goes wild **E**
My teacher is a monster! (no, I am not) **E**

Brown, Peter, 1935-
Brown, P. Children make terrible pets **E**
Brown, P. Chowder **E**
Brown, P. The curious garden **E**

Brown, Richard E.
(il) Clark, D. C. A kid's guide to Washington, D.C. **917**

Brown, Rod
(il) Lester, J. From slave ship to freedom road **306.3**
(il) Shange, N. Freedom's a-callin' me **811**
(il) Shange, N. We troubled the waters **811**

Brown, Roslind Varghese
Tunisia **961.1**

Brown, Ruth
A dark, dark tale **E**
Gracie the lighthouse cat **E**

Brown, Stephanie Gwyn
Bang! Boom! Roar! **E**

Brown, Susan Taylor
Hugging the rock **Fic**

Brown, Tameka Fryer
Around our way on neighbors' day **E**
My cold plum lemon pie bluesy mood **E**

Brown, Tami Lewis
The map of me **Fic**
Soar, Elinor! **92**

Brown, Tricia
Salaam **297.3**

Browne, Anthony
The little bear book **E**
Little Beauty **E**
Me and you **E**
My brother **E**
My dad **E**
My mom **E**
One gorilla **513.2**
Piggybook **E**
Silly Billy **E**
Voices in the park **E**
What if...? **E**

Brownell, Shawn
(il) Peacock, C. A. Mommy far, Mommy near **E**

Brownie & Pearl go for a spin. **E**
Brownie & Pearl grab a bite. Rylant, C. **E**
Brownie & Pearl hit the hay. Rylant, C. **E**
Brownie & Pearl see the sights. Rylant, C. **E**
Brownie & Pearl step out. Rylant, C. **E**
Brownie & Pearl take a dip. Rylant, C. **E**

Brownie Groundhog and the February fox. Blackaby, S. **E**

BROWNIES (GIRL SCOUTS) *See* Girl Scouts

Browning, Diane
Signed, Abiah Rose **E**

Brownlie, Ali
South Africa in our world **968.06**
Sudan in our world **962.4**

Broyles, Anne
Priscilla and the hollyhocks **E**

Bruce Coville. Parker-Rock, M. **92**
Bruce Hale. Parker-Rock, M. **92**

Bruchac, James
The girl who helped thunder and other Native American folktales **398.2**
Bruchac, J. How Chipmunk got his stripes **398.2**
Bruchac, J. Turtle's race with Beaver **398.2**

Bruchac, Joseph
Bruchac, J. The girl who helped thunder and other Native American folktales **398.2**
Bruchac, J. Buffalo song **92**
Bruchac, J. Dragon castle **Fic**
The arrow over the door **Fic**
Bearwalker **Fic**
Between earth & sky **398.2**
A boy called Slow: the true story of Sitting Bull **92**
Crazy Horse's vision **E**
The dark pond **Fic**
The first strawberries **398.2**
How Chipmunk got his stripes **398.2**
My father is taller than a tree **E**
Night wings **Fic**
Pushing up the sky: seven Native American plays for children **812**
Skeleton man **Fic**
Thirteen moons on a turtle's back **398.2**
The Trail of Tears **970.004**
Turtle's race with Beaver **398.2**
Caduto, M. J. Keepers of the night **398.2**
Dragon castle **Fic**
Squanto's journey **Fic**

About
Parker-Rock, M. Joseph Bruchac **92**

Bruchac, Margaret M.
Grace, C. O. 1621 **394.264**

Bruel, Nick
Bad Kitty **E**
A Bad Kitty Christmas **E**
Bad Kitty gets a bath **Fic**
Bad kitty meets the baby **Fic**
Bad Kitty vs. Uncle Murray **Fic**
Happy birthday Bad Kitty **Fic**
Little red bird **E**
(il) Bruel, R. O. Bob and Otto **E**
(il) King-Smith, D. Dinosaur trouble **Fic**
(il) King-Smith, D. The mouse family Robin-

Buchanan, James, 1791-1868
         About
Burgan, M. James Buchanan   **92**

BUCHENWALD (GERMANY: CONCENTRA-TION CAMP)
   See also Concentration camps

Bucher, Katherine Toth
Al-Hazza, T. C. Books about the Middle East   **016**

Buchholz, Rachel
How to survive anything   **646.7**

Bucholz, Dinah
The unofficial Narnia cookbook   **641.594**

The **buck** stops here. Provensen, A.   **973**

Buck, Nola
A Christmas goodnight   **E**

BUCKINGHAM PALACE (LONDON, ENG-LAND) -- FICTION
The mouse with the question mark tail   **Fic**

Buckley, Annie
Be a better babysitter   **649**

Buckley, Carol
Just for elephants   **639.9**
Tarra & Bella   **599.67**

Buckley, James
The Child's World encyclopedia of the NFL **796.332**
Ultimate guide to baseball   **796.357**
Ultimate guide to football   **796.332**
(ed) The Child's World encyclopedia of base-ball   **796.357**

Buckley, Michael
(il) Kel Gilligan's daredevil stunt show   **E**
The Everafter War   **Fic**
The fairy-tale detectives   **Fic**
The inside story   **Fic**
Magic and other misdemeanors   **Fic**
Once upon a crime   **Fic**
The problem child   **Fic**
Tales from the hood   **Fic**
The unusual suspects   **Fic**

Buckley, Susan
Kids make history   **973**
Journeys for freedom   **973**
Leacock, E. Journeys in time   **973**
Leacock, E. Places in time   **911**

Buckmaster, Marjorie L.
Freshwater fishes   **639.34**

Bud, not Buddy. Curtis, C. P.   **Fic**

Budd, Warren
Ames, L. J. Draw 50 endangered animals   **743**

Buddha. Demi   **294.3**
Buddha stories. Demi   **294.3**
Buddhism. Ganeri, A.   **294.3**

BUDDHISM
   See also Religions
Buddhism. Nardo, D.   **294.3**

BUDDHISM

Brown, D. Far beyond the garden gate: Alexandra David-Neel's journey to Lhasa   **92**
Chodzin, S. The wisdom of the crows and other Buddhist tales   **294.3**
Ganeri, A. Buddhism   **294.3**
George, C. What makes me a Buddhist?   **294.3**
Hawker, F. Buddhism in Thailand   **294.3**
Kimmel, E. C. Boy on the lion throne   **92**
Levin, J. Japanese mythology   **299.5**
Nardo, D. Buddhism   **294.3**
Osborne, M. P. One world, many religions   **200**

BUDDHISM -- FICTION
Gershator, P. Sky sweeper   **E**
Thong, R. Fly free!   **E**

BUDDHISM -- PRAYERS
   See also Prayers
Buddhism in Thailand. Hawker, F.   **294.3**

BUDDHIST ART
   See also Art

BUDDHIST LEADERS
Cotter, C. Kids who rule   **920**
Demi Buddha   **294.3**
Kimmel, E. C. Boy on the lion throne   **92**

Buddy. Herlong, M. H.   **Fic**

The Buddy files [series]
Butler, D. H. The case of the fire alarm   **Fic**
Butler, D. H. The case of the library monster   **Fic**
Butler, D. H. The case of the lost boy   **Fic**
Butler, D. H. The case of the missing family   **Fic**
Butler, D. H. The case of the mixed-up mutts   **Fic**

BUDGET
Wiseman, B. Budgeting   **332.024**
Budgeting. Wiseman, B.   **332.024**

BUDGETS, PERSONAL *See* Personal finance

Budnitz, Paul
The hole in the middle   **E**

Budzik, Mary
Punctuation: the write stuff!   **428**

Buehner, Caralyn
Fanny's dream   **E**
Goldilocks and the three bears   **398.2**
Snowmen all year   **E**
Snowmen at night   **E**
Superdog   **E**

Buehner, Mark
(il) Barracca, D. The adventures of Taxi Dog **813**
(il) Buehner, C. Fanny's dream   **E**
(il) Buehner, C. Goldilocks and the three bears   **398.2**
(il) Buehner, C. Snowmen all year   **E**
(il) Buehner, C. Snowmen at night   **E**
(il) Buehner, C. Superdog   **E**
(il) Nolen, J. Harvey Potter's balloon farm   **E**

BUFFALO (N.Y.) -- FICTION
Grandits, J. The travel game   **E**
The **buffalo** are back. George, J. C.   **599.64**

Burke, Lisa
Backyard   **507.8**
Kitchen   **507.8**
Burkert, Nancy Ekholm
(il) Mouse & Lion   **E**
Burkert, Rand
Mouse & Lion   **E**
Burks, Justin Fox
(il) Plumley, A. P. Sewing school   **646.2**
Burleigh, Robert
The adventures of Mark Twain by Huckleberry
   Finn   **92**
Abraham Lincoln comes home   **92**
Clang-clang! Beep-beep!   **E**
Edward Hopper paints his world   **92**
Flight: the journey of Charles Lindbergh   **629.13**
Fly, Cher Ami, fly!   **940.4**
Good-bye, Sheepie   **E**
Home run   **811**
Hoops   **811**
Napoleon   **92**
Night flight   **629.13**
One giant leap   **629.45**
Paul Cezanne   **92**
Stealing home   **92**
Tiger of the snows   **92**
Toulouse-Lautrec   **92**
Volcanoes   **551.2**
Zoom, zoom   **E**
BURLESQUE (LITERATURE)
   See also Comedy; Parody; Satire
BURLESQUE (THEATER)
   See also Theater
BURN OUT (PSYCHOLOGY)
   See also Job satisfaction; Job stress; Mental
   health; Motivation (Psychology); Occupa-
   tional health and safety; Stress (Psychology)
Burn, Doris
Andrew Henry's meadow   **E**
Burnett, Frances Hodgson
A little princess   **Fic**
The secret garden   **Fic**
        About
Lives of the writers   **809**
Burnie, David
Bird   **598**
How animals work   **591.4**
The Kingfisher nature encyclopedia   **508**
Light   **535**
The **burning** bridge. Flanagan, J.   **Fic**
Burningham, John
Tug-of-war   **398.2**
(il) Picnic   **E**
(il) The Way to the zoo   **E**
Edwardo   **E**
It's a secret   **E**

John Burningham   **92**
John Patrick Norman McHennessy   **E**
Mr. Gumpy's motor car   **E**
Mr. Gumpy's outing   **E**
There's going to be a baby   **E**
        About
Burningham, J. John Burningham   **92**
Burns. Landau, E.   **617.1**
BURNS AND SCALDS
Landau, E. Burns   **617.1**
Markle, S. Bad burns   **617.1**
BURNS AND SCALDS -- FICTION
Abbott, T. Firegirl   **Fic**
Burns, Batt
The king with horse's ears and other Irish folk-
   tales   **398.2**
Burns, Brian
Basketball step-by-step   **796.323**
Burns, Khephra
Mansa Musa   **Fic**
Burns, Kylie
What's going on?   **507.8**
Burns, Loree Griffin
Beetle busters   **595.76**
Citizen scientists   **590.72**
Handle with care   **595.78**
The hive detectives   **638**
Tracking trash   **551.46**
Burr, Aaron, 1756-1836
        About
Fradin, D. B. Duel!   **973.4**
Burr, Dan
(il) Hailstone, R. The white ox   **92**
Burroway, Janet
Lord, J. V. The giant jam sandwich   **E**
BURROWING ANIMALS
McKay, S. Animals under our feet   **590**
Miller, S. S. Secret lives of burrowing beasts   **591.7**
BURROWING ANIMALS -- FICTION
Fleming, D. Underground   **E**
Burstein, John
Can we get along?   **179**
I said no!   **158**
Why are you picking on me?   **302.3**
Burton, Virginia Lee
(il) Andersen, H. C. The emperor's new clothes   **E**
Katy and the big snow   **E**
Life story   **560**
The little house   **E**
Mike Mulligan and his steam shovel   **E**
A **bus** called Heaven. Graham, B.   **E**
The **bus** ride.   **E**
BUS TRAVEL -- FICTION
Angleberger, T. Emperor Pickletine rides the
   bus   **Fic**
The great good summer   **Fic**

Calmenson, Stephanie

Jazzmatazz!   **E**

Late for school!   **E**

May I pet your dog?   **636.7**

Rosie   **636.7**

Cole, J. Why did the chicken cross the road? and other riddles, old and new   **793.73**

(comp) The Eentsy, weentsy spider: fingerplays and action rhymes   **796.1**

(comp) Miss Mary Mack and other children's street rhymes   **796.1**

Calvert, Pam

Multiplying menace   **E**

Princess Peepers   **E**

Calvert, Patricia

The ancient Inca   **985**

Vasco da Gama   **92**

Calvin can't fly. Berne, J.   **E**

Calvin Coconut: hero of Hawaii. Salisbury, G.   **Fic**

Calvin Coconut: kung fooey. Salisbury, G.   **Fic**

Calvin Coconut: trouble magnet. Salisbury, G.   **Fic**

Cam Jansen and the mystery at the haunted house. Adler, D. A.   **Fic**

Cam Jansen and the mystery of the stolen diamonds. Adler, D. A.   **Fic**

Cam Jansen and the Secret Service mystery. Adler, D. A.   **Fic**

Cam Jansen and the snowy day mystery. Adler, D. A.   **Fic**

Cam Jansen and the Sports Day mysteries. Adler, D. A.   **Fic**

Cam Jansen and the summer camp mysteries. Adler, D. A.   **Fic**

Cam Jansen and the Valentine baby mystery. Adler, D. A.   **Fic**

Cam Jansen and the wedding cake mystery. Adler, D. A.   **Fic**

Cam Jansen, the mystery of the dinosaur bones. Adler, D. A.   **Fic**

Cam Jansen, the mystery at the monkey house. Adler, D. A.   **Fic**

Cam Jansen, the mystery of the Babe Ruth baseball. Adler, D. A.   **Fic**

Cam Jansen, the mystery of the carnival prize. Adler, D. A.   **Fic**

Cam Jansen, the mystery of the circus clown. Adler, D. A.   **Fic**

Cam Jansen, the mystery of the gold coins. Adler, D. A.   **Fic**

Cam Jansen, the mystery of the monster movie. Adler, D. A.   **Fic**

Cam Jansen, the mystery of the stolen corn popper. Adler, D. A.   **Fic**

Cam Jansen, the mystery of the U.F.O. Adler, D. A.   **Fic**

Cam Jansen, the Triceratops Pops mystery. Adler, D. A.   **Fic**

Camaros. Niver, H. M.   **629.222**

CAMBODIA

Lord, M. A song for Cambodia   **92**

CAMBODIA -- ANTIQUITIES

Sobol, R. The mysteries of Angkor Wat   **959.6**

CAMBODIA -- FICTION

Half spoon of rice   **Fic**

CAMBODIA -- HISTORY -- 1975-

Sonneborn, L. The Khmer Rouge   **959.604**

CAMELS

Barnes, J. Camels and llamas at work   **636.2**

CAMELS

See also Desert animals; Mammals

CAMELS -- FICTION

Azad's camel   **E**

Graber, J. Muktar and the camels   **E**

Nimmo, J. The secret kingdom   **Fic**

Camels and llamas at work. Barnes, J.   **636.2**

CAMERAS

See also Photography; Photography -- Equipment and supplies

CAMERAS -- FICTION

Pichon, L. Penguins   **E**

Wiesner, D. Flotsam   **E**

Cameron, Ann

Colibri   **Fic**

Gloria's way   **Fic**

The lightning catcher   **Fic**

Spunky tells all   **Fic**

The stories Julian tells   **Fic**

Cameron, Chad

(il) Fall mixed up   **E**

Cameron, Marie

(il) Chodzin, S. The wisdom of the crows and other Buddhist tales   **294.3**

Cameroon. Sheehan, S.   **967.11**

CAMEROON

Sheehan, S. Cameroon   **967.11**

CAMEROON -- FICTION

Alexander, L. The fortune-tellers   **E**

Rockliff, M. My heart will not sit down   **E**

Camille McPhee fell under the bus. Tracy, K.   **Fic**

Camisa, Kathryn

Hairy tarantulas   **595.4**

Cammuso, Frank

Knights of the lunch table: the battling bands   **741.5**

Knights of the lunch table: the dodgeball chronicles   **741.5**

Knights of the lunch table: the dragon players   **741.5**

The Misadventures of Salem Hyde   **Fic**

(il) Otto's backwards day   **741.5**

Otto's orange day   **741.5**

Camo girl. Magoon, K.   **Fic**

CAMOUFLAGE (BIOLOGY)

Frogs!   **597.8**

Helman, A. Hide and seek **591.47**
Lunis, N. See-through animals **591.47**
Mitchell, S. K.   Animals with crafty camouflage **591.47**
Pryor, K. J. Clever camouflage **591.47**
Racanelli, M. Camouflaged creatures **591.47**
Schwartz, D. M. Where else in the wild? **591.4**
Schwartz, D. M. Where in the wild? **591.4**
Yaw, V. Color-changing animals **591.47**

CAMOUFLAGE (BIOLOGY)
    See also Animal defenses
Stockdale, S. Stripes of all types **591.47**

CAMOUFLAGE (MILITARY SCIENCE)
Mooney, C. Becoming invisible **623**

CAMOUFLAGE (MILITARY SCIENCE)
    See also Military art and science; Naval art and science

Camouflaged creatures. Racanelli, M. **591.47**

CAMPAIGN FUNDS
    See also Elections; Politics

CAMPAIGN LITERATURE
    See also Literature; Politics

CAMPAIGN MANAGEMENT -- UNITED STATES
Donovan, S. Getting elected **324.7**

CAMPAIGNS, POLITICAL *See* Politics

Campanella, Roy, 1921-1993
    About
Adler, D. A. Campy **92**

Campbell, Bebe Moore
Stompin' at the Savoy **E**

Campbell, Bruce
(il) Hawker, F. Buddhism in Thailand **294.3**
(il) Hawker, F. Christianity in Mexico **282**
(il) Hawker, F. Hinduism in Bali **294.5**
(il) Hawker, F. Islam in Turkey **297**
(il) Hawker, F. Judaism in Israel **296**
(il) Hawker, F. Sikhism in India **294.6**

Campbell, K. G.
Lester's dreadful sweaters **E**
The Mermaid and the Shoe **E**
(il) Flora and Ulysses **Fic**
(il) Tea party rules **E**

Campbell, Margaret Christine
Discovering atoms **539.7**

Campbell, Nicola I.
Shi-shi-etko **E**

Campbell, Richard P.
(il) Campbell, S. C. Growing patterns **513**
(il) Campbell, S. C. Wolfsnail **594**
(il) Mysterious patterns **516.15**

Campbell, Rod
Dear zoo **E**

Campbell, Sarah C.
Growing patterns **513**
Mysterious patterns **516.15**

Wolfsnail **594**

Campbell, Scott
Eversole, R. H. East Dragon, West Dragon **E**
(il) Hug machine **E**

Campbell-Hinshaw, Kelly
Ancient Mexico **709.3**

Camper, Cathy
Bugs before time **560**
Lowriders in space **741.5**

Campfire Graphic Novels Series
Helfand, L. Conquering Everest **741.5**

Campfire Mallory. Friedman, L. B. **Fic**

CAMPING
Champion, N. Fire and cooking **796.54**
George, J. C. Pocket guide to the outdoors **796.5**
George, K. O. Toasting marshmallows **811**

CAMPING
    See also Outdoor recreation

CAMPING -- FICTION
Gibbs, S. Spy camp **Fic**
Longstreth, G. G. Yes, let's **E**
Watt, M. Scaredy Squirrel Goes Camping **E**

CAMPING -- POETRY
George, K. O. Toasting marshmallows **811**

The **camping** trip that changed America. **979.4**

Camping with the president. Wadsworth, G. **92**

Campion, Pascal
(il) Kids go! **782.42**

Campoy, F. Isabel
Ada, A. F. Ten little puppies **398.8**
Tales our abuelitas told **398.2**
(comp) Pio peep! **398.8**

CAMPS
    See also Recreation

CAMPS -- FICTION
Charlie Joe Jackson's guide to summer vacation **Fic**
Cotler, S. Cheesie Mack is cool in a duel **Fic**
Dionne, E. Ollie and the science of treasure hunting **Fic**
Justin Case **Fic**

CAMPS -- SONGS
Mosquitoes are ruining my summer! **782.42**

Campy. Adler, D. A. **92**

Can an old dog learn new tricks? Silverman, B. **590**
Can hens give milk? Stuchner, J. B. **E**
Can I play too? Willems, M. **E**
The **Can** Man. **E**
Can we get along? Burstein, J. **179**
Can we save the tiger? Jenkins, M. **591.68**
Can we share the world with tigers? **599.75**
Can you find it? Cressy, J. **750**
Can you greet the whole wide world? Evans, L. **413**
Can you guess my name? Sierra, J. **398.2**
Can you hear it? Lach, W. **780**
Can you make a scary face? Thomas, J. **E**
Can you see me? Lewin, T. **E**

Candy experiments. Leavitt, L. **507.8**

Candy shop. Wahl, J. **E**

Candy smash. Davies, J. **Fic**

The **candymakers.** Mass, W. **Fic**

Cane toad. Somervill, B. A. **597.8**

Caney, Steven
 Steven Caney's ultimate building book **624**

Canga, Chris
 (il) Brezenoff, S. The burglar who bit the Big Apple **Fic**
 Brezenoff, S. The painting that wasn't there **Fic**
 (il) Brezenoff, S. The zombie who visited New Orleans **Fic**

The **canine** connection: stories about dogs and people. Hearne, B. G. **S**

Cann, Helen
 (il) Manger **E**
 (il) The raiders **Fic**
 (il) The shipwreck **Fic**
 (il) The snowstorm **Fic**
 (il) Guo Yue Little Leap Forward **Fic**
 (il) Milligan, B. Brigid's cloak **398.2**
 (il) The shipwreck **Fic**
 (il) Watts, M. The Bible for children from Good Books **220.9**

CANNABIS *See* Marijuana

Cannarella, Deborah
 Kansas **978.1**

Cannavale, Matthew C.
 Florida, 1513-1821 **975.9**
 North Carolina, 1524-1776 **975.6**

Cannell, Jon
 (il) Holmes, M. T. A giraffe goes to Paris **E**
 (il) Holmes, M. T. My travels with Clara **599.66**

CANNIBALISM
 See also Ethnology; Human behavior

CANNING AND PRESERVING
 See also Cooking; Food -- Preservation; Industrial chemistry

Cannon, A. E.
 Sophie's fish **E**

Cannon, Annie
 (il) Crenson, V. Horseshoe crabs and shorebirds **577.7**

Cannon, Annie Jump, 1863-1941
 About
 Gerber, C. Annie Jump Cannon, astronomer **92**

Cannon, Janell
 Crickwing **E**
 Stellaluna **E**

Cannon, Kevin
 (il) Ottaviani, J. T-Minus: the race to the moon **629.45**

Cannon, Zander
 (il) Ottaviani, J. T-Minus: the race to the moon **629.45**

Canoeing and kayaking. Thorpe, Y. **797.1**

CANOES AND CANOEING
 Thorpe, Y. Canoeing and kayaking **797.1**

CANOES AND CANOEING
 See also Boats and boating; Water sports

CANOES AND CANOEING -- FICTION
 Hobbs, W. Take me to the river **Fic**
 Williams, V. B. Three days on a river in a red canoe **E**

CANONIZATION
 See also Christian saints; Rites and ceremonies

Cans. Blaxland, W. **671**

CANS
 Blaxland, W. Cans **671**

Canterbury tales. Cohen, B. **821**

Canto familiar. Soto, G. **811**

Cantone, Anna-Laura
 (il) French, V. The Daddy Goose treasury **E**
 (il) Goodhart, P. Three little ghosties **E**

Cantrell, Charlie
 A friend for Einstein **E**

Cantrell, Katie
 (il) Dunston, M. The magic of giving **E**

Canwell, Diane
 Sutherland, J. Aircraft carriers **623.82**
 Sutherland, J. Container ships and oil tankers **623.82**
 Sutherland, J. Cruise ships **623.82**
 Sutherland, J. Submarines **623.82**

Capaccio, George
 ADD and ADHD **616.85**
 Jupiter **523.4**
 Mars **523.4**
 The sun **523.7**

Capaldi, Gina
 A boy named Beckoning: the true story of Dr. Carlos Montezuma, Native American hero **92**
 (il) Red Bird sings: the story of Zitkala-Sa **92**

Caparo, Antonio Javier
 (il) Broach, E. Treasure on Superstition Mountain **Fic**
 (il) The magic thief **Fic**
 (il) The magician's bird **Fic**

CAPE COD (MASS.)
 Clifford, B. Real pirates **910.4**

CAPE COD (MASS.) -- FICTION
 Millet, L. The fires beneath the sea **Fic**
 Pennypacker, S. The summer of the gypsy moths **Fic**

Cape Hatteras National Seashore. Reed, J. **975.6**

CAPE HATTERAS NATIONAL SEASHORE (N.C.)
 Reed, J. Cape Hatteras National Seashore **975.6**

CAPE VERDE -- FICTION
 Bates, J. C. Seaside dream **E**

Caper, William
American bison **599.64**
CAPITAL ACCUMULATION *See* Saving and investment
Capital days. **92**
CAPITAL FORMATION *See* Saving and investment
CAPITALISTS AND FINANCIERS
See also Businesspeople
CAPITALS (CITIES)
See also Cities and towns
Caple, Kathy
Duck & Company **E**
The friendship tree **E**
Caple, Laurie A.
(il) Arnold, C. When mammoths walked the earth **569**
CAPOEIRA (DANCE)
Ancona, G. Capoeira **793.3**
Haney, J. Capoeira **793.3**
Cappon, Manuela
(il) Platt, R. London **942**
(il) Platt, R. New York City **974.7**
Caps for sale. Slobodkina, E. **E**
Captain Invincible and the space shapes. Murphy, S. J. **516**
CAPTAIN MARVEL (FICTIONAL CHARACTER)
Baltazar, A. Billy Batson and the magic of Shazam!: Mr. Mind over matter **741.5**
Captain Nobody. Pitchford, D. **Fic**
Captain Raptor and the moon mystery. O'Malley, K. **E**
Captain Raptor and the space pirates. O'Malley, K. **E**
Captain Sky Blue. Egielski, R. **E**
Captain Small Pig. Waddell, M. **E**
CAPTAIN UNDERPANTS (FICTITIOUS CHARACTER)
Pilkey, D. Captain Underpants and the tyrannical retaliation of the Turbo Toilet 2000 **Fic**
Captured history [series]
Nardo, D. Assassination and its aftermath **973.92**
Capucilli, Alyssa
Biscuit **E**
Biscuit's new trick **E**
Katy Duck and the tip-top tap shoes **E**
Pedro's burro **E**
CAPYBARA
Ganeri, A. Capybara **599.35**
CAR ACCIDENTS *See* Traffic accidents
CAR DRIVERS *See* Automobile drivers
CAR INDUSTRY *See* Automobile industry
CAR POOLS
See also Traffic engineering; Transportation
CAR RACING *See* Automobile racing

CAR TRAVEL *See* Automobile travel
CAR WHEELS *See* Wheels
CAR WRECKS *See* Traffic accidents
Caramba and Henry. **E**
Carbajal, Richard
(il) Littlefield, H. The rooftop adventure of Minnie and Tessa, factory fire survivors **741.5**
Carbaugh, Sam
(il) Timekeeping **529**
Carbaugh, Samuel
(il) Mooney, C. George Washington **92**
CARBOHYDRATES
King, H. Carbohydrates for a healthy body **613.2**
CARBOHYDRATES
See also Biochemistry; Nutrition
Carbohydrates for a healthy body. King, H. **613.2**
CARBON
See also Chemical elements
CARBON DIOXIDE GREENHOUSE EFFECT
See Global warming
Carbonated beverages. Furgang, A. **613.2**
CARBONATED BEVERAGES
Furgang, A. Carbonated beverages **613.2**
Carbone, Elisa Lynn
Blood on the river **Fic**
Heroes of the surf **E**
Night running **E**
Storm warriors **Fic**
CARCINOMA *See* Cancer
CARD GAMES
See also Games
CARD TRICKS
See also Card games; Magic tricks; Tricks
Card, Vanessa
(il) Barnes, T. The Kingfisher children's illustrated Bible **220.9**
Cardboard. TenNapel, D. **Fic**
The **cardboard** box book. Walsh, D. **745.54**
The **cardboard** piano. Perkins, L. R. **E**
Cardenas, Teresa
Oloyou **398.2**
CARDIAC DISEASES *See* Heart diseases
CARDIFF (N.Y.) -- ANTIQUITIES
Murphy, J. The giant and how he humbugged America **974.7**
Cardillo, Margaret
Just being Audrey **92**
Cardinale, Christopher
(il) Lyon, G. E. Which side are you on? **782.42**
CARDINALS
Gibbs, S. The last musketeer **Fic**
CARDIOVASCULAR SYSTEM
Corcoran, M. K. The circulatory story **612.1**
Gold, J. C. Learning about the circulatory and lymphatic systems **612.1**
Jakab, C. The circulatory system

Cat the Cat, who is that? Willems, M.   **E**

The **cat** who walked across France. Banks, K.   **E**

The **cat** who went to heaven. Coatsworth, E. J.   **Fic**

The **cat** with seven names.   **E**

The **cat's** pajamas. Edwards, W.   **428**

CATACOMBS

     See also Burial; Cemeteries; Christian antiquities; Tombs

Catalano, Dominic

     (il) Brimner, L. D. Trick or treat, Old Armadillo **E**

Catalanotto, Peter

     Monkey and Robot   **E**

     More of Monkey & Robot   **E**

     (il) Burleigh, R. Good-bye, Sheepie   **E**

     Emily's art   **E**

     No more pumpkins   **Fic**

     Question Boy meets Little Miss Know-It-All **E**

     The secret lunch special   **Fic**

     The Veteran's Day visitor   **Fic**

     (il) Lyon, G. E. Mother to tigers   **92**

CATALOGING

     Cataloging correctly for kids   **025.3**

CATALOGING

     See also Bibliographic control; Documentation; Library science; Library technical processes

Cataloging correctly for kids.   **025.3**

CATALOGING OF MUSIC

     See also Cataloging

CATALOGUING *See* Cataloging

CATAMARANS

     See also Boats and boating

Catanese, P. W.

     Dragon games   **Fic**

     Happenstance found   **Fic**

CATAPULT

     Gurstelle, W. The art of the catapult   **623.4**

CATASTROPHES *See* Disasters

CATASTROPHES (GEOLOGY)

     See also Geology

Catboy. Walters, E.   **Fic**

Catch that baby! Coffelt, N.   **E**

Catch the wind, harness the sun. Caduto, M. J.   **333.79**

Catch you later, traitor.   **Fic**

Catcher. Glaser, J.   **796.357**

Catchpool, Michael

     The cloud spinner   **E**

Cate, Annette LeBlanc

     Look up!   **598**

     The magic rabbit   **E**

Cate, Marijke ten

     (il) Heide, I. v. d. A strange day   **E**

Catel, Patrick

     Surviving stunts and other amazing feats   **613.6**

CATERING

     See also Cooking; Food service

Caterpillar Inc.

     My big book of trucks & diggers   **621.8**

Caterpillar to butterfly. Marsh, L.   **595.78**

Caterpillars. Latimer, J. P.   **595.7**

CATERPILLARS

     See also Butterflies; Moths

     Engle, M. Summer birds: the butterflies of Maria Merian   **92**

     Heiligman, D. From caterpillar to butterfly **595.78**

     Latimer, J. P. Caterpillars   **595.7**

     Marsh, L. Caterpillar to butterfly   **595.78**

     Murawski, D. Face to face with caterpillars **595.7**

     Pasternak, C. How to raise monarch butterflies   **595.78**

     Singer, M. Caterpillars   **595.7**

     Swope, S. Gotta go! Gotta go!   **E**

     Trueit, T. S. Caterpillars   **595.7**

Caterpillars. Trueit, T. S.   **595.7**

Caterpillars. Singer, M.   **595.7**

CATERPILLARS -- FICTION

     Bruel, R. O. Bob and Otto   **E**

     Carle, E. The very hungry caterpillar   **E**

     Elwell, P. Adios, Oscar!   **E**

     Jarrett, C. Arabella Miller's tiny caterpillar **E**

     Lionni, L. Inch by inch   **E**

     Swope, S. Gotta go! Gotta go!   **E**

     Ten little caterpillars   **E**

     The worm whisperer   **Fic**

Cates, Karin

     The Secret Remedy Book   **E**

CATFISH

     Gray, S. H. Walking catfish   **597**

CATHEDRAL OF ST. JOHN THE DIVINE (NEW YORK, N.Y.) -- FICTION

     Me and Momma and Big John   **E**

CATHEDRALS

     Macaulay, D. Building the book Cathedral **726.6**

     Macaulay, D. Built to last   **729**

CATHEDRALS -- FICTION

     Me and Momma and Big John   **E**

Catherine II, the Great, Empress of Russia, 1729-1796

           About

     Krull, K. Lives of extraordinary women   **920**

Catherine's story. Moore, G.   **E**

Catherine, called Birdy. Cushman, K.   **Fic**

CATHOLIC CHURCH

     See also Christian sects; Christianity

CATHOLIC CHURCH -- BISHOPS

     See also Bishops

CATHOLIC CHURCH -- CHARITIES

     See also Charities

CATHOLIC CHURCH -- CLERGY

     See also Clergy; Priests

CATHOLIC CHURCH -- FICTION

I am cat **E**

The Maine coon's haiku **811.54**

Cats and kittens. Johnson, J. **636.8**

CATS IN ART

Ames, L. J. Draw 50 cats **743**

The cats in Krasinski Square. Hesse, K. **E**

The cats in the doll shop. McDonough, Y. Z. **Fic**

Cats' night out. Stutson, C. **E**

Cats, cats! Nelson-Schmidt, M. **E**

CATSKILL MOUNTAINS (N.Y.) -- FICTION

Irving, W. Washington Irving's Rip van Winkle **Fic**

Kimmel, E. A. Rip Van Winkle's return **E**

Weeks, S. As simple as it seems **Fic**

Catt, Thessaly

Migrating with the Arctic tern **598**

Migrating with the caribou **599.65**

Migrating with the humpback whale **599.5**

Migrating with the monarch butterfly **595.7**

Migrating with the salmon **597**

Migrating with the wildebeest **599.64**

CATTLE

Aliki Milk from cow to carton **637**

Boynton, S. Amazing cows **636.2**

Diemer, L. Cows **636.2**

Gibbons, G. The milk makers **637**

LaRochelle, D. Moo! **E**

Montgomery, S. Temple Grandin **636**

Peterson, C. Clarabelle **636.2**

Steele, C. Cattle ranching in the American West **636**

Van Rynbach, I. The taxing case of the cows **324.6**

CATTLE

See also Domestic animals; Mammals

CATTLE -- FICTION

Bar-el, D. Audrey (cow) **Fic**

Cattle ranching in the American West. Steele, C. **636**

Catusanu, Mircea

The strange case of the missing sheep **E**

Caught. Haddix, M. P. **Fic**

Caught by the sea. Paulsen, G. **818**

Cauley, Lorinda Bryan

Clap your hands **E**

CAUSATION

See also Metaphysics; Philosophy

CAUSES OF DISEASES *See* Diseases -- Causes

CAUTIONARY TALES AND VERSES *See* Didactic fiction; Didactic poetry; Fables; Parables

Cavallaro, Michael

L. Frank Baum's The Wizard of Oz **741.5**

Cavanaugh, Nancy J.

This journal belongs to Ratchet **Fic**

Cavanaugh, Terence W.

Bookmapping **372.6**

Keane, N. J. The tech-savvy booktalker **021.7**

CAVE DRAWINGS *See* Cave drawings and paintings

CAVE DRAWINGS AND PAINTINGS

Discovery in the cave **944**

CAVE DRAWINGS AND PAINTINGS -- FICTION

Barron, T. A. Ghost hands **E**

The first drawing **E**

McCully, E. A. The secret cave **E**

Sloat, T. There was an old man who painted the sky **E**

CAVE DWELLERS

Lynette, R. Who lives in a deep, dark cave? **591.7**

Miller, S. S. Secret lives of cave creatures **591.7**

CAVE DWELLERS

See also Prehistoric peoples

CAVE DWELLERS -- FICTION

Barnett, M. Oh no! Not again! **E**

The first drawing **E**

Winter, J. Kali's song **E**

CAVE ECOLOGY

Banting, E. Caves **577.5**

CAVE ECOLOGY

See also Ecology

CAVE PAINTINGS *See* Cave drawings and paintings

Cave, Kathryn

One child, one seed **E**

Caves. Banting, E. **577.5**

CAVES

Banting, E. Caves **577.5**

Discovery in the cave **944**

Lynette, R. Who lives in a deep, dark cave? **591.7**

Taylor, P. L. The secret of Priest's Grotto **940.53**

CAVES -- FICTION

Wilson, N. D. Leepike Ridge **Fic**

CAVES -- NEPAL -- MUSTANG (DISTRICT)

Athans, S. K. Secrets of the sky caves **796.522**

Cavities and toothaches. Landau, E. **617.6**

The **cay.** Taylor, T. **Fic**

Cazet, Denys

Elvis the rooster almost goes to heaven **E**

Minnie and Moo and the haunted sweater **E**

Minnie and Moo, hooves of fire **Fic**

Minnie and Moo, wanted dead or alive **E**

The octopus **E**

Will you read to me? **E**

The **cazuela** that the farm maiden stirred. **E**

CD-I TECHNOLOGY

See also Compact discs; Optical storage devices

CD-ROMS

See also Compact discs; Optical storage devices

CDS (COMPACT DISCS) *See* Compact discs

Ceccoli, Nicoletta

(il) Bernheimer, K. The girl in the castle inside the museum **E**

(il) Helgerson, J. Horns & wrinkles **Fic**

Saint-Saens's Danse Macabre **784.2**

CELERY

See also Vegetables

Celeste's Harlem Renaissance. Tate, E. E. **Fic**

Celestine, drama queen. Ives, P. **E**

CELIBACY

See also Clergy; Religious life

CELL PHONES *See* Cellular telephones

Cell systems. McManus, L. **570**

CELLO

See also Stringed instruments

Cells. Lee, K. F. **571.6**

CELLS

Cohen, M. What is cell theory? **571.6**

Green, J. Inside animals **571**

Johnson, R. L. Mighty animal cells **571.6**

Lee, K. F. Cells **571.6**

McManus, L. Cell systems **570**

Rand, C. DNA and heredity **572.8**

CELLS

See also Biology; Physiology; Reproduction

CELLULAR TELEPHONES

Spilsbury, R. The telephone **621.385**

CELLULAR TELEPHONES

See also Telephone

CELTIC ART

See also Art

CELTIC CIVILIZATION

Green, J. Ancient Celts **936**

CELTIC LEGENDS

See also Legends

CELTIC MYTHOLOGY

See also Mythology

CELTIC MYTHOLOGY -- FICTION

McQuerry, M. D. Beyond the door **Fic**

CELTS

Green, J. Ancient Celts **936**

CEMENT

See also Adhesives; Building materials; Ceramics; Masonry; Plaster and plastering

CEMETERIES

See also Burial; Public health; Sanitation

CEMETERIES -- FICTION

Gaiman, N. The graveyard book graphic novel Volume 1 **741.5**

The graveyard book graphic novel Volume 2 **741.5**

Cendrars, Blaise

Shadow **841**

Cendrillon. San Souci, R. **398.2**

CENSORSHIP

Adams, H. R. Ensuring intellectual freedom and access to information in the school library media program **027.8**

CENSORSHIP

See also Intellectual freedom

CENSORSHIP -- FICTION

Downey, J. S. The ninja librarians **Fic**

CENSUS

See also Population; Statistics; Vital statistics

CENSUS -- FICTION

Davies, J. Tricking the Tallyman **E**

CENTENARIANS

Art from her heart: folk artist Clementine Hunter **92**

Bartoletti, S. C. Kids on strike! **331.892**

Brown, D. Far beyond the garden gate: Alexandra David-Neel's journey to Lhasa **92**

Freedman, R. Indian chiefs **970.004**

Warren, A. Pioneer girl **92**

The **Center** for Cartoon Studies presents Annie Sullivan and the trials of Helen Keller. **362.4**

The **center** of everything. Urban, L. **Fic**

Centerburg tales. McCloskey, R. **Fic**

Centipede. Povey, K. D. **595.6**

CENTIPEDES

Elkin, M. 20 fun facts about centipedes **595.6**

Povey, K. D. Centipede **595.6**

CENTRAL AMERICA -- FICTION

Colato Lainez, R. My shoes and I **E**

Voelkel, J. The end of the world club **Fic**

Voelkel, J. Middleworld **Fic**

CENTRAL AMERICAN COOKING

Behnke, A. Cooking the Central American way **641.5**

CENTRAL HIGH SCHOOL (LITTLE ROCK, ARK.)

Walker, P. R. Remember Little Rock **379**

CENTRAL PACIFIC RAILROAD

Halpern, M. Railroad fever **385**

Perritano, J. The transcontinental railroad **385**

CENTRAL PACIFIC RAILROAD -- FICTION

Yin Coolies **E**

Centsibility. Roderick, S. **332.024**

Cepeda, Joe

(il) Cub's big world **E**

(il) Elya, S. M. N is for Navidad **E**

(il) Montes, M. Juan Bobo goes to work **398.2**

(il) Pattison, D. S. The journey of Oliver K. Woodman **E**

(il) Reiche, D. I, Freddy **Fic**

CERAMIC MATERIALS *See* Ceramics

CERAMICS

Blaxland, W. Plates and mugs **620.1**

Llimos, A. Easy clay crafts in 5 steps **738.1**

CERAMICS

See also Industrial chemistry; Materials

CERAMISTS

Andrews-Goebel, N. The pot that Juan built **738**

Dave, the potter **92**

Cerato, Mattia

(il) Kalz, J. An A-MAZE-ing amusement park adventure **793.73**

Cerberus. Tracy, K. **398.2**

(il) Sheridan, S. I'm me!   E
(il) Tierney, F. Lion's lunch?   E

CHAMBERS OF COMMERCE
    See also Commerce

Chambliss, Maxie
  (il) Bunting, E. Baby can   E
  (il) Cole, J. When you were inside Mommy **612.6**

Chameleon chameleon. Cowley, J.   **597.95**

CHAMELEONS
  Cowley, J. Chameleon chameleon   **597.95**

CHAMELEONS -- FICTION
  Carle, E. The mixed-up chameleon   E
  Gravett, E. Blue chameleon   E
  Na, I. S. Hide & seek   E
  Perlman, J. The delicious bug   E

The **champ!** Bolden, T.   **92**
Champ's story. North, S.   E
The **champion** of children. Bogacki, T.   **92**

Champion, Neil
  Finding food and water   **613.6**
  Finding your way   **613.6**
  Fire and cooking   **796.54**
  In an emergency   **613.6**
  Making shelter   **613.6**

Champions of breakfast. Rex, A.   Fic
Champions of the ocean. Hodgkins, F.   **920**
Champions of the wilderness. Malnor, B.   **920**
Champions of wild animals. Malnor, C.   **920**

Champlain, Samuel de, 1567-1635
        About
  MacLeod, E. Samuel de Champlain   **92**

Champlin, Connie
  Storytelling with puppets   **372.66**

Champollion, Jean Francois, 1790-1832
        About
  Rumford, J. Seeker of knowledge   **92**

Chan, Peter
  (il) Secrets of the crown   Fic

CHANCE -- FICTION
  Kinney, J. Diary of a wimpy kid   Fic

Chancellor, Deborah
  Happy and healthy   **646.7**

Chandra, Deborah
  George Washington's teeth   E

Chanel, Coco, 1883-1971
        About
  Matthews, E. Different like Coco   **92**

Chang, Perry
  Hart, J. Florida   **975.9**

CHANGE (PSYCHOLOGY)
    See also Psychology

CHANGE -- FICTION
  Martins, I. M. Where do we go when we disappear?   E
  Moonpenny Island   Fic
  Standiford, N. Switched at birthday   Fic

Change it! Mason, A.   **530**

CHANGE OF STATE (PHYSICS)
  Lawrence, E. Water   **530.4**

Changeling. Sherman, D.   Fic

CHANGELINGS -- FICTION
  The boy who lost Fairyland   Fic

Changing Africa. Bowden, R.   **960**
Changing climate. Bailey, G.   **551.6**
Changing life on Earth. Hartman, E.   **576.8**
Changing materials. Oxlade, C.   **530.4**
Changing materials [series]
  Oxlade, C. Changing shape   **620.1**
  Oxlade, C. Cooling   **530.4**
  Oxlade, C. Heating   **530.4**
  Oxlade, C. Mixing and separating   **541**
Changing shape. Oxlade, C.   **620.1**
Changing states. Hurd, W.   **530.4**
Changing Woman and her sisters. Tchana, K. H.   **398.2**
Changing you! Saltz, G.   **612.6**

Chanticleer and the fox. Cooney, B.   E

Chantler, Scott
  Tower of treasure   **741.5**

CHANUKAH *See* Hanukkah
Chanukah lights. Rosen, M. J.   E
A **Chanukah** Noel. Jennings, S.   E
The **Chanukkah** guest. Kimmel, E. A.   **296.4**

CHAOS (SCIENCE)
    See also Dynamics; Science; System theory

CHAPBOOKS
    See also Books; Folklore; Literature; Pamphlets; Periodicals; Wit and humor

CHAPLAINS
    See also Clergy

Chaplin, Charlie, 1889-1977
        About
  Fleischman, S. Sir Charlie   **92**

Chapman, Caroline
  Battles & weapons: exploring history through art   **355**

Chapman, Garry
  Coffee   **641.3**

Chapman, Gaye
  (il) Hunt, J. Precious Little   E

Chapman, Jane
  I'm not sleepy!   E
  (il) Bright, P. The not-so-scary Snorklum   E
  Sing a song of sixpence   **398.8**
  (il) Corderoy, T. The little white owl   E
  (il) Davies, N. One tiny turtle   **597.92**
  (il) Godwin, L. Happy and Honey   E
  (il) Warnes, T. Daddy hug   E
  (il) Wilson, K. Bear snores on   E
  (il) Wilson, K. Bear's loose tooth   E
  (il) Wilson, K. Where is home, Little Pip?   E

Chapman, Mark David

How we know what we know about our changing climate   Jiang, Hong **363.7**

The sea, the storm, and the mangrove tangle   **E**

(il) Viorst, J. If I were in charge of the world and other worries **811**

Cheryl Harness history [series]

Harness, C. The adventurous life of Myles Standish **92**

Harness, C. The tragic tale of Narcissa Whitman and a faithful history of the Oregon Trail **92**

The **Cheshire** Cheese cat. Deedy, C. A. **Fic**

Cheshire, Simon

The curse of the ancient mask and other case files **Fic**

The pirate's blood and other case files **Fic**

The treasure of Dead Man's Lane and other case files **Fic**

Chess. King, D. **794.1**

CHESS

Basman, M. Chess for kids **794.1**

King, D. Chess **794.1**

CHESS

See also Board games

CHESS -- FICTION

Blackwood, G. Curiosity **Fic**

Chess for kids. Basman, M. **794.1**

Chess rumble. Neri, G. **Fic**

Chess! I love it, I love it, I love it! Gilson, J. **Fic**

Chess, Victoria

(il) Schwartz, A. Ghosts! **398.2**

(il) Zalben, J. B. Brenda Berman, wedding expert **Fic**

Chessa, Francesca

(il) Brown, A. Love-a-duck **E**

Holly's red boots **E**

(il) Shields, G. Library Lily **E**

Chester. Imai, A. **E**

Chester. **E**

Chester Raccoon and the acorn full of memories. Penn, A. **E**

Chester's way. Henkes, K. **E**

Chesworth, Michael

(il) Ashman, L. Creaky old house **E**

(il) Lewis, M. Morgy makes his move **Fic**

(il) Lewis, M. Morgy's musical summer **Fic**

(il) Miller, H. This is your life cycle **595.7**

Cheung, Hyechong

K is for Korea **951.9**

Cheung, Irvin

(il) McQuinn, A. My friend Mei Jing **E**

Chevelles. Portman, M. **629.222**

CHEWING GUM -- FICTION

Montijo, R. Chews your destiny **Fic**

Chews your destiny. Montijo, R. **Fic**

The **Cheyenne.** De Capua, S. **970.004**

The **Cheyenne.** Cunningham, K. **970.004**

Cheyenne again. Bunting, E. **E**

CHEYENNE INDIANS

Cunningham, K. The Cheyenne **970.004**

De Capua, S. The Cheyenne **970.004**

Ehrlich, A. Wounded Knee: an Indian history of the American West **970.004**

CHEYENNE INDIANS -- FICTION

Bunting, E. Cheyenne again **E**

Goble, P. Death of the iron horse **E**

Chiang, Yeng-Fong

Krasno, R. Cloud weavers **398.2**

CHICAGO (ILL.) -- ANTIQUITIES

See also Antiquities

CHICAGO (ILL.) -- BIOGRAPHY

See also Biography

CHICAGO (ILL.) -- CLIMATE

See also Climate

CHICAGO (ILL.) -- COMMERCE

See also Commerce

CHICAGO (ILL.) -- ECONOMIC CONDITIONS

See also Economic conditions

CHICAGO (ILL.) -- FICTION

Balliett, B. Hold fast **Fic**

Cooper, F. Willie and the All-Stars **E**

Peck, R. Fair weather **Fic**

CHICAGO (ILL.) -- HISTORY

Hurd, O. Chicago history for kids **977.3**

CHICAGO (ILL.) -- MAPS

See also Maps

CHICAGO (ILL.) -- POLITICS AND GOVERNMENT

See also Municipal government; Politics

CHICAGO (ILL.) -- POPULATION

See also Population

CHICAGO (ILL.) -- RACE RELATIONS

See also Race relations

CHICAGO (ILL.) -- STATISTICS

See also Statistics

Chicago history for kids. Hurd, O. **977.3**

Chicagoland Detective Agency [series]

Robbins, T. The drained brains caper **741.5**

CHICANERY *See* Deception

CHICANOS *See* Mexican Americans

Chichester-Clark, Emma

Goldilocks and the three bears **398.2**

Little Miss Muffet counts to ten **E**

Melrose and Croc: an adventure to remember **E**

Piper **E**

(il) McNaughton, C. Not last night but the night before **E**

(il) Morpurgo, M. Hansel and Gretel **398.2**

(il) Morpurgo, M. The McElderry book of Aesop's fables **398.2**

(il) The Pied Piper of Hamelin **398.2**

(il) Pirotta, S. The McElderry book of Grimms' fairy tales **398.2**

CHURCH OF JESUS CHRIST OF LATTER-DAY SAINTS

Bial, R. Nauvoo **289.3**

George, C. What makes me a Mormon? **289.3**

CHURCH SCHOOLS

See also Private schools; Schools

CHURCH WORK WITH YOUTH

See also Church work; Youth

CHURCH YEAR

See also Calendars; Religious holidays; Worship

Church, Caroline

One more hug for Madison **E**

One smart goose **E**

(il) Emmett, J. Leaf trouble **E**

(il) Puttock, S. Little lost cowboy **E**

(il) Symes, R. Harriet dancing **E**

Churchill, Winston Sir, 1874-1965

About

Franklin and Winston **940.53**

Selbert, K. War dogs **E**

Chwast, Seymour

(il) Had gadya **296.4**

(il) Hanft, J. E. Miracles of the Bible **221.9**

(il) The miracles of Passover **296.4**

Ch'in Shih-huang, Emperor of China, 259-210 B.C.

About

O'Connor, J. The emperor's silent army **931**

Ciardi, John

You read to me, I'll read to you **811**

Ciarleglio, Lauren

New Hampshire **974.2**

Cicada summer. Beaty, A. **Fic**

CICADAS

Pringle, L. P. Cicadas! **595.7**

CIGARETTES

See also Smoking; Tobacco

CIGARS

See also Smoking; Tobacco

Cinco de Mayo. Hoyt-Goldsmith, D. **394.26**

CINCO DE MAYO

Hoyt-Goldsmith, D. Cinco de Mayo **394.26**

Mattern, J. Celebrate Cinco de Mayo **394.26**

Otto, C. Celebrate Cinco de Mayo **394.26**

Tait, L. Cinco de Mayo **394.26**

Cinco de Mayo. Tait, L. **394.26**

CINCO DE MAYO (HOLIDAY)

See also Holidays

Cinder Rabbit. Hazen, L. E. **Fic**

Cinderella. **398.2**

CINDERELLA (LEGENDARY CHARACTER) -- FICTION

Cinderella **398.2**

Cinderella Smith. Barden, S. **Fic**

Cinderella Smith [series]

Barden, S. The super secret mystery **Fic**

Cinderella's rat. Meddaugh, S. **E**

Cinders. Brett, J. **E**

CINEMA *See* Motion pictures

CINEMATOGRAPHY

See also Photography

Cinnamon baby. **E**

CIPHER AND TELEGRAPH CODES

See also Ciphers; Telegraph

CIPHERS

Bell-Rehwoldt, S. Speaking secret codes **652**

Blackwood, G. L. Mysterious messages **652**

Gilbert, A. Codes and ciphers **652**

Gregory, J. Breaking secret codes **652**

Gregory, J. Making secret codes **652**

Mitchell, S. K. Spy codes and ciphers **652**

CIPHERS

See also Signs and symbols

CIPHERS -- FICTION

Mr. and Mrs. Bunny-- detectives extraordinaire! **FIC**

CIRCLE

See also Geometry; Shape

Circle dogs. Henkes, K. **516**

Circle of secrets. Little, K. G. **Fic**

Circle opens quartet [series]

Pierce, T. Magic steps **Fic**

Circle unbroken. Raven, M. **E**

Circle, square, Moose. Bingham, K. **E**

Circles. Loughrey, A. **516**

Circles, stars, and squares. Brocket, J. **516**

The **circulatory** story. Corcoran, M. K. **612.1**

The **circulatory** system. Jakab, C.

CIRCULATORY SYSTEM *See* Cardiovascular system

Circulatory system. Tieck, S. **612.1**

CIRCUMNAVIGATION *See* Voyages around the world

Circus. Ehlert, L. **E**

CIRCUS

See also Amusements

Covert, R. Sawdust and spangles: the amazing life of W.C. Coup **92**

Dodds, D. A. Where's Pup? **E**

Fleischman, P. Sidewalk circus **E**

Fleming, C. The great and only Barnum **92**

Helfer, R. The world's greatest elephant **791.3**

Hoff, S. Oliver **E**

Laidlaw, R. On parade **791.8**

McCaughrean, G. The kite rider **Fic**

Schubert, L. Ballet of the elephants **791.8**

Yep, L. When the circus came to town **Fic**

Circus. Munro, R. **E**

CIRCUS -- FICTION

The farmer and the clown **E**

Gravett, E. Wolf won't bite! **E**

Harrison, H. E. Extraordinary Jane   **E**
Klise, K. The Greatest Star on Earth   **Fic**
Klise, K. The show must go on!   **Fic**
My bike   **E**
Oppel, K. The Boundless   **Fic**
Second banana   **E**
Slavin, B. Big Top Otto   **741.5**

CIRCUS EXECUTIVES
Covert, R. Sawdust and spangles: the amazing life
   of W.C. Coup   **92**
Fleming, C. The great and only Barnum   **92**
Peck, R. Fair weather   **Fic**
Prince, A. J. Twenty-one elephants and still stand-
   ing   **E**
Schubert, L. Ballet of the elephants   **791.8**
Circus family dog. Clements, A.   **E**

CIRCUS IN ART
Stone, T. L. Sandy's circus   **92**
Circus opposites. Macdonald, S.   **E**

CIRCUS PERFORMERS
Andreasen, D. The giant of Seville   **E**
Peck, R. Fair weather   **Fic**
Rubinstein, R. E. Zishe the strongman   **92**

CIRCUS PERFORMERS -- FICTION
Kelly, L. Chained   **Fic**
Larwood, K. Freaks   **Fic**
Wild boy and the black terror   **Fic**
The circus ship. Van Dusen, C.   **E**
Cis, Valeria
   (il) Krebs, L. The Beeman   **E**
   (il) Portnoy, M. A. Tale of two Seders   **E**

CITIES AND TOWNS
Boisrobert, A. Popville   **E**
Burleigh, R. Clang-clang! Beep-beep!   **E**
Cities   **307.76**
Millard, A. A street through time   **936**
Low, W. Machines go to work in the city   **E**

CITIES AND TOWNS -- FICTION
The bear's song   **E**
Castillo, L. Nana in the city   **E**
Light, S. Have you seen my dragon?   **E**
Low, W. Machines go to work in the city   **E**
Shulevitz, U. Dusk   **E**

CITIES AND TOWNS -- GROWTH
   See also Internal migration; Population
Citizen scientists. Burns, L. G.   **590.72**
CitizenKid [series]
   Milway, K. S. The good garden   **Fic**
   This child, every child   **305.23**
   Wyatt, V. How to build your own country   **320.4**
Citizenship. Raatma, L.   **323.6**

CITIZENSHIP
Barraclough, S. Honesty   **179**
If the World Were a Village   **304.6**
Wyatt, V. How to build your own country   **320.4**

CITIZENSHIP

   See also Constitutional law; Political ethics;
   Political science

CITIZENSHIP -- UNITED STATES
Raatma, L. Citizenship   **323.6**
Citrin, Michael
   Mack, T. The fall of the Amazing Zalindas   **Fic**
   Mack, T. The mystery of the conjured man   **Fic**

CITRUS FRUITS
   See also Fruit
City 1 2 3. Milich, Z.   **E**
City alphabet. Schwartz, J.   **E**

CITY AND TOWN LIFE
Baker, J. Home   **E**
The bear ate your sandwich   **E**
Bluemle, E. Tap tap boom boom   **E**
Bradby, M. Momma, where are you from?   **E**
Downer, A. Wild animal neighbors   **591.75**
Fleischman, P. Sidewalk circus   **E**
Freedman, R. Immigrant kids   **325**
Guest, E. H. Iris and Walter   **E**
Hill, I. Building stories   **E**
Last stop on Market Street   **E**
Rotner, S. Senses in the city   **E**
Schwartz, J. City alphabet   **E**
Stewart, S. The journey   **E**

CITY AND TOWN LIFE
   See also Cities and towns; Urban sociology

CITY AND TOWN LIFE -- FICTION
Burleigh, R. Zoom, zoom   **E**
Cold snap   **E**
Disalvo-Ryan, D. City green   **E**
File under: 13 suspicious incidents   **Fic**
The hula hoopin' queen   **E**
Manning, M. J. Laundry day   **E**
Peggy   **E**
Rockliff, M. The Grudge Keeper   **E**
Turnage, S. The ghosts of Tupelo Landing   **Fic**
Ward, H. The town mouse and the country mouse   **E**
Yaccarino, D. Doug unplugged!   **E**

CITY AND TOWN LIFE -- FICTION
Brown, P. Mr. Tiger goes wild   **E**

CITY AND TOWN LIFE -- MAINE -- FICTION
Robinson, M. L. Bright Island   **Fic**

**CITY AND TOWN LIFE -- MISSISSIPPI -- FIC-
TION**
Scattergood, A. Glory be   **Fic**

**CITY AND TOWN LIFE -- NEW YORK (STATE)
-- NEW YORK -- FICTION**
Little Bird takes a bath   **E**

CITY AND TOWN LIFE -- POETRY
Hopkins, L. B. City I love   **811**
Kennedy, X. J. City kids   **811**
Moore, L. Mural on Second Avenue, and other city
   poems   **811**

**CITY AND TOWN LIFE -- VERMONT -- FIC-
TION**

Blakemore, M. F. The spy catchers of Maple Hill **Fic**

City chickens. Heppermann, C. **636.5**

City colors. Milich, Z. **E**

City Dog, Country Frog. **E**

City green. Disalvo-Ryan, D. **E**

City I love. Hopkins, L. B. **811**

City in peril! Collicutt, P. **741.5**

City kids. Kennedy, X. J. **811**

CITY LIFE See City and town life

The city of Ember. DuPrau, J. **Fic**

The city of Ember. **741.5**

City of fire. Yep, L. **Fic**

The City of gold and lead. Christopher, J. **Fic**

City of orphans. Avi **Fic**

City of spies. **741.5**

CITY PLANNING

Cities **307.76**

CITY PLANNING -- CITIZEN PARTICIPATION

See also Political participation; Social action

CITY PLANNING -- ROME

Macaulay, D. City: a story of Roman planning and construction **711**

City signs. Milich, Z. **302.23**

CITY TAVERN (PHILADELPHIA, PA.) -- FICTION

Staib, W. A feast of freedom **Fic**

A city tossed and broken. Blundell, J. **Fic**

CITY TRAFFIC

Bee, W. And the cars go... **E**

CITY TRAFFIC -- FICTION

Twenty big trucks in the middle of the street **E**

City witch, country switch. Wax, W. **E**

City: a story of Roman planning and construction. Macaulay, D. **711**

CIVIC LEADERS

Bolden, T. Maritcha **92**

CIVICS See Citizenship; Political science

CIVIL DEFENSE

See also Military art and science

CIVIL DISOBEDIENCE

Gandhi **954.03**

Scandiffio, L. People who said no **303.48**

CIVIL DISOBEDIENCE

See also Resistance to government

CIVIL ENGINEERING

Caney, S. Steven Caney's ultimate building book **624**

Fantastic feats and failures **624**

Macaulay, D. City: a story of Roman planning and construction **711**

Macaulay, D. Underground **624**

Sullivan, G. Built to last **624**

CIVIL ENGINEERING

See also Engineering

CIVIL ENGINEERS

Ehrlich, A. Wounded Knee: an Indian history of the American West **970.004**

Sneed, D. The man who invented the ferris wheel **92**

CIVIL ENGINEERS -- UNITED STATES -- BIOGRAPHY

Davis, K. G. Mr. Ferris and his wheel **92**

CIVIL GOVERNMENT See Political science

CIVIL LIBERTY See Freedom

CIVIL RIGHTS

Krull, K. A kid's guide to America's Bill of Rights **342**

Leavitt, A. J. The Bill of Rights in translation **342**

My Name Is Truth **92**

Thomas, W. D. What are citizens' basic rights? **323**

When thunder comes **811**

CIVIL RIGHTS

See also Constitutional law; Human rights; Political science

CIVIL RIGHTS (INTERNATIONAL LAW) See Human rights

CIVIL RIGHTS -- FICTION

McKissack, P. C. Cyborg **Fic**

Stella by starlight **Fic**

CIVIL RIGHTS -- UNITED STATES -- HISTORY

Baxter, R. The Bill of Rights **342.73**

Kanefield, T. The girl from the tar paper school **92**

CIVIL RIGHTS ACTIVISTS

Adler, D. A. A picture book of Thurgood Marshall **347**

Amoroso, C. Rosa Parks **92**

Bausum, A. Freedom Riders **323.1**

Belle, the last mule at Gee's Bend **E**

Bradby, M. More than anything else **E**

Bridges, R. Through my eyes: the autobiography of Ruby Bridges **92**

Brimner, L. D. Booker T. Washington **92**

Brimner, L. D. We are one: the story of Bayard Rustin **92**

Coleman, W. Racism on trial **345**

Coretta Scott **92**

Donaldson, M. Ruby Bridges **92**

Dray, P. Yours for justice, Ida B. Wells **92**

Farris, C. K. March on! **92**

Farris, C. My brother Martin **92**

Foran, J. Martin Luther King, Jr. Day **394.26**

Freedman, R. Freedom walkers **323.1**

Greenfield, E. Paul Robeson **92**

Gunderson, J. X: the biography of Malcolm X **92**

Haskins, J. Delivering justice **92**

Haskins, J. John Lewis in the lead **92**

Holland, L. J. Dr. Martin Luther King Jr.'s I have a dream speech in translation **323.1**

Jeffrey, L. S. Celebrate Martin Luther King, Jr., Day **394.26**

Kittinger, J. S. Rosa's bus **323.1**

Cloudy with a chance of meatballs. Barrett, J.　**E**

Clover Twig and the magical cottage. Umansky, K.　**Fic**

Clown fish and sea anemones work together. Rustad, M. E. H.　**597**

The **clown** of God. DePaola, T.　**398.2**

CLOWNFISH

Rustad, M. E. H. Clown fish and sea anemones work together　**597**

CLOWNS

See also Circus; Entertainers

CLOWNS -- FICTION

De Guzman, M. Henrietta Hornbuckle's circus of life　**Fic**

Dodds, D. A. Where's Pup?　**E**

The farmer and the clown　**E**

CLUBS

Shea, T. The robotics club　**629.8**

CLUBS -- FICTION

Abdul-Jabbar, K. Sasquatch in the paint　**Fic**

Herrera, R. Hope is a ferris wheel　**Fic**

The **clue** of the linoleum lederhosen. Anderson, M. T.　**Fic**

The **clueless** girl's guide to being a genius. Repka, J.　**Fic**

Clues in the attic. Meister, C.　**741.5**

Clutton-Brock, Juliet

Cat　**599.75**

Cneut, Carll

(il) Kockere, G. D. Willy　**E**

(il) Ten moonstruck piglets　**E**

COACH DRIVERS

Kay, V. Rough, tough Charley　**92**

COACHING (ATHLETICS)

See also Athletics; Physical education; Sports

Coachman, Alice

About

Malaspina, A. Touch the sky　**796.42**

Coal. Green, R.　**553.2**

COAL

See also Fuel

Benduhn, T. Oil, gas, and coal　**665.5**

Green, R. Coal　**553.2**

Hartman, E. Fossil fuels　**333.8**

COAL GAS See Gas

COAL GASIFICATION

See also Coal

COAL LIQUEFACTION

See also Coal

COAL MINERS

See also Miners

Bartoletti, S. C. Growing up in coal country　**331.3**

COAL MINERS -- FICTION

Kehret, P. The ghost's grave　**Fic**

White, R. Little Audrey　**Fic**

COAL MINERS -- UNITED STATES -- HISTORY -- 19TH CENTURY

Nelson, S. D. Digging a hole to heaven　**Fic**

COAL MINES AND MINING

Bartoletti, S. C. Growing up in coal country　**331.3**

Yep, L. The traitor　**Fic**

COAL MINES AND MINING

See also Coal; Mines and mineral resources

COAL MINES AND MINING -- FICTION

Nelson, S. D. Digging a hole to heaven　**Fic**

COAL MINES AND MINING -- SONGS

Lyon, G. E. Which side are you on?　**782.42**

COAL OIL See Petroleum

COAL TAR PRODUCTS

See also Petroleum

Coalson, Glo

(il) Scott, A. H. On Mother's lap　**E**

The **coast** mappers. Morrison, T.　**623.89**

COASTAL ECOLOGY

See also Ecology

High tide for horseshoe crabs　**595.4**

COASTAL LANDFORMS See Coasts

COASTAL ZONE MANAGEMENT

See also Coasts; Regional planning

COASTS

Pyers, G. The biodiversity of coasts　**577.5**

A **coat** for the moon and other Jewish tales. Schwartz, H.　**398.2**

The **coat** of many colors. Koralek, J.　**222**

COATS

Taback, S. Joseph had a little overcoat　**398.2**

COATS -- FICTION

Hest, A. The purple coat　**E**

COATS -- FOLKLORE

Aylesworth, J. My grandfather's coat　**E**

Coatsworth, Elizabeth Jane

The cat who went to heaven　**Fic**

Cobb, Jane

What'll I do with the baby-o?　**E**

Cobb, Rebecca

Missing mommy　**E**

Cobb, Vicki

Cobb, V. I fall down　**531**

Fireworks　**662**

How to really fool yourself　**152.1**

I face the wind　**551.51**

I fall down　**531**

I get wet　**532**

I see myself　**535**

Junk food　**664**

Open your eyes　**612.8**

Science experiments you can eat　**507.8**

See for yourself　**507.8**

Sneakers　**685**

This place is wet　**574.5**

We dare you!　**507.8**

COMPUTERS -- CARTOONS AND CARICA-TURES
> *See also* Cartoons and caricatures

COMPUTERS -- EDUCATIONAL USE *See*
Computer-assisted instruction

COMPUTERS -- FICTION
Black, P. J. Urban outlaws **Fic**
Diamand, E. Flood and fire **Fic**

COMPUTERS AND CHILDREN
> *See also* Children; Computers

COMPUTERS AND PEOPLE WITH DISABILI-TIES
> *See also* Computers; People with disabilities

Conahan, Carolyn
(il) Bayrock, F. Bubble homes and fish farts **590**
The big wish **E**

CONCENTRATION CAMPS
Bunting, E. One candle **E**

CONCEPT FORMATION *See* Concept learning

CONCEPT LEARNING
Mineko Mamada Which is round? Which is bigger? **E**

CONCEPT LEARNING
> *See also* Concepts; Psychology of learning

CONCEPTS
Fisher, V. Everything I need to know before I'm five **E**
Freymann, S. Food for thought **E**
Jocelyn, M. Same same **E**

CONCEPTS
> *See also* Perception

CONCERTS
Potter, A. Jubilee! **92**

CONCERTS
> *See also* Amusements; Music

CONCERTS -- FICTION
Draper, S. M. The silver secret **Fic**
Zoola Palooza **E**
The conch bearer. Divakaruni, C. B. **Fic**

CONCORD (MASS.) -- FICTION
Look, L. Alvin Ho **Fic**

CONCORD (MASS.), BATTLE OF, 1775
Brown, D. Let it begin here! **973.3**
Fradin, D. B. Let it begin here! **973.3**

CONCRETE -- TESTING
> *See also* Strength of materials

CONCRETE CONSTRUCTION
> *See also* Building

Concrete poetry. Bodden, V. **809.1**

CONDENSERS (STEAM)
> *See also* Steam engines

CONDORS
Goldish, M. California condors **598**
Harasymiw, N. D. Condors in danger **598.9**
Condors in danger. Harasymiw, N. D. **598.9**

CONDUCT OF LIFE

Barker, D. Maybe right, maybe wrong **370.1**
Bredsdorff, B. The Crow-girl **Fic**
Curtis, J. L. I'm gonna like me **E**
Graves, S. But why can't I? **152.4**
Graves, S. Not fair, won't share **152.4**
MacGregor, C. Think for yourself **170**
McIntyre, T. The behavior survival guide for kids **158**
Medearis, A. S. Seven spools of thread **E**
Of thee I sing **179**
O'Neill, A. Estela's swap **E**
Pryor, K. J. Cooperation **177**
Pryor, K. J. Courage **179**
Pryor, K. J. Honesty **177**
Pryor, K. J. Kindness **177**
Pryor, K. J. Respect **177**
Pryor, K. J. Tolerance **177**
Rosenthal, A. K. Cookies **E**
Tang, G. Math fables **513**
Van Draanen, W. Flipped **Fic**

CONDUCT OF LIFE
> *See also* Ethics; Human behavior; Life skills

CONDUCT OF LIFE -- FICTION
Abouet, M. Akissi **Fic**
Betty Bunny didn't do it **E**
Derrick, D. G. Animals don't, so I won't! **E**
Foreman, M. Friends **E**
Harper, J. Miles to the finish **E**
Here comes Santa Cat **E**
Idle, M. Flora and the penguin **E**
McDonnell, P. The monsters' monster **E**
Rau, D. M. Robot, Go Bot! **E**
Schneider, J. The meanest birthday girl **E**
Tan, S. Rules of summer **E**

CONDUCT OF LIFE -- GRAPHIC NOVELS
Cammuso, F. Knights of the lunch table: the dragon players **741.5**

CONDUCT OF LIFE -- LITERARY COLLEC-TIONS
Gavin, J. School for princes **398.209**

CONDUCTING
> *See also* Music

Conducting action research to evaluate your school library. Sykes, J. A. **027.8**
Conducting basic and advanced searches. Porterfield, J. **025.04**

CONDUCTORS (MUSIC)
Krull, K. Lives of the musicians **920**
Rubin, S. G. Music was IT: young Leonard Bernstein **92**

CONDUCTORS (MUSIC)
> *See also* Musicians; Orchestra

Cone, Claribel, 1864-1929
About
Fillion, S. Miss Etta and Dr. Claribel **92**
Cone, Etta, 1870-1949

Berkes, M. C. Over in Australia **782.42**

Berkes, M. Over in the forest **E**

Blackstone, S. My granny went to market **E**

Blechman, N. Night light **E**

Bodach, V. Tally charts **510**

Brown, M. W. Another important book **E**

Browne, A. One gorilla **513.2**

Butler, J. Bedtime in the jungle **E**

Cabrera, J. One, two, buckle my shoe **E**

Carle, E. 10 little rubber ducks **E**

Carter, D. A. 600 black spots **E**

Carter, D. A. Lots of bots **E**

Carter, D. A. One red dot **E**

Cave, K. One child, one seed **E**

Chichester-Clark, E. Little Miss Muffet counts to
ten **E**

Christelow, E. Five little monkeys jumping on the
bed **E**

Cohn, S. One wolf howls **599.77**

Count me in **513.2**

Counting crows **E**

Crews, D. Ten black dots **E**

Cuyler, M. 100th day worries **E**

Degman, L. 1 zany zoo **E**

Denise, A. Pigs love potatoes **E**

Dickinson, R. Over in the hollow **E**

Dobbins, J. Driving my tractor **E**

Donaldson, J. One Ted falls out of bed **E**

Ehrhardt, K. This Jazz man **E**

Elliott, D. One little chicken **E**

Emberley, R. Ten little beasties **E**

Engels, C. Knick knack paddy whack **782.42**

Falwell, C. Turtle splash! **E**

Feelings, M. Moja means one **E**

Fisher, V. How high can a dinosaur count? **513**

Fleming, D. Shout! Shout it out! **E**

Fleming, D. Count! **513**

Floca, B. Five trucks **E**

Formento, A. These bees count! **E**

Formento, A. This tree counts! **E**

Fox, M. Let's count goats! **E**

Franco, B. Bird songs **E**

Freymann, S. Food for thought **E**

Geisert, A. Roman numerals I to MM **513.5**

Giganti, P. Each orange had 8 slices **513.5**

Giganti, P. How many snails? **513**

Goldstone, B. Greater estimations **519.5**

Gravett, E. The rabbit problem **E**

Guy, G. F. Fiesta! **E**

Halfmann, J. Eggs 1 2 3 **591.4**

Harris, T. Tally cat keeps track **E**

Hawk, F. Count down to Fall **508.2**

Hays, A. J. Kindergarten countdown **E**

Himmelman, J. 10 little hot dogs **E**

Hines, A. G. 1, 2, buckle my shoe **E**

Hip hip hooray! it's Family Day! **E**

Hoban, T. Let's count **513.2**

Holub, J. Apple countdown **E**

Horáček, P. One spotted giraffe **E**

How many jelly beans? **513.2**

How much is a million? **513**

Hughes, S. Olly and me 1 2 3 **E**

Hutchins, P. 1 hunter **E**

Hutchins, P. Ten red apples **E**

Jane, P. Little goblins ten **E**

Jay, A. 1 2 3 **E**

Jonas, A. Splash! **E**

Katz, K. Ten tiny babies **E**

Keats, E. J. Over in the meadow **E**

Kerr, J. One night in the zoo **E**

Langstaff, J. M. Over in the meadow **782.42**

Lee, H. V. 1, 2, 3 go! **495.1**

Leuck, L. One witch **E**

Levine, A. A. Monday is one day **E**

Ljungkvist, L. Follow the line **E**

Lobel, A. 10 hungry rabbits **E**

Lobel, A. One lighthouse, one moon **E**

Long, E. One drowsy dragon **E**

Lottridge, C. B. One watermelon seed **E**

MacDonald, M. R. How many donkeys? **398.2**

Maloney, P. One foot two feet **E**

Mannis, C. D. One leaf rides the wind **E**

Marino, G. One too many **E**

Markle, S. How many baby pandas? **599.78**

Marshall, N. Numbers **E**

Martin, B. Chicka chicka 1, 2, 3 **E**

Marzollo, J. Help me learn subtraction **513.2**

Marzollo, J. Help me learn numbers 0-20 **E**

Marzollo, J. Ten little Christmas presents **E**

Math-terpieces **510**

McGrath, B. B. Teddy bear counting **E**

Melvin, A. Counting birds **E**

Merriam, E. 12 ways to get to 11 **510**

Milich, Z. City 1 2 3 **E**

Moerbeek, K. Count 1 to 10 **E**

Mora, P. Uno, dos, tres: one, two, three **E**

Morales, Y. Just a minute **398.2**

Moss, L. Zin! zin! zin! a violin **E**

Murphy, S. J. Coyotes all around **519.5**

Murphy, S. J. Jack the builder **513**

Murphy, S. J. Just enough carrots **513.2**

Murphy, S. J. Leaping lizards **E**

Murphy, S. J. Mall mania **513**

Murray, A. One two that's my shoe! **E**

Norman, K. Ten on the sled **E**

Numeroff, L. J. When sheep sleep **E**

One family **E**

Otoshi, K. One **E**

Otoshi, K. Zero **E**

Pallotta, J. Ocean counting **E**

Pamintuan, M. Twelve haunted rooms of Halloween **E**

Paul, A. W. Count on Culebra   **E**

Peters, L. W. Frankie works the night shift   **E**

Pistoia, S. Counting   **513.211**

Raschka, C. Five for a little one   **E**

Reasoner, C. One blue fish   **E**

Roop, P. Down East in the ocean   **E**

Rose, D. L. One nighttime sea   **513.2**

Rose, D. L. The twelve days of winter   **E**

Rosen, M. J. Chanukah lights   **E**

Rubin, A. How many fish?   **513**

Sayre, A. P. One is a snail, ten is a crab   **E**

Schertle, A. 1, 2, I love you   **E**

Schmandt-Besserat, D. The history of counting   **513.2**

Schwartz, D. M. On beyond a million   **513.5**

Sebe, M. Let's count to 100!   **E**

Seeger, L. V. One boy   **E**

Sendak, M. Bumble-Ardy   **E**

Sendak, M. One was Johnny   **E**

Shields, C. D. Wombat walkabout   **E**

Stiegemeyer, J. Gobble-gobble crash!   **E**

Stiegemeyer, J. Seven little bunnies   **E**

Tafuri, N. The big storm   **E**

Tang, G. Math fables   **513**

Ten moonstruck piglets   **E**

Thompson, L. How many cats?   **E**

Thompson, L. Little Quack   **E**

Thong, R. One is a drummer   **E**

Thornhill, J. The wildlife 1 2 3   **E**

Trapani, I. Haunted party   **E**

Tudor, T. 1 is one   **E**

Wadsworth, O. A. Over in the meadow   **E**

Wells, R. Emily's first 100 days of school   **E**

Werner, S. Bugs by the numbers   **595.7**

Williams, S. Let's go visiting   **E**

Wilson, K. A frog in the bog   **E**

Winter, J. Josefina   **513.2**

Yoon, S. One, two, buckle my shoe   **E**

Young, C. Ten birds   **E**

Zelinsky, P. O. Knick-knack paddywhack!   **782.42**

Zuffi, S. Art 123   **E**

COUNTING -- FICTION

Happy punks 1 2 3   **E**

Savage, S. Ten orange pumpkins   **E**

Tullet, H. 10 times 10   **E**

Counting birds. Melvin, A.   **E**

Counting by 7s. Sloan, H. G.   **Fic**

Counting crows.   **E**

Counting on Grace. Winthrop, E.   **Fic**

COUNTRIES *See* Nations

Countries in our world [series]

Brownlie, A. South Africa in our world   **968.06**

Brownlie, A. Sudan in our world   **962.4**

Countries of the world [series]

Bean, R. United Kingdom   **941**

Croy, A. Colombia   **986.1**

Croy, A. Guatemala   **972.81**

Croy, A. Spain   **946**

Croy, E. United States   **973**

Dalal, A. K. India   **954**

Dalal, A. K. Laos   **959.4**

Deckker, Z. Brazil   **981**

Deckker, Z. Poland   **943.8**

Deckker, Z. Portugal   **946.9**

Giles, B. Nigeria   **966.9**

Green, J. Cuba   **972.91**

Green, J. Greece   **949.5**

Green, J. Jamaica   **972.92**

Green, J. Vietnam   **959.7**

Gruber, B. Mexico   **972**

Jackson, B. New Zealand   **993**

Mace, V. South Africa   **968**

McQuinn, C. Ireland   **941.5**

Phillips, C. Japan   **952**

Phillips, C. Sweden   **948.5**

Russell, H. Germany   **943**

Samuels, C. Iraq   **956.7**

Shields, S. D. Turkey   **956.1**

Turner, K. Australia   **994**

Whitfield, S. Afghanistan   **958.1**

Williams, B. Canada   **971**

Young, E. Israel   **956.94**

COUNTRY AND WESTERN MUSIC *See* Country music

The **country** bunny and the little gold shoes. Heyward, D.   **E**

Country explorers [series]

Oluonye, M. N. Nigeria   **966.9**

Riehecky, J. China   **951**

Streissguth, T. Mexico   **972**

COUNTRY LIFE

Barbour, K. Mr. Williams   **92**

Crews, D. Bigmama's   **92**

Guest, E. H. Iris and Walter   **E**

Waddell, M. Tiny's big adventure   **E**

COUNTRY LIFE -- FICTION

Blakemore, M. F. The spy catchers of Maple Hill   **Fic**

Ransom, C. Rebel McKenzie   **Fic**

COUNTRY LIFE -- ILLINOIS -- FICTION

Peck, R. A long way from Chicago   **Fic**

COUNTRY LIFE -- JAPAN

Art and life in rural Japan   **952**

COUNTRY LIFE -- VIRGINIA -- FICTION

Ransom, C. Rebel McKenzie   **Fic**

COUNTRY MUSIC

Bertholf, B. Long gone lonesome history of country music   **781.642**

George-Warren, H. Honky-tonk heroes & hillbilly angels   **920**

Country road ABC. Geisert, A.   **E**

COUNTY GOVERNMENT

The **cow** who clucked. Fleming, D. E
Cowboy Boyd and Mighty Calliope. Moser, L. E
Cowboy country. Scott, A. H. 978
Cowboy Jose. Elya, S. M. E
Cowboy Ned and Andy. Stein, D. E. E
Cowboy up! Flood, N. B. E
COWBOYS
 Bill Pickett, rodeo-ridin' cowboy 636.2
 Lester, J. Black cowboy, wild horses E
COWBOYS *See* Cowhands
COWBOYS -- FICTION
 Cowpoke Clyde and Dirty Dawg E
 Dicamillo, K. Leroy Ninker saddles up Fic
 Moser, L. Cowboy Boyd and Mighty Calliope E
Cowboys and coffin makers. Coulter, L. 331.7
Cowboys and the wild West. Staton, H. 978
Cowcher, Helen
 Desert elephants 599.67
Cowdrey, Richard
 (il) Fletcher, R. The Sandman E
Cowell, Cressida
 That rabbit belongs to Emily Brown E
Cowen-Fletcher, Jane
 Hello puppy! E
Cowgirl Kate and Cocoa. Silverman, E. E
The **cowgirl** way. George-Warren, H. 978
Cowgirls. Branzei, S. 920.72
COWGIRLS *See* Cowhands
 Branzei, S. Cowgirls 920.72
 Green, C. R. Calamity Jane 978
COWHANDS
 Bill Pickett, rodeo-ridin' cowboy 636.2
 Freedman, R. In the days of the vaqueros 636.2
 George-Warren, H. The cowgirl way 978
 Olson, T. How to get rich on a Texas cattle drive 978
 Scott, A. H. Cowboy country 978
 Staton, H. Cowboys and the wild West 978
COWHANDS
 See also Frontier and pioneer life; Ranch life
COWHANDS -- FICTION
 Bruins, D. The legend of Ninja Cowboy Bear E
 Elya, S. M. Cowboy Jose E
 Frisch, A. A night on the range E
 Gribnau, J. Kick the cowboy E
 Hemphill, H. The adventurous deeds of Deadwood Jones Fic
 Janni, R. Every cowgirl needs a horse E
 Janni, R. Every cowgirl needs dancing boots E
 Kimmel, E. A. Little Britches and the rattlers E
 Langdo, B. Tornado Slim and the magic cowboy hat E
 Lawson, D. M. Tex E
 Lester, J. Black cowboy, wild horses E
 Montijo, R. The Halloween Kid E
 Schur, M. Gullible Gus Fic
 Silverman, E. Cowgirl Kate and Cocoa E

Stein, D. E. Cowboy Ned and Andy E
Timberlake, A. The dirty cowboy E
COWHANDS -- SONGS
 See also Music; Songs
Cowing, Sue
 You will call me Drog Fic
Cowles, Rose
 (il) The amazing International Space Station 629
 (il) Science detectives 507
Cowley, Joy
 Chameleon chameleon 597.95
 Red-eyed tree frog 597.8
 Snake and Lizard Fic
Cowlick! Ditchfield, C. E
Cowpoke Clyde and Dirty Dawg. E
Cows. Diemer, L. 636.2
COWS *See* Cattle
COWS -- FICTION
 Alsdurf, P. It's milking time E
 Bar-el, D. Audrey (cow) Fic
 Cazet, D. Minnie and Moo, hooves of fire Fic
 LaRochelle, D. Moo! E
 MacLachlan, P. Fly away Fic
Cows sweat through their noses. Seuling, B. 590
Cows to the rescue. Himmelman, J. E
Cox, Alexander
 (ed) Who's in charge? 320.3
Cox, Carole
 Shakespeare kids 792.9
Cox, David
 (il) Walker, K. I hate books! Fic
Cox, Judy
 Butterfly buddies Fic
 Carmen learns English E
 Go to sleep, Groundhog! E
 My family plays music E
 Nora and the Texas terror Fic
 One is a feast for Mouse E
 Puppy power Fic
 Ukulele Hayley Fic
Cox, Lynne
 Elizabeth, queen of the seas E
Cox, Steve
 (il) Fine, A. The diary of a killer cat Fic
 (il) Kroll, S. Stuff! E
 (il) Paxton, T. The marvelous toy 782.42
Coxe, Molly
 Branley, F. M. The Big Dipper 523.8
Coxon, Michele
 Termites on a stick 599.8
Coy, John
 Eyes on the goal Fic
 Hoop genius E
 Love of the game Fic
 Strong to the hoop E
 Top of the order Fic

See also Insects

CRICKETS -- FICTION

Bunting, E. Christmas cricket   E

Carle, E. The very quiet cricket   E

Feldman, T. Harry Cat and Tucker Mouse: Tucker's beetle band   E

Norac, C. Swing Cafe   E

Selden, G. The cricket in Times Square   **Fic**

Wheeler, L. Old Cricket   E

Crickets in the dark. Gonzales, D.   **595.7**

Crickwing. Cannon, J.   E

Crictor. Ungerer, T.   E

CRIME

Schroeder, A. Robbers!   **364.15**

Somervill, B. A. Graphing crime   **364**

CRIME

See also Administration of criminal justice; Social problems

CRIME -- FICTION

Pullman, P. Two crafty criminals!   **Fic**

CRIME PREVENTION

See also Crime

CRIME PREVENTION -- TECHNOLOGICAL INNOVATIONS

Batman science   **600**

CRIME STORIES *See* Mystery fiction

CRIMES AGAINST HUMANITY

See also Crime

CRIMES OF HATE *See* Hate crimes

CRIMES WITHOUT VICTIMS

See also Crime; Criminal law

Crimi, Carolyn

Dear Tabby   E

Rock 'n' roll Mole   E

CRIMINAL INVESTIGATION

Arroyo, S. L. How crime fighters use math   **363.2**

Graham, I. Forensic technology   **363.2**

Perritano, J. Science beats crime   **363.2**

Townsend, J. Famous forensic cases   **363.2**

CRIMINAL INVESTIGATION

See also Law enforcement

CRIMINAL INVESTIGATION -- FICTION

Stealing the game   **Fic**

CRIMINAL LAW

See also Law

CRIMINAL PSYCHOLOGY

See also Psychology

CRIMINALISTICS *See* Forensic sciences

CRIMINALS

See also Crime

CRIMINALS -- FICTION

Anderson, J. D. Minion   **Fic**

Black, P. J. Urban outlaws   **Fic**

Fork-tongue charmers   **Fic**

Masterminds   **Fic**

CRIMINALS -- IDENTIFICATION

See also Criminal investigation; Identification

CRIMINOLOGY *See* Crime

The **crimson** cap. Howard, E.   **Fic**

Crinkleroot's guide to giving back to nature. Arnosky, J.   **333.95**

CRIPPLED CHILDREN *See* Children with physical disabilities

CRISIS MANAGEMENT

See also Management; Problem solving

Crisp, Dan

(il) Butler, D. H. The case of the library monster   **Fic**

Crispin at the edge of the world. Avi   **Fic**

Crispin: the cross of lead. Avi   **Fic**

Criss cross. Perkins, L. R.   **Fic**

Crist, James J.

Siblings   **306.8**

What to do when you're sad & lonely   **158**

What to do when you're scared & worried   **158**

CRITICAL THINKING

See also Decision making; Logic; Problem solving; Reasoning; Thought and thinking

CRITICISM

See also Aesthetics; Literature; Rhetoric

Critter sitter. Richards, C.   E

CRO-MAGNONS

See also Prehistoric peoples

The **Croaky** Pokey! Long, E.   E

Croatia. Cooper, R.   **949.7**

CROATIA

Cooper, R. Croatia   **949.7**

CROCHETING

See also Needlework

CROCKERY *See* Pottery

Crockett, Davy, 1786-1836

About

Green, C. R. Davy Crockett   **976.8**

Miller, B. Davy Crockett gets hitched   **398.2**

Crockett, Sally Ann Thunder Ann Whirlwind

About

Kellogg, S. Sally Ann Thunder Ann Whirlwind Crockett   **398.2**

Miller, B. Davy Crockett gets hitched   **398.2**

The **crocodile** blues. Polhemus, C.   E

Crocodile tears. Horowitz, A.   **Fic**

Crocodile vs. wildebeest. Meinking, M.   **597.98**

CROCODILES

See also Reptiles

Bodden, V. Crocodiles   **597.98**

Gibbons, G. Alligators and crocodiles   **597.98**

Hamilton, S. L. Attacked by a crocodile   **597.98**

Jackson, T. Saltwater crocodile   **597.98**

Markle, S. Crocodiles   **597.98**

Meinking, M. Crocodile vs. wildebeest   **597.98**

Pringle, L. P. Alligators and crocodiles!   **597.98**

Simon, S. Crocodiles & alligators   **597.98**

Sheehan, S. Cuba **972.91**
Tracy, K. We visit Cuba **972.91**
Cuba. Green, J. **972.91**
CUBA -- FICTION
Colon, E. Good-bye, Havana! Hola, New York! **E**
Flores-Gabis, E. 90 miles to Havana **Fic**
A mango in the hand **E**
Wells, R. My Havana **Fic**
CUBA -- HISTORY -- 1909-1933 -- FICTION
The drum dream girl **E**
Engle, M. The wild book **Fic**
CUBA -- SOCIAL LIFE AND CUSTOMS
Ada, A. F. Under the royal palms **813**
Sheen, B. Foods of Cuba **641.5**
CUBAN AMERICANS
Parker-Rock, M. Alma Flor Ada **92**
CUBAN AMERICANS -- FICTION
Colon, E. Good-bye, Havana! Hola, New York! **E**
Corbett, S. Free baseball **Fic**
Sacre, A. La Noche Buena **E**
CUBAN COOKING
Sheen, B. Foods of Cuba **641.5**
Cuban Missile Crisis. Stein, R. C. **972.91**
CUBAN MISSILE CRISIS, 1962
Stein, R. C. Cuban Missile Crisis **972.91**
CUBAN MISSILE CRISIS, 1962 -- FICTION
Wiles, D. Countdown **Fic**
CUBAN REFUGEES -- FICTION
Flores-Gabis, E. 90 miles to Havana **Fic**
CUBANS
Bernier-Grand, C. T. Alicia Alonso **92**
CUBANS -- FICTION
Lupica, M. Heat **Fic**
CUBE ROOT
See also Arithmetic
Cubes. Olson, N. **516**
CUBES
Olson, N. Cubes **516**
CUBIC EQUATIONS
See also Equations
CUBIC MEASUREMENT *See* Volume (Cubic content)
CUBISM
See also Art
CUCHULAIN (LEGENDARY CHARACTER)
See also Legendary characters
The **cuckoo's** haiku. Rosen, M. J. **811**
Cuckoo. Cucu. Ehlert, L. **398.2**
CUCKOOS -- FICTION
Stead, P. C. A home for Bird **E**
Cuddle up, goodnight. Cleminson, K. **E**
Cuevas, Michelle
The masterwork of a painting elephant **Fic**
Cuffari, Richard
(il) Cohen, B. Thank you, Jackie Robinson **Fic**
Cuffe-Perez, Mary

Skylar **Fic**
Cullen, Lynn
Dear Mr. Washington **Fic**
Cullum, Carolyn N.
The storytime sourcebook II **027.62**
CULTIVATED PLANTS
See also Agriculture; Gardening; Plants
CULTS
See also Religions
CULTS -- FICTION
Flanagan, J. Halt's peril **Fic**
Flanagan, J. The kings of Clonmel **Fic**
Cultural atlas for young people [series]
Corbishley, M. The Middle Ages **940.1**
Murray, J. Africa **960**
A cultural history of women in America [series]
Bingham, J. The Great Depression **973.91**
Coster, P. A new deal for women **305.4**
Gorman, J. L. The modern feminist movement **305.4**
Stearman, K. Women of today **305.4**
Cultural Journeys. Gates, P. **372**
CULTURAL PLURALISM -- UNITED STATES -- HISTORY
Stefoff, R. A different mirror for young people **305.8**
CULTURAL POLICY
See also Culture; Intellectual life
CULTURAL PROPERTY -- PROTECTION
Abouraya, K. L. Hands around the library **962.055**
CULTURAL RELATIONS
See also Intellectual cooperation; International cooperation; International relations
CULTURAL TOURISM
See also Tourist trade
Cultural traditions in Mexico. Peppas, L. **394.26**
Cultural traditions in my world [series]
Peppas, L. Cultural traditions in Mexico **394.26**
CULTURE
Banting, E. England **942**
Foo Yuk Yee Malaysia **959.5**
Kent, D. Mexico **972**
Listen, Slowly **Fic**
Sheehan, S. Malta **945.8**
CULTURE CONFLICT
Walker, N. Why do we fight? **303.6**
CULTURE CONFLICT
See also Ethnic relations; Ethnopsychology; Race relations
Culture in action [series]
Bliss, J. Art that moves **791.43**
Bliss, J. Preening, painting, and piercing **391**
Guillain, C. Punk **781.66**
Hensley, L. Art for all **701**
Mack, J. Journals and blogging **808**
Miles, L. Making a recording **781.49**

Hanukkah moon **E**

Dabcovich, Lydia

The polar bear son **398.2**

Dabek, Lisa

About

Montgomery, S. Quest for the tree kangaroo **599.2**

Dabija, Violeta

(il) A leaf can be **E**

A rock can be **552**

(il) Water can be **E**

Dabrowski, Kristen

My first monologue book **812**

My second monologue book **812**

My third monologue book **812**

Dacey, Bob

(il) Firestone, M. What's the difference between a frog and a toad? **597.8**

(il) Koontz, R. M. What's the difference between a butterfly and a moth? **595.7**

(il) Manushkin, F. Miriam's cup **222**

The **dachshund**. Schweitzer, K. **636.7**

DaCosta, Barbara

Nighttime Ninja **E**

Dad and Pop. Bennett, K. **E**

Dad, Jackie, and me. Uhlberg, M. **E**

DADAISM -- FICTION

Jackson, S. Mimi's Dada Catifesto **E**

Dadblamed Union Army cow. Fletcher, S. **E**

Daddo, Andrew

Goodnight, me **E**

Daddy Adventure Day. Keane, D. **E**

Daddy calls me doodlebug. Lester, J. D. **E**

The **Daddy** Goose treasury. French, V. **E**

Daddy hug. Warnes, T. **E**

Daddy makes the best spaghetti. Hines, A. G. **E**

Daddy, papa, and me. Newman, L. **E**

Daffodil, crocodile. Jenkins, E. **E**

The **dagger** Quick. Eames, B. **Fic**

Dahl, Michael

Guardian of Earth **Fic**

The man behind the mask **Fic**

Nap time for Kitty **E**

Dahl, Roald

The BFG **Fic**

Charlie and the chocolate factory **Fic**

The enormous crocodile **Fic**

James and the giant peach **Fic**

The magic finger **Fic**

Matilda **Fic**

About

Dahl, R. The missing golden ticket and other splendiferous secrets **92**

Dahl, R. More about Boy **92**

Dahlia. McClintock, B. **E**

Daigle, Stephan

Charles, V. M. The birdman **E**

Daigneault, Sylvie

(il) Milway, K. S. The good garden **Fic**

The **Daily** Comet. Asch, F. **E**

Daily life in a Plains Indian village, 1868. Terry, M. B. H. **970.004**

DAIRIES See Dairying

DAIRY PROCESSING

Malam, J. Journey of a glass of milk **637**

DAIRY-FREE COOKING

See also Cooking

DAIRYING

Aliki Milk from cow to carton **637**

Gibbons, G. The milk makers **637**

Peterson, C. Clarabelle **636.2**

Peterson, C. Extra cheese, please! **637**

DAIRYING

See also Agriculture; Livestock industry

Daisy Dawson is on her way! Voake, S. **Fic**

Daisy gets lost. Raschka, C. **E**

Dakin, Glenn

The Society of Dread **Fic**

The Society of Unrelenting Vigilance **Fic**

Dakins, Todd

(il) The art of stone skipping and other fun old-time games **790.1**

Dakos, Kalli

A funeral in the bathroom **811**

DAKOTA INDIANS

Bruchac, J. A boy called Slow: the true story of Sitting Bull **92**

The Christmas coat **92**

Ehrlich, A. Wounded Knee: an Indian history of the American West **970.004**

Freedman, R. Indian chiefs **970.004**

Turner, A. W. Sitting Bull remembers **92**

Zimmerman, D. J. Saga of the Sioux **970.004**

Dalai Lama XIV, 1935-

About

Cotter, C. Kids who rule **920**

Kimmel, E. C. Boy on the lion throne **92**

Dalal, A. Kamala

India **954**

Laos **959.4**

Dale Earnhardt, Jr. Rappoport, K. **92**

Dale, Anna

Magical mischief **Fic**

Dale, Penny

(il) Fine, A. Jamie and Angus together **Fic**

Dalen & Gole. Deas, M. **741.5**

Dalena, Antonello

(il) Salati, G. Race for the Ultrapods **741.5**

Daley, Michael J.

Space station rat **Fic**

DALMATIANS -- FICTION

Bauer, M. G. Just a dog **Fic**

Dalton, John, 1766-1844

Posada, M. Dandelions **583**

DANDELIONS -- FICTION

Middleton, C. Nibbles: a green tale **E**

Daneshvari, Gitty

Class is not dismissed! **Fic**

School of Fear **Fic**

The **Danger** Box. Balliett, B. **Fic**

Danger in space. Holden, H. M. **629.45**

Danger zone: dieting and eating disorders [series]

Zahensky, B. A. Diet fads **613.2**

The **dangerous** alphabet. Gaiman, N. **E**

DANGEROUS ANIMALS

Jenkins, S. Never smile at a monkey **591.6**

Stewart, M. Deadliest animals **591.6**

DANGEROUS ANIMALS

See also Animals

The **dangerous** book for boys. Iggulden, C. **031.02**

Dangerous crossing. Krensky, S. **Fic**

Daniel at the Siege of Boston, 1776. Calkhoven, L. **Fic**

Daniel Boone. Green, C. R. **976.9**

Daniel Boone's great escape. Spradlin, M. P. **92**

Daniel Hale Williams. **92**

Daniel, Alan

(il) Howe, D. Bunnicula **Fic**

Daniel, Noel

(ed) Grimm, J. Fairy tales of the Brothers Grimm **398.2**

DANISH LANGUAGE

See also Language and languages; Norwegian language; Scandinavian languages

DANISH LITERATURE

See also Literature; Scandinavian literature

Danks, Fiona

Run wild! **790.1**

Schofield, J. Make it wild **796.5**

Danneberg, Julie

The big test **E**

Family reminders **Fic**

Monet paints a day **E**

Danny and the dinosaur. Hoff, S. **E**

Danny is done with diapers. O'Connell, R. **E**

Danny's drawing book. Heap, S. **E**

Danny's first snow. Gore, L. **E**

Dant, Traci

Some kind of love **811**

Danticat, Edwidge, 1969-

Danticat, E. Eight days **E**

Danzig, Dianne

Babies don't eat pizza **649**

Danziger, Paula

Amber Brown goes fourth **Fic**

Amber Brown is feeling blue **Fic**

Amber Brown is green with envy **Fic**

Amber Brown is not a crayon **Fic**

Amber Brown sees red **Fic**

Amber Brown wants extra credit **Fic**

Forever Amber Brown **Fic**

I, Amber Brown **Fic**

It's Justin Time, Amber Brown **E**

You can't eat your chicken pox, Amber Brown **Fic**

Darbyshire, Kristen

Put it on the list **E**

Dare the wind. Fern, T. **92**

Dare to be scared 4. San Souci, R. **S**

Dare, Virginia, b. 1587

About

Haddix, M. P. Sabotaged **Fic**

Daredevil. McCarthy, M. **E**

The **daring** adventures of Penhaligon Brush. Rogan, S. J. **Fic**

The **daring** book for girls. Buchanan, A. J. **031.02**

The **daring** book for girls. Buchanan, A. J. **646.700**

The **daring** Miss Quimby. Whitaker, S. **92**

Darius Bell and the glitter pool. Hirsch, O. **Fic**

The **dark.** **E**

DARK AGES *See* Middle Ages

Dark Emperor and other poems of the night. **811**

Dark fiddler: the life and legend of Nicolo Paganini. Frisch, A. **92**

The **dark** game. Janeczko, P. B. **327.12**

The **dark** is rising. Cooper, S. **Fic**

Dark life. Falls, K. **Fic**

DARK MATTER (ASTRONOMY)

See also Matter

Dark night. Monfreid, D. d. **E**

The **dark** pond. Bruchac, J. **Fic**

The **dark** stairs. Byars, B. C. **Fic**

Dark's tale. Grabien, D. **Fic**

A **dark,** dark tale. Brown, R. **E**

The **dark-thirty.** McKissack, P. C. **S**

Darkfall. Hardy, J. **Fic**

Darkness creeping. Shusterman, N. **S**

Darksolstice. Llewellyn, S. **Fic**

Darling, Christina

(comp) Classic horse stories **808.8**

Darling, Kathy

Cobb, V. We dare you! **507.8**

Darling, Louis

(il) Butterworth, O. The enormous egg **Fic**

(il) Cleary, B. Beezus and Ramona **Fic**

(il) Cleary, B. Henry and Beezus **Fic**

(il) Cleary, B. Henry and Ribsy **Fic**

(il) Cleary, B. Henry Huggins **Fic**

(il) Cleary, B. The mouse and the motorcycle **Fic**

(il) Cleary, B. Ramona the pest **Fic**

(il) Cleary, B. Runaway Ralph **Fic**

Darrow, Sharon

Yafi's family **E**

Darth Paper strikes back. Angleberger, T. **Fic**

Darwin. McGinty, A. B. **92**

Darwin, Beatrice

Davis, Tony

Roland Wright: brand-new page **Fic**

Roland Wright: future knight **Fic**

Davy Crockett. Green, C. R. **976.8**

Davy Crockett gets hitched. Miller, B. **398.2**

Dawes, Dominique, 1976-

About

Washburn, K. Heart of a champion **796.440**

Dawson, Arthur L.

(il) Jackson Issa, K. Howard Thurman's great hope **92**

Dawson, Kate

(jt. auth) Aronica-Buck, B. Over the moon **811**

Dawson, Scott

(il) Rosenstock, B. Fearless **92**

(il) Tarshis, L. I survived the shark attacks of 1916 **Fic**

Dawson, Willow

(il) Becker, H. The big green book of the big blue sea **577.7**

Lila & Ecco's do-it-yourself comics club **741.5**

DAY

Bailey, J. Sun up, sun down **525**

Heidbreder, R. Noisy poems for a busy day **811**

Murphy, S. J. It's about time! **529**

Ormerod, J. Miss Mouse's day **E**

Rau, D. M. Day and night **508**

DAY

See also Chronology; Time

DAY -- FICTION

Cabrera, J. Here we go round the mulberry bush **E**

Carluccio, M. The sounds around town **E**

Cleminson, K. Cuddle up, goodnight **E**

Durango, J. Angels watching over me **E**

Franco, B. Bird songs **E**

George, J. C. Morning, noon, and night **E**

Gomi, T. The great day **E**

Hopgood, T. Wow! said the owl **E**

Lamb, A. Tell me the day backwards **E**

Levine, A. A. Monday is one day **E**

The loud book! **E**

Martin, R. Moon dreams **E**

Melvin, A. Counting birds **E**

Milgrim, D. Time to get up, time to go **E**

Ormerod, J. Miss Mouse's day **E**

Roode, D. Little Bea **E**

Rosenthal, A. K. Yes Day! **E**

Rylant, C. All in a day **E**

Spanyol, J. Little neighbors on Sunnyside Street **E**

Viorst, J. Alexander and the terrible, horrible, no good, very bad day **E**

Williams, V. B. Lucky song **E**

Yee, W. H. Summer days and nights **E**

Day and night. Rau, D. M. **508**

A day at the New Amsterdam Theatre. Amendola, D. **792.6**

Day by day. Gal, S. **E**

The **day** Dirk Yeller came to town. Casanova, M. **E**

DAY DREAMS *See* Fantasy

The **day** I had to play with my sister. Bonsall, C. N. **E**

A day in the life of Murphy. Provensen, A. **E**

Day in the life. rain forest animals [series]

Ganeri, A. Capybara **599.35**

A day in the life. Rain forest animals [series]

Ganeri, A. Anaconda **597.96**

Ganeri, A. Howler monkey **599.8**

Ganeri, A. Jaguar **599.75**

Ganeri, A. Lemur **599.8**

Ganeri, A. Macaw **598**

Ganeri, A. Orangutan **599.8**

Ganeri, A. Piranha **597**

Ganeri, A. Poison dart frog **597.8**

Ganeri, A. Tarantula **595.4**

A day in the life. sea animals [series]

Spilsbury, L. Dolphin **599.5**

Spilsbury, L. Jellyfish **593.5**

Spilsbury, L. Octopus **594**

Spilsbury, L. Sea turtle **597.92**

Spilsbury, L. Seal **599.79**

A day in the life: desert animals [series]

Ganeri, A. Arabian oryx **599.64**

Ganeri, A. Fennec fox **599.77**

Ganeri, A. Meerkat **599.74**

Ganeri, A. Scorpion **595.4**

A **day** in the office of Doctor Bugspit. Gravel, E. **741.5**

The **day** Jimmy's boa ate the wash. Noble, T. H. **E**

The **day** Leo said I hate you. Harris, R. H. **E**

Day light, night light. Branley, F. M. **535**

The **day** of Ahmed's secret. Heide, F. P. **E**

DAY OF ATONEMENT *See* Yom Kippur

Day of the Dead. Johnston, T. **394.2**

DAY OF THE DEAD

See also Holidays

The **day** Ray got away. Johnson, A. **E**

The **day** the animals came. Weller, F. W. **E**

The **day** the babies crawled away. **E**

The **day** the cow sneezed. Flora, J. **E**

The **day** the crayons quit. Daywalt, D. **E**

The **day** the dinosaurs died. Brown, C. L. **567.9**

The **day** Tiger Rose said goodbye. **E**

A **day** with Dad. Holmberg, B. R. **E**

A **day** with paramedics. Shepherd, J. **362.18**

A **day** with Wilbur Robinson. Joyce, W. **E**

Day, Alexandra

Carl and the puppies **E**

Carl's sleepy afternoon **E**

Frank and Ernest **E**

Frank and Ernest play ball **E**

Day, Alyson

(ed) Creech, S. The great unexpected **Fic**

Cowcher, H. Desert elephants **599.67**

Guiberson, B. Z. Cactus hotel **583**

Johansson, P. The dry desert **577.5**

Johnson, R. L. A walk in the desert **577.54**

Lynch, W. Sonoran Desert **577.5**

Pyers, G. The biodiversity of deserts **577.5**

DESERT ECOLOGY

See also Ecology

Desert elephants. Cowcher, H. **599.67**

DESERT FAUNA See Desert animals

Desert giant. Bash, B. **583**

DESERT PLANTS

Johnson, R. L. A walk in the desert **577.54**

DESERT PLANTS

See also Deserts; Plant ecology; Plants

Desert Rose and her highfalutin hog. Jackson, A. **E**

DESERTIFICATION

See also Climate; Deserts

DESERTION AND NONSUPPORT

See also Divorce; Domestic relations

DESERTS

Serafini, F. Looking closely across the desert **578.7**

DESERTS -- FICTION

Flanagan, J. Erak's ransom **Fic**

Gonzalez, M. C. My colors, my world **E**

DESIGN

Henry, S. Making amazing art **745.5**

Oldham, T. Kid made modern **745.5**

Design and engineering for STEM [series]

Oxlade, C. Gadgets and games **688.7**

Spilsbury, R. Hi-tech clothes **746.9**

Design it! Arato, R. **745.2**

DESIGN PERCEPTION See Pattern perception

Design your own butterfly garden. Harkins, S. S. **638**

DESIGN, INDUSTRIAL See Industrial design

Arato, R. Design it! **745.2**

DESIGNED GENETIC CHANGE See Genetic engineering

DESIGNER DRUGS

LeVert, S. Ecstasy **362.29**

DESIGNERS

See also Artists

Designing a school library media center for the future. Erikson, R. **027.8**

Desimini, Lisa

(il) Aardema, V. Anansi does the impossible! **398.209**

(il) Annino, J. G. She sang promise: the story of Betty Mae Jumper, Seminole tribal leader **92**

(il) Doodle dandies **811**

(il) Lewis, J. P. The snowflake sisters **E**

Desk stories. O'Malley, K. **741.5**

Desmond, Viola Irene

About

Warner, J. Viola Desmond won't be budged! **92**

The **desperate** dog writes again. Christelow, E. **E**

Desperate journey. Murphy, J. **Fic**

Despite all obstacles: La Salle and the conquest of the Mississippi. Goodman, J. E. **92**

Desrocher, Jack

(il) Doeden, M. Eat right! **613.2**

(il) Donovan, S. Keep your cool! **616.85**

(il) Johnson, R. L. Amazing DNA **572.8**

(il) Johnson, R. L. Mighty animal cells **571.6**

(il) Nelson, S. K. Stay safe! **613.6**

Desrosiers, Sylvie

Hocus Pocus **E**

Dessert first. Durand, H. **Fic**

DESSERTS

Bowers, S. Ghoulish goodies **641.5**

DeVore, J. Ballerina cookbook **641.8**

Dunnington, R. Sweet eats **641.8**

DESSERTS

See also Cooking

DESSERTS -- FICTION

Bosch, P. This book is not good for you **Fic**

Destination solar system [series]

Sparrow, G. Destination Uranus, Neptune, and Pluto **523.4**

Destination Uranus, Neptune, and Pluto. Sparrow, G. **523.4**

Destination: Rocky Mountains. Grupper, J. **978**

DESTITUTION See Poverty

DETECTIVE AND MYSTERY STORIES

Pastis, S. Timmy failure : now look what you've done **Fic**

Shouldn't you be in school? **Fic**

Teague, D. Saving Lucas Biggs **Fic**

Wild boy and the black terror **Fic**

DETECTIVE AND MYSTERY STORIES See Mystery fiction

Detective Blue. **E**

Detective Dinosaur. Skofield, J. **E**

Detective Dinosaur undercover. Skofield, J. **E**

Detective Dinosaur: lost and found. Skofield, J. **E**

Detective Gordon. **Fic**

DETECTIVES

See also Police

DETECTIVES -- FICTION

The case of the stolen sixpence **Fic**

Grey, M. Hermelin the detective mouse **E**

Lawrence, C. P.K. Pinkerton and the pistol-packing widows **Fic**

Pastis, S. Timmy failure : now look what you've done **Fic**

Venable, C. A. F. Raining cats and detectives **Fic**

DETECTOR DOGS

Castaldo, N. F. Sniffer dogs **636.7**

The **detention** club. Yoo, D. **Fic**

DETERGENT POLLUTION OF RIVERS, LAKES, ETC. See Water pollution

Holub, J. Why do birds sing? **598**

Holub, J. Why do cats meow? **636.8**

Holub, J. Why do snakes hiss? **597.96**

Marshall, E. Fox and his friends **E**

Marshall, E. Three by the sea **E**

Marshall, J. Fox be nimble **E**

Marshall, J. Fox on stage **E**

Marshall, J. Fox on the job **E**

Marshall, J. Fox outfoxed **E**

McMullan, K. Pearl and Wagner: four eyes **E**

McMullan, K. Pearl and Wagner: one funny day **E**

Dial-a-ghost. Ibbotson, E. **Fic**

Diamand, Emily

Flood and fire **Fic**

Raiders' ransom **Fic**

Diamant-Cohen, Betsy

(ed) Children's services **027.62**

Booktalking bonanza **028.5**

Crash course in library services to preschool children **027.62**

Early literacy programming en Espanol **027.6**

A **diamond** in the desert. Fitzmaurice, K. **Fic**

Diamond Jim Dandy and the sheriff. Burell, S. **E**

Diamond life. Smith, C. R. **796.357**

The **diamond** of Darkhold. DuPrau, J. **Fic**

Diamond, Donna

(il) Paterson, K. Bridge to Terabithia **Fic**

DIAMONDS

Moore, H. The story behind diamonds **553.8**

DIARIES

Mack, J. Journals and blogging **808**

Stewart, S. The journey **E**

Wilson, N. H. Mountain pose **Fic**

DIARIES

See also Literature

DIARIES -- FICTION

Cavanaugh, N. J. This journal belongs to Ratchet **Fic**

Fleischman, P. The Matchbox diary **E**

Friedman, L. B. Too good to be true **Fic**

LaFleur, S. Listening for Lucca **Fic**

Patron, S. Behind the masks **Fic**

Sternberg, J. The top-secret diary of Celie Valentine **Fic**

DIARISTS

Frank, A. The diary of a young girl: the definitive edition **92**

Halilbegovich, N. My childhood under fire **949.7**

Hurwitz, J. Anne Frank: life in hiding **940.53**

Metselaar, M. Anne Frank: her life in words and pictures **92**

Rol, R. v. d. Anne Frank, beyond the diary **940.53**

Rubin, S. G. The Anne Frank Case: Simon Wiesenthal's search for the truth **92**

Diary of a baby wombat. French, J. **E**

Diary of a fly. Cronin, D. **E**

The **diary** of a killer cat. Fine, A. **Fic**

Diary of a spider. Cronin, D. **E**

Diary of a wimpy kid. Kinney, J. **Fic**

Diary of a wimpy kid [series]

Diary of a wimpy kid: dog days. Kinney, J. **Fic**

Diary of a wimpy kid: Greg Heffley's journal. Kinney, J. **Fic**

Diary of a wimpy kid: Rodrick rules. Kinney, J. **Fic**

Diary of a wimpy kid: the last straw. Kinney, J. **Fic**

Kinney, J. Diary of a wimpy kid **Fic**

Kinney, J. The third wheel **Fic**

DIARY OF A WIMPY KID (MOTION PICTURE)

Kinney, J. The wimpy kid movie diary **791.43**

Diary of a wombat. French, J. **E**

Diary of a worm. **E**

The **diary** of a young girl: the definitive edition. Frank, A. **92**

The **diary** of Melanie Martin; or, How I survived Matt the Brat, Michelangelo, and the Leaning Tower of Pizza. Weston, C. **Fic**

Dias, Bartholomeu, 1450?-1500

About

Fritz, J. Around the world in a hundred years **910.92**

Diaz, David

(il) Andrews-Goebel, N. The pot that Juan built **738**

(il) Bernier-Grand, C. T. Cesar **811**

(il) Bernier-Grand, C. T. Pablo Picasso **709.2**

(il) Brown, M. W. The little scarecrow boy **E**

(il) Bunting, E. Smoky night **E**

(il) Charest, E. M. Before you came **E**

(il) Chocolate, D. El barrio **E**

(il) De colores **782.42**

(il) Ford, C. Ocean's child **E**

(il) Jackson, J. Let there be peace on earth **782.42**

(il) Krull, K. Pocahontas **92**

(il) Krull, K. Wilma unlimited: how Wilma Rudolph became the world's fastest woman **92**

(il) Martin de Porres **282.092**

(il) Me, Frida **E**

(il) Sharing the seasons **811**

(il) Soto, G. Neighborhood odes **811**

(il) Wilbur, R. The disappearing alphabet **811**

DiCamillo, Kate

Dicamillo, K. Two for one **Fic**

Because of Winn-Dixie **Fic**

Dicamillo, K. Bink & Gollie **Fic**

Flora and Ulysses **Fic**

Great joy **E**

Leroy Ninker saddles up **Fic**

Louise **E**

The magician's elephant **Fic**

Mercy Watson fights crime **Fic**

Mercy Watson goes for a ride **Fic**

Mercy Watson to the rescue **Fic**

Mercy Watson: something wonky this way

DRILLING AND BORING (EARTH AND ROCKS)

Gray, S. H. Geology the study of rocks   **551**

DRINKING CUPS -- FICTION

Polacco, P. The blessing cup   **E**

Stanley, D. The cup and the crown   **Fic**

The **drinking** gourd. Monjo, F. N.   **E**

DRINKING OF ALCOHOLIC BEVERAGES

Gottfried, T. Alcohol   **362.292**

DRINKING PROBLEM See Alcoholism; Drinking of alcoholic beverages

DRINKING WATER

Kerley, B. A cool drink of water   **363.6**

DRINKING WATER

See also Water; Water supply

DRINKS See Alcoholic beverages; Beverages; Liquors

Drip, drop. Weeks, S.   **E**

Driscoll, Michael

A child's introduction to poetry   **808.81**

Drita, my homegirl. Lombard, J.   **Fic**

Drive. Clement, N.   **E**

Driven. Mitchell, D.   **92**

DRIVERS, AUTOMOBILE See Automobile drivers

Driving my tractor. Dobbins, J.   **E**

Drizzle. Van Cleve, K.   **Fic**

DROMEDARIES See Camels

Dronzek, Laura

(il) Henkes, K. Birds   **E**

(il) It is night   **E**

(il) Moonlight   **E**

(il) Shannon, G. Rabbit's gift   **398.2**

(il) Shannon, G. Tippy-toe chick, go!   **E**

(il) Shannon, G. White is for blueberry   **E**

Drop it, Rocket. Hills, T.   **E**

A **drop** of blood. Showers, P.   **612.1**

A **drop** of water. Wick, W.   **553.7**

DROPOUTS

See also Students; Youth

DROUGHT -- FICTION

Marino, G. Meet me at the moon   **E**

Droughts. Fradin, J. B.   **363.34**

DROUGHTS

Chin, J. Island   **508**

Fradin, J. B. Droughts   **363.34**

DROUGHTS

See also Meteorology

DROUGHTS -- FICTION

Conway, D. Lila and the secret of rain   **E**

Enderle, D. Crosswire   **Fic**

Hamilton, V. Drylongso   **Fic**

Jackson, A. Rainmaker   **Fic**

McKinnon, H. R. Franny Parker   **Fic**

Stanton, K. Papi's gift   **E**

Van Cleve, K. Drizzle   **Fic**

DROUGHTS -- FOLKLORE

Aardema, V. Bringing the rain to Kapiti Plain   **398.2**

DROUGHTS -- UNITED STATES

Cooper, M. L. Dust to eat   **973.917**

Garland, S. Voices of the dust bowl   **973.917**

A **drowned** maiden's hair. Schlitz, L. A.   **Fic**

The **drowned** vault. Wilson, N. D.   **Fic**

Drucker, Malka

Portraits of Jewish American heroes   **920**

DRUG ABUSE

Allman, T. Drugs   **616.86**

LeVert, S. Ecstasy   **362.29**

DRUG ABUSE

See also Social problems; Substance abuse

DRUG ABUSE -- FICTION

Elliott, Z. Bird   **E**

DRUG ABUSE -- TREATMENT

See also Therapeutics

DRUG EDUCATION

See also Health education

Drug facts [series]

Gottfried, T. Alcohol   **362.292**

Gottfried, T. Marijuana   **362.29**

LeVert, S. Ecstasy   **362.29**

LeVert, S. Steroids   **362.29**

Menhard, F. R. The facts about inhalants   **362.29**

DRUG RESISTANCE IN MICROORGANISMS

See also Microorganisms

DRUG THERAPY

See also Therapeutics

Drugs. Allman, T.   **616.86**

DRUGS

See also Pharmacy; Therapeutics

DRUGS -- ABUSE See Drug abuse

DRUGS AND CRIME

See also Crime; Drugs

DRUIDS AND DRUIDISM

Farmer, N. The Sea of Trolls   **Fic**

DRUIDS AND DRUIDISM

See also Celts; Religions

DRUIDS AND DRUIDISM -- FICTION

Farmer, N. The Islands of the Blessed   **Fic**

Farmer, N. The Land of the Silver Apples   **Fic**

Farmer, N. The Sea of Trolls   **Fic**

DRUM See Drums

Drum city. Guidone, T.   **E**

The **drum** dream girl.   **E**

Drumbeat in our feet. Keeler, P. A.   **793.3**

Drummer boy of John John. Greenwood, M.   **786.9**

Drummer Hoff. Emberley, B.   **398.8**

DRUMMERS (MUSICIANS) -- FICTION

The drum dream girl   **E**

Drummond, Allan

(il) Borden, L. The journey that saved Curious George   **92**

Energy island   **333.9**

DWELLINGS *See* Domestic architecture; Houses; Housing

DWELLINGS -- DESIGN AND CONSTRUCTION -- FICTION
Bean, J. Building our house **E**

DWELLINGS -- FICTION
Auxier, J. The Night Gardener **Fic**
Blakemore, M. F. The Water Castle **Fic**
Columbus, C. House of secrets **Fic**
dePaola, T. Jack **E**
Hyewon Yum This is our house **E**
Kirk, D. Library mouse **E**
Still life **Fic**

DwellStudio (Firm)
Good morning, toucan **E**
Goodnight, owl **E**

Dwight Eisenhower. Mara, W. **92**

Dwyer, Helen
Earthquakes! **551.2**
Floods! **551.48**
Tsunamis! **551.46**

Dyckman, Ame
Boy and Bot **E**
Tea party rules **E**
Wolfie the bunny **E**

Dyer, Alan
Mission to the moon **629.45**

Dyer, Brooke
(il) Santa Claus and the Three Bears **Fic**
(il) Yolen, J. Sleep, black bear, sleep **E**

Dyer, Heather
Ibby's magic weekend **Fic**

Dyer, Jane
(il) Appelt, K. Oh my baby, little one **E**
(il) Babies on the go **E**
(il) Beaumont, K. Move over, Rover **E**
(il) Krull, K. A woman for president **92**
(il) Lewis, R. A. Every year on your birthday **E**
(il) Lewis, R. A. I love you like crazy cakes **E**
(il) Melmed, L. K. Hurry! Hurry! Have you heard? **E**
(il) Rosenthal, A. K. Cookies **E**
(il) Santa Claus and the Three Bears **Fic**
(il) Spinelli, E. Sophie's masterpiece **E**

Dyer, Sarah
Batty **E**
Monster day at work **E**

DYES AND DYEING
See also Color; Pigments; Textile chemistry; Textile industry

DYING PATIENTS *See* Terminally ill
Dying to meet you. Klise, K. **Fic**

Dylan, Bob
Man gave names to all the animals **782.42**
About
When Bob met Woody **92**

Dynamic drag racers. Sandler, M. **629.228**
DYNAMICS
See also Mathematics; Mechanics

DYSFUNCTIONAL FAMILIES -- FICTION
Loftin, N. Nightingale's nest **Fic**
Lupica, M. Heavy hitters **Fic**
Child, L. Maude the not-so-noticeable Shrimpton **E**

DYSLEXIA -- FICTION
Engle, M. The wild book **Fic**

Dyson, Marianne J.
Home on the moon **629.45**

DYSTOPIAN FICTION
London, A. Proxy **Fic**
Lowry, L. Son **Fic**
MacHale, D. J. SYLO **Fic**

DYSTOPIAN FICTION
See also Fantasy fiction; Science fiction

DYSTOPIAS
See also Political science

E

E-I-E-I-O! **E**
E-MAIL
See also Data transmission systems; Telecommunication

E-mergency. Lichtenheld, T. **E**
Each kindness. **E**
Each living thing. Ryder, J. **E**
Each orange had 8 slices. Giganti, P. **513.5**

Eagen, Rachel
NASCAR **796.72**

Eager. Fox, H. **Fic**

Eager, Edward
Half magic **Fic**

Eagle Strike. Horowitz, A. **Fic**
EAGLES
See also Birds; Birds of prey
Gish, M. Eagles **598**
Markle, S. Eagles **598**
Read, T. C. Exploring the world of eagles **598**
Riggs, K. Eagles **598.9**
Wilcox, C. Bald eagles **598**

EAGLES -- FOLKLORE
Gregorowski, C. Fly, eagle, fly! **398.2**

Eamer, Claire
Before the World Was Ready **509**
Lizards in the sky **591.4**
The world in your lunch box **641.3**

Eames, Brian
The dagger Quick **Fic**

EAR
See also Head
Ganeri, A. Hearing **612.8**
Halvorson, K. Inside the ears **612.8**
Larsen, C. S. Crust and spray **612.8**

Cole, H. On the way to the beach — **E**
Formento, A. This tree counts! — **E**
Franco, B. Pond circle — **E**
Muldrow, D. We planted a tree — **E**
Shelby, A. The man who lived in a hollow tree — **E**

ECOLOGY -- FOLKLORE
The Barefoot book of Earth tales — **398.2**
MacDonald, M. R. Surf war! — **398.2**

Ecology the study of ecosystems. Gray, S. H. — **577**

ECOLOGY, HUMAN See Human ecology

ECONOMIC BOTANY
See also Agriculture; Botany

ECONOMIC CONDITIONS
McNeese, T. The Great Depression, 1929-1940 — **973.917**

ECONOMIC FORECASTING
See also Business cycles; Economics; Forecasting

ECONOMIC GEOLOGY
See also Geology

ECONOMIC HISTORY See Economic conditions

ECONOMIC POLICY -- UNITED STATES
Heinrichs, A. The great recession — **330.9**

ECONOMIC RECESSIONS See Recessions

ECONOMIC SUSTAINABILITY See Sustainable development

ECONOMIC ZOOLOGY
See also Zoology

ECONOMICS
Managing money — **332.02**
Payment methods — **332.4**

ECONOMISTS
Twenty-two cents — **92**

ECONOMY See Saving and investment

Ecosystems. Housel, D. J. — **577**
Ecosystems [series]
Banting, E. Caves — **577.5**

ECOSYSTEMS See Ecology

Ecosystems at risk. Aitken, S. — **551.6**

ECOTERRORISM
See also Environmental movement; Terrorism

ECOTOURISM
See also Tourist trade

Ecoworks [series]
Hunter, N. How carbon footprints work — **363.7**

ECSTASY (DRUG)
LeVert, S. Ecstasy — **362.29**

Ecuador. Foley, E. — **986.6**
ECUADOR
Foley, E. Ecuador — **986.6**

Ed and Kip. Chorao, K. — **E**
Ed Emberley's big green drawing book. Emberley, E. — **741.2**
Ed Emberley's big red drawing book. Emberley, E. — **741.2**
Ed Emberley's bye-bye, big bad bullybug! Ember-

ley, E. — **E**
Ed Emberley's drawing book of faces. Emberley, E. — **743**
Ed Emberley's drawing book: make a world. Emberley, E. — **741.2**
Ed Emberley's fingerprint drawing book. Emberley, E. — **741.2**
Ed Emberley's great thumbprint drawing book. Emberley, E. — **741.2**

EDAPHOLOGY See Soil ecology

EDDAS
See also Old Norse literature; Poetry; Scandinavian literature

Eddie & the gang with no name [series]
Bateman, C. Running with the Reservoir Pups — **Fic**
Eddie gets ready for school. Milgrim, D. — **E**
Eddie the raccoon. Friend, C. — **E**
Eddie's garden. Garland, S. — **E**
Eddie's kitchen. Garland, S. — **E**
Eddie's toolbox. Garland, S. — **E**
Eddie's war. Saller, C. F. — **Fic**

Edens, Cooper
(comp) Princess stories — **398.2**

Ederle, Gertrude, 1905-2003
About
Adler, D. A. America's champion swimmer: Gertrude Ederle — **92**
Krull, K. Lives of the athletes — **796**

EDGAR ALLAN POE AWARDS
See also Literary prizes; Mystery fiction
Edgar Allan Poe's apple pie. Lewis, J. P. — **811**
Edgar Allan's official crime investigation notebook. Amato, M. — **Fic**
Edgar Degas: paintings that dance. Cocca-Leffler, M. — **709**

Edgar, Elsbeth
The Visconti house — **Fic**

Edge books: kitchen science [series]
Bell-Rehwoldt, S. Science experiments that surprise and delight — **507.8**
Lew, K. Science experiments that fly and move — **507.8**
Wheeler-Toppen, J. Science experiments that explode and implode — **507.8**
Wheeler-Toppen, J. Science experiments that fizz and bubble — **507.8**

Edge books: making and breaking codes [series]
Bell-Rehwoldt, S. Speaking secret codes — **652**
Gregory, J. Breaking secret codes — **652**
Gregory, J. Making secret codes — **652**

Edge books. Paper airplanes [series]
Harbo, C. L. Paper airplanes: Captain, level 4 — **745.592**
Harbo, C. L. Paper airplanes: Copilot, level 2 — **745.592**
Harbo, C. L. Paper airplanes: Flight school, level

See also English literature; Satire

ENGLISH SPEECHES

See also English literature; Speeches

ENGLISH WIT AND HUMOR

See also English literature; Wit and humor

English, fresh squeezed! Shields, C. D.   **811**

English, Karen

The baby on the way   **E**

Francie   **Fic**

Hot day on Abbott Avenue   **E**

Nikki & Deja   **Fic**

Nikki & Deja: birthday blues   **Fic**

Nikki & Deja: the newsy news newsletter   **Fic**

Nikki and Deja: election madness   **Fic**

Skateboard party   **Fic**

Speak to me   **E**

ENGRAVERS

Judge, L. Yellowstone Moran   **92**

Woodruff, E. Fearless   **Fic**

ENGRAVERS

See also Artists

ENGRAVING

See also Art; Graphic arts; Illustration of books; Pictures

Enigma. Base, G.   **Fic**

ENIGMAS *See* Curiosities and wonders; Riddles

Enigmatic events. Blackwood, G. L.   **904**

The **enormous** crocodile. Dahl, R.   **Fic**

The **enormous** egg. Butterworth, O.   **Fic**

Enormous smallness.   **92**

Enos, Randall, 1936-

Mocha Dick   **Fic**

Enright, Amanda

(il) Rustad, M. E. H. Animals in fall   **578.4**

(il) Rustad, M. E. H. Fall apples   **634**

(il) Rustad, M. E. H. Fall harvests   **631.5**

Rustad, M. E. H. Fall leaves   **581.4**

(il) Rustad, M. E. H. Fall pumpkins   **635**

(il) Rustad, M. E. H. Fall weather   **508.2**

ENSEMBLES (MATHEMATICS) *See* Set theory

ENSEMBLES (MUSIC)

See also Music; Musical form; Musicians

ENSIGNS *See* Flags

Ensuring intellectual freedom and access to information in the school library media program. Adams, H. R.   **027.8**

ENTERPRISES *See* Business enterprises

ENTERTAINERS

Green, C. R. Buffalo Bill Cody   **978**

Krull, K. Fartiste   **Fic**

Weatherford, C. B. Oprah   **92**

Wills, C. A. Annie Oakley: a photographic story of a life   **92**

ENTERTAINERS -- FICTION

Ackerman, K. Song and dance man   **E**

Byars, B. C. The Golly sisters go West   **E**

Krull, K. Fartiste   **Fic**

Say, A. Kamishibai man   **E**

ENTERTAINING

Beery, B. Barbara Beery's pink princess party cookbook   **641.5**

ENTERTAINING

See also Etiquette; Home economics

Entertainment. Lusted, M. A.   **791**

ENTERTAINMENTS *See* Amusements

ENTOZOA *See* Parasites

ENTRÉES (COOKING)

Delicious vegetarian main dishes   **641.5**

Meaty main dishes   **641.82**

ENTREPRENEURS

Goldsworthy, S. Steve Jobs   **92**

Venezia, M. Steve Jobs & Steve Wozniak   **92**

ENTREPRENEURS

See also Businesspeople; Self-employed

ENTREPRENEURSHIP

See also Business; Capitalism; Small business

Jenkins, E. Lemonade in winter   **E**

ENURESIS

Bennett, H. J. Max Archer, kid detective: the case of the wet bed   **616.85**

ENVIRONMENT

Gray, S. H. Ecology the study of ecosystems   **577**

Environment action! [series]

Barnham, K. Recycle   **363.7**

Environment in focus [series]

Jakab, C. Waste management   **363.7**

ENVIRONMENTAL DEGRADATION

Stille, D. R. Nature interrupted   **577**

ENVIRONMENTAL DEGRADATION

See also Environment; Natural disasters

ENVIRONMENTAL DEGRADATION -- FICTION

Samworth, K. Aviary Wonders Inc. Spring Catalog and Instruction Manual   **Fic**

Environmental engineer. Horn, G.   **628**

ENVIRONMENTAL ETHICS

See also Ethics

ENVIRONMENTAL HEALTH

See also Environmental influence on humans; Public health

ENVIRONMENTAL HEALTH ENGINEERING *See* Sanitary engineering

ENVIRONMENTAL INFLUENCE ON HUMANS

See also Adaptation (Biology); Human ecology; Human geography

ENVIRONMENTAL LAW

See also Environmental policy; Environmental protection; Law

ENVIRONMENTAL LOBBY *See* Environmental movement

Exploring habitats [series]

Lynette, R. Who lives in a colorful coral reef? **591.7**

Lynette, R. Who lives in a deep, dark cave? **591.7**

Lynette, R. Who lives in a wet, wild rain forest? **591.7**

Lynette, R. Who lives on a towering mountain? **591.7**

Lynette, R. Who lives on the icy, cold tundra **591.7**

Exploring immigration. Ollhoff, J. **304.8**

Exploring our solar system [series]

Jefferis, D. Galaxies **523.1**

Jefferis, D. Space probes **629.43**

Jefferis, D. Star spotters **522**

Jefferis, D. The stars **523.8**

Exploring space robots. Kops, D. **629.46**

Exploring space travel. Waxman, L. H. **629.45**

Exploring the connection between children's literature and music. Carlow, R. **372**

Exploring the elements [series]

Kaner, E. Who likes the rain? **551.57**

Kaner, E. Who likes the snow? **551.57**

Kaner, E. Who likes the wind? **551.51**

Exploring the International Space Station. Waxman, L. H. **629.44**

Exploring the past. Croy, A. **930.1**

Exploring the solar system. Carson, M. K. **523.2**

Exploring the solar system. Tourville, A. D. **523.2**

Exploring the world of [series]

Read, T. C. Exploring the world of coyotes **599.77**

Read, T. C. Exploring the world of eagles **598**

Read, T. C. Exploring the world of seals and walruses **599.79**

Read, T. C. Exploring the world of wolves **599.77**

Exploring the world of coyotes. Read, T. C. **599.77**

Exploring the world of eagles. Read, T. C. **598**

Exploring the world of mammals. **599**

Exploring the world of seals and walruses. Read, T. C. **599.79**

Exploring the world of wolves. Read, T. C. **599.77**

EXPLOSIONS

Richardson, G. Kaboom! **500**

Wheeler-Toppen, J. Science experiments that explode and implode **507.8**

EXPLOSIVES

See also Chemistry

EXPOSED CHILDREN *See* Abandoned children

EXPRESS HIGHWAYS

See also Roads; Traffic engineering

EXPRESS SERVICE

See also Railroads; Transportation

EXPRESSIONISM (ART)

See also Art

EXTINCT ANIMALS

Jenkins, M. Can we save the tiger? **591.68**

Newland, S. Extinction! **576.8**

EXTINCT ANIMALS

See also Animals

EXTINCT CITIES

See also Archeology; Cities and towns

Barber, N. Lost cities **930.1**

EXTINCT CITIES -- FICTION

McKinlay, M. Below **Fic**

EXTINCTION (BIOLOGY)

See also Biology

Brown, C. L. The day the dinosaurs died **567.9**

Jenkins, M. Can we save the tiger? **591.68**

Newland, S. Extinction! **576.8**

EXTINCTION OF SPECIES, MASS *See* Mass extinctions

Extinction! Newland, S. **576.8**

Extra cheese, please! Peterson, C. **637**

Extra credit. Clements, A. **Fic**

Extra yarn. Barnett, M. **E**

EXTRAGALACTIC NEBULAE *See* Galaxies

The extraordinary adventures of Ordinary Boy [series]

Boniface, W. The hero revealed **Fic**

The **extraordinary** education of Nicholas Benedict. Stewart, T. L. **Fic**

Extraordinary endangered animals. Guerive, G. **333.95**

Extraordinary Ernie and Marvelous Maud. Watts, F. **Fic**

Extraordinary Jane. Harrison, H. E. **E**

The **extraordinary** Mark Twain (according to Susy) Kerley, B. **92**

EXTRASENSORY PERCEPTION

See also Parapsychology

EXTRASENSORY PERCEPTION -- FICTION

Lester, J. The old African **Fic**

Nelson, N. Bringing the boy home **Fic**

Rhodes, J. P. Ninth Ward **Fic**

EXTRASOLAR PLANETS

Kops, D. Exploring exoplanets **523.2**

Miller, R. Seven wonders beyond the solar system **523.8**

Portman, M. Are there other Earths? **523.2**

Wittenstein, V. O. Planet hunter **523.2**

EXTRASOLAR PLANETS

See also Planets

EXTRASOLAR PLANETS -- POETRY

Prelutsky, J. The swamps of Sleethe **811**

EXTRATERRESTRIAL BASES

See also Civil engineering

EXTRATERRESTRIAL BEINGS

Erickson, J. Alien abductions **001.9**

Saint-Exupery, A. d. The little prince **Fic**

EXTRATERRESTRIAL BEINGS

See also Life on other planets

EXTRATERRESTRIAL BEINGS -- FICTION

Alien encounter **Fic**

Brake, M. Alien Hunter's Handbook **576.8**

Brawer, M. Archie takes flight — Fic
DiTerlizzi, T. The battle for WondLa — Fic
Rex, A. Smek for president! — Fic

EXTRATERRESTRIAL BEINGS -- GRAPHIC NOVELS
Deas, M. Dalen & Gole — 741.5
Sfar, J. The little prince — 741.5

EXTRATERRESTRIAL BEINGS -- POETRY
Prelutsky, J. The swamps of Sleethe — 811

EXTRATERRESTRIAL LIFE See Life on other planets

EXTRAVEHICULAR ACTIVITY (SPACE FLIGHT)
Vogt, G. Spacewalks — 629.45

EXTRAVEHICULAR ACTIVITY (SPACE FLIGHT)
See also Space flight

Extreme animals. Davies, N. — 590
Extreme biology. — 570
Extreme rocks & minerals! Smithsonian Institution — 552
Extreme scientists. Jackson, D. M. — 509

EXTREME SPORTS
Hile, L. Surviving extreme sports — 796
Woods, M. Xtreme! Extreme sports facts and stats — 796

EXTREME SPORTS
See also Sports

Extreme survival [series]
Catel, P. Surviving stunts and other amazing feats — 613.6
Hile, L. Animal survival — 591.5
Hile, L. Surviving extreme sports — 796
Hurley, M. Surviving the wilderness — 613.6
Extreme weather. Simpson, K. — 551.6

EXTREME WEATHER
Evans, B. It's raining fish and spiders — 551.6

Eyckerman, Merel
(il) George, L. M. Back to school Tortoise — E
Eye. Macaulay, D. — 612.8

EYE
Cobb, V. Open your eyes — 612.8
Eye to eye — 573.88
Fielding, B. Animal eyes — 591.4
Larsen, C. S. Crust and spray — 612.8
Macaulay, D. Eye — 612.8
Markle, S. Lost sight — 617.7
Miller, S. S. All kinds of eyes — 591.4
Parker, V. Having an eye test — 617.7
Simon, S. Eyes and ears — 612.8

EYE
See also Face; Head

EYE -- FICTION
Auxier, J. Peter Nimble and his fantastic eyes — Fic
Kostecki-Shaw, J. S. My travelin' eye — E
An eye for art. — 708

An eye for color: the story of Josef Albers. Wing, N. — 92
The eye of the whale. — 599.5

Eye on energy [series]
Wheeler, J. C. Alternative cars — 629.222
Eye on the universe. Cole, M. D. — 522
Eye to eye. — 573.88

Eye to eye with endangered species [series]
Rodriguez, C. Bats — 599.4
Rodriguez, C. Cougars — 599.75
Stearns, P. M. Manatees — 599.5
Stearns, P. M. Whooping cranes — 598
An eyeball in my garden. — 811

EYEGLASSES -- FICTION
Brown, M. T. Arthur's eyes — E
Calvert, P. Princess Peepers — E
Giff, P. R. Watch out, Ronald Morgan! — E
McMullan, K. Pearl and Wagner: four eyes — E
Park, B. Junie B., first grader (at last!) — Fic
Eyes and ears. Simon, S. — 612.8
The eyes of the Amaryllis. Babbitt, N. — Fic
Eyes on the goal. Coy, J. — Fic

Eyewitness books [series]
Macquitty, M. Shark — 597.3
Mound, L. A. Insect — 595.7
Whalley, P. Butterfly & moth — 595.78

Eyewitness disaster [series]
Dwyer, H. Earthquakes! — 551.2
Dwyer, H. Floods! — 551.48
Dwyer, H. Tsunamis! — 551.46
Royston, A. Hurricanes! — 551.55
Royston, A. Storms! — 551.55
Eyewitness ocean. — 551.46

F

F is for fiesta. Elya, S. M. — E
F is for firefighting. — 628.9
The fabled fifth graders of Aesop Elementary School. Fleming, C. — Fic
Fables. Lobel, A. — Fic

FABLES
See also Fiction; Literature
The ant and the grasshopper — E
Bannerman, H. The story of Little Babaji — 823
Brett, J. Town mouse, country mouse — 398.24
Brown, M. Once a mouse — 398.2
Buhler, C. v. But who will bell the cats? — E
Cooney, B. Chanticleer and the fox — E
D'Aulaire, I. The two cars — E
Demi Buddha stories — 294.3
DePaola, T. Tomie dePaola's Favorite nursery tales — 398.2
Downard, B. The race of the century — 398.2
Forest, H. The contest between the Sun and the Wind — 398.2
Galdone, P. The monkey and the crocodile — 398.2

AUTHOR, TITLE, AND SUBJECT INDEX
TWENTY-SECOND EDITION

Crane, J. The clouds above **741.5**

Deutsch, B. Hereville: how Mirka got her sword **741.5**

Espinosa, R. The courageous princess **741.5**

Flight explorer **741.5**

Fuji, M. The big adventures of Majoko, volume 1 **741.5**

Hale, D. Rapunzel's revenge **741.5**

Kibuishi, K. Amulet, book one: The Stonekeeper **741.5**

Kovac, T. Wonderland **741.5**

Medley, L. Castle waiting **741.5**

Nytra, D. The secret of the stone frog **741.5**

Petersen, D. Mouse Guard: Fall 1152 **741.5**

Petersen, D. Mouse Guard: Winter 1152 **741.5**

Smith, J. Bone: out from Boneville **741.5**

Smith, J. Bone: Rose **741.5**

Smith, J. Bone: tall tales **741.5**

Soo, K. Jellaby: monster in the city **741.5**

Thompson, J. Magic Trixie **741.5**

FANTASY GRAPHIC NOVELS

    See also Graphic novels

Fantasy league. Lupica, M. **Fic**

FANTASY POETRY

    See also Poetry

FANTASY TELEVISION PROGRAMS

    See also Television programs

FANTASY WRITERS

Colbert, D. The magical worlds of Harry Potter **823**

Ellis, S. From reader to writer **372.62**

Peterson-Hilleque, V. J.K. Rowling, extraordinary author **92**

FANZINES

    See also Periodicals

Far beyond the garden gate: Alexandra David-Neel's journey to Lhasa. Brown, D. **92**

Far far away. Segal, J. **E**

Far from shore. Webb, S. **591.7**

FAR NORTH *See* Arctic regions

Far-flung adventures [series]

Stewart, P. Fergus Crane **Fic**

Far-out guide to asteroids and comets. Carson, M. K. **523.4**

Far-out guide to Earth. Carson, M. K. **525**

Far-out guide to Jupiter. Carson, M. K. **523.4**

Far-out guide to Mars. Carson, M. K. **523.4**

Far-out guide to Mercury. Carson, M. K. **523.4**

Far-out guide to Neptune. Carson, M. K. **523.4**

Far-out guide to Saturn. Carson, M. K. **523.4**

Far-out guide to the icy dwarf planets. Carson, M. K. **523.4**

Far-out guide to the moon. Carson, M. K. **523.3**

Far-out guide to the solar system [series]

Carson, M. K. Far-out guide to asteroids and comets **523.4**

Carson, M. K. Far-out guide to Earth **525**

Carson, M. K. Far-out guide to Jupiter **523.4**

Carson, M. K. Far-out guide to Mars **523.4**

Carson, M. K. Far-out guide to Mercury **523.4**

Carson, M. K. Far-out guide to Neptune **523.4**

Carson, M. K. Far-out guide to Saturn **523.4**

Carson, M. K. Far-out guide to the icy dwarf planets **523.4**

Carson, M. K. Far-out guide to the moon **523.3**

Carson, M. K. Far-out guide to the sun **523.7**

Carson, M. K. Far-out guide to Uranus **523.4**

Carson, M. K. Far-out guide to Venus **523.4**

Far-out guide to the sun. Carson, M. K. **523.7**

Far-out guide to Uranus. Carson, M. K. **523.4**

Far-out guide to Venus. Carson, M. K. **523.4**

Far-out science projects about Earth's sun and moon. Gardner, R. **523**

Faraway home. Kurtz, J. **E**

A **faraway** island. **Fic**

Farber, E. S.

Seagulls don't eat pickles **Fic**

Farber, Norma

How the hibernators came to Bethlehem **E**

Faria, Rosana

(il) Cottin, M. The black book of colors **E**

Farías, Carolina

(il) When Christmas feels like home **E**

Farley follows his nose. Johnston, L. **E**

Farley, Brianne

Ike's incredible ink **E**

Farley, Robin

Mia and the too big tutu **E**

Farley, Walter

The Black Stallion **Fic**

Farlow, James Orville

Bringing dinosaur bones to life **567.9**

Farm. Cooper, E. **E**

FARM ANIMALS *See* Domestic animals

FARM BUILDINGS

    See also Buildings

FARM CROPS *See* Farm produce

FARM EQUIPMENT *See* Agricultural machinery

FARM FAMILIES

    See also Family

FARM LABORERS *See* Agricultural laborers

FARM LIFE

Bateman, T. April foolishness **E**

Gammell, S. Once upon MacDonald's farm **E**

Geisert, A. Thunderstorm **E**

Hodge, D. Up we grow! **630**

Katz, J. Meet the dogs of Bedlam Farm **636.7**

Lindsey, K. Sweet potato pie **E**

Purmell, A. Apple cider making days **E**

FARM LIFE

    See also Country life; Farmers

FARM LIFE -- CALIFORNIA -- FICTION

Unusual chickens for the exceptional poultry farm-

FASTS AND FEASTS -- ISLAM *See* Islamic holidays

FASTS AND FEASTS -- JUDAISM *See* Jewish holidays

Fat cat. MacDonald, M. R.   **398.209**

FATALLY ILL PATIENTS *See* Terminally ill

FATE AND FATALISM

    See also Philosophy

FATE AND FATALISM -- FICTION

Echo   **Fic**

The **fate** of Achilles. Landmann, B.   **883**

FATHER AND CHILD -- FICTION

Are the dinosaurs dead, Dad?   **E**

The bear's sea escape   **E**

Cummings, T. Giddy-up, daddy!   **E**

Koehler, F. How to cheer up dad   **E**

Marino, G. Following Papa's song   **E**

When a dad says "I love you"   **E**

Father's Day. Rockwell, A. F.   **E**

FATHER'S DAY

    See also Holidays

FATHER'S DAY -- FICTION

Rockwell, A. F. Father's Day   **E**

FATHER-CHILD RELATIONSHIP

    See also Children; Fathers; Parent-child relationship

FATHER-CHILD RELATIONSHIP -- FICTION

Are the dinosaurs dead, Dad?   **E**

Cummings, T. Giddy-up, daddy!   **E**

Koehler, F. How to cheer up dad   **E**

Marino, G. Following Papa's song   **E**

Paulsen, G. Road trip   **Fic**

When a dad says "I love you"   **E**

FATHER-DAUGHTER RELATIONSHIP

A bear in war   **E**

Biden, J. Don't forget, God bless our troops **355.1**

FATHER-DAUGHTER RELATIONSHIP

    See also Daughters; Father-child relationship; Fathers

FATHER-DAUGHTER RELATIONSHIP -- FICTION

Cavanaugh, N. J. This journal belongs to Ratchet   **Fic**

Christopher, L. Flyaway   **Fic**

Gephart, D. Olivia Bean, trivia queen   **Fic**

Lord, C. Half a chance   **Fic**

Raschka, C. Everyone can learn to ride a bicycle **E**

Saturday is Dadurday   **E**

Say, A. The favorite daughter   **E**

Smith, R. Chupacabra   **Fic**

Sovern, M. J. The meaning of Maggie   **813.6**

Surfer Chick   **E**

Van Draanen, W. Sammy Keyes and the killer cruise   **Fic**

FATHER-SON RELATIONSHIP

    See also Father-child relationship; Fathers; Sons

FATHER-SON RELATIONSHIP -- FICTION

Applesauce   **E**

Baker-Smith, G. Farther   **Fic**

Beaty, D. Knock knock   **E**

Brawer, M. Archie takes flight   **Fic**

Brawer, M. Water planet rescue   **Fic**

Buzzeo, T. One cool friend   **E**

Collins, P. L. The Deer watch   **E**

Durand, H. Mitchell goes bowling   **E**

Ering, T. B. The Almost fearless Hamilton Squidlegger   **E**

Fitzmaurice, K. A diamond in the desert   **Fic**

My father's arms are a boat   **E**

Night sky dragons   **Fic**

Poulsen, D. A. Old Man   **Fic**

FATHER-SON RELATIONSHIP -- GRAPHIC NOVELS

TenNapel, D. Cardboard   **Fic**

FATHERS

Browne, A. My dad   **E**

Herb, S. Connecting fathers, children, and reading   **028.5**

FATHERS

    See also Family; Men

FATHERS -- FICTION

Almond, D. My dad's a birdman   **Fic**

Bennett, K. Dad and Pop   **E**

Bennett, K. Your daddy was just like you   **E**

Bouchard, H. Harvey   **741.5**

Bransford, N. Jacob Wonderbar and the cosmic space kapow   **Fic**

Browne, A. My dad   **E**

Bunting, E. Pop's bridge   **E**

Carle, E. Mister Seahorse   **E**

Clement, N. Drive   **E**

Davies, J. The magic trap   **Fic**

Gaiman, N. Fortunately, the milk   **Fic**

Gantos, J. I am not Joey Pigza   **Fic**

Gephart, D. Olivia Bean, trivia queen   **Fic**

Glass, B. R. Blue-ribbon dad   **E**

Hill, K. Bo at Ballard Creek   **Fic**

Hof, M. Against the odds   **Fic**

Kang, H. Chengli and the Silk Road caravan   **Fic**

Mason, S. Moon pie   **Fic**

My tattooed dad   **E**

Pendziwol, J. Marja's skis   **E**

Qiong, Y. L. A New Year's reunion   **E**

Resau, L. Star in the forest   **Fic**

Rockwell, A. F. Father's Day   **E**

Rosenberg, L. Tyrannosuarus dad   **E**

Saturday is Dadurday   **E**

Smith, H. A. Keeping the night watch   **Fic**

Thompson, J. E. The girl from Felony Bay   **Fic**

Van Draanen, W. Sammy Keyes and the showdown in Sin City   **Fic**

See also Child psychology; Fear

FEAR IN CHILDREN -- FICTION

Rosenthal, E. I'll save you Bobo!   **E**

Fear itself. Clements, A.   **Fic**

FEAR OF THE DARK

Otis and the puppy   **E**

FEAR OF THE DARK

See also Fear; Fear in children

FEAR OF THE DARK -- FICTION

The dark   **E**

Otis and the puppy   **E**

Schneider, J. Bedtime monsters   **E**

Fearing, Mark

The great Thanksgiving escape   **E**

(il) How Martha saved her parents from green beans   **E**

(il) The three little aliens and the big bad robot   **E**

(il) A very witchy spelling bee   **E**

Fearless. Rosenstock, B.   **92**

Fearless. Woodruff, E.   **Fic**

Fearless Jack. Johnson, P. B.   **398.2**

Fearnley, Jan

Martha in the middle   **E**

Milo Armadillo   **E**

Mr. Wolf's pancakes   **E**

FEAST DAYS *See* Religious holidays

FEAST OF DEDICATION *See* Hanukkah

A **feast** of freedom. Staib, W.   **Fic**

FEAST OF LIGHTS *See* Hanukkah

Feasting bedbugs, mites, and ticks. Gleason, C.   **614.4**

Feathered dinosaurs. Lessem, D.   **567.9**

Feathers. Woodson, J.   **Fic**

FEATHERS

Feathers   **598.1**

Feathers.   **598.1**

Feathers for lunch. Ehlert, L.   **813**

FECES

Albee, S. Poop happened!   **363.7**

Berkowitz, J. Jurassic poop   **567.9**

Cusick, D. Get the scoop on animal poop   **590**

The Scoop on Poop   **E**

Track that scat!   **591.47**

Feder, Jane

Spooky friends   **E**

FEDERAL COURTS *See* Courts -- United States

FEDERAL GOVERNMENT

See also Constitutional law; Political science; Republics

FEDERAL RESERVE BANKS

See also Banks and banking

FEDERAL-STATE RELATIONS

See also Federal government; State governments

Federle, Tim

Better Nate than ever   **Fic**

Five, six, seven, Nate!   **Fic**

Feed the children first.   **940**

FEEDING BEHAVIOR IN ANIMALS *See* Animals -- Food

Feeding friendsies. Bloom, S.   **E**

Feeding the sheep. Schubert, L.   **E**

FEEDS

See also Animals -- Food

Feel the force! Adams, T.   **530**

FEELING *See* Perception; Touch

Feeling better. Rashkin, R.   **616.89**

Feelings. Aliki   **152.4**

Feelings. Balouch, K.   **E**

Feelings, Muriel

Jambo means hello   **E**

Moja means one   **E**

Feelings, Tom

(il) Feelings, M. Jambo means hello   **E**

(il) Feelings, M. Moja means one   **E**

(il) Lester, J. To be a slave   **326**

(il) Soul looks back in wonder   **811**

Feeney, Siri Weber

(il) Allen, K. The first American flag   **929.9**

(il) Mortensen, L. Writing the U.S. Constitution   **342**

Feeney, Stephanie

Sun and rain   **996.9**

FEET *See* Foot

Fehlau, Dagmar

(il) Bunting, E. My robot   **E**

Feiffer, Jules

Bark, George   **E**

Rupert Can Dance   **E**

(il) Feiffer, K. Henry, the dog with no tail   **E**

(il) Feiffer, K. My side of the car   **E**

(il) Juster, N. The annotated Phantom tollbooth **813**

(il) Juster, N. The odious Ogre   **E**

(il) Juster, N. The phantom tollbooth   **Fic**

Lowry, L. The birthday ball   **Fic**

Feiffer, Kate

But I wanted a baby brother!   **E**

Double pink   **E**

Henry, the dog with no tail   **E**

My mom is trying to ruin my life   **E**

My side of the car   **E**

President Pennybaker   **E**

The problem with the Puddles   **Fic**

Feigenbaum, Aaron

American alligators   **597.98**

Emergency at Three Mile Island   **621.48**

Feiler, Bruce S.

Walking the Bible   **222**

Feinberg, Barbara

Welcome to Lizard Motel   **028.5**

Feinstein, Stephen

Barack Obama   **92**

Fiestas: a year of Latin American songs of celebration. Orozco ... **782.42**

Fifty cents and a dream. Asim, J. ... **370.92**

Figgs & phantoms. Raskin, E. ... **Fic**

Fight for freedom. Bobrick, B. ... **973.3**

FIGHTER PLANES

   Abramson, A. S. Fighter planes up close ... **623.74**

Fighter planes up close. Abramson, A. S. ... **623.74**

FIGHTING *See* Battles; Boxing; Bullfights; Dueling; Fencing; Gladiators; Military art and science; Naval art and science; Self-defense; Self-defense for women; War

Fighting fire! Cooper, M. L. ... **363.37**

Fighting for equality. Boomhower, R. E. ... **92**

The **fighting** ground. Avi ... **Fic**

Figley, Marty Rhodes

   John Greenwood's journey to Bunker Hill ... **973.3**

   Prisoner for liberty ... **92**

FIGURE DRAWING

   See also Artistic anatomy; Drawing

FIGURE PAINTING

   See also Artistic anatomy; Painting

Figure skating. McDougall, C. ... **796.91**

FIGURE SKATING *See* Ice skating

FIGURES OF SPEECH

   It's raining cats and dogs ... **616.85**

File under: 13 suspicious incidents. ... **Fic**

FILIPINO AMERICANS -- FICTION

   Postcards from Pismo ... **Fic**

Filippenko, Alexei V.

          About

   Jackson, E. B. The mysterious universe ... **523.8**

Filling the family tree. Ollhoff, J. ... **929**

Fillion, Susan

   Miss Etta and Dr. Claribel ... **92**

Fillmore, Millard, 1800-1874

          About

   Gottfried, T. Millard Fillmore ... **92**

FILM ADAPTATIONS

   See also Motion pictures

FILM DIRECTION *See* Motion pictures -- Production and direction

FILM DIRECTORS *See* Motion picture producers and directors

FILM FESTIVALS

   See also Festivals

FILM NOIR

   See also Motion pictures

FILM PRODUCERS *See* Motion picture producers and directors

FILM PRODUCTION *See* Motion pictures -- Production and direction

FILMMAKING *See* Motion pictures -- Production and direction

Filmmaking & documentaries. Hill, Z. B. ... **791.43**

FILMS *See* Filmstrips; Motion pictures

FILMSTRIPS

   See also Audiovisual materials; Photography

FINANCE, PERSONAL *See* Personal finance

FINANCIAL CRASHES *See* Financial crises

FINANCIAL CRISES

   Heinrichs, A. The great recession ... **330.9**

FINANCIAL PANICS *See* Financial crises

FINANCIAL PLANNING, PERSONAL *See* Personal finance

FINANCIERS

   Goldsworthy, S. Richard Branson ... **92**

FINCHES

   Pericoli, M. The true story of Stellina ... **E**

Finchler, Judy

   Miss Malarkey leaves no reader behind ... **E**

Find a face. Robert, F. ... **E**

Find the constellations. Rey, H. A. ... **523.8**

Find the right site. Truesdell, A. ... **025.04**

Find where the wind goes. Jemison, M. C. ... **92**

Find your way online. Rabbat, S. ... **025.04**

A **finder's** magic. Pearce, P. ... **Fic**

A **finders-keepers** place. Leal, A. H. ... **Fic**

Finding a voice : women's fight for equality in U.S. society [series]

   Gelletly, L. A woman's place in early America ... **305.4**

Finding Buck McHenry. Slote, A. ... **Fic**

Finding family. Bolden, T. ... **Fic**

Finding food and water. Champion, N. ... **613.6**

Finding home. Markle, S. ... **599.2**

Finding Providence: the story of Roger Williams. Avi ... **92**

Finding Ruby Starling. Rivers, K. ... **Fic**

Finding Serendipity. ... **Fic**

Finding spring. ... **E**

Finding the worm. ... **Fic**

FINDING THINGS *See* Lost and found possessions

Finding your way. Champion, N. ... **613.6**

Findlay, Diane

   (ed) LibrarySparks: library lessons ... **027.62**

A **fine** St. Patrick's day. Wojciechowski, S. ... **E**

A **fine** white dust. Rylant, C. ... **Fic**

Fine, Anne

   The diary of a killer cat ... **Fic**

   Jamie and Angus together ... **Fic**

Fine, Edith Hope

   Armando and the blue tarp school ... **E**

Fine, Howard

   (il) Moore, L. Beware, take care ... **811**

   (il) Palatini, M. Piggie pie! ... **E**

The **finest** hours. Sherman, C. ... **910.916**

FINGER GAMES *See* Finger play

FINGER PAINTING

   See also Child artists; Painting

FINGER PLAY

FIRE PREVENTION
See also Fires

FIRE STATIONS *See* Fire departments

Fire truck. Sis, P.   **E**

Fire truck. Bingham, C.   **628.9**

Fire trucks on the move. Jango-Cohen, J.   **628.9**

Fire! Godkin, C.   **577.2**

Fire! Fuego! Brave bomberos. Elya, S. M.   **E**

Fire, bed, & bone. Branford, H.   **Fic**

FIREARMS INDUSTRY

  Wyckoff, E. B. The man behind the gun: Samuel Colt and his revolver   **92**

Firebird. Pirotta, S.   **398.2**

Firebird. Copeland, M.   **E**

Fireboy to the rescue! Miller, E.   **613.6**

The firefighters. Whiting, S.   **E**

Firefighters A to Z. Demarest, C. L.   **628.9**

Firefighters at work. Kenney, K. L.   **628.9**

Firefighters! speeding! spraying! saving! Hubbell, P.   **E**

FIREFLIES -- FICTION

  Carle, E. The very lonely firefly   **E**

  Little, K. G. The time of the fireflies   **Fic**

  Nutt, R. Amy's light   **E**

Firefly animal rescue series

  Bow, P. Chimpanzee rescue   **599.8**

Firefly July and other very short poems. Janeczko, P. B.   **811**

Firegirl. Abbott, T.   **Fic**

The firehouse light. Nolan, J.   **363.3**

The firekeeper's son. Park, L. S.   **E**

FIREMEN AND FIREWOMEN *See* Fire fighters

FIREPLACES

  See also Architecture -- Details; Buildings; Heating; Space heaters

FIREPROOFING

  See also Fire insurance; Fire prevention

FIRES

  Champion, N. Fire and cooking   **796.54**

  Cooper, M. L. Fighting fire!   **363.37**

  Marrin, A. Flesh & blood so cheap   **974.7**

FIRES

  See also Accidents; Disasters; Fire

FIRES -- CHICAGO (ILL.)

  Murphy, J. The great fire   **977.3**

FIRES -- FICTION

  Choldenko, G. Al Capone does my homework **Fic**

  Garretson, D. Wildfire run   **Fic**

  Munro, R. Go! go! go!   **E**

The fires beneath the sea. Millet, L.   **Fic**

The fires of Merlin. Barron, T. A.   **Fic**

Fireside, Bryna J.

  Private Joel and the Sewell Mountain seder **Fic**

Firestone, Mary

  Top 50 reasons to care about giant pandas   **599.78**

  Top 50 reasons to care about rhinos   **599.66**

Top 50 reasons to care about tigers   **599.75**

What's the difference between a frog and a toad?   **597.8**

Fireworks. Rau, D. M.   **662**

FIREWORKS

  See also Amusements

FIREWORKS

  Cobb, V. Fireworks   **662**

  Rau, D. M. Fireworks   **662**

FIRMS *See* Business enterprises

FIRST AID

  See also Health self-care; Home accidents; Medicine; Nursing; Rescue work; Sick

The first American flag. Allen, K.   **929.9**

First Americans [series]

  Bjorklund, R. The Hopi   **970.004**

  Burgan, M. The Arapaho   **978**

  De Capua, S. The Cheyenne   **970.004**

  De Capua, S. The Choctaw   **970.004**

  De Capua, S. The Comanche   **970.004**

  De Capua, S. The Menominee   **970.004**

  De Capua, S. The Shawnee   **970.004**

  De Capua, S. The Shoshone   **970.004**

  Hicks, T. A. The Chumash   **970.004**

  King, D. C. The Haida   **970.004**

  King, D. C. The Huron   **970.004**

  King, D. C. The Inuit   **970.004**

  King, D. C. The Mohawk   **970.004**

  King, D. C. The Nez Perce   **970.004**

  King, D. C. The Ojibwe   **970.004**

  King, D. C. The Powhatan   **970.004**

  King, D. C. The Seminole   **970.004**

First big book of dinosaurs. Hughes, C. D.   **567.9**

First big book of the ocean. Hughes, C. D.   **551.4**

The first Christmas. Williams, S.   **232.9**

First day. Mackall, D. D.   **E**

First day in grapes. Perez, L. K.   **E**

First day of school. Rockwell, A. F.   **E**

First day of school. Barber, N.   **372**

FIRST DAY OF SCHOOL -- FICTION

  Diesen, D. The pout-pout fish goes to school   **E**

  Foxy   **E**

  Ganz-Schmitt, S. Planet Kindergarten   **E**

  Rosenberry, V. Vera's first day of school   **E**

  Schmid, P. Oliver and his alligator   **E**

  You're wearing that to school?!   **E**

  Yum, H. Mom, it's my first day of kindergarten! **E**

The first day of winter. Fleming, D.   **E**

First dive to shark dive. Lourie, P.   **797.2**

The first drawing.   **E**

First facts. Data mania [series]

  Aboff, M. Pigs, cows, and probability   **519.2**

First facts. Whales and dolphins up close [series]

  Rake, J. S. Blue whales up close   **599.5**

  Rake, J. S. Humpback whales up close   **599.5**

First facts: easy origami [series]

Foley, Tim
  (il) Yomtov, N. The Bambino: the story of Babe Ruth's legendary 1927 season **92**
Folgueira, Rodrigo
  Ribbit! **E**
Foli, Gianluca
  (il) Cali, D. The bear with the sword **E**
FOLIAGE See Leaves
Folk. Handyside, C. **781.62**
FOLK ART
  Art from her heart: folk artist Clementine Hunter **92**
FOLK ART
  See also Art; Art and society
FOLK ARTISTS
  Aston, D. H. Dream something big **E**
FOLK BELIEFS See Folklore; Superstition
FOLK DANCING
  See also Dance
The **Folk** Keeper. Billingsley, F. **Fic**
FOLK LITERATURE
  Fredericks, A. D. African legends, myths, and folk-tales for readers theatre **812**
  Gobble You Up! **398.2**
  MacDonald, M. R. When the lights go out **027.62**
FOLK LITERATURE
  See also Folklore; Literature
FOLK LORE See Folklore
FOLK MUSIC
  Alcorn, S. Odetta, the queen of folk **92**
  Handyside, C. Folk **781.62**
FOLK MUSIC
  See also Music
FOLK MUSIC -- FICTION
  Passing the music down **E**
FOLK MUSIC -- UNITED STATES
  Seeger, R. C. American folk songs for children in home, school, and nursery school **782.42**
FOLK MUSICIANS
  Alcorn, S. Odetta, the queen of folk **92**
  Christensen, B. Woody Guthrie, poet of the people **782.421**
  Krull, K. Lives of the musicians **920**
FOLK SONGS
  The 12 days of Christmas **782.42**
  De colores and other Latin-American folk songs for children **781.62**
  Engels, C. Knick knack paddy whack **782.42**
  Favorite folk songs **782.42**
  Isadora, R. 12 days of Christmas **782.42**
  Langstaff, J. M. Frog went a-courtin' **782.42**
  Langstaff, J. M. Oh, a-hunting we will go **782.42**
  Langstaff, J. M. Over in the meadow **782.42**
  Leodhas, S. N. Always room for one more **782.42**
  Let's sing together **782.42**
  Long, L. The twelve days of Christmas **782.42**
  Ray, J. The twelve days of Christmas **782.42**
  Rueda, C. Let's play in the forest while the wolf is not around **782.42**
  Spirin, G. The twelve days of Christmas **782.42**
  Taback, S. There was an old lady who swallowed a fly **782.421**
FOLK SONGS
  See also Folklore; Songs; Vocal music
FOLK SONGS -- UNITED STATES
  Cabrera, J. Old MacDonald had a farm **782.42**
  The Farmer in the dell **782.42**
  The Fox went out on a chilly night **782.42**
  Hopkinson, D. Home on the range **92**
  I hear America singing! **782.42**
  Isadora, R. Old Mikamba had a farm **E**
  Pinkney, B. Hush, little baby **782.42**
  Quattlebaum, M. Jo MacDonald saw a pond **E**
  Sleepytime songs **782.42**
  Voake, C. Tweedle dee dee **782.42**
FOLK TALES See Folklore; Legends
FOLKLORE
  Alley, Z. B. There's a wolf at the door **398.2**
  Andrews, J. Rude stories **398.2**
  The August House book of scary stories **398.2**
  Aylesworth, J. Goldilocks and the three bears **398.2**
  Aylesworth, J. The mitten **398.2**
  Aylesworth, J. My grandfather's coat **E**
  The Barefoot book of Earth tales **398.2**
  Barton, B. The little red hen **398.2**
  Barton, B. The three bears **398.2**
  Berner, R. S. Definitely not for little ones **398.2**
  Blackstone, S. Storytime **398.2**
  The Blue fairy book **398.2**
  Brett, J. Gingerbread baby **398.2**
  Buehner, C. Goldilocks and the three bears **398.2**
  Cech, J. Rapunzel **398.2**
  Chapman, J. Sing a song of sixpence **398.8**
  Chichester-Clark, E. Goldilocks and the three bears **398.2**
  Clayton, S. P. Amazons! **398.2**
  Cousins, L. Yummy **398.2**
  Crews, N. Jack and the beanstalk **398.2**
  Daly, J. Sivu's six wishes **E**
  Daly, N. Pretty Salma **E**
  Davis, A. A hen for Izzy Pippik **Fic**
  Davis, D. Fandango stew **E**
  DePaola, T. Tomie dePaola's Favorite nursery tales **398.2**
  Doherty, B. Fairy tales **398.2**
  Egielski, R. The gingerbread boy **398.21**
  Ehrlich, A. A treasury of princess stories **398.2**
  Elya, S. M. Little Roja Riding Hood **E**
  Elya, S. M. Rubia and the three osos **398.2**
  Emberley, E. Chicken Little **398.2**
  Emberley, E. The red hen **398.2**
  Ernst, L. C. Little Red Riding Hood: a newfangled prairie tale **398.2**

Fleischman, P. Glass slipper, gold sandal **398.2**

Forest, H. The contest between the Sun and the Wind **398.2**

Forest, H. The little red hen **398.2**

French, V. Henny Penny **398.2**

Galdone, P. The gingerbread boy **398.2**

Galdone, P. Henny Penny **398.2**

Galdone, P. The little red hen **398.2**

Galdone, P. The three bears **398.2**

Grimm, J. The twelve dancing princesses **398.2**

Grimm, J. The story of Little Red Riding Hood **398.2**

Harris, J. My monster notebook **398.2**

Hartman, B. The Lion storyteller book of animal tales **398.2**

Hausman, G. Horses of myth **398.2**

Hennessy, B. G. The boy who cried wolf **398.2**

Isadora, R. The fisherman and his wife **398.2**

Isadora, R. Hansel and Gretel **398.2**

Kajikawa, K. Tsunami! **398.2**

Karlin, B. James Marshall's Cinderella **398.2**

Kellogg, S. Chicken Little **398.2**

Kellogg, S. The three little pigs **398.24**

Ketteman, H. The three little gators **E**

Kimmel, E. A. The fisherman and the turtle **398.2**

Kimmel, E. A. Gershon's monster **398.2**

Kimmel, E. A. The gingerbread man **398.21**

Kimmel, E. A. The runaway tortilla **398.2**

Kimmelman, L. The Little Red Hen and the Passover matzah **398.2**

Lester, J. John Henry **398.2**

Livo, N. J. Tales to tickle your funny bone **398.2**

MacDonald, M. R. Conejito **398.2**

MacDonald, M. R. Five-minute tales **398.2**

MacDonald, M. R. Look back and see **027.62**

MacDonald, M. R. Shake-it-up tales! **372.6**

MacDonald, M. R. The storyteller's start-up book **372.64**

MacDonald, M. R. Three-minute tales **398.2**

MacDonald, M. R. When the lights go out **027.62**

Marshall, J. Goldilocks and the three bears **398.2**

McGovern, A. Too much noise **398.2**

McGrath, B. B. The little red elf **E**

Mitton, T. The storyteller's secrets **398.2**

Moerbeek, K. Aesop's fables: a pop-up book of classic tales **398.2**

Muth, J. J. Stone soup **398.2**

Nishizuka, K. The beckoning cat **398.2**

Olson, A. N. Ask the bones: scary stories from around the world **398.2**

Olson, A. N. More bones **398.2**

O'Malley, K. The great race **398.2**

Osborne, M. P. The brave little seamstress **398.2**

Palatini, M. Lousy rotten stinkin' grapes **398.2**

Pinkney, J. The lion & the mouse **E**

Pinkney, J. The little red hen **398.2**

Princess stories **398.2**

The runaway piggy **398.2**

Sabuda, R. Beauty & the beast **398.2**

Sage, A. Rapunzel **398.2**

San Souci, R. Short & shivery **398.2**

San Souci, R. Sister tricksters **398.2**

Schwartz, A. Ghosts! **398.2**

Schwartz, A. I saw you in the bathtub, and other folk rhymes **398.2**

Schwartz, A. In a dark, dark room, and other scary stories **398.2**

Schwartz, A. Scary stories 3 **398.2**

Schwartz, A. There is a carrot in my ear, and other noodle tales **398.2**

Schwartz, H. A coat for the moon and other Jewish tales **398.2**

Shannon, G. More stories to solve **398.2**

Shannon, G. Stories to solve **398.2**

Shepard, A. One-Eye! Two-Eyes! Three-Eyes! **398.2**

Shulevitz, U. The treasure **398.2**

Sierra, J. Can you guess my name? **398.2**

Sierra, J. The gruesome guide to world monsters **398**

Sierra, J. Nursery tales around the world **398.2**

Souhami, J. King Pom and the fox **398.2**

Souhami, J. Sausages **398.2**

Spirin, G. Goldilocks and the three bears **398.2**

Steven, K. C. Stories for a fragile planet **398.2**

Sturges, P. The Little Red Hen (makes a pizza) **398.2**

Tchana, K. H. Changing Woman and her sisters **398.2**

Three bears Goldilocks and the three bears **398.2**

Willey, M. The 3 bears and Goldilocks **398.2**

Yolen, J. Fairy tale feasts **641.5**

Yolen, J. Not one damsel in distress **398.22**

Yolen, J. Touch magic **028.5**

Zelinsky, P. O. Rapunzel **398.22**

Zemach, M. The three little pigs **398.2**

FOLKLORE -- AFRICA

Aardema, V. Bringing the rain to Kapiti Plain **398.2**

African tales **398.2**

Beautiful blackbird **398.2**

Bryan, A. Ashley Bryan's African tales, uh-huh **398.2**

Fredericks, A. D. African legends, myths, and folktales for readers theatre **812**

Gregorowski, C. Fly, eagle, fly! **398.2**

Grifalconi, A. The village of round and square houses **398.2**

Haley, G. E. A story, a story **398.2**

Kimmel, E. A. Anansi and the magic stick **398.24**

Kimmel, E. A. Anansi and the moss-covered rock **398.2**

Kimmel, E. A. Anansi and the talking melon **398.24**

101 success secrets for gifted kids **155.45**

Fontichiaro, Kristin
(ed) Growing schools **370.71**
Go straight to the source **020**
Podcasting 101 **006.7**

Foo Yuk Yee
Malaysia **959.5**

Foo, the flying frog of Washtub Pond. Yang, B. **E**

Food. Reilly, K. M. **641.3**

FOOD
Andrew Zimmern's field guide to exceptionally weird, wild, & wonderful foods **394.12**
Blaxland, W. Chinese food **641.59**
Butterworth, C. How Did That Get in My Lunchbox? **641.3**
D'Amico, J. The science chef **641.3**
Food and faith **204**
Gardner, R. Ace your food science project **664**
Head, H. Healthy eating **613.2**
Hewitt, S. Your food **641.3**
Kelly, S. M. Yummy! **E**
McClure, N. To market, to market **381**
Miller, J. Food science **641.3**
Peterson, C. Seed soil sun **641.3**
Podwal, M. H. A sweet year **296.4**
Reilly, K. M. Food **641.3**
Robbins, K. Food for thought **641.3**
Rotner, S. Where does food come from? **664**
Thornhill, J. Who wants pizza? **641.3**
Tuminelly, N. Cool cake & cupcake food art **641.8**
Tuminelly, N. Cool creepy food art **641.5**
Tuminelly, N. Cool fruit & veggie food art **641.5**
Tuminelly, N. Cool holiday food art **641.5**
Tuminelly, N. Cool sandwich food art **641.8**
Tuminelly, N. Cool snack food art **641.5**
Verdick, E. Mealtime **E**
Wells, R. Yoko **E**
The world in your lunch box **641.3**

FOOD -- CALORIC CONTENT
See also Food -- Composition

FOOD -- CHOLESTEROL CONTENT
See also Food -- Composition

FOOD -- COMPOSITION
The world in your lunch box **641.3**

FOOD -- ENVIRONMENTAL ASPECTS
Gaarder-Juntti, O. What in the world is green food? **641.3**

FOOD -- FIBER CONTENT
Royston, A. Water and fiber for a healthy body **613.2**

FOOD -- FIBER CONTENT
See also Food -- Composition

FOOD -- FICTION
Doremus, G. Empty Fridge **E**
How Martha saved her parents from green beans **E**
McGhee, A. The case of the missing donut **E**

Rodgers, G. Chukfi Rabbit's big, bad belly-ache **398.2**
The seven silly eaters **E**

FOOD -- HISTORY
The world in your lunch box **641.3**

FOOD -- LAW AND LEGISLATION
See also Law; Legislation

FOOD -- MEXICO -- HISTORY
Blaxland, W. Mexican food **641.59**

FOOD -- MICROBIOLOGY
See also Microbiology

FOOD -- PICTORIAL WORKS
Menzel, P. What the world eats **641.3**

FOOD -- POETRY
The popcorn astronauts **811.6**

FOOD -- PRESERVATION
Pringle, L. Ice! **621.5**

FOOD -- SODIUM CONTENT
See also Food -- Composition

FOOD -- SONGS
Arnosky, J. Gobble it up! **E**
Carle, E. Today is Monday **782.421**

FOOD ADDITIVES
See also Food -- Analysis; Food -- Preservation

FOOD ADULTERATION AND INSPECTION
See also Consumer protection; Public health
Food allergies. Landau, E. **616.97**

FOOD ALLERGY
Ballard, C. Explaining food allergies **616.97**
Landau, E. Food allergies **616.97**

FOOD ALLERGY
See also Allergy
Food and faith. **204**
Food and farming. Parker, S. **630**

FOOD ASSISTANCE PROGRAMS See Food relief

FOOD BANKS
See also Food relief
Food chain reactions [series]
Slade, S. What if there were no bees? **577.4**
Slade, S. What if there were no gray wolves? **577.3**
Slade, S. What if there were no lemmings? **577.5**
Slade, S. What if there were no sea otters? **577.7**

FOOD CHAINS (ECOLOGY)
Callery, S. Ocean **577.7**
Callery, S. Polar lands **577.5**
Crenson, V. Horseshoe crabs and shorebirds **577.7**
Farrell, C. Plants out of place **581.6**
Fisher, A. L. The story goes on **E**
Fleisher, P. Forest food webs **577.3**
Franco, B. Pond circle **E**
Godkin, C. Wolf island **577**
Hooks, G. Freshwater feeders **577.6**
Hooks, G. Makers and takers **577.7**
Jenkins, S. How many ways can you catch a

FREEDOM OF ASSOCIATION
   See also Civil rights; Freedom
FREEDOM OF CONSCIENCE
   See also Conscience; Freedom; Toleration
FREEDOM OF INFORMATION
   Adams, H. R. Ensuring intellectual freedom and access to information in the school library media program   **027.8**
FREEDOM OF INFORMATION
   See also Civil rights; Intellectual freedom
FREEDOM OF MOVEMENT
   See also Civil rights; Freedom
FREEDOM OF RELIGION
   See also Civil rights; Freedom; Toleration
FREEDOM OF SPEECH
   See also Censorship; Civil rights; Freedom; Intellectual freedom
FREEDOM OF THE PRESS
   See also Civil rights; Freedom; Intellectual freedom; Press
Freedom on the menu. Weatherford, C. B.   **E**
Freedom Riders. Bausum, A.   **323.1**
Freedom ship. Rappaport, D.   **Fic**
Freedom song.   **E**
Freedom song. Walker, S. M.   **E**
Freedom stone. Kluger, J.   **Fic**
Freedom struggle. Rossi, A.   **973.7**
Freedom Summer. Rubin, S. G.   **323.11**
Freedom Summer. Wiles, D.   **E**
Freedom walkers. Freedman, R.   **323.1**
Freedom!   **741.5**
Freedom's a-callin' me. Shange, N.   **811**
Freeman, Don
  Corduroy   **E**
  Earl the squirrel   **E**
  Quiet! there's a canary in the library   **E**
Freeman, Elizabeth, 1744?-1829
       About
  Mumbet's Declaration of Independence   **92**
Freeman, Evelyn B.
  Temple, C. A. Children's books in children's hands   **028.5**
Freeman, Judy
  Books kids will sit still for 3   **011.6**
Freeman, Laura
  (il) English, K. Nikki & Deja   **Fic**
  (il) English, K. Nikki & Deja: birthday blues   **Fic**
  (il) English, K. Nikki & Deja: the newsy news newsletter   **Fic**
  (il) English, K. Nikki and Deja: election madness   **Fic**
  Skateboard party   **Fic**
Freeman, Martha
  Mrs. Wow never wanted a cow   **E**
  The trouble with cats   **Fic**
  Who is stealing the 12 days of Christmas?   **Fic**

  Who stole Grandma's million-dollar pumpkin pie?   **Fic**
  Who stole Halloween?   **Fic**
  Who stole New Year's Eve?   **Fic**
  Who stole Uncle Sam?   **Fic**
Freeman, Tor
  Olive and the big secret   **E**
Freese, Susan M.
  Craigslist   **381**
Freeze frame. Macy, S.   **796.98**
FREEZING *See* Cryobiology; Frost; Ice; Refrigeration
FREIGHT
   See also Maritime law; Materials handling; Railroads; Transportation
FRENCH AMERICANS
  Englar, M. French colonies in America   **970.01**
FRENCH CANADIANS
  Englar, M. French colonies in America   **970.01**
FRENCH CANADIANS -- FOLKLORE
  Kimmel, E. A. The flying canoe   **398.2**
French colonies in America. Englar, M.   **970.01**
FRENCH COOKING
  Blaxland, W. French food   **641.5**
  LaRoche, A. Recipe and craft guide to France **641.5**
  Locricchio, M. The cooking of France   **641.59**
  Wagner, L. Cool French cooking   **641.594**
FRENCH COOKING
   See also Cooking
FRENCH COOKING -- FICTION
  Minette's feast   **E**
French ducks in Venice. Freymann-Weyr, G.   **Fic**
French food. Blaxland, W.   **641.5**
FRENCH LANGUAGE
   See also Language and languages; Romance languages
FRENCH LANGUAGE -- DICTIONARIES
  Corbeil My first French English visual dictionary   **443**
  Kudela, K. R. My first book of French words   **443**
FRENCH LANGUAGE -- DICTIONARIES -- ENGLISH
   See also Encyclopedias and dictionaries
FRENCH LANGUAGE -- VOCABULARY
  Russo, M. Peter is just a baby   **E**
FRENCH LITERATURE
   See also Literature; Romance literature
FRENCH PAINTING
  Johnson, D. B. Magritte's marvelous hat   **E**
  Sellier, M. Renoir's colors   **759.05**
FRENCH POETRY
  Cendrars, B. Shadow   **841**
FRENCH POETRY
   See also French literature; Poetry
The **French** Revolution. Riggs, K.   **944.04**
French, Jackie

(il) Dicamillo, K. Two for one   **Fic**
(il) Dicamillo, K. Bink & Gollie   **Fic**
(il) Durand, H. Mitchell goes bowling   **E**
(il) Durand, H. Mitchell's license   **E**
Let's do nothing!   **E**
Fudge-a-mania. Blume, J.   **Fic**
FUEL
    Ollhoff, J. Fossil fuels   **333.8**
FUEL
    See also Combustion; Energy resources; Engines; Fire; Home economics
FUEL CELLS
    Lew, K. Goodbye, gasoline   **621.31**
Fuge, Charles
    Astonishing animal ABC   **E**
FUGITIVE SLAVES
    Fradin, D. B. The price of freedom   **973.7**
    Heinrichs, A. The Underground Railroad   **326**
    Morrow, B. O. A good night for freedom   **E**
    Raatma, L. The Underground Railroad   **973.7**
    Under the freedom tree   **811.54**
FUGITIVE SLAVES
    See also Slaves
FUGITIVE SLAVES -- FICTION
    Cole, H. Unspoken   **E**
    Tarshis, L. I survived the Battle of Gettysburg, 1863   **E**
FUGITIVE SLAVES -- POETRY
    Under the freedom tree   **811.54**
Fuhrken, Charles
    What every middle school teacher needs to know about reading tests (from someone who has written them)   **428**
Fuji, Machiko
    The big adventures of Majoko, volume 1   **741.5**
Fujiwara, Yumiko
    Honey   **638**
Fukuda, Toyofumi
    (il) Komiya, T. Life-size zoo   **590**
The **full** belly bowl. Aylesworth, J.   **E**
Full house. Dodds, D. A.   **513**
The **full** moon. Duey, K.   **Fic**
Full moon and star.   **E**
A **full** moon is rising. Singer, M.   **811**
Full, full, full of love. Cooke, T.   **E**
Fuller, Sandy Ferguson
    My cat, coon cat   **E**
Fullick, Ann
    Rebuilding the body   **617.9**
Fullman, Joe
    (jt. auth) Chrisp, P. History year by year   **909**
Fullner, Sheryl Kindle
    The shoestring library   **025.1**
Fulton, Robert, 1765-1815
About
    Herweck, D. Robert Fulton   **92**

FUMIGATION
    See also Communicable diseases; Insecticides
Fun & funky knits. Junor, B.   **746.43**
Fun adventure crafts [series]
    Llimos, A. Haunted house adventure crafts   **745.5**
Fun fact file: bugs! [series]
    Elkin, M. 20 fun facts about centipedes   **595.6**
    Nelson, M. 20 fun facts about dragonflies   **595.7**
Fun holiday crafts kids can do [series]
    Bledsoe, K. E. Chinese New Year crafts   **745.594**
Fun with Chinese cooking. Lee, F.   **641.5**
Fun with Roman numerals. Adler, D. A.   **513**
FUNCTIONAL COMPETENCIES *See* Life skills
FUNCTIONAL EQUATIONS
    See also Equations; Functions
FUNCTIONAL LITERACY
    See also Literacy
FUNCTIONS
    See also Differential equations; Mathematical analysis; Mathematics; Set theory
FUND RAISING -- FICTION
    Cazet, D. Minnie and Moo, hooves of fire   **Fic**
    Lopez, D. Ask my mood ring how I feel   **Fic**
FUNDAMENTAL LIFE SKILLS *See* Life skills
FUNDAMENTAL RIGHTS *See* Civil rights; Human rights
Fundamentals of children's services. Sullivan, M.   **027.62**
Fundamentals of school library media management. Martin, B. S.   **025.1**
A **funeral** in the bathroom.   **811**
FUNERAL RITES AND CEREMONIES
    See also Manners and customs; Rites and ceremonies
FUNERAL RITES AND CEREMONIES -- FICTION
    Howe, J. Kaddish for Grandpa in Jesus' name, amen   **E**
Fungi. Wearing, J.   **579**
FUNGI
    Wearing, J. Fungi   **579**
FUNGI
    See also Agricultural pests; Pests; Plants
Funke, Cornelia Caroline
    Dragon rider   **Fic**
    Inkdeath   **Fic**
    Inkheart   **Fic**
    Inkspell   **Fic**
    The princess knight   **E**
    Princess Pigsty   **E**
    The wildest brother   **E**
FUNNIES *See* Comic books, strips, etc.
Funny business.   **920**
Funny cartooning for kids. Artell, M.   **741**
Funny Farm. Teague, M.   **E**
The **funny** little woman. Mosel, A.   **398.2**

<cite></cite>

Gautama Buddha

About

Demi Buddha **294.3**

Gavin, Jamila

School for princes **398.209**

Tales from India **398.2**

Gavril, David

(il) Van Leeuwen, J. Chicken soup **E**

GAWAIN (LEGENDARY CHARACTER)

Morpurgo, M.   Sir Gawain and the Green
Knight **398.2**

GAY AUTHORS

See also Authors; Gay men

GAY FATHERS -- FAMILY RELATIONSHIPS

This is my family a first look at same sex parents **306.874**

GAY MEN'S WRITINGS

See also Literature

GAY PARENTS

This is my family a first look at same sex parents **306.874**

GAY PRIDE PARADES -- FICTION

This day in June **E**

GAY RIGHTS

See also Civil rights

GAY YOUTH

See also Youth

GAY YOUTH -- UNITED STATES

Seba, J. Gallup guides for youth facing persistent
prejudice **306.76**

Gay, Marie-Louise

(il) Caramba and Henry **E**

Princess pistachio **E**

Roslyn Rutabaga and the biggest hole on earth **E**

When Stella was very very small **E**

(il) Howe, J. Houndsley and Catina **E**

(il) Wishinsky, F. Please, Louise! **E**

GAYS -- FICTION

London, A. Proxy **Fic**

GAZA STRIP -- FICTION

The story of Hurry **E**

GAZETTEERS

See also Geography

Gazlay, Suzy

Managing green spaces **333.7**

GEARING

See also Machinery; Power transmission;
Wheels

Gecko. Craats, R. **639.3**

Geckos. Hernandez-Divers, S. **639.3**

GECKOS

Craats, R. Gecko **639.3**

Hernandez-Divers, S. Geckos **639.3**

GECKOS -- FICTION

Galante, C. Willowood **Fic**

GECKOS -- FOLKLORE

MacDonald, M. R. Go to sleep, Gecko! **398.2**

Gee Whiz. **Fic**

Gee, Joshua

Encyclopedia horrifica **001.9**

Gee, Maggie

About

Moss, M.   Sky high: the true story of Maggie
Gee **92**

Geehan, Wayne

(il) Calvert, P. Multiplying menace **E**

Geek Chic. Palatini, M. **Fic**

Geeks, girls, and secret identities. Jung, M. **Fic**

Geese. Bailer, D. **598**

GEESE

See also Birds; Poultry

Bailer, D. Geese **598**

Best, C. Goose's story **E**

Ehrlich, H. M. Louie's goose **E**

Freedman, C. Gooseberry Goose **E**

Greenstein, E. The goose man **92**

Sayre, A. P. Honk, honk, goose! **598**

GEESE -- FICTION

Alone together **E**

Duck & Goose go to the beach **E**

Dunrea, O. Gideon **E**

Loth, S. Zelda the Varigoose **E**

Willems, M. That is not a good idea! **E**

Geeslin, Campbell

Elena's serenade **E**

The **geezer** in the freezer. Wright, R. **E**

Gehrig, Lou, 1903-1941

About

Adler, D. A. Lou Gehrig **796.357**

Gehry, Frank

About

Bodden, V. Frank Gehry **92**

Geiger, Beth

Clean water **363.7**

Geisert, Arthur

Country road ABC **E**

Hogwash **E**

Ice **E**

Lights out **E**

Roman numerals I to MM **513.5**

Thunderstorm **E**

GEISHAS

See also Entertainers

Geister, David

(il) Surviving the Hindenburg **363.12**

Geister, David

(il) Swain, G. Riding to Washington **E**

Gelletly, LeeAnne

A woman's place in early America **305.4**

Gellman, Ellie B.

Netta and her plant **E**

Gem. Hobbie, H. **E**

Echo **Fic**

GERMINATION

Benbow, A. Sprouting seed science projects **580.7**

GERMS *See* Bacteria; Germ theory of disease; Microorganisms

Germs make me sick! Berger, M. **616.9**

Geronimo, Apache Chief, 1829-1909

About

Ehrlich, A. Wounded Knee: an Indian history of the American West **970.004**

Gerrell, Spike

(il) Bennett, H. J. Max Archer, kid detective: the case of the wet bed **616.85**

Gerritsen, Paula

Nuts **E**

Gershator, Phillis

Listen, listen **E**

Moo, moo, brown cow, have you any milk? **E**

Sky sweeper **E**

Time for a hug **E**

Who's awake in springtime? **E**

Who's in the forest? **E**

Gershon's monster. Kimmel, E. A. **398.2**

Gershwin's Rhapsody in Blue. **E**

Gershwin, George, 1898-1937

About

Gershwin's Rhapsody in Blue **E**

Krull, K. Lives of the musicians **920**

Gerson, Mary-Joan

Why the sky is far away **398.2**

Gerstein, Francine

(jt. auth) Fromer, L. My noisy body **612**

Fromer, L. My achy body **612**

Fromer, L. My messy body **612**

(jt. auth) Fromer, L. My noisy body **612**

Fromer, L. My stretchy body **612.6**

Gerstein, Mordicai

Carolinda clatter! **E**

Leaving the nest **E**

Minifred goes to school **E**

Sparrow Jack **E**

The white ram **E**

The wild boy **155.45**

(il) Lipson, E. R. Applesauce season **E**

(il) Prevert, J. How to paint the portrait of a bird **E**

(il) The camping trip that changed America **979.4**

(il) The first drawing **E**

A book **E**

Dear hot dog **811**

How to bicycle to the moon to plant sunflowers **E**

The man who walked between the towers **791**

The night world **E**

Gertrude is Gertrude is Gertrude is Gertrude. Winter, J. **92**

Gervais, Bernadette

Pittau, F. Out of sight **590**

GESTALT PSYCHOLOGY

See also Consciousness; Perception; Psychology; Senses and sensation; Theory of knowledge

Get all tied up. Mooney, C. **623.88**

Get art smart [series]

Benduhn, T. What is color? **701**

Benduhn, T. What is shape? **701**

Fitzgerald, S. What is texture? **701**

Meredith, S. What is form? **701**

Meredith, S. What is line? **701**

Meredith, S. What is space? **701**

Get connected. Rau, D. M. **745.594**

Get happy. Doyle, M. **E**

Get into Art! Brooks, S. **E**

Get on board: the story of the Underground Railroad. Haskins, J. **326**

Get organized without losing it. Fox, J. S. **371.3**

Get the scoop on animal poop. Cusick, D. **590**

Get to know your pet [series]

Johnson, J. Cats and kittens **636.8**

Johnson, J. Dogs and puppies **636.7**

Johnson, J. Guinea pigs **636.9**

Johnson, J. Hamsters and gerbils **636.9**

Johnson, J. Rabbits **636.9**

Johnson, J. Rats and mice **636.9**

Get up and go! Carlson, N. L. **E**

Getting elected. Donovan, S. **324.7**

Getting near to baby. Couloumbis, A. **Fic**

GETTING READY FOR BED *See* Bedtime

Getting stronger, getting fit. Hunt, J. **613.7**

Getting there. Konrad, M. S. **388**

Getting to know the world's greatest artists [series]

Venezia, M. Diego Velazquez **92**

Venezia, M. Faith Ringgold **92**

Venezia, M. Horace Pippin **92**

Getting to know the world's greatest inventors & scientists [series]

Daniel Hale Williams **92**

Venezia, M. Charles Drew **92**

Venezia, M. Luis Alvarez **92**

Venezia, M. Stephen Hawking **92**

Venezia, M. Steve Jobs & Steve Wozniak **92**

Venezia, M. Thomas Edison **92**

Venezia, M. The Wright brothers **92**

Getting your zzzzs. Cleland, J. **E**

Gettysburg. Gregory, J. **973.7**

GETTYSBURG (PA.)

Lincoln's Gettysburg address **759.13**

GETTYSBURG (PA.), BATTLE OF, 1863

Gregory, J. Gettysburg **973.7**

Murphy, J. The long road to Gettysburg **973.7**

Weber, J. L. Summer's bloodiest days **973.7**

What was the Battle of Gettysburg? **973.7**

GETTYSBURG (PA.), BATTLE OF, 1863 -- FIC-TION

Calkhoven, L. Will at the Battle of Gettysburg, 1863 — **Fic**

Gutman, D. Abner & me — **Fic**

Hopkinson, D. Billy and the rebel — **E**

Noble, T. H. The last brother — **E**

Tarshis, L. I survived the Battle of Gettysburg, 1863 — **E**

Gewirtz, Adina Rishe

Zebra forest — **Fic**

Gewirtz, Elaine Waldorf

The bulldog — **636.7**

Fetch this book — **636.7**

Geyer, Mark

Moriarty, C. The inquisitor's apprentice — **Fic**

Geyer, Mark Edward

(il) The watcher in the shadows — **Fic**

GEYSERS

> *See also* Geology; Geothermal resources; Physical geography; Water

Ghahremani, Susie

(il) What will hatch? — **E**

Ghana. Levy, P. — **966.7**

GHANA

Levy, P. Ghana — **966.7**

Medearis, A. S. Seven spools of thread — **E**

GHANA -- BIOGRAPHY

Emmanuel's dream — **92**

GHANA -- FICTION

Daly, N. Pretty Salma — **E**

Medearis, A. S. Seven spools of thread — **E**

Milway, K. S. One hen — **E**

GHANA -- SOCIAL LIFE AND CUSTOMS

Garner, L. African crafts — **745.5**

GHANA EMPIRE

McKissack, P. C. The royal kingdoms of Ghana, Mali, and Songhay — **966.2**

Gherman, Beverly

First mothers — **973.09**

Norman Rockwell — **759.13**

Sparky: the life and art of Charles Schulz — **92**

Ghetto cowboy. Neri, G. — **Fic**

Ghigna, Charles

Barn storm — **E**

Ghigna, Debra

Ghigna, C. Barn storm — **E**

Ghiuselev, Iassen

(il) Ruskin, J. The king of the Golden River — **Fic**

The **ghost** and Mrs. Hobbs. DeFelice, C. C. — **Fic**

The **ghost** catcher. Hamilton, M. — **398.2**

GHOST DANCE

Ehrlich, A. Wounded Knee: an Indian history of the American West — **970.004**

Ghost girl. Ray, D. — **Fic**

Ghost hands. Barron, T. A. — **E**

Ghost Hawk. Cooper, S. — **Fic**

Ghost hunt. Hawes, J. — **133.1**

Ghost hunt 2. Hawes, J. — **133.1**

Ghost hunter. Paver, M. — **Fic**

Ghost Mysteries [series]

DeFelice, C. C. The ghost of Fossil Glen — **Fic**

A **ghost** named Fred. Benchley, N. — **E**

The **ghost** of Crutchfield Hall. Hahn, M. D. — **Fic**

The **ghost** of Cutler Creek. DeFelice, C. C. — **Fic**

The **ghost** of Fossil Glen. DeFelice, C. C. — **Fic**

The **ghost** of Poplar Point. DeFelice, C. C. — **Fic**

The **ghost** prison. Delaney, J. — **Fic**

The **ghost** sitter. Griffin, P. R. — **Fic**

GHOST STORIES

Abela, D. The ghosts of Gribblesea Pier — **Fic**

Allison, J. Gilda Joyce, psychic investigator: the bones of the holy — **Fic**

Auxier, J. The Night Gardener — **Fic**

Barnholdt, L. Girl meets ghost — **Fic**

Barrows, A. Ivy + Bean and the ghost that had to go — **Fic**

Bauer, M. D. The blue ghost — **Fic**

The beasts of Clawstone Castle — **Fic**

Benchley, N. A ghost named Fred — **E**

Black, H. Doll bones — **Fic**

Compestine, Y. C. Boy dumplings — **E**

Cooper, S. Ghost Hawk — **Fic**

Cushman, D. Dirk Bones and the mystery of the haunted house — **E**

Cuyler, M. Skeleton hiccups — **E**

The death of Yorik Mortwell — **Fic**

DeFelice, C. C. The ghost and Mrs. Hobbs — **Fic**

DeFelice, C. C. The ghost of Cutler Creek — **Fic**

DeFelice, C. C. The ghost of Fossil Glen — **Fic**

DeFelice, C. C. The ghost of Poplar Point — **Fic**

Delaney, J. The ghost prison — **Fic**

Del Negro, J. Passion and poison — **S**

Dickens, C. A Christmas carol — **Fic**

Eeckhout, E. There's no such thing as ghosts! — **E**

Galdone, P. The teeny-tiny woman — **398.2**

Goodhart, P. Three little ghosties — **E**

Grabenstein, C. The black heart crypt — **Fic**

Grabenstein, C. The crossroads — **Fic**

Grabenstein, C. The Hanging Hill — **Fic**

Griffin, P. R. The ghost sitter — **Fic**

Hahn, M. D. All the lovely bad ones — **Fic**

Hahn, M. D. The ghost of Crutchfield Hall — **Fic**

Hahn, M. D. Wait till Helen comes — **Fic**

Herman, E. Hubknuckles — **E**

Home sweet horror — **E**

Ibbotson, E. Dial-a-ghost — **Fic**

Irving, W. The Legend of Sleepy Hollow — **Fic**

Kehret, P. The ghost's grave — **Fic**

Kelley, J. The girl behind the glass — **Fic**

Kelly, D. A. The pinstripe ghost — **Fic**

Kimmel, E. C. Scaredy Kat — **Fic**

Witch Baby and me after dark **Fic**

Witch Baby and me on stage **Fic**

The **glitch** in sleep. Hulme, J. **Fic**

Glitter girls and the great fake out. Cabot, M. **Fic**

Global babies. Global Fund for Children (Organization) **E**

Global baby girls. **E**

Global Fund for Children (Organization)

American babies **E**

Global babies **E**

(comp) Global baby girls **E**

GLOBAL POSITIONING SYSTEM

See also Navigation

Global warming. Royston, A. **363.7**

Global warming. Morris, N. **363.7**

GLOBAL WARMING

See also Climate; Solar radiation

Arnold, C. A warmer world **363.738**

Markle, S. Waiting for ice **599.786**

Meyer, S. Adapting to flooding and rising sea levels **363.34**

Global warming. Simon, S. **363.7**

GLOBE THEATRE (LONDON, ENGLAND)

Aliki William Shakespeare & the Globe **792.09**

Chrisp, P. Welcome to the Globe **792**

GLOBE THEATRE (LONDON, ENGLAND) -- FICTION

All the world's a stage **Fic**

Cooper, S. King of shadows **Fic**

GLOBES

Pastis, S. Timmy failure : now look what you've done **Fic**

GLOBES

See also Maps

Gloria's way. Cameron, A. **Fic**

The **glorious** adventures of the Sunshine Queen. McCaughrean, G. **Fic**

The **glorious** flight: across the Channel with Louis Bleriot, July 25, 1909. Provensen, A. **92**

Glory be. Scattergood, A. **Fic**

The **glory** wind. Sherrard, V. **Fic**

GLOSSARIES *See* Encyclopedias and dictionaries

Glow-in-the-dark animals. Lunis, N. **572**

GLOW-IN-THE-DARK BOOKS

See also Picture books for children; Toy and movable books

Glucksman, Jodi

(jt. auth) Aronica-Buck, B. Over the moon **811**

Gnoli, Domenico

(il) Juster, N. Alberic the Wise and other journeys **S**

The **gnome's** eye. Kerz, A. **Fic**

GNOMES

See also Folklore

GNOSTICISM

See also Church history -- 30-600, Early church; Philosophy; Religions

GNUS

Catt, T. Migrating with the wildebeest **599.64**

Meinking, M. Crocodile vs. wildebeest **597.98**

Walden, K. Wildebeests **599.64**

Go. Kidd, C. **740**

Go away, big green monster! Emberley, E. **E**

Go easy on energy. Bullard, L. **333.79**

Go figure! Ball, J. **793.74**

Go fly a bike! Haduch, B. **629.227**

Go green [series]

Lanz, H. Shopping choices **381**

Go out and play! Rose, J. **796**

Go straight to the source. Fontichiaro, K. **020**

Go to bed, monster! Wing, N. **E**

Go to sleep, Gecko! MacDonald, M. R. **398.2**

Go to sleep, Groundhog! Cox, J. **E**

Go west, Amelia Bedelia! Parish, H. **E**

Go! go! Bobo: colors. Basher, S. **E**

Go! go! go! Munro, R. **E**

Go, go America. Yaccarino, D. **973**

Go, go, grapes! Sayre, A. P. **641.3**

Go, shapes, go! Fleming, D. **E**

Goal! **E**

Goal! Woods, M. **796.334**

Goal! science projects with soccer. Goodstein, M. **507.8**

Goal!: the fire and fury of soccer's greatest moment. Stewart, M. **796.334**

The **goat-faced** girl. **398.2**

The **goatnappers.** Jordan, R. **Fic**

GOATS

Polacco, P. G is for goat **E**

GOATS -- FICTION

Berry, L. What floats in a moat? **E**

Cole, H. Trudy **E**

Fox, M. Let's count goats! **E**

Gorbachev, V. That's what friends are for **E**

Huck runs amuck! **E**

Jordan, R. The goatnappers **Fic**

Jordan, R. Lost Goat Lane **Fic**

Kimmelman, L. The three bully goats **E**

Nyeu, T. Bunny days **E**

One little chicken **E**

Palatini, M. The three silly billies **E**

Polacco, P. Oh, look! **E**

Rocco, J. Wolf! wolf! **E**

Sharmat, M. Gregory, the terrible eater **E**

Unicorn thinks he's pretty great **E**

Waddell, M. Captain Small Pig **E**

Westera, M. Sheep and Goat **Fic**

GOATS -- FOLKLORE

Galdone, P. The three Billy Goats Gruff **398.2**

Gobble it up! Arnosky, J. **E**

Gobble You Up! **398.2**

Gobble, gobble. Falwell, C. **E**

Grimly, Gris

  (il) The death of Yorik Mortwell   **Fic**

  (il) DiPucchio, K. S. Sipping spiders through a straw   **782.42**

  (il) Gaiman, N. The dangerous alphabet   **E**

  (il) Irving, W. The Legend of Sleepy Hollow   **Fic**

The **Grimm** conclusion.   **Fic**

The **Grimm** Legacy. Shulman, P.   **Fic**

Grimm's fairy tales. Grimm, J.   **398.2**

Grimm, Jacob, 1785-1863

  The twelve dancing princesses   **398.2**

Adaptations

  Berner, R. S. Definitely not for little ones   **398.2**

  Hettinga, D. R. The Brothers Grimm   **430**

  Pirotta, S. The McElderry book of Grimms' fairy tales   **398.2**

Grimm, Wilhelm, 1786-1859

  (jt. auth) Grimm, J. The twelve dancing princesses   **398.2**

Adaptations

  Isadora, R. Hansel and Gretel   **398.2**

About

  Hettinga, D. R. The Brothers Grimm   **430**

Grin and bear it. Landry, L.   **E**

Grindley, Sally

  It's my school   **E**

Grisham, John

  Grisham, J. Theodore Boone: kid lawyer   **Fic**

  Theodore Boone: the abduction   **Fic**

  Theodore Boone: kid lawyer   **Fic**

GRIST MILLS See Flour mills

GRIZZLY BEAR

  Greene, J. D. Grizzly bears   **599.78**

  Markle, S. Grizzly bears   **599.78**

  Sartore, J. Face to face with grizzlies   **599.78**

GRIZZLY BEAR -- FICTION

  Eat like a bear   **E**

Grizzly bears. Markle, S.   **599.78**

Grizzly bears. Greene, J. D.   **599.78**

Grizzly dad. Harrison, J.   **E**

The **Grizzly** Gazette. Murphy, S. J.   **513**

Grobler, Piet

  (il) All the wild wonders   **808.81**

  (il) Lujan, J. Colors! Colores!   **861**

  (il) Naidoo, B. Aesop's fables   **398.2**

GROCERY TRADE

  See also Food industry

Groenink, Chuck

  (il) Santa Clauses   **811.6**

Grogan, John

  Marley   **636.7**

Groner, Judyth Saypol

  My first Hebrew word book   **492.4**

Groom, Juliet

  Silent night   **E**

GROOMING FOR GIRLS

The care & keeping of you   **613.04**

GROOMING, PERSONAL See Personal grooming

The gross and goofy body [series]

  Stewart, M. Germ wars!   **571.9**

  Stewart, M. Give me a hand   **591.4**

  Stewart, M. Here we grow   **612.7**

  Stewart, M. Moving and grooving   **612.7**

  Stewart, M. The skin you're in   **591.47**

  Stewart, M. You've got nerve!   **612.8**

Gross body invaders. Owen, R.   **578.6**

Gross body science [series]

  Donovan, S. Hawk & Drool   **612.3**

  Donovan, S. Rumble & spew   **612.3**

  Larsen, C. S. Crust and spray   **612.8**

  Lew, K. Clot & scab   **617.1**

  Lew, K. Itch & ooze   **616.5**

GROSS NATIONAL PRODUCT

  See also Economics; Statistics; Wealth

Gross, Elly Berkovits, 1929-

About

  Gross, E. B. Elly   **92**

Grossberg, Blythe

  Asperger's rules!   **618.92**

GROTTOES See Caves

The **grouchy** ladybug. Carle, E.   **E**

GROUND EFFECT MACHINES See Air-cushion vehicles

Ground zero dogs. Goldish, M.   **636.7**

The **groundbreaking,** chance-taking life of George Washington Carver and science & invention in America. Harness, C.   **92**

Grounded.   **Fic**

Grounded. Klise, K.   **Fic**

GROUNDHOG DAY

  Gibbons, G. Groundhog day!   **394.26**

GROUNDHOG DAY -- FICTION

  Cox, J. Go to sleep, Groundhog!   **E**

  Hill, S. L. Punxsutawney Phyllis   **E**

Groundhog day! Gibbons, G.   **394.26**

Groundhog gets a say. Swallow, P. C.   **E**

GROUNDS MAINTENANCE

  See also Gardening

GROUNDWATER

  See also Water

GROUP DECISION MAKING

  See also Decision making

GROUP MEDICAL SERVICE See Health insurance

GROUP PROBLEM SOLVING

  See also Problem solving

GROUP RELATIONS TRAINING

  See also Interpersonal relations

GROUP THEORY

  See also Algebra; Mathematics; Number theory

GUNS -- UNITED STATES -- HISTORY
Mara, W. The gunsmith **683.4**
The **gunsmith.** Mara, W. **683.4**
GUNSMITHING *See* Firearms industry
GUNSMITHS
Wyckoff, E. B. The man behind the gun: Samuel
Colt and his revolver **92**
Gunter, Veronika Alice
Pet science **636**
The ultimate indoor games book **793**
Gunzi, Christiane
Murrell, D. J. Mega trucks **629.224**
Guo Yue
Little Leap Forward **Fic**
Gurihiru (Group of artists)
(il) Drama **741.5**
Gurstelle, William
The art of the catapult **623.4**
Gus & me. Richards, K. **E**
Gus and Grandpa and the two-wheeled bike. Mills,
C. **E**
Gustafson, Scott
Favorite nursery rhymes from Mother Goose **398.8**
Gustavson, Adam
Dirty rats **599.35**
(il) Silent star **796.357**
(il) Blumenthal, D. The blue house dog **E**
(il) Borden, L. The A+ custodian **E**
(il) Borden, L. The last day of school **Fic**
(il) Borden, L. The lost-and-found tooth **Fic**
(il) Jingle bells **E**
(il) Kay, V. Rough, tough Charley **92**
(il) Kimmelman, L. Mind your manners, Alice
Roosevelt! **E**
(il) Lendroth, S. Calico Dorsey **Fic**
(il) Ludwig, T. Better than you **E**
(il) The trouble with May Amelia **Fic**
(il) Weber, E. The Yankee at the seder **Fic**
Gut bugs, dust mites, and other microorganisms you
can't live without. Weakland, M. **579**
Gut-wrenching gravity and other fatal forces. Clay-
bourne, A. **531**
Gutenberg, Johann, 1397?-1468
About
Koscielniak, B. Johann Gutenberg and the amazing
printing press **686.2**
Rumford, J. From the good mountain **E**
Skelton, M. Endymion Spring **Fic**
Guthrie, James
Last song **E**
Guthrie, Woody, 1912-1967
About
Christensen, B. Woody Guthrie, poet of the peo-
ple **782.421**
Krull, K. Lives of the musicians **920**
When Bob met Woody **92**

Gutierrez, Akemi
(il) Ramos, J. I'm just like my mom/I'm just like
my dad **E**
Gutierrez, Rudy
(il) Dorros, A. Mama and me **E**
(il) Golio, G. Spirit seeker **788.7**
(il) Dorros, A. Papa and me **E**
Gutman, Dan
Abner & me **Fic**
Babe & me **Fic**
Casey back at bat **811**
The Christmas genie **Fic**
The homework machine **Fic**
Honus & me **Fic**
Jackie & me **Fic**
Jim & me **Fic**
Mickey & me **Fic**
Mission unstoppable **Fic**
My weird writing tips **808.042**
Never say genius **Fic**
Ray & me **Fic**
The return of the homework machine **Fic**
Roberto & me **Fic**
Satch & me **Fic**
Shoeless Joe & me **Fic**
(ed) Recycle this book **333.72**
Guts. Simon, S. **612.3**
Guttersnipe. Cutler, J. **E**
Guy, Ginger Foglesong
Fiesta! **E**
Perros! Perros! Dogs! Dogs! **E**
Guy-write. Fletcher, R. **808.06**
Guyana. Jermyn, L. **988.1**
GUYANA
Jermyn, L. Guyana **988.1**
Guyku. Raczka, B. **811**
Guys read. **818**
Guys read [series]
Brown, D. The sports pages **S**
Guys read **818**
Other worlds **S**
Guys read: funny business. **S**
Guys read: thriller. Scieszka Jon, E. **S**
Guyton, Tyree
About
Magic trash **92**
Gym shorts [series]
Hicks, B. Basketball Bats **Fic**
Hicks, B. Doubles troubles **Fic**
Hicks, B. Goof-off goalie **Fic**
Hicks, B. Scaredy-cat catcher **Fic**
Hicks, B. Swimming with Sharks **Fic**
Hicks, B. Track attack **Fic**
Gymnastics. Veitch, C. **796.44**
GYMNASTICS
See also Athletics; Exercise; Sports

Gymnastics. Schwartz, H. E. **796.4**

GYMNASTICS

Burford, M. Grace, gold and glory **796.440**

Schwartz, H. E. Gymnastics **796.4**

Veitch, C. Gymnastics **796.44**

Washburn, K. Heart of a champion **796.440**

Wendorff, A. Gymnastics **796.44**

Gymnastics. Wendorff, A. **796.44**

GYMNASTICS -- FICTION

Isadora, R. Jake at gymnastics **E**

GYPSIES -- FICTION

Pinfold, L. The Django **E**

Rutkoski, M. The Cabinet of Wonders **Fic**

GYPSUM

> *See also* Minerals

H

H.I.V.E. Walden, M. **Fic**

H.O.R.S.E. Myers, C. **Fic**

Haake, Martin

(il) Donovan, S. Bob the Alien discovers the Dewey decimal system **025.4**

(il) Donovan, S. Pingpong Perry experiences how a book is made **070.5**

Haas, Jessie

Bramble and Maggie give and take **Fic**

Bramble and maggie spooky season **Fic**

Bramble and Maggie **Fic**

Sugaring **E**

Haas, Rick de

Peter and the winter sleepers **E**

Haas, Robert B.

I dreamed of flying like a bird **779**

HABEAS CORPUS

> *See also* Civil rights; Constitutional law; Criminal procedure; Martial law

Haber, Tiffany Strelitz

The monster who lost his mean **E**

HABIT

> *See also* Human behavior; Psychology

HABITAT (ECOLOGY)

Base, G. The water hole **E**

Blackaby, S. Nest, nook & cranny **811**

Fleming, D. Where once there was a wood **639.9**

Jenkins, S. I see a kookaburra! **591.7**

Parker, S. Animal habitats **591.7**

A place for bats **599.4**

Riggs, K. Gorillas **599.884**

Riggs, K. Leopards **599.75**

Riggs, K. Moose **599.65**

Singer, M. A strange place to call home **571.1**

Stetson, E. Kids' easy-to-create wildlife habitats **639.9**

VanCleave, J. P. Janice Vancleave's ecology for every kid **577**

HABITAT (ECOLOGY)

> *See also* Ecology

HABITAT (ECOLOGY) -- FICTION

Violet Mackerel's natural habitat **Fic**

HABITATIONS OF DOMESTIC ANIMALS *See* Animal housing

HABITS OF ANIMALS *See* Animal behavior

Hachiko. Turner, P. S. **636**

Hachiko waits. Newman, L. **Fic**

HACKENSACK MEADOWLANDS (N.J.)

Yezerski, T. Meadowlands **577.690**

Hacohen, Dean

Tuck me in! **E**

Had gadya. **296.4**

Hadadi, Hoda

(il) Cunnane, K. Deep in the Sahara **E**

Haddix, Margaret Peterson, 1964-

Caught **Fic**

Found **Fic**

Risked **Fic**

Sabotaged **Fic**

Sent **Fic**

Torn **Fic**

Haddon, Mark

Boom! **Fic**

Footprints on the Moon **E**

Hader, Berta

The big snow **E**

Hader, Elmer Stanley

Hader, B. The big snow **E**

Hades. O'Connor, G. **398.209**

HADES (GREEK DEITY) -- COMIC BOOKS, STRIPS, ETC.

O'Connor, G. Hades **398.209**

Haduch, Bill

Go fly a bike! **629.227**

Hafner, Marylin

(il) Berger, M. Germs make me sick! **616.9**

(il) Dodds, D. A. Teacher's pets **E**

M & M and the bad news babies **E**

(il) Horvath, P. The Pepins and their problems **Fic**

(il) Prelutsky, J. It's Christmas! **811**

(il) Prelutsky, J. It's Thanksgiving! **811**

(il) Ross, P. Meet M & M **E**

Hagen, George

Gabriel Finley and the raven's riddle **Fic**

Hagglund, Betty

Epic treks **910.4**

Hague, Bradley

Alien deep **551.2**

Hague, Michael

(il) The hobbit **Fic**

(il) Aylesworth, J. Little Bitty Mousie **E**

(il) Lofting, H. The voyages of Doctor Dolittle **Fic**

Hahn, Mary Downing

All the lovely bad ones **Fic**

The ghost of Crutchfield Hall **Fic**

book **743**

McGee, R. Paper crafts for Halloween **745.594**

HALLOWEEN

See also Holidays

HALLOWEEN -- FICTION

Bramble and maggie spooky season **Fic**

Brendler, C. Not very scary **E**

Cronin, D. Click, clack, boo **E**

The monsterator **E**

Savage, S. Ten orange pumpkins **E**

Seeger, L. V. Dog and Bear **E**

Shivery Shades of Halloween **E**

White, R. The treasure of Way Down Deep **Fic**

Watt, M. Scaredy Squirrel Prepares for Halloween **E**

HALLOWEEN -- GRAPHIC NOVELS

Thompson, J. Scary Godmother **741.5**

HALLOWEEN -- POETRY

Fritsch, P. Pennsylvania Dutch Halloween scherenschnitte **745.594**

Halloween goodnight. Cushman, D. **E**

Halloween is-- Gibbons, G. **394.26**

The Halloween Kid. Montijo, R. **E**

Halloween night. Murray, M. D. **E**

Hallowell, George

Wagons ho! **E**

Hallowilloween. Brown, C. **811**

Halls, Kelly Milner

In search of Sasquatch **001.9**

Mysteries of the mummy kids **393**

Saving the Baghdad Zoo **636.088**

Tales of the cryptids **001.9**

(ed) Girl meets boy **S**

HALLUCINATIONS AND ILLUSIONS

See also Abnormal psychology; Parapsychology; Subconsciousness; Visions

Halperin, Wendy Anderson

Peace **172**

(il) Aylesworth, J. The full belly bowl **E**

(il) Bruchac, J. My father is taller than a tree **E**

(il) Galbraith, K. O. Planting the wild garden **581.4**

(il) Gold, A. Thank you, God, for everything **E**

(il) The Secret Remedy Book **E**

Halpern, Monica

Railroad fever **385**

Underground towns, treetops, and other animal hiding places **591.47**

Halpern, Shari

(il) The apple pie tree **583**

(il) Sturges, P. I love planes! **E**

(il) Sturges, P. I love school! **E**

(il) Sturges, P. I love trains! **E**

Halpert, Herbert

Chase, R. The Jack tales **398.2**

Halpin, Abigail

(il) Brauner, B. The magic mistake **Fic**

(il) Cheng, A. The year of the book **Fic**

Krishnaswami, U. The grand plan to fix everything **Fic**

(il) Cox, J. Nora and the Texas terror **Fic**

(il) Patron, S. Maybe yes, maybe no, maybe maybe **Fic**

(il) Snyder, L. Penny Dreadful **Fic**

Halsey, Megan

(il) Cousins of clouds **811**

(il) Hubbell, P. Airplanes **E**

(il) Hubbell, P. Boats **E**

(il) Hubbell, P. Cars **E**

(il) Older, J. Telling time **529**

Rockwell, A. F. Four seasons make a year **E**

(il) Rockwell, A. F. Little shark **597**

(il) Rockwell, A. F. One bean **635**

(il) Valentine be mine **E**

(il) Zimmer, T. V. Steady hands **811**

Halt's peril. Flanagan, J. **Fic**

Halvorsen, Gail

About

Tunnell, M. Candy bomber **92**

Halvorson, Karin

Inside the brain **612.8**

Inside the ears **612.8**

Inside the heart **612.17**

Hama, Larry

The battle of Iwo Jima **940.54**

Hamaker, Steve

(il) Quest for the Spark **Fic**

Hamanaka, Sheila

All the colors of the earth **813**

Grandparents song **E**

Hambleton, Vicki

(jt. auth) Greenwood, C. So, you wanna be a writer? **808**

Hamburg, Jennifer

A moose that says moo **E**

Hamer, Fannie Lou Townsend, 1917-1977

About

Let it shine **920**

Hamilton, Alexander, 1757-1804

About

Fradin, D. B. Duel! **973.4**

Fritz, J. Alexander Hamilton **92**

Hamilton, Emma Walton

Andrews, J. The very fairy princess **E**

(ed) Julie Andrews' collection of poems, songs, and lullabies **808.8**

Hamilton, John

How a bill becomes a law **328**

Tsunamis **551.46**

Hamilton, K. R.

Police officers on patrol **E**

Red Truck **E**

Hamilton, Libby

Horse: the essential guide for young equestri-

Hanukkah lights **811**
Heiligman, D. Celebrate Hanukkah **296.4**
Heller, E. S. Menorah under the sea **296.4**
Lehman-Wilzig, T. Hanukkah around the world **296.4**
Melmed, L. K. Eight winter nights **296.4**
Roth, S. L. Hanukkah, oh Hanukkah **782.42**
The story of Hanukkah **296.4**
Ziefert, H. Hanukkah haiku **296.4**

HANUKKAH

See also Jewish holidays

HANUKKAH -- FICTION

The eighth menorah **E**
Hershel and the Hanukkah Goblins **E**
Pinkwater, D. M. Beautiful Yetta's Hanukkah Kitten **E**
Brown, B. Hanukkah in Alaska **E**
Kimmel, E. A. Simon and the bear **E**
Sadie's almost marvelous menorah **E**

HANUKKAH -- POETRY

Hanukkah lights **811**

HANUKKAH -- SONGS

Baum, M. I have a little dreidel **782.42**
Roth, S. L. Hanukkah, oh Hanukkah **782.42**
Hanukkah around the world. Lehman-Wilzig, T. **296.4**
Hanukkah at Valley Forge. Krensky, S. **E**
Hanukkah haiku. Ziefert, H. **296.4**
The **Hanukkah** hop. **E**
Hanukkah in Alaska. Brown, B. **E**
Hanukkah lights. Martin, D. **E**
Hanukkah lights. **811**
The **Hanukkah** mice. Kroll, S. **E**
Hanukkah moon. Da Costa, D. **E**

HANUKKAH STORIES

Baum, M. I have a little dreidel **782.42**
Da Costa, D. Hanukkah moon **E**
Glaser, L. Hoppy Hanukkah! **E**
The Hanukkah hop **E**
Jennings, S. A Chanukah Noel **E**
Rosen, M. J. Chanukah lights **E**
The story of Hanukkah **296.4**
Hanukkah, oh Hanukkah. Roth, S. L. **782.42**

Hapipi, Rafiz

Foley, E. El Salvador **972.84**
Happenstance found. Catanese, P. W. **Fic**

HAPPINESS

Graves, S. I'm not happy **152.4**

HAPPINESS

See also Emotions

HAPPINESS -- FICTION

Schwartz, A. 100 things that make me happy **E**
Taro Miura The tiny king **E**
Happy. Van Hout, M. **E**
Happy 100th day! Milord, S. **E**
Happy and healthy. Chancellor, D. **646.7**

Happy and Honey. Godwin, L. **E**
Happy bees. Yorinks, A. **E**
Happy belly, happy smile. Isadora, R. **E**
Happy birdday, Tacky! Lester, H. **E**
Happy birthday Bad Kitty. Bruel, N. **Fic**
Happy birthday to you! Raven, M. **782.42**
Happy birthday, Hamster. Lord, C. **E**
Happy Birthday, Madame Chapeau. Beaty, A. **E**
Happy birthday, Mallory! Friedman, L. B. **Fic**
Happy birthday, Martin Luther King. Marzollo, J. **323**
Happy birthday, Moon. Asch, F. **E**
Happy birthday, Sophie Hartley. Greene, S. **Fic**
Happy birthday, Tree. **E**
Happy Cat. Henry, S. **E**
Happy endings. Pulver, R. **E**
Happy Halloween, Mittens. Schaefer, L. M. **E**
Happy Hippo, angry Duck. Boynton, S. **E**

Happy Honey [series]

Godwin, L. Happy and Honey **E**
Happy like soccer. Boelts, M. **Fic**
Happy New Year, Mallory! Friedman, L. B. **Fic**
Happy Nowruz. Batmanglij, N. **641.5**
Happy Pig Day! Willems, M. **E**
Happy punks 1 2 3. **E**
Happy, happy Chinese New Year! Demi **394.26**

Haptie, Charlotte

Otto and the flying twins **Fic**

Haque, Jameel

Kwek, K. Pakistan **954.91**

Harada, Violet H.

(ed) Growing schools **370.71**
Assessing for learning **027.8**
Inquiry learning through librarian-teacher partnerships **371.1**
Hughes-Hassell, S. School reform and the school library media specialist **027.8**

Harasimowicz, Ellen

(il) Burns, L. G. Beetle busters **595.76**
(il) Burns, L. G. Citizen scientists **590.72**
(il) Burns, L. G. Handle with care **595.78**
(il) Burns, L. G. The hive detectives **638**

Harasymiw, N. D.

Condors in danger **598.9**

Harbo, Christopher L.

Easy animal origami **736**
Easy holiday origami **736**
Easy ocean origami **736**
Easy origami toys **736**
The kids' guide to paper airplanes **745.592**
Paper airplanes: Captain, level 4 **745.592**
Paper airplanes: Copilot, level 2 **745.592**
Paper airplanes: Flight school, level 1 **745.592**
Paper airplanes: Pilot, level 3 **745.592**
Harbor. Crews, D. **E**

HARBORS

(il) Alien encounter **Fic**

Dreamer, wisher, liar **Fic**

Gigi in the big city **E**

Henry's heart **E**

Imaginative inventions **609**

Just Grace and the super sleepover **Fic**

Just Grace and the trouble with cupcakes **Fic**

Just Grace gets crafty **Fic**

Just Grace **Fic**

Just Grace and the double surprise **Fic**

Just Grace and the snack attack **Fic**

Just Grace and the Terrible Tutu **Fic**

Just Grace goes green **Fic**

Just Grace walks the dog **Fic**

Mimi and Lulu **E**

Pink me up **E**

The power of cute **E**

Still Just Grace **Fic**

When Randolph turned rotten **E**

Harper, Dan

Sit, Truman! **E**

Harper, Jamie

Miles to the finish **E**

Miles to go **E**

(il) Warner, S. EllRay Jakes is not a chicken! **Fic**

(il) Warner, S. EllRay Jakes is not a rock star **Fic**

(il) Warner, S. Only Emma **Fic**

Harper, Jessica

Uh-oh, Cleo **Fic**

Underpants on my head **Fic**

Harper, Lee

The Emperor's cool clothes **E**

Snow! Snow! Snow! **E**

(il) Myers, W. D. Looking for the easy life **E**

Harper, Meghan

Reference sources and services for youth **025.5**

Harper, Suzanne

Earnest, P. The real spy's guide to becoming a
spy **327.12**

A gaggle of goblins **Fic**

Harrell, Rob

Monster on the Hill **741.5**

Harriet and the Promised Land. Lawrence, J. **811**

Harriet Beecher Stowe and the Beecher preachers.
Fritz, J. **813**

Harriet dancing. Symes, R. **E**

Harriet Tubman and the Underground Railroad.
Adler, D. A. **973.7**

Harriet's had enough. Guest, E. H. **E**

Harriet, the spy. Fitzhugh, L. **Fic**

Harrington, David

(il) Balsley, T. Maccabee! **296.4**

Harrington, Janice N.

Busy-busy Little Chick **E**

Harrington, Janice N.

The chicken-chasing queen of Lamar County **E**

Going north **E**

Harrington, Karen

Courage for beginners **Fic**

Sure signs of crazy **Fic**

Harris, Andrew

(il) Cobb, V. Your body battles a broken bone **617.1**

(il) Cobb, V. Your body battles a cavity **617.6**

(il) Cobb, V. Your body battles a cold **616.2**

(il) Cobb, V. Your body battles a skinned knee **617.1**

(il) Cobb, V. Your body battles a stomachache **616.3**

(il) Cobb, V. Your body battles an earache **617.8**

(il) Harris, T. Tally cat keeps track **E**

Harris, Ashley Rae

Tupac Shakur **92**

Harris, Brian

(il) Hodge, D. Up we grow! **630**

(il) Hodge, D. Watch me grow! **630**

Harris, Caroline

Whales and dolphins **599.5**

Wild weather **551.55**

Harris, Christopher

Mayer, B. Libraries got game **025.2**

Harris, Jacqueline L.

Science in ancient Rome **509**

Harris, Jim, 1955-

(il) When you're a pirate dog and other pirate poems **811**

Harris, Joe

The belly book **E**

Harris, John

My monster notebook **398.2**

Strong stuff **398.2**

Holmes, M. T. A giraffe goes to Paris **E**

Jingle bells **E**

Harris, Joseph

Space exploration **629.4**

Harris, Laurie Lanzen

(ed) Biography for beginners: women who made a
difference **920.003**

(ed) Colonial America and the Revolutionary
War **973.2**

Harris, Lewis

A taste for red **Fic**

Harris, Lois V.

Mary Cassatt **92**

Harris, Nathaniel

Ancient Maya **972**

Harris, Pamela K.

Welcome to Switzerland **949.4**

Harris, Robie H.

The day Leo said I hate you **E**

Goodbye, Mousie **E**

It's not the stork! **612.6**

It's so amazing! **612.6**

Mail Harry to the moon! **E**

(il) Seeger, P. Abiyoyo **398.2**

(il) Taylor, M. D. The gold Cadillac **Fic**

HAZARDOUS OCCUPATIONS

    See also Occupations

HAZARDOUS SUBSTANCES

    See also Materials

**HAZARDOUS SUBSTANCES -- TRANSPORTA-
TION**

    See also Transportation

HAZARDOUS WASTES

    See also Hazardous substances; Industrial
waste; Refuse and refuse disposal

Hazelaar, Cor

(il) Shelby, A. The man who lived in a hollow
tree **E**

Hazen, Barbara Shook

Digby **E**

Hazen, Lynn E.

The amazing trail of Seymour Snail **Fic**

Cinder Rabbit **Fic**

HDTV. Hirschmann, K. **384.55**

HDTV (TELEVISION) *See* High definition television

He has shot the president! Brown, D. **973.7**

He laughed with his other mouths. Anderson, M.
T. **Fic**

He will go fearless. Lawlor, L. **Fic**

He Zhihong

(il) Gower, C. Long-Long's New Year **E**

He's got the whole world in his hands. Nelson,
K. **782.25**

HEAD

Allen, K. The human head **611**

HEAD

    See also Anatomy

Head lice. Royston, A. **616.5**

Head, body, legs. Paye **398.2**

Head, Honor

Healthy eating **613.2**

Keeping clean **613.4**

Keeping fit **613.7**

Head-to-toe health [series]

Landau, E. Asthma **616.2**

Landau, E. Bites and stings **617.1**

Landau, E. Broken bones **617.1**

Landau, E. Bumps, bruises, and scrapes **617.1**

Landau, E. Burns **617.1**

Landau, E. Cavities and toothaches **617.6**

Landau, E. Chickenpox **616.9**

Landau, E. The common cold **616.2**

Landau, E. Earaches **617.8**

Landau, E. Food allergies **616.97**

Landau, E. Sprains and strains **617.1**

Landau, E. Strep throat **616.9**

Landau, E. Warts **616.5**

HEADACHE

    See also Pain

The **headless** cupid. Snyder, Z. K. **Fic**

The **Headless** Horseman rides tonight. Prelutsky,
J. **811**

Headline science [series]

Lew, K. Goodbye, gasoline **621.31**

Nardo, D. Climate crisis **363.7**

Nardo, D. Cure quest **616**

Stille, D. R. Great shakes **551.2**

Stille, D. R. Nature interrupted **577**

VanVoorst, J. Rise of the thinking machines **629.8**

Heads. Van Fleet, M. **E**

HEADS OF STATE

    See also Executive power; Statesmen

Heads or tails. Gantos, J. **Fic**

Heale, Jay

Democratic Republic of the Congo **967.51**

Madagascar **969.1**

Tanzania **967.8**

HEALERS -- FICTION

Quirk, K. A girl called Problem **Fic**

HEALING

    See also Therapeutics

The **healing** spell. Little, K. G. **Fic**

The Healing Wars [series]

Hardy, J. Blue fire **Fic**

Hardy, J. The shifter **Fic**

The healing wars [series]

Hardy, J. Darkfall **Fic**

Health. Durrie, K. **613.2**

HEALTH

    See also Medicine; Physiology; Preventive
medicine

HEALTH

Durrie, K. Health **613.2**

Harris, R. H. What's so yummy? **613.2**

Head, H. Healthy eating **613.2**

Miller, E. The monster health book **613**

Read, L. Keeping well **613**

Rooney, A. Health and medicine **610**

Schaefer, A. Staying healthy **613**

Stoyles, P. The A-Z of health **616**

HEALTH -- INFORMATION SERVICES

Lukenbill, W. B. Health information in a changing
world **372**

HEALTH -- STUDY AND TEACHING *See* Health
education

Health alert [series]

Bjorklund, R. Cerebral palsy **616.8**

Bjorklund, R. Cystic fibrosis **616.3**

Bjorklund, R. Epilepsy **616.8**

Brill, M. T. Down syndrome **616.85**

Calamandrei, C. Fever **616**

Capaccio, G. ADD and ADHD **616.85**

Colligan, L. H. Sleep disorders **616.8**

Colligan, L. H. Tick-borne illnesses **616.9**

Hendra, Sue

(il) Hicks, B. J. Monsters don't eat broccoli   E

Hendricks, Donald

(il) McAlister, C. Brave Donatella and the Jasmine thief   E

Hendricks, Jeff

LeVert, S. Ecstasy   **362.29**

Hendrix, Jimi

About

Golio, G. Jimi: sounds like a rainbow: a story of young Jimi Hendrix

Hendrix, John

(il) A boy called Dickens   **Fic**

Shooting at the stars   E

(il) Rutherford B., who was he?   **811.54**

John Brown   92

(il) Hopkinson, D. Abe Lincoln crosses a creek   E

(il) Nurse, soldier, spy: the story of Sarah Edmonds, a Civil War hero   92

Hendry, Linda

Dog crafts   **745.5**

(il) Hood, S. Pup and Hound hatch an egg   E

Heneghan, Judith

Once there was a seed   **581.4**

Heney, Clare

Cottrell Boyce, F. The unforgotten coat   **Fic**

(il) Cottrell Boyce, F. The un-forgotten coat   **Fic**

Hengel, Katherine

It's a baby Australian fur seal!   **599.79**

Henham, R. D.

The red dragon codex   **Fic**

Henie, Sonja, 1912-1969

About

Krull, K. Lives of the athletes   **796**

Henkes, Kevin

Penny and her song   E

Bird Lake moon   **Fic**

Birds   E

The birthday room   **Fic**

Chester's way   E

Circle dogs   **516**

A good day   E

Jessica   E

Julius, the baby of the world   E

Kitten's first full moon   E

My garden   E

Old Bear   E

Olive's ocean   **Fic**

Owen   E

Protecting Marie   **Fic**

Sheila Rae, the brave   E

So happy!   E

Sun & Spoon   **Fic**

Wemberly worried   E

Words of stone   **Fic**

Chrysanthemum   E

Little white rabbit   E

Penny and her marble   E

The year of Billy Miller   **Fic**

(jt. auth) Henkes, K. Penny and her doll   E

(il) Lilly's purple plastic purse   E

Hennessy, B. G.

Because of you   E

The boy who cried wolf   **398.2**

Henny Penny. French, V.   **398.2**

Henny Penny. Galdone, P.   **398.2**

Henri Matisse. Welton, J.   **92**

Henri's scissors. Winter, J.   **92**

Henrichs, Wendy

I am Tama, lucky cat   **398.2**

When Anju loved being an elephant   E

Henrietta Hornbuckle's circus of life. De Guzman, M.   **Fic**

Henrietta King, la patrona.   **976.4**

HENRIETTA MARIE (SHIP)

Cerullo, M. M. Shipwrecks   **910.4**

Henrique, Paulo

(il) Conway, G. Crawling with zombies   **741.5**

Henry Aaron's dream. Tavares, M.   **92**

Henry and Beezus. Cleary, B.   **Fic**

Henry and Mudge. Rylant, C.   E

Henry and Mudge and a very Merry Christmas. Rylant, C.   E

Henry and Mudge and Annie's good move. Rylant, C.   E

Henry and Mudge and the bedtime thumps. Rylant, C.   E

Henry and Mudge and the best day of all. Rylant, C.   E

Henry and Mudge and the careful cousin. Rylant, C.   E

Henry and Mudge and the great grandpas. Rylant, C.   E

Henry and Mudge and the happy cat. Rylant, C.   E

Henry and Mudge and the snowman plan. Rylant, C.   E

Henry and Mudge and the starry night. Rylant, C.   E

Henry and Mudge get the cold shivers. Rylant, C.   E

Henry and Mudge in the family trees. Rylant, C.   E

Henry and Mudge in the green time. Rylant, C.   E

Henry and Mudge in the sparkle days. Rylant, C.   E

Henry and Ribsy. Cleary, B.   **Fic**

Henry and the cannons. Brown, D.   **973.3**

Henry and the kite dragon. Hall, B. E.   E

Henry and the Valentine surprise. Carlson, N. L.   E

Henry hikes to Fitchburg. Johnson, D. B.   E

Henry Huggins. Cleary, B.   **Fic**

Henry in love. McCarty, P.   E

Henry Knox.   **92**

Henry Reed, Inc. Robertson, K.   **Fic**

Henry the fourth. Murphy, S. J.   **513**

Henry's first-moon birthday. Look, L.   E

Here come the humpbacks! **599.5**
Here comes Destructosaurus! Reynolds, A. **E**
Here comes Grandma! Lord, J. **E**
Here comes Jack Frost. Kohara, K. **E**
Here comes McBroom! Fleischman, S. **Fic**
Here comes Mother Goose. Opie, I. A. **398.8**
Here comes Santa Cat. **E**
Here comes the Easter Cat! **E**
Here comes the garbage barge! Winter, J. **E**
Here comes the strikeout. Kessler, L. P. **E**
Here I am. Kim, P. **E**
Here lies Linc. Ray, D. **Fic**
Here lies the librarian. Peck, R. **Fic**
Here there be monsters. Newquist, H. P. **594**
Here we go round the mulberry bush. Cabrera, J. **E**
Here we go round the mulberry bush. Fatus, S. **782.42**
Here we grow. Stewart, M. **612.7**
Here's a little poem. **811**
Here's looking at me. Raczka, B. **757**
Here, kitty, kitty. Mora, P. **E**
HEREDITY
  Rand, C. DNA and heredity **572.8**
  Simons, R. Too many Sunday dinners **616.3**
HEREDITY
  See also Biology; Breeding
HERESY
  See also Religion
Hereville: how Mirka got her sword. Deutsch, B. **741.5**
Hergé, 1907-1983
  Herge The adventures of Tintin, vol. 1 **741.5**
Herlong, M.H.
  Buddy **Fic**
Herman and Rosie. **E**
Herman, Charlotte
  First rain **E**
Herman, Emily
  Hubknuckles **E**
Hermelin the detective mouse. Grey, M. **E**
Hermes, Patricia
  Emma Dilemma and the camping nanny **Fic**
  Emma Dilemma and the new nanny **Fic**
  Emma Dilemma and the soccer nanny **Fic**
  Emma Dilemma and the two nannies **Fic**
  Emma Dilemma, the nanny, and the best horse ever **Fic**
  Emma Dilemma, the nanny, and the secret ferret **Fic**
The **hermit** crab. Goodrich, C. **E**
HERMITS
  Arnosky, J. Crinkleroot's guide to giving back to nature **333.95**
Hernandez de la Cruz, Maria
  Endredy, J. The journey of Tunuri and the Blue Deer **398.2**
Hernandez, Leeza

Dog gone! **E**
  (il) Donovan, S. Bored Bella learns about fiction and nonfiction **025.4**
  (il) McCallum, A. Eat your math homework **641.5**
Hernandez, Roger E.
  The Civil War, 1840s-1890s **973.7**
  Early explorations: the 1500s **970.01**
  New Spain: 1600-1760s **973.1**
Hernandez-Divers, Sonia
  Geckos **639.3**
Hero dad. Hardin, M. **E**
A **hero** for WondLa. DiTerlizzi, T. **Fic**
The **hero** of Little Street. Rogers, G. **E**
Hero of the high seas. Cooper, M. L. **92**
Hero on a bicycle. Hughes, S. **Fic**
The **hero** revealed. Boniface, W. **Fic**
The **hero** Schliemann. Schlitz, L. A. **92**
Hero's Guide [series]
  The hero's guide to storming the castle **Fic**
The Hero's guide ; book 3 [series]
  The Hero's Guide to Being an Outlaw **Fic**
The **Hero's** Guide to Being an Outlaw. **Fic**
The **hero's** guide to saving your kingdom. Healy, C. **Fic**
The **hero's** guide to storming the castle. **Fic**
Heroes. Mochizuki, K. **E**
Heroes [series]
  McCaughrean, G. Hercules **292**
  McCaughrean, G. Odysseus **292**
  McCaughrean, G. Perseus **292**
HEROES -- FICTION
  Clements, A. About average **Fic**
  Donaldson, J. Superworm **E**
  Foxlee, K. Ophelia and the marvelous boy **Fic**
  Garza, X. Maximilian and the mystery of the Guardian Angel **Fic**
  The hero's guide to storming the castle **Fic**
  Legends of Zita the spacegirl **741.5**
  The orphan army **Fic**
  Quest for the Spark **Fic**
  Rocco, J. Blizzard **E**
  Slack, M. Elecopter **E**
  Supertruck **E**
HEROES -- PAKISTAN -- BIOGRAPHY
  Winter, J. Malala, a brave girl from Pakistan/Iqbal, a brave boy from Pakistan **920**
HEROES AND HEROINES
  28 days **973.04**
  Haven, K. F. Reluctant heroes **920**
  Of thee I sing **179**
  Roop, P. Tales of famous heroes **920**
  Winter, J. Peaceful heroes **920**
HEROES AND HEROINES
  See also Adventure and adventurers
HEROES AND HEROINES -- FICTION
  Healy, C. The hero's guide to saving your king-

Your food **641.3**
Your local environment **333.72**
Hey batta batta swing! Cook, S. **796.357**
Hey Canada! Bowers, V. **971**
Hey diddle diddle. Bunting, E. **E**
Hey rabbit! Ruzzier, S. **E**
Hey there, stink bug! Bulion, L. **595.7**
Hey! listen to this. **028.5**
Hey, Al. Yorinks, A. **E**
Heyer, Carol
  (il) O'Malley, K. Once upon a royal superbaby **E**
Heyman, Alissa
  (ed) The big book of pirates **S**
Heyman, Ken
  (il) Morris, A. Hats, hats, hats **391**
Heyward, DuBose
  The country bunny and the little gold shoes **E**
Heyworth, Heather
  (il) Troupe, T. K. If I were a ballerina **792.8**
Hi, cat! Keats, E. J. **E**
Hi, Fly Guy! Arnold, T. **E**
Hi, Koo! Muth, J. J. **811**
Hi-tech clothes. Spilsbury, R. **746.9**
Hiaasen, Carl
  Flush **Fic**
  Hoot **Fic**
  Scat **Fic**
Hiawatha. Longfellow, H. W. **811**
HIBERNATION
  Baines, R. A den is a bed for a bear **599.78**
HIBERNATION
  See also Animal behavior
HIBERNATION -- FICTION
  Banks, K. The bear in the book **E**
  Bear has a story to tell **E**
Hibernation station. Meadows, M. **E**
HICCUPS -- FICTION
  Cuyler, M. Skeleton hiccups **E**
Hickory dickory dock. Baker, K. **E**
Hickox, Rebecca
  The golden sandal **398.2**
Hicks, Barbara Jean
  Jitterbug jam **E**
  Monsters don't eat broccoli **E**
Hicks, Betty
  The worm whisperer **Fic**
  Basketball Bats **Fic**
  Doubles troubles **Fic**
  Goof-off goalie **Fic**
  Out of order **Fic**
  Scaredy-cat catcher **Fic**
  Swimming with Sharks **Fic**
  Track attack **Fic**
Hicks, Faith Erin
  (il) Into the woods **741.5**
  (il) The Sound of Thunder **741.5**

  (il) The unkindness of ravens **741.5**
Hicks, Mark A.
  (il) Kuntz, L. Celebrate the USA **973**
Hicks, Terry Allan
  The Chumash **970.004**
  Earth and the moon **525**
  Karate **796.8**
  Obesity **616.3**
  Saturn **523.4**
  Why do leaves change color? **575**
Hidden. Dauvillier, L. **741.5**
The **hidden** boy. Berkeley, J. **Fic**
The **hidden** children. Greenfeld, H. **940.53**
HIDDEN CHILDREN (HOLOCAUST)
  See also Jewish children in the Holocaust
The **hidden** gallery. Wood, M. **Fic**
Hidden hippo. Gannij, J. **590**
HIDDEN TREASURE *See* Buried treasure
Hidden world of the Aztec. Lourie, P. **972**
Hidden worlds: looking through a scientist's microscope. Kramer, S. **502.8**
Hide & seek. Na, I. S. **E**
Hide and seek. Grant, K. **Fic**
Hide and Seek. Fox, N. **614.4**
Hide and seek. Helman, A. **591.47**
Hide and Seek. Carter, D. A. **E**
Hide and seek first words. Sirett, D. **793.73**
Hide and seek fog. Tresselt, A. R. **E**
HIDE-AND-SEEK -- FICTION
  Chase, K. Oliver's tree **E**
  Na, I. S. Hide & seek **E**
  Where is Pim? **E**
Hide-and-squeak. Frederick, H. V. **E**
Hiding Edith. Kacer, K. **940.53**
Hiding from the Nazis. **940.53**
HIEROGLYPHICS
  Giblin, J. The riddle of the Rosetta Stone **493**
  Rumford, J. Seeker of knowledge **92**
HIEROGLYPHICS
  See also Inscriptions; Writing
Hierstein, Judith
  (il) Garland, S. Voices of the dust bowl **973.917**
Higgins, Anne Keenan
  (il) Ain, B. Starring Jules (as herself) **E**
  (il) Ain, B. Starring Jules (in drama-rama) **Fic**
Higgins, F. E.
  The Black Book of Secrets **Fic**
  The bone magician **Fic**
Higgins, Nadia
  Jennifer Lawrence **791.450**
  Splash! Learn about water **546**
Higgins, Simon
  Moonshadow **Fic**
  The nightmare ninja **Fic**
Higgledy-piggledy chicks. Joosse, B. M. **E**
Higglety pigglety pop! Sendak, M. **Fic**

HOLIDAYS

Douglass, S. L. Ramadan   **297.3**

Gibbons, G. Halloween is--   **394.26**

Hopkins, L. B. Days to celebrate   **051**

Jones, L. Kids around the world celebrate! **394.26**

Kenney, K. L. Cool holiday parties   **793.2**

Peppas, L. Cultural traditions in Mexico   **394.26**

Webb, L. S. Holidays of the world cookbook for students   **641.5**

Holidays [series]

Murray, J. Ramadan   **297.3**

HOLIDAYS -- FICTION

French, J. Christmas wombat   **E**

HOLIDAYS -- MEXICO

Peppas, L. Cultural traditions in Mexico   **394.26**

HOLIDAYS -- POETRY

Hines, A. G. Winter lights   **811**

HOLIDAYS -- UNITED STATES

Red, white, and boom!   **E**

Holidays and festivals [series]

Dickmann, N. Ramadan and Id-ul-Fitr   **297.3**

Rissman, R. Martin Luther King, Jr. Day   **394.26**

Holidays around the world [series]

Heiligman, D. Celebrate Christmas   **394.26**

Heiligman, D. Celebrate Diwali   **294.5**

Heiligman, D. Celebrate Halloween   **394.26**

Heiligman, D. Celebrate Hanukkah   **296.4**

Heiligman, D. Celebrate Independence Day **394.26**

Heiligman, D. Celebrate Passover   **296.4**

Heiligman, D. Celebrate Ramadan & Eid al-Fitr   **297.3**

Heiligman, D. Celebrate Rosh Hashanah and Yom Kippur   **296.4**

Heiligman, D. Celebrate Thanksgiving   **394.26**

Otto, C. Celebrate Chinese New Year   **394.26**

Otto, C. Celebrate Cinco de Mayo   **394.26**

Otto, C. Celebrate Kwanzaa   **394.26**

Otto, C. Celebrate Valentine's Day   **394.26**

Holidays of the world cookbook for students. Webb, L. S.   **641.5**

HOLIDAYS, HINDU *See* Hindu holidays

HOLIDAYS, JEWISH *See* Jewish holidays

Holinaty, Josh

(il) You just can't help it!   **599.9**

HOLISTIC MEDICINE

See also Alternative medicine; Medicine

Holland, Gay W.

(il) Glaser, L. Hello, squirrels!   **599.3**

Holland, Leslie J.

Dr. Martin Luther King Jr.'s I have a dream speech in translation   **323.1**

Holland, Mary

Ferdinand Fox's first summer   **599.775**

Holland, Richard

(il) Landman, T. Mary's penny   **E**

(il) Mark, J. The museum book   **069**

Holland, Trish

Ford, C. Ocean's child   **E**

Hollar, Sherman

(ed) Ecology   **577**

Hollar, Sherman

(ed) Ancient Egypt   **932**

Hollihan, Kerrie Logan

Elizabeth I--the people's queen   **942.05**

Rightfully ours   **324.6**

Isaac Newton and physics for kids   **92**

Theodore Roosevelt for kids   **92**

Holling, Holling C.

Paddle-to-the-sea   **Fic**

Holly's red boots. Chessa, F.   **E**

Hollyer, Beatrice

Our world of water   **363.6**

HOLLYWOOD (CALIF.) -- FICTION

Williams, M. The Fizzy Whiz kid   **Fic**

Holm, Jennifer L.

(ed) Comics Squad   **741.5**

The fourteenth goldfish   **Fic**

Babymouse: queen of the world   **741.5**

Brave new pond   **741.5**

Middle school is worse than meatloaf   **Fic**

Our only May Amelia   **Fic**

Penny from heaven   **Fic**

Squish, Super Amoeba   **741.5**

Turtle in paradise   **Fic**

The trouble with May Amelia   **Fic**

Holm, Matthew

(ed) Comics Squad   **741.5**

Holm, J. L. Babymouse: queen of the world **741.5**

Holm, J. L. Brave new pond   **741.5**

(jt. auth) Holm, J. L. Squish, Super Amoeba **741.5**

Holm, Sharon Lane

(il) The best birthday parties ever!   **793.2**

Holmberg, Bo R.

A day with Dad   **E**

Holmes, Benjamin C., fl. 1846-1870

About

Sherman, P. Ben and the Emancipation Proclamation   **E**

Holmes, Janet A.

Have you seen Duck?   **E**

Holmes, Jeremy

(il) Florian, D. Poem-mobiles   **811**

Holmes, Mary Tavener

A giraffe goes to Paris   **E**

My travels with Clara   **599.66**

Holmes, Sara Lewis

Operation Yes   **Fic**

HOLMES, SHERLOCK (FICTIONAL CHARACTER) -- FICTION

Lane, A. Black ice   **Fic**

Lane, A. Rebel fire   **Fic**

Holmes, Thom

Hot diggity dog. Sylver, A. **641.3**
Hot dog! **973.91**
Hot hand. Lupica, M. **Fic**
Hot hot rods. Sandler, M. **629.228**
Hot rod hamster. **E**
Hot rod hamster. **E**
Hot, hot roti for Dada-ji. Zia, F. **E**
HOTEL EXECUTIVES
  Barasch, L. Knockin' on wood **92**
HOTELS AND MOTELS
  Mara, W. The innkeeper **647.9**
  Turnage, S. The ghosts of Tupelo Landing **Fic**
HOTELS AND MOTELS -- FICTION
  Carman, P. The field of wacky inventions **Fic**
  Milford, K. Greenglass House **Fic**
Hottest motorcycles. Woods, B. **629.227**
Hottest muscle cars. Woods, B. **629.222**
Hottest NASCAR machines. Kelley, K. C. **796.72**
Hottest race cars. Egan, E. **796.72**
Hottest sports cars. Woods, B. **629.222**
Hottest, coldest, highest, deepest. Jenkins, S. **910**
Houblon, Marie
  A world of colors **535.6**
Houdini. Krull, K. **92**
Houdini. Biskup, A. **92**
The Houdini box. Selznick, B. **Fic**
Houdini, Harry, 1874-1926
  About
  Biskup, A. Houdini **92**
  Carlson, L. M. Harry Houdini for kids **92**
  Fleischman, S. Escape! **92**
  Krull, K. Houdini **92**
  Selznick, B. The Houdini box **Fic**
Houle, Michelle E.
  Lindsey Williams **92**
Hound and hare. Berner, R. S. **Fic**
Hound dog true. Urban, L. **Fic**
The Hound dog's haiku. **811**
Houndsley and Catina. Howe, J. **E**
Houran, Lori Haskins
  A trip into space **629.4**
The house. Lewis, J. P. **811**
The House at Pooh Corner. Milne, A. A. **Fic**
The house Baba built. Young, E. **92**
A house between homes. Stewart, S. **362.7**
HOUSE CLEANING
  See also Cleaning; Home economics; House-
  hold sanitation
HOUSE CONSTRUCTION
  Barton, B. Building a house **690**
  Bean, J. Building our house **E**
  Newhouse, M. The house that Max built **690**
HOUSE CONSTRUCTION
  See also Building; Domestic architecture
HOUSE CONSTRUCTION -- FICTION
  Beil, K. M. Jack's house **E**

Moore, I. A house in the woods **E**
HOUSE DECORATION *See* Interior design
HOUSE FLIES *See* Flies
A house for Hermit Crab. Carle, E. **E**
HOUSE FURNISHING *See* Interior design
The house in the night. Swanson, S. M. **E**
A house in the woods. Moore, I. **E**
The house of a million pets. Hodgman, A. **92**
The house of Dies Drear. Hamilton, V. **Fic**
House of dolls. Block, F. L. **Fic**
The house of Hades. Riordan, R. **Fic**
House of many ways. Jones, D. W. **Fic**
House of secrets. Columbus, C. **Fic**
House of secrets [series]
  Battle of the beasts **Fic**
The house on East 88th Street. Waber, B. **E**
HOUSE PAINTING
  See also House construction
HOUSE PLANTS
  See also Cultivated plants; Flower gardening;
  Plants; Window gardening
The house that George built. **975.3**
The house that Max built. Newhouse, M. **690**
HOUSE TRAILERS *See* Mobile homes; Travel
  trailers and campers
The house with a clock in its walls. Bellairs, J. **Fic**
House, Katherine L.
  Lighthouses for kids **387.1**
  The White House for kids **975.3**
House, Silas
  Eli the Good **Fic**
HOUSEBOATS
  See also Boats and boating
HOUSEFLY
  I, fly **595.77**
HOUSEHOLD APPLIANCES *See* Household
  equipment and supplies
  Oxlade, C. Gadgets and games **688.7**
HOUSEHOLD BUDGETS
  See also Cost and standard of living; Personal
  finance
HOUSEHOLD EMPLOYEES -- FICTION
  Angleberger, T. Horton Halfpott **Fic**
  Auxier, J. The Night Gardener **Fic**
  Blundell, J. A city tossed and broken **Fic**
  The Golem's latkes **E**
  Parish, H. Amelia Bedelia bakes off **E**
  Parish, P. Amelia Bedelia **E**
  Parish, P. An Amelia Bedelia celebration **E**
  Stevermer, C. Magic below stairs **Fic**
  Stewart, S. The friend **E**
  Venuti, K. C. Leaving the Bellweathers **Fic**
  Zahler, D. The thirteenth princess **Fic**
HOUSEHOLD EQUIPMENT AND SUPPLIES
  Ernst, L. C. How things work in the house **640**
HOUSEHOLD MOVING *See* Moving

climate. Cherry, L.   **363.7**
How weird is it. Hillman, B.   **500**
How you were born. Cole, J.   **612.6**
How your body works. Stewart, D. E.   **612**
How's your health [series]
  Royston, A. Asthma   **616.2**
  Royston, A. Cuts, bruises, and breaks   **617.1**
  Royston, A. Head lice   **616.5**
  Royston, A. Tooth decay   **617.6**
How's your health? [series]
  Royston, A. Allergies   **616.97**
How-to-do-it manuals for librarians [series]
  Alire, C. Serving Latino communities   **027.6**
  Herb, S. Connecting fathers, children, and reading   **028.5**
  Martin, B. S. Fundamentals of school library media management   **025.1**
How? Ripley, C.   **031.02**
Howard Thurman's great hope. Jackson Issa, K. **92**
Howard, Arthur
  (il) Byars, B. C. The SOS file   **Fic**
  (il) Cuyler, M. 100th day worries   **E**
  (il) Cuyler, M. Hooray for Reading Day!   **E**
  Hoodwinked   **E**
  (il) Mr. Putter & Tabby drop the ball   **E**
  (il) Mr. Putter & Tabby ring the bell   **E**
  (il) Mr. Putter & Tabby turn the page   **E**
  (il) Rylant, C. Mr. Putter & Tabby pour the tea   **E**
  (il) Scanlon, L. G. Noodle & Lou   **E**
  (il) Slater, T. Smooch your pooch   **E**
Howard, Elizabeth Fitzgerald
  Aunt Flossie's hats (and crab cakes later)   **E**
  Virgie goes to school with us boys   **E**
Howard, Ellen
  The crimson cap   **Fic**
Howard, Paul
  (il) Cooke, T. Full, full, full of love   **E**
  (il) Henderson, K. Look at you!   **E**
Howarth, Craigh
  (il) Mair, J. S. The perfect gift   **E**
Howarth, Daniel
  (il) Glaser, L. Hoppy Hanukkah!   **E**
  (il) Glaser, L. Hoppy Passover!   **E**
  (il) Roth, C. Will you still love me?   **E**
Howatt, Sandra J.
  Sleepyheads   **E**
Howe, Deborah
  Bunnicula   **Fic**
Howe, Ian
  Jennings, M. Soccer step-by-step   **796.334**
Howe, James
  Howe, D. Bunnicula   **Fic**
  Howe, J. Addie on the inside   **Fic**
  Howe, J. Totally Joe   **Fic**
  Brontorina   **Fic**
  Dew drop dead   **Fic**

Horace and Morris but mostly Dolores   **E**
Houndsley and Catina   **E**
Kaddish for Grandpa in Jesus' name, amen   **E**
Otter and odder   **E**
Pinky and Rex   **E**
Totally Joe   **Fic**
When you go to kindergarten   **372.21**
Howe, Peter
  Waggit again   **Fic**
  Waggit's tale   **Fic**
  Warriors of the black shroud   **Fic**
Howe, Samuel Gridley, 1801-1876
        About
  Alexander, S. H. She touched the world: Laura Bridgman, deaf-blind pioneer   **92**
Howe, William Howe, 5th Viscount, 1729-1814
        About
  Murphy, J. The crossing   **973.3**
Howell, Brian
  Sports   **796**
  The US Civil War and Reconstruction   **973.8**
Howell, Troy
  (il) Friddell, C. Goliath   **975.2**
  The dragon of Cripple Creek   **Fic**
  (il) Osborne, M. P. Favorite Greek myths   **292**
Howells, Tania
  (il) Button, L. Willow's whispers   **E**
Howitt, Mary Botham
  The spider and the fly   **821**
Howl's moving castle. Jones, D. W.   **Fic**
Howland, Naomi
  Latkes, latkes, good to eat   **E**
  Princess says goodnight   **E**
Howler monkey. Ganeri, A.   **599.8**
Howley, Matthew
  (il) Gale, E. K. The Zoo at the Edge of the World   **Fic**
Howling hurricanes. Spilsbury, L.   **551.55**
Howse, Jennifer
  Inclined planes   **621.8**
  Levers   **621.8**
  NASCAR Sprint Cup   **796.72**
  Trees   **582.16**
Hoy, William, 1862-1961
        About
  Silent star   **796.357**
Hoyt, Ard
  (il) Anderson, L. H. The hair of Zoe Fleefenbacher goes to school   **E**
  (il) Brendler, C. Winnie Finn, worm farmer   **E**
  (il) Casanova, M. The day Dirk Yeller came to town   **E**
  (il) Casanova, M. Some dog!   **E**
  (il) Casanova, M. Utterly otterly day   **E**
  (il) Demas, C. Saying goodbye to Lulu   **E**
  (il) Meadows, M. Piggies in the kitchen   **E**

Kochalka, J. Johnny Boo: the best little ghost in the world! **741.5**

Krosoczka, J. J. Lunch Lady and the League of Librarians **741.5**

Lemke, D. Zinc Alloy: Super Zero **741.5**

Lynch, J. Mo and Jo: fighting together forever **741.5**

Mack, J. Hippo and Rabbit in three short tales **E**

Morse, S. Magic Pickle **741.5**

Pien, L. Long Tail Kitty **741.5**

Robbins, T. The drained brains caper **741.5**

Roman, D. Astronaut Academy: Zero gravity **741.5**

Rosenstiehl, A. Silly Lilly and the four seasons **741.5**

Sava, S. C. Hyperactive **741.5**

Sias, R. Zoe and Robot: let's pretend **741.5**

Smith, J. Little Mouse gets ready **741.5**

Sonishi, K. Leave it to PET!: the misadventures of a recycled super robot, vol. 1 **741.5**

Spires, A. Binky the space cat **741.5**

Thompson, J. Magic Trixie **741.5**

Trondheim, L. Tiny Tyrant **741.5**

Wight, E. Frankie Pickle and the closet of doom **741.5**

HUMOROUS GRAPHIC NOVELS

See also Graphic novels

HUMOROUS PICTURES *See* Comic books, strips, etc.

HUMOROUS POETRY

Brown, C. Flamingoes on the roof **811**

Brown, C. Hallowilloween **811**

Brown, C. Soup for breakfast **811**

Ciardi, J. You read to me, I'll read to you **811**

Florian, D. Laugh-eteria **811**

For laughing out loud **811**

Katz, A. Oops! **811**

Katz, A. Poems I wrote when no one was looking **811**

Levy, D. Maybe I'll sleep in the bathtub tonight **811**

Lobel, A. Odd owls & stout pigs **811**

Prelutsky, J. I've lost my hippopotamus **811**

Prelutsky, J. Behold the bold umbrellaphant **811**

Prelutsky, J. The new kid on the block: poems **811**

Prelutsky, J. A pizza the size of the sun **811**

Prelutsky, J. Something big has been here **811**

Shapiro, K. J. I must go down to the beach again **811**

Silverstein, S. Don't bump the glump and other fantasies **811**

Silverstein, S. Every thing on it **811**

Silverstein, S. Falling up **811**

Silverstein, S. A light in the attic **811**

Silverstein, S. Runny Babbit **811**

Silverstein, S. Where the sidewalk ends **811**

Viorst, J. If I were in charge of the world and other worries **811**

When you're a pirate dog and other pirate poems **811**

Wilson, K. What's the weather inside? **811**

HUMOROUS POETRY

See also Poetry; Wit and humor

HUMOROUS STOIRES

Novak, B. J. The book with no pictures **E**

HUMPBACK WHALE

The eye of the whale **599.5**

HUMPBACK WHALE -- FICTION

Marino, G. Following Papa's song **E**

Here come the humpbacks! **599.5**

Humpback whales up close. Rake, J.S. **599.5**

Humphrey, Paul

Building a castle **728.8**

Humpty Dumpty. Kubler, A. **E**

Humpty Dumpty and friends. Lipchenko, O. **398.8**

The hundred dresses. Estes, E. **Fic**

A hundred horses. Lean, S. **Fic**

Huneck, Stephen

Sally goes to Heaven **E**

Huneck, Stephen

Even bad dogs go to heaven **636.7**

Sally goes to the beach **E**

HUNGARIAN COOKING

Hargittai, M. Cooking the Hungarian way **641.5**

HUNGARY -- FICTION

Cheng, A. The lace dowry **Fic**

Seredy, K. The Good Master **Fic**

Seredy, K. The white stag **Fic**

HUNGER

Namioka, L. The hungriest boy in the world **E**

HUNGER -- FICTION

Lobel, A. 10 hungry rabbits **E**

Namioka, L. The hungriest boy in the world **E**

Rawlings, M. K. The secret river **Fic**

Salerno, S. Harry hungry! **E**

HUNGER STRIKES

See also Demonstrations; Fasting; Nonviolence; Passive resistance; Resistance to government

The **hungriest** boy in the world. Namioka, L. **E**

The **hungry** coat. Demi **398.2**

The **hungry** ghost of Rue Orleans. Quattlebaum, M. **E**

The **hungry** little monkey. Blackford, A. **E**

HUNS

Helget, N. Barbarians **940.1**

Kroll, S. Barbarians! **940.1**

Hunt, Irene

Across five Aprils **Fic**

Hunt, Jamie

Getting stronger, getting fit **613.7**

Tired of being teased **616.3**

The truth about diets **613.2**

Hunt, Judith A.

(il) Kenney, K. L. Ellis Island **304.8**

I am Jazz! Herthel, J.   **E**
I am Malala.   **92**
I am me. Kuskin, K.   **E**
I am not going to school today.   **E**
I am not Joey Pigza. Gantos, J.   **Fic**
I am phoenix: poems for two voices. Fleischman, P.   **811**
I am Sacagawea. Norwich, G.   **978.004**
I am small. Dodd, E.   **E**
I am so strong.   **E**
I am Tama, lucky cat. Henrichs, W.   **398.2**
I am the book. Hopkins, L. B.   **811**
I am the darker brother.   **811**
I am the dog. Pinkwater, D. M.   **E**
I am too absolutely small for school. Child, L.   **E**
I and I. Medina, T.   **92**
I broke my trunk! Willems, M.   **E**
I came from the water.   **972.940**
I can be anything.   **E**
I can do it myself! Adams, D.   **E**
I can help. Costello, D.   **E**
I can read book [series]
  Bonsall, C. N. The case of the hungry stranger   **E**
  Brenner, B. Wagon wheels   **E**
  Brown, C. L. After the dinosaurs   **569**
  Brown, C. L. Beyond the dinosaurs   **560**
  Brown, C. L. The day the dinosaurs died   **567.9**
  Byars, B. C. The Golly sisters go West   **E**
  Capucilli, A. Pedro's burro   **E**
  Cazet, D. Elvis the rooster almost goes to heaven   **E**
  Cazet, D. Minnie and Moo and the haunted sweater   **E**
  Cazet, D. Minnie and Moo, wanted dead or alive   **E**
  Cazet, D. The octopus   **E**
  Coerr, E. The big balloon race   **E**
  Coerr, E. The Josefina story quilt   **E**
  Cushman, D. Dirk Bones and the mystery of the haunted house   **E**
  Cushman, D. Inspector Hopper   **E**
  Dizzy dinosaurs   **811**
  Farley, R. Mia and the too big tutu   **E**
  George, J. C. Goose and Duck   **E**
  Gilman, G. Dixie   **E**
  Gorbachev, V. Ms. Turtle the babysitter   **E**
  Hamsters, shells, and spelling bees   **811**
  Hanukkah lights   **811**
  Hazen, B. S. Digby   **E**
  Hill, S. Ruby's perfect day   **E**
  Hoban, L. Arthur's Christmas cookies   **E**
  Hoban, L. Silly Tilly's Thanksgiving dinner   **E**
  Hoff, S. Danny and the dinosaur   **E**
  Hoff, S. The littlest leaguer   **E**
  Hoff, S. Oliver   **E**
  Hoff, S. Sammy the seal   **E**
  Hurd, E. T. Johnny Lion's book   **E**
  Kenah, K. The best seat in second grade   **E**

Kessler, L. P. Here comes the strikeout   **E**
Kessler, L. P. Kick, pass, and run   **E**
Kessler, L. P. Last one in is a rotten egg   **E**
Little, J. Emma's yucky brother   **E**
Lobel, A. Frog and Toad are friends   **E**
Lobel, A. Grasshopper on the road   **E**
Lobel, A. Mouse soup   **E**
Lobel, A. Mouse tales   **E**
Lobel, A. Owl at home   **E**
Lobel, A. Small pig   **E**
Lobel, A. Uncle Elephant   **E**
Maestro, M. What do you hear when cows sing?   **793.73**
McCully, E. A. The grandma mix-up   **E**
Minarik, E. H. Little Bear   **E**
Minarik, E. H. Little Bear and the Marco Polo   **E**
Minarik, E. H. No fighting, no biting!   **E**
Monjo, F. N. The drinking gourd   **E**
Mozelle, S. Zack's alligator and the first snow   **E**
Parish, P. Amelia Bedelia   **E**
Parish, H. Amelia Bedelia bakes off   **E**
Prelutsky, J. It's Christmas!   **811**
Prelutsky, J. It's Thanksgiving!   **811**
Prelutsky, J. It's snowing! it's snowing!   **811**
Schaefer, L. M. Happy Halloween, Mittens   **E**
Schaefer, L. M. Mittens   **E**
Schwartz, A. Ghosts!   **398.2**
Schwartz, A. I saw you in the bathtub, and other folk rhymes   **398.2**
Schwartz, A. In a dark, dark room, and other scary stories   **398.2**
Schwartz, A. There is a carrot in my ear, and other noodle tales   **398.2**
Scotton, R. Splat the cat sings flat   **E**
Skofield, J. Detective Dinosaur   **E**
Skofield, J. Detective Dinosaur: lost and found   **E**
Skofield, J. Detective Dinosaur undercover   **E**
Thomson, S. L. Amazing whales!   **599.5**
Turner, A. W. Dust for dinner   **E**
Weeks, S. Drip, drop   **E**
Wiseman, B. Morris and Boris at the circus   **E**
Wyler, R. Magic secrets   **793.8**
Yorinks, A. Flappy and Scrappy   **E**
I can read chapter book [series]
  Avi Finding Providence: the story of Roger Williams   **92**
I can read mystery book [series]
  Benchley, N. A ghost named Fred   **E**
I can say a prayer. Piper, S.   **242**
I could be, you could be. Owen, K.   **E**
I could do that! White, L.   **92**
I dare you not to yawn.   **E**
I didn't do it. Graves, S.   **177**
I didn't do it. MacLachlan, P.   **811**
I don't want a cool cat! Dodd, E.   **E**
I don't want to go to school! Blake, S.   **E**

Bullard, L. Rashad's Ramadan and Eid al-Fitr **297.3**

Ida B. Wells. Myers, W. D. **92**

Idaho. Kent, D. **979.6**

IDAHO

Kent, D. Idaho **979.6**

Stanley, J. Idaho **979.6**

Stefoff, R. Idaho **979.6**

Idaho. Stefoff, R. **979.6**

Idaho. Stanley, J. **979.6**

IDAHO -- FICTION

Tracy, K. Camille McPhee fell under the bus **Fic**

Tracy, K. The reinvention of Bessica Lefter **Fic**

IDAHO TERRITORY -- HISTORY -- 19TH CEN-TURY -- FICTION

Prisoner 88 **Fic**

IDEALISM

See also Philosophy

IDENTITY

Marsden, C. The gold-threaded dress **Fic**

IDENTITY (PSYCHOLOGY)

See also Personality; Psychology; Self

IDENTITY (PSYCHOLOGY) -- FICTION

Birdie's big-girl hair **E**

The black reckoning **Fic**

Kinsey-Warnock, N. True colors **Fic**

Lichtenheld, T. Exclamation mark **E**

Lowry, L. Son **Fic**

Perkins, L. R. Criss cross **Fic**

Standiford, N. Switched at birthday **Fic**

IDEOLOGY

See also Philosophy; Political science; Psychology; Theory of knowledge; Thought and thinking

IDITAROD TRAIL SLED DOG RACE, ALASKA

Miller, D. S. The great serum race **798.8**

IDITAROD TRAIL SLED DOG RACE, ALASKA -- FICTION

Shahan, S. Ice island **Fic**

Idle, Molly

(il) Crow, K. Zombelina **E**

Flora and the flamingo **E**

Flora and the penguin **E**

Tea Rex **E**

If. Kipling, R. **821**

If all the animals came inside. **E**

If America were a village. Smith, D. J. **973**

If animals kissed good night-- Paul, A. W. **E**

If I had a raptor. O'Connor, G. **E**

If I never forever endeavor. Meade, H. **E**

If I ran the circus. Seuss **E**

If I ran the zoo. Seuss **E**

If I were a ballerina. Troupe, T. K. **792.8**

If I were a jungle animal. Ellery, A. **E**

If I were in charge of the world and other worries. Viorst, J. **811**

If It Rains Pancakes. Cleary, B. P. **811.5**

If not for the cat. Prelutsky, J. **811**

If rocks could sing. McGuirk, L. **E**

If stones could speak. Aronson, M. **936**

If the shoe fits. Bell, K. **Fic**

If the World Were a Village. **304.6**

If you decide to go to the moon. McNulty, F. **629.45**

If you find this. **Fic**

If you give a dog a donut. Numeroff, L. J. **E**

If you give a mouse a cookie. Numeroff, L. J. **E**

If you give a T-rex a bone. Myers, T. **567.9**

If you lived here. Laroche, G. **392**

If you lived here you'd be home by now. Briant, E. **E**

If you love a nursery rhyme. **398.8**

If you made a million. Schwartz, D. M. **332.024**

If you want to see a whale. Fogliano, J. **E**

If you were a chocolate mustache. **811**

If you were a dog. Hibbert, C. **E**

If you were a panda bear. Minor, F. **E**

If you were there in 1776. Brenner, B. **973.3**

If you're a monster and you know it. Emberley, R. **E**

If you're happy and you know it. Cabrera, J. **E**

If you're happy and you know it! Ormerod, J. **E**

If you're hoppy. Sayre, A. P. **E**

If you're reading this, it's too late. Bosch, P. **Fic**

. . . if your name was changed at Ellis Island. Levine, E. **325**

IGBO (AFRICAN PEOPLE) -- FICTION

Saint-Lot, K. N. Amadi's snowman **E**

Iggulden, Conn

The dangerous book for boys **031.02**

Tollins **Fic**

Iggulden, Hal

Iggulden, C. The dangerous book for boys **031.02**

IGLOOS

See also Houses; Inuit

Ignatow, Amy

The long-distance dispatch between Lydia Goldblatt and Julie Graham-Chang **Fic**

The popularity papers **Fic**

Words of (questionable) wisdom from Lydia Goldblatt & Julie Graham-Chang **Fic**

Igneous rock. Faulkner, R. **552**

IGUANAS

Jango-Cohen, J. Let's look at iguanas **597.95**

Lunis, N. Black spiny-tailed iguana **597.95**

Lunis, N. Green iguanas **639.3**

IGUANAS -- FICTION

Orloff, K. K. I wanna iguana **E**

Paul, A. W. Count on Culebra **E**

Robbins, J. The new girl . . . and me **E**

Vernon, U. Dragonbreath: curse of the were-wie-ner **Fic**

Iguanas in the snow and other winter poems. Alarcon, F. X. **811**

IGUANODON

See also Dinosaurs

INFORMATION LITERACY -- STUDY AND TEACHING

Callison, D. The blue book on information age inquiry, instruction and literacy **028.7**

Grassian, E. S. Information literacy instruction **025.5**

Information literacy instruction. Grassian, E. S. **025.5**

INFORMATION RESOURCES

Fontichiaro, K. Go straight to the source **020**

Gaines, A. Master the library and media center **020**

INFORMATION RETRIEVAL -- STUDY AND TEACHING

Grassian, E. S. Information literacy instruction **025.5**

INFORMATION SCIENCE

See also Communication

INFORMATION SERVICES

See also Information resources

INFORMATION SOURCES *See* Information resources

INFORMATION SUPERHIGHWAY *See* Computer networks; Information networks; Internet

INFORMATION TECHNOLOGY

Keane, N. J. The tech-savvy booktalker **021.7**

Scheeren, W. O. Technology for the school librarian **025.04**

Solway, A. Communication **303.4**

INFORMATION TECHNOLOGY

See also Technology

INFORMATION TECHNOLOGY -- STUDY AND TEACHING -- CASE STUDIES

Growing schools **370.71**

INFORMATION THEORY

See also Communication

INFORMATION, FREEDOM OF *See* Freedom of information

Ingalls, Ann

The little piano girl **E**

Inglese, Judith

(il) King, D. I see the sun in Afghanistan **E**

Ingman, Bruce

(il) Ahlberg, A. Hooray for bread **E**

(il) Ahlberg, A. The pencil **E**

(il) Ahlberg, A. Everybody was a baby once, and other poems **811**

(il) Ahlberg, A. Previously **E**

(il) Ahlberg, A. The runaway dinner **E**

(il) Cabral, O. The seven sneezes **E**

(il) Feiffer, K. Double pink **E**

When Martha's away **E**

Ingpen, Robert R.

(il) Barrie, J. M. Peter Pan and Wendy **Fic**

(il) Carroll, L. Alice's adventures in Wonderland **Fic**

Dickens **92**

(il) Grahame, K. The wind in the willows **Fic**

Ingraham, Erick

(il) Calhoun, M. Cross-country cat **E**

Ingram, Jay

Funston, S. It's all in your head **612.8**

INHALANT ABUSE

Menhard, F. R. The facts about inhalants **362.29**

INHERITANCE (BIOLOGY) *See* Heredity

INHERITANCE AND SUCCESSION -- FICTION

Giles, S. M. The body thief **Fic**

Klise, K. Till death do us bark **Fic**

Naylor, P. R. Emily's fortune **Fic**

O'Dell, K. The aviary **Fic**

INHERITANCE AND TRANSFER TAX

See also Estate planning; Inheritance and succession; Internal revenue; Taxation

INITIATION RITES

See also Rites and ceremonies

INJUNCTIONS

See also Constitutional law; Labor unions

INJURIES *See* Accidents; First aid; Wounds and injuries

INK

Farley, B. Ike's incredible ink **E**

The **ink** garden of brother Theophane. Millen, C. M. **E**

INK PAINTING

Peot, M. Inkblot **751.4**

Inkblot. Peot, M. **751.4**

Inkdeath. Funke, C. C. **Fic**

Inkheart. Funke, C. C. **Fic**

Inkspell. Funke, C. C. **Fic**

INLAND NAVIGATION

See also Navigation; Shipping; Transportation

INNER CITIES

See also Cities and towns

Innerst, Stacy

(il) Brewer, P. The Beatles were fab (and they were funny) **782.421**

(il) Brewer, P. Lincoln tells a joke **92**

(il) Johnston, T. Levi Strauss gets a bright idea or **E**

Innes, Stephanie

A bear in war **E**

The **innkeeper.** Mara, W. **647.9**

Innocenti, Roberto

(il) Collodi, C. The adventures of Pinocchio **Fic**

(il) Lewis, J. P. The house **811**

Innovation in sports [series]

Fitzpatrick, J. Skateboarding **796.22**

Gigliotti, J. Football **796.332**

Kelley, K. C. Golf **796.352**

Kelley, K. C. Soccer **796.334**

Labrecque, E. Basketball **796.323**

Teitelbaum, M. Baseball **796.357**

INTEGRATED CURRICULUM *See* Interdisciplinary approach in education

INTEGRATED SCHOOLS *See* School integration

INTEGRATION IN EDUCATION *See* School integration; Segregation in education

INTEGRATION, RACIAL *See* Race relations

INTELLECT
See also Psychology

INTELLECT -- FICTION
Chatterton, M. The Brain finds a leg   **Fic**

INTELLECTUAL COOPERATION
See also International cooperation

INTELLECTUAL FREEDOM
Scales, P. R. Protecting intellectual freedom in your school library   **025.2**

INTELLECTUAL FREEDOM
See also Freedom

Intellectual freedom front lines [series]
Scales, P. R. Protecting intellectual freedom in your school library   **025.2**

INTELLECTUAL LIFE
See also Culture

INTELLIGENCE AGENTS *See* Spies

INTELLIGENCE OF ANIMALS *See* Animal intelligence

INTELLIGENCE SERVICE
Earnest, P. The real spy's guide to becoming a spy   **327.12**

INTELLIGENCE SERVICE
See also Public administration; Research

INTELLIGENCE TESTS
See also Child psychology; Educational psychology

INTELLIGENT BUILDINGS
See also Buildings

INTEMPERANCE *See* Alcoholism; Temperance

INTERACTIVE MEDIA *See* Multimedia

INTERACTIVE MULTIMEDIA *See* Multimedia

INTERBEHAVIORIAL PSYCHOLOGY *See* Behaviorism

INTERCOMMUNICATION SYSTEMS
See also Electronic apparatus and appliances; Telecommunication

INTERCOUNTRY ADOPTION *See* International adoption

INTERCOUNTRY ADOPTION -- FICTION
Goyangi means cat   **E**
Peacock, C. A. Red thread sisters   **Fic**
Red butterfly   **Fic**

INTERCULTURAL EDUCATION *See* Multicultural education

INTERDISCIPLINARY APPROACH IN EDUCATION
Larson, J. C. Bringing mysteries alive for children and young adults   **028.5**

INTERDISCIPLINARY APPROACH IN EDUCATION
See also Curriculum planning

INTEREST (ECONOMICS)
See also Banks and banking; Business mathematics; Capital; Finance; Loans

INTEREST GROUPS *See* Lobbying; Political action committees

The intergalactic bed & breakfast [series]
Aliens on vacation   **Fic**

INTERGENERATIONAL RELATIONS -- FICTION
Casarosa, E. La Luna   **E**
The hula hoopin' queen   **E**

INTERGOVERNMENTAL TAX RELATIONS
See also Taxation

INTERIOR DECORATION *See* Interior design

INTERIOR DESIGN
Weaver, J. It's your room   **747**

INTERIOR DESIGN
See also Art; Decoration and ornament; Design; Home economics

Interjections.   **428**

INTERLIBRARY LOANS
See also Library circulation; Library cooperation

INTERMEDIATE SCHOOLS *See* Middle schools

INTERNAL COMBUSTION ENGINES
See also Engines

INTERNAL MIGRATION
See also Colonization; Population

INTERNAL REVENUE
See also Taxation

INTERNAL REVENUE LAW
See also Law

INTERNATIONAL ADOPTION
Skrypuch, M. F. Last airlift   **959.704**

INTERNATIONAL ADOPTION
See also Adoption

INTERNATIONAL AGENCIES
See also International cooperation

INTERNATIONAL ARBITRATION
See also International cooperation; International law; International relations; International security; Treaties

The international cookbook for kids. Locricchio, M.   **641.5**

INTERNATIONAL COOPERATION
Shoveller, H. Ryan and Jimmy   **361.7**

INTERNATIONAL COOPERATION
See also Cooperation; International law; International relations

INTERNATIONAL COPYRIGHT *See* Copyright

INTERNATIONAL LAW
See also Law

INTERNATIONAL POLICE

Will puberty last my whole life? **613**

INTERPLANETARY VISITORS *See* Extraterrestrial beings

INTERPLANETARY VOYAGES

See also Astronautics; Fiction

Brawer, M. Water planet rescue **Fic**

Goodman, S. E. How do you burp in space? **629.45**

INTERPRETATION OF CULTURAL AND NATURAL RESOURCES -- UNITED STATES

Carson, M. K. The park scientists **333.78**

INTERPRETERS

Adler, D. A. A picture book of Sacagawea **978**

Blumberg, R. Shipwrecked!: the true adventures of a Japanese boy **92**

The crossing **E**

O'Dell, S. Streams to the river, river to the sea **Fic**

INTERRACIAL ADOPTION

Levy, D. A. The misadventures of the family Fletcher **Fic**

INTERRACIAL ADOPTION

See also Adoption; Race relations

INTERRACIAL ADOPTION -- FICTION

The year of the baby **Fic**

INTERRACIAL MARRIAGE

The case for loving **306.846**

INTERRACIAL RELATIONS *See* Race relations

Interrupted journey. Lasky, K. **639.9**

Interrupting chicken. Stein, D. E. **E**

INTERSTATE COMMERCE

See also Commerce

INTERSTELLAR COMMUNICATION

See also Life on other planets; Telecommunication

Interstellar pig. Sleator, W. **Fic**

INTERVENTION (INTERNATIONAL LAW)

See also International law; War

INTERVIEWS

See also Conversation

INTESTINES

Cobb, V. Your body battles a stomachache **616.3**

Donovan, S. Rumble & spew **612.3**

INTI RAYMI FESTIVAL

Krebs, L. Up and down the Andes **985**

INTIFADA, 1987-1992

See also Israel-Arab conflicts

INTIFADA, 2000-

See also Israel-Arab conflicts

INTIMACY (PSYCHOLOGY)

See also Emotions; Interpersonal relations; Love; Psychology

Intner, Carol F.

Homework help from the library **025.5**

Intner, Sheila S., 1935-

(ed) Cataloging correctly for kids **025.3**

Into the classroom. McKeown, R. **370.71**

Into the deep. Sheldon, D. **92**

Into the firestorm. Hopkinson, D. **Fic**

Into the sea. Guiberson, B. Z. **597.92**

Into the trap. Moodie, C. **Fic**

Into the unknown. **910.4**

Into the woods. Gardner, L. **Fic**

Into the woods. **741.5**

INTOLERANCE *See* Fanaticism; Toleration

INTOXICANTS *See* Alcohol; Alcoholic beverages; Liquors

INTOXICATION *See* Alcoholism; Temperance

Intriago, Patricia

Dot **E**

INTUITION

See also Philosophy; Psychology; Rationalism; Theory of knowledge

The **Inuit**. King, D. C. **970.004**

INUIT

Cunningham, K. The Inuit **970.004**

Fatty legs **92**

Jordan-Fenton, C. A stranger at home **92**

King, D. C. The Inuit **970.004**

Lourie, P. Whaling season **599.5**

Martin, J. B. The lamp, the ice, and the boat called Fish **919**

Proud to be Inuvialuit **970.004**

The **Inuit**. Cunningham, K. **970.004**

INUIT -- ART

Rivera, R. Arctic adventures **920**

INUIT -- BIOGRAPHY

When I was eight **371.829**

INUIT -- CANADA -- FICTION

Hobbs, W. Never say die **Fic**

INUIT -- CANADA

Fatty legs **92**

Rivera, R. Arctic adventures **920**

INUIT -- CULTURAL ASSIMILATION -- CANADA

Not my girl **E**

INUIT -- FICTION

Ford, C. Ocean's child **E**

George, J. C. Nutik, the wolf pup **E**

Joosse, B. M. Mama, do you love me? **306.874**

Littlewood, K. Immi's gift **E**

Scott, A. H. On Mother's lap **E**

The shipwreck **Fic**

Sloat, T. Berry magic **E**

The snowstorm **Fic**

Taylor, T. Ice drift **Fic**

INUIT -- FOLKLORE

Brett, J. The three snow bears **398.2**

Dabcovich, L. The polar bear son **398.2**

INUIT -- FOLKLORE

See also Folklore

INUIT -- GREENLAND -- FICTION

The raiders **Fic**

INUIT WOMEN -- BIOGRAPHY

Parry, R. Heart of a shepherd **Fic**

Rumford, J. Silent music **E**

IRAQ WAR, 2003-2011 -- PERSONAL NARRA-TIVES

Dennis, B. Nubs **636.7**

Falvey, D. Letters to a soldier **956.7**

Goldish, M. Baghdad pups **956.7**

Ireland. Blashfield, J. F. **941.7**

Ireland. McQuinn, C. **941.5**

IRELAND

Blashfield, J. F. Ireland **941.7**

IRELAND -- ANTIQUITIES

Green, J. Ancient Celts **936**

IRELAND -- FICTION

Creech, S. The great unexpected **Fic**

IRELAND -- HISTORY

Feed the children first **940**

IRELAND -- HISTORY -- FAMINE, 1845-1852

Fradin, D. B. The Irish potato famine **941.508**

Feed the children first **940**

IRELAND -- SOCIAL LIFE AND CUSTOMS

Sheen, B. Foods of Ireland **641.5**

Ireland, Norma Olin

(comp) Index to fairy tales **398.2**

Irena Sendler and the children of the Warsaw Ghetto. **92**

Irena's jars of secrets. **92**

The **iridescence** of birds. **92**

Iris and Walter. Guest, E. H. **E**

IRISH -- CANADA -- FICTION

Curtis, C. P. The madman of Piney Woods **Fic**

IRISH AMERICANS -- FICTION

Barker, M. P. Mending horses **Fic**

IRISH COOKING

Sheen, B. Foods of Ireland **641.5**

IRISH LITERATURE

See also Literature

The **Irish** potato famine. Fradin, D. B. **941.508**

Iroaganachi, John

Achebe, C. How the leopard got his claws **Fic**

Iron. Sparrow, G. **546**

IRON

See also Chemical elements; Metals

Sparrow, G. Iron **546**

The **iron** dragon. Pryor, B. **Fic**

The **iron** giant. **Fic**

Iron Hans. Mitchell, S. **398.2**

IRON IN THE BODY

See also Iron; Minerals in the body

IRON ORES

See also Iron; Ores

Iron thunder. Avi **Fic**

The **iron** trial. Black, H. **Fic**

Ironhand. Fletcher, C. **Fic**

IRONWORK

See also Decoration and ornament; Iron;

Metalwork

The **Iroquois.** Dolbear, E. J. **970.004**

IROQUOIS INDIANS

Dolbear, E. J. The Iroquois **970.004**

IROQUOIS INDIANS -- FOLKLORE

Sherman, P. The sun's daughter **398.2**

IRRIGATION

Kamkwamba, W. The boy who harnessed the wind **92**

IRRIGATION

See also Agricultural engineering; Hydraulic engineering; Water resources development; Water supply

IRRIGATION -- MALAWI

Kamkwamba, W. The boy who harnessed the wind **92**

Irving, Washington

The Legend of Sleepy Hollow **Fic**

Washington Irving's Rip van Winkle **Fic**

Kimmel, E. A. Rip Van Winkle's return **E**

Zornow, J. The legend of Sleepy Hollow **741.5**

About

Harness, C. The literary adventures of Washington Irving **92**

Irwin, Bindi, 1998-

(jt. auth) Black, J. A year in the life of Bindi **333.72**

Is everyone ready for fun? Thomas, J. **E**

Is it a fact? [series]

Silverman, B. Can an old dog learn new tricks? **590**

Is it larger? Is it smaller? Hoban, T. **516**

Is it red? Is it yellow? Is it blue? Hoban, T. **E**

Is my cat a tiger? Bidner, J. **636.8**

Is my dog a wolf? Bidner, J. **636.7**

Is my hamster wild? Newcomb, R. **636.9**

Is singing for you? Landau, E. **783**

Is the flute for you? Landau, E. **788**

Is the guitar for you? Landau, E. **787.87**

Is the trumpet for you? Landau, E. **788**

Is the violin for you? Landau, E. **787.2**

Is there a dog in this book? Schwarz, V. **E**

Is there life in outer space? Branley, F. M. **576.8**

Is there really a human race? Curtis, J. L. **E**

Is your buffalo ready for kindergarten? Vernick, A. **E**

Is your mama a llama? Guarino, D. **813**

Isaac Asimov's 21st century library of the universe [series]

Asimov, I. The Milky Way and other galaxies **523.1**

Isaac Newton. Steele, P. **92**

Isaac Newton. Krull, K. **92**

Isaac Newton and physics for kids. Hollihan, K. L. **92**

Isaacs, Anne

Dust Devil **E**

Meanwhile, back at the ranch **E**

Pancakes for supper! **E**

Junior worldmark encyclopedia of the nations. 910.3

Junior Worldmark encyclopedia of the states. 973

JUNK *See* Waste products

Junk drawer jewelry. Di Salle, R.   **745.594**

Junk drawer physics. Mercer, B.   **530**

Junk food. Cobb, V.   **664**

Junk food. Currie, S.   **613.2**

JUNK IN SPACE *See* Space debris

Junkyard science. Young, K. R.   **507.8**

The **junkyard** wonders. Polacco, P.   **Fic**

Junor, Betty

    Fun & funky knits   **746.43**

Jupiter. Landau, E.   **523.4**

Jupiter. Capaccio, G.   **523.4**

JUPITER (PLANET)

    Capaccio, G. Jupiter   **523.4**

    Carson, M. K. Far-out guide to Jupiter   **523.4**

    Landau, E. Jupiter   **523.4**

    Mist, R. Jupiter and Saturn   **523.45**

JUPITER (PLANET)

    See also Planets

Jupiter and Saturn. Mist, R.   **523.45**

Jurassic poop. Berkowitz, J.   **567.9**

JURISPRUDENCE *See* Law

JURISTS *See* Lawyers

Jurmain, Suzanne

    The forbidden schoolhouse   **92**

    The worst of friends   **973.4**

Just a dog. Bauer, M. G.   **Fic**

Just a dream. Van Allsburg, C.   **E**

Just a drop of water. Cerra, K. O.   **Fic**

Just a minute. Morales, Y.   **398.2**

Just a second. Jenkins, S.   **529**

Just add water.   **546**

Just because. Elliott, R.   **E**

Just behave, Pablo Picasso!   **709.2**

Just being Audrey. Cardillo, M.   **92**

Just Desserts. Durand, H.   **Fic**

Just enough carrots. Murphy, S. J.   **513.2**

Just fine the way they are.   **388**

Just for elephants. Buckley, C.   **639.9**

Just for kids! [series]

    Hart, C. You can draw cartoon animals   **741.5**

Just Grace. Harper, C. M.   **Fic**

Just Grace and the double surprise. Harper, C. M.   **Fic**

Just Grace and the snack attack. Harper, C. M.   **Fic**

Just Grace and the super sleepover. Harper, C. M.   **Fic**

Just Grace and the Terrible Tutu. Harper, C. M.   **Fic**

Just Grace and the trouble with cupcakes. Harper, C. M.   **Fic**

Just Grace gets crafty. Harper, C. M.   **Fic**

Just Grace goes green. Harper, C. M.   **Fic**

Just Grace walks the dog. Harper, C. M.   **Fic**

Just how long can a long string be!? Baker, K.   **E**

Just in case. Morales, Y.   **E**

Just in case. Viorst, J.   **E**

Just in time, Abraham Lincoln. Polacco, P.   **Fic**

Just like a baby. Havill, J.   **E**

Just like Josh Gibson. Johnson, A.   **E**

Just one bite. Schaefer, L. M.   **591.4**

Just So Stories. Kipling, R.   **E**

Just the basics [series]

    Franklin, P. School library collection development   **025.2**

Just the right size. Davies, N.   **591.4**

Just what Mama needs. Glenn, S. M.   **E**

Juster, Norton, 1929-

    Alberic the Wise and other journeys   **S**

    The annotated Phantom tollbooth   **813**

    The hello, goodbye window   **E**

    Neville   **E**

    The odious Ogre   **E**

    The phantom tollbooth   **Fic**

    About

    Juster, N. The annotated Phantom tollbooth   **813**

JUSTICE

    See also Ethics; Law; Virtue

JUSTICE LEAGUE (FICTIONAL CHARACTERS)

    See also Fictional characters; Superheroes

JUSTICES OF THE PEACE

    White, L. I could do that!   **92**

Justin and the best biscuits in the world.   **Fic**

Justin Bieber. Yasuda, A.   **92**

Justin Bieber: first step 2 forever. Bieber, J.   **92**

Justin Case. Vail, R.   **Fic**

Justin Case.   **Fic**

Justin Fisher declares war! Preller, J.   **Fic**

Jutte, Jan

    (il) Joosse, B. M. Roawr!   **E**

    (il) Joosse, B. M. Sleepover at gramma's house   **E**

JUVENILE DELINQUENCY

    Mead, A. Junebug in trouble   **Fic**

JUVENILE DELINQUENCY

    See also Crime; Social problems

JUVENILE DELINQUENCY -- FICTION

    Mead, A. Junebug in trouble   **Fic**

    Sachar, L. Holes   **Fic**

Juvenile diabetes. Glaser, J.   **616.4**

JUVENILE PROSTITUTION

    See also Juvenile delinquency; Prostitution

Jyotirmayee Mohapatra. Woog, A.   **92**

K

K is for Korea. Cheung, H.   **951.9**

Kaboom! Richardson, G.   **500**

Kacer, Kathy

    Hiding Edith   **940.53**

Kaddish for Grandpa in Jesus' name, amen. Howe, J.   **E**

(il) The Scoop on Poop **E**

Kelly, Joseph

(il) Kerrin, J. S. Martin Bridge blazing ahead! **Fic**

(il) Kerrin, J. S. Martin Bridge in high gear! **Fic**

(il) Kerrin, J. S. Martin Bridge on the lookout! **Fic**

(il) Kerrin, J. S. Martin Bridge out of orbit! **Fic**

(il) Kerrin, J. S. Martin Bridge sound the alarm! **Fic**

(il) Kerrin, J. S. Martin Bridge: onwards and up-wards! **Fic**

(il) Kerrin, J. S. Martin Bridge: ready for take-off! **Fic**

(il) Kerrin, J. S. Martin Bridge: the sky's the lim-it **Fic**

(il) Parker, M. B. A paddling of ducks **E**

Kelly, Katy

Lucy Rose, big on plans **Fic**

Lucy Rose, busy like you can't believe **Fic**

Lucy Rose, here's the thing about me **Fic**

Lucy Rose, working myself to pieces and bits **Fic**

Melonhead **Fic**

Melonhead and the big stink **Fic**

Melonhead and the undercover operation **Fic**

Kelly, Lynne

Chained **Fic**

Kelly, Mij

Where giants hide **E**

Kelly, Sheila M.

Families **306.85**

Yummy! **E**

Rotner, S. I'm adopted! **362.7**

Rotner, S. Shades of people **E**

Kelly, Sophia

What a beast! **398**

Kelsey, Elin

Canadian dinosaurs **567.9**

Not your typical book about the environment **333.72**

You are stardust **E**

Wild ideas **153.4**

Strange new species **578**

Kelsey, Marybeth

A recipe 4 robbery **Fic**

Kelson, Ellen

(il) Let's build a playground **790.06**

Kemble, Mai S.

(il) Urdahl, C. Polka-dot fixes kindergarten **E**

Kemer, Eric

Gardner, R. Easy genius science projects with tem-perature and heat **536**

Kemly, Kathleen Hadam

(il) Bruhn, A. Inside the human body **612**

(il) Smucker, A. E. Golden delicious **634**

KEMPO *See* Kung fu

Kempter, Christa

Wally and Mae **E**

When Mama can't sleep **E**

Kenah, Katharine

The best seat in second grade **E**

Kendall, Gideon

(il) Hulme, J. The glitch in sleep **Fic**

(il) Hulme, J. The split second **Fic**

(il) Nielsen, J. A. Elliot and the goblin war **Fic**

(il) Nielsen, J. A. Elliot and the pixie plot **Fic**

(il) Nielsen, J. A. Elliot and the Yeti threat **Fic**

(il) Plourde, L. Dino pets go to school **E**

Kendall, Martha E.

The Erie Canal **386**

Kendall, Russ

(il) Waters, K. Sarah Morton's day **974.4**

Kendo. Ellis, C. **796.8**

KENDO

Ellis, C. Kendo **796.8**

KENKEN

See also Puzzles

Kennaway, Adrienne

(il) This is the mountain **577.5**

(il) Wilson, J. V. Bumblebee **595.7**

Kennedy family

About

Krull, K. The brothers Kennedy **920**

Kennedy, Anne

(il) Spinelli, E. Miss Fox's class goes green **E**

(il) Spinelli, E. Miss Fox's class shapes up **E**

Kennedy, Anne Vittur

The Farmer's away! baa! neigh! **E**

Kennedy, Caroline

(ed) A family of poems **808.81**

(ed) Poems to learn by heart **821.008**

Kennedy, Dorothy M.

(comp) Knock at a star **811**

Kennedy, Doug

(il) Bardoe, C. The ugly dinosaur **E**

Kennedy, Edward Moore, 1932-2009

About

Krull, K. The brothers Kennedy **920**

Kennedy, Emma

Wilma Tenderfoot: the case of the frozen hearts **Fic**

Wilma Tenderfoot: the case of the putrid poison **Fic**

Kennedy, John E.

Puppet planet **791.5**

Kennedy, John F.

About

Cooper, I. Jack **973**

Kennedy, John F. (John Fitzgerald), 1917-1963

About

Adler, D. A. A picture book of John F. Kenne-dy **973.922**

Heiligman, D. High hopes **92**

Krull, K. The brothers Kennedy **920**

Nardo, D. Assassination and its aftermath **973.92**

Rappaport, D. Jack's path of courage **92**

Kennedy, Marlane

The dog days of Charlotte Hayes **Fic**

Zigazak! **E**

Kimmelman, Leslie

Hot dog! **973.91**

Everybody bonjours! **E**

In the doghouse **E**

The Little Red Hen and the Passover matzah **398.2**

Mind your manners, Alice Roosevelt! **E**

The three bully goats **E**

Kimonos. **E**

Kimura, Ken

999 Frogs Wake Up **E**

999 tadpoles **E**

Kinard, Kami

The boy prediction **Fic**

The **kind** of friends we used to be. Dowell, F. O. **Fic**

KINDERGARTEN

Howe, J. When you go to kindergarten **372.21**

Marx, T. Kindergarten day USA and China **371.82**

Sturges, P. I love school! **E**

KINDERGARTEN

See also Elementary education; Schools

KINDERGARTEN -- FICTION

Ganz-Schmitt, S. Planet Kindergarten **E**

Lloyd, J. The Best Thing About Kindergarten **E**

The **kindergarten** cat. Lewis, J. P. **E**

Kindergarten countdown. Hays, A. J. **E**

Kindergarten day USA and China. Marx, T. **371.82**

Kindergarten diary. Portis, A. **E**

Kindergators [series]

Hands off, Harry! **E**

Kindersley, Anabel

Children just like me **305.23**

Kindersley, Barnabas

Kindersley, A. Children just like me **305.23**

KINDERTRANSPORTS (RESCUE OPERA-TIONS) -- FICTION

Perl, L. Isabel's War **Fic**

The **kindhearted** crocodile. **E**

Kindness. Pryor, K. J. **177**

KINDNESS

Barraclough, S. Sharing **177**

Graves, S. I'm not happy **152.4**

Pryor, K. J. Kindness **177**

KINDNESS -- FICTION

Princesse Camcam Fox's garden **E**

Each kindness **E**

Heiman, D. It's a-- it's a-- it's a mitzvah! **296.1**

Kindred souls. MacLachlan, P. **Fic**

Kindschi, Tara

4-H guide to raising chickens **636.5**

KINEMATICS

Waters, J. All kinds of motion **531**

Kinerk, Robert

Clorinda **E**

Oh, how Sylvester can pester! **811**

KINESIOLOGY

See also Human locomotion; Physical fitness

KINETIC ART

See also Art

KINETIC SCULPTURE

See also Kinetic art; Sculpture

KINETICS See Dynamics; Motion

King Arthur and his Knights of the Round Table. Green, R. L. **398.2**

King Arthur and the Round Table. Talbott, H. **398.2**

King Arthur's very great grandson. Kraegel, K. **E**

King Bidgood's in the bathtub. Wood, A. **E**

King for a day. Khan, R. **E**

King George: what was his problem? Sheinkin, S. **973.3**

King Hugo's huge ego. Van Dusen, C. **E**

King Jack and the dragon. Bently, P. **E**

King Midas. Demi **398.2**

King Midas and the golden touch. Craft, C. **398.209**

The **King** of Little Things. Lepp, B. **E**

The **King** of Quizzical Island. **E**

King of shadows. Cooper, S. **Fic**

The **king** of the Golden River. Ruskin, J. **Fic**

King of the mound. Tooke, W. **Fic**

King of the wind. Henry, M. **Fic**

KING PHILIP'S WAR, 1675-1676

See also Native Americans -- Wars; United States -- History -- 1600-1775, Colonial period

King Pom and the fox. Souhami, J. **398.2**

KING RANCH (TEX.)

Henrietta King, la patrona **976.4**

The **king** who barked. Jones, C. F. **636**

The **king** with horse's ears and other Irish folktales. Burns, B. **398.2**

The **king's** taster. Oppel, K. **E**

King, B. B.

About

Boynton, S. Sandra Boynton's One shoe blues **782.42**

King, Bart

Bart's king-sized book of fun **793**

King, Caro

Seven sorcerers **Fic**

King, Coretta Scott, 1927-2006

About

Coretta Scott **92**

King, Daniel

Chess **794.1**

King, Dave

(il) Sirett, D. Hide and seek first words **793.73**

King, David C.

Children's encyclopedia of American history **973**

Delaware **975.1**

First people **970.004**

The Haida **970.004**

The Huron **970.004**

The Inuit **970.004**

The gingerbread pirates **E**

Klaffke, Ben

(il) Landau, E. Smokejumpers **628.9**

Klages, Ellen

The green glass sea **Fic**

White sands, red menace **Fic**

Klass, David

Stuck on Earth **Fic**

Klassen, Jon

Barnett, M. Extra yarn **E**

(il) Barnett, M. Sam and Dave dig a hole **E**

(il) The dark **E**

I want my hat back **E**

Stutson, C. Cats' night out **E**

This is not my hat **E**

(il) The unseen guest **Fic**

(il) Wood, M. The hidden gallery **Fic**

(il) Wood, M. The mysterious howling **Fic**

Klatt, Kathy Fling

(jt. auth) Ghoting, S. N. STEP into storytime **027.62**

Klausmeier, Jesse

Open this little book **E**

Klavan, Laurence

City of spies **741.5**

Klee, Paul, 1879-1940

About

Paul Klee for children **759.949**

Klein, Laurie Allen

(il) Balloon trees **633.8**

(il) Solar system forecast **551.5**

Klein, Ted

Rhode Island **974.5**

Kleven, Elisa

(il) De colores and other Latin-American folk songs for children **781.62**

(il) Dorros, A. Abuela **E**

(il) Durango, J. Angels watching over me **E**

(il) Hurd, T. The weaver **E**

The apple doll **E**

The friendship wish **E**

Welcome home, Mouse **E**

(il) One little chicken **E**

(il) Orozco Diez deditos. Ten little fingers & other play rhymes and action songs from Latin America **782.42**

(il) Orozco Fiestas: a year of Latin American songs of celebration **782.42**

(il) Thong, R. Wish **398**

KLEZMER MUSIC -- FICTION

Yolen, J. B.U.G. **Fic**

Klimley, A. Peter

About

Mallory, K. Swimming with hammerhead sharks **597.3**

Klimo, Kate

The dragon in the driveway **Fic**

The dragon in the library **Fic**

The dragon in the sock drawer **Fic**

The dragon in the volcano **Fic**

Kline, Michael P.

(il) Blobaum, C. Geology rocks! **551**

(il) Breen, M. The kids' book of weather forecasting **551.63**

(il) Johmann, C. Bridges! **624.2**

(il) Olien, R. Kids care! **361.2**

Kline, Suzy

Horrible Harry in room 2B **Fic**

Song Lee and the I hate you notes **Fic**

Song Lee and the Leech Man **Fic**

(il) Remkiewicz, F. Song Lee in Room 2B **Fic**

Kling, Kevin

Big little brother **E**

Big little mother **E**

Klinger, Shula

(il) Patt, B. Best friends forever **Fic**

Klinting, Lars

What do you want? **E**

The **klipfish** code. Casanova, M. **Fic**

Klipper, Barbara

Programming for children and teens with autism spectrum disorder **027.6**

Klise, Kate

Grammy Lamby and the secret handshake **E**

The Greatest Star on Earth **Fic**

Homesick **Fic**

The show must go on! **Fic**

Dying to meet you **Fic**

Grounded **Fic**

Over my dead body **Fic**

Regarding the bathrooms **Fic**

Regarding the bees **Fic**

Regarding the fountain **Fic**

Regarding the sink **Fic**

Regarding the trees **Fic**

Stand straight, Ella Kate **E**

Till death do us bark **Fic**

Shall I knit you a hat? **E**

Klise, M. Sarah

(il) Klise, K. Grammy Lamby and the secret handshake **E**

(il) Klise, K. The Greatest Star on Earth **Fic**

(il) Klise, K. The show must go on! **Fic**

(il) Klise, K. Dying to meet you **Fic**

Klise, K. Over my dead body **Fic**

(il) Klise, K. Regarding the bathrooms **Fic**

(il) Klise, K. Regarding the bees **Fic**

(il) Klise, K. Regarding the fountain **Fic**

(il) Klise, K. Regarding the sink **Fic**

(il) Klise, K. Regarding the trees **Fic**

(il) Klise, K. Stand straight, Ella Kate **E**

(il) Klise, K. Till death do us bark **Fic**

(il) Shall I knit you a hat? **E**

KLONDIKE RIVER VALLEY (YUKON) -- GOLD DISCOVERIES -- FICTION

Hobbs, W. Jason's gold   Fic

Kloske, Geoffrey

Once upon a time, the end   E

Klosterman, Lorrie

Meningitis   616.8

Klug, Dave

(il) Cobb, V. See for yourself   507.8

Kluger, Jeffrey

Freedom stone   Fic

Knapman, Timothy

Guess what I found in Dragon Wood?   E

Mungo and the spiders from space   E

Knapp, Ron

Bloodsucking creatures   591.5

Mummy secrets uncovered   393

Knapp, Ruthie

Who stole Mona Lisa?   E

The **Kneebone** boy. Potter, E.   Fic

Kneeknock Rise. Babbitt, N.   Fic

Kneen, Maggie

(il) King-Smith, D. Babe   Fic

Chocolate moose   E

Kneib, Martha

Chad   967.43

Pietrzyk, L. Maryland   975.2

Knick knack paddy whack. Engels, C.   782.42

Knick-knack paddywhack! Zelinsky, P. O.   782.42

Knight, Christopher G.

(il) Lasky, K. Interrupted journey   639.9

(il) Lasky, K. The most beautiful roof in the world   577.3

(il) Silk & venom   595.4

Knight, Hilary

(il) Kay Thompson's Eloise   E

Knight, Joan

Charlotte in Giverny   Fic

Charlotte in London   Fic

Charlotte in New York   Fic

Charlotte in Paris   Fic

Knight, Margaret, 1838-1914

About

Kulling, M. In the bag!   E

McCully, E. A. Marvelous Mattie   92

Thimmesh, C. Girls think of everything   920

Knight, Margy Burns

Talking walls   721

Knightley Academy. Schneider, R.   Fic

Knights. Riggs, K.   940.1

Knights. Durman, L.   940.1

Knights and castles [series]

Durman, L. Knights   940.1

Durman, L. Siege   355.4

KNIGHTS AND KNIGHTHOOD

Adkins, J. What if you met a knight?   940.1

Durman, L. Knights   940.1

Gibbons, G. Knights in shining armor   394

Park, L. The medieval knights   940.1

Riggs, K. Knights   940.1

Thomas, S. M. Good night, Good Knight   E

KNIGHTS AND KNIGHTHOOD

See also Middle Ages; Nobility

KNIGHTS AND KNIGHTHOOD -- FICTION

The dragon & the knight   E

Kraegel, K. King Arthur's very great grandson   E

Larson, M. A. Pennyroyal Academy   Fic

Rogue Knight   Fic

KNIGHTS AND KNIGHTHOOD -- FOLKLORE

Hodges, M. Saint George and the dragon   398.2

Paterson, K. Parzival   398.2

Knights in shining armor. Gibbons, G.   394

Knights of the kitchen table. Scieszka, J.   Fic

Knights of the lunch table: the battling bands. Cammuso, F.   741.5

Knights of the lunch table: the dodgeball chronicles. Cammuso, F.   741.5

Knights of the lunch table: the dragon players. Cammuso, F.   741.5

KNIGHTS OF THE ROUND TABLE *See* Arthurian romances

The knights' tales [series]

Morris, G. The adventures of Sir Lancelot the Great   Fic

Knit your bit.   E

KNITTING

Bradberry, S. Kids knit!   746.43

Junor, B. Fun & funky knits   746.43

Shall I knit you a hat?   E

KNITTING

See also Needlework

KNITTING -- FICTION

Knit your bit   E

Knitty Kitty. Elliott, D.   E

KNIVES

See also Hardware; Weapons

Knives and forks. Blaxland, W.   683

Knock at a star.   811

Knock knock. Beaty, D.   E

Knock on wood.   811

Knock, knock! Freymann, S.   817

Knockin' on wood. Barasch, L.   92

Knorr, Laura

(il) Ulmer, W. K. A isn't for fox   E

KNOTS AND SPLICES

Mooney, C. Get all tied up   623.88

Sadler, J. A. Knotting   746.42

KNOTS AND SPLICES

See also Navigation; Rope

Knots in my yo-yo string. Spinelli, J.   813

Knots on a counting rope. Martin, B.   E

Knott, Cheryl Denise

Spiders on the case **Fic**

Vision of beauty: the story of Sarah Breedlove Walker **B**

A voice of her own: the story of Phillis Wheatley, slave poet **92**

The librarian who measured the earth **520**

The man who made time travel **526**

Silk & venom **595.4**

Lassieur, Allison

Trade and commerce in the early Islamic world **381**

The ancient Romans **937**

Louisiana **976.3**

Last airlift. Skrypuch, M. F. **959.704**

The last apprentice [series]

Delaney, J. Attack of the Fiend **Fic**

Delaney, J. Clash of the demons **Fic**

Delaney, J. Curse of the bane **Fic**

Delaney, J. Night of the soul-stealer **Fic**

Delaney, J. Rage of the fallen **Fic**

Delaney, J. Revenge of the witch **Fic**

Delaney, J. The Spook's Bestiary **Fic**

Delaney, J. The Spook's tale and other horrors **S**

Delaney, J. Wrath of the Bloodeye **Fic**

Rise of the huntress **Fic**

The **last** battle. Lewis, C. S. **Fic**

The **last** best days of summer. Hobbs, V. **Fic**

The **last** brother. Noble, T. H. **E**

The **last** day of kindergarten. Loewen, N. **E**

The **last** day of school. Borden, L. **Fic**

The **last** invisible boy. Kuhlman, E. **Fic**

The **last** laugh. Aruego, J. **E**

Last laughs. Lewis, J. P. **818**

The **last** Martin. Friesen, J. **Fic**

The **last** musketeer. Gibbs, S. **Fic**

Last one in is a rotten egg. Kessler, L. P. **E**

The **last** present. Mass, W. **Fic**

The **last** ride of Caleb O'Toole. Pierpoint, E. **Fic**

The **last** river. Waldman, S. **978**

Last song. Guthrie, J. **E**

Last stop on Market Street. **E**

The **last** synapsid. Mason, T. **Fic**

The **last** train. Titcomb, G. **E**

Last-but-not-least lola [series]

Last-but-not-least lola and the wild chicken **Fic**

Last-but-not-least lola and the wild chicken. **Fic**

Late for school. Martin, S. **782.42**

Late for school! Calmenson, S. **E**

Latham, Donna

Backyard Biology **570.78**

Amazing biome projects you can build yourself **577**

Ecology **577**

Latham, Irene

Dear Wandering Wildebeest **811**

Leaving Gee's Bend **Fic**

Lathrop, Dorothy P.

(il) Animals of the Bible **220.8**

(il) Field, R. Hitty: her first hundred years **Fic**

Latif, Zawiah Abdul

Gish, S. Ethiopia **963**

Hassig, S. M. Somalia **967.73**

Heale, J. Madagascar **969.1**

Kagda, F. Algeria **965**

Kagda, S. Lithuania **947.93**

Levy, P. Sudan **962.4**

Sheehan, S. Lebanon **956.92**

Latimer, Alex

The boy who cried ninja **E**

Latimer, Jonathan P.

Caterpillars **595.7**

Latimer, Miriam

(il) The sunflower sword **E**

(il) Harvey, M. Shopping with Dad **E**

(il) The sunflower sword **E**

LATIN AMERICA

Delacre, L. Salsa stories **S**

LATIN AMERICA -- CIVILIZATION

Green is a chile pepper **E**

LATIN AMERICA -- FICTION

Delacre, L. Salsa stories **S**

Hurwitz, J. New shoes for Silvia **E**

Stanton, K. Papi's gift **E**

LATIN AMERICA -- POLITICS AND GOVERNMENT

See also Politics

LATIN AMERICA -- SOCIAL LIFE AND CUSTOMS

Orozco Fiestas: a year of Latin American songs of celebration **782.42**

Latin America and the Caribbean. Solway, A. **780.9**

LATIN AMERICAN ART

Lane, K. Come look with me: Latin American art **709**

LATIN AMERICAN ART

See also Art

LATIN AMERICAN LITERATURE

See also Literature

LATIN AMERICAN LITERATURE -- BIBLIOGRAPHY

Schon, I. Recommended books in Spanish for children and young adults, 2004-2008 **011.6**

LATIN AMERICANS -- POETRY

Under the mambo moon **811**

LATIN LANGUAGE

See also Language and languages

LATIN LITERATURE

See also Literature

LATINO AUTHORS

See also American authors

LATINOS (U.S.)

Hernandez, R. E. The Civil War, 1840s-1890s **973.7**

Otfinoski, S. The new republic: 1760-1840s **973.3**

Portraits of Hispanic American heroes **920**

Weller, F. W. The day the animals came   **E**

LATINOS (U.S.) -- HISTORY -- 20TH CENTURY

Tonatiuh, D. Separate is never equal   **379.2**

LATITUDE

   See also Earth; Geodesy; Nautical astronomy

The **latke** who couldn't stop screaming. Snicket,
  L.   **E**

Latkes, latkes, good to eat. Howland, N.   **E**

Latno, Mark

  The paper boomerang book   **745.54**

Latrobe, Kathy Howard

  The children's literature dictionary   **028.5**

LATTER-DAY SAINTS *See* Church of Jesus Christ
  of Latter-day Saints

Latvia. Barlas, R.   **947.96**

LATVIA

  Barlas, R. Latvia   **947.96**

Latyk, Olivier

  (il) Martin, R. Moon dreams   **E**

  (il) Rees, D. Jeannette Claus saves Christmas   **E**

Lau, Ruth

  Berg, E. Senegal   **966.3**

Lauber, Patricia

  Be a friend to trees   **582.16**

  What you never knew about beds, bedrooms, and
    pajamas   **392**

  What you never knew about fingers, forks, & chop-
    sticks   **394.1**

  Who eats what?   **577**

Laugesen, Malene

  (il) Cummins, J. Flying solo   **92**

Laugh & learn [series]

  Crist, J. J. Siblings   **306.8**

  Fox, J. S. Get organized without losing it   **371.3**

  Verdick, E. Don't behave like you live in a cave **395**

Laugh-eteria. Florian, D.   **811**

Laughing out loud, I fly. Herrera, J. F.   **811**

LAUGHTER

  See also Emotions

  McKee, D. Elmer   **E**

LAUNDRESSES -- FICTION

  Yeoman, J. The wild washerwomen   **E**

LAUNDRY

  See also Cleaning; Home economics; House-
    hold sanitation

LAUNDRY -- FICTION

  Bunting, E. Washday   **E**

Laundry day. Manning, M. J.   **E**

Laura Ingalls Wilder. Berne, E. C.   **92**

Laura Secord: a story of courage. Lunn, J. L. S. **Fic**

Laure, Jason

  Altman, L. J. Arkansas   **976.7**

  Blauer, E. Mali   **966.2**

  Blauer, E. Mauritania   **966.1**

  McDaniel, M. New Mexico   **972**

Laurell, RoseAleta

About

  King, M. G. Librarian on the roof!   **027.4**

Lauren, Jill

  That's like me!   **371.9**

Laurent, Richard

  (il) Bauer, C. F. Leading kids to books through
    magic   **027.62**

  (il) Bauer, C. F. Leading kids to books through
    puppets   **027.62**

Lauw, Darlene

  Light   **535**

  Water   **553.7**

Laval, Thierry

  Colors   **E**

Lavallee, Barbara

  (il) Cobb, V. This place is wet   **574.5**

  (il) Joosse, B. M. Mama, do you love me? **306.874**

  (il) Joosse, B. M. Papa, do you love me?   **E**

  (il) Mora, P. Uno, dos, tres: one, two, three   **E**

Lavery, Brian

  Legendary journeys: ships   **387.2**

LAW

  Hamilton, J. How a bill becomes a law   **328**

LAW

  See also Political science

LAW -- UNITED STATES

  Rodger, E. What is the judicial branch?   **347.73**

LAW -- VOCATIONAL GUIDANCE

  See also Professions; Vocational guidance

LAW ENFORCEMENT

  Bad news for outlaws   **92**

LAW REFORM

  See also Law

Law, Felicia

  Atlas of Southwest and Central Asia   **950**

  Atlas of the Far East and Southeast Asia   **950**

Law, Ingrid

  Savvy   **Fic**

  Scumble   **Fic**

Law, Ruth, b. 1887

About

  Ruth Law thrills a nation   **629.13**

Law, Stephen

  Really, really big questions   **100**

Law, Westley Wallace, 1923-2002

About

  Haskins, J. Delivering justice   **92**

Lawler, Janet

  Rain Forest Colors   **591.734**

Lawlor, Laurie

  He will go fearless   **Fic**

  Helen Keller: rebellious spirit   **92**

  Muddy as a duck puddle and other American simi-
    les   **425**

  The school at Crooked Creek   **Fic**

Lawlor, Veronica

Rustad, M. E. H. Fall leaves **581.4**

LEAVES

See also Plants

LEAVES -- FICTION

Berger, C. The little yellow leaf **E**

Briant, E. If you lived here you'd be home by now **E**

Ehlert, L. Leaf Man **E**

Emmett, J. Leaf trouble **E**

A leaf can be **E**

O'Malley, K. Lucky leaf **E**

Rawlinson, J. Fletcher and the falling leaves **E**

Stein, D. E. Leaves **E**

Leaving Gee's Bend. Latham, I. **Fic**

Leaving the Bellwethers. Venuti, K. C. **Fic**

Leaving the nest. Gerstein, M. **E**

Leavitt, Amie Jane

The Bill of Rights in translation **342**

The Declaration of Independence in translation **973.3**

Leavitt, Loralee

Candy experiments **507.8**

Lebanon. Sheehan, S. **956.92**

LEBANON

Sheehan, S. Lebanon **956.92**

LEBANON -- FICTION

Heide, F. P. Sami and the time of the troubles **E**

Lebaron, Joyce

(jt. auth) Hellweg, P. The American Heritage student thesaurus **428**

Lebaron, Susannah

(jt. auth) Hellweg, P. The American Heritage student thesaurus **428**

LeBlanc, Andre

The red piano **92**

Lebron James. Yasuda, A. **92**

Lebron James. Gatto, K. **92**

Lechner, John

The clever stick **E**

Leck, James

The adventures of Jack Lime **Fic**

LECTURERS

Bardhan-Quallen, S. Ballots for Belva **92**

Boomhower, R. E. Fighting for equality **92**

LECTURES AND LECTURING

See also Public speaking; Rhetoric; Teaching

Ledger, Heath, 1979-2008

About

Watson, S. Heath Ledger **92**

Lee, Bruce, 1940-1973

About

Krull, K. Lives of the athletes **796**

Mochizuki, K. Be water, my friend **92**

Lee, Chinlun

(il) Rosen, M. Totally wonderful Miss Plumberry **E**

Lee, Claudia M.

(ed) Messengers of rain and other poems from Latin America **861**

Lee, Cora

The great motion mission **530**

The great number rumble **510**

Lee, Dom

(il) Baseball saved us **E**

(il) Mochizuki, K. Be water, my friend **92**

(il) Mochizuki, K. Heroes **E**

(il) Mochizuki, K. Passage to freedom **940.53**

(il) Yoo, P. Sixteen years in sixteen seconds **92**

Lee, Dora

Biomimicry **608**

Lee, Frances

Fun with Chinese cooking **641.5**

Lee, H. Chuku

Beauty and the beast **398.2**

Lee, Ho Baek

While we were out **E**

(il) Park, L. S. Bee-bim bop! **E**

Lee, Huy Voun

(il) Jacobs, P. D. Fire drill **E**

1, 2, 3 go! **495.1**

At the beach **495.1**

(il) Sayre, A. P. Honk, honk, goose! **598**

Lee, Insu

(il) Yep, L. Auntie Tiger **E**

Lee, Janet, 1954-

McCann, J. Return of the Dapper Men **741.5**

Lee, Jeanne M.

(il) Fang, L. The Ch'i-lin purse **398.209**

Lee, Jenny

Elvis and the underdogs **Fic**

Lee, Kimberly Fekany

Cells **571.6**

Lee, Mark

Twenty big trucks in the middle of the street **E**

Lee, Milly

Landed **Fic**

Lee, Paul

(il) Golenbock, P. Hank Aaron **796.357**

(il) Lasky, K. A voice of her own: the story of Phillis Wheatley, slave poet **92**

Lee, Richard B.

Africans thought of it! **609**

Lee, Robert E. (Robert Edward), 1807-1870

About

Benoit, P. The surrender at Appomattox **973.7**

Murphy, J. A savage thunder **973.7**

Rosenberg, A. The Civil War **920**

Stark, K. Marching to Appomattox **973.7**

Lee, Sammy, 1920-

About

Yoo, P. Sixteen years in sixteen seconds **92**

Lee, Spike

CHILDREN'S CORE COLLECTION
TWENTY-SECOND EDITION

first-century librarians   **027.62**

Wichman, E. T. Librarian's guide to passive programming   **025.5**

Winter, J. The librarian of Basra   **92**

LIBRARIANS -- FICTION

Bottner, B. Miss Brooks' Story Nook   **E**

Downey, J. S. The ninja librarians   **Fic**

Seagulls don't eat pickles   **Fic**

LIBRARIANS -- GRAPHIC NOVELS

Krosoczka, J. J. Lunch Lady and the League of Librarians   **741.5**

LIBRARIANS -- LEGAL STATUS, LAWS, ETC. -- UNITED STATES

Russell, C. Complete copyright for K-12 librarians and educators   **346.04**

LIBRARIANS -- RATING

Sykes, J. A. Conducting action research to evaluate your school library   **027.8**

LIBRARIANS -- UNITED STATES -- HANDBOOKS, MANUALS, ETC

Crews, K. D. Copyright law for librarians and educators   **346.04**

Librarians at work. Kenney, K. L.   **020**

LIBRARIANS' UNIONS

     See also Labor unions

LIBRARIANSHIP *See* Library science

LIBRARIES

Abouraya, K. L. Hands around the library **962.055**

Bruss, D. Book! book! book!   **E**

Buzzeo, T. Inside the books   **E**

Gaines, A. Master the library and media center **020**

King, M. G. Librarian on the roof!   **027.4**

Myron, V. Dewey the library cat   **636.8**

Numeroff, L. J. Beatrice doesn't want to   **E**

Sawa, M. The library book   **027**

Winter, J. Biblioburro   **E**

Winter, J. The librarian of Basra   **92**

LIBRARIES -- ACQUISITIONS

     See also Libraries -- Collection development; Library technical processes

LIBRARIES -- ACTIVITY PROGRAMS -- UNITED STATES

Wichman, E. T. Librarian's guide to passive programming   **025.5**

LIBRARIES -- ADMINISTRATION

MacDonell, C. Essential documents for school libraries   **025.1**

School library management   **025.1**

Tips and other bright ideas for elementary school libraries.   **025.1**

LIBRARIES -- CATALOGING *See* Cataloging

LIBRARIES -- CENSORSHIP

     See also Censorship

LIBRARIES -- COLLECTION DEVELOPMENT

Franklin, P. School library collection development   **025.2**

Sullivan, M. Fundamentals of children's services   **027.62**

LIBRARIES -- COOPERATION *See* Library cooperation

LIBRARIES -- EGYPT -- ALEXANDRIA

Abouraya, K. L. Hands around the library **962.055**

LIBRARIES -- EXHIBITIONS

Skaggs, G. Look, it's books!   **021.7**

LIBRARIES -- FICTION

Barden, S. The super secret mystery   **Fic**

Becker, B. A Library book for bear   **E**

The boy & the book   **E**

Downey, J. S. The ninja librarians   **Fic**

The fantastic flying books of Mr. Morris Lessmore   **E**

Grabenstein, C. Escape from Mr. Lemoncello's library   **Fic**

Kohara, K. The Midnight Library   **E**

LIBRARIES -- FINANCE *See* Library finance

LIBRARIES -- HANDBOOKS, MANUALS, ETC.

Stephens, C. G. Library 101   **027.8**

LIBRARIES -- LAW AND LEGISLATION

Chmara, T. Privacy and confidentiality issues **344**

LIBRARIES -- LAW AND LEGISLATION

     See also Law; Legislation

LIBRARIES -- PUBLIC RELATIONS

     See also Libraries and community

LIBRARIES -- SPECIAL COLLECTIONS

Gallaway, B. Game on!   **025.2**

Mayer, B. Libraries got game   **025.2**

Scheeren, W. O. Technology for the school librarian   **025.04**

LIBRARIES -- SPECIAL COLLECTIONS -- AUDIOBOOKS

Grover, S. Listening to learn   **372.4**

LIBRARIES -- SPECIAL COLLECTIONS -- GRAPHIC NOVELS

Brenner, R. E. Understanding manga and anime   **025.2**

Fagan, B. D. Comic book collections for libraries   **025.2**

Goldsmith, F. The readers' advisory guide to graphic novels   **025.2**

Graphic novels beyond the basics   **025.2**

Serchay, D. S. The librarian's guide to graphic novels for children and tweens   **025.2**

LIBRARIES -- SPECIAL COLLECTIONS -- SEXUAL MINORITIES

Naidoo, J. C. Rainbow family collections   **028.1**

LIBRARIES -- STANDARDS

American Association of School Librarians Standards for the 21st-century learner in action   **025.5**

LIBRARIES -- STATISTICS

     See also Statistics

LIBRARIES -- UNITED STATES

The frugal librarian   **025.1**

Ellis, S. From reader to writer **372.62**

Winter, J. Gertrude is Gertrude is Gertrude is Gertrude **92**

Yolleck, J. Paris in the spring with Picasso **E**

LITERARY FORGERIES

   See also Counterfeits and counterfeiting; Forgery

LITERARY LANDMARKS

   See also Historic buildings; Literature -- History and criticism

LITERARY PROPERTY *See* Copyright; Intellectual property

LITERARY RECREATIONS

   Garland, M. Super snow day: seek and find **E**

LITERARY RECREATIONS

   See also Amusements

LITERARY STYLE

   See also Literature

LITERATURE

   Fleming, D. The everything book **E**

LITERATURE

   See also Humanities; Language arts

LITERATURE -- COLLECTIONS

   Classic horse stories **808.8**

   DePaola, T. Joy to the world **808.8**

   Hey! listen to this **028.5**

   Killer koalas from outer space **808.8**

   The Norton anthology of children's literature **808.8**

   Sawyer, R. The way of the storyteller **372.6**

LITERATURE -- COMPETITIONS

   See also Contests; Literary prizes

LITERATURE -- DICTIONARIES

   See also Encyclopedias and dictionaries

LITERATURE -- EVALUATION *See* Best books; Book reviewing; Books and reading; Criticism; Literature -- History and criticism

LITERATURE -- STUDY AND TEACHING

   Cavanaugh, T. W. Bookmapping **372.6**

   Hall, S. Using picture storybooks to teach literary devices **016**

   Saccardi, M. Books that teach kids to write **028.5**

Literature for youth [series]

   Crew, H. S. Women engaged in war in literature for youth **016**

   Garcha, R. The world of Islam in literature for youth **016**

Lithgow, John

   Micawber **E**

LITHOGRAPHERS

   Burleigh, R. Toulouse-Lautrec **92**

LITHOGRAPHERS

   See also Artists

LITHOGRAPHY

   See also Color printing; Printing; Prints

Lithuania. Kagda, S. **947.93**

LITHUANIA

Kagda, S. Lithuania **947.93**

LITIGATION

   See also Law

Litten, Kristyna

   (il) This day in June **E**

LITTERING *See* Refuse and refuse disposal

Little Audrey. White, R. **Fic**

Little ballet star. Geras, A. **E**

Little Bea. Roode, D. **E**

Little Bea and the snowy day. Roode, D. **E**

Little Bear. Minarik, E. H. **E**

Little Bear and the Marco Polo. Minarik, E. H. **E**

The **little** bear book. Browne, A. **E**

Little Bear's little boat. Bunting, E. **E**

Little Beauty. Browne, A. **E**

LITTLE BIGHORN, BATTLE OF THE, 1876

   Anderson, P. C. George Armstrong Custer **92**

   Turner, A. W. Sitting Bull remembers **92**

   Walker, P. R. Remember Little Bighorn **973.8**

Little bird. **E**

Little Bird takes a bath. **E**

A **little** bit of love. Platt, C. **E**

The **little** bitty bakery. Muir, L. **E**

A **little** bitty man and other poems for the very young. **831**

Little Bitty Mousie. Aylesworth, J. **E**

Little black crow. Raschka, C. **E**

Little blog on the prairie. Bell, C. D. **Fic**

Little blue and little yellow. Lionni, L. **E**

Little Blue Truck. **E**

Little boat. Docherty, T. **E**

A **little** book of slime. Twist, C. **590**

A **little** book of sloth. Cooke, L. **599.3**

Little boy. McGhee, A. **E**

Little Britches and the rattlers. Kimmel, E. A. **E**

LITTLE BROWN BAT

   Markle, S. The case of the vanishing little brown bats **599.4**

Little Chick. Hest, A. **E**

Little Chicken's big day. Davis, K. **E**

Little Cub. Dunrea, O. **E**

Little diva. La Chanze **E**

Little divas. Boles, P. M. **Fic**

Little Dog. Jahn-Clough, L. **E**

Little dog lost. Carnesi, M. **636.7**

Little dog, lost. Bauer, M. D. **Fic**

The **little** dump truck. Cuyler, M. **E**

The **little** engine that could. Piper, W. **E**

The **little** engine that could. **E**

Little Fox goes to the end of the world. Tompert, A. **E**

Little goblins ten. Jane, P. **E**

Little Gold Star. Hayes, J. **398.2**

Little Gold Star. San Souci, R. **398.2**

The **little** hands big fun craft book. Press, J. **745.5**

Little Hoot. Rosenthal, A. K. **E**

Little Horse. Byars, B. C.   **Fic**

The **little** house. Burton, V. L.   **E**

Little house [series]

   Wilder, L. I. By the shores of Silver Lake   **Fic**

   Wilder, L. I. Little house in the big woods   **Fic**

   Wilder, L. I. The long winter   **Fic**

   Wilder, L. I. On the banks of Plum Creek   **Fic**

The **Little** House cookbook.   **641.5**

Little house in the big woods. Wilder, L. I.   **Fic**

Little house on the prairie. Wilder, L. I.   **Fic**

A **Little** House traveler. Wilder, L. I.   **92**

The **little** island.   **E**

Little Joe. Wallace, S. N.   **Fic**

Little kids first big book of animals. Hughes, C. D.   **590**

Little kids first big book of why. Shields, A. **031.02**

LITTLE LEAGUE BASEBALL

   See also Baseball

LITTLE LEAGUE BASEBALL -- FICTION

   Northrop, M. Plunked   **Fic**

   The way home looks now   **Fic**

Little Leap Forward. Guo Yue   **Fic**

Little lions, bull baiters & hunting hounds. Crosby, J.   **636.7**

The **little** little girl with the big big voice. Balouch, K.   **E**

Little Lola.   **E**

Little lost cowboy. Puttock, S.   **E**

LITTLE MAGAZINES

   See also Periodicals

Little Mama forgets. Cruise, R.   **E**

The **Little** Matador. Hector, J.   **E**

The **little** match girl. Pinkney, J.   **E**

The **little** match girl. Andersen, H. C.   **Fic**

Little Melba and her big trombone.   **92**

The **Little** Mermaid. Sabuda, R.   **E**

Little Miss Muffet counts to ten. Chichester-Clark, E.   **E**

Little Mist. McAllister, A.   **E**

The **little** moon princess. Lee, Y.   **E**

Little mouse. Murray, A.   **E**

Little Mouse gets ready. Smith, J.   **741.5**

Little Mouse's big book of fears. Gravett, E.   **E**

Little Mouse's big secret. Battut, É.   **E**

Little Naomi, Little Chick.   **E**

Little neighbors on Sunnyside Street. Spanyol, J. **E**

Little newts. Goldish, M.   **597.8**

Little Night. Morales, Y.   **E**

The **little** old lady who was not afraid of anything. **E**

Little One Step. James, S.   **E**

Little owl lost. Haughton, C.   **E**

Little Owl's day.   **E**

Little Owl's night. Srinivasan, D.   **E**

Little panda. Ryder, J.   **599.74**

A **little** peace. Kerley, B.   **327.1**

Little people and a lost world. Goldenberg, L. **599.93**

The **little** piano girl. Ingalls, A.   **E**

Little Poems for Tiny Ears. Oliver, L.   **E**

The **little** prince. Sfar, J.   **741.5**

The **little** prince. Saint-Exupery, A. d.   **Fic**

The **little** prince: deluxe pop-up book. Saint-Exupery, A. d.   **Fic**

A **little** princess. Burnett, F. H.   **Fic**

Little Quack. Thompson, L.   **E**

Little Quack's bedtime. Thompson, L.   **E**

Little Rabbit lost. Horse, H.   **E**

The **little** rabbit who liked to say moo. Allen, J. **E**

Little Rat makes music. Bang-Campbell, M.   **E**

Little Red. Roberts, L.   **E**

Little red bird. Bruel, N.   **E**

The **little** red elf. McGrath, B. B.   **E**

The **little** red hen. Pinkney, J.   **398.2**

The **little** red hen. Forest, H.   **398.2**

The **little** red hen. Galdone, P.   **398.2**

The **little** red hen. Barton, B.   **398.2**

The **Little** Red Hen (makes a pizza) Sturges, P.   **398.2**

The **Little** Red Hen and the Passover matzah. Kimmelman, L.   **398.2**

Little Red Henry.   **E**

The **little** red lighthouse and the great gray bridge. Swift, H. H.   **E**

The **Little** Red Pen. Crummel, S. S.   **E**

Little Red Riding Hood. Pinkney, J.   **398.2**

Little Red Riding Hood. Spirin, G.   **398.2**

Little Red Riding Hood. Hyman, T. S.   **398.2**

Little Red Riding Hood. Grimm, J.   **398.2**

Little Red Riding Hood.   **E**

Little Red Riding Hood. Ziefert, H.   **398.2**

Little Red Riding Hood: a newfangled prairie tale. Ernst, L. C.   **398.2**

Little Red Writing. Holub, J.   **E**

LITTLE ROCK (ARK.) -- HISTORY -- 20TH CENTURY -- FICTION

   Levine, K. The lions of Little Rock   **Fic**

Little Roja Riding Hood. Elya, S. M.   **E**

Little Rooster's diamond button. MacDonald, M. R.   **398.2**

Little Santa. Agee, J.   **E**

The **little** scarecrow boy. Brown, M. W.   **E**

The **little** school bus. Roth, C.   **E**

Little shark. Rockwell, A. F.   **597**

The **little** ships.   **813**

Little sister and the month brothers. De Regniers, B. S.   **398.2**

Little Sister is not my name. Draper, S. M.   **Fic**

LITTLE THEATER MOVEMENT

   See also Theater

Little Toot. Gramatky, H.   **E**

Little treasures. Ogburn, J. K.   **413**

Little trucks with big jobs. Maass, R.   **629.224**

Little Tug. Savage, S.   **E**

Little Vampire. **741.5**
Little White Duck. Liu, N. **741.5**
The little white owl. Corderoy, T. **E**
Little white rabbit. Henkes, K. **E**
Little wolf's song. Teckentrup, B. **E**
Little women. Alcott, L. M. **Fic**
Little world math concepts [series]
Mattern, J. Even or odd? **513**
Little world social studies [series]
Hord, C. My safe community **331.7**
Hord, C. Need it or want it? **332.024**
The little yellow leaf. Berger, C. **E**
Little yoga. Whitford, R. **613.7**
Little you. **E**
Little, Jean
Emma's yucky brother **E**
About
Ellis, S. From reader to writer **372.62**
Little, Kimberley Griffiths
The time of the fireflies **Fic**
Circle of secrets **Fic**
The healing spell **Fic**
The little, little house. Souhami, J. **398.2**
Littlefield, Holly
The rooftop adventure of Minnie and Tessa, factory fire survivors **741.5**
The **littlest** dinosaur's big adventure. Foreman, M. **E**
The littlest evergreen. Cole, H. **E**
The littlest leaguer. Hoff, S. **E**
The littlest llama. Buxton, J. **E**
The littlest mountain. Rosenstock, B. **E**
Littlewood, Karin
(il) Conway, D. The most important gift of all **E**
(il) Cornwell, N. Christophe's story **Fic**
(il) Hoffman, M. The color of home **E**
Immi's gift **E**
(il) Lobel, G. Moonshadow's journey **E**
(il) Moore, G. Catherine's story **E**
LITURGIES
See also Public worship; Rites and ceremonies
Litwin, Eric
Pete the cat: I love my white shoes **E**
Litwin, Laura Baskes
Write horror fiction in 5 simple steps **808.3**
Litzinger, Rosanne
(il) Nishizuka, K. The beckoning cat **398.2**
(il) Paul, A. W. Snail's good night **E**
(il) Stewig, J. W. The animals watched **222**
Liu Yi
(il) Tracking Tyrannosaurs **567.91**
Liu, Jae Soo
Yellow umbrella **E**
Liu, Na
Little White Duck **741.5**

Liu-Perkins, Christine
At home in her tomb **931**
Lively Elizabeth! what happens when you push. Bergman, M. **E**
Lively plant science projects. Benbow, A. **580.7**
Lives cut short [series]
Anderson, J. J. John Lennon **92**
Harris, A. R. Tupac Shakur **92**
Watson, S. Heath Ledger **92**
Lives of extraordinary women. Krull, K. **920**
The lives of stars. Croswell, K. **523.8**
Lives of the artists. Krull, K. **709.2**
Lives of the athletes. Krull, K. **796**
Lives of the explorers. **920**
Lives of the great artists. Ayres, C. **709**
Lives of the musicians. Krull, K. **920**
Lives of the presidents. Krull, K. **920**
Lives of the scientists. **509.2**
Lives of the writers. **809**
Lives: poems about famous Americans. **811**
LIVESTOCK See Domestic animals; Livestock industry
LIVESTOCK -- HANDLING
Montgomery, S. Temple Grandin **636**
LIVESTOCK INDUSTRY
See also Agriculture; Economic zoology
Living color. Jenkins, S. **591.47**
LIVING EARTH THEORY See Gaia hypothesis
LIVING SKILLS See Life skills
Living stories. Zoe, T. **970.004**
Living sunlight. Bang, M. **572**
Living well [series]
Gray, S. H. Living with juvenile rheumatoid arthritis **616.7**
Living wild [series]
Gish, M. Alligators **597.98**
Gish, M. Bats **599.4**
Gish, M. Bison **599.64**
Gish, M. Eagles **598**
Gish, M. Gorillas **599.8**
Gish, M. Hummingbirds **598**
Gish, M. Jaguars **599.75**
Gish, M. Kangaroos **599.2**
Gish, M. Killer whales **599.5**
Gish, M. Komodo dragons **597.95**
Gish, M. Leopards **599.75**
Gish, M. Moose **599.65**
Gish, M. Owls **598**
Gish, M. Pandas **599.78**
Gish, M. Rhinoceroses **599.66**
Gish, M. Whales **599.5**
Hanel, R. Penguins **598**
Hanel, R. Tigers **599.75**
Helget, N. L. Swans **598**
LIVING WILLS
See also Wills

2645

Living with juvenile rheumatoid arthritis. Gray, S. H. **616.7**

Living with mom and living with dad. Walsh, M. **E**

Livingston, Myra Cohn
Calendar **E**

Livingstone, David, 1813-1873
About
Bodden, V. To the heart of Africa **916**

Livo, Norma J.
Tales to tickle your funny bone **398.2**

Liwska, Renata
(il) The Christmas quiet book **E**
(il) Cuffe-Perez, M. Skylar **Fic**
Red wagon **E**
(il) The loud book! **E**
(il) The quiet book **E**

Lizano, Marc, 1970-
(il) Dauvillier, L. Hidden **741.5**

Lizard music. Pinkwater, D. M. **Fic**

Lizards. Bjorklund, R. **639.3**

Lizards. Bishop, N. **597.95**

LIZARDS
See also Reptiles
Bishop, N. Lizards **597.95**
Bjorklund, R. Lizards **639.3**
Collard III, S. B. Sneed B. Collard III's most fun book ever about lizards **597.95**
Lunis, N. Black spiny-tailed iguana **597.95**
Somervill, B. A. Monitor lizard **597.95**
Stewart, M. Salamander or lizard? **597.8**

LIZARDS -- FICTION
Becker, B. Holbrook **Fic**
Cowley, J. Snake and Lizard **Fic**
Cummings, P. Harvey Moon, museum boy **E**
Donaldson, J. Superworm **E**
Leedy, L. The great graph contest **E**
Murphy, S. J. Leaping lizards **E**
Pinkwater, D. M. Lizard music **Fic**
Wiesner, D. Art & Max **E**

Lizards in the sky. Eamer, C. **591.4**

Lizzie Newton and the San Francisco earthquake. Krensky, S. **979.4**

Lizzie nonsense. Ormerod, J. **E**

Ljungkvist, Laura
Follow the line **E**
Follow the line to school **E**

Llama, llama red pajama. Dewdney, A. **E**

LLAMAS
Barnes, J. Camels and llamas at work **636.2**

LLAMAS -- FICTION
Buxton, J. The littlest llama **E**
Dewdney, A. Llama, llama red pajama **E**
Guarino, D. Is your mama a llama? **813**

LLAMAS AS PETS -- FICTION
Maria had a little llama/ María tenía una llamita **E**

Llanas, Sheila Griffin
Women of the U.S. Navy **359**

Llewellyn, Claire
Cooking with fruits and vegetables **641.3**
Cooking with meat and fish **641.6**

Llewellyn, Sam
Darksolstice **Fic**
The well between the worlds **Fic**

Llimos, Anna
Easy bead crafts in 5 steps **745.58**
Easy cardboard crafts in 5 steps **745.5**
Easy clay crafts in 5 steps **738.1**
Easy cloth crafts in 5 steps **745.5**
Easy earth-friendly crafts in 5 steps **745.5**
Easy paper crafts in 5 steps **745.54**
Haunted house adventure crafts **745.5**

Lloyd Jones, Rob
Wild boy **Fic**

Lloyd, Alison
Year of the tiger **Fic**

Lloyd, Jennifer
The Best Thing About Kindergarten **E**

Lloyd, Megan
(il) Berger, M. Chirping crickets **595.7**
(il) Berger, M. Look out for turtles! **597.92**
(il) Branley, F. M. Earthquakes **551.2**
(il) Branley, F. M. Volcanoes **551.2**
(il) Edwards, P. D. The mixed-up rooster **E**
(il) Guiberson, B. Z. Cactus hotel **583**
Kimmel, E. A. The gingerbread man **398.21**
(il) The little old lady who was not afraid of anything **E**
(il) Miller, B. Davy Crockett gets hitched **398.2**
(il) White, B. Betsy Ross **92**
(il) White, L. Too many turkeys **E**

Lloyd, Natalie
A snicker of magic **Fic**

Lloyd, Sam
Doctor Meow's big emergency **E**
Mr. Pusskins and Little Whiskers **E**

Lloyd-Jones, Sally
How to get a job by me, the boss **E**
Poor Doreen **E**
Song of the stars **E**

LMNO peas. Baker, K. **E**

Loaders. Askew, A. **624.1**

LOANS -- FICTION
Milway, K. S. One hen **E**

LOBBYING
Schwartz, H. E. Political activism **322.4**

LOBBYING
See also Politics; Propaganda

Lobel, Adrianne
(il) Lobel, A. The frogs and toads all sang **811**
(il) Lobel, A. Odd owls & stout pigs **811**
10 hungry rabbits **E**
Lena's sleep sheep **E**

The voyages of Doctor Dolittle **Fic**

Lofts, Pamela

(il) Fox, M. Hunwick's egg **E**

(il) Fox, M. Koala Lou **E**

LOG CABINS AND HOUSES

See also House construction; Houses

A log's life. **577.3**

Logan, Bob

The Sea of Bath **E**

Logan, Claudia

The 5,000-year-old puzzle **932**

Logan, Harriet

(jt. auth) Faulkner, M. A zeal of zebras **590**

LOGARITHMS

See also Algebra; Mathematics -- Tables; Trigonometry -- Tables

LOGGING

See also Forests and forestry

LOGIC

See also Intellect; Philosophy; Science -- Methodology

Logue, Mary

Sleep like a tiger **E**

Loizeaux, William

Clarence Cochran, a human boy **Fic**

Loki's wolves. Marr, M. **Fic**

Lola at the library. **E**

Lola's fandango. **E**

LOLLIPOPS -- FICTION

Krall, D. The great lollipop caper **E**

Lomax, John Avery, 1867-1948

About

Hopkinson, D. Home on the range **92**

Lombard, Jenny

Drita, my homegirl **Fic**

Lomberg, Michelle

Horse **636.1**

Spider **639**

Lon Po Po. Young, E. **398.2**

London. Platt, R. **942**

LONDON (ENGLAND)

Horowitz, A. The Falcon's Malteser **Fic**

Pullman, P. I was a rat! **Fic**

Rubbino, S. A walk in London **942**

LONDON (ENGLAND) -- FICTION

The case of the stolen sixpence **Fic**

Colfer, E. The hangman's revolution **Fic**

Colfer, E. The reluctant assassin **Fic**

Edge, C. Twelve minutes to midnight **Fic**

Hopkinson, D. The Great Trouble **Fic**

Jinks, C. How to catch a bogle **Fic**

Larwood, K. Freaks **Fic**

Pullman, P. Two crafty criminals! **Fic**

Schlitz, L. A. Splendors and glooms **Fic**

LONDON (ENGLAND) -- HISTORY

Platt, R. London **942**

Wells-Cole, C. Charles Dickens **823**

The **London** Eye mystery. Dowd, S. **Fic**

London, Alex

Proxy **Fic**

London, C. Alexander

We are not eaten by yaks **Fic**

We dine with cannibals **Fic**

London, Jack

About

Lives of the writers **809**

London, Jonathan

Bruchac, J. Thirteen moons on a turtle's back **398.2**

Baby whale's journey **E**

Froggy builds a tree house **E**

Froggy goes to Hawaii **E**

Froggy learns to swim **E**

Hippos are huge! **599.63**

I'm a truck driver **E**

A plane goes ka-zoom! **E**

A train goes clickety-clack **E**

A truck goes rattley-bumpa **E**

LONELINESS

See also Emotions

LONELINESS -- FICTION

Battersby, K. Squish Rabbit **E**

Bauer, M. D. Little dog, lost **Fic**

Brun-Cosme, N. Big Wolf & Little Wolf **E**

The cat with seven names **E**

DeFelice, C. C. Signal **Fic**

Dunrea, O. Little Cub **E**

Elliott, R. Zoo girl **E**

Hannigan, K. Emmaline and the bunny **Fic**

Herman and Rosie **E**

Murphy, S. Pearl verses the world **Fic**

Sherry, K. Turtle Island **E**

A **long** and uncertain journey: the 27,000 mile voyage of Vasco da Gama. Goodman, J. E. **910**

Long ball. Stewart, M. **796.357**

LONG DISTANCE RUNNING See Marathon running

LONG DISTANCE TELEPHONE SERVICE

See also Telephone

Long gone lonesome history of country music. Bertholf, B. **781.642**

LONG ISLAND (N.Y.) -- FICTION

Korman, G. Zoobreak **Fic**

Marino, N. Neil Armstrong is my uncle **Fic**

Winter, J. Here comes the garbage barge! **E**

LONG LIFE See Longevity

A **long** piece of string. Wondriska, W. **E**

The **long** road to Gettysburg. Murphy, J. **973.7**

Long shot. Lupica, M. **Fic**

Long Tail Kitty. Pien, L. **741.5**

A **long** way away. Viva, F. **E**

A **long** way from Chicago. Peck, R. **Fic**

The **long** winter. Wilder, L. I. **Fic**

Here comes Grandma! **E**

Where is Catkin? **E**

Lord, John Vernon

The giant jam sandwich **E**

Lord, Leonie

(il) Waddell, M. The super hungry dinosaur **E**

Lord, Michelle

Animal school **596**

A song for Cambodia **92**

Lords of Trillium. **Fic**

Lorenz, Konrad

About

Greenstein, E. The goose man **92**

Lorig, Richard

Lorig, S. Such a silly baby! **E**

Lorig, Steffanie

Such a silly baby! **E**

LOS ANGELES (CALIF.) -- FICTION

Bunting, E. Smoky night **E**

Cohn, R. Two steps forward **Fic**

Kelly, D. A. The L.A. Dodger **Fic**

Pinkwater, D. M. The Neddiad **Fic**

Politi, L. Juanita **E**

Politi, L. Pedro, the angel of Olvera Street **E**

Woods, B. The red rose box **Fic**

LOS ANGELES DODGERS (BASEBALL TEAM)

Winter, J. You never heard of Sandy Koufax!? **92**

Los gatos black on Halloween. Montes, M. **E**

Loser. Spinelli, J. **Fic**

LOSING THINGS See Lost and found possessions

LOSS (PSYCHOLOGY)

See also Psychology

LOSS (PSYCHOLOGY) -- FICTION

Ehrlich, A. The girl who wanted to dance **E**

Like pickle juice on a cookie **Fic**

McKay, H. Binny for short **Fic**

Orr, W. Missing! A cat called Buster **Fic**

Pennypacker, S. The summer of the gypsy moths **Fic**

Ransom, C. Rebel McKenzie **Fic**

Lost & found. Tan, S. **S**

Lost and found. Clements, A. **Fic**

Lost and found. LaMarche, J. **E**

Lost and found. Jeffers, O. **E**

The **lost** and found pony. Dockray, T. **E**

LOST AND FOUND POSSESSIONS

Cushman, D. Mystery at the Club Sandwich **E**

Kellogg, S. The missing mitten mystery **E**

LOST AND FOUND POSSESSIONS -- FICTION

Ben draws trouble **E**

Have you seen my monster? **E**

If you find this **Fic**

Manning, M. J. Laundry day **E**

The troublemaker **E**

Wells, R. Max and Ruby at the Warthogs' wedding **E**

Bunting, E. Have you seen my new blue socks? **E**

Henkes, K. Penny and her marble **E**

Mister Whistler **Fic**

Where are my books? **E**

Yoon, S. Found **E**

LOST ARCHITECTURE

See also Architecture

Lost boy. Newbery, L. **Fic**

Lost boy. Yolen, J. **92**

The **lost** children. Cohagan, C. **Fic**

LOST CHILDREN -- FICTION

The bear's sea escape **E**

Nelson, K. Baby Bear **E**

Lost cities. Barber, N. **930.1**

Lost city. Lewin, T. **985**

The **Lost** Colony of Roanoke. Fritz, J. **975.6**

The **lost** garden. Yep, L. **979.4**

Lost Goat Lane. Jordan, R. **Fic**

Lost in babylon. Lerangis, P. **Fic**

Lost in Lexicon. Noyce, P. **Fic**

Lost in the sun. **Fic**

LOST ITEMS -- FICTION

Martin, A. M. Rain Reign **Fic**

The **lost** lake. Say, A. **E**

LOST POSSESSIONS See Lost and found possessions

Lost sight. Markle, S. **617.7**

The **lost** stories. Flanagan, J. **S**

LOST THINGS See Lost and found possessions

The **lost** treasure of Tuckernuck. Fairlie, E. **Fic**

LOST TRIBES OF ISRAEL

See also Jews

The **lost** years of Merlin. Barron, T. A. **Fic**

Lost! A dog called Bear. Orr, W. **Fic**

The **lost-and-found** tooth. Borden, L. **Fic**

Losure, Mary

The Fairy Ring, or, Elsie and Frances Fool the World **398**

Loth, Sebastian

Zelda the Varigoose **E**

Clementine **E**

Remembering Crystal **E**

Lots and lots of coins. Reid, M. S. **737.4**

Lots of bots. Carter, D. A. **E**

Lots of dots. Frazier, C. **E**

Lots of spots. Ehlert, L. **E**

Lottie Paris lives here. **E**

Lottie's new beach towel. Mathers, P. **E**

Lottridge, Celia Barker

The listening tree **Fic**

One watermelon seed **E**

Stories from Adam and Eve to Ezekiel **220.9**

Stories from the life of Jesus **232.9**

Lotu, Denize

Running the road to ABC **E**

Lou Gehrig. Adler, D. A. **796.357**

MAN *See* Human beings

MAN -- ANTIQUITY *See* Human origins

MAN -- INFLUENCE ON NATURE *See* Human influence on nature

MAN -- ORIGIN *See* Human origins

The **man** behind the gun: Samuel Colt and his revolver. Wyckoff, E. B. **92**

The **man** behind the mask. Dahl, M. **Fic**

The **man** from the land of Fandango. **E**

The **man** from the other side. Orlev, U. **Fic**

Man gave names to all the animals. Dylan, B. **782.42**

MAN IN SPACE *See* Space flight

The **Man** in the Moon. Joyce, W. **E**

Man walks on the Moon. Bodden, V. **629.45**

The **man** who flies with birds. Vogel, C. G. **598**

The **man** who invented basketball. Wyckoff, E. B. **92**

The **man** who invented basketball: James Naismith and his amazing game. Wyckoff, E. B. **92**

The **man** who invented the ferris wheel. Sneed, D. **92**

The **man** who invented the laser. Wyckoff, E. B. **92**

The **man** who lived in a hollow tree. Shelby, A. **E**

The **man** who made time travel. **526**

The **man** who walked between the towers. Gerstein, M. **791**

MAN, PREHISTORIC *See* Fossil hominids; Prehistoric peoples

MAN-WOMAN RELATIONSHIP
    See also Interpersonal relations

MANAGEMENT OF CONFLICT *See* Conflict management

Managing children's services in the public library. Fasick, A. M. **027.62**

Managing green spaces. Gazlay, S. **333.7**

Managing money. **332.02**

Managing your digital footprint. Grayson, R. **004.6**

The **manatee** scientists. Lourie, P. **599.5**

Manatees. Stearns, P. M. **599.5**

MANATEES

Arnosky, J. Jim Arnosky's All about manatees **599.5**

Goldish, M. Florida manatees **599.5**

Lourie, P. The manatee scientists **599.5**

Skerry, B. Face to face with manatees **599.5**

Stearns, P. M. Manatees **599.5**

Manchess, Gregory

(il) Waldman, S. The last river **978**

Mandel, Peter

Jackhammer Sam **E**

Mandela. Kramer, A. **92**

Mandela. Cooper, F. **968.06**

Mandela, Nelson

About

Cooper, F. Mandela **968.06**

Kramer, A. Mandela **92**

Mandela, N. Nelson Mandela: long walk to freedom **92**

Peaceful protest: the life of Nelson Mandela **968.06**

Nelson, K. Nelson Mandela **968.06**

Mandelbaum, Jack

About

Warren, A. Surviving Hitler **940.53**

Mandell, Muriel

A donkey reads **398.2**

Manders, John

(il) Demas, C. Pirates go to school **E**

(il) Dodds, D. A. Minnie's Diner **E**

(il) Friend, C. The perfect nest **E**

(il) Lauber, P. What you never knew about beds, bedrooms, and pajamas **392**

(il) Lauber, P. What you never knew about fingers, forks, & chopsticks **394.1**

(il) McClatchy, L. Dear Tyrannosaurus Rex **E**

(il) McGinley, P. A year without a Santa Claus **E**

(il) Tripp, J. Pete & Fremont **Fic**

(il) Zuckerman, A. 2030 **600**

Manfish: a story of Jacques Cousteau. Berne, J. **92**

Manfredi, Frederica

(il) De Campi, A. Kat & Mouse: Teacher torture **741.5**

MANGA

Fuji, M. The big adventures of Majoko, volume 1 **741.5**

Sonishi, K. Leave it to PET!: the misadventures of a recycled super robot, vol. 1 **741.5**

MANGA
    See also Graphic novels

MANGA -- STUDY AND TEACHING

Brenner, R. E. Understanding manga and anime **025.2**

Manga math mysteries [series]

Thielbar, M. The ancient formula **741.5**

Mangelsen, Thomas D.

(il) Hirschi, R. Our three bears **599.78**

(il) Searching for grizzlies **599.78**

Manger. **E**

Mangled by a hurricane! Aronin, M. **551.55**

A **mango** in the hand. **E**

MANGOES -- FICTION

A mango in the hand **E**

MANGROVE ECOLOGY

The mangrove tree **577.6**

The **mangrove** tree. **577.6**

MANHATTAN (NEW YORK, N.Y.)

Vila, L. Building Manhattan **974.7**

Maniac Magee. Spinelli, J. **Fic**

MANIC-DEPRESSIVE ILLNESS -- FICTION

Leal, A. H. A finders-keepers place **Fic**

Mills, C. One square inch **Fic**

Wilson, J. The illustrated Mum **Fic**

MANIPULATIVES

See also Audiovisual materials; Mathematics -- Study and teaching; Teaching -- Aids and devices

Manivong, Laura
  Escaping the tiger   **Fic**

Mankiller, Wilma
          About
  Krull, K. Lives of extraordinary women **920**
  Sonneborn, L. Wilma Mankiller **92**

Manley, Candace
  Skeeter's dream **Fic**

Manley, Effa, 1900-1981
          About
  She loved baseball: the Effa Manley story **92**

Mann, Bethany
  Hines-Stephens, S. Show off **790.1**

Mann, Charles C.
  Before Columbus **970.01**

Mann, Elizabeth
  Hoover Dam **627**
  The Parthenon **726**
  The Roman Colosseum **937**
  Statue of Liberty **974.7**
  Taj Mahal **954**
  Tikal **972.81**

Mann, Janet
          About
  Turner, P. S. The dolphins of Shark Bay **599.53**

Mann, Jennifer K.
  Two speckled eggs **E**
  (il) Turkey Tot **E**

Manna, Anthony L.
  The orphan **398.2**

MANNED SPACE FLIGHT *See* Space flight
  Goodman, S. E. How do you burp in space? **629.45**
  Holden, H. M. The coolest job in the universe **629.44**

Manners. Aliki **395**

MANNERS *See* Courtesy; Etiquette

Manners mash-up: a goofy guide to good behavior. **395**

Manning, Jane
  (il) Millie Fierce Sleeps Out **E**
  (il) Jane, P. Little goblins ten **E**
  (il) Katz, B. Nothing but a dog **E**
  (il) There's no place like school **811**
  (il) Weeks, S. Drip, drop **E**
  (il) Weeks, S. Mac and Cheese **E**

Manning, Matthew K.
  Ali Baba and the forty thieves **741.5**

Manning, Maurie
  Kitchen dance **E**
  Laundry day **E**

Manning, Mick
  (jt. auth) Granström, B. Nature adventures **508**
  The Beatles **92**

Charles Dickens **92**
Tail-end Charlie **940.54**
Under your skin **612**
Woolly mammoth **569**

Manning, Peyton
          About
  Rappoport, K. Peyton Manning **796.332**
  Wilner, B. Peyton Manning **92**

Mannis, Celeste Davidson
  Julia Morgan built a castle **92**
  One leaf rides the wind **E**

Manny's cows. Becker, S. **E**

Manolito Four-Eyes. Lindo, E. **Fic**

Manolito Four-Eyes [series]
  Lindo, E. Manolito Four-Eyes **Fic**
  Lindo, E. Manolito Four-Eyes: the 2nd volume of the great encyclopedia of my life **Fic**
  Lindo, E. Manolito Four-Eyes: the 3rd volume of the great encyclopedia of my life **Fic**

Manolito Four-Eyes: the 2nd volume of the great encyclopedia of my life. Lindo, E. **Fic**

Manolito Four-Eyes: the 3rd volume of the great encyclopedia of my life. Lindo, E. **Fic**

Mansa Musa. Burns, K. **Fic**

Manta rays. Wearing, J. **597**

Mantha, John
  (il) What was the Battle of Gettysburg? **973.7**
  (il) MacLeod, E. Samuel de Champlain **92**

Mantle, Ben
  (il) Moser, L. Perfect Soup **E**

Mantle, Mickey, 1931-1995
          About
  Gutman, D. Mickey & me **Fic**

MANTODEA
  Maley, A. H. 20 fun facts about praying mantises **595.7**

MANUAL WORKERS *See* Labor; Working class

MANUFACTURES
  Slavin, B. Transformed **670**

MANUFACTURING EXECUTIVES
  Kulling, M. It's a snap! **92**
  Wyckoff, E. B. The man behind the gun: Samuel Colt and his revolver **92**

MANUSCRIPTS
  See also Archives; Bibliography; Books

MANUSCRIPTS -- FICTION
  Beebe, K. Brother Hugo and the bear **E**

Manushkin, Fran
  How Mama brought the spring **E**
  The belly book **E**
  Miriam's cup **222**
  The Shivers in the fridge **E**

Many luscious lollipops: a book about adjectives. Heller, R. **428**

Many moons. Thurber, J. **813**

Many moons. Thurber, J. **E**

Marks, Alan
- (il) Markle, S. Snow school   **E**
- Markle, S. Family pack   **E**
- (il) Markle, S. Finding home   **599.2**
- (il) Markle, S. Hip-pocket papa   **597.8**
- (il) Markle, S. A mother's journey   **598**
- High tide for horseshoe crabs   **595.4**
- (il) Markle, S. Waiting for ice   **599.786**

Marks, Diana F.
- Children's book award handbook   **028.5**

Marks, Jennifer L.
- Bobcats   **599.75**
- Clouded leopards   **599.75**
- Jaguars   **599.75**

MARKSMEN
- Wills, C. A. Annie Oakley: a photographic story of a life   **92**

Markuson, Carolyn A.
- Erikson, R. Designing a school library media center for the future   **027.8**

Marley. Grogan, J.   **636.7**

Marley, Bob
About
- Medina, T. I and I   **92**

Marlow, Layn
- Hurry up and slow down   **E**

MARMOTS
- Gibbons, G. Groundhog day!   **394.26**

MARMOTS -- FICTION
- April Fool, Phyllis!   **E**
- Blackaby, S. Brownie Groundhog and the February fox   **E**
- Cherry, L. How Groundhog's garden grew   **E**
- Cox, J. Go to sleep, Groundhog!   **E**
- Elish, D. The attack of the frozen woodchucks   **Fic**
- Hill, S. L. Punxsutawney Phyllis   **E**
- Mr. and Mrs. Bunny-- detectives extraordinaire!   **FIC**
- Olson, J. Tickle, tickle! itch, twitch!   **E**
- Swallow, P. C. Groundhog gets a say   **E**

Marooned. Kraske, R.   **92**

Marquez, Francisca
- (il) Houran, L. H. A trip into space   **629.4**

Marr, Melissa, 1972-
- Loki's wolves   **Fic**
- Odin's ravens   **Fic**

MARRIAGE
- *See also* Family; Sacraments

MARRIAGE -- FICTION
- Buehner, C. Fanny's dream   **E**
- Lyons, K. S. Ellen's broom   **E**

MARRIAGE CUSTOMS AND RITES
- *See also* Manners and customs; Marriage; Rites and ceremonies; Weddings
- Lyons, K. S. Ellen's broom   **E**

MARRIED PEOPLE

- *See also* Family; Marriage

Marrin, Albert
- Marrin, A. Flesh & blood so cheap   **974.7**
- Oh, rats!   **599.35**

Marriott, Pat
- (il) Aiken, J. The wolves of Willoughby Chase **Fic**

Mars. Capaccio, G.   **523.4**

Mars. Landau, E.   **523.4**

MARS (PLANET)
- Capaccio, G. Mars   **523.4**
- Carson, M. K. Far-out guide to Mars   **523.4**
- Landau, E. Mars   **523.4**

MARS (PLANET)
- *See also* Planets

MARS (PLANET) -- EXPLORATION
- Rusch, E. The mighty Mars rovers   **523.43**

MARS (PLANET) -- EXPLORATION
- *See also* Planets -- Exploration

MARS (PLANET) -- FICTION
- Gall, C. There's nothing to do on Mars   **E**

MARS PROBES
- Rusch, E. The mighty Mars rovers   **523.43**

MARS PROBES
- *See also* Mars (Planet); Space probes

Marsalis, Wynton, 1961-
- Jazz A-B-Z   **781.65**
- Squeak! rumble! whomp! whomp! whomp!   **E**

Marschall, Ken
- Inside the Titanic   **910.4**

Marschark, Marc
- (jt. auth) Hauser, P. C. How deaf children learn   **371.91**

Marsden, Carolyn, 1950-
- Marsden, C. The gold-threaded dress   **Fic**
- Silk umbrellas   **Fic**
- Take me with you   **Fic**
- When heaven fell   **Fic**

Marsden, John
- Tan, S. Lost & found   **S**

MARSH ECOLOGY
- Johansson, P. Marshes and swamps   **577.6**
- Wechsler, D. Marvels in the muck   **578.7**

MARSH ECOLOGY
- *See also* Ecology

Marsh, Laura
- Caterpillar to butterfly   **595.78**
- Polar bears   **599.78**
- Amazing animal journeys   **591.56**
- Butterflies   **595.7**
- Elephants   **599.67**
- Whales   **599.5**

Marsh, Othniel Charles, 1831-1899
About
- Goldish, M. The fossil feud   **560**
- Johnson, R. L. Battle of the dinosaur bones **560.973**

Marshall Armstrong is new to our school. Mackin-

The **Mayflower.** Greenwood, M.   **974.4**
MAYFLOWER (SHIP)
   Greenwood, M. The Mayflower   **974.4**
MAYFLOWER COMPACT (1620
   Greenwood, M. The Mayflower   **974.4**
Mayo, Margaret
   Zoom, rocket, zoom!   **E**
   Choo choo clickety-clack!   **E**
   Roar!   **E**
Mayor, Adrienne
   The Griffin and the Dinosaur   **398.245**
MAYORS
   Hodges, M. Dick Whittington and his cat   **398.2**
   Otfinoski, S. Grover Cleveland   **92**
   Shelton, P. Y. Child of the civil rights movement   **323.1**
Mayr, Diane
   Run, Turkey run   **E**
Mays, Carl, 1891-1971
          About
   Gutman, D. Ray & me   **Fic**
Mays, Willie, 1931-
          About
   You never heard of Willie Mays?!   **796.357**
MAZATEC INDIANS -- FICTION
   Ramirez, A. Napi   **E**
MAZE GARDENS
     See also Gardens
The **maze** of bones. Riordan, R.   **Fic**
MAZE PUZZLES
   Kalz, J. An A-MAZE-ing amusement park adventure   **793.73**
   Lankford, M. D. Mazes around the world   **793.73**
   Munro, R. Amazement park   **793.73**
   Munro, R. Mazeways: A to Z   **793.73**
MAZE PUZZLES
     See also Puzzles
Mazellan, Ron
   (il) Irena's jars of secrets   **92**
Mazer, Anne
   Spilling ink   **808.3**
Mazer, Norma Fox
   Has anyone seen my Emily Greene?   **E**
MAZES *See* Maze gardens; Maze puzzles
Mazes around the world. Lankford, M. D.   **793.73**
Mazeways: A to Z. Munro, R.   **793.73**
Mazorlig, Thomas
   (ed) Boruchowitz, D. E. Sugar gliders   **636.935**
McAlister, Caroline
   Brave Donatella and the Jasmine thief   **E**
McAllister, Angela
   Little Mist   **E**
   My mom has x-ray vision   **E**
   Yuck! That's not a monster!   **E**
McAllister, Ian
   Salmon bears   **599.78**

   The sea wolves   **599.77**
McArdle, Paula
   (il) Shelby, A. The adventures of Molly Whuppie and other Appalachian folktales   **398.2**
McArthur, Meher
   An ABC of what art can be   **700**
McAuley, Adam
   (il) Ann and Nan are anagrams   **Fic**
McBratney, Sam
   Guess how much I love you   **E**
   When I'm big   **E**
McBroom's wonderful one-acre farm. Fleischman, S.   **Fic**
McCall Smith, Alexander, 1948-
   The great cake mystery   **Fic**
   The Mystery of Meerkat Hill   **Fic**
   The mystery of the missing lion   **Fic**
McCallum, Ann
   Eat your math homework   **641.5**
McCann, Jim
   Return of the Dapper Men   **741.5**
McCann, Michelle Roehm
   Girls who rocked the world   **920.72**
McCarthy, Colin
   Reptile   **597.9**
McCarthy, Mary
   A closer look   **E**
McCarthy, Meghan
   (il) Earmuffs for everyone!   **92**
   Daredevil   **E**
   The incredible life of Balto   **636.7**
   Aliens are coming!   **791.44**
   Astronaut handbook   **629.45**
   The incredible life of Balto   **636.7**
   Pop!   **664**
   Seabiscuit   **798.4**
McCarthy, Pat
   Friends of the earth   **304.2**
McCarthy, Steve
   (il) Sally go round the stars   **398.8**
McCarthy, Tom
          About
   Montgomery, S. Saving the ghost of the mountain   **599.75**
McCartney, Paul
          About
   Brewer, P. The Beatles were fab (and they were funny)   **782.421**
McCarty, Nick
   Marco Polo   **92**
McCarty, Peter
   Chloe   **E**
   First snow for Pedro   **E**
   Henry in love   **E**
   Hondo and Fabian   **E**
   Jeremy draws a monster   **E**

Beautiful warrior **E**
The bobbin girl **E**
(il) Fern, T. Dare the wind **92**
First snow **E**
The grandma mix-up **E**
Marvelous Mattie **92**
Mirette on the high wire **E**
My heart glow: Alice Cogswell, Thomas Gallaudet and the birth of American sign language **92**
Queen of the diamond **92**
The secret cave **E**
Squirrel and John Muir **E**
Wonder horse **E**
(il) Rappaport, D. The secret seder **E**
(il) Rockwell, T. How to eat fried worms **Fic**
(il) Schertle, A. 1, 2, I love you **E**
(il) Van Rynbach, I. The taxing case of the cows **324.6**
(il) Weaver, T. Cat jumped in! **E**

McCurdy, Michael
(il) Fradin, D. B. The founders **920**
(il) Fradin, D. B. The signers **973.3**
Walden then & now **818**
(il) Osborne, M. P. American tall tales **398.2**

McDaniel, Deanna
Gentle reads **028.5**

McDaniel, Melissa
Arizona **979.1**
New Mexico **972**
North Dakota **978.4**

McDaniels, Preston
(il) Dowell, F. O. Phineas L. MacGuire . . . blasts off! **Fic**
(il) Dowell, F. O. Phineas L. MacGuire . . . gets slimed! **Fic**

McDee, Katie
(il) Bridget and Bo build a blog **Fic**

McDermott, Gerald
Anansi the spider **398.2**
Arrow to the sun **398.2**
Coyote: a trickster tale from the American Southwest **398.2**
Creation **E**
Jabuti the tortoise **398.2**
Monkey **398.2**
Papagayo **E**
Pig-Boy **398.2**
Raven **398.2**
Zomo the Rabbit **398.24**

McDonald, Jill
(il) Gershator, P. Who's in the forest? **E**

McDonald, Megan
Ant and Honey Bee **E**
Cloudy with a chance of boys **Fic**
Hen hears gossip **E**
It's picture day today! **E**

Jessica Finch in Pig Trouble **E**
Judy Moody **Fic**
Judy Moody & Stink: the mad, mad, mad, mad treasure hunt **Fic**
Judy Moody goes to Hollywood **791.43**
Judy Moody, girl detective **Fic**
Judy moody and stink and the big bad blackout **Fic**
Judy Moody, Mood Martian **Fic**
The rule of three **Fic**
Stink and the ultimate thumb-wrestling smackdown **Fic**
Stink: the incredible shrinking kid **Fic**
Shoe dog **E**
Stink and the Midnight Zombie Walk **Fic**
Stink and the shark sleepover **Fic**
(il) Elya, S. M. Fairy trails **E**

McDonnell, Christine
Goyangi means cat **E**
Dog wants to play **E**

McDonnell, Patrick
Me . . . Jane **92**
The monsters' monster **E**
A perfectly messed-up story **E**
South **E**

McDonough, Yona Zeldis
The cats in the doll shop **Fic**
The doll shop downstairs **Fic**
The doll with the yellow star **Fic**
Louisa **92**
Peaceful protest: the life of Nelson Mandela **968.06**

McDougall, Chros
Figure skating **796.91**
Track & field **796.42**
Volleyball **796.325**

McDowell, Marilyn Taylor
Carolina Harmony **Fic**
The **McElderry** book of Aesop's fables. Morpurgo, M. **398.2**
The **McElderry** book of Greek myths. Kimmel, E. A. **292**
The **McElderry** book of Grimms' fairy tales. Pirotta, S. **398.2**

McElligot's pool. Seuss **E**

McElligott, Matthew
Bean thirteen **E**
Benjamin Franklinstein lives! **Fic**
Benjamin Franklinstein meets the Fright brothers **Fic**
Even monsters need haircuts **E**
The lion's share **E**

McElmurry, Jill
(il) Hopkins, H. J. The tree lady **92**
(il) Little Blue Truck **E**
Mario makes a move **E**
When Otis courted Mama **E**
(il) Heide, F. P. The one and only Marigold **E**

Boy, Bird, and Dog	E
Drawing lessons from a bear	E
Emma in charge	E
Mole music	E
No!	E
Pig Pig returns	E
Pigs aplenty, pigs galore!	813
Sylvie & True	E
The teddy bear	E
Water boy	E
Weezer changes the world	E
McPhail, D. Waddles	E
(il) Numeroff, L. J. When sheep sleep	E
(il) Rockwell, T. Emily Stew	811
(il) Spinelli, E. When Papa comes home tonight	E

McPhee, Marc E.
Farmer, L. S. J. Neal-Schuman technology management handbook for school library media centers — 025.1

McPherson, James M.
Fields of fury — 973.7

McPherson, Stephanie Sammartino
Iceberg right ahead! — 910.4

McQuerry, Maureen Doyle
Beyond the door — Fic

McQuinn, Anna
Leo loves baby time	E
Lola at the library	E
My friend Jamal	E
My friend Mei Jing	E
The sleep sheep	E
McQuinn, C. Ireland	941.5

McQuinn, Colm
Ireland — 941.5

McReynolds, Linda
Eight days gone — 629.45

McSwigan, Marie
Snow treasure — Fic

McWhorter, Diane
A dream of freedom — 323.1

McWhorter, Heather
(il) Willey, M. Clever Beatrice — 398.2

McWilliam, Howard
(il) Markle, S. What If You Had Animal Teeth? E
(il) When a dragon moves in — E

Me . . . Jane. McDonnell, P.	92
Me and Meow. Gudeon, A.	E
Me and Momma and Big John.	E
Me and my bike. Ander	E
Me and my dad. Morgan, S.	E
Me and my dragon. Biedrzycki, D.	E
Me and Rolly Maloo. Wong, J. S.	Fic
Me and Uncle Romie. Hartfield, C.	E
Me and you. Browne, A.	E
Me hungry! Tankard, J.	E
Me too!	E

| Me with you. Dempsey, K. | E |

MÉTIS -- FICTION
Erdrich, L. Chickadee — Fic

Me, Frida. — E

Mead, Alice
| Junebug | Fic |
| Junebug in trouble | Fic |

Mead, Wendy
The Merchant — 381.09

Bennett, C. Montana	978.6
McDaniel, M. Arizona	979.1
Top 10 birds for kids	636.6
Stefoff, R. Utah	979.2

Meade, Holly
(il) Bartoletti, S. C. Naamah and the ark at night	E
(il) Elliott, D. In the sea	811
(il) Best, C. Goose's story	E
(il) Brenner, T. And then comes Halloween	E
(il) Elliott, D. In the wild	811
(il) Elliott, D. On the farm	E
(il) Gershator, P. Sky sweeper	E
(il) Ho, M. Hush!	782.4
(il) Lindbergh, R. On morning wings	223
If I never forever endeavor	E
Inside, inside, inside	E
John Willy and Freddy McGee	E

Meadowlands. Yezerski, T. — 577.690

MEADOWLANDS (N.J.)
Yezerski, T. Meadowlands — 577.690

MEADOWS -- FICTION
| Cole, H. On Meadowview Street | E |
| Katō, Y. In the meadow | E |

MEADOWS -- POETRY
Sidman, J. Butterfly eyes and other secrets of the meadow — 811

Meadows, Michelle
Piggies in pajamas	E
Hibernation station	E
Piggies in the kitchen	E

MEAL PLANNING See Menus; Nutrition

Mealer, Bryan
(jt. auth) Kamkwamba, W. The boy who harnessed the wind — 92

MEALS FOR SCHOOL CHILDREN See School children -- Food

MEALS ON WHEELS PROGRAMS
See also Food relief

Mealtime. Verdick, E.	E
The meanest birthday girl. Schneider, J.	E
The meaning of Maggie. Sovern, M. J.	813.6

MEANNESS See Bad behavior

| Meanwhile. Shiga, J. | 741.5 |
| Meanwhile, back at the ranch. | E |

Measure it! [series]
Adamson, T. K. How do you measure length and distance? — 530.8

MEDEA (GREEK MYTHOLOGY)

    See also Legendary characters

Medearis, Angela Shelf

    Seven spools of thread   **E**

MEDIA CENTERS (EDUCATION) *See* Instructional materials centers

MEDIA LITERACY

    See also Literacy

Media literacy [series]

    Botzakis, S. Pretty in print   **050**

MEDICAID

    Lynette, R. What to do when your family can't afford healthcare   **368.3**

MEDICAL BOTANY

    See also Botany; Medicine; Pharmacy

MEDICAL CARE

    Barber, N. Going to the hospital   **362.1**

    Murphy, L. ABC doctor   **610**

    Parker, V. Going to the hospital   **362.1**

    Singer, M. I'm getting a checkup   **610**

MEDICAL CARE

    See also Public health

MEDICAL CARE -- ETHICAL ASPECTS *See* Medical ethics

MEDICAL CARE -- FICTION

    Archer, D. Big Bad Wolf   **E**

    Harper, J. Uh-oh, Cleo   **Fic**

    Lawrence, I. The giant-slayer   **Fic**

    Urgency emergecy! Itsy bitsy spider   **E**

MEDICAL CARE FOR THE POOR *See* Medicaid; Poor -- Medical care

MEDICAL CHARITIES

    See also Charities; Medical care; Public health

MEDICAL DRAMA (FILMS)

    See also Motion pictures

MEDICAL DRAMA (TELEVISION PROGRAMS)

    See also Television programs

MEDICAL ETHICS

    Fullick, A. Rebuilding the body   **617.9**

MEDICAL ETHICS

    See also Bioethics; Ethics; Professional ethics

MEDICAL GENETICS

    See also Genetics; Pathology

MEDICAL INSURANCE *See* Health insurance

MEDICAL JURISPRUDENCE

    See also Forensic sciences

MEDICAL MISSIONS

    See also Medicine

    Medical mysteries. Auden, S.   **610**

MEDICAL PHOTOGRAPHY

    See also Photography; Photography -- Scientific applications

MEDICAL PRACTICE

    See also Medicine

MEDICAL PROFESSION *See* Medical personnel; Medical practice; Medicine

MEDICAL SCIENCES *See* Medicine

MEDICAL SELF-CARE *See* Health self-care

MEDICAL SERVICES *See* Medical care

MEDICAL TECHNOLOGISTS

    Mullins, M. Surgical technologist   **617**

MEDICAL TECHNOLOGY

    Rooney, A. Health and medicine   **610**

    Sandvold, L. B. Revolution in medicine   **610**

MEDICAL TECHNOLOGY

    See also Medicine

MEDICAL TRANSPLANTATION *See* Transplantation of organs, tissues, etc.

MEDICAL WASTES

    See also Refuse and refuse disposal

MEDICAL ZOOLOGY

    See also Medicine; Zoology

MEDICATION ABUSE

    See also Drug abuse; Substance abuse

Medici, Patricia, 1972-

        About

    The tapir scientist   **599.66**

MEDICINE

    Fullick, A. Rebuilding the body   **617.9**

    Goldsmith, C. Cutting-edge medicine   **610**

    Lew, K. Bat spit, maggots, and other amazing medical wonders   **610**

    Murphy, L. ABC doctor   **610**

    Rooney, A. Health and medicine   **610**

    Silverstein, A. Tapeworms, foot fungus, lice, and more   **616**

    Singer, M. I'm getting a checkup   **610**

MEDICINE

    See also Life sciences; Therapeutics

MEDICINE -- BIOGRAPHY

    See also Biography

MEDICINE -- ENCYCLOPEDIAS

    Encyclopedia of health   **610**

    Stoyles, P. The A-Z of health   **616**

MEDICINE -- ETHICAL ASPECTS *See* Medical ethics

MEDICINE -- HISTORY

    Romanek, T. Science, medicine, and math in the early Islamic world   **509.56**

MEDICINE -- LAW AND LEGISLATION

    See also Law; Legislation

MEDICINE -- MISCELLANEA

    See also Curiosities and wonders

MEDICINE -- RESEARCH

    Auden, S. Medical mysteries   **610**

    Dendy, L. A. Guinea pig scientists   **616**

    Piddock, C. Outbreak   **614.4**

MEDICINE -- RESEARCH

    See also Research

Wilkinson, P. Gandhi **92**

Winter, J. Gertrude is Gertrude is Gertrude is Gertrude **92**

Yolleck, J. Paris in the spring with Picasso **E**

Zora Hurston and the chinaberry tree **813**

MEMOIRS See Autobiographies; Autobiography; Biography

MEMORIAL DAY

    See also Holidays

MEMORY

Adler, D. A. Cam Jansen and the snowy day mystery **Fic**

Bunting, E. The memory string **E**

Cleary, B. P. Mrs. Riley Bought Five Itchy Aardvarks and other painless tricks for memorizing science facts **500**

MEMORY

    See also Brain; Educational psychology; Intellect; Psychology; Psychophysiology; Thought and thinking

MEMORY -- FICTION

Young, C. Nancy knows **E**

Fleischman, P. The Matchbox diary **E**

Stone, P. The boy on Cinnamon Street **Fic**

The **Memory** Bank. Coman, C. **Fic**

The **memory** coat. Woodruff, E. **E**

The **memory** string. Bunting, E. **E**

MEMPHIS (TENN.) -- FICTION

Polacco, P. John Philip Duck **E**

Vawter, V. Paperboy **Fic**

MEN -- BIOGRAPHY

    See also Biography

MEN -- DISEASES

    See also Diseases

MEN -- PSYCHOLOGY

    See also Psychology

MEN -- SOCIETIES

    See also Clubs; Societies

MEN IN BUSINESS See Businessmen

MEN'S CLOTHING

    See also Clothing and dress

Menchin, Scott

(il) Cronin, D. Wiggle **E**

(il) McGhee, A. Song of middle C **E**

What if everything had legs? **E**

(il) Shannon, G. Chicken scratches **811**

Menchu, Rigoberta

The girl from Chimel **92**

The honey jar **398.2**

The secret legacy **398.2**

    About

Krull, K. Lives of extraordinary women **920**

Menchu, R. The girl from Chimel **92**

Mendel, Gregor, 1822-1884

    About

Bardoe, C. Gregor Mendel **92**

Van Gorp, L. Gregor Mendel **92**

Mendelson, Edward

(ed) Lear, E. Edward Lear **821**

Mendez, Sean

One world kids cookbook **641.59**

Mendez, Simon

(il) Wilson, H. Seashore **551.4**

(il) Wilson, K. Mama, why? **E**

Mendez, Sylvia, 1936-

    About

Tonatiuh, D. Separate is never equal **379.2**

Mending horses. Barker, M. P. **Fic**

Menendez, Francisco, b. ca. 1700

    About

Turner, G. T. Fort Mose **975.9**

Meng, Cece

I will not read this book **E**

Menhard, Francha Roffe

The facts about inhalants **362.29**

Meningitis. Klosterman, L. **616.8**

MENINGITIS

Klosterman, L. Meningitis **616.8**

MENNONITES -- FICTION

Migrant **E**

MENNONITES -- POETRY

Forler, N. Winterberries and apple blossoms **811**

The **Menominee.** De Capua, S. **970.004**

MENOMINEE INDIANS

De Capua, S. The Menominee **970.004**

MENORAH -- FICTION

The eighth menorah **E**

Sadie's almost marvelous menorah **E**

Menorah under the sea. Heller, E. S. **296.4**

Menorahs, mezuzas, and other Jewish symbols. Chaikin, M. **296.4**

Menotti, Andrea

How many jelly beans? **513.2**

Menotti, Gian Carlo

Amahl and the night visitors **232.9**

MENSTRUATION

Gravelle, K. The period book **612.6**

Jukes, M. Growing up: it's a girl thing **612.6**

MENSTRUATION

    See also Reproduction

MENSURATION

Long, L. Measurement mania **372.7**

MENTAL ARITHMETIC

    See also Arithmetic

MENTAL DEPRESSION See Depression (Psychology)

MENTAL HEALTH

    See also Happiness; Health

MENTAL HEALTH SERVICES

    See also Medical care

MENTAL ILLNESS

    See also Abnormal psychology; Diseases

Politi, L. Juanita   **E**
Politi, L. Pedro, the angel of Olvera Street   **E**
The quiet place   **E**
Resau, L. Star in the forest   **Fic**
Ryan, P. M. Becoming Naomi Leon   **Fic**
Ryan, P. M. Esperanza rising   **Fic**
Soto, G. Baseball in April, and other stories   **S**
Soto, G. Facts of life   **S**
Soto, G. Local news   **S**
Soto, G. Petty crimes   **S**
Soto, G. The skirt   **Fic**
Soto, G. Too many tamales   **813**
Tafolla, C. Fiesta babies   **E**
Tafolla, C. What can you do with a rebozo?   **E**
Tonatiuh, D. Dear Primo   **E**
When Christmas feels like home   **E**

MEXICAN AMERICANS -- POETRY
Ada, A. F. Gathering the sun   **811**
Bernier-Grand, C. T. Cesar   **811**
Herrera, J. F. Laughing out loud, I fly   **811**
Soto, G. Canto familiar   **811**

MEXICAN AMERICANS -- SOCIAL LIFE AND CUSTOMS
Hoyt-Goldsmith, D. Celebrating a Quinceanera   **395.2**
Tait, L. Cinco de Mayo   **394.26**

MEXICAN ART
Campbell-Hinshaw, K. Ancient Mexico   **709.3**
Count me in   **513.2**
Mexican food. Blaxland, W.   **641.5**
Mexican food. Blaxland, W.   **641.59**

MEXICAN LITERATURE
See also Latin American literature; Literature

MEXICANS -- FICTION
Hobbs, W. Crossing the wire   **Fic**
Jaramillo, A. La linea   **Fic**
Mexico. Kent, D.   **972**

MEXICO
Gruber, B. Mexico   **972**
Hawker, F. Christianity in Mexico   **282**
Junior Worldmark encyclopedia of the Mexican states   **972**
Streissguth, T. Mexico   **972**
Mexico. Streissguth, T.   **972**
Mexico. Gruber, B.   **972**

MEXICO -- ANTIQUITIES
Campbell-Hinshaw, K. Ancient Mexico   **709.3**
Cooke, T. Ancient Aztec   **972**
Harris, N. Ancient Maya   **972**
Kops, D. Palenque   **972**

MEXICO -- FICTION
Anaya, R. A. The first tortilla   **Fic**
Capucilli, A. Pedro's burro   **E**
Dorros, A. Numero uno   **E**
Dorros, A. Julio's magic   **E**
Elya, S. M. Cowboy Jose   **E**

Fine, E. H. Armando and the blue tarp school   **E**
Fleischman, S. The dream stealer   **Fic**
Garza, X. Lucha libre: the Man in the Silver Mask   **Fic**
Geeslin, C. Elena's serenade   **E**
Goldman, J. Uncle monarch and the Day of the Dead   **E**
Johnston, T. Day of the Dead   **394.2**
Madrigal, A. H. Erandi's braids   **E**
Mora, P. Uno, dos, tres: one, two, three   **E**
Playing loteria   **E**
Ramirez, A. Napi   **E**
Resau, L. What the moon saw   **Fic**
Ryan, P. M. Becoming Naomi Leon   **Fic**
Tonatiuh, D. Dear Primo   **E**
Winter, J. Josefina   **513.2**

MEXICO -- HISTORY
Lourie, P. On the Texas trail of Cabeza de Vaca   **92**
Mattern, J. Celebrate Cinco de Mayo   **394.26**
Otfinoski, S. The new republic: 1760-1840s   **973.3**
Serrano, F. The poet king of Tezcoco   **92**
Kent, D. Mexico   **972**

MEXICO -- SOCIAL LIFE AND CUSTOMS
Augustin, B. The food of Mexico   **394.1**
Hoyt-Goldsmith, D. Cinco de Mayo   **394.26**
Mattern, J. Celebrate Cinco de Mayo   **394.26**
Otto, C. Celebrate Cinco de Mayo   **394.26**
Tait, L. Cinco de Mayo   **394.26**
Winter, J. Calavera abecedario   **E**
Johnston, T. Day of the Dead   **394.2**
Peppas, L. Cultural traditions in Mexico   **394.26**

Meyer, Kerstin
(il) Funke, C. C. The princess knight   **E**
(il) Funke, C. C. Princess Pigsty   **E**
(il) Funke, C. C. The wildest brother   **E**
(il) Steinhofel, A. An elk dropped in   **Fic**

Meyer, Susan
Adapting to flooding and rising sea levels   **363.34**
Black radishes   **Fic**
New shoes   **E**

Meyers, Mark
(il) Kelly, D. A. The Fenway foul-up   **Fic**
(il) Kelly, D. A. The L.A. Dodger   **Fic**
(il) Kelly, D. A. The pinstripe ghost   **Fic**

Meyers, Matthew
(il) Bartholomew Biddle and the very big wind   **Fic**

Meyers, Susan
Everywhere babies   **E**
Bear in the air   **E**
Kittens! Kittens! Kittens!   **E**

MEZUZAH -- FICTION
The Shema in the mezuzah   **E**

Mezzanotte, Jim
Police   **363.2**

Mhlophe, Gcina
African tales   **398.2**

Brown, J. Star Wars **741.5**

Dowell, F. O. The second life of Abigail Walker **Fic**

Drama **741.5**

Gale, E. K. The Bully Book **Fic**

Kinard, K. The boy prediction **Fic**

My life as a joke **Fic**

Sovern, M. J. The meaning of Maggie **813.6**

Taylor, C. Ready to wear **Fic**

Tracy, K. Bessica Lefter bites back **Fic**

The year of the fortune cookie **Fic**

MIDDLE-BORN CHILDREN -- FICTION

Pincus, G. The 14 fibs of Gregory K **Fic**

The **middle-child** blues. Crow, K. **E**

Middleman, Amy B.

(ed) Pfeifer, K. G. American Medical Assocation boy's guide to becoming a teen **613**

(ed) Pfeifer, K. G. American Medical Association girl's guide to becoming a teen **613**

Middleton, Charlotte

Nibbles: a green tale **E**

Middleton, Julie

Are the dinosaurs dead, Dad? **E**

Middleworld. Voelkel, J. **Fic**

Midnight for Charlie Bone. Nimmo, J. **Fic**

Midnight forests. Hines, G. **92**

The **Midnight** Library. Kohara, K. **E**

Midnight magic. Avi **Fic**

The **midnight** tunnel. Frazier, A. **Fic**

Midsummer knight. Rogers, G. **E**

The **midwife's** apprentice. Cushman, K. **Fic**

MIDWIVES

Let it shine **920**

Wells, R. Mary on horseback **92**

MIDWIVES

See also Childbirth; Natural childbirth; Nurses

MIDWIVES -- FICTION

Cushman, K. The midwife's apprentice **Fic**

Van Steenwyk, E. Prairie Christmas **E**

Mierka, Gregg A.

Nathanael Greene **92**

Migdale, Lawrence

(il) Hoyt-Goldsmith, D. Celebrating a Quinceanera **395.2**

(il) Hoyt-Goldsmith, D. Celebrating Ramadan **297.3**

(il) Hoyt-Goldsmith, D. Cinco de Mayo **394.26**

(il) Hoyt-Goldsmith, D. Three Kings Day **394.26**

Migheli, Roberta

(il) Salati, G. Race for the Ultrapods **741.5**

Mighty animal cells. Johnson, R. L. **571.6**

The **mighty** asparagus. Radunsky, V. **E**

Mighty Casey. Preller, J. **E**

Mighty easy motivators [series]

Bauer, C. F. Leading kids to books through crafts **027.62**

Bauer, C. F. Leading kids to books through magic **027.62**

Bauer, C. F. Leading kids to books through puppets **027.62**

The **mighty** Lalouche. **E**

Mighty machines [series]

Askew, A. Bulldozers **624.1**

Askew, A. Cranes **624.1**

Askew, A. Diggers **624.1**

Askew, A. Loaders **624.1**

Lindeen, M. Ships **623.82**

Lindeen, M. Tractors **629.225**

Lindeen, M. Trains **625.1**

Lindeen, M. Trucks **629.224**

Mighty Maddie. Murphy, S. J. **389**

The **mighty** Mars rovers. Rusch, E. **523.43**

The **mighty** Miss Malone. Curtis, C. P. **Fic**

Mighty Monty. Hurwitz, J. **Fic**

The **mighty** Quinn. **Fic**

Mighty rivers. Green, J. **551.48**

Migrant. **E**

MIGRANT AGRICULTURAL LABORERS -- FICTION

Migrant **E**

MIGRANT LABOR

Adler, D. A. A picture book of Cesar Chavez **92**

Cooper, M. L. Dust to eat **973.917**

Dolores Huerta **331.4**

Jimenez, F. The Christmas gift: El regalo de Navidad **E**

Krull, K. Harvesting hope **92**

Perez, L. K. First day in grapes **E**

Stanley, J. Children of the Dust Bowl **371.9**

MIGRANT LABOR -- FICTION

Engle, M. Silver people **Fic**

Tonatiuh, D. Pancho Rabbit and the coyote **E**

Migrating with the Arctic tern. Catt, T. **598**

Migrating with the caribou. Catt, T. **599.65**

Migrating with the humpback whale. Catt, T. **599.5**

Migrating with the monarch butterfly. Catt, T. **595.7**

Migrating with the salmon. Catt, T. **597**

Migrating with the wildebeest. Catt, T. **599.64**

MIGRATIONS OF NATIONS

Helget, N. Barbarians **940.1**

MIGRATORY WORKERS *See* Migrant labor

Mike Fink. Kellogg, S. **398.22**

Mike Mulligan and his steam shovel. Burton, V. L. **E**

Mikis and the donkey. Dumon Tak, B. **E**

Mikolaycak, Charles

(il) Prokofiev, S. Peter and the wolf **E**

Milelli, Pascal

(il) Whelan, G. Waiting for the owl's call **E**

Miles Davis. Lynette, R. **788.9**

Miles to go. Harper, J. **E**

Miles to the finish. Harper, J. **E**

Miles, Lisa

Ducks **636.5**

Investing **332.6**

Pigs **636.4**

Reduce, reuse, and recycle **363.7**

Sheep **636.3**

Swimming **797.2**

Minders of make-believe. Neuburger, E. K. **070.5**

MINE ACCIDENTS -- CHILE

Aronson, M. Trapped **363.1**

Scott, E. Buried alive! **363.11**

MINE SURVEYING

   See also Mining engineering; Prospecting; Surveying

Mine! **E**

Mine's the best. Bonsall, C. N. **E**

Mine, all mine. Heller, R. **428**

Mineko Mamada

Which is round? Which is bigger? **E**

MINERALOGY *See* Minerals; Natural history

Minerals. Spilsbury, R. **549**

MINERALS

   See also Geology

Aston, D. H. A rock is lively **552**

Davis, B. J. Minerals, rocks, and soil **552**

Green, D. Rocks and minerals **552**

Rocks and minerals **552**

Royston, A. Vitamins and minerals for a healthy body **613.2**

Smithsonian Institution Extreme rocks & minerals! **552**

Spilsbury, R. Minerals **549**

Tomecek, S. Everything rocks and minerals **552**

Tomecek, S. Rocks & minerals **552**

VanCleave, J. P. Janice VanCleave's rocks and minerals **552**

MINERALS IN HUMAN NUTRITION

   See also Food; Minerals; Nutrition

MINERALS IN THE BODY

   See also Metabolism; Minerals; Minerals in the body

Minerals, rocks, and soil. Davis, B. J. **552**

MINERS

Lyon, G. E. Which side are you on? **782.42**

Scott, E. Buried alive! **363.11**

MINERS -- FICTION

Wiseman, D. Jeremy Visick **Fic**

Minerva Louise and the red truck. Stoeke, J. M. **E**

Minerva the monster. Kirwan, W. **E**

MINES AND MINERAL RESOURCES

   See also Economic geology; Natural resources; Raw materials

Minette's feast. **E**

Ming Lo moves the mountain. Lobel, A. **E**

Mini Mia and her darling uncle. Lindenbaum, P. **E**

Mini racer. Dempsey, K. **E**

MINIATURE GARDENS

   See also Gardens; Miniature objects

Miniature horses. Lunis, N. **636.1**

MINIATURE PAINTING

   See also Miniature objects; Painting

The **miniature** schnauzer. Biniok, J. **636.7**

The **miniature** world of Marvin & James. Broach, E. **Fic**

MINIBIKES

   See also Bicycles; Motorcycles

Minifred goes to school. Gerstein, M. **E**

MINING ENGINEERING

   See also Civil engineering; Coal mines and mining; Engineering; Mines and mineral resources

Minion. Anderson, J. D. **Fic**

Minister, Peter

Amazing giant sea creatures **591.77**

(il) Greenwood, M. Amazing giant dinosaurs **567.9**

(il) Woodward, J. Dinosaurs eye to eye **567.9**

MINISTERS (DIPLOMATIC AGENTS) *See* Diplomats

MINISTERS OF THE GOSPEL *See* Clergy

Minji's salon. Choung **E**

Minkel, Walter

How to do The three bears with two hands **791.5**

Minn and Jake. Wong, J. S. **Fic**

Minnesota. Brill, M. T. **977.6**

Minnesota. Schwabacher, M. **977.6**

Minnesota. Harmon, D. **977.6**

MINNESOTA

Brill, M. T. Minnesota **977.6**

Harmon, D. Minnesota **977.6**

Root, P. Big belching bog **577.6**

Schwabacher, M. Minnesota **977.6**

MINNESOTA -- FICTION

Applegate, K. Home of the brave **Fic**

Blume, L. M. M. The rising star of Rusty Nail **Fic**

Friend, C. Barn boot blues **Fic**

Hattemer, K. The vigilante poets of Selwyn Academy **Fic**

Lasky, K. Marven of the Great North Woods **E**

Lorbiecki, M. Paul Bunyan's sweetheart **E**

Lovelace, M. H. Betsy-Tacy **Fic**

Paulsen, G. The winter room **Fic**

Wilder, L. I. On the banks of Plum Creek **Fic**

MINNESOTA -- HISTORY -- 20TH CENTURY -- FICTION

Hayles, M. Breathing room **Fic**

Minnie and Moo and the haunted sweater. Cazet, D. **E**

Minnie and Moo, hooves of fire. Cazet, D. **Fic**

Minnie and Moo, wanted dead or alive. Cazet, D. **E**

Minnie's Diner. Dodds, D. A. **E**

Minnow and Rose. Young, J. **Fic**

MINNOWS -- FICTION

Sauer, T. Nugget and Fang **E**

MINOR ARTS *See* Decorative arts

MINOR LEAGUE BASEBALL

    See also Baseball

MINOR PLANETS *See* Asteroids

Minor, Florence

    If you were a panda bear   **E**

Minor, Wendell

  (il) Aldrin, B. Reaching for the moon   **92**

  (il) Aldrin, B. Look to the stars   **629.4**

  (il) Brown, M. W. Nibble nibble   **811**

  (il) Burleigh, R. Abraham Lincoln comes home **92**

  Burleigh, R. Edward Hopper paints his world   **92**

  (il) Burleigh, R. Night flight   **629.13**

  (il) Ehrlich, A. Rachel   **92**

  (il) George, J. C. The buffalo are back   **599.64**

  (il) George, J. C. Everglades   **975.9**

  (il) George, J. C. Luck   **E**

  (il) George, J. C. Morning, noon, and night   **E**

  (il) George, J. C. The wolves are back   **599.77**

  (il) Henry Knox   **92**

  Minor, F. If you were a panda bear   **E**

  My farm friends   **E**

  Yankee Doodle America   **973.3**

  (il) Titcomb, G. The last train   **E**

  (il) Turner, A. W. Abe Lincoln remembers   **973.7**

  (il) Turner, A. W. Sitting Bull remembers   **92**

MINORITIES -- UNITED STATES -- HISTORY

  Stefoff, R. A different mirror for young people   **305.8**

MINORITIES IN ENGINEERING

    See also Engineering

MINORITIES IN LITERATURE

  Gilton, D. L. Multicultural and ethnic children's literature in the United States   **028.5**

MINORITIES IN MOTION PICTURES

    See also Motion pictures

MINORITY BUSINESS ENTERPRISES

    See also Business enterprises; Minorities

MINORITY WOMEN

    See also Minorities; Women

MINORITY YOUTH

    See also Minorities; Youth

MINSTRELS

    See also Poets

MINSTRELS -- FICTION

  Vining, E. G. Adam of the road   **Fic**

Minter, Daniel

  (il) Lyons, K. S. Ellen's broom   **E**

  (il) Medearis, A. S. Seven spools of thread   **E**

  (il) Reynolds, S. The first marathon: the legend of Pheidippides   **938**

MINTS

    See also Money

Minty: a story of young Harriet Tubman. Schroeder, A.   **305.5**

Mira's Diary. Moss, M.   **Fic**

Miracle mud.   **796.357**

MIRACLES

  Hanft, J. E. Miracles of the Bible   **221.9**

MIRACLES -- FICTION

  The question of miracles   **Fic**

MIRACLES -- FOLKLORE

  DePaola, T. The clown of God   **398.2**

The **miracles** of Passover.   **296.4**

Miracles of the Bible. Hanft, J. E.   **221.9**

The **miraculous** journey of Edward Tulane. DiCamillo, K.   **Fic**

Mirallès, 1959-

  (il) Waluk   **741.5**

Miranda Cosgrove. Yasuda, A.   **92**

Miranda's beach day. Keller, H.   **E**

Miranda, Anne

  To market, to market   **E**

Mirandy and Brother Wind. McKissack, P. C.   **E**

Mirette on the high wire. McCully, E. A.   **E**

Miriam (Biblical figure)

About

  Jules, J. Miriam in the desert   **222**

  Manushkin, F. Miriam's cup   **222**

Miriam in the desert. Jules, J.   **222**

Miriam's cup. Manushkin, F.   **222**

Miron, Marie-Charlotte

  My Little Handbook of Experiments   **E**

Mirpuri, Gouri

  (jt. auth) Cooper, R. Indonesia   **959.8**

Mirror. Morpurgo, M.   **E**

Mirror. Baker, J.   **E**

Mirror mirror. Singer, M.   **811**

The **mirror** of Merlin. Barron, T. A.   **Fic**

A **mirror** to nature. Yolen, J.   **811**

MIRRORS

  Cobb, V. I see myself   **535**

MIRRORS -- FICTION

  Morpurgo, M. Mirror   **E**

The **misadventures** of Maude March. Couloumbis, A.   **Fic**

Misadventures of Millicent Madding [series]

  Tacang, B. Bully-be-gone   **Fic**

The **Misadventures** of Salem Hyde. Cammuso, F.   **Fic**

The **misadventures** of the family Fletcher. Levy, D. A.   **Fic**

The **misadventures** of the magician's dog. Sackett, F.   **Fic**

MISCARRIAGE

    See also Pregnancy

MISCELLANEOUS FACTS *See* Books of lists; Curiosities and wonders

Miss Bindergarten celebrates the 100th day of kindergarten. Slate, J.   **E**

Miss Bridie chose a shovel. Connor, L.   **E**

Miss Brooks loves books (and I don't) Bottner, B. **E**

Monkey and Robot. Catalanotto, P.   **E**
The **monkey** and the crocodile. Galdone, P.   **398.2**
Monkey colors. Lunde, D.   **E**
Monkey see monkey draw. Beard, A.   **E**
Monkey Truck. Slack, M. H.   **E**
Monkey with a tool belt. Monroe, C.   **E**
Monkey with a tool belt and the seaside shenanigans. Monroe, C.   **E**
Monkeys. Bodden, V.   **599.8**
MONKEYS
  Bodden, V. Monkeys   **599.8**
  Bustos, E. Going ape!   **599.8**
  Ganeri, A. Howler monkey   **599.8**
  Jiang The magical Monkey King   **398.209**
  Lunde, D. Monkey colors   **E**
  Sayre, A. P. Meet the howlers   **599.8**
  Stewart, M. No monkeys, no chocolate   **633.7**
MONKEYS
  See also Primates
MONKEYS -- BEHAVIOR
  See also Animal behavior
MONKEYS -- FICTION
  Catalanotto, P. Monkey and Robot   **E**
  Second banana   **E**
  Two little monkeys   **E**
  Warning: do not open this book!   **E**
MONKEYS -- FOLKLORE
  Galdone, P. The monkey and the crocodile   **398.2**
  Jiang The magical Monkey King   **398.209**
  McDermott, G. Monkey   **398.2**
Monkeys and dog days. Banks, K.   **E**
MONKS
  Norris, K. The holy twins: Benedict and Scholastica   **271**
MONKS -- FICTION
  Beebe, K. Brother Hugo and the bear   **E**
Monks, Lydia
  (il) Donaldson, J. What the ladybug heard   **E**
MONOLOGUES
  Dabrowski, K. My first monologue book   **812**
  Dabrowski, K. My second monologue book   **812**
  Dabrowski, K. My third monologue book   **812**
  Schlitz, L. A. Good masters! Sweet ladies!   **940.1**
MONONUCLEOSIS -- FICTION
  Weissman, E. B. The short seller   **Fic**
MONOPOLIES
  See also Commerce; Economics
MONORAIL RAILROADS
  See also Railroads
MONOTHEISM
  See also Religion; Theism
Monroe, Chris
  (il) Kling, K. Big little brother   **E**
  (il) Kling, K. Big little mother   **E**
  Monkey with a tool belt   **E**
  Monkey with a tool belt and the seaside shenani-

gans   **E**
  Sneaky sheep   **E**
Monroe, James, 1758-1831
About
  Naden, C. J. James Monroe   **92**
Monroe, Mary Alice
  Turtle summer   **597.92**
Monroy, Manuel
  (il) Amado, E. What are you doing?   **E**
Monsieur Marceau.   **B**
Monsoon. Krishnaswami, U.   **E**
Monsoon afternoon. Sheth, K.   **E**
MONSOONS
  See also Meteorology
MONSOONS -- FICTION
  Krishnaswami, U. Monsoon   **E**
  Sheth, K. Monsoon afternoon   **E**
Monster [series]
  Trondheim, L. Monster Christmas   **741.5**
Monster bones. Bailey, J.   **567.9**
Monster chefs. Anderson, B.   **E**
Monster Christmas. Trondheim, L.   **741.5**
Monster day at work. Dyer, S.   **E**
Monster fliers. MacLeod, E.   **567.9**
Monster Goose. Sierra, J.   **811**
The **monster** health book. Miller, E.   **613**
Monster hunt. Arnosky, J.   **001.9**
A **monster** is coming! Harrison, D. L.   **E**
Monster mess! Cuyler, M.   **E**
Monster on the Hill. Harrell, R.   **741.5**
Monster parade. Corey, S.   **E**
The **monster** princess. MacHale, D. J.   **E**
Monster trucks on the move. Nelson, K. L.   **796.7**
The **monster** who ate darkness. Dunbar, J.   **E**
The **monster** who lost his mean.   **E**
The **monsterator.**   **E**
Monsters. Malam, J.   **398.2**
MONSTERS
  See also Animals -- Folklore; Curiosities and wonders; Folklore; Mythology
  Arnosky, J. Monster hunt   **001.9**
  Bruchac, J. The dark pond   **Fic**
  DiPucchio, K. S. Sipping spiders through a straw   **782.42**
  Gee, J. Encyclopedia horrifica   **001.9**
  Halls, K. M. Tales of the cryptids   **001.9**
  Harris, J. My monster notebook   **398.2**
  Kelly, S. What a beast!   **398**
  Malam, J. Monsters   **398.2**
  Matthews, R. Strange animals   **001.9**
  Orr, T. The monsters of Hercules   **398.2**
  Reinhart, M. Dragons & Monsters   **398**
  Sierra, J. The gruesome guide to world monsters   **398**
  Sierra, J. Monster Goose   **811**
  Van Leeuwen, J. Amanda Pig and the awful, scary

This is the mountain **577.5**

MOUNTAIN ECOLOGY

    See also Ecology

MOUNTAIN FAUNA *See* Mountain animals

MOUNTAIN LIFE

    See also Country life

MOUNTAIN LIFE -- FICTION

    Dowell, F. O. Dovey Coe **Fic**

    Hemingway, E. M. Road to Tater Hill **Fic**

    Mountain lions. Shores, E. L. **599.75**

A **mountain** of mittens. Plourde, L. **E**

MOUNTAIN PLANTS

    See also Plant ecology; Plants

Mountain pose. Wilson, N. H. **Fic**

MOUNTAINEERING

    Athans, S. K. Secrets of the sky caves **796.522**

    Athans, S. K. Tales from the top of the world **796.52**

    Berne, E. C. Summiting Everest **796.522**

    Burleigh, R. Tiger of the snows **92**

    Cleare, J. Epic climbs **796.52**

    Coburn, B. Triumph on Everest: a photobiography of Sir Edmund Hillary **92**

    Helfand, L. Conquering Everest **741.5**

    Jenkins, S. The top of the world **796.52**

    Skreslet, L. To the top of Everest **796.52**

MOUNTAINEERING

    See also Outdoor life

MOUNTAINEERING EXPEDITIONS -- EVEREST, MOUNT (CHINA AND NEPAL) -- PICTORIAL WORKS

    Berne, E. C. Summiting Everest **796.522**

MOUNTAINEERING -- FICTION

    Birdseye, T. Storm Mountain **Fic**

    Patneaude, D. A piece of the sky **Fic**

MOUNTAINEERING -- NEPAL -- MUSTANG (DISTRICT)

    Athans, S. K. Secrets of the sky caves **796.522**

MOUNTAINEERS

    Burleigh, R. Tiger of the snows **92**

    Coburn, B. Triumph on Everest: a photobiography of Sir Edmund Hillary **92**

    Helfand, L. Conquering Everest **741.5**

    Krull, K. Lives of the athletes **796**

    Mortenson, G. Listen to the wind **371.82**

    Mortenson, G. Three cups of tea **371.82**

MOUNTAINEERS -- BIOGRAPHY

    Athans, S. K. Tales from the top of the world **796.52**

Mountains. Simon, S. **551.4**

MOUNTAINS

    Jennings, T. Massive mountains **551.4**

    Levy, J. Discovering mountains **577.5**

    Sheehan, T. F. Mountains **551.4**

    Simon, S. Mountains **551.4**

    Zoehfeld, K. W. How mountains are made **551.4**

Mountains. Sheehan, T. F. **551.4**

MOUNTAINS -- FICTION

Broach, E. Revenge of Superstition Mountain **Fic**

Mourlevat, Jean-Claude

    The pull of the ocean **Fic**

MOURNING *See* Bereavement

MOURNING CUSTOMS *See* Funeral rites and ceremonies

Mourning, Tuesday

    (il) Billy and Milly, short and silly! **E**

    (il) Calvert, P. Princess Peepers **E**

    (il) Jackson, A. Eggs over Evie **Fic**

Mouse. Savage, S. **599.35**

MOUSE *See* Mice

Mouse & Lion. **E**

Mouse and Mole, a perfect Halloween. Yee, W. H. **E**

Mouse and Mole, a winter wonderland. Yee, W. H. **E**

Mouse and Mole, secret valentine. Yee, W. H. **E**

The **mouse** and the motorcycle. Cleary, B. **Fic**

Mouse bird snake wolf. Almond, D. **Fic**

The **mouse** family Robinson. King-Smith, D. **Fic**

Mouse guard. **741.5**

Mouse guard. Petersen, D. E. **741.5**

Mouse guard. **741.5**

Mouse Guard: Fall 1152. Petersen, D. **741.5**

Mouse Guard: Winter 1152. Petersen, D. **741.5**

Mouse mess. Riley, L. A. **E**

Mouse shapes. Walsh, E. S. **E**

Mouse soup. Lobel, A. **E**

Mouse tales. Lobel, A. **E**

Mouse was mad. Urban, L. **E**

The **mouse** with the question mark tail. **Fic**

Mousie love. Chaconas, D. **E**

Mousterpiece. Zalben, J. B. **E**

MOUTH

    Korb, R. My mouth **612.3**

    Miller, S. S. All kinds of mouths **591.4**

MOUTH

    See also Face; Head

MOUTH -- DISEASES

    Donovan, S. Hawk & Drool **612.3**

MOUTH -- DISEASES

    See also Diseases

MOVABLE BOOKS *See* Toy and movable books

Move it! Mason, A. **531**

Move over, Rover. Beaumont, K. **E**

Move! Jenkins, S. **E**

MOVEMENT DISORDERS

    See also Disabilities; Nervous system -- Diseases

MOVEMENTS OF ANIMALS *See* Animal locomotion

A **movie** in my pillow. Argueta, J. **861**

MOVIES *See* Motion pictures

Moving. Parker, V. **648**

MOVING

    Barber, N. Moving to a new house **648**

    Glasser, D. New kid, new scene **373.1**

Sovern, M. J. The meaning of Maggie **813.6**

MULTIPLICATION

Leedy, L. 2 x 2 **513.2**

Long, L. Marvelous multiplication **513**

Murphy, S. J. Double the ducks **513**

Tang, G. The best of times **513**

MULTIPLICATION

See also Arithmetic

MULTIPLICATION -- FICTION

Calvert, P. Multiplying menace **E**

Dodds, D. A. Minnie's Diner **E**

Multiplying menace. Calvert, P. **E**

MULTIRACIAL PEOPLE *See* Racially mixed people

Mumbet's Declaration of Independence. **92**

Mummies. Sloan, C. **393**

MUMMIES

See also Archeology; Burial; Human remains (Archeology)

Bolton, A. Pyramids and mummies **932**

Carney, E. Mummies **393**

Deem, J. M. Bodies from the bog **573.3**

Deem, J. M. Bodies from the ice **393**

Halls, K. M. Mysteries of the mummy kids **393**

Knapp, R. Mummy secrets uncovered **393**

Markle, S. Outside and inside mummies **393**

Perritano, J. Mummies in the library **513.2**

Rau, D. M. Mummies **393**

Robson, D. The mummy **393**

Sloan, C. Mummies **393**

Mummies. Rau, D. M. **393**

Mummies. Carney, E. **393**

MUMMIES -- FICTION

Spooky friends **E**

Mummies in the library. Perritano, J. **513.2**

The **mummy.** Robson, D. **393**

Mummy secrets uncovered. Knapp, R. **393**

Munan, Heidi

(jt. auth) Foo Yuk Yee Malaysia **959.5**

Munari, Bruno

Bruno Munari's zoo **E**

Muncaster, Harriet

I am a witch's cat **E**

Muncha! Muncha! Muncha! Fleming, C. **E**

Münchhausen, Karl Friedrich Hieronymus, Freiherr von, 1720-1797

About

Janisch, H. Fantastic adventures of Baron Munchausen **Fic**

Mundy, Robyn

Epic voyages **910.4**

Mung-mung! Park, L. S. **413**

Mungo and the spiders from space. Knapman, T. **E**

MUNICIPAL ART

See also Art; Cities and towns

MUNICIPAL ENGINEERING

See also Engineering; Public works

MUNICIPAL GOVERNMENT

See also Local government; Political science

MUNICIPALITIES *See* Cities and towns; Municipal government

Muñoz, Claudio

(il) Medina, M. Tia Isa wants a car **E**

Muñoz, William

(il) The horse and the Plains indians **978**

Patent, D. H. The right dog for the job **362.4**

Patent, D. H. Saving Audie **636.7**

Munro, Roxie

Amazement park **793.73**

Busy builders **595.7**

Circus **E**

Go! go! go! **E**

Hatch! **598**

Inside-outside dinosaurs **567.9**

Mazeways: A to Z **793.73**

Rodeo **791.8**

(il) Spradlin, M. P. Texas Rangers **976.4**

Munsey, Lizzie

(ed) Knowledge Encyclopedia **031**

Munsinger, Lynn

(il) Crimi, C. Rock 'n' roll Mole **E**

(il) Elliott, L. A string of hearts **E**

(il) Greenberg, D. Crocs! **E**

(il) Lester, H. Happy birdday, Tacky! **E**

(il) Lester, H. Hooway for Wodney Wat **E**

(il) Lester, H. The Loch Mess monster **E**

(il) Lester, H. The sheep in wolf's clothing **E**

(il) Lester, H. Tacky's Christmas **E**

(il) Lester, H. Three cheers for Tacky **E**

(il) Lester, H. Wodney Wat's wobot **E**

(il) Lewis, J. P. Spot the plot **811**

(il) Manners mash-up: a goofy guide to good behavior **395**

(il) Numeroff, L. J. Beatrice doesn't want to **E**

(il) Numeroff, L. J. The Jellybeans and the big Book Bonanza **E**

(il) Numeroff, L. J. The Jellybeans and the big camp kickoff **E**

(il) Numeroff, L. J. Ponyella **E**

(il) Rose, D. L. Birthday zoo **E**

Muntean, Michaela

Do not open this book! **E**

MUPPET SHOW (TELEVISION PROGRAM)

Jim Henson **92**

Murakami, Yasunari

(il) Kimura, K. 999 Frogs Wake Up **E**

(il) Kimura, K. 999 tadpoles **E**

Mural on Second Avenue, and other city poems. Moore, L. **811**

MURAL PAINTING AND DECORATION

See also Decoration and ornament; Interior design; Painting

See also Investments

MUTUALISM (BIOLOGY) *See* Symbiosis

Muhammad, d. 632

About

Demi Muhammad   **297**

My 1st graphic novel [series]

Meister, C. Clues in the attic   **741.5**

Mortensen, L. The missing monster card   **741.5**

My abuelita. Johnston, T.   **E**

My achy body. Fromer, L.   **612**

My America. Gilchrist, J. S.   **E**

My America.   **811**

My American government [series]

Thomas, W. D. What are citizens' basic rights? **323**

Thomas, W. D. What is a constitution?   **342**

My art book.   **745.5**

My baby and me. Reiser, L.   **E**

My baby blue jays. Berendt, J.   **598**

My baseball book. Gibbons, G.   **796.357**

My basketball book. Gibbons, G.   **796.323**

My basmati bat mitzvah. Freedman, P. J.   **Fic**

My bear Griz. McGinness, S.   **E**

My best friend. Rodman, M. A.   **E**

My best friend is as sharp as a pencil. Piven, H. **E**

My Bibi always remembers. Buzzeo, T.   **E**

My big book of trucks & diggers. Caterpillar Inc. **621.8**

My big brother. Cohen, M.   **E**

My big brother. Fisher, V.   **E**

My bike.   **E**

My blue is happy.   **E**

My body [series]

Korb, R. My brain   **612.8**

Korb, R. My mouth   **612.3**

Korb, R. My muscles   **612.7**

Korb, R. My nose   **612.2**

Korb, R. My spine   **612.7**

Korb, R. My stomach   **612.3**

My brain. Korb, R.   **612.8**

My brother. Browne, A.   **E**

My brother Bert. Hughes, T.   **E**

My brother Charlie.   **E**

My brother Martin. Farris, C.   **92**

My brother Sam is dead. Collier, J. L.   **Fic**

My brother the robot. Grabenstein, C.   **Fic**

My brother's book. Sendak, M.   **811**

My brother, my sister, and I. Watkins, Y. K. **Fic**

My bus.   **E**

My car. Barton, B.   **E**

My cat copies me. Kwon   **E**

My cat, coon cat. Fuller, S. F.   **E**

My cat, the silliest cat in the world. Bachelet, G. **E**

My childhood under fire. Halilbegovich, N.   **949.7**

My Chinatown. Mak, K.   **E**

My Chincoteague pony. Jeffers, S.   **E**

My cold plum lemon pie bluesy mood. Brown, T.

F.   **E**

My cold went on vacation. Rausch, M.   **E**

My colors, my world. Gonzalez, M. C.   **E**

My community [series]

Macken, J. E. The dinosaur museum   **567.9**

My dad. Browne, A.   **E**

My dad's a birdman. Almond, D.   **Fic**

My dad, my hero. Long, E.   **E**

My daddy is a giant. Norac, C.   **E**

My daddy, Dr. Martin Luther King, Jr.   **323.092**

My Dadima wears a sari. Sheth, K.   **E**

My Daniel. Conrad, P.   **Fic**

My diary. Tibo, G.   **E**

My diary from here to there. Perez, A. I.   **E**

My dog is as smelly as dirty socks. Piven, H. **E**

My dog Jack is fat. Bunting, E.   **E**

My dog Lyle. Goldfinger, J. P.   **E**

My dog may be a genius. Prelutsky, J.   **811**

My dog thinks I'm a genius. Ziefert, H.   **E**

My dog, Buddy. Milgrim, D.   **E**

My dog, my cat. Fletcher, A.   **E**

My family plays music. Cox, J.   **E**

My family tree [series]

Newman, L. Mommy, mama, and me   **E**

My family, mi familia [series]

Mora, P. Here, kitty, kitty   **E**

Mora, P. Wiggling pockets   **E**

My farm friends. Minor, W.   **E**

My father is taller than a tree. Bruchac, J. **E**

My father knows the names of things. Yolen, J. **E**

My father's arms are a boat.   **E**

My father's hands. Ryder, J.   **E**

My father's shop. Ichikawa, S.   **E**

My favorite recipes. Karmel, A.   **641.5**

My feet. Aliki   **612**

My first acting series

Dabrowski, K. My second monologue book   **812**

Dabrowski, K. My third monologue book   **812**

My first airplane ride. Hubbell, P.   **E**

My first bird. Bozzo, L.   **636.6**

My first book of French words. Kudela, K. R. **443**

My first book of German words. Kudela, K. R. **433**

My first book of Japanese words. Kudela, K. R. **495.6**

My first book of Mandarin Chinese words. Kudela, K. R. **495.1**

My first book of Spanish words. Kudela, K. R. **463**

My first cat. Bozzo, L.   **636.8**

My first Chinese New Year. Katz, K.   **E**

My first day.   **591.3**

My first day at a new school. Guillain, C.   **371**

My first dog. Bozzo, L.   **636.7**

My first fish. Bozzo, L.   **639.34**

My first French English visual dictionary. Corbeil **443**

My first ghost.   **E**

My pig Amarillo. Ichikawa, S.   **E**
My pony Jack. Meister, C.   **E**
My preschool. Rockwell, A. F.   **E**
My pup. O'Hair, M.   **E**
My race car. Rex, M.   **629.228**
My readers [series]
  Day, A. Carl and the puppies   **E**
  Feldman, T. Harry Cat and Tucker Mouse: Harry to
   the rescue!   **E**
  Feldman, T. Harry Cat and Tucker Mouse: starring
   Harry   **E**
  Feldman, T. Harry Cat and Tucker Mouse: Tucker's
   beetle band   **E**
  Keenan, S. Castle   **623**
  Keenan, S. Jet plane   **629.133**
My rhinoceros. Agee, J.   **E**
My robot. Bunting, E.   **E**
My rotten redheaded older brother. Polacco, P.   **E**
My rows and piles of coins. Mollel, T. M.   **E**
My safe community. Hord, C.   **331.7**
My school in the rain forest. Ruurs, M.   **370.9**
My science notebook [series]
  Podesto, M. The body   **612**
  Podesto, M. Dinosaurs   **567.9**
My second monologue book. Dabrowski, K.   **812**
My secret war diary, by Flossie Albright. Williams,
  M.   **Fic**
My senses. Read, L.   **612.8**
My shining star. Wells, R.   **649**
My shoes and I. Colato Lainez, R.   **E**
My side of the car. Feiffer, K.   **E**
My side of the mountain trilogy. George, J. C.   **Fic**
My snake Blake.   **E**
My soccer book. Gibbons, G.   **796.334**
My sort of fairy tale ending. Staniszewski, A.   **Fic**
My special day at Third Street School. Bunting, E. **E**
My spine. Korb, R.   **612.7**
My stomach. Korb, R.   **612.3**
My stretchy body. Fromer, L.   **612.6**
My tattooed dad.   **E**
My teacher for President. Winters, K.   **E**
My teacher is a dinosaur. Leedy, L.   **560**
My teacher is a monster! (no, I am not) Brown, P. **E**
My third monologue book. Dabrowski, K.   **812**
My three best friends and me, Zulay.   **E**
My travelin' eye. Kostecki-Shaw, J. S.   **E**
My travels with Clara. Holmes, M. T.   **599.66**
My turn to learn [series]
  Marshall, N. Colors   **E**
  Marshall, N. My turn to learn opposites   **E**
  Marshall, N. My turn to learn shapes   **E**
My turn to learn opposites. Marshall, N.   **E**
My turn to learn shapes. Marshall, N.   **E**
My Uncle Martin's big heart. Watkins, A. F.   **92**
My Uncle Martin's words of love for America. **323.1**
My very first Mother Goose. Opie, I. A.   **398.8**

My very own room. Perez, A. I.   **E**
My very unfairy tale life. Staniszewski, A.   **Fic**
My village.   **808.81**
My visit to the aquarium. Aliki   **639.34**
My weird writing tips. Gutman, D.   **808.042**
My wild sister and me. Wewer, I.   **E**
My world of discovery. Wilkes, A.   **031**
MYANMAR -- FICTION
  Perkins, M. Bamboo people   **Fic**
MYANMAR -- POLITICS AND GOVERNMENT
  Rose, S. Aung San Suu Kyi   **92**
MYCOLOGY *See* Fungi
Myers, Christopher
  (il) Copeland, M. Firebird   **E**
  My pen   **E**
  H.O.R.S.E.   **Fic**
  We are America   **811**
  (il) Jazz   **811**
  (il) Looking like me   **E**
  Black cat   **E**
  Lies and other tall tales   **398.2**
  We are America   **811**
  Wings   **E**
  (il) Myers, W. D. Blues journey   **811**
  (il) Myers, W. D. Harlem   **811**
Myers, Jack
  The puzzle of the platypus   **590**
Myers, Jill J.
  Responding to cyber bullying   **371.5**
Myers, Laurie
  Byars, B. C. Cat diaries   **S**
  Byars, B. C. Dog diaries   **S**
  Byars, B. C. The SOS file   **Fic**
  Escape by night   **Fic**
  Lewis and Clark and me   **Fic**
Myers, Matthew
  (il) Bartholomew Biddle and the very big wind **Fic**
  (il) Battle Bunny   **E**
  (il) Dipucchio, K. Clink   **E**
  (il) E-I-E-I-O!   **E**
  (il) Rosenberg, L. Tyrannosuarus dad   **E**
Myers, Tim
  Basho and the river stones   **E**
  The furry-legged teapot   **398.2**
  If you give a T-rex a bone   **567.9**
Myers, Walter Dean, 1937-2014
  Jazz   **811**
  Lawrence, J. The great migration   **759.13**
  Looking like me   **E**
  Malcolm X   **92**
  Blues journey   **811**
  The blues of Flats Brown   **E**
  Harlem   **811**
  Ida B. Wells   **92**
  I've seen the promised land   **92**
  Looking for the easy life   **E**

Mystery at the Club Sandwich. Cushman, D.   **E**

MYSTERY COMIC BOOKS, STRIPS, ETC.

    See also Comic books, strips, etc.

MYSTERY FICTION

Adler, D. A. Cam Jansen and the mystery at the haunted house   **Fic**

Adler, D. A. Cam Jansen and the mystery of the stolen diamonds   **Fic**

Adler, D. A. Cam Jansen and the Secret Service mystery   **Fic**

Adler, D. A. Cam Jansen and the snowy day mystery   **Fic**

Adler, D. A. Cam Jansen and the Sports Day mysteries   **Fic**

Adler, D. A. Cam Jansen and the summer camp mysteries   **Fic**

Adler, D. A. Cam Jansen and the Valentine baby mystery   **Fic**

Adler, D. A. Cam Jansen and the wedding cake mystery   **Fic**

Adler, D. A. Cam Jansen, the mystery of the dinosaur bones   **Fic**

Adler, D. A. Cam Jansen, the mystery at the monkey house   **Fic**

Adler, D. A. Cam Jansen, the mystery of the Babe Ruth baseball   **Fic**

Adler, D. A. Cam Jansen, the mystery of the carnival prize   **Fic**

Adler, D. A. Cam Jansen, the mystery of the circus clown   **Fic**

Adler, D. A. Cam Jansen, the mystery of the gold coins   **Fic**

Adler, D. A. Cam Jansen, the mystery of the monster movie   **Fic**

Adler, D. A. Cam Jansen, the mystery of the stolen corn popper   **Fic**

Adler, D. A. Cam Jansen, the mystery of the U.F.O.   **Fic**

Adler, D. A. Cam Jansen, the Triceratops Pops mystery   **Fic**

Adler, D. A. Young Cam Jansen and the 100th day of school mystery   **E**

Adler, D. A. Young Cam Jansen and the dinosaur game   **E**

Allison, J. Gilda Joyce, psychic investigator   **Fic**

Allison, J. Gilda Joyce, psychic investigator: the bones of the holy   **Fic**

Allison, J. Gilda Joyce: the dead drop   **Fic**

Allison, J. Gilda Joyce: the ghost sonata   **Fic**

Allison, J. Gilda Joyce: the Ladies of the Lake   **Fic**

Amato, M. Edgar Allan's official crime investigation notebook   **Fic**

Anderson, M. T. Agent Q, or the smell of danger!   **Fic**

Anderson, M. T. Jasper Dash and the flame-pits of Delaware   **Fic**

Angleberger, T. Horton Halfpott   **Fic**

Aronson, S. Beyond lucky   **Fic**

Avi City of orphans   **Fic**

Baccalario, P. The long-lost map   **Fic**

Bachmann, S. The Cabinet of Curiosities   **S**

Balliett, B. The Calder game   **Fic**

Balliett, B. Chasing Vermeer   **Fic**

Balliett, B. Hold fast   **Fic**

Balliett, B. The Wright 3   **Fic**

Barden, S. The super secret mystery   **Fic**

Barnett, M. The case of the case of mistaken identity   **Fic**

Barnett, M. The ghostwriter secret   **Fic**

Barnett, M. It happened on a train   **Fic**

Barnholdt, L. Girl meets ghost   **Fic**

Barrett, T. The 100-year-old secret   **Fic**

Barrett, T. The Beast of Blackslope   **Fic**

Beil, M. D. The Red Blazer Girls: the ring of Rocamadour   **Fic**

Beil, M. D. The Red Blazer Girls: The vanishing violin   **Fic**

Beil, M. The Red Blazer Girls: the mistaken masterpiece   **Fic**

Berk, J. Strike three, you're dead   **Fic**

Berlin, E. The potato chip puzzles   **Fic**

Berlin, E. The puzzling world of Winston Breen   **Fic**

Biedrzycki, D. Ace Lacewing, bug detective: the big swat   **E**

Blakemore, M. F. The spy catchers of Maple Hill   **Fic**

Bonsall, C. N. The case of the hungry stranger   **E**

Brezenoff, S. The burglar who bit the Big Apple   **Fic**

Brezenoff, S. The painting that wasn't there   **Fic**

Brezenoff, S. The zombie who visited New Orleans   **Fic**

Broach, E. Masterpiece   **Fic**

Broach, E. Missing on Superstition Mountain   **Fic**

Broach, E. Revenge of Superstition Mountain   **Fic**

Broach, E. Shakespeare's secret   **Fic**

Buckley, M. The Everafter War   **Fic**

Buckley, M. The inside story   **Fic**

Buckley, M. Magic and other misdemeanors   **Fic**

Buckley, M. Once upon a crime   **Fic**

Buckley, M. The problem child   **Fic**

Buckley, M. Tales from the hood   **Fic**

Buckley, M. The unusual suspects   **Fic**

Butler, D. H. The case of the fire alarm   **Fic**

Butler, D. H. The case of the library monster   **Fic**

Butler, D. H. The case of the lost boy   **Fic**

Butler, D. H. The case of the missing family   **Fic**

Butler, D. H. The case of the mixed-up mutts   **Fic**

Byars, B. C. The dark stairs   **Fic**

Cadenhead, M. Sally's bones   **Fic**

Carey, B. Poison most vial   **Fic**

The case of the missing carrot cake   **E**

The case of the stolen sixpence   **Fic**

Odyssey, S. T. The Wizard of Dark Street **Fic**

Patron, S. Behind the masks **Fic**

Park, L. S. Trust no one **Fic**

Pieces and players **Fic**

Princess Academy **Fic**

Princess for a week **Fic**

Pullman, P. Two crafty criminals! **Fic**

Raskin, E. The mysterious disappearance of Leon (I mean Noel) **Fic**

Raskin, E. The tattooed potato and other clues **Fic**

Raskin, E. The Westing game **Fic**

Riddell, C. Ottoline and the yellow cat **Fic**

Roberts, W. D. The view from the cherry tree **Fic**

Rockliff, M. The case of the July 4th jinx **E**

Rockliff, M. The case of the missing moose **Fic**

Rockliff, M. The case of the poisoned pig **Fic**

Runholt, S. Adventure at Simba Hill **Fic**

Runholt, S. The mystery of the third Lucretia **Fic**

Rylant, C. The case of the missing monkey **E**

Schlitz, L. A. Splendors and glooms **Fic**

Selzer, A. I put a spell on you **Fic**

Sharmat, M. W. Nate the Great **E**

Sharmat, M. W. Nate the Great and the hungry book club **Fic**

Sherry, M. Walls within walls **Fic**

Shouldn't you be in school? **Fic**

Simont, M. Nate the Great and the stolen base **E**

Skofield, J. Detective Dinosaur **E**

Skofield, J. Detective Dinosaur undercover **E**

Skofield, J. Detective Dinosaur: lost and found **E**

Snicket, L. The composer is dead **E**

Sobol, D. J. Encyclopedia Brown and the case of the carnival crime **Fic**

Sobol, D. J. Encyclopedia Brown and the case of the midnight visitor **Fic**

Sobol, D. J. Encyclopedia Brown and the case of the secret UFOs **Fic**

Sobol, D. J. Encyclopedia Brown and the case of the treasure hunt **Fic**

Sobol, D. J. Encyclopedia Brown takes the cake! **Fic**

Sobol, D. J. Encyclopedia Brown, boy detective **Fic**

Sobol, D. J. Encyclopedia Brown, super sleuth **Fic**

Springer, N. The case of the cryptic crinoline **Fic**

Springer, N. The case of the gypsy good-bye **Fic**

Springer, N. The case of the missing marquess **Fic**

St. Antoine, S. Three bird summer **Fic**

Standiford, N. The secret tree **Fic**

Stanley, D. The mysterious matter of I.M. Fine **Fic**

Stewart, P. The curse of the night wolf **Fic**

Stewart, P. Phantom of Blood Alley **Fic**

Strickland, B. The sign of the sinister sorcerer **Fic**

Stroud, J. The whispering skull **Fic**

Teplin, S. The clock without a face **Fic**

Thompson, J. E. The girl from Felony Bay **Fic**

The trouble with chickens **Fic**

The unseen guest **Fic**

Updale, E. Johnny Swanson **Fic**

Draanen, W. v. Sammy Keyes and the art of deception **Fic**

Draanen, W. v. Sammy Keyes and the cold hard cash **Fic**

Draanen, W. v. Sammy Keyes and the curse of Moustache Mary **Fic**

Draanen, W. v. Sammy Keyes and the dead give-away **Fic**

Draanen, W. v. Sammy Keyes and the Hollywood mummy **Fic**

Draanen, W. v. Sammy Keyes and the hotel thief **Fic**

Draanen, W. v. Sammy Keyes and the psycho Kitty Queen **Fic**

Draanen, W. v. Sammy Keyes and the runaway elf **Fic**

Draanen, W. v. Sammy Keyes and the search for Snake Eyes **Fic**

Draanen, W. v. Sammy Keyes and the Sisters of Mercy **Fic**

Draanen, W. v. Sammy Keyes and the skeleton man **Fic**

Draanen, W. v. Sammy Keyes and the wedding crasher **Fic**

Draanen, W. v. Sammy Keyes and the wild things **Fic**

Van Draanen, W. Sammy Keyes and the killer cruise **Fic**

Van Draanen, W. Sammy Keyes and the night of skulls **Fic**

Van Draanen, W. Sammy Keyes and the show-down in Sin City **Fic**

Wallace, C. The pumpkin mystery **E**

Walters, E. The money pit mystery **Fic**

Warner, P. The secret of the skeleton key **Fic**

The watcher in the shadows **Fic**

Watson, G. Edison's gold **Fic**

When did you see her last? **Fic**

Who could that be at this hour? **Fic**

Who stole New Year's Eve? **Fic**

Winters, B. H. The mystery of the missing everything **Fic**

Wright, B. R. The dollhouse murders **Fic**

Ylvisaker, A. The luck of the Buttons **Fic**

MYSTERY FILMS

See also Motion pictures

MYSTERY GRAPHIC NOVELS

Collicutt, P. City in peril! **741.5**

Conway, G. Crawling with zombies **741.5**

De Campi, A. Kat & Mouse: Teacher torture **741.5**

Explorer **S**

Kibuishi, K. Amulet, book one: The Stonekeep-er **741.5**

NATIVE AMERICANS -- RELIGION

  See also Religion

NATIVE AMERICANS -- RELOCATION

  Bjornlund, L. D. The Trail of Tears   **970.004**

  Bruchac, J. The Trail of Tears   **970.004**

NATIVE AMERICANS -- RITES AND CERE-MONIES

  Ancona, G. Powwow   **394.2**

NATIVE AMERICANS -- RITES AND CERE-MONIES

  See also Rites and ceremonies

NATIVE AMERICANS -- SOUTH AMERICA -- FOLKLORE

  Knutson, B. Love and roast chicken   **398.2**

NATIVE AMERICANS -- SOUTHWESTERN STATES

  Baylor, B. When clay sings   **970.004**

NATIVE AMERICANS -- UNITED STATES

  Green, C. R. Sacagawea   **978.004**

NATIVE AMERICANS -- WARS

  Anderson, P. C. George Armstrong Custer   **92**

  Ehrlich, A. Wounded Knee: an Indian history of the American West   **970.004**

  Zimmerman, D. J. Saga of the Sioux   **970.004**

NATIVE AMERICANS -- WEST (U.S.)

  Ehrlich, A. Wounded Knee: an Indian history of the American West   **970.004**

NATIVE AMERICANS -- WOMEN *See* Native American women

NATIVE PLANTS

  See also Plants

Natterson, Cara

The care & keeping of you 2   **613**

Natti, Susanna

  (il) Adler, D. A. Cam Jansen and the mystery at the haunted house   **Fic**

  (il) Adler, D. A. Cam Jansen and the mystery of the stolen diamonds   **Fic**

  (il) Adler, D. A. Cam Jansen and the Secret Service mystery   **Fic**

  (il) Adler, D. A. Cam Jansen and the snowy day mystery   **Fic**

  (il) Adler, D. A. Cam Jansen and the Valentine baby mystery   **Fic**

  (il) Adler, D. A. Cam Jansen, the mystery of the dinosaur bones   **Fic**

  (il) Adler, D. A. Cam Jansen, the mystery at the monkey house   **Fic**

  (il) Adler, D. A. Cam Jansen, the mystery of the carnival prize   **Fic**

  (il) Adler, D. A. Cam Jansen, the mystery of the circus clown   **Fic**

  (il) Adler, D. A. Cam Jansen, the mystery of the gold coins   **Fic**

  (il) Adler, D. A. Cam Jansen, the mystery of the monster movie   **Fic**

  (il) Adler, D. A. Cam Jansen, the mystery of the stolen corn popper   **Fic**

  (il) Adler, D. A. Cam Jansen, the mystery of the U.F.O.   **Fic**

  (il) Adler, D. A. Cam Jansen, the Triceratops Pops mystery   **Fic**

  (il) Adler, D. A. Young Cam Jansen and the 100th day of school mystery   **E**

  (il) Adler, D. A. Young Cam Jansen and the dinosaur game   **E**

  (il) Giff, P. R. Watch out, Ronald Morgan!   **E**

NATURAL AREAS -- FICTION

  Joyner, A. Boris on the move   **E**

NATURAL CHILDBIRTH

  See also Childbirth

NATURAL CYCLES *See* Cycles

Natural disasters.   **363.34**

NATURAL DISASTERS

  See also Disasters

  Bailey, G. Fragile planet   **363.34**

  Claybourne, A. 100 deadliest things on the planet   **591.6**

  Garbe, S. The Worst wildfires of all time   **363.34**

  Guiberson, B. Z. Disasters   **904**

  Hile, L. Animal survival   **591.5**

  Langley, A. Hurricanes, tsunamis, and other natural disasters   **363.34**

  Natural disasters   **363.34**

  Rusch, E. Eruption!   **363.34**

  Simon, S. Seymour Simon's extreme earth records   **550**

  Somervill, B. A. Graphing natural disasters   **363.34**

  Trammel, H. K. Wildfires   **634.9**

NATURAL DISASTERS -- FICTION

  Clements, A. About average   **Fic**

NATURAL FOODS

  Apte, S. Eating green   **630**

  Johanson, P. Fake foods   **613.2**

NATURAL FOODS

  See also Food

NATURAL GAS

  Benduhn, T. Oil, gas, and coal   **665.5**

NATURAL GAS

  See also Fuel; Gases

NATURAL HISTORY

  Burnie, D. The Kingfisher nature encyclopedia **508**

  Burton, V. L. Life story   **560**

  Castella, K. Discovering nature's alphabet   **E**

  Kelsey, E. Strange new species   **578**

  Morrison, G. Nature in the neighborhood   **508**

NATURAL HISTORY

  See also Science

NATURAL HISTORY -- AFRICA

  This is the mountain   **577.5**

NATURAL HISTORY -- ALASKA

  Miller, D. S. Arctic lights, arctic nights   **591.4**

Nature's wonders [series]

  Heinrichs, A. The Nile **962**

  Kras, S. L. The Galapagos Islands **986.6**

  Kummer, P. K. The Great Lakes **977**

Nature's yucky! 2: the desert southwest. Landstrom, L. A. **591.7**

Nature: a child's eye view [series]

  Fujiwara, Y. Honey **638**

NATURECRAFT *See* Nature craft

NATUROPATHY

    See also Alternative medicine; Therapeutics

Naujokaitis, Pranas T.

  The totally awesome epic quest of the brave boy knight **741.5**

Nault, Jennifer

  Volcanoes **551.2**

NAUTICAL ALMANACS

    See also Almanacs; Navigation

NAUTICAL ASTRONOMY

    See also Astronomy

NAUTICAL CHARTS

    See also Maps; Navigation

Nauvoo. Bial, R. **289.3**

NAVAHO INDIANS *See* Navajo Indians

The **Navajo.** Cunningham, K. **970.004**

NAVAJO CHILDREN

    See also Native American children; Navajo Indians

NAVAJO INDIANS

  Cunningham, K. The Navajo **970.004**

  Ehrlich, A. Wounded Knee: an Indian history of the American West **970.004**

  Flood, N. B. Cowboy up! **E**

  Roessel, M. Songs from the loom **746.1**

NAVAJO INDIANS -- FICTION

  Miles, M. Annie and the Old One **Fic**

  O'Dell, S. Sing down the moon **Fic**

NAVAJO WOMEN

    See also Native American women; Navajo Indians

NAVAL AIR BASES *See* Air bases

NAVAL ARCHITECTURE

    See also Architecture

NAVAL ART AND SCIENCE -- GRAPHIC NOVELS

  Weigel, J. Thunder from the sea **741.5**

NAVAL OFFICERS

  Berne, J. Manfish: a story of Jacques Cousteau **92**

  Blumberg, R. Commodore Perry in the land of the Shogun **952**

  Cooper, M. L. Hero of the high seas **92**

  Yaccarino, D. The fantastic undersea life of Jacques Cousteau **92**

NAVAL PERSONNEL *See* Sailors

Navas, Juan Pablo

  (il) Scieszka, J. Melvin's valentine **E**

Navigating Early. Vanderpool, C. **Fic**

NAVIGATION

  Borden, L. Sea clocks **526**

  Fern, T. Dare the wind **92**

  Kirk, S. T is for tugboat **623.82**

  The man who made time travel **526**

  Young, K. R. Across the wide ocean **623.89**

NAVIGATION (AERONAUTICS)

    See also Aeronautics

NAVIGATION (ASTRONAUTICS)

    See also Astrodynamics; Astronautics

NAVIGATORS *See* Explorers; Sailors

Navigators [series]

  Smith, M. Ancient Egypt **932**

Naylor, Phyllis Reynolds

  Alice in rapture, sort of **Fic**

  Alice in-between **Fic**

  Alice the brave **Fic**

  All but Alice **Fic**

  Emily's fortune **Fic**

  Faith, hope, and Ivy June **Fic**

  Outrageously Alice **Fic**

  Roxie and the Hooligans **Fic**

  Shiloh **Fic**

  Starting with Alice **Fic**

NAZI HUNTERS

  Rubin, S. G. The Anne Frank Case: Simon Wiesenthal's search for the truth **92**

Nazoa, Aquiles

  A small Nativity **E**

NBA FINALS (BASKETBALL)

    See also Basketball; Sports tournaments

NCAA Basketball. Bekkering, A. **796.323**

Neal, Christopher Silas

  (il) Messner, K. Over and under the snow **591.4**

Neal-Schuman guide to recommended children's books and media for use with every elementary subject. Matthew, K. I. **011.6**

Neal-Schuman technology management handbook for school library media centers. Farmer, L. S. J. **025.1**

NEANDERTHALS

    See also Fossil hominids

NEAR EAST *See* Middle East

NEAR-DEATH EXPERIENCES

    See also Death

NEAR-EARTH OBJECTS

    See also Solar system

Nearly nonsense. Singh, R. **398.2**

The **neat** line. Edwards, P. D. **E**

NEATNESS *See* Cleanliness; Orderliness

Nebraska. Bjorklund, R. **978.2**

Nebraska. Heinrichs, A. **978.2**

NEBRASKA

  Bjorklund, R. Nebraska **978.2**

  Bringle, J. Nebraska **978.2**

Nespeca, Sue McCleaf
Picture books plus   **028.5**
Nesquens, Daniel
My tattooed dad   **E**
Ness, Evaline
Sam, Bangs & Moonshine   **E**
NEST BUILDING
    See also Animal behavior; Animals -- Habitations
A **nest** for Celeste. Cole, H.   **Fic**
Nest, nook & cranny. Blackaby, S.   **811**
The **Netherlands.** Docalavich, H.   **949.2**
NETHERLANDS -- COLONIES -- AMERICA
Huey, L. M. American archaeology uncovers the Dutch colonies   **974.7**
NETHERLANDS -- FICTION
Borden, L. The greatest skating race   **Fic**
Coville, B. Hans Brinker   **E**
DeJong, M. The wheel on the school   **Fic**
Fleming, C. Boxes for Katje   **E**
Hof, M. Mother number zero   **Fic**
Kuijer, G. The book of everything   **Fic**
Willems, M. Knuffle Bunny free   **E**
NETHERLANDS -- HISTORY -- 17TH CENTURY -- FICTION
Rogers, G. The hero of Little Street   **E**
NETHERLANDS -- HISTORY -- 1940-1945, GERMAN OCCUPATION
Frank, A. The diary of a young girl: the definitive edition   **92**
Hurwitz, J. Anne Frank: life in hiding   **940.53**
Metselaar, M. Anne Frank: her life in words and pictures   **92**
Reiss, J. The upstairs room   **92**
Rol, R. v. d. Anne Frank, beyond the diary   **940.53**
NETHERLANDS
Docalavich, H. The Netherlands   **949.2**
Nethery, Mary
Dennis, B. Nubs   **636.7**
Larson, K. Two Bobbies   **636.08**
Netta and her plant. Gellman, E. B.   **E**
Nettleton, Pamela Hill
William Shakespeare   **822.3**
Neubecker, Robert
(il) Florian, D. Shiver me timbers   **E**
(il) Time (out) for monsters!   **E**
(il) Bagert, B. School fever   **811**
(il) Cuyler, M. Tick tock clock   **E**
(il) Kimmel, E. C. The top job   **E**
(il) Lund, D. Monsters on machines   **E**
What little boys are made of   **E**
Wow! America!   **E**
Wow! city!   **E**
Wow! Ocean!   **E**
Wow! school!   **E**
(il) Weeks, S. Sophie Peterman tells the truth!   **E**

Neuburger, Emily K.
Juster, N. The annotated Phantom tollbooth   **813**
A Caldecott celebration   **741.6**
Golden legacy   **070.5**
Minders of make-believe   **070.5**
Neufeld, Juliana
(il) Grabenstein, C. My brother the robot   **Fic**
(il) Treasure hunters   **Fic**
Neugebauer, Michael
Chimpanzee Children of Gombe   **599.8**
Neumeier, Rachel
The Floating Islands   **Fic**
NEUROLOGY *See* Nervous system
NEUROSCIENCES
    See also Medicine
NEUTRON WEAPONS
    See also Nuclear weapons
NEUTRONS
    See also Atoms; Particles (Nuclear physics)
Nevada. Stefoff, R.   **979.3**
Nevada. Roza, G.   **979.3**
NEVADA
Karst, K. Area 51   **001.9**
Nevada. Heinrichs, A.   **979.3**
NEVADA -- FICTION
Lawrence, C. P.K. Pinkerton and the pistol-packing widows   **Fic**
NEVADA -- HISTORY -- 19TH CENTURY -- FICTION
Lawrence, C. P.K. Pinkerton and the petrified man   **Fic**
Lawrence, C. P.K. Pinkerton and the pistol-packing widows   **Fic**
Never Ever. Empson, J.   **E**
Never forgotten.   **Fic**
Never say boo! Pulver, R.   **E**
Never say die. Hobbs, W.   **Fic**
Never say genius. Gutman, D.   **Fic**
Never smile at a monkey. Jenkins, S.   **591.6**
Never take a shark to the dentist and other things not to do. Barrett, J.   **E**
Never to forget: the Jews of the Holocaust. Meltzer, M.   **940.53**
Neville. Juster, N.   **E**
Neville, Emily Cheney
It's like this, Cat   **Fic**
Nevins, Daniel
(il) Ehrlich, A. With a mighty hand   **220.95**
Nevius, Carol
Baseball hour   **796.357**
Building with Dad   **E**
Karate hour   **E**
Soccer hour   **E**
The **new** Americans. Maestro, B.   **970.02**
NEW AMSTERDAM THEATRE (NEW YORK, N.Y.)

Amendola, D. A day at the New Amsterdam Theatre **792.6**

The **new** baby at your house. Cole, J. **306.875**

A **new** beginning. Pfeffer, W. **394.26**

A **new** brother or sister. Guillain, C. **306.8**

NEW BUSINESS ENTERPRISES

See also Business enterprises

New clothes for New Year's Day. Bae **E**

A **new** deal for women. Coster, P. **305.4**

New dinos. Tanaka, S. **567.9**

NEW ENGLAND -- FICTION

Alcott, L. M. Little women **Fic**

Connor, L. Crunch **Fic**

Hall, D. Ox-cart man **E**

Isaacs, A. Pancakes for supper! **E**

Jacobson, J. R. Small as an elephant **Fic**

MacLachlan, P. Your moon, my moon **E**

Waite, M. P. The witches of Dredmoore Hollow **Fic**

NEW ENGLAND -- HISTORY

Hyatt, P. R. The quite contrary man **92**

NEW ENGLAND -- HISTORY -- 1775-1865 -- FICTION

Barker, M. P. Mending horses **Fic**

New France, 1534-1763. Worth, R. **971.01**

The **new** girl . . . and me. Robbins, J. **E**

NEW GUINEA

Montgomery, S. Quest for the tree kangaroo **599.2**

New Hampshire. Ciarleglio, L. **974.2**

New Hampshire. Kent, D. **974.2**

NEW HAMPSHIRE

Ciarleglio, L. New Hampshire **974.2**

Kent, D. New Hampshire **974.2**

Otfinoski, S. New Hampshire **974.2**

New Hampshire. Otfinoski, S. **974.2**

NEW HAMPSHIRE -- FICTION

Banks, K. Dillon Dillon **Fic**

Bertrand, L. Granite baby **E**

Blos, J. W. A gathering of days: a New England
girl's journal, 1830-32 **Fic**

Bruchac, J. Night wings **Fic**

Lord, C. Half a chance **Fic**

Wallace, R. Wicked cruel **Fic**

NEW HAMPSHIRE -- HISTORY

Auden, S. New Hampshire, 1603-1776 **974.2**

New Hampshire, 1603-1776. Auden, S. **974.2**

New Jersey. Mattern, J. **974.9**

NEW JERSEY

Kent, D. New Jersey **974.9**

King, D. C. New Jersey **974.9**

Mattern, J. New Jersey **974.9**

Moragne, W. New Jersey **974.9**

New Jersey. King, D. C. **974.9**

New Jersey. Moragne, W. **974.9**

New Jersey. Kent, D. **974.9**

NEW JERSEY -- FICTION

Bauer, A. C. E. No castles here **Fic**

Green, T. Football hero **Fic**

Holm, J. L. Penny from heaven **Fic**

Tarshis, L. I survived the shark attacks of 1916 **Fic**

Zucker, N. F. Callie's rules **Fic**

NEW JERSEY -- HISTORY

Yezerski, T. Meadowlands **577.690**

NEW JERSEY -- HISTORY -- FICTION

Carbone, E. Heroes of the surf **E**

New Jersey 1609-1776. Doak, R. S. **974.9**

The **new** jumbo book of easy crafts. Sadler, J.
A. **745.5**

New kid. Green, T. **Fic**

The **new** kid on the block: poems. Prelutsky, J. **811**

New kid, new scene. Glasser, D. **373.1**

New Mexico. Burgan, M. **978.9**

New Mexico. Brezina, C. **978.9**

New Mexico. McDaniel, M. **972**

New Mexico. Burgan, M. **978.9**

NEW MEXICO -- FICTION

Abraham, S. G. Cecilia's year **Fic**

Cervantes, J. Tortilla sun **Fic**

Hawkins, A. R. The year money grew on trees **Fic**

Klages, E. The green glass sea **Fic**

Klages, E. White sands, red menace **Fic**

Mora, P. Abuelos **E**

Stanley, D. Saving Sky **Fic**

A **new** nation. Maestro, B. **973.3**

NEW NEGRO MOVEMENT *See* Harlem Renaissance

New old shoes. Blessing, C. **E**

NEW ORLEANS (LA.)

Miller, W. Rent party jazz **E**

NEW ORLEANS (LA.) -- FICTION

Brezenoff, S. The zombie who visited New Orleans **Fic**

Cole, H. A nest for Celeste **Fic**

Herlong, M. H. Buddy **Fic**

Miller, W. Rent party jazz **E**

Philbrick, R. Zane and the hurricane **Fic**

Quattlebaum, M. The hungry ghost of Rue Orleans **E**

Rhodes, J. P. Ninth Ward **Fic**

Schroeder, A. Satchmo's blues **E**

Uhlberg, M. A storm called Katrina **E**

Watson, R. A place where hurricanes happen **E**

Woods, B. Saint Louis Armstrong Beach **Fic**

NEW ORLEANS (LA.) -- RACE RELATIONS

Bridges, R. Through my eyes: the autobiography of
Ruby Bridges **92**

Donaldson, M. Ruby Bridges **92**

New red bike! Ransome, J. **E**

The **new** republic: 1760-1840s. Otfinoski, S. **973.3**

New research techniques. Randolph, R. P. **001.4**

New shoes. **E**

New shoes for Silvia. Hurwitz, J. **E**

The **New** small person. **E**

The runaway king **Fic**

The shadow throne **Fic**

Elliot and the goblin war **Fic**

Elliot and the pixie plot **Fic**

Elliot and the Yeti threat **Fic**

Nielsen, Shaw

(il) Friedman, C. How do you feed a hungry giant? **E**

Nielsen, Susin

Dear George Clooney **Fic**

Word nerd **Fic**

Niemann, Christoph

The potato king **E**

Pet dragon **E**

The police cloud **E**

Subway **E**

That's how! **E**

Niepold, Mil

Oooh! Picasso **730.9**

Nigeria. Oluonye, M. N. **966.9**

Nigeria. Giles, B. **966.9**

NIGERIA

Giles, B. Nigeria **966.9**

Oluonye, M. N. Nigeria **966.9**

Onyefulu, I. Ikenna goes to Nigeria **966.9**

NIGERIA -- FICTION

Saint-Lot, K. N. Amadi's snowman **E**

NIGHT

Bailey, J. Sun up, sun down **525**

Banks, K. The night worker **E**

Murphy, S. J. It's about time! **529**

Rau, D. M. Day and night **508**

Rose, D. L. One nighttime sea **513.2**

Thompson, L. Polar bear night **E**

While You Were Sleeping **031.02**

NIGHT

See also Chronology; Time

NIGHT -- FICTION

Boyd, L. Flashlight **E**

Hannah's Night **E**

The night world **E**

NIGHT -- FOLKLORE

Caduto, M. J. Keepers of the night **398.2**

NIGHT -- POETRY

Dark Emperor and other poems of the night **811**

Switching on the moon **811**

Night at the fair. Crews, D. **E**

The **night** before Christmas. Moore, C. C. **811**

The **night** before Christmas. Moore, C. C. **811**

The **night** before Christmas. Moore, C. C. **811**

Night boat to freedom. Raven, M. **E**

The **Night** Eater. Juan, A. **E**

The **night** fairy. Schlitz, L. A. **Fic**

Night flight. Burleigh, R. **629.13**

The **Night** Gardener. Auxier, J. **Fic**

Night golf. Miller, W. **E**

The **Night** has ears. **398.9**

The **night** is singing. Davies, J. **E**

Night light. Blechman, N. **E**

Night lights. Gal, S. **E**

Night noises. Fox, M. **E**

The **night** of Las Posadas. DePaola, T. **E**

Night of the howling dogs. Salisbury, G. **Fic**

Night of the Moon. Khan, H. **E**

Night of the pumpkinheads. Rosen, M. J. **E**

Night of the soul-stealer. Delaney, J. **Fic**

Night of the Veggie Monster. McClements, G. **E**

A **night** on the range. Frisch, A. **E**

Night owl. **E**

Night running. Carbone, E. L. **E**

Night shift. Hartland, J. **E**

Night shift daddy. Spinelli, E. **E**

Night sky dragons. **Fic**

Night Sky Wheel Ride. Fitch, S. **811**

Night wings. Bruchac, J. **Fic**

The **night** worker. Banks, K. **E**

The **night** world. **E**

Night's nice. Emberley, B. **E**

The **nightingale**. Mitchell, S. **Fic**

The **nightingale**. Andersen, H. C. **E**

The **nightingale**. Andersen, H. C. **E**

Nightingale's nest. Loftin, N. **Fic**

Nightingale, Florence, 1820-1910

About

Demi Florence Nightingale **92**

Gorrell, G. K. Heart and soul: the story of Florence Nightingale **92**

Springer, N. The case of the cryptic crinoline **Fic**

NIGHTINGALES -- FICTION

Andersen, H. C. The nightingale **E**

Andersen, H. C. The nightingale **E**

Mitchell, S. The nightingale **Fic**

The **nightmare** ninja. Higgins, S. **Fic**

Nightmare plagues [series]

Aronin, M. Tuberculosis **616.9**

Person, S. Bubonic plague **614.5**

Person, S. Malaria **614.5**

Reingold, A. Smallpox **614.5**

Rudolph, J. The flu of 1918 **614.5**

NIGHTMARES -- FICTION

Schwarz, V. The Sleepwalkers **Fic**

Nightmares: poems to trouble your sleep. Prelutsky, J. **811**

Nightshade chronicles [series]

Lords of Trillium **Fic**

Nightshade City. Wagner, H. **Fic**

The Nightsiders [series]

The orphan army **Fic**

Nightsong. Berk, A. **E**

Nighttime Ninja. DaCosta, B. **E**

Nighty night, little green monster. Emberley, E. **E**

Nihoff, Tim

Let it shine **920**

Macy, S. Bylines: a photobiography of Nellie Bly **92**

Martin, J. B. The chiru of high Tibet **599.64**

Marzollo, J. Happy birthday, Martin Luther King **323**

Maupin, M. Benjamin Banneker **92**

McCurdy, M. Walden then & now **818**

McDonnell, P. Me . . . Jane **92**

Michelson, R. As good as anybody: Martin Luther King Jr. and Abraham Joshua Heschel's amazing march toward freedom **92**

Miller, W. Richard Wright and the library card **92**

My Uncle Martin's words of love for America **323.1**

Myers, W. D. Ida B. Wells **92**

Myers, W. D. I've seen the promised land **92**

Parker-Rock, M. Joseph Bruchac **92**

Pinkney, A. D. Dear Benjamin Banneker **520**

Rappaport, D. Martin's big words: the life of Dr. Martin Luther King, Jr. **92**

Rissman, R. Martin Luther King, Jr. Day **394.26**

Rose, S. Aung San Suu Kyi **92**

Selznick, B. The Houdini box **Fic**

Sitarski, A. Cold light **572**

Springer, N. The case of the cryptic crinoline **Fic**

Swain, G. Riding to Washington **E**

Turner, P. S. A life in the wild **92**

Watkins, A. F. My Uncle Martin's big heart **92**

Whiting, J. W.E.B. Du Bois **92**

Winter, J. The watcher: Jane Goodall's life with the chimps **92**

Yaccarino, D. The fantastic undersea life of Jacques Cousteau **92**

NONGRADED SCHOOLS

   See also Ability grouping in education; Education -- Experimental methods; Schools

Noni the pony. Lester, A. **E**

NONINDIGENOUS PESTS

Batten, M. Aliens from Earth **578.6**

Burns, L. G. Beetle busters **595.76**

Drake, J. Alien invaders **578.6**

Jackson, C. Alien invasion **578.6**

Metz, L. What can we do about invasive species? **578.6**

Souza, D. M. Plant invaders **581.6**

NONINDIGENOUS PESTS

   See also Biological invasions; Pests

NONLINGUISTIC COMMUNICATION *See* Nonverbal communication

Nonna's birthday surprise. Bastianich, L. **E**

NONOBJECTIVE ART *See* Abstract art

NONPUBLIC SCHOOLS *See* Church schools; Private schools

NONSENSE VERSES

Doyen, D. Once upon a twice **E**

Florian, D. Bing bang boing **811**

His shoes were far too tight **821**

Lear, E. The complete verse and other nonsense **821**

Lear, E. Edward Lear **821**

Lear, E. Edward Lear's The duck & the kangaroo **821**

Lear, E. The owl and the pussycat **821**

Prelutsky, J. The frogs wore red suspenders **811**

Prelutsky, J. Ride a purple pelican **811**

Prelutsky, J. Scranimals **811**

Silverstein, S. Every thing on it **811**

Silverstein, S. Falling up **811**

Silverstein, S. A light in the attic **811**

Silverstein, S. Where the sidewalk ends **811**

Willard, N. A visit to William Blake's inn **811**

NONSENSE VERSES

   See also Children's poetry; Humorous poetry; Wit and humor

NONVERBAL COMMUNICATION

Jackson, D. M. Every body's talking **153.6**

NONVERBAL COMMUNICATION

   See also Communication

NONVIOLENT NONCOOPERATION *See* Passive resistance

NONWORD STORIES *See* Stories without words

Noodle & Lou. Scanlon, L. G. **E**

Noodle pie. Starke, R. **Fic**

Noodle's knitting. Webster, S. **E**

Noon, Steve

   Millard, A. A street through time **936**

Noonie's masterpiece. Railsback, L. **Fic**

Noordeman, Arjen

   (il) Hearst, M. Unusual creatures **590**

Noordeman, Jelmer

   (il) Hearst, M. Unusual creatures **590**

Nora and the Texas terror. Cox, J. **Fic**

Nora's ark. Kinsey-Warnock, N. **E**

Nora's ark. **E**

Norac, Carl

   My daddy is a giant **E**

   My mommy is magic **E**

   Swing Cafe **E**

Norcliffe, James

   The boy who could fly **Fic**

NORDIC PEOPLES *See* Teutonic peoples

Nordqvist, Sven

   Tomtes' Christmas porridge **E**

Norling, Beth

   (il) Herrick, S. Naked bunyip dancing **Fic**

Norman Rockwell. Gherman, B. **759.13**

Norman, Kimberly

   I know a wee piggy **E**

   Ten on the sled **E**

Norris, Kathleen

   The holy twins: Benedict and Scholastica **271**

Norris, Martin

   (il) Walsh, D. The cardboard box book **745.54**

NORTHWEST TERRITORIES
Andre We feel good out here **970.004**
McLeod, T. The Delta is my home **970.004**
Zoe, T. Living stories **970.004**
NORTHWEST, PACIFIC -- HISTORY -- 19TH CENTURY -- FICTION
Mackey, H. Dreamwood **Fic**
The **Norton** anthology of children's literature. **808.8**
Norton, Mary
Bed-knob and broomstick **Fic**
The **Norumbegan quartet** [series]
Anderson, M. T. The empire of gut and bone **Fic**
Anderson, M. T. The Game of Sunken Places **Fic**
Anderson, M. T. The suburb beyond the stars **Fic**
NORVELT (PA.) -- HISTORY -- 20TH CENTURY -- FICTION
Gantos, J. From Norvelt to nowhere **Fic**
NORWAY -- FICTION
Preus, M. West of the moon **Fic**
NORWAY -- HISTORY -- 19TH CENTURY -- FICTION
Preus, M. West of the moon **Fic**
NORWEGIAN LANGUAGE
See also Language and languages; Scandinavian languages
NORWEGIAN LITERATURE
See also Literature; Scandinavian literature
Norwich, Grace
I am Harriet Tubman **973.7**
I am Sacagawea **978.004**
Mar, J. The body book for boys **612.6**
Norworth, Jack
Take me out to the ball game **782.42**
Nory Ryan's song. Giff, P. R. **Fic**
NOSE
Korb, R. My nose **612.2**
Ganeri, A. Smell **612.8**
Larsen, C. S. Crust and spray **612.8**
Miller, S. S. All kinds of noses **591.4**
NOSE
See also Face; Head
NOSE -- FICTION
Brown, M. T. Arthur's nose **E**
Nostradamus. Doft, T. **133.3**
Nostradamus, 1503-1566
About
Doft, T. Nostradamus **133.3**
Nosy Rosie. Keller, H. **E**
Not a box. Portis, A. **E**
Not a buzz to be found. Glaser, L. **595.7**
Not a drop to drink. Burgan, M. **363.6**
Not a stick. Portis, A. **E**
Not all princesses dress in pink. Yolen, J. **E**
Not fair, won't share. Graves, S. **152.4**
Not in Room 204. Riggs, S. **E**
Not inside this house! Lewis, K. **E**

Not last night but the night before. McNaughton, C. **E**
Not me! Killen, N. **E**
Not my girl. **E**
Not one damsel in distress. Yolen, J. **398.22**
A **not** scary story about big scary things. Williams, C. K. **E**
Not very scary. Brendler, C. **E**
Not yet, Rose. Hill, S. L. **E**
Not your parents' money book. Chatzky, J. **332.024**
Not your typical book about the environment. Kelsey, E. **333.72**
Not-quite-so-easy origami. Meinking, M. **736**
The **not-so-scary** Snorklum. Bright, P. **E**
NOTE-TAKING
Green, J. Write it down **371.3**
NOTE-TAKING
See also Reporters and reporting; Study skills
NOTEBOOKS
See also Books
NOTEBOOKS, ARTISTS' *See* Artists' notebooks
Notes from a liar and her dog. Choldenko, G. **Fic**
Notes from the dog. Paulsen, G. **Fic**
Nothing. Agee, J. **E**
Nothing but a dog. Katz, B. **E**
Nothing but trouble. Stauffacher, S. **92**
Nothing here but stones. Oswald, N. **Fic**
Nothing like a puffin. Soltis, S. **E**
Noullet, Georgette
Bed hog **E**
Nouns. Heinrichs, A. **428**
Nouns and verbs have a field day. Pulver, R. **E**
NOVA SCOTIA -- FICTION
Bastedo, J. Free as the wind **E**
Race the wild wind **E**
NOVA SCOTIA -- POETRY
Grant, S. Up home **811**
Novak, B. J.
The book with no pictures **E**
Novak, Matt
A wish for you **E**
NOVELISTS
Abrams, D. Gary Soto **92**
Adler, D. A. A picture book of Harriet Beecher Stowe **92**
The adventures of Mark Twain by Huckleberry Finn **92**
Alderson, B. Thumbelina **E**
Andersen, H. C. The nightingale **E**
Anderson, W. T. Pioneer girl: the story of Laura Ingalls Wilder **92**
Berne, E. C. Laura Ingalls Wilder **92**
Bledsoe, L. J. How to survive in Antarctica **998**
Bond, V. Zora and me **Fic**
Brown, M. Pablo Neruda **92**
Colbert, D. The magical worlds of Harry Potter **823**

Ross, T. Three little kittens and other favorite nursery rhymes **398.8**

Sally go round the stars **398.8**

Scieszka, J. Truckery rhymes **811**

Seibold, J. O. Other goose **398.8**

Sierra, J. Monster Goose **811**

Taback, S. This is the house that Jack built **398.8**

This little piggy **398.8**

Tildes, P. L. Will you be mine? **398.8**

Tortillitas para mama and other nursery rhymes **398.8**

Trapani, I. Rufus and friends: rhyme time **398.8**

Trapani, I. Rufus and friends: school days **398.8**

Wadsworth, O. A. Over in the meadow **E**

Wright, B. F. The real Mother Goose **398.8**

NURSERY RHYMES -- DICTIONARIES

The Oxford dictionary of nursery rhymes **398.8**

NURSERY RHYMES -- FICTION

Fox, M. Good night, sleep tight **E**

NURSERY RHYMES, SPANISH AMERICAN

Arrorro mi nino **398.8**

Pio peep! **398.8**

NURSERY SCHOOLS

Henkes, K. Wemberly worried **E**

NURSERY SCHOOLS

See also Elementary education; Schools

NURSERY SCHOOLS -- FICTION

Dinosaur vs. school **E**

Little Naomi, Little Chick **E**

Sadie and the big mountain **E**

Nursery tales around the world. Sierra, J. **398.2**

NURSES

Annino, J. G. She sang promise: the story of Betty Mae Jumper, Seminole tribal leader **92**

Demi Florence Nightingale **92**

Glasscock, S. How nurses use math **610.73**

Gorrell, G. K. Heart and soul: the story of Florence Nightingale **92**

Jones, C. Sarah Emma Edmonds was a great pretender **92**

Kenney, K. L. Nurses at work **610.73**

Krensky, S. Clara Barton **92**

Nurse, soldier, spy: the story of Sarah Edmonds, a Civil War hero **92**

Rosenberg, A. The Civil War **920**

Somervill, B. A. Clara Barton **92**

Springer, N. The case of the cryptic crinoline **Fic**

Wade, M. D. Amazing civil war nurse Clara Barton **92**

Wells, R. Mary on horseback **92**

NURSES -- ENGLAND -- BIOGRAPHY

Demi Florence Nightingale **92**

Nurses at work. Kenney, K. L. **610.73**

NURSING

See also Medicine; Therapeutics

NURSING HOMES

See also Hospitals; Institutional care; Longterm care facilities

The **Nutcracker.** Anderson, A. **E**

Nutcracker. Hoffmann, E. T. A. **Fic**

The **Nutcracker.** Spinner, S. **E**

The **nutcracker.** Schulman, J. **Fic**

The **Nutcracker.** Koppe, S. **Fic**

The **nutcracker.** Cech, J. **E**

The **Nutcracker.** Kain, K. **E**

The **Nutcracker.** Jeffers, S. **E**

NUTCRACKER (BALLET)

Anderson, A. The Nutcracker **E**

Tallulah's Nutcracker **E**

The **Nutcracker** doll. DePalma, M. N. **E**

Nutik, the wolf pup. George, J. C. **E**

NUTRITION

Butterworth, C. How Did That Get in My Lunchbox? **641.3**

Cleary, B. P. Apples, cherries, red raspberries **641.3**

Cleary, B. P. Green beans, potatoes, and even tomatoes **641.3**

Currie, S. Junk food **613.2**

Doeden, M. Eat right! **613.2**

Durrie, K. Health **613.2**

Edwards, H. Talking about your weight **613.2**

Furgang, A. Salty and sugary snacks **613.2**

Gardner, R. Ace your exercise and nutrition science project: great science fair ideas **613**

Harris, R. H. What's so yummy? **613.2**

Head, H. Healthy eating **613.2**

Hunt, J. The truth about diets **613.2**

Johanson, P. Fake foods **613.2**

King, H. Carbohydrates for a healthy body **613.2**

Leedy, L. The edible pyramid **613.2**

Miller, E. The monster health book **613**

Powell, J. Fats for a healthy body **613.2**

Rau, D. M. Going vegetarian **613.2**

Royston, A. Proteins for a healthy body **613.2**

Royston, A. Vitamins and minerals for a healthy body **613.2**

Royston, A. Water and fiber for a healthy body **613.2**

Schaefer, A. Healthy food **613.2**

Simons, R. Bigger isn't always better **613.2**

Thompson, H. Cookies or carrots? **613.2**

Verdick, E. Mealtime **E**

Watson, S. Mystery meat **613.2**

The world in your lunch box **641.3**

NUTRITION

See also Health; Physiology; Therapeutics

Head, H. Healthy eating **613.2**

Kelly, S. M. Yummy! **E**

Rau, D. M. Going vegetarian **613.2**

Nuts. Cook, K. **Fic**

Nuts. Gerritsen, P. **E**

NUTS

Olivia and the fairy princesses. Falconer, I. **E**
Olivia Bean, trivia queen. Gephart, D. **Fic**
Olivia goes to Venice. **E**
Olivia Kidney. Potter, E. **Fic**
Olivia's birds. Bouler, O. **598**
Ollhoff, Jim
  Beginning genealogy **929**
  The Black Death **616.9**
  Collecting primary records **929**
  DNA **929**
  Exploring immigration **304.8**
  Filling the family tree **929**
  The flu **616.2**
  Fossil fuels **333.8**
  Geothermal, biomass, and hydrogen **333.79**
  The germ detectives **616.9**
  Indian mythology **294**
  Japanese mythology **398.2**
  Malaria **616.9**
  Mayan and Aztec mythology **972.81**
  Middle Eastern Mythology **398.209**
  Nuclear energy **333.79**
  Smallpox **616.9**
  Solar power **333.79**
  Using your research **929**
  What are germs? **616**
  Wind and water **333.9**
  World in crisis **333.79**
Ollie and the lost toy. Richards, L. **E**
Ollie and the science of treasure hunting. Dionne, E. **Fic**
Ollie the purple elephant. Krosoczka, J. J. **E**
Ollie's Halloween. Dunrea, O. **E**
Olly and me 1 2 3. Hughes, S. **E**
Olofsdotter, Marie
  (il) Adler, D. A. A picture book of Cesar Chavez **92**
Oloyou. Cardenas, T. **398.2**
Olshan, Matthew
  The mighty Lalouche **E**
Olson, Arielle North
  Ask the bones: scary stories from around the world **398.2**
  More bones **398.2**
Olson, Gillia M.
  Polar bears' search for ice **599.78**
Olson, Julie
  Tickle, tickle! itch, twitch! **E**
Olson, Nathan
  Cones **516**
  Cubes **516**
  Cylinders **516**
  Pyramids **516**
  Spheres **516**
Olson, Tod
  How to get rich in the California Gold Rush **979.4**
  How to get rich on a Texas cattle drive **978**

  How to get rich on the Oregon Trail **978**
Olson-Brown, Ellen
  Ooh la la polka dot boots **E**
Oluonye, Mary N.
  Nigeria **966.9**
Olwell, Robert
  Doak, R. S. South Carolina, 1540-1776 **975.7**
Olympians [series]
  O'Connor, G. Hades **398.209**
  O'Connor, G. Zeus **741.5**
OLYMPIC ATHLETES
  Burford, M. Grace, gold and glory **796.440**
  Queen of the track **796.42**
OLYMPIC ATHLETES
  See also Athletes
OLYMPIC GAMES
  Bobrick, B. A passion for victory: the story of the Olympics in ancient and early modern times **796.4**
  Butterfield, M. Events **796.48**
  Butterfield, M. History **796.48**
  Butterfield, M. Scandals **796.48**
  Macy, S. Freeze frame **796.98**
  Macy, S. Swifter, higher, stronger **796.48**
  Queen of the track **796.42**
  Washburn, K. Heart of a champion **796.440**
OLYMPIC GAMES
  See also Athletics; Contests; Games; Sports
OLYMPIC GAMES, 1996 (ATLANTA, GA.)
  See also Olympic games
OLYMPIC GAMES, 2012 (LONDON, ENG-LAND)
  See also Olympic games
Olympic National Park. Jankowski, S. **979.7**
OLYMPIC NATIONAL PARK (WASH.)
  Jankowski, S. Olympic National Park **979.7**
OLYMPICS *See* Olympic games
The Olympics [series]
  Butterfield, M. Events **796.48**
  Butterfield, M. History **796.48**
  Butterfield, M. Scandals **796.48**
OMAN
  Ejaz, K. We visit Oman **953.53**
  Nye, N. S. The turtle of Oman **Fic**
OMAN -- FICTION
  Nye, N. S. The turtle of Oman **Fic**
Omega City. **Fic**
Ommen, Sylvia van
  (il) Westera, M. Sheep and Goat **Fic**
Omololu, Cynthia Jaynes
  When it's six o'clock in San Francisco **E**
On a beam of light. Berne, J. **92**
On a medieval day. Arato, R. **S**
On a road in Africa. Doner, K. **636.08**
On a windy night. Day, N. R. **E**
On angel wings. Morpurgo, M. **Fic**
On beyond a million. Schwartz, D. M. **513.5**

One leaf rides the wind. Mannis, C. D. **E**
The **one** left behind. Roberts, W. D. **Fic**
One lighthouse, one moon. Lobel, A. **E**
One little chicken. **E**
One little chicken. Elliott, D. **E**
One million things [series]
  Woodward, J. Planet Earth **550**
One moon, two cats. Godwin, L. **E**
One more hug for Madison. Church, C. **E**
One night in the Coral Sea. Collard, S. B. **593.6**
One night in the Everglades. Larsen, L. **577**
One night in the zoo. Kerr, J. **E**
One nighttime sea. Rose, D. L. **513.2**
One of us. Moss, P. **E**
ONE PARENT FAMILY See Single-parent families
One peace. Wilson, J. **305.23**
One plastic bag. **363.728**
One potato, two potato. DeFelice, C. C. **E**
One rainy day. Salzano, T. **E**
One red apple. Ziefert, H. **634**
One red dot. Carter, D. A. **E**
One Saturday evening. Baker, B. **E**
One small place in a tree. Brenner, B. **577.3**
One smart goose. Church, C. **E**
One special day. **E**
One spooky night. Stone, K. **E**
One spotted giraffe. Horáček, P. **E**
One square inch. Mills, C. **Fic**
One starry night. **E**
One Ted falls out of bed. Donaldson, J. **E**
One Times Square. McKendry, J. **974.7**
One tiny turtle. Davies, N. **597.92**
One too many. Marino, G. **E**
One true bear. Dewan, T. **E**
One two that's my shoe! Murray, A. **E**
One was Johnny. Sendak, M. **E**
One watermelon seed. Lottridge, C. B. **E**
One well. Strauss, R. **553.7**
One witch. Leuck, L. **E**
One wolf howls. Cohn, S. **599.77**
One world kids cookbook. Mendez, S. **641.59**
One world kids cookbook. Mendez, S. **641.5**
One world, many religions. Osborne, M. P. **200**
One world, one day. Kerley, B. **305.23**
One year in Beijing. Wang Xiaohong **E**
One, two, buckle my shoe. Yoon, S. **E**
One, two, buckle my shoe. Cabrera, J. **E**
One-Eye! Two-Eyes! Three-Eyes! Shepard, A. **398.2**
One-handed catch. Auch, M. J. **Fic**
One-of-a-kind stamps and crafts. Ross, K. **761**
Ones and twos. Jocelyn, M. **E**
Ong, Jacqueline
  Sheehan, P. Cote d'Ivoire **966.68**
Ong, Wilson
  (il) James, H. F. Paper son **Fic**

Onion John. Krumgold, J. **Fic**
Onion juice, poop, and other surprising sources of alternative energy. Weakland, M. **333.79**
Onishi, Satoru
  Who's hiding? **E**
ONLINE AUTHORSHIP
  Bridget and Bo build a blog **Fic**
ONLINE CHAT GROUPS
  See also Conversation
Online etiquette and safety. Cornwall, P. **004.6**
ONLINE MARKETING See Internet marketing
ONLINE SELLING See Internet marketing
ONLINE SOCIAL NETWORKS
  Freese, S. M. Craigslist **381**
  Richardson, W. Blogs, wikis, podcasts, and other powerful Web tools for classrooms **371.3**
  Schwartz, H. E. Safe social networking **302.302**
ONLINE SOCIAL NETWORKS -- FICTION
  Baskin, N. R. Runt **Fic**
Only a witch can fly. McGhee, A. **E**
ONLY CHILD
  See also Children; Family size
ONLY CHILD -- FICTION
  Adderson, C. Jasper John Dooley **Fic**
  Best, C. What's so bad about being an only child? **E**
Only Emma. Warner, S. **Fic**
Only one neighborhood. Harshman, M. **E**
Only one year. **Fic**
The **only** ones. Starmer, A. **Fic**
Only passing through: the story of Sojourner Truth. Rockwell, A. F. **92**
Only the mountains do not move. Reynolds, J. **305.8**
Only the names remain. Bealer, A. W. **970.004**
The **only** thing worse than witches. Magaziner, L. **Fic**
Only you can save mankind. Pratchett, T. **Fic**
Onoda, Yuta
  (il) Lewis, G. Wild wings **Fic**
ONTARIO
  Greenwood, B. A pioneer sampler **971**
ONTARIO -- FICTION
  Sherrard, V. The glory wind **Fic**
ONTOLOGY
  See also Philosophy
Onward. Johnson, D. **92**
Onyefulu, Ifeoma
  The girl who married a ghost **398.2**
  Ikenna goes to Nigeria **966.9**
  Play **E**
Oobleck, slime, & dancing spaghetti. Williams, J. **507.8**
Oodles of animals. Ehlert, L. **E**
Ooh la la polka dot boots. Olson-Brown, E. **E**
Ookpik. Hiscock, B. **598**
Oonark, Jessie, 1906-1985
                    About

Orange pear apple bear. Gravett, E.　　　**E**

ORANGES -- FICTION

Alvarez, J. A gift of gracias　　　**E**

Aston, D. H. An orange in January　　　**E**

Rocklin, J. One day and one amazing morning on Orange Street　　　**Fic**

Oranges on Golden Mountain. Partridge, E.　　　**E**

Orangutan. Ganeri, A.　　　**599.8**

ORANGUTAN

Bredeson, C. Orangutans up close　　　**599.8**

Ganeri, A. Orangutan　　　**599.8**

Laman, T. Face to face with orangutans　　　**599.8**

Mattern, J. Orangutans　　　**599.8**

ORANGUTAN -- FICTION

Antle, B. Suryia swims! : the true story of how an orangutan learned to swim　　　**E**

Daddo, A. Goodnight, me　　　**E**

Orangutanka.　　　**E**

Orangutans. Mattern, J.　　　**599.8**

ORANGUTANS -- FICTION

Orangutanka　　　**E**

Orangutans up close. Bredeson, C.　　　**599.8**

Orani. Nivola, C. A.　　　**945**

ORATIONS See Speeches

ORATORY See Public speaking

Orb weavers. Markle, S.　　　**595.4**

Orback, Craig

(il) The Can Man　　　**E**

(il) Figley, M. R. John Greenwood's journey to Bunker Hill　　　**973.3**

(il) Figley, M. R. Prisoner for liberty　　　**92**

(il) Krensky, S. Paul Bunyan　　　**398.2**

(il) Mortensen, L. Paul Revere's ride　　　**92**

(il) Thomas, P. Nature's paintbox　　　**811**

ORBITAL LABORATORIES See Space stations

ORBITAL RENDEZVOUS (SPACE FLIGHT)

See also Space flight; Space stations; Space vehicles

ORBITING VEHICLES See Artificial satellites; Space stations

Orca footprints [series]

Mulder, M. Brilliant!　　　**339.79**

Mulder, M. Every last drop　　　**333.91**

Orca young readers [series]

Hyde, N. I owe you one　　　**Fic**

Leach, S. Jake Reynolds: chicken or eagle?　　　**Fic**

Peterson, L. J. The ballad of Knuckles McGraw　　　**Fic**

Orchard, Eric

(il) Edge, C. Twelve minutes to midnight　　　**Fic**

ORCHESTRA

Ganeri, A. The young person's guide to the orchestra　　　**784.2**

Koscielniak, B. The story of the incredible orchestra　　　**784.2**

ORCHESTRA -- FICTION

Cummings, P. Boom bah!　　　**E**

Snicket, L. The composer is dead　　　**E**

ORCHESTRAL MUSIC

See also Instrumental music; Music; Orchestra

ORDERLINESS

Lester, H. The Loch Mess monster　　　**E**

Murphy, S. J. Mighty Maddie　　　**389**

Reynolds, A. Here comes Destructosaurus!　　　**E**

ORDERLINESS -- FICTION

Arnold, T. Fix this mess!　　　**E**

Lester, H. The Loch Mess monster　　　**E**

McDonnell, P. A perfectly messed-up story　　　**E**

Prigger, M. S. Aunt Minnie McGranahan　　　**E**

ORDERLINESS -- GRAPHIC NOVELS

Wight, E. Frankie Pickle and the closet of doom　　　**741.5**

ORDINATION

See also Rites and ceremonies; Sacraments

ORDNANCE

See also Military art and science

ORE DEPOSITS

See also Geology

Oregon. Roza, G.　　　**979.5**

Oregon. Kent, D.　　　**979.5**

OREGON

Kent, D. Oregon　　　**979.5**

Roza, G. Oregon　　　**979.5**

OREGON -- FICTION

Beard, D. B. Operation Clean Sweep　　　**Fic**

Cox, J. Nora and the Texas terror　　　**Fic**

McDonald, M. Cloudy with a chance of boys　　　**Fic**

McDonald, M. The rule of three　　　**Fic**

The mighty Quinn　　　**Fic**

Noe, K. S. Something to hold　　　**Fic**

Parry, R. Heart of a shepherd　　　**Fic**

Patneaude, D. A piece of the sky　　　**Fic**

Platt, R. B. Hellie Jondoe　　　**Fic**

Schroeder, L. It's Raining Cupcakes　　　**Fic**

Young, J. A book for black-eyed Susan　　　**Fic**

OREGON NATIONAL HISTORIC TRAIL -- FICTION

Pierpoint, E. The last ride of Caleb O'Toole　　　**Fic**

The **Oregon** Trail. Friedman, M.　　　**978**

OREGON TRAIL

Friedman, M. The Oregon Trail　　　**978**

Olson, T. How to get rich on the Oregon Trail　　　**978**

OREGON TRAIL

See also Overland journeys to the Pacific; United States

OREGON TRAIL -- FICTION

Pierpoint, E. The last ride of Caleb O'Toole　　　**Fic**

Stanley, D. Roughing it on the Oregon Trail　　　**Fic**

Van Leeuwen, J. Bound for Oregon　　　**Fic**

ORES

See also Minerals

The **orphan** army. **Fic**
The **orphan** boy. Mollel, T. M. **398.21**
The **orphan** of Awkward Falls. Graves, K. **Fic**
ORPHANAGES
 See also Charities; Children -- Institutional
 care
ORPHANAGES -- FICTION
 Stewart, T. L. The extraordinary education of Nich-
 olas Benedict **Fic**
ORPHANS
 Almond, D. Heaven Eyes **Fic**
 Blackwood, G. L. Shakespeare's scribe **Fic**
 Bredsdorff, B. The Crow-girl **Fic**
 Horowitz, A. Eagle Strike **Fic**
 Horowitz, A. Stormbreaker **Fic**
 I came from the water **972.940**
 Ibbotson, E. Dial-a-ghost **Fic**
 Skrypuch, M. F. Last airlift **959.704**
 Warren, A. We rode the orphan trains **362.73**
 Woodson, J. Locomotion **Fic**
 Yep, L. The magic paintbrush **Fic**
ORPHANS
 See also Children
ORPHANS -- FICTION
 Almond, D. The Boy who swam with piranhas **Fic**
 Barker, M. P. Mending horses **Fic**
 Black, P. J. Urban outlaws **Fic**
 Creech, S. The great unexpected **Fic**
 Edge, C. Twelve minutes to midnight **Fic**
 Elliott, R. Zoo girl **E**
 Gaiman, N. The graveyard book graphic novel
 Volume 1 **741.5**
 Graff, L. A tangle of knots **Fic**
 The graveyard book graphic novel Volume 2 **741.5**
 Hopkinson, D. The Great Trouble **Fic**
 Kinsey-Warnock, N. True colors **Fic**
 Nielsen, J. A. The false prince **Fic**
 Rooftoppers **Fic**
 Schlitz, L. A. Splendors and glooms **Fic**
 Sloan, H. G. Counting by 7s **Fic**
 Stewart, T. L. The extraordinary education of Nich-
 olas Benedict **Fic**
 Streatfeild, N. Ballet shoes **Fic**
ORPHANS -- SIERRA LEONE -- BIOGRAPHY
 DePrince, E. Ballerina dreams **92**
Orr, Tamra
 LeVert, S. Massachusetts **974.4**
 Moragne, W. New Jersey **974.9**
 Orr, T. B. The food of China **394.1**
 Alaska **979.8**
 California **979.4**
 Coins and other currency **332.4**
 Florida **975.9**
 The food of Greece **394.1**
 A kid's guide to earning money **650.1**
 The monsters of Hercules **398.2**

Oklahoma **976.6**
Qatar **953.6**
Saint Lucia **972.98**
The sirens **398.2**
Orr, Wendy
 Lost! A dog called Bear **Fic**
 Missing! A cat called Buster **Fic**
 Mokie & Bik **Fic**
 Mokie & Bik go to sea **Fic**
 The princess and her panther **E**
Orsini, Cheryl
 (il) Musgrove, M. Lucy the good **Fic**
Ortakales, Denise
 (il) Brenner, B. Good morning, garden **E**
Ortega. Fergus, M. **Fic**
ORTHODONTICS
 See also Dentistry; Orthopedics
ORTHOPEDICS
 See also Medicine; Surgery
Orwell's luck. Jennings, R. W. **Fic**
ORYX
 Ganeri, A. Arabian oryx **599.64**
Osborn, Kathy
 (il) Ablow, G. A horse in the house, and other
 strange but true animal stories **590**
Osborne, Mary Pope
 American tall tales **398.2**
 The brave little seamstress **398.2**
 Favorite Greek myths **292**
 Kate and the beanstalk **398.2**
 New York's bravest **E**
 One world, many religions **200**
 The Random House book of Bible stories **220.9**
 Osborne, W. Sleeping Bobby **398.2**
Osborne, Will
 Sleeping Bobby **398.2**
Osburn, Jennifer
 Selfridge, B. A teen's guide to creating Web pages
 and blogs **006.7**
Oscar and the bat. Waring, G. **E**
Oscar and the very hungry dragon. Krause, U. **E**
Oscar's half birthday. Graham, B. **E**
Oskarsson, Bardur
 (il) The flat rabbit **E**
Osnaya, Ricardo
 (il) Manning, M. K. Ali Baba and the forty
 thieves **741.5**
OSPREYS -- FICTION
 Lewis, G. Wild wings **Fic**
OSTEOPATHIC MEDICINE
 See also Medicine
Osteoporosis. Hoffmann, G. **616.7**
OSTEOPOROSIS
 Hoffmann, G. Osteoporosis **616.7**
OSTROGOTHS *See* Goths
Osuna Perez, Gloria

Creepy backyard invaders **578.7**

Disgusting food invaders **615.9**

Gross body invaders **578.6**

Icky house invaders **578.6**

Valentine's Day origami **736**

Woods, M. Ace! **796.342**

Woods, M. Goal! **796.334**

Woods, M. Xtreme! Extreme sports facts and stats **796**

Owens, Gail

(il) Hurwitz, J. The adventures of Ali Baba Bernstein **Fic**

(il) Sobol, D. J. Encyclopedia Brown and the case of the treasure hunt **Fic**

Owens, Jesse, 1913-1980

About

Adler, D. A. A picture book of Jesse Owens **796.42**

Krull, K. Lives of the athletes **796**

Owens, L. L.

The life cycle of a snail **594**

The **owl** and the pussycat. Lear, E. **821**

Owl at home. Lobel, A. **E**

Owl babies. Waddell, M. **E**

Owl howl. Friester, P. **E**

Owl moon. Yolen, J. **E**

Owls. Gibbons, G. **598**

Owls. Bodden, V. **598.9**

Owls. Gish, M. **598**

OWLS

Bodden, V. Owls **598.9**

Gibbons, G. Owls **598**

Gish, M. Owls **598**

Gonzales, D. Owls in the dark **598**

Hiscock, B. Ookpik **598**

Nate the Great on the Owl Express **E**

Sattler, H. R. The book of North American owls **598.9**

Thomson, R. The life cycle of an owl **598**

OWLS -- FICTION

Chapman, J. I'm not sleepy! **E**

Hoot owl, master of disguise **E**

Jennings, P. Odd, weird, and little **Fic**

Kohara, K. The Midnight Library **E**

Little Owl's day **E**

Night owl **E**

OWLS -- GRAPHIC NOVELS

Runton, A. Owly: The way home and The bittersweet summer **741.5**

OWLS -- POETRY

Lear, E. The owl and the pussycat **821**

Lobel, A. Odd owls & stout pigs **811**

Owls in the dark. Gonzales, D. **598**

Owly and Wormy, friends all aflutter! Runton, A. **E**

Owly: The way home and The bittersweet summer. Runton, A. **741.5**

Owney, the mail-pouch pooch. Kerby, M. **E**

Owsley, Anthony

(il) Ouch! **616**

Ox, house, stick. Robb, D. **411**

Ox-cart man. Hall, D. **E**

Oxenbury, Helen

(il) Bently, P. King Jack and the dragon **E**

(il) Burningham, J. There's going to be a baby **E**

(il) Carroll, L. Alice's adventures in Wonderland **Fic**

(il) Fox, M. Ten little fingers and ten little toes **E**

(il) The Helen Oxenbury nursery collection **398.8**

(il) Hest, A. Charley's first night **E**

(il) Hest, A. When Charley Met Grampa **E**

(il) Krauss, R. The growing story **E**

(il) Root, P. Big Momma makes the world **E**

(il) Rosen, M. We're going on a bear hunt **E**

(il) Trivizas, E. The three little wolves and the big bad pig **398.24**

(il) Waddell, M. Farmer duck **E**

The **Oxford** book of story poems. **808.81**

The **Oxford** companion to children's literature. Carpenter, H. **809**

The **Oxford** dictionary of nursery rhymes. **398.8**

The **Oxford** encyclopedia of children's literature. **809**

Oxford world's classics [series]

The Bible: Authorized King James Version **220.5**

Oxlade, Chris

Gadgets and games **688.7**

Gaming technology **794.8**

Oxley, Jennifer

(il) Aronson, B. The chicken problem **E**

OXPECKERS (BIRDS)

Rustad, M. E. H. Zebras and oxpeckers work together **599.66**

OXYGEN

See also Chemical elements; Gases

OZ (IMAGINARY PLACE)

Cavallaro, M. L. Frank Baum's The Wizard of Oz **741.5**

Oz, Amos, 1939-

Suddenly in the depths of the forest **Fic**

OZARK MOUNTAINS -- FICTION

Rawls, W. Where the red fern grows **Fic**

OZONE LAYER

Jakubiak, D. J. What can we do about ozone loss? **363.7**

OZONOSPHERE *See* Ozone layer

P

P. Zonka lays an egg. **E**

P.K. Pinkerton and the petrified man. Lawrence, C. **Fic**

P.K. Pinkerton and the pistol-packing widows. Lawrence, C. **Fic**

P.S. Be Eleven. Williams-Garcia, R. **Fic**

(il) Gray, R. Have you heard the nesting bird? **E**

Pak, Soyung

Dear Juno **E**

Pakistan. Sonneborn, L. **954.91**

Pakistan. Kwek, K. **954.91**

PAKISTAN

Hinman, B. We visit Pakistan **954.91**

Kwek, K. Pakistan **954.91**

Sonneborn, L. Pakistan **954.91**

PAKISTAN -- FICTION

D'Adamo, F. Iqbal **Fic**

Khan, R. King for a day **E**

Khan, R. Silly chicken **E**

Williams, K. L. Four feet, two sandals **E**

PAKISTAN -- POLITICS AND GOVERNMENT

Naden, C. J. Benazir Bhutto **92**

PAKISTANI AMERICANS -- FICTION

Khan, H. Night of the Moon **E**

Khan, R. Big red lollipop **E**

Mobin-Uddin, A. The best Eid ever **E**

PAKISTANIS

Winter, J. Malala, a brave girl from Pakistan/Iqbal, a brave boy from Pakistan **920**

Pakkala, Christine

Last-but-not-least lola and the wild chicken **Fic**

Pal, Erika

(il) Azad's camel **E**

Palace of dreams. Jacobson, A. **Fic**

PALACES

See also Buildings

Palacio, R. J.

Wonder **Fic**

Palacios, Sara

(il) Brown, M. Marisol McDonald and the clash bash

Palatini, Margie

No nap! yes nap! **E**

The cheese **E**

Bad boys get henpecked! **E**

Boo-hoo moo **E**

Earthquack! **E**

Geek Chic **Fic**

Goldie and the three hares **E**

Gorgonzola **E**

Hogg, Hogg & Hog **E**

Lousy rotten stinkin' grapes **398.2**

Piggie pie! **E**

Three French hens **E**

The three silly billies **E**

Pale Male. Schulman, J. **598**

Palen, Debbie

(il) Gravelle, K. The period book **612.6**

Palenque. Kops, D. **972**

PALENQUE SITE (MEXICO)

Kops, D. Palenque **972**

Paleo bugs. Bradley, T. J. **560**

PALEO-INDIANS

See also Native Americans -- History; Prehistoric peoples

PALEOANTHROPOLOGY

Aronson, M. The skull in the rock **569.9**

PALEOART

Scaly spotted feathered frilled **567.9**

PALEONTOLOGISTS

Brown, D. Rare treasure: Mary Anning and her remarkable discoveries **560**

Fern, T. Barnum's bones **560.9**

Goldish, M. The fossil feud **560**

Johnson, R. L. Battle of the dinosaur bones **560.973**

Ray, D. K. Dinosaur mountain **567.9**

PALEONTOLOGY

Bonner, H. When dinos dawned, mammals got munched, and Pterosaurs took flight **567.9**

Gray, S. H. Paleontology the study of prehistoric life **560**

Greenwood, M. Amazing giant dinosaurs **567.9**

Parker, S. Age of the Dinosaur **567.9**

Scaly spotted feathered frilled **567.9**

Tanaka, S. New dinos **567.9**

Zoehfeld, K. W. Dinosaur parents, dinosaur young **567.9**

PALEONTOLOGY

See also Historical geology; Zoology

PALEONTOLOGY -- UNITED STATES -- HISTORY -- 19TH CENTURY

Johnson, R. L. Battle of the dinosaur bones **560.973**

Paleontology the study of prehistoric life. Gray, S. H. **560**

PALEOZOOLOGY *See* Paleontology

PALESTINE -- FICTION

Speare, E. G. The bronze bow **Fic**

PALESTINIAN ARABS

Ellis, D. Three wishes **956.94**

Marx, T. Sharing our homeland **956.04**

PALESTINIAN ARABS -- FICTION

Abdel-Fattah, R. Where the streets had a name **Fic**

PALESTINIAN ARABS -- FOLKLORE

MacDonald, M. R. Tunjur! Tunjur! Tunjur! **398.2**

PALESTINIANS *See* Palestinian Arabs

Paley, Jane

Hooper finds a family **Fic**

Paley, Joan

(il) Guiberson, B. Z. The emperor lays an egg **598.47**

(il) Halfmann, J. Star of the sea **593.9**

PALINDROMES

Agee, J. Jon Agee's palindromania! **428**

PALINDROMES

See also Literary recreations; Word games

PALINDROMES -- FICTION

Shulman, M. Mom and Dad are palindromes **E**

PALLIATIVE TREATMENT

See also Therapeutics

The **paper** boomerang book. Latno, M. **745.54**
Paper craft fun for holidays [series]

McGee, R. Paper crafts for Chinese New Year **745.594**

McGee, R. Paper crafts for Christmas **745.594**

McGee, R. Paper crafts for Day of the Dead **745.594**

McGee, R. Paper crafts for Halloween **745.594**

McGee, R. Paper crafts for Kwanzaa **745.594**

McGee, R. Paper crafts for Valentine's Day **745.594**

PAPER CRAFTS

Carter, D. A. Hide and Seek **E**

Castleforte, B. Papertoy monsters **745.592**

Dobson, C. Wind power **333.9**

Fritsch, P. Pennsylvania Dutch Halloween scherenschnitte **745.594**

Garza, C. L. Making magic windows **745.54**

Harbo, C. L. The kids' guide to paper airplanes **745.592**

Harbo, C. L. Paper airplanes: Captain, level 4 **745.592**

Harbo, C. L. Paper airplanes: Copilot, level 2 **745.592**

Harbo, C. L. Paper airplanes: Flight school, level 1 **745.592**

Harbo, C. L. Paper airplanes: Pilot, level 3 **745.592**

Henry, S. Paper folding **736**

Latno, M. The paper boomerang book **745.54**

Llimos, A. Easy paper crafts in 5 steps **745.54**

McGee, R. Paper crafts for Chinese New Year **745.594**

McGee, R. Paper crafts for Christmas **745.594**

McGee, R. Paper crafts for Day of the Dead **745.594**

McGee, R. Paper crafts for Halloween **745.594**

McGee, R. Paper crafts for Kwanzaa **745.594**

McGee, R. Paper crafts for Valentine's Day **745.594**

The paper airplane book **629**

Staake, B. Look! Another book! **E**

Torres, L. Rock your party **745.54**

Tremaine, J. Paper tricks **793.8**

PAPER CRAFTS

See also Handicraft

Paper crafts for Chinese New Year. McGee, R. **745.594**

Paper crafts for Christmas. McGee, R. **745.594**

Paper crafts for Day of the Dead. McGee, R. **745.594**

Paper crafts for Halloween. McGee, R. **745.594**

Paper crafts for Kwanzaa. McGee, R. **745.594**

Paper crafts for Valentine's Day. McGee, R. **745.594**

The **paper** crane. Bang, M. **E**

Paper folding. Henry, S. **736**

PAPER FOLDING *See* Origami; Paper crafts

PAPER MAKING *See* Papermaking

PAPER MANUFACTURE *See* Papermaking

PAPER MONEY

Forest, C. The dollar bill in translation **332.4**

PAPER MONEY

See also Money

Paper products. Langley, A. **676**

PAPER SCULPTURE *See* Paper crafts

Paper son. James, H. F. **Fic**

Paper tricks. Tremaine, J. **793.8**

PAPER WORK *See* Paper crafts

PAPERBACK BOOKS

See also Books; Editions

The **paperboy**. Pilkey, D. **E**

Paperboy. Vawter, V. **Fic**

PAPERHANGING

See also Interior design

PAPERMAKING

Langley, A. Paper products **676**

PAPERMAKING

See also Manufactures; Paper

Papertoy monsters. Castleforte, B. **745.592**

Papi's gift. Stanton, K. **E**

PAPIER-MÂCHÉ *See* Paper crafts

Papp, Robert

(il) Noble, T. H. The last brother **E**

(il) Shefelman, J. J. Anna Maria's gift **Fic**

Pappy's handkerchief. Scillian, D. **E**

Paprocki, Greg

(il) Math-terpieces **510**

Papua New Guinea. Gascoigne, I. **995.3**

PAPUA NEW GUINEA

Gascoigne, I. Papua New Guinea **995.3**

PARACHUTE TROOPS

Stone, T. L. Courage has no color, the true story of the Triple Nickles **940.54**

PARACHUTES

See also Aeronautics

Parade. Crews, D. **E**

PARADE FLOATS *See* Parades

PARADES

Count me in **513.2**

Crews, D. Parade **E**

Sweet, M. Balloons over Broadway **92**

PARADES

See also Festivals; Pageants

PARADES -- FICTION

This day in June **E**

Paraguay. Jermyn, L. **989.2**

PARAGUAY

Jermyn, L. Paraguay **989.2**

PARALLEL UNIVERSES -- FICTION

Lipsyte, R. The twinning project **Fic**

PARALYSIS, CEREBRAL *See* Cerebral palsy

PARAMEDICAL PERSONNEL *See* Allied health personnel; Emergency medical technicians

PARAMEDICS, EMERGENCY *See* Emergency medical technicians

PARANORMAL FICTION

Mass, W. The last present **Fic**

The best birthday parties ever! **793.2**

Danks, F. Run wild! **790.1**

DeVore, J. Ballerina cookbook **641.8**

Duncan, K. The good fun! book **642**

Kenney, K. L. Cool family parties **793.2**

Kenney, K. L. Cool holiday parties **793.2**

Kenney, K. L. Cool international parties **793.2**

Kenney, K. L. Cool slumber parties **793.2**

Kenney, K. L. Cool sports parties **793.2**

Kenney, K. L. Cool theme parties **793.2**

McGillian, J. K. Sleepover party! **793.2**

Regan, L. Party games **790.1**

Rose, D. L. Birthday zoo **E**

Torres, L. Rock your party **745.54**

PARTIES

 See also Entertaining

PARTIES -- FICTION

Bardhan-Quallen, S. Duck, Duck, Moose! **E**

Brendler, C. Not very scary **E**

Park, L. S. Xander's panda party **E**

Skateboard party **Fic**

PARTNERSHIP

 See also Business enterprises

Partridge, Elizabeth

Dogtag summer **Fic**

Oranges on Golden Mountain **E**

Restless spirit: the life and work of Dorothea Lange **770**

Party games. Regan, L. **790.1**

A **party** in Ramadan. Mobin-Uddin, A. **E**

Parzival. Paterson, K. **398.2**

Paschen, Elise

(ed) Poetry speaks to children **811**

(ed) Poetry speaks: who I am **808.81**

Paschkis, Julie

(il) Brown, M. Pablo Neruda **92**

P. Zonka lays an egg **E**

Mooshka **E**

(il) Baum, M. I have a little dreidel **782.42**

(il) Engle, M. Summer birds: the butterflies of Maria Merian **92**

(il) Fleischman, P. Glass slipper, gold sandal **398.2**

(il) Khan, H. Night of the Moon **E**

(il) Knock on wood **811**

(il) Lord, J. Albert the Fix-it Man **E**

(il) Lord, J. Here comes Grandma! **E**

(il) Lord, J. Where is Catkin? **E**

(il) MacDonald, M. R. Fat cat **398.209**

(il) MacDonald, M. R. The great smelly, slobbery, small-tooth dog **398.2**

(il) Paye Head, body, legs **398.2**

(il) Paye Mrs. Chicken and the hungry crocodile **398.2**

(il) Rodriguez, R. Building on nature **92**

(il) Rodriguez, R. Through Georgia's eyes **92**

(il) Wong, J. S. Twist **811**

Pascoe, Elaine

Plants without seeds **586**

Pascual and the kitchen angels. DePaola, T. **E**

Passage to freedom. Mochizuki, K. **940.53**

Passing the music down. **E**

Passion and poison. Del Negro, J. **S**

A **passion** for victory: the story of the Olympics in ancient and early modern times. Bobrick, B. **796.4**

PASSION PLAYS

 See also Bible plays; Mysteries and miracle plays; Religious drama; Theater

PASSIONS *See* Emotions

PASSIVE RESISTANCE

Demi Gandhi **954.03**

Wilkinson, P. Gandhi **92**

PASSIVE RESISTANCE

 See also Resistance to government

Passover. Ziefert, H. **296.4**

PASSOVER

Had gadya **296.4**

Heiligman, D. Celebrate Passover **296.4**

Kimmel, E. A. Wonders and miracles **296.4**

The longest night **E**

Manushkin, F. Miriam's cup **222**

The miracles of Passover **296.4**

Schecter, E. The family Haggadah **296.4**

Ziefert, H. Passover **296.4**

PASSOVER

 See also Jewish holidays

PASSOVER -- FICTION

Cohen, D. B. Nachshon, who was afraid to swim **E**

Fireside, B. J. Private Joel and the Sewell Mountain seder **Fic**

Glaser, L. Hoppy Passover! **E**

Portnoy, M. A. Tale of two Seders **E**

Rappaport, D. The secret seder **E**

Weber, E. The Yankee at the seder **Fic**

PASSOVER -- FOLKLORE

Kimmelman, L. The Little Red Hen and the Passover matzah **398.2**

PASTEL DRAWING

 See also Drawing

Pastel, Elyse

(il) Hazen, L. E. Cinder Rabbit **Fic**

Pasternak, Carol

How to raise monarch butterflies **595.78**

Pasteur, Louis, 1822-1895

     About

Hyde, N. What is germ theory? **615**

Miles, L. Louis Pasteur **509.2**

Ollhoff, J. The germ detectives **616.9**

Zamosky, L. Louis Pasteur **92**

PASTIMES *See* Amusements; Games; Recreation

PASTORAL PEOPLES *See* Nomads

PASTORAL POETRY

 See also Poetry

PASTORS *See* Clergy; Priests

PASTRY

    See also Baking; Cooking

PASTURES

    See also Agriculture; Land use

Pat-a-cake. Kubler, A.   **398.8**

PATAGONIA (ARGENTINA AND CHILE) -- FICTION

Barron, T. A. Ghost hands   **E**

Patch, Sam, 1807-1829

About

Cummins, J. Sam Patch   **92**

PATCHWORK

    See also Needlework

The **patchwork** path. Stroud, B.   **E**

The **patchwork** quilt. Flournoy, V.   **E**

PATCHWORK QUILTS *See* Quilts

The **patchwork** Torah. Ofanansky, A.   **E**

Pateman, Robert

Bolivia   **984**

Patent, Dorothy Hinshaw

The horse and the Plains indians   **978**

Dogs on duty   **355.4**

The right dog for the job   **362.4**

Saving Audie   **636.7**

When the wolves returned   **599.77**

Slinky, Scaly, Slithery Snakes   **597.96**

PATENTS

    See also Manufactures

PATENTS

Earmuffs for everyone!   **92**

Paterson, John

The Flint Heart   **Fic**

Paterson, Katherine

Bread and roses, too   **Fic**

Bridge to Terabithia   **Fic**

Brother Sun, Sister Moon   **E**

(ed) Giving thanks   **E**

The great Gilly Hopkins   **Fic**

The light of the world   **232.9**

Lyddie   **Fic**

Park's quest   **Fic**

Parzival   **398.2**

The same stuff as stars   **Fic**

The tale of the mandarin ducks   **398.24**

(jt. auth) Paterson, J. The Flint Heart   **Fic**

About

Ellis, S. From reader to writer   **372.62**

Path of the pronghorn. Urbigkit, C.   **599.65**

PATHOLOGY

    See also Medicine

PATIENCE

De Goldi, K. The ACB with Honora Lee   **Fic**

PATIENCE

    See also Human behavior; Virtue

PATIENCE -- FICTION

Fogliano, J. If you want to see a whale   **E**

Marilyn's monster   **E**

Waiting is not easy!   **E**

Patience Wright. Shea, P. D.   **92**

Patkau, Karen

(il) Lottridge, C. B. One watermelon seed   **E**

Creatures great and small   **591.4**

Creatures yesterday and today   **591.3**

Patneaude, David

A piece of the sky   **Fic**

Patricelli, Leslie

Be quiet, Mike!   **E**

The birthday box   **E**

Higher! higher!   **E**

Potty   **E**

Tubby   **E**

Patricia von Pleasantsquirrel. Proimos, J.   **E**

Patrick in A teddy bear's picnic and other stories. Hayes, G.   **741.5**

Patrick's dinosaurs. Carrick, C.   **E**

Patrick, Saint, 373?-463?

About

DePaola, T. Patrick: patron saint of Ireland   **92**

Patrick: patron saint of Ireland. DePaola, T.   **92**

PATRIOTIC POETRY

    See also Poetry

PATRIOTIC SONGS *See* National songs

PATRIOTISM

Park, L. S. When my name was Keoko   **Fic**

PATRIOTISM

    See also Citizenship; Human behavior; Loyalty

PATRIOTISM -- FICTION

Calkhoven, L. Daniel at the Siege of Boston, 1776   **Fic**

Wilson, K. How to bake an American pie   **E**

Patrol. Myers, W. D.   **E**

Patron, Susan

Behind the masks   **Fic**

The higher power of Lucky   **Fic**

Maybe yes, maybe no, maybe maybe   **Fic**

PATRONS OF THE ARTS

Fritz, J. Leonardo's horse   **730.92**

Patt, Beverly

Best friends forever   **Fic**

Patten, Brian

The big snuggle-up   **E**

Patten, E. J.

Return to Exile   **Fic**

PATTERN PERCEPTION

Cleary, B. P. A-B-A-B-A--a book of pattern play   **515**

Pistoia, S. Patterns   **152.14**

Spotty, stripy, swirly   **152.14**

PATTERN PERCEPTION

    See also Perception

PERSIAN GULF REGION

O'Neal, C. We visit Iraq **956.7**

Tracy, K. We visit Saudi Arabia **953.8**

PERSIAN LEGENDS

Laird, E. Shahnameh **891**

PERSIAN POETRY

Demi Rumi **92**

Persiani, Tony

(il) Barton, C. The Day-Glo brothers **535.6**

Person, Stephen

Arctic fox **599.77**

Bubonic plague **614.5**

The coral reef **578.7**

Cougar **599.75**

Devastated by a volcano! **551.2**

Malaria **614.5**

Saving animals from oil spills **628.1**

Struck by lightning! **551.56**

PERSONAL APPEARANCE

Platt, R. They wore what?! **391**

Simons, R. At home in your body **613**

PERSONAL APPEARANCE -- FICTION

Clements, A. About average **Fic**

PERSONAL APPEARANCE -- GRAPHIC NOVELS

Telgemeier, R. Smile **741.5**

Personal best [series]

Gifford, C. Basketball **796.323**

Gifford, C. Soccer **796.334**

Gifford, C. Swimming **797.2**

Gifford, C. Track and field **796.42**

PERSONAL CLEANLINESS See Hygiene

PERSONAL CONDUCT See Conduct of life

PERSONAL FINANCE

Bochner, R. The new totally awesome money book for kids (and their parents) **332.024**

Chatzky, J. Not your parents' money book **332.024**

Hall, A. Show me the money **332.024**

Hall, M. Credit cards and checks **332.7**

Hall, M. Your allowance **332.024**

Hord, C. Need it or want it? **332.024**

Larson, J. S. Do I need it? or do I want it? **332.024**

Larson, J. S. What can you do with money? **332.024**

Lynette, R. What to do when your family has to cut costs **332.024**

Managing money **332.02**

Minden, C. Investing **332.6**

Mitten, E. K. Goods or services? **332.024**

Orr, T. A kid's guide to earning money **650.1**

Payment methods **332.4**

Roderick, S. Centsibility **332.024**

Schwartz, D. M. If you made a million **332.024**

PERSONAL FREEDOM See Freedom

PERSONAL GROOMING

Chancellor, D. Happy and healthy **646.7**

PERSONAL GROOMING

See also Hygiene; Personal appearance

PERSONAL HEALTH See Health

PERSONAL HEALTH SERVICES See Medical care

PERSONAL HYGIENE See Hygiene

PERSONAL LIFE SKILLS See Life skills

PERSONAL LOANS

See also Consumer credit; Loans

PERSONAL NAMES

See also Names

PERSONAL NAMES -- FICTION

Henkes, K. Penny and her doll **E**

PERSONAL NAMES -- FOLKLORE

Mosel, A. Tikki Tikki Tembo **398.2**

PERSONAL NARRATIVES See Autobiographies; Biography

PERSONAL SPACE

See also Interpersonal relations; Nonverbal communication; Space and time

PERSONAL TIME MANAGEMENT See Time management

PERSONALITY

See also Consciousness; Psychology

PERSONS

See also Human beings

PERSPECTIVE

See also Descriptive geometry; Geometrical drawing; Optics; Painting

PERSPECTIVE (PHILOSOPHY) -- FICTION

Girl meets boy **S**

PERSUASION (PSYCHOLOGY)

See also Communication; Conformity

PERSUASION (RHETORIC) See Public speaking; Rhetoric

PERU -- ANTIQUITIES

Gruber, B. Ancient Inca **985**

PERU -- FICTION

Lacey, J. Island of Thieves **Fic**

PERU -- SOCIAL LIFE AND CUSTOMS

Krebs, L. Up and down the Andes **985**

Sheen, B. Foods of Peru **641.5**

PERUVIAN COOKING

Sheen, B. Foods of Peru **641.5**

PESACH See Passover

Peskimo (Company)

(il) Franceschelli, C. Alphablock **E**

Peskowitz, Miriam

(jt. auth) Buchanan, A. J. The daring book for girls **646.700**

Peskowitz, Miriam

Buchanan, A. J. The daring book for girls **031.02**

PESSIMISM -- FICTION

Mack, J. Good news, bad news **E**

PEST CONTROL

See also Agricultural pests; Economic zoology; Pests

funerals, and other fatal circumstances **Fic**

(il) Look, L. Alvin Ho: allergic to girls, school, and other scary things **Fic**

All the things I love about you **E**

(il) Rosenthal, A. K. Bedtime for Mommy **E**

Singer, M. A stick is an excellent thing **811**

(il) Snyder, L. Any which wall **Fic**

Phantom of Blood Alley. Stewart, P. **Fic**

The **phantom** tollbooth. Juster, N. **Fic**

PHANTOMS *See* Apparitions; Ghosts

Pharaoh. Kennett, D. **932**

Pharaoh's boat. Weitzman, D. L. **932**

The **Pharaohs'** armies. Park, L. **355**

PHARMACEUTICAL CHEMISTRY

    See also Chemistry

PHARMACOLOGY

    See also Medicine

PHARMACY

Petersen, C. The apothecary **615**

PHARMACY

    See also Chemistry; Medicine

PHEASANTS

    See also Birds; Game and game birds

Pheidippides, fl. 490 B.C.

          About

Reynolds, S. The first marathon: the legend of Pheidippides **938**

Phelan, Glen

Invisible force **531**

Phelan, Matt

(il) Bluffton **741.5**

Marilyn's monster **E**

(il) Park, L. S. Xander's panda party **E**

(il) Birdsall, J. Flora's very windy day **E**

(il) Birney, B. G. The seven wonders of Sassafras Springs **Fic**

(il) Mazer, A. Spilling ink **808.3**

(il) Patron, S. The higher power of Lucky **Fic**

Around the world **741.5**

The storm in the barn **741.5**

(il) Robbins, J. The new girl . . . and me **E**

(il) Robbins, J. Two of a kind **E**

(il) Rockwell, A. F. Big George: how a shy boy became President Washington **92**

(il) Spinelli, E. Where I live **Fic**

(il) Stott, A. Always **E**

(il) Stott, A. I'll be there **E**

Phelps, Michael, 1985-

          About

Torsiello, D. P. Michael Phelps **92**

PHILADELPHIA (PA.)

Anderson, L. H. Fever, 1793 **Fic**

Staton, H. Independence Hall **974.8**

PHILADELPHIA (PA.) -- FICTION

Anderson, L. H. Fever, 1793 **Fic**

De Angeli, M. L. Thee, Hannah! **Fic**

Neri, G. Ghetto cowboy **Fic**

Smith, R. I. Q.: book two, The White House **Fic**

PHILADELPHIA (PA.) -- HISTORY

Murphy, J. An American plague **614.5**

PHILADELPHIA (PA.) -- HISTORY -- 19TH CENTURY -- FICTION

Blackwood, G. Curiosity **Fic**

Philadelphia chickens. Boynton, S. **782.42**

PHILADELPHIA PHILLIES (BASEBALL TEAM) -- FICTION

Berk, J. Strike three, you're dead **Fic**

PHILANTHROPISTS

Alexander, S. H. She touched the world: Laura Bridgman, deaf-blind pioneer **92**

Figley, M. R. Prisoner for liberty **92**

Glaser, L. Emma's poem **974.7**

Henrietta King, la patrona **976.4**

Kulling, M. It's a snap! **92**

Lasky, K. Vision of beauty: the story of Sarah Breedlove Walker **B**

Let it shine **920**

Liberty's voice: the story of Emma Lazarus **92**

Mitchell, D. Driven **92**

Ray, D. Ghost girl **Fic**

Reusser, K. Celebrities giving back **361.7**

Wadsworth, G. First Girl Scout **369.463**

Weatherford, C. B. Dear Mr. Rosenwald **Fic**

Weatherford, C. B. Oprah **92**

Philbrick, Rodman

Zane and the hurricane **Fic**

Philbrick, W. R.

The mostly true adventures of Homer P. Figg **Fic**

The young man and the sea **Fic**

Philip Hall likes me, I reckon maybe. Greene, B. **Fic**

Philip Reid saves the statue of freedom. **973**

Philip, Neil

(ed) A Braid of lives **970.004**

(ed) Weave little stars into my sleep **782.42**

Phillipps, Julie C.

Wink: the ninja who wanted to be noticed **E**

Wink: the ninja who wanted to nap **E**

Phillips, Chad

(il) Marzollo, J. Help me learn numbers 0-20 **E**

(il) Marzollo, J. Help me learn subtraction **513.2**

Phillips, Charles

Japan **952**

Sweden **948.5**

Phillips, Craig

(il) Holub, J. Zeus and the thunderbolt of doom **E**

Phillips, Dave

(il) Jacobson, A. Palace of dreams **Fic**

Phillips, Gary R.

(il) Blessing, C. New old shoes **E**

Phillips, John

Leonardo da Vinci **92**

Phillips, L. D. (Lodner Darvontis), 1825-1869

About

Fleming, C. Papa's mechanical fish   E

Phillips, Lily Renee

About

Robbins, T. Lily Renée, escape artist   940.53

Phillips-Duke, Barbara J.

(il) Hazen, B. S. Digby   E

Phillis sings out freedom. Malaspina, A.   92

Phillis's big test. Clinton, C.   92

PHILOLOGISTS

Berner, R. S. Definitely not for little ones   398.2

Ellis, S. From reader to writer   372.62

Hettinga, D. R. The Brothers Grimm   430

Pirotta, S. The McElderry book of Grimms' fairy tales   398.2

PHILOLOGISTS -- GREAT BRITAIN -- BIOGRAPHY

Bryant, J. The right word   92

PHILOLOGY *See* Language and languages; Linguistics

PHILOSOPHERS

Demi Buddha   294.3

Demi The legend of Lao Tzu and the Tao te ching   299.5

Jun Lim Socrates   183

Love, D. A. Of numbers and stars   92

PHILOSOPHY

Law, S. Really, really big questions   100

What do you believe?   200

PHILOSOPHY -- ENCYCLOPEDIAS

See also Encyclopedias and dictionaries

PHILOSOPHY -- HISTORIOGRAPHY

See also Historiography

PHILOSOPHY AND RELIGION

See also Philosophy; Religion

PHILOSOPHY OF NATURE

Goble, P. All our relatives   970.004

Philpot, Chris

(il) Buchholz, R. How to survive anything   646.7

Phineas Gage: a gruesome but true story about brain science. Fleischman, J.   362.1

Phineas L. MacGuire . . . blasts off! Dowell, F. O.   Fic

Phineas L. MacGuire . . . gets slimed! Dowell, F. O.   Fic

Phineas L. Macguire erupts! Dowell, F. O.   Fic

Phobiapedia. Levy, J.   616.85

PHOBIAS

Levy, J. Phobiapedia   616.85

PHOBIAS

See also Fear; Neuroses

PHOBIAS -- FICTION

Daneshvari, G. Class is not dismissed!   Fic

Daneshvari, G. School of Fear   Fic

LaFaye, A. Water steps   Fic

PHOENIX (MYTHICAL BIRD)

See also Mythical animals

PHOENIX (MYTHICAL BIRD) -- FICTION

Demi The girl who drew a phoenix   E

PHONETICS

See also Language and languages; Sound

PHONOGRAPH RECORDS *See* Sound recordings

PHOSPHORESCENCE

See also Luminescence; Radioactivity

Phosphorus. Beatty, R.   546

PHOSPHORUS

Beatty, R. Phosphorus   546

A photo for Greta. Alter, A.   E

PHOTOBIOLOGY

Ocean sunlight   571.4

PHOTODOCUMENTATION *See* Documentary photography

PHOTOGRAPHERS

Bond, R. In the belly of an ox: the unexpected photographic adventures of Richard and Cherry Kearton   92

Crews, D. Bigmama's   92

Eliza's cherry trees   92

Freedman, R. Kids at work   331.3

Gerstein, M. Sparrow Jack   E

Martin, J. B. Snowflake Bentley   551.57

Partridge, E. Restless spirit: the life and work of Dorothea Lange   770

Rosenberg, A. The Civil War   920

Winthrop, E. Counting on Grace   Fic

PHOTOGRAPHERS

See also Artists

PHOTOGRAPHERS -- FICTION

Alter, A. A photo for Greta   E

Winthrop, E. Counting on Grace   Fic

PHOTOGRAPHERS -- UNITED STATES -- BIOGRAPHY

Gordon Parks   92

PHOTOGRAPHIC CHEMISTRY

See also Chemistry

PHOTOGRAPHS

Nardo, D. The Blue marble   525.022

PHOTOGRAPHS -- HISTORY

Nardo, D. The Blue marble   525.022

PHOTOGRAPHY

Gordon Parks   92

Kaufman, E. Numbers everywhere   E

PHOTOGRAPHY -- DIGITAL TECHNIQUES *See* Digital photography

PHOTOGRAPHY -- FICTION

Lord, C. Half a chance   Fic

PHOTOGRAPHY -- HISTORY

Kulling, M. It's a snap!   92

PHOTOGRAPHY OF ANIMALS

Haas, R. B. I dreamed of flying like a bird   779

PHOTOGRAPHY OF ANIMALS

Ponce de Leon, Juan, 1460?-1521
About
Fritz, J. Around the world in a hundred years **910.92**
POND ANIMALS
The secret pool **577.63**
POND ANIMALS -- FICTION
Duck says don't! **E**
Pond babies. Falwell, C. **E**
Pond circle. Franco, B. **E**
POND ECOLOGY
> See also Ecology
POND ECOLOGY -- FICTION
Fleming, D. In the small, small pond **813**
Franco, B. Pond circle **E**
Quattlebaum, M. Jo MacDonald saw a pond **E**
Wallace, N. E. Pond walk **E**
A **pond** full of ink. **839.31**
Pond walk. Wallace, N. E. **E**
PONDS
Bredeson, C. Baby animals of lakes and ponds **591.7**
Bruchac, J. The dark pond **Fic**
Serafini, F. Looking closely around the pond **578.7**
PONDS
> See also Water
PONDS -- FICTION
Bruchac, J. The dark pond **Fic**
Bunting, E. Frog and friends **E**
Duck says don't! **E**
Falwell, C. Pond babies **E**
Falwell, C. Scoot! **E**
Wallace, N. E. Pond walk **E**
Yang, B. Foo, the flying frog of Washtub Pond **E**
PONDS -- POETRY
Sidman, J. Song of the water boatman **811**
PONIES
> See also Horses
PONIES -- FICTION
Angleberger, T. Crankee Doodle **E**
Lester, A. Noni the pony **E**
Pons, Bernadette
(il) Dokas, D. Muriel's red sweater **E**
PONTIAC'S CONSPIRACY, 1763-1765
> See also Native Americans -- Wars; United
> States -- History -- 1600-1775, Colonial period
PONY EXPRESS
Kay, V. Whatever happened to the Pony Express? **383**
Spradlin, M. P. Off like the wind! **383**
Thompson, G. Riding with the mail **383**
PONY EXPRESS
> See also Express service; Postal service
The pony whisperer [series]
Rising, J. The word on the yard **Fic**
Ponyella. Numeroff, L. J. **E**
POODLES -- FICTION
Dipucchio, K. Gaston **E**

The **pool** of fire. Christopher, J. **Fic**
Poole, Amy Lowry
The pea blossom **E**
Poop happened! Albee, S. **363.7**
Poop-eaters. Prischmann, D. A. **595.7**
POOR
Bial, R. Tenement **974.7**
Hopkinson, D. Shutting out the sky **307**
Saul, L. Ways to help disadvantaged youth **362.7**
POOR
> See also Poverty; Public welfare
POOR -- MEDICAL CARE
> See also Medical care
Poor Doreen. **E**
A **poor** excuse for a dragon. Hayes, G. **E**
POOR RELIEF See Charities; Domestic economic
assistance; Public welfare
POP ART
Christensen, B. Fabulous! **92**
Rubin, S. G. Andy Warhol **92**
Rubin, S. G. Whaam!: the art & life of Roy Lichtenstein **92**
POP ART
> See also Art
Pop culture bios: action movie stars [series]
Higgins, N. Jennifer Lawrence **791.450**
Pop culture revolutions [series]
Rosinsky, N. M. Graphic content! **741.5**
POP MUSICIANS
Bieber, J. Justin Bieber: first step 2 forever **92**
Orgill, R. Skit-scat raggedy cat: Ella Fitzgerald **92**
Pinkney, A. D. Ella Fitzgerald **92**
Yasuda, A. Justin Bieber **92**
Pop! Bradley, K. B. **530.4**
Pop! McCarthy, M. **664**
Pop's bridge. Bunting, E. **E**
Pop-up. Wickings, R. **070.5**
A **pop-up** book of nursery rhymes. Reinhart, M. **398.8**
POP-UP BOOKS
The 12 days of Christmas **782.42**
Adams, T. Feel the force! **530**
Baruzzi, A. The true story of Little Red Riding Hood **E**
Bataille, M. 10 **E**
Bataille, M. ABC3D **E**
Belloc, H. Jim who ran away from his nurse and was eaten by a lion **E**
Boisrobert, A. Popville **E**
Campbell, R. Dear zoo **E**
Carter, D. A. 600 black spots **E**
Carter, D. A. Blue 2 **E**
Carter, D. A. Lots of bots **E**
Carter, D. A. One red dot **E**
Carter, D. A. White noise **E**
Carter, D. A. Yellow square **E**

Baylor, B. When clay sings   **970.004**
Kenney, K. L. Super simple clay projects   **738.1**
Park, L. S. A single shard   **Fic**
POTTERY
    See also Ceramics; Clay industry; Decoration and ornament; Decorative arts; Tableware
POTTERY -- FICTION
Look, L. Polka Dot Penguin Pottery   **E**
Park, L. S. A single shard   **Fic**
POTTERY, AMERICAN *See* American pottery
Potts, Aiden
The smash! smash! truck   **363.7**
Potty. Patricelli, L.   **E**
Potty animals. Vestergaard, H.   **E**
Pouch! Stein, D. E.   **E**
POUGHKEEPSIE (N.Y.) -- FICTION
Graff, L. A tangle of knots   **Fic**
Poulsen, David A.
Old Man   **Fic**
POULTRY
    See also Birds; Domestic animals
The **pout-pout** fish. Diesen, D.   **E**
The **pout-pout** fish goes to school. Diesen, D.   **E**
Poverty. Mason, P.   **362.5**
POVERTY
    See also Economic conditions; Social problems
POVERTY
Mason, P. Poverty   **362.5**
Tejubehan (Singer) Drawing from the City   **745**
POVERTY -- FICTION
Davis, A. A hen for Izzy Pippik   **FIC**
Jimmy the greatest!   **E**
Povey, Karen D.
Centipede   **595.6**
Pow, Tom
Tell me one thing, Dad   **E**
Powell, Barbara Johns, 1935-1991
      About
Kanefield, T. The girl from the tar paper school **92**
Powell, Ben
Stock, C. Skateboarding step-by-step   **796.22**
Powell, Consie
(il) Bevis, M. E. Wolf song   **E**
Powell, Eric
(il) Sniegoski, T. Billy Hooten, Owlboy   **Fic**
Powell, Jillian
Explaining cystic fibrosis   **616.3**
Fats for a healthy body   **613.2**
Powell, John Wesley, 1834-1902
      About
Ray, D. K. Down the Colorado   **92**
Waldman, S. The last river   **978**
Powell, Martin
The tall tale of Paul Bunyan: the graphic novel   **741.5**

Powell, Patricia Hruby
Josephine   **92**
Powell, William J., 1916-
      About
Michelson, R. Twice as good   **796.352**
POWER (MECHANICS)
Claybourne, A. Pushes and pulls   **531**
Hillman, B. How strong is it?   **620.1**
Spilsbury, R. What is energy?   **621**
POWER (MECHANICS)
    See also Mechanical engineering; Mechanics
POWER (SOCIAL SCIENCES)
    See also Political science
POWER (SOCIAL SCIENCES) -- FICTION
Demi The greatest power   **E**
POWER OF ATTORNEY
    See also Law
The **power** of cute. Harper, C. M.   **E**
The **power** of Un. Etchemendy, N.   **Fic**
POWER PLANTS, NUCLEAR *See* Nuclear power plants
Power play. O'Donnell, L.   **741.5**
POWER POLITICS *See* Balance of power; Cold war
POWER RESOURCES *See* Energy resources
POWER RESOURCES -- FICTION
Frank Einstein and the Electro-Finger   **Fic**
POWER RESOURCES CONSERVATION *See* Energy conservation
POWER RESOURCES DEVELOPMENT *See* Energy development
POWER SUPPLY *See* Energy resources
POWER TOOLS
    See also Tools
POWER TRANSMISSION
    See also Mechanical engineering; Power (Mechanics)
POWER TRANSMISSION, ELECTRIC *See* Electric lines; Electric power distribution
Power up to fight pollution. Bullard, L.   **363.7**
Power up! Learn about energy. Vogel, J.   **333.79**
Powerful medicine [series]
Markle, S. Bad burns   **617.1**
Markle, S. Faulty hearts   **612.1**
Markle, S. Leukemia   **616.99**
Markle, S. Lost sight   **617.7**
Markle, S. Shattered bones   **617.1**
Markle, S. Wounded brains   **617**
Powerful words. Hudson, W.   **081**
Powerless. Cody, M.   **Fic**
Powers, Don T.
(il) Hartnett, S. The silver donkey   **Fic**
The **Powhatan.** King, D. C.   **970.004**
POWHATAN INDIANS
Brimner, L. D. Pocahontas   **92**
King, D. C. The Powhatan   **970.004**

Lester, J. Let's talk about race **305.8**
Marsden, C. The gold-threaded dress **Fic**
Polacco, P. Mr. Lincoln's way **E**
Schwartz, J. Short **612.6**
Yep, L. The traitor **Fic**

PREJUDICES
See also Attitude (Psychology); Emotions;
Interpersonal relations

PREJUDICES -- FICTION
Barker, M. P. Mending horses **Fic**

Preller, James
Home sweet horror **E**
Justin Fisher declares war! **Fic**
Mighty Casey **E**
A pirate's guide to first grade **E**
Six innings **Fic**

Prelutsky, Jack
(comp) The 20th century children's poetry treasury **811**
(comp) For laughing out loud **811**
Be glad your nose is on your face and other poems **811**
Behold the bold umbrellaphant **811**
The carnival of the animals **811**
The dragons are singing tonight **811**
The frogs wore red suspenders **811**
Good sports **811**
The Headless Horseman rides tonight **811**
If not for the cat **811**
It's Christmas! **811**
It's snowing! it's snowing! **811**
It's Thanksgiving! **811**
It's Valentine's Day **811**
My dog may be a genius **811**
The new kid on the block: poems **811**
Nightmares: poems to trouble your sleep **811**
A pizza the size of the sun **811**
Pizza, pigs, and poetry **808.1**
Ride a purple pelican **811**
Scranimals **811**
Something big has been here **811**
The swamps of Sleethe **811**
Tyrannosaurus was a beast **811**
What a day it was at school! **811**
(ed) The Random House book of poetry for children **811**
(comp) Read a rhyme, write a rhyme **811**
(comp) Read-aloud rhymes for the very young **811**
Seuss Hooray for Diffendoofer Day! **E**
(ed) There's no place like school **811**
The wizard **E**
I've lost my hippopotamus **811**
Stardines swim high across the sky and other poems **811**

PREMATURE BABIES -- FICTION
Kantorovitz, S. The very tiny baby **E**

PREMENSTRUAL SYNDROME
See also Menstruation

PREMIERS See Prime ministers

PRENATAL CARE
See also Pregnancy

Prentzas, G. S.
Arkansas **976.7**
Georgia **975.8**
Wyoming **978.7**

PREPARATION GUIDES FOR EXAMINATIONS See Examinations -- Study guides

PREPARED CEREALS
See also Breakfasts; Food
Rex, A. Unlucky charms **Fic**

Prepositions. Heinrichs, A. **428**

PRESCHOOL CHILDREN See Children

Preschool favorites. Briggs, D. **372.6**

Preschool to the rescue. Sierra, J. **E**

PRESENTS See Gifts

PRESERVATION OF BIODIVERSITY See Biodiversity conservation

PRESERVATION OF FOOD See Food -- Preservation

PRESERVATION OF NATURAL RESOURCES See Conservation of natural resources

PRESERVATION OF NATURAL SCENERY See Landscape protection; Natural monuments; Nature conservation

PRESERVATION OF WILDLIFE See Wildlife conservation

Preserve our planet [series]
Delano, M. F. Earth in the hot seat **363.7**

President George Washington. Allen, K. **92**
The **president** is shot! Holzer, H. **973.7**
President of the whole fifth grade. Winston, S. **Fic**
President Pennybaker. Feiffer, K. **E**
President taft is stuck in the bath. Barnett, M. **E**

PRESIDENTIAL ADVISERS
Let it shine **920**

PRESIDENTIAL CANDIDATES
Bardhan-Quallen, S. Ballots for Belva **92**
Blashfield, J. F. Hillary Clinton **92**
Krull, K. The brothers Kennedy **920**
Krull, K. A woman for president **92**
Let it shine **920**
Murphy, J. A savage thunder **973.7**
Raatma, L. Shirley Chisholm **92**

Presidential pets. **973**

PRESIDENTS
Abramson, J. Obama **92**
Adler, D. A. George Washington **92**
Adler, D. A. A picture book of Dolley and James Madison **92**
Adler, D. A. A picture book of John and Abigail Adams **92**
Adler, D. A. A picture book of John F. Kenne-

PROTECTION OF ENVIRONMENT *See* Environmental protection

PROTECTION OF GAME *See* Game protection

PROTECTION OF NATURAL SCENERY *See* Landscape protection; Natural monuments; Nature conservation

PROTECTION OF WILDLIFE *See* Wildlife conservation

PROTEINS
Royston, A. Proteins for a healthy body   **613.2**

PROTEINS
See also Biochemistry; Nutrition

Proteins for a healthy body. Royston, A.   **613.2**

PROTEST MARCHES AND RALLIES *See* Demonstrations

PROTEST MOVEMENTS
Scandiffio, L. People who said no   **303.48**

PROTEST MOVEMENTS -- FICTION
Violet Mackerel's pocket protest   **Fic**

PROTESTANTISM
See also Christianity; Church history

PROTESTS, DEMONSTRATIONS, ETC. *See* Demonstrations

Protists. Arato, R.   **579**

PROTISTS
Arato, R. Protists   **579**

The **protoctist** kingdom. Zabludoff, M.   **579**

PROTOCTISTA
Zabludoff, M. The protoctist kingdom   **579**

PROTONS
See also Atoms; Particles (Nuclear physics)

PROTOPLASM
See also Biology; Life (Biology)

Protopopescu, Orel
Thelonious Mouse   **E**

PROTOZOA
Arato, R. Protists   **579**
Graham, I. Microscopic scary creatures   **591.6**

PROTOZOA
See also Microorganisms

Proud as a peacock, brave as a lion. Barclay, J.   **E**

A **proud** taste for scarlet and miniver. Konigsburg, E. L.   **Fic**

Proud to be Inuvialuit.   **970.004**

Prove it! Glass, S.   **507**

Provensen, Alice
The buck stops here   **973**
A day in the life of Murphy   **E**
The glorious flight: across the Channel with Louis Bleriot, July 25, 1909   **92**
(il) Willard, N. A visit to William Blake's inn **811**

Provensen, Martin
Provensen, A. The glorious flight: across the Channel with Louis Bleriot, July 25, 1909   **92**
(il) Willard, N. A visit to William Blake's inn **811**

PROVERBS

The Night has ears   **398.9**

PROVERBS
See also Folklore; Quotations

PROVERBS -- FICTION
Gregorich, B. Waltur paints himself into a corner and other stories   **E**
A mango in the hand   **E**

PROVIDENCE (R.I.) -- FICTION
Johnson, P. The amazing adventures of John Smith, Jr., aka Houdini   **Fic**

PROVIDENCE AND GOVERNMENT OF GOD
See also God

Prowling the seas. Turner, P. S.   **591.7**

Proxy. London, A.   **Fic**

Prudence wants a pet. Daly, C.   **E**

PRUNING
See also Forests and forestry; Fruit culture; Gardening; Trees

Pryor, Bonnie
The iron dragon   **Fic**
Simon's escape   **Fic**

Pryor, Kimberley Jane
Amazing armor   **591.47**
Clever camouflage   **591.47**
Cooperation   **177**
Courage   **179**
Honesty   **177**
Kindness   **177**
Mimicry and relationships   **591.47**
Respect   **177**
Tolerance   **177**
Tricky behavior   **591.47**
Venom, poison, and electricity   **591.6**
Warning colors   **591.47**

The **PS** brothers. Boelts, M.   **Fic**

Psalm 23. Moser, B.   **223**

Psalms for young children. Delval   **223**

PSEUDONYMS
See also Names; Personal names

PSI (PARAPSYCHOLOGY) *See* Parapsychology

Pssst! Rex, A.   **E**

PSYCHE (GREEK DEITY)
Craft, M. Cupid and Psyche   **292.1**

PSYCHE (GREEK DEITY)
See also Gods and goddesses

PSYCHIATRIC HOSPITALS
See also Hospitals

PSYCHIATRIC HOSPITALS -- FICTION
Edge, C. Twelve minutes to midnight   **Fic**

PSYCHIATRY
See also Medicine

PSYCHIC ABILITY -- FICTION
Barnholdt, L. Girl meets ghost   **Fic**
Stroud, J. The screaming staircase   **Fic**
Stroud, J. The whispering skull   **Fic**

PSYCHIC PHENOMENA *See* Parapsychology

PSYCHICAL RESEARCH *See* Parapsychology

PSYCHICS

    See also Parapsychology; Persons

PSYCHOANALYSIS

    See also Psychology

PSYCHOKINESIS

    See also Parapsychology; Spiritualism

PSYCHOKINESIS -- FICTION

    LaMarche, J. Up   E

PSYCHOLOGICAL STRESS *See* Stress (Psychology)

PSYCHOLOGICAL TESTS

    See also Psychology

PSYCHOLOGICAL WARFARE

    See also Applied psychology; Military art and science; Morale; Propaganda; War

PSYCHOLOGY

    Funston, S. It's all in your head   **612.8**

    Totally human   **612**

    Winston, R. M. L. What goes on in my head? **612.8**

    Young, K. R. Experiments to do on your family   **507.8**

PSYCHOLOGY

    See also Brain; Philosophy; Soul

PSYCHOLOGY OF LEARNING

    See also Animal intelligence; Child psychology; Education; Educational psychology; Memory

PSYCHOLOGY OF RELIGION

    See also Psychology; Religion

PSYCHOLOGY, PATHOLOGICAL

    Ouch!   **616**

PSYCHOPHYSIOLOGY

    See also Nervous system; Physiology; Psychology

PSYCHOSOMATIC MEDICINE

    See also Abnormal psychology; Medicine; Mind and body; Psychoanalysis

PSYCHOTHERAPY

    Rashkin, R. Feeling better   **616.89**

PSYCHOTHERAPY

    See also Psychiatry; Therapeutics

PTERANODON

    See also Dinosaurs; Pterosaurs

Pterodactyl. Peterson, S.   **567.9**

PTERODACTYLS

    Lessem, D. Flying giants of dinosaur time   **567.9**

PTERODACTYLS

    See also Dinosaurs

PTEROSAURS

    Ewart, C. Fossil   E

    Lessem, D. Flying giants of dinosaur time   **567.9**

    MacLeod, E. Monster fliers   **567.9**

PTEROSAURS

    See also Dinosaurs

PTEROSAURS -- FICTION

    Ewart, C. Fossil   E

Pu Yi, 1906-1967

    About

    Cotter, C. Kids who rule   **920**

PUBERTY

    Boy talk   **612.6**

    The care & keeping of you   **613.04**

    The care & keeping of you 2   **613**

    It's perfectly normal   **613.9**

    Jukes, M. Growing up: it's a girl thing   **612.6**

    Katz, A. Girl in the know   **612.6**

    Madaras, L. On your mark, get set, grow!   **612.6**

    Madaras, L. Ready, set, grow!   **612.6**

    Madaras, L. The what's happening to my body? book for boys   **612.6**

    Madaras, L. The what's happening to my body? book for girls   **612.6**

    Mar, J. The body book for boys   **612.6**

    Pfeifer, K. G. American Medical Assocation boy's guide to becoming a teen   **613**

    Pfeifer, K. G. American Medical Association girl's guide to becoming a teen   **613**

    Plaisted, C. Girl talk   **612.6**

    Saltz, G. Changing you!   **612.6**

    Will puberty last my whole life?   **613**

PUBERTY -- FICTION

    Greene, S. Sophie Hartley and the facts of life   Fic

PUBLIC ADMINISTRATION

    See also Local government; Municipal government; Political science

PUBLIC ASSISTANCE *See* Public welfare

PUBLIC BUILDINGS

    See also Buildings; Public works

PUBLIC DEBTS

    See also Debt; Loans; Public finance

PUBLIC DEMONSTRATIONS *See* Demonstrations

Public enemy number two. Horowitz, A.   Fic

PUBLIC FIGURES *See* Celebrities

PUBLIC HEALTH

    Mimi's Village   Fic

PUBLIC HEALTH

    See also Health; Human services; Social problems; State medicine

PUBLIC HYGIENE *See* Public health

PUBLIC LIBRARIES

    Fasick, A. M. Managing children's services in the public library   **027.62**

    Squires, T. Library partnerships   **021.2**

PUBLIC LIBRARIES

    See also Libraries

PUBLIC OPINION

    See also Freedom of conscience; Political psychology; Political science; Social psychology

PUBLIC PLAYGROUNDS *See* Playgrounds

AUTHOR, TITLE, AND SUBJECT INDEX
TWENTY-SECOND EDITION

Pulling dogs. Rajczak, K.   **636.7**

Pullman, Philip, 1946-

  Clockwork   **Fic**

  I was a rat!   **Fic**

  Two crafty criminals!   **Fic**

PULSARS

    See also Astronomy

Pulver, Robin

  Christmas kitten   E

  Happy endings   E

  Never say boo!   E

  Nouns and verbs have a field day   E

  Punctuation takes a vacation   E

  Saturday is Dadurday   E

  Silent letters loud and clear   E

  Thank you, Miss Doover   E

PUMAS

  Hamilton, S. L. Ambushed by a cougar   **599.75**

  Person, S. Cougar   **599.75**

  Rodriguez, C. Cougars   **599.75**

  Shores, E. L. Mountain lions   **599.75**

PUMAS -- FICTION

  Mora, P. Dona Flor   E

PUMPING MACHINERY

    See also Engines; Hydraulic engineering

PUMPKIN

  Cave, K. One child, one seed   E

  Esbaum, J. Seed, sprout, pumpkin, pie   **635**

  The fierce yellow pumpkin   E

  Fridell, R. Life cycle of a pumpkin   **635**

  Gibbons, G. The pumpkin book   **635**

  Holub, J. The garden that we grew   E

  Hubbell, W. Pumpkin Jack   E

  Malam, J. Grow your own soup   **635**

  Pfeffer, W. From seed to pumpkin   **583**

  Rotten pumpkin   **577.16**

  Rustad, M. E. H. Fall pumpkins   **635**

  Serfozo, M. Plumply, dumply pumpkin   E

PUMPKIN -- FICTION

  Catalanotto, P. No more pumpkins   **Fic**

  Cuyler, M. The bumpy little pumpkin   E

  Duke, K. Ready for pumpkins   E

  The fierce yellow pumpkin   E

  Holub, J. The garden that we grew   E

  Hubbell, W. Pumpkin Jack   E

  Jacobson, J. Andy Shane and the pumpkin trick   **Fic**

  McNamara, M. How many seeds in a pumpkin?   E

  Mortimer, A. Pumpkin cat   E

  Moulton, M. K. The very best pumpkin   E

  Rockwell, A. F. Apples and pumpkins   E

  Rosen, M. J. Night of the pumpkinheads   E

  Savage, S. Ten orange pumpkins   E

  Serfozo, M. Plumply, dumply pumpkin   E

  Tegen, K. The story of the Jack O'Lantern   E

  Thomas, J. Pumpkin trouble   E

  Titherington, J. Pumpkin, pumpkin   E

Wallace, C. The pumpkin mystery   E

Wallace, N. E. Pumpkin day!   E

The **pumpkin** book. Gibbons, G.   **635**

Pumpkin butterfly. Mordhorst, H.   **811**

Pumpkin cat. Mortimer, A.   E

Pumpkin day! Wallace, N. E.   E

Pumpkin eye. Fleming, D.   E

Pumpkin Jack. Hubbell, W.   E

The **pumpkin** mystery. Wallace, C.   E

Pumpkin soup. Cooper, H.   E

Pumpkin trouble. Thomas, J.   E

Pumpkin, pumpkin. Titherington, J.   E

PUNCTUALITY

    See also Time; Virtue

Punctuation. Heinrichs, A.   **428**

PUNCTUATION

  Bruno, E. K. A punctuation celebration!   **428**

  Budzik, M. Punctuation: the write stuff!   **428**

  Cleary, B. P. The punctuation station   **428**

  Truss, L. Eats, shoots & leaves   **428**

  Truss, L. The girl's like spaghetti   **428**

  Truss, L. Twenty-odd ducks   **428**

PUNCTUATION -- FICTION

  Carr, J. Greedy Apostrophe   E

  Pulver, R. Punctuation takes a vacation   E

A **punctuation** celebration! Bruno, E. K.   **428**

The **punctuation** station. Cleary, B. P.   **428**

Punctuation takes a vacation. Pulver, R.   E

Punctuation: the write stuff! Budzik, M.   **428**

PUNISHMENT IN SCHOOLS *See* School discipline

Punk. Guillain, C.   **781.66**

PUNK CULTURE -- JUVENILE FICTION

  Happy punks 1 2 3   E

PUNK ROCK MUSIC

  Guillain, C. Punk   **781.66**

Punk wig. Ries, L.   E

PUNS

    See also Wit and humor

PUNS -- FICTION

  Agee, J. Mr. Putney's quacking dog   E

  Hall, M. Cat tale   E

Punxsutawney Phyllis. Hill, S. L.   E

Pup and Hound hatch an egg. Hood, S.   E

The **pup** who cried wolf. Kurtz, C.   **Fic**

Puppet planet. Kennedy, J. E.   **791.5**

PUPPETEERS

  Jim Henson   **92**

  Sweet, M. Balloons over Broadway   **92**

PUPPETEERS -- FICTION

  Catmull, K. Summer and Bird   **Fic**

PUPPETS -- FICTION

  Schlitz, L. A. Splendors and glooms   **Fic**

PUPPETS -- POETRY

  Bryan, A. Ashley Bryan's Puppets   **811**

PUPPETS AND PUPPET PLAYS

Bauer, C. F. Leading kids to books through puppets **027.62**

Bryan, A. Ashley Bryan's Puppets **811**

Champlin, C. Storytelling with puppets **372.66**

D'Cruz Make your own puppets **791.5**

Exner, C. R. Practical puppetry A-Z **791.5**

Jim Henson **92**

Kennedy, J. E. Puppet planet **791.5**

Minkel, W. How to do The three bears with two hands **791.5**

Stanley, D. Mozart, the wonder child **92**

Sweet, M. Balloons over Broadway **92**

PUPPETS AND PUPPET PLAYS

See also Drama; Folk drama; Theater

PUPPETS AND PUPPET PLAYS -- FICTION

Angleberger, T. The surprise attack of Jabba the Puppett **Fic**

Schlitz, L. A. Splendors and glooms **Fic**

PUPPIES *See* Dogs

Arlon, P. Puppies and kittens **636.7**

Puppies and kittens. Arlon, P. **636.7**

Puppies and piggies. Rylant, C. **E**

Puppy power. Cox, J. **Fic**

The **puppy** who wanted a boy. Thayer, J. **E**

PURIFICATION OF WATER *See* Water purification

PURIM

Kimmel, E. A. The story of Esther **222**

PURIM -- FICTION

Goldin, B. D. Cakes and miracles **E**

PURITANS -- FICTION

Speare, E. G. The witch of Blackbird Pond **Fic**

Purmell, Ann

Apple cider making days **E**

Christmas tree farm **E**

Maple syrup season **E**

The **purple** balloon. Raschka, C. **155.9**

The **purple** coat. Hest, A. **E**

Purple Little Bird. Foley, G. **E**

The **purple** smurfs. Delporte, Y. **741.5**

Push button. Aliki **E**

The **pushcart** war. Merrill, J. **Fic**

Pushes and pulls. Claybourne, A. **531**

Pushing up the sky: seven Native American plays for children. Bruchac, J. **812**

Puss in boots. Cech, J. **398.2**

Puss in boots. Galdone, P. **398.2**

Puss in boots. Perrault, C. **398.24**

Put inclined planes to the test. Walker, S. M. **621.8**

Put it all together. Cornwall, P. **808**

Put it on the list. Darbyshire, K. **E**

Put levers to the test. Walker, S. M. **621.8**

Put pulleys to the test. Walker, S. M. **621.8**

Put screws to the test. Walker, S. M. **621.8**

Put wedges to the test. Walker, S. M. **621.8**

Put wheels and axles to the test. Walker, S. M. **621.8**

Puttapipat, Niroot

The musicians of Bremen **398.2**

Putting on a play. Jacobs, P. D. **792**

Puttock, Simon

Little lost cowboy **E**

PUYALLUP ASSEMBLY CENTER (PUYALLUP, WASH.) -- FICTION

Larson, K. Dash **Fic**

Patt, B. Best friends forever **Fic**

Puybaret, Eric

(il) Berne, J. Manfish: a story of Jacques Cousteau **92**

(il) Cech, J. The nutcracker **E**

(il) Harburg, E. Y. Over the rainbow **782.42**

(il) Lipton, L. Puff, the magic dragon

(il) Moore, C. C. The night before Christmas **811**

(il) When you wish upon a star **782.42**

(il) Yarrow, P. Puff the magic dragon pop-up book **E**

The **puzzle** of the platypus. Myers, J. **590**

PUZZLES

Carter, D. A. 600 black spots **E**

Carter, D. A. Blue 2 **E**

Carter, D. A. One red dot **E**

Clark, D. C. A kid's guide to Washington, D.C. **917**

Hillenbrand, W. Mother Goose picture puzzles **398.8**

Horvath, D. What dat? **E**

Kidslabel (Firm) Spot 7 animals **793.73**

Kidslabel (Firm) Spot 7 Christmas **793.73**

Kidslabel (Firm) Spot 7 School **793.73**

Kidslabel (Firm) Spot 7 spooky **793.73**

Kidslabel (Firm) Spot 7 Toys **793.73**

Marzollo, J. I spy school days **793.73**

Munro, R. Circus **E**

Nickle, J. Alphabet explosion! **793.73**

Onishi, S. Who's hiding? **E**

Steiner, J. Look-alikes **793.73**

Steiner, J. Look-alikes around the world **793.73**

Steiner, J. Look-alikes Christmas **793.73**

Steiner, J. Look-alikes, jr. **793.73**

Wick, W. Can you see what I see? **793.73**

Wick, W. Can you see what I see? Cool collections **793.73**

Wick, W. Can you see what I see? Dream machine **793.73**

Wick, W. Can you see what I see? On a scary, scary night **793.73**

Wick, W. Can you see what I see? Seymour and the juice box boat **793.73**

Wick, W. Can you see what I see? toyland express **793.73**

Wick, W. Can you see what I see?: once upon a time **793.73**

Wick, W. Can you see what I see?: Treasure ship **793.73**

RAIN FORESTS -- FICTION

Engle, M. Silver people   **Fic**

Na, I. S. Hide & seek   **E**

RAIN FORESTS -- PICTORIAL WORKS

Duke, K. In the rainforest   **577.34**

Rain makes applesauce. Scheer, J.   **E**

Rain play. Cotten, C.   **E**

Rain player. Wisniewski, D.   **398.2**

Rain Reign. Martin, A. M.   **Fic**

Rain school.   **E**

The **rain** stomper. Boswell, A. K.   **E**

The **rain** train. De Roo, E.   **E**

Rain! Ashman, L.   **E**

RAINBOW

See also Meteorology

Rainbow family collections. Naidoo, J. C.   **028.1**

Rainbow Street Shelter [series]

Orr, W. Lost! A dog called Bear   **Fic**

Orr, W. Missing! A cat called Buster   **Fic**

RAINFALL *See* Rain

Rainforest romp. Mitton, T.   **591.7**

Rainforests. Fusco Castaldo, N.   **577.3**

RAINFORESTS *See* Rain forests

Raining cats and detectives. Venable, C. A. F.   **Fic**

Raining cats and dogs. Moses, W.   **428**

Rainis, Kenneth G.

Gardner, R. Ace your animal science project   **590.7**

Gardner, R. Ace your chemistry science project   **540.7**

Rainmaker. Jackson, A.   **Fic**

Rainstorm. Lehman, B.   **E**

Raising boy readers. Sullivan, M.   **028.5**

Raising dragons. Nolen, J.   **E**

Raising voices. Sima, J.   **027.62**

Raj, the bookstore tiger. Pelley, K. T.   **E**

Rajczak, Kristen

Pulling dogs   **636.7**

Rescue dogs   **636.7**

Raji Codell, Esme

(jt. auth) Codell, R. E. Seed by seed   **634.11**

Rake, Jody Sullivan

Blue whales up close   **599.5**

The human skeleton   **611**

Humpback whales up close   **599.5**

The mystery of whale strandings   **599.5**

Rakkety Tam. Jacques, B.   **Fic**

Raleigh's page. Armstrong, A.   **Fic**

Raleigh, Walter Sir, 1552?-1618

About

Armstrong, A. Raleigh's page   **Fic**

RALLIES (PROTEST) *See* Demonstrations

Ralph Masiello's Halloween drawing book. Masiello, R.   **743**

Ralph Masiello's robot drawing book. Masiello, R.   **743**

Ralph S. Mouse. Cleary, B.   **Fic**

Ralston, Birgitta

Snow play   **796**

Rama, Sue

Keane, D. Daddy Adventure Day   **E**

Miller, H. Subway ride   **388.4**

Park, L. S. Yum! Yuck!   **413**

Ramadan. Murray, J.   **297.3**

RAMADAN

See also Islamic holidays

Ramadan. Douglass, S. L.   **297.3**

RAMADAN

Bullard, L. Rashad's Ramadan and Eid al-Fitr   **297.3**

Dickmann, N. Ramadan and Id-ul-Fitr   **297.3**

Douglass, S. L. Ramadan   **297.3**

Heiligman, D. Celebrate Ramadan & Eid al-Fitr   **297.3**

Hoyt-Goldsmith, D. Celebrating Ramadan   **297.3**

Jeffrey, L. S. Celebrate Ramadan   **297.3**

MacMillan, D. M. Ramadan and Id al-Fitr   **297.3**

Murray, J. Ramadan   **297.3**

Whitman, S. Under the Ramadan moon   **297.3**

RAMADAN -- FICTION

Addasi, M. The white nights of Ramadan   **E**

Jalali, R. Moon watchers   **E**

Katz, K. My first Ramadan   **E**

Khan, H. Night of the Moon   **E**

Mobin-Uddin, A. A party in Ramadan   **E**

Robert, N. b. Ramadan moon   **E**

Ramadan and Id al-Fitr. MacMillan, D. M.   **297.3**

Ramadan and Id-ul-Fitr. Dickmann, N.   **297.3**

Ramadan moon. Robert, N. b.   **E**

RAMAYANA

Arni, S. Sita's Ramayana   **741.5**

The **Ramayana** and Hinduism. Ganeri, A.   **294.5**

Ramirez, Antonio

Napi   **E**

Ramirez, Jose

Cumpiano, I. Quinito's neighborhood   **E**

Ramona and her father. Cleary, B.   **Fic**

Ramona and her mother. Cleary, B.   **Fic**

Ramona forever. Cleary, B.   **Fic**

Ramona Quimby, age 8. Cleary, B.   **Fic**

Ramona the brave. Cleary, B.   **Fic**

Ramona the pest. Cleary, B.   **Fic**

Ramona's world. Cleary, B.   **Fic**

Ramos, Jorge

I'm just like my mom/I'm just like my dad   **E**

Ramos, Mario

I am so strong   **E**

RAMOTSWE, PRECIOUS (FICTITIOUS CHARACTER) -- FICTION

McCall Smith, A. The Mystery of Meerkat Hill   **Fic**

Rampersad, Arnold

(ed) African American Poetry   **811**

(ed) Hughes, L. Langston Hughes   **811**

Ramsden, Ashley

Seven fathers   **398.2**

Ramsey, Calvin Alexander

Belle, the last mule at Gee's Bend   **E**

Ruth and the Green Book   **E**

RANCH LIFE

Freedman, R. In the days of the vaqueros   **636.2**

Steele, C. Cattle ranching in the American West **636**

Urbigkit, C. The guardian team   **636.7**

RANCH LIFE

    See also Farm life; Frontier and pioneer life

RANCH LIFE -- CALIFORNIA -- FICTION

Gee Whiz   **Fic**

RANCH LIFE -- FICTION

Gee Whiz   **Fic**

Meanwhile, back at the ranch   **E**

RANCH LIFE -- WEST (U.S.)

Branzei, S. Cowgirls   **920.72**

RANCHERS

Fern, T. E. Buffalo music   **E**

Henrietta King, la patrona   **976.4**

Rand McNally Goodes World Atlas.   **912**

Rand, Ann

I know a lot of things   **E**

Sparkle and spin   **E**

Rand, Betseygail

Big Bunny   **E**

Rand, Casey

DNA and heredity   **572.8**

Glass squid and other spectacular squid   **594**

Graphing sports   **796**

Human reproduction   **612.6**

Temperature   **536**

Time   **530.1**

Rand, Colleen

Rand, B. Big Bunny   **E**

Rand, Paul

Rand, A. I know a lot of things   **E**

Rand, A. Sparkle and spin   **E**

Rand, Ted

(il) Bunting, E. The memory string   **E**

(il) Cleary, B. The hullabaloo ABC   **E**

(il) George, J. C. Nutik, the wolf pup   **E**

(il) Martin, B. Barn dance!   **E**

(il) Martin, B. The ghost-eye tree   **E**

(il) Martin, B. Knots on a counting rope   **E**

(il) Prelutsky, J. If not for the cat   **811**

Randall, Alison L.

The wheat doll   **E**

Randolph Caldecott. Marcus, L. S.   **741.6**

Randolph, Ryan P.

New research techniques   **001.4**

The **Random** House book of Bible stories. Osborne, M. P.   **220.9**

The **Random** House book of poetry for children. **811**

Ranger's apprentice [series]

Flanagan, J. The battle for Skandia   **Fic**

Flanagan, J. The burning bridge   **Fic**

Flanagan, J. The emperor of Nihon-Ja   **Fic**

Flanagan, J. Erak's ransom   **Fic**

Flanagan, J. Halt's peril   **Fic**

Flanagan, J. The icebound land   **Fic**

Flanagan, J. The kings of Clonmel   **Fic**

Flanagan, J. The lost stories   **S**

Flanagan, J. The ruins of Gorlan   **Fic**

Flanagan, J. The siege of Macindaw   **Fic**

Flanagan, J. The sorcerer of the north   **Fic**

Rania

The sandwich swap   **E**

Rankin, Jeannette, 1880-1973

About

Krull, K. Lives of extraordinary women   **920**

Rankin, Joan

The popcorn astronauts   **811.6**

(il) Borden, L. Off to first grade   **E**

(il) Ruddell, D. A whiff of pine, a hint of skunk **811**

(il) Wilson, K. A frog in the bog   **E**

Rankin, Laura

(il) Ruthie and the (not so) very busy day   **E**

Ruthie and the (not so) teeny tiny lie   **E**

(il) Underwood, D. A balloon for Isabel   **E**

Ransford, Sandy

Horse & pony breeds   **636.1**

Horse & pony care   **636.1**

The Kingfisher illustrated horse & pony encyclopedia   **636.1**

Ransom, Candice

Big rigs on the move   **629.224**

The lifesaving adventure of Sam Deal, shipwreck rescuer   **741.5**

The old blue pickup truck   **E**

Rebel McKenzie   **Fic**

Scrapbooking just for you!   **745.593**

Ransome, Arthur, 1884-1967

About

Ellis, S. From reader to writer   **372.62**

Ransome, James

(il) My Name Is Truth   **92**

(il) Cline-Ransome, L. Before there was Mozart: the story of Joseph Boulogne, Chevalier de Saint-George   **92**

Cline-Ransome, L. Young Pele   **92**

(il) Hopkinson, D. Sky boys   **E**

(il) Hopkinson, D. Sweet Clara and the freedom quilt   **E**

(il) Howard, E. F. Aunt Flossie's hats (and crab cakes later)   **E**

(il) Jordan, D. Baby blessings   **242**

(il) McKissack, P. C. Let my people go   **Fic**

(il) Mitchell, M. K. Uncle Jed's barbershop   **E**

(il) Mitchell, M. K. When grandmama sings   **E**

Gunner, football hero   **E**

New red bike!   **E**

Ollhoff, J. Using your research **929**

RESEARCH -- CITIZEN PARTICIPATION
Burns, L. G. Citizen scientists **590.72**

RESEARCH AIRCRAFT -- UNITED STATES
Karst, K. Area 51 **001.9**

RESEARCH AND DEVELOPMENT *See* Research

RESEARCH PAPER WRITING *See* Report writing

Researching people, places, and events. Cefrey, H. **001.4**

RESERVOIRS -- FICTION
McKinlay, M. Below **Fic**

Resi, Putu
Hawker, F. Hinduism in Bali **294.5**

RESIDENCES *See* Domestic architecture; Houses

RESISTANCE OF MATERIALS *See* Strength of materials

RESISTANCE TO GOVERNMENT
Scandiffio, L. People who said no **303.48**

RESISTANCE TO GOVERNMENT
See also Political ethics; Political science

RESISTANCE TO GOVERNMENT -- FICTION
Hall, T. Away **Fic**
The **Resisters.** Nylund, E. S. **Fic**

RESORTS
See also Recreation

RESORTS -- FICTION
Monroe, C. Monkey with a tool belt and the seaside shenanigans **E**

RESOURCE MANAGEMENT *See* Conservation of natural resources

Respect. Pryor, K. J. **177**

RESPECT
Barraclough, S. Fair play **175**
Pryor, K. J. Respect **177**

RESPIRATION
See also Physiology

RESPIRATORY ORGANS *See* Respiratory system

Respiratory system. Tieck, S. **612.2**

RESPIRATORY SYSTEM
See also Anatomy; Physiology

RESPIRATORY SYSTEM
Gold, S. D. Learning about the respiratory system **611**
Simon, S. Lungs **612.2**
Tieck, S. Respiratory system **612.2**

Responding to cyber bullying. Myers, J. J. **371.5**
Responding to the culture of bullying and disrespect. Beaudoin **371.5**

RESPONSIBILITY
Parker, V. Acting responsibly **179**

RESPONSIBILITY
See also Ethics

RESPONSIBILITY -- FICTION

Don't spill the milk **E**

REST
See also Health; Hygiene
Kuskowski, A. Cool relaxing **613.7**

REST HOMES -- FICTION
De Goldi, K. The ACB with Honora Lee **Fic**

RESTAURANTS -- FICTION
Stimpson, C. Jack and the baked beanstalk **E**

Restless spirit: the life and work of Dorothea Lange. Partridge, E. **770**

RESTRAINT OF TRADE
See also Commerce; Commercial law

RETAIL EXECUTIVES
Blumenthal, K. Mr. Sam **92**
Goldsworthy, S. Richard Branson **92**
Weatherford, C. B. Dear Mr. Rosenwald **Fic**

RETAIL TRADE
See also Commerce

RETAIL TRADE -- FICTION
Carling, A. L. Mama & Papa have a store **E**
Reinhardt, D. The summer I learned to fly **Fic**
Schwartz, J. Our corner grocery store **E**
The **retired** kid. Agee, J. **E**

RETIREMENT
See also Leisure; Old age

RETIREMENT -- FICTION
Luxbacher, I. Mr. Frank **E**
Return of the Dapper Men. McCann, J. **741.5**
The **return** of the homework machine. Gutman, D. **Fic**
The **Return** of Zita the Spacegirl. Hatke, B. **741.5**
Return to Exile. Patten, E. J. **Fic**
Return to sender. Alvarez, J. **Fic**

Reuben, Susan
Food and faith **204**

Reusing things. Barraclough, S. **363.7**

Reusser, Kayleen
Celebrities giving back **361.7**
Recipe and craft guide to Indonesia **641.5**

REVELATION
See also God; Supernatural; Theology

Revell, Cindy
(il) Waldman, D. Clever Rachel **398.2**
(il) Waldman, D. A sack full of feathers **398.2**

REVENGE -- FICTION
Davies, N. The Lion who stole my arm **Fic**
Revenge of Superstition Mountain. Broach, E. **Fic**
Revenge of the Dinotrux. Gall, C. **E**
Revenge of the witch. Delaney, J. **Fic**

REVENUE *See* Tariff; Taxation

Revere, Paul, 1735-1818
About
Fritz, J. And then what happened, Paul Revere? **92**
Giblin, J. The many rides of Paul Revere **92**
Lawson, R. Mr. Revere and I **Fic**
Mortensen, L. Paul Revere's ride **92**

(il) Colfer, E. Artemis Fowl: the graphic novel | **741.5**

Rigaud, Louis
(jt. auth) Boisrobert, A. Popville | **E**

Riggs, Kate
Alligators | **597.98**
Bats | **599.4**
Eagles | **598.9**
Gorillas | **599.884**
Kangaroos | **599.2**
Killer whales | **599.53**
Leopards | **599.75**
Moose | **599.65**
Sea lions | **599.79**
Whales | **599.5**
Woodpeckers | **598.7**
Dolphins | **599.5**
Elephants | **599.67**
The French Revolution | **944.04**
Gladiators | **937**
Knights | **940.1**
Pirates | **910.4**
Samurai | **952**
Wolfgang Amadeus Mozart | **92**
Wolves | **599.77**

Riggs, Shannon
Not in Room 204 | **E**

RIGHT AND LEFT (POLITICAL SCIENCE)
See also Political parties; Political science
The **right** dog for the job. Patent, D. H. | **362.4**
The **right** fight. Lynch, C. | **Fic**

RIGHT OF PRIVACY
Chmara, T. Privacy and confidentiality issues | **344**
Grayson, R. Managing your digital footprint | **004.6**
Jakubiak, D. J. A smart kid's guide to Internet privacy | **005.8**

RIGHT OF PRIVACY
See also Civil rights

RIGHT OF PROPERTY
See also Civil rights; Property

RIGHT TO COUNSEL
See also Civil rights

RIGHT TO DIE
See also Death; Medical ethics; Medicine --
Law and legislation

RIGHT TO HEALTH CARE
See also Human rights

RIGHT TO KNOW *See* Freedom of information
The **right** word. Bryant, J. | **92**
The **Right-Under** Club. Deriso, C. H. | **Fic**

**RIGHTEOUS GENTILES IN THE HOLO-
CAUST**
See also Holocaust, 1939-1945; World War,
1939-1945 -- Jews -- Rescue
Rightfully ours. Hollihan, K. L. | **324.6**
RIGHTS OF ANIMALS *See* Animal rights

RIGHTS, HUMAN *See* Human rights

Riglietti, Serena
(il) Cooper, S. The magician's boy | **Fic**

Rigsby, Mike
Amazing rubber band cars | **745.592**

Riki's birdhouse. Wellington, M. | **E**
Rikki-tikki-tavi. Pinkney, J. | **E**
Riley and Rose in the picture. Gretz, S. | **E**

Riley, James
Half upon a time | **Fic**

Riley, Linnea Asplind
Mouse mess | **E**

Riley, Peter D.
Electricity | **537**
Forces | **531**
Light | **535**
Materials | **620.1**
Sound | **534**

Riley-Webb, Charlotte
(il) Brown, T. F. Around our way on neighbors'
day | **E**
(il) Lindsey, K. Sweet potato pie | **E**
(il) Miller, W. Rent party jazz | **E**

Rim, Sujean
(il) Birdie's big-girl hair | **E**
Birdie's big-girl dress | **E**
Birdie's big-girl shoes | **E**

Rinaldo, Denise
White House Q & A | **975.3**

Rinck, Maranke
I feel a foot! | **E**
The **Ring** of Five. McNamee, E. | **Fic**

Ringgold, Faith
(il) Brooks, G. Bronzeville boys and girls | **811**
Tar Beach | **E**

About
Venezia, M. Faith Ringgold | **92**

Rinker, Sherri Duskey
Goodnight, goodnight, construction site | **E**
Steam train, dream train | **E**
The **Rio** Grande. Marsico, K. | **978.8**

RIO GRANDE VALLEY
Marsico, K. The Rio Grande | **978.8**

Riordan, Rick
(jt. auth) Collar, O. The Red Pyramid | **Fic**
The blood of Olympus | **Fic**
The house of Hades | **Fic**
The lightning thief | **Fic**
The Mark of Athena | **Fic**
Percy Jackson's Greek Gods | **Fic**
The Serpent's Shadow | **Fic**
The throne of fire | **Fic**
The maze of bones | **Fic**
The son of Neptune | **Fic**
Vespers rising | **Fic**
Venditti, R. The lightning thief: the graphic nov-

Springer, N. Rowan Hood, outlaw girl of Sherwood Forest **Fic**

Robin Hood and the golden arrow. San Souci, R. **398.2**

The **robin** makes a laughing sound. Wolf, S. **598**

Robinet, Harriette Gillem
Forty acres and maybe a mule **Fic**
Walking to the bus-rider blues **Fic**

Robins. Hudak, H. C. **598**

ROBINS
Hudak, H. C. Robins **598**

ROBINS
See also Birds

Robinson, Aminah Brenda Lynn
(il) Sophie **E**

Robinson, Anthony
Hamzat's journey **947**

Robinson, Barbara
The best Christmas pageant ever **Fic**

Robinson, Bill, 1878-1949
About
Dillon, L. Rap a tap tap **792.7**

Robinson, Charles
(il) Levitin, S. Journey to America **Fic**
(il) Smith, D. B. A taste of blackberries **Fic**

Robinson, Christian
(il) Dipucchio, K. Gaston **E**
(il) Harlem's little blackbird **782.421**
Last stop on Market Street **E**
(il) Ashman, L. Rain! **E**
(il) Powell, P. H. Josephine **92**

Robinson, Fay
Schafer, S. Tigers **599.75**

Robinson, Fiona
What animals really like **E**

Robinson, Jackie, 1919-1972
About
Adler, D. A. A picture book of Jackie Robinson **796.357**
Amoroso, C. Jackie Robinson **92**
Burleigh, R. Stealing home **92**
Gutman, D. Jackie & me **Fic**
Krensky, S. Play ball, Jackie! **E**
Krull, K. Lives of the athletes **796**
O'Sullivan, R. Jackie Robinson plays ball **92**
Robinson, S. Jackie Robinson **796.357**
Robinson, S. Jackie's gift **E**
Robinson, S. Promises to keep: how Jackie Robinson changed America **92**
Stout, G. Baseball heroes **796.357**
Teammates **796.357**
Testing the ice: a true story about Jackie Robinson **92**
Uhlberg, M. Dad, Jackie, and me **E**

Robinson, James
Inventions **609**

Robinson, Jill
(jt. auth) Bekoff, M. Jasper's story **599.78**

Robinson, Jo Ann, 1942-
About
Freedman, R. Freedom walkers **323.1**

Robinson, Laura
Cyclist bikelist **796.6**

Robinson, Mabel L.
Bright Island **Fic**

Robinson, Michelle
What to do if an elephant stands on your foot **E**

Robinson, Sharon
Jackie's gift **E**
Jackie Robinson **796.357**
Promises to keep: how Jackie Robinson changed America **92**
Safe at home **Fic**
Slam dunk! **Fic**
Testing the ice: a true story about Jackie Robinson **92**

Robinson, Tim
(il) Sheinkin, S. King George: what was his problem? **973.3**
(il) Sheinkin, S. Two miserable presidents **973.7**
(il) Sheinkin, S. Which way to the wild West? **978**

Robinson, Tom
Basketball **796.323**

ROBINSONADES
See also Adventure fiction; Imaginary voyages

The **robot** book. Brown, H. **E**

Robot City [series]
Collicutt, P. City in peril! **741.5**

Robot explorers. Miller, R. **629.43**

Robot technology. Graham, I. **629.8**

Robot Zot! Scieszka, J. **E**

Robot, Go Bot! Rau, D. M. **E**

ROBOTICS *See* Robots

Robotics [series]
Chaffee, J. How to build a prize-winning robot **629.8**
Freedman, J. Robots through history **629.8**
Payment, S. Robotics careers **629.8**
Shea, T. The robotics club **629.8**

Robotics careers. Payment, S. **629.8**

The **robotics** club. Shea, T. **629.8**

Robots. Rau, D. M. **629.8**

ROBOTS
See also Machinery; Mechanical movements
Allman, T. The Nexi robot **629.8**
Chaffee, J. How to build a prize-winning robot **629.8**
Freedman, J. Robots through history **629.8**
Graham, I. Robot technology **629.8**
Kops, D. Exploring space robots **629.46**
Mason, A. Robots: from everyday to out of this

world Jill **629.8**
Miller, R. Robot explorers **629.43**
Payment, S. Robotics careers **629.8**
Rau, D. M. Robots **629.8**
Shea, T. The robotics club **629.8**
VanVoorst, J. Rise of the thinking machines **629.8**
Woog, A. SCRATCHbot **629.8**

ROBOTS -- CARTOONS AND COMICS
Rau, D. M. Robot, Go Bot! **E**

ROBOTS -- FICTION
Arnold, T. Fix this mess! **E**
Blackwood, G. Curiosity **Fic**
Catalanotto, P. Monkey and Robot **E**
Dyckman, A. Boy and Bot **E**
Frank Einstein & the antimatter motor **Fic**
Grabenstein, C. My brother the robot **Fic**
Legends of Zita the spacegirl **741.5**
Pearl and Wagner **E**
Rau, D. M. Robot, Go Bot! **E**
Robertson, M. P. Frank n stan **Fic**
Samworth, K. Aviary Wonders Inc. Spring Catalog
 and Instruction Manual **Fic**
Scaletta, K. The winter of the robots **Fic**
Yaccarino, D. Doug unplugged! **E**

ROBOTS -- GRAPHIC NOVELS
Collicutt, P. City in peril! **741.5**
Lemke, D. Zinc Alloy: Super Zero **741.5**
McCann, J. Return of the Dapper Men **741.5**
Sias, R. Zoe and Robot: let's pretend **741.5**

ROBOTS -- SONGS
Hale, N. The twelve bots of Christmas **E**

ROBOTS IN ART
Masiello, R. Ralph Masiello's robot drawing
 book **743**
Stephens, J. Robots! **743**
Robots through history. Freedman, J. **629.8**
Robots! Stephens, J. **743**
Robots: from everyday to out of this world. Mason,
A. **629.8**
Robson, David
 The mummy **393**
Roca, Francois
 Brown, T. L. Soar, Elinor! **92**
 Paterson, K. The light of the world **232.9**
 Prince, A. J. Twenty-one elephants and still stand-
  ing **E**
Rocco, John
 (il) Eaton, J. C. How to train a train **E**
 (il) Paterson, J. The Flint Heart **Fic**
 (il) Patten, E. J. Return to Exile **Fic**
 (il) Riordan, R. Percy Jackson's Greek Gods **Fic**
 Blackout **E**
 Blizzard **E**
 (il) Kudlinski, K. V. Boy were we wrong about the
  solar system! **523.2**
 Moonpowder **E**

Wolf! wolf! **E**
Roche, Art
 Cartooning **741.5**
Roche, Denis
 (il) Evans, L. Can you greet the whole wide
  world? **413**
 (il) London, J. A plane goes ka-zoom! **E**
 (il) London, J. A train goes clickety-clack **E**
 (il) London, J. A truck goes rattley-bumpa **E**
Rochelle, Belinda
 (ed) Words with wings **811**
Rock. Handyside, C. **781.66**
Rock 'n' roll Mole. Crimi, C. **E**
ROCK AND ROLL MUSIC *See* Rock music
A **rock** can be . . . **552**
ROCK CLIMBING *See* Mountaineering
**ROCK DRAWINGS, PAINTINGS, AND EN-
GRAVINGS**
 See also Archeology; Prehistoric art
ROCK GARDENS
 See also Gardens
A **rock** is lively. Aston, D. H. **552**
ROCK MUSIC
Appelt, K. Bats around the clock **E**
Boynton, S. Dog train **782.42**
George-Warren, H. Shake, rattle, & roll **781.66**
Handyside, C. Rock **781.66**
Stamaty, M. A. Shake, rattle & turn that noise
 down! **781.66**
ROCK MUSIC
 See also Music; Popular music
ROCK MUSIC -- FICTION
Appelt, K. Bats around the clock **E**
Crimi, C. Rock 'n' roll Mole **E**
Winters, B. H. The secret life of Ms. Finkleman **Fic**
ROCK MUSIC -- GRAPHIC NOVELS
Cammuso, F. Knights of the lunch table: the bat-
 tling bands **741.5**
ROCK MUSIC -- VOCATIONAL GUIDANCE
Anniss, M. Recording and promoting your mu-
 sic **780.23**
ROCK MUSICIANS
Anderson, J. J. John Lennon **92**
Aretha, D. Awesome African-American rock and
 soul musicians **781.644**
Collins, T. Elvis **92**
Elvis **92**
Golio, G. Jimi: sounds like a rain-
 bow: a story of young Jimi Hendrix
Rappaport, D. John's secret dreams **92**
Stamaty, M. A. Shake, rattle & turn that noise
 down! **781.66**
When Bob met Woody **92**
**ROCK MUSICIANS -- ENGLAND -- BIOGRA-
PHY**
Behnke, A. M. Death of a dreamer **782.421**

Ryan, Susannah
Maestro, B. Coming to America: the story of immigration **325**

Rybolt, Leah M.
Gardner, R. Ace your science project about the senses **612.8**

Rybolt, Thomas R.
Gardner, R. Ace your food science project **664**
Gardner, R. Ace your physical science project **530**
Gardner, R. Ace your science project about the senses **612.8**

Rycroft, Nina
(il) Cummings, P. Boom bah! **E**

Ryder, Joanne
Dance by the light of the moon **E**
A dragon's guide to the care and feeding of humans **Fic**
Each living thing **E**
Little panda **599.74**
My father's hands **E**
A pair of polar bears **599.78**

Rylander, Chris
The fourth stall **Fic**

Rylant, Cynthia
Cat Heaven **E**
Dog Heaven **E**
Moonlight: the Halloween cat **E**
All in a day **E**
Alligator boy **E**
Annie and Snowball and the Book Bugs Club **E**
Annie and Snowball and the cozy nest **E**
Annie and Snowball and the dress-up birthday **E**
Annie and Snowball and the shining star **E**
Annie and Snowball and the wintry freeze **E**
Appalachia **974**
The beautiful stories of life **292**
Brownie & Pearl grab a bite **E**
Brownie & Pearl hit the hay **E**
Brownie & Pearl see the sights **E**
Brownie & Pearl step out **E**
Brownie & Pearl take a dip **E**
The case of the missing monkey **E**
A fine white dust **Fic**
Henry and Mudge **E**
Henry and Mudge and a very Merry Christmas **E**
Henry and Mudge and Annie's good move **E**
Henry and Mudge and the bedtime thumps **E**
Henry and Mudge and the best day of all **E**
Henry and Mudge and the careful cousin **E**
Henry and Mudge and the great grandpas **E**
Henry and Mudge and the happy cat **E**
Henry and Mudge and the snowman plan **E**
Henry and Mudge and the starry night **E**
Henry and Mudge get the cold shivers **E**
Henry and Mudge in the family trees **E**
Henry and Mudge in the green time **E**

Henry and Mudge in the sparkle days **E**
Missing May **Fic**
Mr. Putter & Tabby clear the decks **E**
Mr. Putter & Tabby pour the tea **E**
Mr. Putter & Tabby drop the ball **E**
Mr. Putter & Tabby ring the bell **E**
Mr. Putter & Tabby turn the page **E**
Poppleton **E**
Puppies and piggies **E**
The relatives came **E**
Snow **E**
When I was young in the mountains **E**
Brownie & Pearl go for a spin **E**
(il) Cat Heaven **E**
(il) Dog Heaven **E**
God got a dog **Fic**

S

S is for story. Hershenhorn, E. **808.3**
Sís, Peter, 1949-
About
Sis, P. The wall **92**
Saab, Julie
Little Lola **E**
Sabatino, Chris
(il) King, B. Bart's king-sized book of fun **793**
SABBATH
Bernhard, D. Y. Around the world in one Shabbat **296.4**
SABBATH
See also Judaism
SABBATH -- FICTION
Fox, T. No baths at camp **E**
The Schmutzy Family **E**
Snyder, L. Baxter, the pig who wanted to be kosher **E**
Sabbeth, Carol
Monet and the impressionists for kids **759.05**
Van Gogh and the Post-Impressionists for kids **759.05**
SABLE ISLAND (N.S.) -- FICTION
Race the wild wind **E**
Sabnani, Nina
(il) Rao, S. My mother's sari **E**
SABOTAGE
See also Offenses against public safety; Strikes; Subversive activities; Terrorism
SABOTAGE -- FICTION
Coman, C. The Memory Bank **Fic**
Sabotaged. Haddix, M. P. **Fic**
Sabuda, Robert
The dragon & the knight **E**
The Little Mermaid **E**
(il) The 12 days of Christmas **782.42**
(jt. auth) Reinhart, M. Dragons & Monsters **398**
Reinhart, M. Fairies and magical creatures **398**

A big night for salamanders **E**

Salariya, David

(il) Graham, I. Microscopic scary creatures **591.6**

Malam, J. Pinnipeds **599.79**

Pipe, J. Swarms **591.5**

Salas, Laura Purdie

A leaf can be **E**

A rock can be . . . **552**

Water can be **E**

Menhard, F. R. The facts about inhalants **362.29**

Amphibians **597.8**

Bookspeak! **811**

Salati, Giorgio

Race for the Ultrapods **741.5**

SALEM (MASS.) -- FICTION

Thompson, P. B. The devil's door **Fic**

SALEM (MASS.) -- HISTORY

Jackson, S. The witchcraft of Salem Village **133.4**

Roach, M. K. In the days of the Salem witchcraft trials **133.4**

Salerno, Steven

(il) Brothers at bat **796.357**

(il) Elya, S. M. Bebe goes shopping **E**

(il) Freeman, M. Mrs. Wow never wanted a cow **E**

(il) Pattison, D. S. 19 girls and me **E**

Harry hungry! **E**

SALES TAX

See also Taxation

Salisbury, Graham

Calvin Coconut: hero of Hawaii **Fic**

Calvin Coconut: kung fooey **Fic**

Calvin Coconut: trouble magnet **Fic**

Night of the howling dogs **Fic**

SALIVA

Donovan, S. Hawk & Drool **612.3**

Saller, Carol Fisher

Eddie's war **Fic**

Salley, Coleen

Epossumondas **398.21**

Epossumondas plays possum **E**

Epossumondas saves the day **E**

Sallie Gal and the Wall-a-kee man. Moses, S. P. **Fic**

Sally and the purple socks. Bechtold, L. **E**

Sally Ann Thunder Ann Whirlwind Crockett. Kellogg, S. **398.2**

Sally go round the stars. **398.8**

Sally goes to Heaven. Huneck, S. **E**

Sally goes to the beach. Huneck, S. **E**

Sally Jean, the Bicycle Queen. Best, C. **E**

Sally Ride. Macy, S. **92**

Sally Ride science [series]

Bridges, A. Clean air **363.7**

Geiger, B. Clean water **363.7**

Ride, S. K. Mission: planet Earth **525**

Ride, S. K. Mission: save the planet **333.72**

Sally the dog [series]

Huneck, S. Sally goes to Heaven **E**

Sally's bones. Cadenhead, M. **Fic**

Salmansohn, Pete, 1947-

Saving birds **333.95**

Salmieri, Daniel

(il) Gibson, A. Around the world on eighty legs **811**

(il) Rubin, A. Those darn squirrels and the cat next door **E**

(il) Rubin, A. Those darn squirrels! **E**

SALMON

See also Fishes

Salmon bears. McAllister, I. **599.78**

Salmon summer. McMillan, B. **639.2**

SALSA MUSICIANS -- UNITED STATES -- BIOGRAPHY

Brown, M. Tito Puente, Mambo King **784.4**

Salsa stories. Delacre, L. **S**

Salsedo, Greg

(il) Dauvillier, L. Hidden **741.5**

Salt. Frost, H. **Fic**

SALT

Furgang, A. Salty and sugary snacks **613.2**

Kurlansky, M. The story of salt **553.6**

Moore, H. The story behind salt **553.6**

Salt in his shoes. Jordan, D. **E**

SALT MARSHES

Wechsler, D. Marvels in the muck **578.7**

SALT WATER AQUARIUMS *See* Marine aquariums

SALT-FREE DIET

See also Cooking; Diet

Salten, Felix

Bambi **Fic**

Saltwater crocodile. Jackson, T. **597.98**

SALTWATER FISHING

See also Fishing

Salty and sugary snacks. Furgang, A. **613.2**

Saltypie. **92**

Saltz, Gail

Amazing you **612.6**

Changing you! **612.6**

Saltzberg, Barney

Chengdu could not, would not, fall asleep **E**

(il) Murphy, S. J. Sluggers' car wash **513**

Beautiful oops! **E**

I want a dog! **E**

Stanley and the class pet **E**

SALUTATIONS *See* Etiquette

Salvadori, Mario George

Levy, M. Earthquakes, volcanoes, and tsunamis **551.2**

SALVAGE

Alter, A. What can you do with an old red shoe? **745.5**

Mitchell, J. S. Crashed, smashed, and mashed **629.222**

Say hello like this. Murphy, M.   E
Say hello to Zorro! Goodrich, C.   E
Say hello! Isadora, R.   E
Say hello, Lily. Lakritz, D.   E
Say something, Perico. Harris, T.   E
Say, Allen
    The favorite daughter   E
    (il) Friedman, I. R. How my parents learned to
    eat   E
    (il) Grandfather's journey   E
    Allison   E
    The bicycle man   E
    Boy in the garden   E
    Drawing from memory   **741.6**
    Erika-san   E
    Kamishibai man   E
    The lost lake   E
    Tea with milk   E
    Tree of cranes   E
    (il) Snyder, D. The boy of the three-year nap **398.2**
Say, Allen, 1937-
    About
    Say, A. Drawing from memory   **741.6**
Sayago, Mauricio Trenard
    (il) Hayes, J. Dance, Nana, dance   **398.2**
Saying goodbye to Lulu. Demas, C.   E
SAYINGS See Epigrams; Proverbs; Quotations
Sayles, Elizabeth
    (il) Kohuth, J. Anne Frank's chestnut tree   E
    (il) Krilanovich, N. Moon child   E
Sayre, April Pulley
    Eat like a bear   E
    Here come the humpbacks!   **599.5**
    Go, go, grapes!   **641.3**
    Touch a butterfly   **635**
    Dig, wait, listen   E
    Honk, honk, goose!   **598**
    If you're hoppy   E
    Meet the howlers   **599.8**
    One is a snail, ten is a crab   E
    Rah, rah, radishes!   **641.3**
    Stars beneath your bed   **551.51**
    Trout are made of trees   **577**
    Turtle, turtle, watch out!   E
    Vulture view   **598**
Sayre, Jeff
    Sayre, A. P. One is a snail, ten is a crab   E
Sazaklis, John
    Royal rodent rescue   Fic
Scales, Pat R.
    Books under fire   **016.098**
    Protecting intellectual freedom in your school library   **025.2**
    Teaching banned books   **098**
Scaletta, Kurtis
    Mamba Point   Fic

    The winter of the robots   **Fic**
The **Scallywags**. Melling, D.   E
Scaly spotted feathered frilled.   **567.9**
Scandals. Butterfield, M.   **796.48**
Scandiffio, Laura
    People who said no   **303.48**
SCANDINAVIA -- CIVILIZATION
    Park, L. The Scandinavian Vikings   **948**
SCANDINAVIAN LANGUAGES
    See also Language and languages
SCANDINAVIAN LITERATURE
    See also Literature
SCANDINAVIAN MYTHOLOGY See Norse mythology
The **Scandinavian** Vikings. Park, L.   **948**
Scanlan, Lawrence
    The big red horse   **798.4**
Scanlon, Liz Garton
    The Good-Pie Party   E
    The great good summer   **Fic**
    All the world   **811**
    Noodle & Lou   E
The **scar.** Moundlic, C.   E
SCARECROWS -- FICTION
    The big snuggle-up   E
    Brown, M. W. The little scarecrow boy   E
Scaredy Kat. Kimmel, E. C.   Fic
Scaredy Squirrel. Watt, M.   E
Scaredy Squirrel Goes Camping. Watt, M.   E
Scaredy Squirrel has a birthday party. Watt, M.   E
Scaredy Squirrel Prepares for Halloween. Watt, M.   E
Scaredy-cat catcher. Hicks, B.   Fic
Scaredy-cat, Splat! Scotton, R.   E
The **scariest** monster in the world. Weatherly, L.   E
Scarum fair. Swaim, J.   **811**
SCARVES
    Manning, M. J. Laundry day   E
Scary creatures [series]
    Clarke, P. Hippos   **599.63**
    Graham, I. Microscopic scary creatures   **591.6**
    Malam, J. Pinnipeds   **599.79**
    Pipe, J. Swarms   **591.5**
Scary Godmother. Thompson, J.   **741.5**
Scary stories 3. Schwartz, A.   **398.2**
Scary stories to tell in the dark. Schwartz, A.   **398.25**
Scary tales [series]
    Home sweet horror   E
Scat. Hiaasen, C.   Fic
Scattergood, Augusta
    Glory be   Fic
SCENE PAINTING
    See also Painting; Theaters -- Stage setting and scenery
SCENERY See Landscape protection; Natural monuments; Views; Wilderness areas

SCENIC BYWAYS
See also Roads
Schaap, Phil
Marsalis, W. Jazz A-B-Z 781.65
Schachner, Judith Byron
(il) Napoli, D. J. The prince of the pond Fic
The Grannyman E
Schachner, J. Skippyjon Jones class action E
Schachner, Judy
(il) Manners mash-up: a goofy guide to good behavior 395
Skippyjon Jones class action E
Schaefer, Adam
Exercise 613.7
Healthy food 613.2
Staying healthy 613
Staying safe 613.6
Steroids 362.29
Schaefer, Carole Lexa
Big Little Monkey E
Dragon dancing E
Schaefer, Lola M.
Frankie Stein E
Frankie Stein starts school E
Happy Halloween, Mittens E
Just one bite 591.4
Loose tooth E
Mittens E
Mittens, where is Max? E
Pick, pull, snap! 582
This is the sunflower E
What's up, what's down? E
One busy day E
One special day E
Schaefer, Valorie
The care & keeping of you 613.04
Schafer, Susan
Lions 599.75
Tigers 599.75
Schaller, George B.
About
Martin, J. B. The chiru of high Tibet 599.64
Turner, P. S. A life in the wild 92
Schanzer, Rosalyn
George vs. George 973.3
How we crossed the West 917
What Darwin saw 92
Scharschmidt, Sherry
(jt. auth) Hacohen, D. Tuck me in! E
Schecter, David
Cruz, A. The woman who outshone the sun 398.21
Schecter, Ellen
The family Haggadah 296.4
Scheer, Julian
Rain makes applesauce E
Scheeren, William O.

Technology for the school librarian 025.04
Scheffler, Axel
(il) Donaldson, J. The gruffalo E
(il) Donaldson, J. The Highway Rat E
(il) Donaldson, J. Superworm E
(il) Donaldson, J. The fish who cried wolf E
(il) Donaldson, J. Stick Man E
(il) Eliot, T. S. Old Possum's book of practical cats 811
SCHEHERAZADE (LEGENDARY CHARACTER)
See also Legendary characters
Schembri, Pamela
Catalanotto, P. No more pumpkins Fic
Catalanotto, P. The secret lunch special Fic
Catalanotto, P. The Veteran's Day visitor Fic
Schenck, Emily
Glasser, D. New kid, new scene 373.1
Scherer, Glenn
Who on earth is Rachel Carson? 92
Schertle, Alice
Little Blue Truck E
Such a little mouse E
Pio peep! 398.8
1, 2, I love you E
Button up! 811
Scheunemann, Pam
Cool beaded jewelry 745.58
Schimel, Lawrence
Let's go see Papa! E
Schindel, John
Busy gorillas 599.8
Schindel, Morton, 1918-
About
Cech, J. Imagination and innovation 791.43
Schindler, S. D.
(il) Beebe, K. Brother Hugo and the bear E
(il) Pearson, S. We're going on a ghost hunt E
(il) Rosenstock, B. Ben Franklin's big splash 92
Armstrong, A. Whittington Fic
(il) Ashman, L. Come to the castle! 940.1
(il) Berger, M. Spinning spiders 595.4
(il) Bildner, P. The unforgettable season 796.357
(il) Choldenko, G. Louder, Lili E
(il) Cuyler, M. Monster mess! E
(il) Cuyler, M. Skeleton hiccups E
(il) Davies, J. Tricking the Tallyman E
(il) Hall, K. Creepy riddles 793.73
(il) Hopkinson, D. Home on the range 92
(il) Hurst, C. O. Terrible storm E
(il) Kay, V. Covered wagons, bumpy trails E
(il) Kay, V. Hornbooks and inkwells E
(il) Krensky, S. How Santa got his job E
(il) Kudlinski, K. V. Boy, were we wrong about dinosaurs! 567.9
(il) Kurlansky, M. The cod's tale 639.2

Harada, V. H. Assessing for learning 027.8

Harada, V. H. Inquiry learning through librarian-teacher partnerships 371.1

Harper, M. Reference sources and services for youth 025.5

Hughes-Hassell, S. School reform and the school library media specialist 027.8

Independent school libraries 025.1

The indispensable librarian 025.1

Lanning, S. Essential reference services for today's school media specialists 025.5

Martin, B. S. Fundamentals of school library media management 025.1

Morris, B. J. Administering the school library media center 027.8

Scales, P. R. Protecting intellectual freedom in your school library 025.2

Scales, P. R. Teaching banned books 098

Scheeren, W. O. Technology for the school librarian 025.04

School library management 025.1

Skaggs, G. Look, it's books! 021.7

Squires, T. Library partnerships 021.2

Stephens, C. G. Library 101 027.8

Sullivan, M. Connecting boys with books 2 028.5

Sykes, J. A. Conducting action research to evaluate your school library 027.8

SCHOOL LIBRARIES
See also Instructional materials centers; Libraries

SCHOOL LIBRARIES -- ACTIVITY PROJECTS

Grimes, S. Reading is our business 027.8

Mackey, B. A librarian's guide to cultivating an elementary school garden 372

SCHOOL LIBRARIES -- BOOK LISTS

Keane, N. J. 101 great, ready-to-use book lists for children 028.5

SCHOOL LIBRARIES -- CATALOGS

Safford, B. R. Guide to reference materials for school library media centers 011.6

SCHOOL LIBRARIES -- CENSORSHIP -- UNITED STATES

Books under fire 016.098

SCHOOL LIBRARIES -- COLLECTION DEVELOPMENT

Baumbach, D. Less is more 025.2

Bishop, K. The collection program in schools 027.8

Franklin, P. School library collection development 025.2

SCHOOL LIBRARIES -- DESIGN AND CONSTRUCTION

Erikson, R. Designing a school library media center for the future 027.8

SCHOOL LIBRARIES -- EVALUATION

Sykes, J. A. Conducting action research to evaluate your school library 027.8

SCHOOL LIBRARIES -- INFORMATION TECHNOLOGY

Growing schools 370.71

SCHOOL LIBRARIES -- LAW AND LEGISLATION -- UNITED STATES

Russell, C. Complete copyright for K-12 librarians and educators 346.04

SCHOOL LIBRARIES -- UNITED STATES -- ADMINISTRATION

The indispensable librarian 025.1

School library collection development. Franklin, P. 025.2

School library management. 025.1

SCHOOL LIFE *See* Students

SCHOOL LIFE -- GRAPHIC NOVELS

Roman, D. Astronaut Academy: Zero gravity 741.5

A school like mine. UNICEF 371.82

SCHOOL LUNCHES *See* School children -- Food

SCHOOL MASCOTS *See* Mascots

SCHOOL MEDIA CENTERS *See* Instructional materials centers

SCHOOL MUSIC *See* Music -- Study and teaching; School songbooks; Singing

SCHOOL NURSES
See also Nurses

School of Fear. Daneshvari, G. Fic

SCHOOL PLAYGROUNDS *See* Playgrounds

SCHOOL PLAYS *See* Children's plays; College and school drama

SCHOOL PRINCIPALS -- FICTION

The Adventures of Captain Underpants Fic

Pilkey, D. Captain Underpants and the tyrannical retaliation of the Turbo Toilet 2000 Fic

SCHOOL PROSE *See* Children's writings

School reform and the school library media specialist. Hughes-Hassell, S. 027.8

SCHOOL REPORTS
See also Report writing

SCHOOL SHOOTINGS
See also Crime; School violence

SCHOOL SONGBOOKS
See also Songbooks; Songs

School spirit. Kimmel, E. C. Fic

SCHOOL SPORTS
See also Sports; Student activities

SCHOOL SPORTS -- FICTION

Abdul-Jabbar, K. Sasquatch in the paint Fic

SCHOOL STORIES

Abbott, T. Firegirl Fic

Adler, D. A. Cam Jansen and the Sports Day mysteries Fic

Adler, D. A. Cam Jansen, the mystery of the carnival prize Fic

Adler, D. A. Young Cam Jansen and the 100th day of school mystery E

Ain, B. Starring Jules (in drama-rama) Fic

Chatterton, M. The Brain finds a leg **Fic**

Cheng, A. Where the steps were **Fic**

Cheng, A. The year of the book **Fic**

Cheshire, S. The pirate's blood and other case files **Fic**

Child, L. Clarice Bean, don't look now **Fic**

Child, L. I am too absolutely small for school **E**

Child, L. Utterly me, Clarice Bean **Fic**

Chodos-Irvine, M. Best best friends **E**

Choldenko, G. A giant crush **E**

Choldenko, G. Louder, Lili **E**

Clark, C. G. Secrets of Greymoor **Fic**

Cleary, B. Dear Mr. Henshaw **Fic**

Cleary, B. Henry Huggins **Fic**

Cleary, B. Muggie Maggie **Fic**

Cleary, B. Ramona forever **Fic**

Cleary, B. Ramona Quimby, age 8 **Fic**

Cleary, B. Ramona the brave **Fic**

Cleary, B. Ramona the pest **Fic**

Cleary, B. Ramona's world **Fic**

Clementine **Fic**

Clementine and the spring trip **Fic**

Clements, A. About average **Fic**

Clements, A. The report card **Fic**

Clements, A. Fear itself **Fic**

Clements, A. Frindle **Fic**

Clements, A. Lost and found **Fic**

Clements, A. Lunch money **Fic**

Clements, A. No talking **Fic**

Clements, A. Room one **Fic**

Clements, A. We the children **Fic**

Cody, M. Powerless **Fic**

Cohen, B. Molly's pilgrim **E**

Cohen, M. First grade takes a test **E**

Cohen, M. Will I have a friend? **E**

Comerford, L. B. Rissa Bartholomew's declaration of independence **Fic**

Comics Squad **741.5**

Cornwell, N. Christophe's story **Fic**

Cousins, L. Maisy goes to preschool **E**

Cox, J. Butterfly buddies **Fic**

Cox, J. Carmen learns English **E**

Cox, J. Nora and the Texas terror **Fic**

Cox, J. Puppy power **Fic**

Cox, J. Ukulele Hayley **Fic**

Coy, J. Love of the game **Fic**

Coy, J. Top of the order **Fic**

Creech, S. Bloomability **Fic**

Creech, S. Hate that cat **Fic**

Creech, S. Love that dog **Fic**

Crews, D. School bus **E**

Crossan, S. The Weight of Water **Fic**

Crummel, S. S. The Little Red Pen **E**

Cuyler, M. 100th day worries **E**

Cuyler, M. Hooray for Reading Day! **E**

Dahl, R. Matilda **Fic**

Daly, N. Bettina Valentino and the Picasso Club **Fic**

D'Amico, C. Ella the Elegant Elephant **E**

Daneshvari, G. Class is not dismissed! **Fic**

Daneshvari, G. School of Fear **Fic**

Danneberg, J. The big test **E**

Danziger, P. Amber Brown is not a crayon **Fic**

Danziger, P. Amber Brown sees red **Fic**

Danziger, P. Amber Brown wants extra credit **Fic**

Davies, J. Candy smash **Fic**

Davies, J. The lemonade crime **Fic**

Davis, E. The secret science alliance and the copy-cat crook **741.5**

De Groat, D. Ants in your pants, worms in your plants! **E**

De Groat, D. No more pencils, no more books, no more teacher's dirty looks! **E**

DeGross, M. Donavan's double trouble **Fic**

DeJong, M. The wheel on the school **Fic**

Demas, C. Pirates go to school **E**

DePaola, T. Meet the Barkers **E**

Diesen, D. The pout-pout fish goes to school **E**

Dinosaur vs. school **E**

DiSalvo, D. The sloppy copy slipup **Fic**

Dodds, D. A. Teacher's pets **E**

Dotty **E**

Dowell, F. O. The kind of friends we used to be **Fic**

Dowell, F. O. Phineas L. MacGuire . . . blasts off! **Fic**

Dowell, F. O. Phineas L. MacGuire . . . gets slimed! **Fic**

Dowell, F. O. Phineas L. Macguire erupts! **Fic**

Dowell, F. O. The secret language of girls **Fic**

Draanen, W. v. Sammy Keyes and the wedding crasher **Fic**

Drama **741.5**

Draper, S. M. The dazzle disaster dinner party **Fic**

Dunston, M. The magic of giving **E**

Durand, H. Dessert first **Fic**

Durand, H. Just Desserts **Fic**

Durand, H. No room for Dessert **Fic**

Dutton, S. Mary Mae and the gospel truth **Fic**

Elish, D. The School for the Insanely Gifted **Fic**

Elkin, M. Samuel's baby **E**

EllRay Jakes Rocks the Holidays! **Fic**

English, K. Nikki & Deja **Fic**

English, K. Nikki & Deja: birthday blues **Fic**

English, K. Nikki & Deja: the newsy news newsletter **Fic**

English, K. Nikki and Deja: election madness **Fic**

English, K. Speak to me **E**

Erskine, K. Mockingbird **Fic**

Falwell, C. David's drawings **E**

Ferraiolo, J. D. The big splash **Fic**

Finchler, J. Miss Malarkey leaves no reader behind **E**

Fine, E. H. Armando and the blue tarp school **E**

Ibbotson, E. The dragonfly pool **Fic**
Ignatow, A. The long-distance dispatch between
  Lydia Goldblatt and Julie Graham-Chang **Fic**
Ignatow, A. The popularity papers **Fic**
Ignatow, A. Words of (questionable) wisdom from
  Lydia Goldblatt & Julie Graham-Chang **Fic**
In loving memory of Gorfman T. Frog **Fic**
The invisible boy **E**
Iwamatsu, A. J. Crow Boy **E**
Jacobs, P. D. Fire drill **E**
Jacobson, J. Andy Shane and the Queen of
  Egypt **Fic**
Jacobson, J. Andy Shane and the very bossy Dolo-
  res Starbuckle **Fic**
Jennings, P. Guinea dog **Fic**
Johnson, V. The great Greene heist **Fic**
Jones, T. L. Silhouetted by the blue **Fic**
Jordan, R. The goatnappers **Fic**
Jules, J. Duck for Turkey Day **E**
Kargman, J. Pirates & Princesses **E**
Kay, V. Hornbooks and inkwells **E**
Kelly, K. Lucy Rose, here's the thing about me **Fic**
Kenah, K. The best seat in second grade **E**
Kerrin, J. S. Martin Bridge in high gear! **Fic**
Kerrin, J. S. Martin Bridge on the lookout! **Fic**
Kerrin, J. S. Martin Bridge: the sky's the limit **Fic**
Kerz, A. Better than weird **Fic**
Kimmel, E. C. The reinvention of Moxie Roos-
  evelt **Fic**
Kimmel, E. C. School spirit **Fic**
Kinney, J. Diary of a wimpy kid **Fic**
Kinney, J. Diary of a wimpy kid: Greg Heffley's
  journal **Fic**
Kinney, J. Diary of a wimpy kid: Rodrick rules **Fic**
Kinney, J. Diary of a wimpy kid: the last straw **Fic**
Kinney, J. The third wheel **Fic**
Kirk, D. Keisha Ann can! **E**
Kleven, E. The apple doll **E**
Kline, S. Horrible Harry in room 2B **Fic**
Kline, S. Song Lee and the I hate you notes **Fic**
Kline, S. Song Lee and the Leech Man **Fic**
Klise, K. Regarding the bathrooms **Fic**
Klise, K. Regarding the bees **Fic**
Klise, K. Regarding the fountain **Fic**
Klise, K. Regarding the sink **Fic**
Klise, K. Regarding the trees **Fic**
Knudsen, M. Argus **E**
Knudson, M. Raymond & Graham: bases load-
  ed **Fic**
Knudson, M. Raymond and Graham rule the
  school **Fic**
Knudson, M. Raymond and Graham, dancing
  dudes **Fic**
Konigsburg, E. L. The view from Saturday **Fic**
Korman, G. Framed **Fic**
Korman, G. No more dead dogs **Fic**

Koster, G. The Peanut-Free Cafe **E**
Krieg, J. Griff Carver, hallway patrol **Fic**
Kuhlman, E. The last invisible boy **Fic**
LaFleur, S. M. Love, Aubrey **Fic**
LaFleur, S. Eight keys **Fic**
Lawlor, L. The school at Crooked Creek **Fic**
Leal, A. H. A finders-keepers place **Fic**
Lehman, B. Museum trip **E**
Lester, H. Hooway for Wodney Wat **E**
Lester, H. Wodney Wat's wobot **E**
Levine, K. The lions of Little Rock **Fic**
Lewis, J. P. The kindergarten cat **E**
Lewis, M. Morgy makes his move **Fic**
Lilly's purple plastic purse **E**
Lin, G. The Year of the Rat **Fic**
Lindo, E. Manolito Four-Eyes **Fic**
Lindo, E. Manolito Four-Eyes: the 2nd volume of
  the great encyclopedia of my life **Fic**
Little Lola **E**
Little Naomi, Little Chick **E**
Ljungkvist, L. Follow the line to school **E**
Loewen, N. The last day of kindergarten **E**
Look, L. Ruby Lu, star of the show **Fic**
Lopez, D. Confetti girl **Fic**
Lord, B. B. In the Year of the Boar and Jackie Rob-
  inson **Fic**
Lotu, D. Running the road to ABC **E**
Lowry, L. Gooney Bird and all her charms **FIC**
Lowry, L. Gooney Bird Greene **Fic**
Lowry, L. Gooney Bird on the map **Fic**
Lowry, L. The birthday ball **Fic**
Lowry, L. Gooney Bird and the room mother **Fic**
Lowry, L. Gooney Bird is so absurd **Fic**
Lowry, L. Gooney the fabulous **Fic**
Lulu and the duck in the park **Fic**
Lupica, M. Long shot **Fic**
Lupica, M. Play Makers **Fic**
Lupica, M. Safe at home **Fic**
Lupica, M. Two-minute drill **Fic**
Lyon, G. E. The pirate of kindergarten **E**
Mackall, D. D. First day **E**
Mackintosh, D. Marshall Armstrong is new to our
  school **E**
MacLachlan, P. Word after word after word **Fic**
Madison, A. Velma Gratch & the way cool butter-
  fly **E**
Margolis, L. Everybody bugs out **Fic**
Margolis, L. Girls acting catty **Fic**
Margolis, L. Girl's best friend **Fic**
Marilyn's monster **E**
Marsden, C. The gold-threaded dress **Fic**
Martin, A. M. Belle Teal **Fic**
Marty McGuire **Fic**
McCall Smith, A. The great cake mystery **Fic**
McCarty, P. Henry in love **E**
McCulloch, M. The other Felix **Fic**

Quackenbush, R. M. First grade jitters **E**

Railsback, L. Noonie's masterpiece **Fic**

Rain school **E**

Rania The sandwich swap **E**

Rankin, L. Ruthie and the (not so) teeny tiny lie **E**

Rathmann, P. Officer Buckle and Gloria **E**

Ray, D. Ghost girl **Fic**

Ray, D. Here lies Linc **Fic**

Reed, L. R. Color chaos! **E**

Rees, D. Uncle Pirate **Fic**

Rees, D. Uncle Pirate to the rescue **Fic**

Reid, B. Perfect snow **E**

Remkiewicz, F. Song Lee in Room 2B **Fic**

Repka, J. The clueless girl's guide to being a genius **Fic**

Reynolds, A. Superhero School **E**

Reynolds, P. The dot **E**

Richards, J. Thunder Raker **Fic**

Riggs, S. Not in Room 204 **E**

Robbins, J. The new girl . . . and me **E**

Robbins, J. Two of a kind **E**

Robinson, M. L. Bright Island **Fic**

Rocket's 100th day of school **E**

Rockliff, M. My heart will not sit down **E**

Rockwell, A. F. First day of school **E**

Rockwell, A. F. My preschool **E**

Rodman, M. A. First grade stinks **E**

Rodman, M. A. Yankee girl **Fic**

Rosen, M. Totally wonderful Miss Plumberry **E**

Rosenberry, V. Vera's first day of school **E**

Rundell, K. Cartwheeling in thunderstorms **Fic**

Rupp, R. Octavia Boone's big questions about life, the universe, and everything **Fic**

Rupp, R. Sarah Simpson's Rules for Living **Fic**

Russo, M. A very big bunny **E**

Rylander, C. The fourth stall **Fic**

Sachar, L. Marvin Redpost: is he a girl? **Fic**

Sachar, L. Sideways stories from Wayside School **Fic**

Salisbury, G. Calvin Coconut: kung fooey **Fic**

Salisbury, G. Calvin Coconut: trouble magnet **Fic**

Saltzberg, B. Stanley and the class pet **E**

Sauer, T. Mostly monsterly **E**

Saunders, K. Beswitched **Fic**

Schachner, J. Skippyjon Jones class action **E**

Schaefer, C. L. Dragon dancing **E**

Schaefer, L. M. Frankie Stein starts school **E**

Schmatz, P. Bluefish **Fic**

Schmid, P. Hugs from Pearl **E**

Schmidt, G. D. The Wednesday wars **Fic**

Schneider, R. Knightley Academy **Fic**

Schneider, R. The secret prince **Fic**

Schotter, R. Doo-Wop Pop **E**

Scieszka, J. Spaceheadz, book 2 **Fic**

Scieszka, J. Spaceheadz, book 3 **Fic**

Scotton, R. Splat the cat **E**

Scotton, R. Splat the cat sings flat **E**

Selzer, A. I put a spell on you **Fic**

Seuling, B. Robert takes a stand **Fic**

Seuss Hooray for Diffendoofer Day! **E**

Shang, W. The great wall of Lucy Wu **Fic**

Shea, B. Big plans **E**

Shefelman, J. J. Anna Maria's gift **Fic**

Sherman, D. The BEDMAS conspiracy **Fic**

Shouldn't you be in school? **Fic**

Shreve, S. R. The flunking of Joshua T. Bates **Fic**

Sierra, J. We love our school! **E**

Simms, L. Rotten teeth **E**

Skateboard party **Fic**

Skye, O. Wonkenstein: the creature from my closet **Fic**

Slade, A. G. Jolted **Fic**

Sonnenblick, J. After ever after **Fic**

Sonnenblick, J. Zen and the art of faking it **Fic**

Spaceheadz **Fic**

Spinelli, E. Miss Fox's class goes green **E**

Spinelli, E. Miss Fox's class shapes up **E**

Spinelli, J. Loser **Fic**

Stagestruck **E**

Stier, C. The terrible secrets of the Tell-All Club **Fic**

Stine, R. L. It's the first day of school--forever! **Fic**

Stone, P. Deep down popular **Fic**

Stout, S. K. Fiona Finkelstein meets her match!! **Fic**

Stuey Lewis against all odds **Fic**

Sturges, P. I love school! **Fic**

Tallulah's Nutcracker **E**

Tallulah's solo **E**

The Tapper twins go to war (with each other) **Fic**

Tarshis, L. Emma-Jean Lazarus fell out of a tree **Fic**

Taylor, C. Ready to wear **Fic**

Ten rules you absolutely must not break if you want to survive the school bus **E**

The terrible two **Fic**

Thomson, M. Keena Ford and the second-grade mixup **Fic**

Towell, K. Skary childrin and the carousel of sorrow **Fic**

Townsend, M. Billy Tartle in Say Cheese! **E**

Tracy, K. Camille McPhee fell under the bus **Fic**

Tracy, K. The reinvention of Bessica Lefter **Fic**

Trueit, T. S. No girls allowed (dogs okay) **Fic**

Underwood, D. A balloon for Isabel **E**

Urban, L. A crooked kind of perfect **Fic**

Urban, L. Hound dog true **Fic**

Urdahl, C. Polka-dot fixes kindergarten **E**

Vail, R. Justin Case **Fic**

Van Draanen, W. Sammy Keyes and the night of skulls **Fic**

Vande Velde, V. 8 class pets + one squirrel ÷ one dog **Fic**

Vernick, A. Is your buffalo ready for kindergarten? **E**

Ain, B. Starring Jules (as herself)	**E**
Ain, B. Starring Jules (in drama-rama)	**Fic**
Anderson, J. D. Sidekicked	**Fic**
Andrews, J. The very fairy princess	**E**
Angleberger, T. Princess Labelmaker to the rescue!	**Fic**
Angleberger, T. The surprise attack of Jabba the Puppett	**Fic**
Auch, M. J. I was a third grade science project	**Fic**
Barden, S. The super secret mystery	**Fic**
Barnholdt, L. Girl meets ghost	**Fic**
Baskin, N. R. Runt	**Fic**
Ben draws trouble	**E**
Best, C. Beatrice spells some lulus and learns to write a letter	**E**
Booraem, E. Texting the underworld	**Fic**
Brauner, B. The magic mistake	**Fic**
Brown, P. My teacher is a monster! (no, I am not)	**E**
Clements, A. About average	**Fic**
Clements, A. Troublemaker	**Fic**
Cohen, B. Molly's pilgrim	**E**
Comics Squad	**741.5**
Cotler, S. Cheesie Mack is running like crazy!	**Fic**
Coville, B. The skull of truth	**Fic**
Cox, J. Ukulele Hayley	**Fic**
Cuyler, M. 100th day worries	**E**
Davies, J. Candy smash	**Fic**
Diesen, D. The pout-pout fish goes to school	**E**
Dinosaur vs. school	**E**
Dowell, F. O. R. The sound of your voice, only really far away	**Fic**
Drama	**741.5**
Each kindness	**E**
EllRay Jakes Rocks the Holidays!	**Fic**
English, K. Nikki & Deja	**FIC**
Fairlie, E. The lost treasure of Tuckernuck	**Fic**
Fleming, D. The Saturday boy	**Fic**
Fletcher, R. Flying solo	**Fic**
Frazier, A. The mastermind plot	**Fic**
Friedman, L. Play it again, Mallory	**Fic**
Fry, M. The Odd Squad	**Fic**
Gantos, J. Joey Pigza swallowed the key	**Fic**
Gilson, J. Bug in a rug	**Fic**
Grabenstein, C. My brother the robot	**Fic**
Graff, L. Absolutely almost	**Fic**
Green, T. New kid	**Fic**
Greene, S. Princess Posey and the first grade boys	**E**
Hale, S. The storybook of legends	**Fic**
Harkrader, L. The adventures of Beanboy	**Fic**
Harper, C. M. Just Grace and the super sleepover	**Fic**
Harper, C. M. Just Grace and the trouble with cupcakes	**Fic**
Harrington, K. Courage for beginners	**Fic**
Hattemer, K. The vigilante poets of Selwyn Academy	
Henkes, K. The year of Billy Miller	**Fic**
Hosford, K. Infinity and me	**E**
The invisible boy	**E**
Jennings, P. Guinea dog 2	**Fic**
Jennings, P. Odd, weird, and little	**Fic**
Johnson, V. The great Greene heist	**Fic**
Joyner, A. Boris for the win	**823.92**
Jung, M. Geeks, girls, and secret identities	**Fic**
Kinard, K. The boy prediction	**Fic**
Kinney, J. Diary of a wimpy kid	**Fic**
Kline, S. Song Lee and the I hate you notes	**Fic**
Larson, M. A. Pennyroyal Academy	**Fic**
Lee, J. Elvis and the underdogs	**Fic**
Lester, H. Hooway for Wodney Wat	**E**
Levine, K. The lions of Little Rock	**Fic**
Levy, D. A. The misadventures of the family Fletcher	**Fic**
Lewis, M. Morgy makes his move	**Fic**
Lipsyte, R. The twinning project	**Fic**
Little Lola	**E**
Little Naomi, Little Chick	**E**
Look, L. Alvin Ho	**Fic**
Lowry, L. Gooney Bird and all her charms	**FIC**
Lulu and the duck in the park	**Fic**
The magician's bird	**Fic**
Messner, K. Marty McGuire digs worms!	**Fic**
The mighty Quinn	**Fic**
My Heart Is Laughing	**398.2**
My three best friends and me, Zulay	**E**
Northrop, M. Plunked	**Fic**
Palacio, R. J. Wonder	**Fic**
Paulsen, G. Vote	**Fic**
Pearl and Wagner	**E**
Pincus, G. The 14 fibs of Gregory K	**Fic**
A poem in your pocket	**Fic**
Polacco, P. Mr. Wayne's masterpiece	**E**
Princess Academy	**Fic**
Reynolds, P. H. Sky color	**Fic**
Robinson, M. L. Bright Island	**Fic**
Rocket's 100th day of school	**E**
Rosenberry, V. Vera's first day of school	**E**
Sadie and the big mountain	**E**
Say, A. The favorite daughter	**E**
Schmid, P. Oliver and his alligator	**E**
Seuss Hooray for Diffendoofer Day!	**E**
Simms, L. Rotten teeth	**E**
Skateboard party	**Fic**
Sloan, H. G. Counting by 7s	**Fic**
Standiford, N. Switched at birthday	**Fic**
Stead, R. Liar & spy	**Fic**
Stealing the game	**Fic**
Stone, P. The boy on Cinnamon Street	**Fic**
Stuey Lewis against all odds	**Fic**
The Tapper twins go to war (with each other)	**Fic**
The terrible two	**Fic**

Schulman, Janet
The nutcracker   **Fic**
Pale Male   **598**
(ed) You read to me & I'll read to you   **E**
Schulz, Charles M.
     About
Amoroso, C. Charles Schulz   **92**
Gherman, B. Sparky: the life and art of Charles Schulz   **92**
Schumacher, Thomas L.
How does the show go on?   **792**
Schuman, Michael
Delaware   **975.1**
Schumann, Bettina
13 women artists children should know   **709**
Schumann, Clara, 1819-1896
     About
Krull, K. Lives of the musicians   **920**
Reich, S. Clara Schumann   **786.2**
Schur, Maxine
Gullible Gus   **Fic**
Schwabach, Karen
The storm before Atlanta   **Fic**
Schwabacher, Martin
Bears   **599.78**
Elephants   **599.67**
Minnesota   **977.6**
Puerto Rico   **972.95**
Schwake, Rainer
(il) 3-D art lab for kids   **702.8**
Schwake, Susan
3-D art lab for kids   **702.8**
Schwalb, Edith
     About
Kacer, K. Hiding Edith   **940.53**
Schwartz, Alvin, 1927-1992
Ghosts!   **398.2**
I saw you in the bathtub, and other folk rhymes **398.2**
In a dark, dark room, and other scary stories **398.2**
More scary stories to tell in the dark   **398.2**
Scary stories 3   **398.2**
Scary stories to tell in the dark   **398.25**
There is a carrot in my ear, and other noodle tales   **398.2**
Schwartz, Amy
(il) Frederick, H. V. Babyberry pie   **E**
(il) Hest, A. The purple coat   **E**
Tiny and Hercules   **E**
What James likes best   **E**
100 things that make me happy   **E**
Dee Dee and me   **E**
Willie and Uncle Bill   **E**
Schwartz, Betty Ann
The splendid spotted snake   **E**
Schwartz, Carol
(il) Slade, S. What if there were no bees? **577.4**

(il) Slade, S. What if there were no gray wolves?   **577.3**
(il) Slade, S. What if there were no lemmings?   **577.5**
(il) Slade, S. What if there were no sea otters? **577.7**
Schwartz, Corey Rosen
The three ninja pigs   **E**
Schwartz, David M.
How much is a million?   **513**
G is for googol   **510**
If you made a million   **332.024**
Millions to measure   **530.8**
On beyond a million   **513.5**
Q is for quark   **500**
Rotten pumpkin   **577.16**
What in the wild?   **508**
Where else in the wild?   **591.4**
Where in the wild?   **591.4**
Schwartz, Ellen
Stealing home   **Fic**
Schwartz, Heather E.
Gymnastics   **796.4**
Political activism   **322.4**
Safe social networking   **302.302**
Snowboarding   **796.93**
Women of the U.S. Air Force   **358.4**
Schwartz, Howard
Olson, A. N. Ask the bones: scary stories from around the world   **398.2**
Olson, A. N. More bones   **398.2**
A coat for the moon and other Jewish tales   **398.2**
Gathering sparks   **E**
Schwartz, Joanne
City alphabet   **E**
Our corner grocery store   **E**
Schwartz, John
Short   **612.6**
Schwartz, Jordan
The art of LEGO design   **688.72**
Schwartz, Roslyn
(il) Splat!   **E**
Schwarz, Renee
Birdfeeders   **690**
Birdhouses   **690**
Making masks   **646.4**
Wind chimes and whirligigs   **745.592**
Schwarz, Viviane
(il) Deacon, A. A place to call home   **E**
Is there a dog in this book?   **E**
The Sleepwalkers   **Fic**
There are no cats in this book!   **E**
Schweitzer, Karen
The beagle   **636.7**
The dachshund   **636.7**
Schweninger, Ann
(il) Van Leeuwen, J. Amanda Pig and the awful,

Haddix, M. P. Torn **Fic**

Haddon, M. Boom! **Fic**

Hall, T. Away **Fic**

Hall, T. The Line **Fic**

Hatke, B. The Return of Zita the Spacegirl **741.5**

Holyoke, P. The Neptune Project **Fic**

Hulme, J. The glitch in sleep **Fic**

Hulme, J. The split second **Fic**

Hurd, T. Bongo fishing **Fic**

The iron giant **Fic**

Jeffrey, M. Max Quick: the pocket and the pendant **Fic**

Klass, D. Stuck on Earth **Fic**

Knapman, T. Mungo and the spiders from space **E**

Legends of Zita the spacegirl **741.5**

Lipsyte, R. The twinning project **Fic**

London, A. Proxy **Fic**

Lowry, L. Son **Fic**

Lowry, L. The giver **Fic**

Lyga, B. Archvillain **Fic**

Marshall, E. Space case **E**

Mass, W. Pi in the sky **Fic**

McElligott, M. Benjamin Franklinstein lives! **Fic**

McKissack, P. C. The clone codes **Fic**

McKissack, P. C. Cyborg **Fic**

Myklusch, M. Jack Blank and the Imagine Nation **Fic**

Naftali, J. The rendering **Fic**

Nylund, E. S. The Resisters **Fic**

O'Malley, K. Captain Raptor and the moon mystery **E**

O'Malley, K. Captain Raptor and the space pirates **E**

The orphan army **Fic**

Other worlds **S**

Pinkwater, D. M. Adventures of a cat-whiskered girl **Fic**

Pinkwater, D. M. Lizard music **Fic**

Prevost, G. The book of time **Fic**

Reeve, P. Larklight **Fic**

Rex, A. Smek for president! **Fic**

Rex, A. The true meaning of Smekday **Fic**

Scaletta, K. The winter of the robots **Fic**

Seegert, S. How to grow up and rule the world **Fic**

Service, P. F. Escape from planet Yastol **Fic**

Sleator, W. The boxes **Fic**

Sleator, W. Interstellar pig **Fic**

Stadler, A. Julian Rodriguez: episode one, Trash crisis on earth **Fic**

Stadler, A. Julian Rodriguez: episode two, Invasion of the relatives **Fic**

Stewart, T. L. The mysterious Benedict Society **Fic**

Teague, M. The doom machine **Fic**

Van Eekhout, G. The boy at the end of the world **Fic**

Vaupel, R. The rules of the universe by Austin W. Hale **Fic**

Verne, J. 20,000 leagues under the sea **Fic**

Webb, P. Six days **Fic**

White, R. You'll like it here (everybody does) **Fic**

Wilson, D. H. A boy and his bot **Fic**

Winterson, J. Tanglewreck **Fic**

Yolen, J. Commander Toad and the voyage home **E**

SCIENCE FICTION

See also Adventure fiction; Fiction

SCIENCE FICTION -- GRAPHIC NOVELS

Gagne, M. The saga of Rex **741.5**

SCIENCE FICTION COMIC BOOKS, STRIPS, ETC.

See also Comic books, strips, etc.

SCIENCE FICTION FILMS

See also Motion pictures

SCIENCE FICTION GRAPHIC NOVELS

Casty Walt Disney's Mickey Mouse and the world to come **741.5**

Collicutt, P. City in peril! **741.5**

Deas, M. Dalen & Gole **741.5**

Farshtey, G. Bionicle #1: rise of the Toa Nuva **741.5**

Flight explorer **741.5**

Guibert, E. Sardine in outer space **741.5**

Hatke, B. The Return of Zita the Spacegirl **741.5**

Hatke, B. Zita the spacegirl **741.5**

Kibuishi, K. Copper **741.5**

Legends of Zita the spacegirl **741.5**

McCann, J. Return of the Dapper Men **741.5**

O'Malley, K. Captain Raptor and the moon mystery **E**

Parker, J. Missile Mouse: rescue on Tankium3 **741.5**

Parker, J. Missile Mouse: the star crusher **741.5**

Roman, D. Astronaut Academy: Zero gravity **741.5**

Shiga, J. Meanwhile **741.5**

Stevenson, R. L. The strange case of Dr. Jekyll and Mr. Hyde **741.5**

SCIENCE FICTION GRAPHIC NOVELS

See also Graphic novels

SCIENCE FICTION POETRY

See also Poetry

SCIENCE FICTION TELEVISION PROGRAMS

See also Television programs

SCIENCE FICTION WRITERS

Ellis, S. From reader to writer **372.62**

Science for every kid series

VanCleave, J. P. Janice Vancleave's ecology for every kid **577**

VanCleave, J. P. Janice VanCleave's engineering for every kid **507.8**

VanCleave, J. P. Janice VanCleave's oceans for every kid **551.46**

Science in ancient China. Beshore, G. W. **509**

Science in ancient Egypt. Woods, G. **509**

Science in ancient Rome. Harris, J. L. **509**

Science matters: simple machines [series]

De Medeiros, J. Pulleys **621.8**
De Medeiros, M. Screws **621.8**
Howse, J. Inclined planes **621.8**
Howse, J. Levers **621.8**
Tomljanovic, T. Wedges **621.8**

SCIENCE MUSEUMS -- WASHINGTON (D.C.) -- GUIDEBOOKS
Korrell, E. B. Awesome adventures at the Smithsonian **069**

Science of sports [series]
Bazemore, S. Soccer: how it works **796.334**
Dreier, D. Baseball **796.357**
Slade, S. Basketball **796.323**

Science of the past [series]
Beshore, G. W. Science in ancient China **509**
Harris, J. L. Science in ancient Rome **509**
Woods, G. Science in ancient Egypt **509**
The **science** of water. Parker, S. **532**
Science on the loose. Becker, H. **507.8**

Science play [series]
Cobb, V. I fall down **531**
Cobb, V. I face the wind **551.51**
Cobb, V. I see myself **535**

SCIENCE PROJECTS
Benbow, A. Awesome animal science projects **590.7**
Benbow, A. Lively plant science projects **580.7**
Benbow, A. Sprouting seed science projects **580.7**
Blobaum, C. Awesome snake science **597.96**
Bonnet, R. L. Home run! **530**
Carson, M. K. Weather projects for young scientists **551.5**
Explore Natural Resources! **333.7**
Gabrielson, C. Stomp rockets, catapults, and kaleidoscopes **507.8**
Gardner, R. Ace your animal science project **590.7**
Gardner, R. Ace your chemistry science project **540.7**
Gardner, R. Ace your ecology and environmental science project **577**
Gardner, R. Ace your exercise and nutrition science project: great science fair ideas **613**
Gardner, R. Ace your food science project **664**
Gardner, R. Ace your forces and motion science project **531**
Gardner, R. Ace your human biology science project **612**
Gardner, R. Ace your math and measuring science project **530.8**
Gardner, R. Ace your physical science project **530**
Gardner, R. Ace your plant science project **580.7**
Gardner, R. Ace your science project about the senses **612.8**
Gardner, R. Ace your science project using chemistry magic and toys **540.7**
Gardner, R. Ace your space science project **520**

Gardner, R. Ace your weather science project **551.5**
Gardner, R. Easy genius science projects with chemistry **540.7**
Gardner, R. Easy genius science projects with electricity and magnetism **537**
Gardner, R. Easy genius science projects with temperature and heat **536**
Gardner, R. Easy genius science projects with weather **551.5**
Gardner, R. Far-out science projects about Earth's sun and moon **523**
Gardner, R. Slam dunk! science projects with basketball **530**
Gardner, R. Stellar science projects about Earth's sky **551.5**
Gardner, R. Super science projects about Earth's soil and water **631.4**
Gardner, R. Super-sized science projects with volume **530.8**
Gardner, R. Wild science projects about Earth's weather **551.5**
Goodstein, M. Ace your sports science project **507.8**
Goodstein, M. Goal! science projects with soccer **507.8**
Goodstein, M. Wheels! **530**
Hopwood, J. Cool distance assistants **507.8**
Hopwood, J. Cool dry ice devices **507.8**
Hopwood, J. Cool gravity activities **531**
Margles, S. Mythbusters science fair book **507.8**
Reilly, K. M. The human body **612**
Reilly, K. M. Planet Earth **333.72**
Science activities for all students **507.8**
Tocci, S. More simple science fair projects, grades 3-5 **507.8**
VanCleave, J. P. Janice VanCleave's big book of play and find out science projects **507.8**
VanCleave, J. P. Janice VanCleave's electricity **537**
VanCleave, J. P. Janice VanCleave's engineering for every kid **507.8**
VanCleave, J. P. Janice VanCleave's guide to the best science fair projects **507.8**
VanCleave, J. P. Janice VanCleave's rocks and minerals **552**
VanCleave, J. P. Janice VanCleave's weather **551.5**
VanCleave, J. P. Step-by-step science experiments in astronomy **520**
VanCleave, J. P. Step-by-step science experiments in energy **531**
VanCleave, J. P. Janice VanCleave's weather **551.5**
Williams, J. Oobleck, slime, & dancing spaghetti **507.8**
Young, K. R. Experiments to do on your family **507.8**

SCIENCE PROJECTS -- FICTION
Scaletta, K. The winter of the robots **Fic**

Draper, S. M. The birthday storm **Fic**

Sayre, A. P. Turtle, turtle, watch out! **E**

The voyage of Turtle Rex **E**

Sea turtles' race to the sea. Allen, K. **597.92**

SEA URCHINS

Gilpin, D. Starfish, urchins & other echino-derms **593**

SEA WATER

See also Water

SEA WATER AQUARIUMS *See* Marine aquariums

SEA WATER CONVERSION

See also Water purification

SEA WAVES *See* Ocean waves

The **sea** wolves. McAllister, I. **599.77**

The **sea,** the storm, and the mangrove tangle. Cherry, L. **E**

SEA-SHORE *See* Seashore

Seabird in the forest. Dunning, J. **598**

Seabiscuit. McCarthy, M. **798.4**

SEABISCUIT (RACE HORSE)

McCarthy, M. Seabiscuit **798.4**

Seabrook, Alexis

(il) Buchanan, A. J. The daring book for girls **646.700**

Seabrooke, Brenda

Wolf pie **Fic**

SEAFARING LIFE

See also Adventure and adventurers; Manners and customs; Voyages and travels

SEAFARING LIFE -- FICTION

Ahlberg, A. The baby in the hat **E**

Conly, J. L. Murder afloat **Fic**

Flanagan, J. The hunters **Fic**

Flanagan, J. The invaders **Fic**

In a village by the sea **E**

Lawrence, I. The buccaneers

Treasure hunters **Fic**

SEAFOOD

Llewellyn, C. Cooking with meat and fish **641.6**

SEAFOOD

See also Food; Marine resources

Seaglass summer. Banerjee, A. **Fic**

Seagulls don't eat pickles. **Fic**

Seahorses. Wearing, J. **597**

Seahorses. Curtis, J. K. **597**

Seahorses, pipefishes, and their kin. Miller, S. S. **597**

Seal. Spilsbury, L. **599.79**

Seal pup rescue. Peterson, B. **E**

SEALS (ANIMALS)

Butterworth, C. See what a seal can do! **599.79**

Cox, L. Elizabeth, queen of the seas **E**

Hengel, K. It's a baby Australian fur seal! **599.79**

Leopard & Silkie **599.79**

Lunis, N. California sea lion **599.7**

Malam, J. Pinnipeds **599.79**

Markovics, J. L. Weddell seal **599.79**

Meinking, M. Polar bear vs. seal **599.75**

Metz, L. Discovering sea lions **599.79**

Peterson, B. Seal pup rescue **E**

Read, T. C. Exploring the world of seals and walruses **599.79**

Spilsbury, L. Seal **599.79**

SEALS (ANIMALS)

See also Mammals; Marine mammals

SEALS (ANIMALS) -- CONSERVATION

Leopard & Silkie **599.79**

SEALS (ANIMALS) -- FICTION

Harvey, J. Astro the Steller sea lion **599.79**

Hoff, S. Sammy the seal **E**

Seeger, L. V. What if? **E**

The **seals** on the bus. Hort, L. **782.421**

SEAMANSHIP *See* Navigation

SEAMEN *See* Sailors

Seamore, the very forgetful porpoise. Edgemon, D. **E**

Search and rescue dog heroes. Bozzo, L. **636.7**

SEARCH AND RESCUE OPERATIONS *See* Rescue work

SEARCH DOGS

Castaldo, N. F. Sniffer dogs **636.7**

Goldish, M. Ground zero dogs **636.7**

SEARCH DOGS

See also Working dogs

SEARCH ENGINES *See* Web search engines

The **search** for delicious. Babbitt, N. **Fic**

The **search** for WondLa. DiTerlizzi, T. **Fic**

The search for WondLa [series]

DiTerlizzi, T. The battle for WondLa **Fic**

Searching for dragons. Wrede, P. C. **Fic**

Searching for grizzlies. **599.78**

Searching for Sarah Rector. Bolden, T. **92**

SEARCHING THE INTERNET *See* Internet searching

Searchlight books. How government does works [series]

Donovan, S. Getting elected **324.7**

Searle, Ronald

(il) Forbes, R. L. Beast Friends Forever **811**

SEAS

See also Earth; Physical geography; Water

Seashore. Wilson, H. **551.4**

SEASHORE

Arnosky, J. Beachcombing **578.7**

Bredeson, C. Baby animals of the seashore **591.7**

Parker, S. Seashore **577.7**

Rotner, S. Senses at the seashore **E**

Serafini, F. Looking closely along the shore **578.7**

Wilson, H. Seashore **551.4**

Seashore. Parker, S. **577.7**

SEASHORE -- FICTION

Bearn, E. Tumtum & Nutmeg: the Rose Cottage

tales **Fic**

Cooper, E. Beach **E**

Mortiz, D. Hush little beachcomber **E**

Roop, P. Down East in the ocean **E**

SEASHORE ECOLOGY

Himmelman, J. Who's at the seashore? **591.7**

Pyers, G. The biodiversity of coasts **577.5**

SEASHORE ECOLOGY

See also Ecology

Seaside dream. Bates, J. C. **E**

A **season** of gifts. Peck, R. **Fic**

Season of secrets. Nicholls, S. **Fic**

Seasons. Rau, D. M. **508.2**

Seasons. Crausaz, A. **508.2**

Seasons [series]

Smith, S. Fall **508.2**

Smith, S. Spring **508.2**

Smith, S. Summer **508.2**

Smith, S. Winter **508.2**

SEASONS

See also Astronomy; Climate; Meteorology

Seasons. Blexbolex **E**

SEASONS

Branley, F. M. Sunshine makes the seasons **508.2**

Crausaz, A. Seasons **508.2**

Esbensen, B. J. Swing around the sun **811**

Feeney, S. Sun and rain **996.9**

Fisher, V. Everything I need to know before I'm five **E**

Gibbons, G. The reasons for seasons **525**

Hines, A. G. Pieces **811**

McKneally, R. Our seasons **508.2**

Morrison, G. Nature in the neighborhood **508**

Rau, D. M. Seasons **508.2**

Rockwell, A. F. Four seasons make a year **E**

Royston, A. Looking at weather and seasons **551.6**

VanCleave, J. P. Janice VanCleave's science around the year **507.8**

Weiner, M. Shakespeare's Seasons **822.3**

SEASONS -- ENCYCLOPEDIAS

Goldstone, B. Awesome autumn **E**

SEASONS -- FICTION

Christensen, B. Plant a little seed **E**

Johnston, T. Winter is coming **E**

Secrets of the seasons **E**

Such a little mouse **E**

A wonderful year **E**

SEASONS -- GRAPHIC NOVELS

Rosenstiehl, A. Silly Lilly and the four seasons **741.5**

SEASONS -- POETRY

Esbensen, B. J. Swing around the sun **811**

Farrar, S. The year comes round **811**

Forest has a song **E**

Gray, R. One big rain **811**

Hines, A. G. Pieces **811**

Janeczko, P. B. Firefly July and other very short poems **811**

Julie Andrews' treasury for all seasons **808.81**

Muth, J. J. Hi, Koo! **811**

The **seasons** of Arnold's apple tree. Gibbons, G. **525**

SEATTLE (WASH.) -- FICTION

Barden, S. Cinderella Smith **Fic**

Seaver, Barton

National Geographic Kids Cookbook **641.5**

Seaweed soup. Murphy, S. J. **511.3**

SEAWEEDS *See* Algae

Seba, Jaime

Gallup guides for youth facing persistent prejudice **306.76**

Sebastian and the balloon. **E**

Sebe, Masayuki

Let's count to 100! **E**

Sebestyen, Ouida

Words by heart **Fic**

SECESSION -- SOUTHERN STATES

See also United States -- History -- 1861-1865, Civil War

Secheret, Jessica

(il) Chasse, J. D. The babysitter's survival guide **649**

SECLUSION *See* Solitude

Second banana. **E**

SECOND HAND TRADE *See* Secondhand trade

A **second** is a hiccup. Hutchins, H. J. **529**

The **second** life of Abigail Walker. Dowell, F. O. **Fic**

Second sight. Blackwood, G. L. **Fic**

SECOND WORLD WAR *See* World War, 1939-1945

SECONDHAND TRADE

A gift for Mama **Fic**

Secord, Laura, d. 1868

About

Lunn, J. L. S. Laura Secord: a story of courage **Fic**

SECRECY -- FICTION

Jung, M. Geeks, girls, and secret identities **Fic**

Lowry, L. Son **Fic**

Secret agents. Gilbert, A. **327.12**

The **secret** box. Lehman, B. **E**

The **secret** cave. McCully, E. A. **E**

The **secret** circus. Wright, J. **E**

The **secret** garden. Burnett, F. H. **Fic**

Secret history of mermaids and creatures of the deep. Berk, A. **398**

The **secret** hum of a daisy. Holczer, T. **Fic**

The **secret** kingdom. Nimmo, J. **Fic**

The **secret** language of girls. Dowell, F. O. **Fic**

The **secret** legacy. Menchu, R. **398.2**

The **secret** life of a snowflake. Libbrecht, K. G. **551.57**

The **secret** life of Ms. Finkleman. Winters, B. H. **Fic**

Secret lives [series]

SEGREGATION IN EDUCATION -- FICTION

Conkling, W. Sylvia and Aki **Fic**

Tuck, P. M. As fast as words could fly **Fic**

Weatherford, C. B. Dear Mr. Rosenwald **Fic**

SEGREGATION IN EDUCATION -- VIRGINIA -- HISTORY -- 20TH CENTURY

Kanefield, T. The girl from the tar paper school **92**

Seguin, Juan Nepomuceno, 1806-1890

About

Chemerka, W. R. Juan Seguin **976.4**

Seibold, J. Otto

(il) Edgemon, D. Seamore, the very forgetful porpoise **E**

Olive the other reindeer **E**

Other goose **398.8**

(il) Sierra, J. Tell the truth, B.B. Wolf **E**

Seidler, Tor

Gully's travels **Fic**

SEINEN

See also Manga

Seiple, Samantha

Ghosts in the fog **940.54**

SEISMIC SEA WAVES *See* Tsunamis

SEISMOGRAPHY *See* Earthquakes

SEISMOLOGY *See* Earthquakes

Seki, Sunny

(il) Yuko-chan and the Daruma doll **E**

Selbert, Kathryn

War dogs **E**

Selden, George

Feldman, T. Harry Cat and Tucker Mouse: starring Harry **E**

The cricket in Times Square **Fic**

The **seldom-ever-shady** glades. Van Wassenhove, S. **811**

SELECTIVE MUTISM -- FICTION

LaFleur, S. Listening for Lucca **Fic**

Lean, S. A dog called Homeless **Fic**

SELF

See also Consciousness; Individuality; Personality

SELF HEALTH CARE *See* Health self-care

SELF IMAGE *See* Personal appearance

Self, David

Christianity **230**

SELF-ACCEPTANCE

Henkes, K. The birthday room **Fic**

Markes, J. Good thing you're not an octopus! **E**

Spinelli, J. Loser **Fic**

SELF-ACCEPTANCE

See also Psychology

SELF-ACCEPTANCE -- FICTION

Howe, J. Addie on the inside **Fic**

Mann, J. K. Two speckled eggs **E**

Bear and duck **E**

Lichtenheld, T. Exclamation mark **E**

SELF-ASSURANCE *See* Self-confidence; Self-reliance

SELF-AWARENESS *See* Self-perception

SELF-CARE, HEALTH *See* Health self-care

SELF-CONFIDENCE

Allen, D. Dancing in the wings **E**

Levine, G. C. The two princesses of Bamarre **Fic**

Moss, W. Being me **158**

Reynolds, P. Ish **E**

Simons, R. At home in your body **613**

SELF-CONFIDENCE

See also Emotions

SELF-CONFIDENCE -- FICTION

Dowell, F. O. The second life of Abigail Walker **Fic**

Lewin, B. You can do it! **E**

Pastis, S. Timmy failure : now look what you've done **Fic**

Princess Academy **Fic**

SELF-CONSCIOUSNESS

See also Psychology

SELF-CONTROL

See also Psychology

SELF-DEFENSE IN ANIMALS *See* Animal defenses

SELF-DESTRUCTIVE BEHAVIOR

See also Psychology

SELF-EMPLOYED

See also Businesspeople

SELF-ESTEEM

Curtis, J. L. I'm gonna like me **E**

Moss, W. Being me **158**

Yep, L. When the circus came to town **Fic**

SELF-ESTEEM

See also Psychology

SELF-ESTEEM -- FICTION

Graff, L. Absolutely almost **Fic**

SELF-EVALUATION IN EDUCATION *See* Educational evaluation

SELF-EXAMINATION, MEDICAL *See* Health self-care

SELF-GOVERNMENT *See* Democracy; Representative government and representation

SELF-HELP MEDICAL CARE *See* Health self-care

SELF-HELP TECHNIQUES

See also Applied psychology; Life skills

SELF-IMPROVEMENT

See also Life skills

SELF-INSTRUCTION

See also Education; Study skills

SELF-LOVE (PSYCHOLOGY) *See* Self-acceptance; Self-esteem

SELF-MEDICATION *See* Health self-care

SELF-PERCEPTION

Gantos, J. Jack on the tracks **Fic**

Van Draanen, W. Flipped **Fic**

Naidoo, J. C. Rainbow family collections **028.1**

SEXUALLY TRANSMITTED DISEASES

    See also Communicable diseases

Seymour Simon's book of trains. Simon, S. **385**

Seymour Simon's extreme earth records. Simon, S. **550**

Seymour Simon's extreme oceans. Simon, S. **551.46**

Sfar, Joann

    (il) Guibert, E. Sardine in outer space **741.5**

    (il) Little Vampire **741.5**

    The little prince **741.5**

Shackles. Wentworth, M. **E**

SHADES AND SHADOWS

    Bulla, C. R. What makes a shadow? **535**

    Claybourne, A. Light and dark **535**

    Hoban, T. Shadows and reflections **779**

SHADES AND SHADOWS

    See also Drawing

SHADES AND SHADOWS -- FICTION

    Leathers, P. The Black rabbit **E**

SHADES AND SHADOWS -- POETRY

    Cendrars, B. Shadow **841**

Shades of black. Pinkney, S. L. **305.23**

Shades of people. Rotner, S. **E**

Shadow. Cendrars, B. **841**

The **shadow** door. Bannister (Person) **741.5**

Shadow of a bull. Wojciechowska, M. **Fic**

The **shadow** of Malabron. Wharton, T. **Fic**

SHADOW PANTOMIMES AND PLAYS

    See also Amateur theater; Pantomimes; Puppets and puppet plays; Shadow pictures; Theater

SHADOW PICTURES

    See also Amusements

Shadow spinner. Fletcher, S. **Fic**

The **shadow** throne. Nielsen, J. A. **Fic**

The **Shadowhand** Covenant. Farrey, B. **Fic**

SHADOWPACT (FICTIONAL CHARACTERS)

    See also Fictional characters; Superheroes

SHADOWS *See* Shades and shadows

SHADOWS -- FICTION

    Edmundson, C. Yeti, turn out the light! **E**

Shadows and moonshine. Aiken, J. **S**

Shadows and reflections. Hoban, T. **779**

SHAFT SINKING *See* Drilling and boring (Earth and rocks)

Shaggy dogs, waggy dogs. Hubbell, P. **E**

Shahan, Sherry

    Ice island **Fic**

    Spicy hot colors: colores picantes **E**

Shahn, Ben

    (il) Reid, A. Ounce, dice, trice **428**

Shahnameh. Laird, E. **891**

Shake & shout. Reid, R. **027.62**

Shake, rattle & turn that noise down! Stamaty, M. A. **781.66**

Shake, rattle, & roll. George-Warren, H. **781.66**

Shake-it-up tales! MacDonald, M. R. **372.6**

Shakespeare kids. Cox, C. **792.9**

The **Shakespeare** stealer. Blackwood, G. L. **Fic**

SHAKESPEARE'S GLOBE (LONDON, ENGLAND)

    Aliki William Shakespeare & the Globe **792.09**

Shakespeare's scribe. Blackwood, G. L. **Fic**

Shakespeare's Seasons. Weiner, M. **822.3**

Shakespeare's secret. Broach, E. **Fic**

Shakespeare's spy. Blackwood, G. L. **Fic**

Shakespeare, William, 1564-1616

About

    Aliki William Shakespeare & the Globe **792.09**

    All the world's a stage **Fic**

    Blackwood, G. L. The Shakespeare stealer **Fic**

    Blackwood, G. L. Shakespeare's scribe **Fic**

    The boy, the bear, the baron, the bard **E**

    Chrisp, P. Welcome to the Globe **792**

    Cooper, S. King of shadows **Fic**

    Coville, B. William Shakespeare's A midsummer night's dream **822.3**

    Coville, B. William Shakespeare's Twelfth night **822.3**

    Cox, C. Shakespeare kids **792.9**

    Lives of the writers **809**

    MacDonald, B. Wicked Will **Fic**

    Nettleton, P. H. William Shakespeare **822.3**

    Raum, E. Twenty-first-century Shakespeare **822.3**

    Schmidt, G. D. The Wednesday wars **Fic**

    Stanley, D. Bard of Avon: the story of William Shakespeare **822.3**

    Weiner, M. Shakespeare's Seasons **822.3**

SHAKESPEARE, WILLIAM, 1564-1616 -- DICTIONARIES

    See also Encyclopedias and dictionaries

SHAKESPEARE, WILLIAM, 1564-1616 -- QUOTATIONS

    See also Quotations

SHAKESPEARE, WILLIAM, 1564-1616 -- STAGE HISTORY

    See also Theater

Shakur, Tupac

About

    Harris, A. R. Tupac Shakur **92**

SHALE GAS

    Squire, A. O. Hydrofracking **622**

Shall I knit you a hat? **E**

SHAMANISM

    See also Religions

SHAMANS

    Nelson, S. D. Black Elk's vision **92**

SHAME

    See also Emotions

Shang, Wendy Wan-Long

    The great wall of Lucy Wu **Fic**

Paulsen, G. The legend of Bass Reeves **Fic**
SHERIFFS -- FICTION
  McGhee, A. The case of the missing donut **E**
  Shea, B. Kid sheriff and the terrible Toads **E**
The Sherlock files [series]
  Barrett, T. The 100-year-old secret **Fic**
Sherlock Holmes and the Baker Street Irregulars [series]
  Mack, T. The fall of the Amazing Zalindas **Fic**
  Mack, T. The mystery of the conjured man **Fic**
SHERLOCK HOLMES FILMS
  See also Motion pictures; Mystery films
Sherlock Holmes. The legend begins [series]
  Lane, A. Black ice **Fic**
  Lane, A. Rebel fire **Fic**
Sherlock, Patti
  Letters from Wolfie **Fic**
Sherman, Casey
  The finest hours **910.916**
Sherman, Deborah
  The BEDMAS conspiracy **Fic**
Sherman, Delia
  Changeling **Fic**
Sherman, Josepha
  Asteroids, meteors, and comets **523.4**
  Neptune **523.4**
  Uranus **523.4**
Sherman, Pat
  Ben and the Emancipation Proclamation **E**
  The sun's daughter **398.2**
Sherman, Patsy O., 1930-
      About
  Thimmesh, C. Girls think of everything **920**
Sherrard, Valerie
  The glory wind **Fic**
  Tumbleweed skies **Fic**
Sherrow, Victoria
  Ancient Africa **939**
  Ohio **977.1**
Sherry, Kevin
  (il) Manners mash-up: a goofy guide to good behavior **395**
  Turtle Island **E**
  I'm the biggest thing in the ocean **E**
Sherry, Maureen
  Walls within walls **Fic**
Sheth, Kashmira
  Tiger in my soup **E**
  Blue jasmine **Fic**
  Boys without names **Fic**
  Monsoon afternoon **E**
  My Dadima wears a sari **E**
Shh! we have a plan. Haughton, C. **E**
Shh! we're writing the Constitution. Fritz, J. **342**
Shhh! Gorbachev, V. **E**
Shhhhh! Everybody's sleeping. Markes, J. **E**

Shi-shi-etko. Campbell, N. I. **E**
Shields, Amy
  Little kids first big book of why **031.02**
Shields, Carol Diggory
  Baby's got the blues **E**
  English, fresh squeezed! **811**
  Wombat walkabout **E**
Shields, Charles J.
  Honduras **972.83**
Shields, Gillian
  Library Lily **E**
  When the world is ready for bed **E**
  When the world was waiting for you **E**
Shields, Sarah D.
  Turkey **956.1**
The **shifter.** Hardy, J. **Fic**
Shiga, Jason
  Meanwhile **741.5**
Shillinglaw, Bruce
  (il) Zoehfeld, K. W. Dinosaur parents, dinosaur young **567.9**
Shiloh. Naylor, P. R. **Fic**
Shimin, Symeon
  (il) Krumgold, J. Onion John **Fic**
Shimko, Bonnie
  The private thoughts of Amelia E. Rye **Fic**
Shimmer. Noel, A. **Fic**
Shimmer & splash. Arnosky, J. **591.77**
Shiner, Michael, 1805-1880
      About
  Hughes, V. Once upon a barbershop **92**
Shining star: the Anna May Wong story. Yoo, P. **92**
SHINTO
  Levin, J. Japanese mythology **299.5**
SHINTO
  See also Religions
SHIP PILOTS
  See also Sailors
The **Shipbuilder.** Heinrichs, A. **973.2**
SHIPBUILDING -- UNITED STATES -- HISTORY
  Heinrichs, A. The Shipbuilder **973.2**
SHIPPING
  See also Transportation
Ships. Lindeen, M. **623.82**
SHIPS
  Barton, B. Boats **387.2**
  Crews, D. Harbor **387.2**
  Jenson-Elliott, C. Pirate ships ahoy! **910.4**
  Kirk, S. T is for tugboat **623.82**
  Lavery, B. Legendary journeys: ships **387.2**
  Lindeen, M. Ships **623.82**
  Weitzman, D. L. Pharaoh's boat **932**
SHIPS -- FICTION
  Avi Iron thunder **Fic**
  By sea **E**

Singer, I. B. Stories for children S

Soto, G. Baseball in April, and other stories S

Soto, G. Facts of life S

Soto, G. Local news S

Soto, G. Petty crimes S

Spinelli, J. The library card S

Stine, R. L. The haunting hour S

Tan, S. Lost & found S

Troll's eye view S

Under my hat S

Under the weather S

You read to me & I'll read to you E

SHORT STORY

    See also Authorship; Fiction; Literature

SHORT STORY WRITERS

Adler, D. A. A picture book of Harriet Beecher Stowe 92

The adventures of Mark Twain by Huckleberry Finn 92

Berner, R. S. Definitely not for little ones 398.2

Bledsoe, L. J. How to survive in Antarctica 998

Bond, V. Zora and me Fic

Bryant, J. A river of words: the story of William Carlos Williams 92

Cooper, F. Coming home 818

Dahl, R. The missing golden ticket and other splendiferous secrets 92

Dahl, R. More about Boy 92

Ellis, S. From reader to writer 372.62

Fleischman, S. The trouble begins at 8 92

Fritz, J. Harriet Beecher Stowe and the Beecher preachers 813

Kerley, B. The extraordinary Mark Twain (according to Susy) 92

McKissack, P. C. A song for Harlem Fic

Miller, W. Richard Wright and the library card 92

Murphy, J. Across America on an emigrant train 385

Myers, C. Lies and other tall tales 398.2

Paulsen, G. Caught by the sea 818

Paulsen, G. How Angel Peterson got his name 813

Paulsen, G. My life in dog years 813

Varmer, H. Hans Christian Andersen 92

Zora Hurston and the chinaberry tree 813

Shortall, Leonard W.

    (il) Sobol, D. J. Encyclopedia Brown, boy detective Fic

Shortcut. Crews, D. E

Shortcut. Macaulay, D. 793.7

Shortelle, Dennis

    Gardner, R. Slam dunk! science projects with basketball 530

The **shortest** day. Pfeffer, W. 394.26

SHORTHAND

    See also Business education; Office practice; Writing

The **Shoshone.** De Capua, S. 970.004

SHOSHONE INDIANS

Adler, D. A. A picture book of Sacagawea 978

De Capua, S. The Shoshone 970.004

Freedman, R. Indian chiefs 970.004

Green, C. R. Sacagawea 978.004

Nelson, M. The life of Sacagawea 978

SHOSHONI INDIANS -- FICTION

The crossing E

Should I share my ice cream? Willems, M. E

Shouldn't you be in school? Fic

Shout! Shout it out! Fleming, D. E

Shoveller, Herb

    Ryan and Jimmy 361.7

Show me the money. Hall, A. 332.024

The **show** must go on! Klise, K. Fic

Show off. Hines-Stephens, S. 790.1

Show way. Woodson, J. E

SHOW WINDOWS

    See also Advertising; Decoration and ornament; Windows

SHOW-AND-TELL PRESENTATIONS -- FICTION

Best, C. Beatrice spells some lulus and learns to write a letter E

Simms, L. Rotten teeth E

The **show-off.** Greene, S. Fic

SHOWERS (PARTIES)

    See also Parties

Showers, Paul

    A drop of blood 612.1

    Hear your heart 612.1

    Sleep is for everyone 612.8

    What happens to a hamburger? 612.3

SHOWING OFF

    See also Human behavior

Showman, Galen

    (il) Gaiman, N. The graveyard book graphic novel Volume 1 741.5

    The graveyard book graphic novel Volume 2 741.5

Shragg, Karen

    Landstrom, L. A. Nature's yucky! 2: the desert southwest 591.7

Shrek! Steig, W. E

Shreve, Susan Richards

    The flunking of Joshua T. Bates Fic

SHREWS -- FICTION

Weiss, E. The taming of Lola E

SHRIMPS

Rustad, M. E. H. Moray eels and cleaner shrimp work together 597

The **shrinking** of Treehorn. Heide, F. P. Fic

Shroades, John

    (il) Klimo, K. The dragon in the driveway Fic

    (il) Klimo, K. The dragon in the library Fic

    (il) Klimo, K. The dragon in the volcano Fic

SHRUBS

See also Plants; Trees

Shulevitz, Uri

Dusk — E

How I learned geography — E

Troto and the trucks — E

Snow — E

So sleepy story — E

The treasure — 398.2

When I wore my sailor suit — E

Shulman, Mark

Ann and Nan are anagrams — Fic

Treasure hunters — Fic

Mom and Dad are palindromes — E

Shulman, Polly

The Grimm Legacy — Fic

The Wells Bequest — Fic

Shurtliff, Liesl

Rump — Fic

Shuster, Joe, 1914-1992

About

Nobleman, M. T. Boys of steel — 92

Shusterman, Neal, 1962-

Darkness creeping — S

(jt. auth) Elfman, E. Tesla's attic — Fic

Shuter, Jane

Ancient China — 931

Shutting out the sky. Hopkinson, D. — 307

Shwatsit! Ditchfield, C. — E

Shy Charles. Wells, R. — E

SHYNESS

See also Emotions

SHYNESS -- FICTION

Choldenko, G. A giant crush — E

Cooper, I. Lucy on the loose — Fic

Dewdney, A. Roly Poly pangolin — E

Lakritz, D. Say hello, Lily — E

Newman, J. The boys — E

Twohy, M. Poindexter makes a friend — E

Urban, L. Hound dog true — Fic

Srinivasan, D. Octopus alone — E

Sias, Ryan

Zoe and Robot: let's pretend — 741.5

Sibbick, John

(il) Scaly spotted feathered frilled — 567.9

Siberell, Anne

Bravo! brava! a night at the opera — 782.1

SIBLING RIVALRY

See also Child psychology; Siblings

SIBLING RIVALRY -- FICTION

Hartnett, S. Sadie and Ratz — Fic

Bye-bye baby brother! — E

Kantorovitz, S. The very tiny baby — E

Siblings. Crist, J. J. — 306.8

SIBLINGS

See also Family

Cole, J. The new baby at your house — 306.875

Crist, J. J. Siblings — 306.8

Danzig, D. Babies don't eat pizza — 649

Dominguez, A. Santiago stays — E

Guillain, C. A new brother or sister — 306.8

Jenkins, S. Sisters & brothers — 591.56

Shapiro, O. Autism and me — 616.85

Sheldon, A. Big sister now — 306.8

Skotko, B. Fasten your seatbelt — 616.85

Telgemeier, R. Sisters — 741.5

SIBLINGS -- FICTION

Armstrong, A. Racing the moon — Fic

Cossi, O. Pemba Sherpa — E

Cotler, S. Cheesie Mack is cool in a duel — Fic

Gewirtz, A. R. Zebra forest — Fic

Jenkins, E. Lemonade in winter — E

McCarty, P. Chloe — E

Nytra, D. The secret of the stone frog — 741.5

One special day — E

Treasure hunters — Fic

The troublemaker — E

Young, C. A few bites — E

Abouet, M. Akissi — Fic

Henkes, K. The year of Billy Miller — Fic

Look, L. Alvin Ho — Fic

MacLachlan, P. Fly away — Fic

O'Neill, C. Annie & Simon — E

Pennypacker, S. The summer of the gypsy moths — Fic

Robertson, M. P. Frank n stan — Fic

Rocklin, J. The five lives of our cat Zook — Fic

Tiger in my soup — E

SIBLINGS -- GRAPHIC NOVELS

Ormerod, J. 101 things to do with baby — E

SIBLINGS -- POETRY

Greenfield, E. Brothers & sisters — 811

SIBLINGS OF PRESIDENTS

Krull, K. The brothers Kennedy — 920

Sibyl-Anne vs. Ratticus. Macherot, R. — 741.5

SICK

See also People with disabilities

SICK -- FICTION

Appelt, K. Mogie — E

Christopher, L. Flyaway — Fic

Lee, J. Elvis and the underdogs — Fic

SICK -- PRAYERS

See also Prayers

A **sick** day for Amos McGee. Stead, P. C. — E

SICKNESS *See* Diseases

Siddals, Mary McKenna

Compost stew — E

Shivery Shades of Halloween — E

Sidekicked. Anderson, J. D. — Fic

Sidekicks. Santat, D. — 741.5

Sidewalk circus. Fleischman, P. — E

Sidewalk flowers. — E

A **single** shard. Park, L. S.   **Fic**

SINGLE WOMEN

    See also Single people; Women

SINGLE-PARENT FAMILIES

  The great big book of families   **306.8**

  Mead, A. Junebug in trouble   **Fic**

SINGLE-PARENT FAMILIES

    See also Family

SINGLE-PARENT FAMILIES -- FICTION

  Gantos, J. Joey Pigza swallowed the key   **Fic**

  Gantos, J. The key that swallowed Joey Pigza   **Fic**

  Lean, S. A dog called Homeless   **Fic**

  The Penderwicks in spring   **Fic**

SINGLE-SEX SCHOOLS

    See also Schools

SINGULARITIES (MATHEMATICS)

    See also Geometry

Siomades, Lorianne

  Katy did it!   **E**

Sioras, Efstathia

  Czech Republic   **943.7**

The **Sioux**. Cunningham, K.   **970.004**

Sipping spiders through a straw. DiPucchio, K. S.   **782.42**

Sir Charlie. Fleischman, S.   **92**

Sir Gawain and the Green Knight. Morpurgo, M.   **398.2**

Sir Reginald's logbook. Hammill, M.   **E**

The **sirens**. Orr, T.   **398.2**

SIRENS (MYTHOLOGY)

  Orr, T. The sirens   **398.2**

Sirett, Dawn

  Hide and seek first words   **793.73**

SIRIUS

    See also Stars

Sirota, Lyn A.

  Giant pandas   **599.78**

Sirrell, Terry

  (il) Masoff, J. Oh, yuck!   **031.02**

Sirrine, Carol

  Cool crafts with old CDs   **745.58**

  Cool crafts with old jeans   **745.5**

  Cool crafts with old t-shirts   **745.5**

  Cool crafts with old wrappers, cans and bottles   **745.5**

Sis, Peter

  Fleischman, S. The 13th floor   **Fic**

  Fleischman, S. The dream stealer   **Fic**

  Fleischman, S. The whipping boy   **Fic**

  Prelutsky, J. The dragons are singing tonight   **811**

  Prelutsky, J. Scranimals   **811**

  Ryan, P. M. The dreamer   **Fic**

  Shannon, G. More stories to solve   **398.2**

  Shannon, G. Stories to solve   **398.2**

  Ballerina!   **E**

  Dinosaur!   **E**

  Fire truck   **E**

  Komodo!   **E**

  Madlenka   **E**

  Madlenka soccer star   **E**

  Tibet   **951**

  The tree of life: a book depicting the life of Charles Darwin, naturalist, geologist & thinker   **92**

  Trucks, trucks, trucks   **E**

  Starry messenger   **520**

  The Pilot and the Little Prince   **92**

    About

  Sis, P. The wall   **92**

Siskind, Frederic B.

  (il) Lewis, J. P. Face bug   **E**

Sisson, Stephanie Roth

  (il) Greene, S. Princess Posey and the first grade boys   **E**

  (il) Greene, S. Princess Posey and the perfect present   **Fic**

  Star stuff   **92**

  (il) Pulver, R. Thank you, Miss Doover   **E**

Sister. Greenfield, E.   **Fic**

Sister Bear.   **398.2**

Sister tricksters. San Souci, R.   **398.2**

Sisters. Telgemeier, R.   **741.5**

SISTERS

    See also Siblings; Women

  Gauch, P. L. Tanya and the red shoes   **E**

  Grandpre, M. The sea chest   **E**

  Johnson, A. A cool moonlight   **Fic**

  Levine, G. C. The two princesses of Bamarre   **Fic**

  Tucker, K. The seven Chinese sisters   **E**

  Williams, V. B. Amber was brave, Essie was smart   **811**

  Woods, B. The red rose box   **Fic**

Sisters & brothers. Jenkins, S.   **591.56**

SISTERS (RELIGIOUS) *See* Nuns

SISTERS -- FICTION

  Bendis, B. M. Takio   **741.5**

  De Lint, C. Seven wild sisters   **Fic**

  Gone Crazy in Alabama   **Fic**

  Hyewon Yum The twins' little sister   **E**

  McKissack, P. The all-I'll-ever-want Christmas doll   **E**

  Nichols, L. Maple and Willow together   **E**

  Paschkis, J. Mooshka   **E**

  Primavera, E. Libby of High Hopes   **Fic**

  Sternberg, J. The top-secret diary of Celie Valentine   **Fic**

  Streatfeild, N. Ballet shoes   **Fic**

  Catmull, K. Summer and Bird   **Fic**

  De Sève, R. Peanut and Fifi have a ball   **E**

  Hayes, J. Don't say a word, mamá = No digas nada, mamá   **E**

  Liniers The big wet balloon   **741.5**

  Maple   **E**

Skateboard party **Fic**

Skateboarding step-by-step. Stock, C. **796.22**

SKATING *See* Ice skating; Roller skating

Skead, Robert

Something to prove **796.357**

Skeens, Matthew

(il) Seuling, B. Cows sweat through their noses **590**

(il) Seuling, B. Your skin weighs more than your brain **612**

Skeeter's dream. Manley, C. **Fic**

Skeletal system. Tieck, S. **612.7**

SKELETON

Baines, R. The bones you own **612.7**

Barner, B. Dem bones **612.7**

Jenkins, S. Bones **612.7**

Lowry, L. Gooney Bird and all her charms **FIC**

Parker, S. The skeleton and muscles **612.7**

Rake, J. S. The human skeleton **611**

Simon, S. Bones **612.7**

Tieck, S. Skeletal system **612.7**

SKELETON

See also Musculoskeletal system

SKELETON -- FICTION

Cadenhead, M. Sally's bones **Fic**

Cuyler, M. Skeleton hiccups **E**

Lowry, L. Gooney Bird and all her charms **FIC**

Rohmann, E. Bone dog **E**

Van Draanen, W. Sammy Keyes and the night of skulls **Fic**

The **skeleton** and muscles. Parker, S. **612.7**

Skeleton hiccups. Cuyler, M. **E**

Skeleton Key. Horowitz, A. **Fic**

Skeleton man. Bruchac, J. **Fic**

The **Skeleton** pirate. Lucas, D. **E**

Skellig. Almond, D. **Fic**

Skelton, Betty

About

McCarthy, M. Daredevil **E**

SKELTON, BETTY, 1926-2011

McCarthy, M. Daredevil **E**

Skelton, Matthew

Endymion Spring **Fic**

The story of Cirrus Flux **Fic**

SKEPTICISM

See also Free thought; Philosophy; Rationalism

Skerry, Brian

(il) Mallory, K. Adventure beneath the sea **551.46**

Face to face with manatees **599.5**

SKETCHBOOKS, ARTISTS' *See* Artists' notebooks

Sketches from a spy tree. Zimmer, T. V. **Fic**

SKETCHING *See* Drawing

Skevington, Andrea

The story of Jesus **232.9**

SKIDOOS *See* Snowmobiles

Skies like these. Hilmo, T. **Fic**

SKIING

Kenney, K. L. Skiing & snowboarding **796.93**

SKIING

See also Winter sports

Skiing & snowboarding. Kenney, K. L. **796.93**

SKIING -- FICTION

Pendziwol, J. Marja's skis **E**

Van Dusen, C. Learning to ski with Mr. Magee **E**

Skillet bread, sourdough, and vinegar pie. Ichord, L. F. **641.5**

Skills in motion [series]

Aikman, L. Pilates step-by-step **613.7**

Atha, A. Fitness for young people **613.7**

Burns, B. Basketball step-by-step **796.323**

Jennings, M. Baseball step-by-step **796.357**

Jennings, M. Magic step-by-step **793.8**

Jennings, M. Soccer step-by-step **796.334**

Jennings, M. Tai chi step-by-step **613.7**

Spilling, M. Yoga step-by-step **613.7**

Stock, C. Skateboarding step-by-step **796.22**

SKIN

Baines, R. Your skin holds you in **612.7**

Cobb, V. Your body battles a skinned knee **617.1**

Faulk, M. The case of the flesh-eating bacteria **616.5**

Gold, S. D. Learning about the musculoskeletal system and the skin **612.7**

Guillain, C. Our skin **612.7**

Lew, K. Itch & ooze **616.5**

Miller, S. S. All kinds of skin **591.4**

Rotner, S. Shades of people **E**

Stewart, M. The skin you're in **591.47**

SKIN

See also Anatomy; Physiology

SKIN -- DISEASES

Johnson, A. A cool moonlight **Fic**

Lew, K. Itch & ooze **616.5**

SKIN -- DISEASES

See also Diseases

SKIN -- DISEASES -- FICTION

Johnson, A. A cool moonlight **Fic**

SKIN DIVING

Berne, J. Manfish: a story of Jacques Cousteau **92**

Yaccarino, D. The fantastic undersea life of Jacques Cousteau **92**

SKIN DIVING

See also Deep diving; Water sports

Skin like milk, hair of silk. Cleary, B. P. **808**

The **skin** you're in. Stewart, M. **591.47**

Skinny-dipping at Monster Lake. Wallace, B. **Fic**

SKIPPING ROPE *See* Rope skipping

Skippyjon Jones class action. Schachner, J. **E**

The **skirt.** Soto, G. **Fic**

SKIS AND SKIING *See* Skiing

Skit-scat raggedy cat: Ella Fitzgerald. Orgill, R. **92**

SKITS

   See also Amusements; Theater

Sklansky, Amy E.

  Out of this world   **811**

  Where do chicks come from?   **636.5**

Skofield, James

  Detective Dinosaur   **E**

  Detective Dinosaur undercover   **E**

  Detective Dinosaur: lost and found   **E**

Skog, Jason

  Acting   **792**

Skotko, Brian

  Fasten your seatbelt   **616.85**

Skreslet, Laurie

  To the top of Everest   **796.52**

Skrypuch, Marsha Forchuk

  Last airlift   **959.704**

Skulduggery Pleasant. Landy, D.   **Fic**

The **skull** in the rock. Aronson, M.   **569.9**

The **skull** of truth. Coville, B.   **Fic**

Skullduggery Pleasant [series]

  Landy, D. The Faceless Ones   **Fic**

Skunkdog. Jenkins, E.   **E**

Skunks. Mason, A.   **599.7**

SKUNKS

  Gonzales, D. Skunks in the dark   **599.7**

  Mason, A. Skunks   **599.7**

  Otfinoski, S. Skunks   **599.7**

Skunks. Otfinoski, S.   **599.7**

SKUNKS -- FICTION

  Avi Poppy's return   **Fic**

  Jenkins, E. Skunkdog   **E**

  Pochocki, E. The blessing of the beasts   **E**

  Schmid, P. A pet for Petunia   **E**

Skunks in the dark. Gonzales, D.   **599.7**

Skurzynski, Gloria

  Are we alone?   **576.8**

  On time   **529**

  This is rocket science   **629.4**

SKY

  Gardner, R. Stellar science projects about Earth's sky   **551.5**

  Wood, A. Blue sky   **E**

SKY

   See also Astronomy; Atmosphere

SKY -- FICTION

  Reynolds, P. H. Sky color   **Fic**

Sky boys. Hopkinson, D.   **E**

Sky color. Reynolds, P. H.   **Fic**

Sky dancers. Kirk, C. A.   **E**

Sky high: the true story of Maggie Gee. Moss, M. **92**

Sky Raiders. Mull, B.   **Fic**

Sky sailors. Bristow, D.   **910.4**

Sky sweeper. Gershator, P.   **E**

Skye, Obert

Wonkenstein: the creature from my closet   **Fic**

Skylar. Cuffe-Perez, M.   **Fic**

Skyscraper. Curlee, L.   **720**

SKYSCRAPERS

  Curlee, L. Skyscraper   **720**

  Macaulay, D. Building big   **720**

  Parker, V. How tall is tall?   **720**

  Price, S. The story behind skyscrapers   **720**

  Stern, S. L. Building greenscrapers   **720**

SKYSCRAPERS

   See also Buildings

SKYSCRAPERS -- EARTHQUAKE EFFECTS

   See also Buildings -- Earthquake effects; Earthquakes

Skywriting. Lewis, J. P.   **811**

Slack, Michael

  (il) Goodman, S. E. How do you burp in space?   **629.45**

  (il) Sauer, T. Nugget and Fang   **E**

  Elecopter   **E**

Slack, Michael H.

  (il) Lewis, J. P. Edgar Allan Poe's apple pie   **811**

  (il) Donovan, S. Hawk & Drool   **612.3**

  (il) Donovan, S. Rumble & spew   **612.3**

  (il) Kelley, E. A. My life as a chicken   **E**

  (il) Larsen, C. S. Crust and spray   **612.8**

  (il) Lew, K. Clot & scab   **617.1**

  (il) Lew, K. Itch & ooze   **616.5**

  Monkey Truck   **E**

Slade, Arthur G.

  Jolted   **Fic**

Slade, Christian

  (il) Aliens on vacation   **Fic**

  (il) Rogan, S. J. The daring adventures of Penhaligon Brush   **Fic**

  (il) Wells, K. Rascal   **Fic**

Slade, Suzanne

  The house that George built   **975.3**

  Friends for freedom   **303.48**

  Basketball   **796.323**

  Climbing Lincoln's steps   **305.8**

  What can we do about the energy crisis?   **333.79**

  What if there were no bees?   **577.4**

  What if there were no gray wolves?   **577.3**

  What if there were no lemmings?   **577.5**

  What if there were no sea otters?   **577.7**

  What's new at the zoo?   **513**

Slam dunk! Robinson, S.   **Fic**

Slam dunk! science projects with basketball. Gardner, R.   **530**

Slammed by a tsunami! Aronin, M.   **551.46**

Slangalicious. O'Reilly, G.   **427**

Slant. Williams, L. E.   **Fic**

Slate, Jenny

  Marcel the Shell with shoes on   **E**

Slate, Joseph

What's the matter, Bunny Blue?   **E**

Smek for president! Rex, A.   **Fic**

Smell. Ganeri, A.   **612.8**

SMELL

    See also Senses and sensation

Boothroyd, J. What is smell?   **612.8**

Ganeri, A. Smell   **612.8**

Hewitt, S. Smell it!   **612.8**

SMELL -- FICTION

Johnston, L. Farley follows his nose   **E**

Keller, H. Nosy Rosie   **E**

Palatini, M. Gorgonzola   **E**

Smell it! Hewitt, S.   **612.8**

Smells like dog. Selfors, S.   **Fic**

Smelly locker. Katz, A.   **782.42**

Smelt, Roselynn

New Zealand   **993**

Smick.   **E**

Smile. Telgemeier, R.   **741.5**

Smile! Hodgkinson, L.   **E**

Smile, Principessa! Enderle, J. R.   **E**

Smiles, Eileen Michaelis

Yolen, J. Apple for the teacher   **782.42**

The **smiley** snowman. Butler, M. C.   **E**

Smiley, Jane

Gee Whiz   **Fic**

The Georges and the Jewels   **Fic**

Smith, Abby Hadassah, 1797-1878

           About

Van Rynbach, I. The taxing case of the cows **324.6**

Smith, Alan

Jennings, M. Baseball step-by-step   **796.357**

Smith, Alex T.

(il) Cottringer, A. Eliot Jones, midnight superhero   **E**

(il) McAllister, A. My mom has x-ray vision   **E**

Foxy and Egg   **E**

Smith, Alvin

(il) Wojciechowska, M. Shadow of a bull   **Fic**

Smith, Anne

(il) Robb, D. Ox, house, stick   **411**

Smith, Brian

(il) Steinberg, D. Sound off!   **741.5**

Smith, Cat Bowman

(il) DeFelice, C. C. Old Granny and the bean thief   **E**

(il) Freeman, M. The trouble with cats   **Fic**

(il) Greene, S. Owen Foote, mighty scientist   **Fic**

(il) MacDonald, A. Too much flapdoodle!   **Fic**

(il) Murphy, S. J. Dave's down-to-earth rock shop   **511.3**

(il) Thomassie, T. Feliciana Feyra LeRoux   **E**

Smith, Charles R.

28 days   **973.04**

(il) Hughes, L. My people   **811**

(il) Kipling, R. If   **821**

Black Jack: the ballad of Jack Johnson   **92**

Diamond life   **796.357**

Stars in the shadows   **796.357**

Twelve rounds to glory: the story of Muhammad Ali   **92**

Smith, Chris

One city, two brothers   **398.2**

Smith, Clete Barrett

Aliens on vacation   **Fic**

Smith, Craig

(il) MacLeod, D. Heather Fell in the Water   **E**

(il) Bell, K. If the shoe fits   **Fic**

(il) Dumbleton, M. Cat   **E**

Smith, Cynthia Leitich

Indian shoes   **Fic**

Jingle dancer   **E**

Smith, Danna

Balloon trees   **633.8**

Pirate nap   **E**

Two at the zoo   **E**

Smith, David J.

If America were a village   **973**

A taste of blackberries   **Fic**

If the World Were a Village   **304.6**

This child, every child   **305.23**

Smith, Duane

(il) Halfmann, J. Seven miles to freedom   **92**

Smith, Elinor, 1911-2010

           About

Brown, T. L. Soar, Elinor!   **92**

Smith, Elwood

(il) Colato Laínez, R. Señor Pancho had a rancho   **E**

(il) Katz, A. Stalling   **E**

(il) Sylver, A. Hot diggity dog   **641.3**

(il) Watanabe, K. No problem!   **153.4**

Smith, Hope Anita

Keeping the night watch   **Fic**

Mother poems   **811**

Smith, Icy

Half spoon of rice   **Fic**

Smith, Jan

(il) Holub, J. Apple countdown   **E**

Smith, Jeff

Bone: out from Boneville   **741.5**

Bone: Rose   **741.5**

Bone: tall tales   **741.5**

Little Mouse gets ready   **741.5**

(il) Sniegoski, T. Quest for the spark   **Fic**

Smith, Jessie Willcox

(il) Spyri, J. Heidi   **Fic**

Smith, Joseph A.

(il) Bardoe, C. Gregor Mendel   **92**

(il) Ginsburg, M. Clay boy   **398.2**

(il) Maltbie, P. I. Claude Monet   **92**

(il) Sugaring   **E**

Baxter, the pig who wanted to be kosher   **E**
Bigger than a bread box   **Fic**
The longest night   **E**
Penny Dreadful   **Fic**

Snyder, Peter Etril
   (il) Forler, N. Winterberries and apple blossoms   **811**

Snyder, Zilpha Keatley
   The Egypt game   **Fic**
   The headless cupid   **Fic**
   William S. and the great escape   **Fic**
   William's midsummer dreams   **Fic**
   The witches of Worm   **Fic**

So B. it. Weeks, S.   **Fic**
So far from the bamboo grove. Watkins, Y. K.   **Fic**
So far from the sea. Bunting, E.   **E**
So happy! Henkes, K.   **E**
So many circles, so many squares. Hoban, T.   **516**
So many days. McGhee, A.   **E**
So sleepy story. Shulevitz, U.   **E**
So what's it like to be a cat? Kuskin, K.   **E**
So you want to be an inventor? St. George, J.   **608**

So, Meilo
   (il) Alex the parrot   **636.6**
   (il) Coombs, K. Water sings blue   **811**
   (il) Look, L. Brush of the gods   **E**
   (il) When thunder comes   **811**
   (il) The 20th century children's poetry treasury   **811**
   (il) Gibfried, D. Brother Juniper   **E**
   (il) O Flatharta, A. Hurry and the monarch   **E**
   (il) Read a rhyme, write a rhyme   **811**
   (il) Schulman, J. Pale Male   **598**
   (il) Simonds, N. Moonbeams, dumplings & dragon boats   **394.26**

So, you wanna be .. [series]
   Greenwood, C. So, you wanna be a writer?   **808**
So, you wanna be a writer? Greenwood, C.   **808**
So, you want to work in fashion? Wooster, P.   **746.9**
So, you want to work in sports? Mattern, J.   **796**

SOAP
   Wagner, L. Cool melt & pour soap   **668**

SOAP BOX DERBIES
   See also Racing

SOAP BUBBLES
   Bradley, K. B. Pop!   **530.4**

SOAP SCULPTURE
   See also Modeling; Sculpture

Soar, Elinor! Brown, T. L.   **92**

Sobol, Donald J.
   Encyclopedia Brown and the case of the carnival crime   **Fic**
   Encyclopedia Brown and the case of the midnight visitor   **Fic**
   Encyclopedia Brown and the case of the secret UFOs   **Fic**
   Encyclopedia Brown and the case of the treasure

hunt   **Fic**
   Encyclopedia Brown cracks the case   **Fic**
   Encyclopedia Brown takes the cake!   **Fic**
   Encyclopedia Brown, boy detective   **Fic**
   Encyclopedia Brown, super sleuth   **Fic**

Sobol, Richard
   The story of silk   **677**
   (il) Hudson, C. W. Construction zone   **690**
   An elephant in the backyard   **636.9**
   The life of rice   **633.1**
   The mysteries of Angkor Wat   **959.6**

Soccer. Kassouf, J.   **796.334**

SOCCER
   See also Ball games; Football; Sports
   Bazemore, S. Soccer: how it works   **796.334**
   Forest, C. Play soccer like a pro   **796.334**
   Gibbons, G. My soccer book   **796.334**
   Gifford, C. My first soccer book   **796.334**
   Gifford, C. Soccer   **796.334**
   Goodstein, M. Goal! science projects with soccer   **507.8**
   Guillain, C. Soccer   **796.334**
   Hamm, M. Winners never quit!   **E**
   Hornby, H. Soccer   **796.334**
   Hyde, N. Soccer science   **796.334**
   Jennings, M. Soccer step-by-step   **796.334**
   Jokulsson, I. Stars of the World Cup   **920**
   Kassouf, J. Soccer   **796.334**
   Kelley, K. C. Soccer   **796.334**
   Pele For the love of soccer!   **92**
   Stewart, M. Goal!: the fire and fury of soccer's greatest moment   **796.334**
   Wendorff, A. Soccer   **796.334**
   Woods, M. Goal!   **796.334**

Soccer. Hornby, H.   **796.334**
Soccer. Kelley, K. C.   **796.334**
Soccer. Guillain, C.   **796.334**
Soccer. Gifford, C.   **796.334**
Soccer. Wendorff, A.   **796.334**

SOCCER -- BIOGRAPHY
   Cline-Ransome, L. Young Pele   **92**

SOCCER -- ENCYCLOPEDIAS
   Gifford, C. The Kingfisher soccer encyclopedia   **796.334**

SOCCER -- FICTION
   Bildner, P. The soccer fence   **E**
   Boelts, M. Happy like soccer   **Fic**
   Maisy plays soccer   **E**
   Soccer star   **E**

SOCCER -- FOLKORE
   MacDonald, M. R. Bat's big game   **398.2**

SOCCER -- POETRY
   Lesynski, L. Crazy about soccer   **811**

SOCCER -- TRAINING
   Gifford, C. My first soccer book   **796.334**
   Gifford, C. Soccer skills   **796.334**

super robot, vol. 1 **741.5**
Sonneborn, Liz
  The Articles of Confederation **342.73**
  Canada **971**
  District of Columbia **975.3**
  France **944**
  The Khmer Rouge **959.604**
  Kuwait **953.67**
  North Korea **951.93**
  Pakistan **954.91**
  Pompeii **937**
  The United States Constitution **342.73**
  Wilma Mankiller **92**
Sonneborn, Scott
  Shell shocker **Fic**
Sonnemair, Jan
  (il) Flood, N. B. Cowboy up! **E**
Sonnenblick, Jordan
  After ever after **Fic**
  Zen and the art of faking it **Fic**
SONNETS
  See also Poetry
Sonnichsen, A. L.
  Red butterfly **Fic**
Sonoran Desert. Lynch, W. **577.5**
SONORAN DESERT
  Lynch, W. Sonoran Desert **577.5**
SONS
  See also Family; Men
SONS AND MOTHERS *See* Mother-son relationship
The **sons** of the Dragon King. Young, E. **398.2**
Soo, Kean
  Jellaby **741.5**
  Jellaby: monster in the city **741.5**
Sootface. San Souci, R. **398.2**
Sophia's war. Avi **Fic**
Sophie. **E**
Sophie and the next-door monsters. Case, C. **E**
Sophie Hartley and the facts of life. Greene, S. **Fic**
Sophie Hartley, on strike. Greene, S. **Fic**
Sophie Peterman tells the truth! Weeks, S. **E**
Sophie Scott goes south. Lester, A. **E**
Sophie Simon solves them all. Graff, L. **Fic**
Sophie's fish. Cannon, A. E. **E**
Sophie's lovely locks. Villnave, E. P. **E**
Sophie's masterpiece. Spinelli, E. **E**
Sophie's squash. Miller, P. Z. **E**
Sophie's wheels. Pearson, D. **E**
SOPRANOS (SINGERS) -- UNITED STATES -- BIOGRAPHY
  Leontyne Price **92**
The **sorcerer** of the north. Flanagan, J. **Fic**
SORCERY *See* Magic; Occultism; Witchcraft
Sorensen, Henri
  (il) Deedy, C. A. The yellow star **Fic**

(il) Fitch, F. M. A book about God **231**
(il) Frost, R. Robert Frost **811**
(il) Huling, J. Ol' Bloo's boogie-woogie band and blues ensemble **398.2**
Soriano, Luis
About
  Brown, M. Waiting for the BiblioBurro **E**
  Winter, J. Biblioburro **E**
Sorrentino, Michela
  (il) The edible alphabet **630**
SORROW *See* Bereavement; Grief; Joy and sorrow
Sort it out! **E**
Sort-of-difficult origami. Alexander, C. **736**
Sorting through spring. **510**
The **SOS** file. Byars, B. C. **Fic**
Sosa, Hernan
  Fine, E. H. Armando and the blue tarp school **E**
Soto, Gary
  Baseball in April, and other stories **S**
  Canto familiar **811**
  Facts of life **S**
  Local news **S**
  Neighborhood odes **811**
  Petty crimes **S**
  The skirt **Fic**
  Taking sides **Fic**
  Too many tamales **813**
About
  Abrams, D. Gary Soto **92**
Sotomayor, Sonia, 1954-
About
  Gitlin, M. Sonia Sotomayor **92**
  McElroy, L. T. Sonia Sotomayor **92**
  Winter, J. Sonia Sotomayor **92**
Souhami, Jessica
  Foxy! **E**
  King Pom and the fox **398.2**
  The little, little house **398.2**
  Sausages **398.2**
SOUL
  See also Future life; Human beings (Theology); Philosophy
SOUL -- FICTION
  The spindlers **Fic**
Soul and R&B. Handyside, C. **781.644**
Soul looks back in wonder. **811**
SOUL MUSIC
  Handyside, C. Soul and R&B **781.644**
SOUL MUSICIANS
  Aretha, D. Awesome African-American rock and soul musicians **781.644**
Soumagnac, Virginie
  (il) Monari, M. Zero kisses for me! **E**
Sound. Riley, P. D. **534**
SOUND

Lindo, E. Manolito Four-Eyes: the 3rd volume of the great encyclopedia of my life **Fic**

Schimel, L. Let's go see Papa! **E**

Trevino, E. B. d. I, Juan de Pareja **Fic**

Wojciechowska, M. Shadow of a bull **Fic**

SPAIN -- HISTORY -- 1936-1939, CIVIL WAR

Serres, A. And Picasso painted Guernica **759**

Spangler, Steve

Naked eggs and flying potatoes **507.8**

SPANIARDS -- UNITED STATES

Hernandez, R. E. New Spain: 1600-1760s **973.1**

Lilly, A. Spanish colonies in America **970.01**

Otfinoski, S. The new republic: 1760-1840s **973.3**

Perritano, J. Spanish missions **266**

Spanish colonies in America. Lilly, A. **970.01**

SPANISH LANGUAGE

Elya, S. M. Fire! Fuego! Brave bomberos **E**

SPANISH LANGUAGE

See also Language and languages; Romance languages

SPANISH LANGUAGE -- DICTIONARIES

Corbeil My first Spanish English visual dictionary **463**

Kudela, K. R. My first book of Spanish words **463**

SPANISH LANGUAGE -- FICTION

Harris, T. Say something, Perico **E**

SPANISH LANGUAGE -- VOCABULARY

Brimner, L. D. Trick or treat, Old Armadillo **E**

The cazuela that the farm maiden stirred **E**

Cox, J. Carmen learns English **E**

Dorros, A. Numero uno **E**

Dorros, A. Mama and me **E**

Dorros, A. Papa and me **E**

Elya, S. M. Rubia and the three osos **398.2**

Elya, S. M. Adios, tricycle **E**

Elya, S. M. Bebe goes shopping **E**

Elya, S. M. Cowboy Jose **E**

Elya, S. M. F is for fiesta **E**

Elya, S. M. Fairy trails **E**

Elya, S. M. N is for Navidad **E**

Elya, S. M. No more, por favor **E**

Elya, S. M. Oh no, gotta go! **E**

Fiesta fiasco **E**

Goldman, J. Uncle monarch and the Day of the Dead **E**

Johnston, T. My abuelita **E**

A mango in the hand **E**

Montes, M. Los gatos black on Halloween **E**

Paul, A. W. Count on Culebra **E**

Pinkwater, D. M. Beautiful Yetta **E**

Winter, J. Calavera abecedario **E**

SPANISH LANGUAGE MATERIALS -- BILINGUAL

Arrorro mi nino **398.8**

Brown, M. Marisol McDonald and the clash bash

Call me tree **E**

Garza, X. Maximilian and the mystery of the Guardian Angel **Fic**

Hayes, J. Don't say a word, mamá = No digas nada, mamá **E**

Hayes, J. Little Gold Star **398.2**

Maria had a little llama/ María tenía una llamita **E**

Perez, A. I. My very own room **E**

Pio peep! **398.8**

Reiser, L. Tortillas and lullabies. Tortillas y cancioncitas **E**

SPANISH LITERATURE

See also Literature; Romance literature

SPANISH LITERATURE -- BIBLIOGRAPHY

Schon, I. Recommended books in Spanish for children and young adults, 2004-2008 **011.6**

Spanish missions. Perritano, J. **266**

SPANISH POETRY -- COLLECTIONS

Messengers of rain and other poems from Latin America **861**

Spanyol, Jessica

Little neighbors on Sunnyside Street **E**

Spark the firefighter. Krensky, S. **E**

Sparkle and spin. Rand, A. **E**

Sparky. **E**

Sparky: the life and art of Charles Schulz. Gherman, B. **92**

SPARRING See Boxing

Sparrow girl. Pennypacker, S. **E**

Sparrow Jack. Gerstein, M. **E**

Sparrow Road. O'Connor, S. **Fic**

Sparrow, Giles

Destination Uranus, Neptune, and Pluto **523.4**

Iron **546**

Sparrows. Post, H. **598**

SPARROWS

Post, H. Sparrows **598**

SPARROWS -- FICTION

Graham, B. Vanilla ice cream **E**

SPARTA (EXTINCT CITY)

Park, L. The Spartan hoplites **938**

The **Spartan** hoplites. Park, L. **938**

The **Spatulatta** cookbook. Gerasole, I. **641.5**

Spaulding, Amy E.

The art of storytelling **372.6**

Speak to me. English, K. **E**

SPEAKING See Debates and debating; Lectures and lecturing; Preaching; Public speaking; Rhetoric; Speech; Voice

Speaking of art. **700**

Speaking secret codes. Bell-Rehwoldt, S. **652**

Speaking volumes. Gilmore, B. **028.5**

SPEAR FISHING

See also Fishing

Speare, Elizabeth George

The bronze bow **Fic**

The sign of the beaver **Fic**

Howse, J. NASCAR Sprint Cup 796.72
Webster, C. Masters Golf Tournament 796.352
Wiseman, B. Boston Marathon 796.42
Wiseman, B. Kentucky Derby 798.4
Wiseman, B. Stanley Cup 796.96
Wiseman, B. Ultimate fighting 796.8
SPORTING EQUIPMENT See Sporting goods
SPORTING GOODS
Blaxland, W. Basketballs 688.7
Rosen, M. J. Balls!: round 2 796.3
Sports. Howell, B. 796
SPORTS
Berman, L. The greatest moments in sports 796
Fridell, R. Sports technology 688.7
Gillman, C. The kids' summer fun book 790.1
Gillman, C. The kids' winter fun book 790.1
Goodstein, M. Ace your sports science project 507.8
Kelley, K. C. Weird sports moments 796
Kenney, K. L. Cool sports parties 793.2
Mason, P. Improving endurance 613.7
Mason, P. Improving flexibility 613.7
Mason, P. Improving speed 613.7
Mattern, J. So, you want to work in sports? 796
Rissman, R. Shapes in sports 516
Rosen, M. J. Balls!: round 2 796.3
Ross, S. Sports technology 688.7
Taylor-Butler, C. Think like a scientist in the gym 530
Watson, S. B. Weird animal sports 796
Watson, S. B. Weird sports of the world 796
Watson, S. B. Weird throwing and kicking sports 796
Weird zone 796.1
SPORTS
See also Play; Recreation
SPORTS -- CORRUPT PRACTICES
Butterfield, M. Scandals 796.48
LeVert, S. Steroids 362.29
SPORTS -- EQUIPMENT AND SUPPLIES See Sporting goods
SPORTS -- FICTION
Brown, D. The sports pages S
Myers, C. H.O.R.S.E. Fic
SPORTS -- GRAPHIC NOVELS
See also Graphic novels
SPORTS -- POETRY
Low, A. The fastest game on two feet and other poems about how sports began 811
Prelutsky, J. Good sports 811
SPORTS -- STATISTICS
Rand, C. Graphing sports 796
SPORTS -- STATISTICS
See also Statistics
SPORTS -- UNITED STATES -- MARKETING
Miracle mud 796.357

SPORTS -- VOCATIONAL GUIDANCE
Howell, B. Sports 796
Sports and my body [series]
Guillain, C. Cycling 796.6
Guillain, C. Soccer 796.334
Guillain, C. Swimming 797.2
Veitch, C. Gymnastics 796.44
SPORTS BROADCASTING See Radio broadcasting of sports; Television broadcasting of sports
Sports camp. Wallace, R. Fic
SPORTS CARDS
See also Sports
SPORTS CARS
See also Automobiles
SPORTS DRAMA (FILMS)
See also Motion pictures
SPORTS DRAMA (TELEVISION PROGRAMS)
See also Television programs
SPORTS FOR PEOPLE WITH DISABILITIES
See also People with disabilities
SPORTS FOR WOMEN
See also Sports
Sports Illustrated kids [series]
Gassman, J. You can't spike your serves Fic
SPORTS IN RADIO See Radio broadcasting of sports
SPORTS MASCOTS See Mascots
SPORTS MEDICINE
See also Medical care; Medicine
The **sports** pages. Brown, D. S
SPORTS RECORDS
See also Sports
Sports records [series]
Doeden, M. The greatest basketball records 796.323
Dougherty, T. The greatest football records 796.332
Sports science [series]
Boudreau, H. Swimming science 797.2
Bow, J. Baseball science 796.357
Bow, J. Cycling science 796.6
Bow, P. Tennis science 796.342
Hyde, N. Soccer science 796.334
Sports Star Champions [series]
Thornley, S. Tim Duncan 796.323
Rappoport, K. Alex Rodriguez 796.357
Rappoport, K. Derek Jeter 796.357
Rappoport, K. Peyton Manning 796.332
Sports stars who care [series]
Rappoport, K. Dale Earnhardt, Jr. 92
Rappoport, K. David Wright 92
Wilner, B. Kevin Garnett 92
Sports starters [series]
Crossingham, J. Spike it volleyball 796.325
SPORTS STORIES See Sports -- Fiction
SPORTS TEAMS
See also Sports
Sports technology. Fridell, R. 688.7

STATUE OF LIBERTY (NEW YORK, N.Y.) -- FICTION

Drummond, A. Liberty!   E

Yolen, J. Naming Liberty   E

STATUES See Monuments; Sculpture

STATUES -- FICTION

Who could that be at this hour?   Fic

STATUTES See Law

Staub, Leslie

(il) Lives; poems about famous Americans   811

Everybody gets the blues   E

Stauffacher, Sue

Gator on the loose!   Fic

Harry Sue   Fic

Nothing but trouble   92

Tillie the terrible Swede   92

Stay safe! Nelson, S. K.   613.6

Stay! Lowry, L.   Fic

Staying healthy. Schaefer, A.   613

Staying safe. Schaefer, A.   613.6

Stead, Erin E.

(il) Bear has a story to tell   E

(il) Fogliano, J. And then it's spring   E

(il) Fogliano, J. If you want to see a whale   E

(il) Stead, P. C. A sick day for Amos McGee   E

Stead, Judy

(il) Raczka, B. Snowy, blowy winter   E

(il) Raczka, B. Spring things   E

(il) Raczka, B. Summer wonders   E

(il) Raczka, B. Who loves the fall?   E

(il) Shirley, D. Best friend on wheels   E

Stead, Philip C.

Bear has a story to tell   E

(il) Sebastian and the balloon   E

Special delivery   E

Hello, my name is Ruby   E

A home for Bird   E

A sick day for Amos McGee   E

Stead, P. C. Jonathan and the big blue boat   E

Stead, Rebecca

Liar & spy   Fic

When you reach me   Fic

Steady hands. Zimmer, T. V.   811

STEALING -- FICTION

Davies, M. Ben rides on   E

Ryan, C. The map to everywhere   Fic

Who could that be at this hour?   Fic

Stealing home. Schwartz, E.   Fic

Stealing home. Burleigh, R.   92

Stealing the game.   Fic

STEAM

See also Heat; Power (Mechanics); Water

STEAM ENGINEERING

See also Engineering

STEAM ENGINES

Zimmermann, K. R. Steam locomotives   385

STEAM ENGINES

See also Engines; Steam engineering

Steam locomotives. Zimmermann, K. R.   385

STEAM LOCOMOTIVES

See also Locomotives

The Stourbridge Lion   625.26

STEAM NAVIGATION

See also Navigation; Steam engineering; Transportation

Steam train, dream train.   E

STEAM TURBINES

See also Steam engines; Steam navigation; Turbines

STEAM-SHOVELS -- FICTION

Burton, V. L. Mike Mulligan and his steam shovel   E

Zimmerman, A. G. Digger man   E

STEAMBOATS

Herweck, D. Robert Fulton   92

STEAMBOATS

See also Boats and boating; Naval architecture; Ocean travel; Shipbuilding; Ships

STEAMPUNK FICTION

Gratz, A. The League of Seven   Fic

Lloyd Jones, R. Wild boy   Fic

STEAMPUNK FICTION

See also Science fiction

STEAMSHIPS See Steamboats

Stearman, Kaye

Women of today   305.4

Stearn, Ted

(il) Jackson, D. M. The name game   929.9

Stearns, Megan

(il) Mooney, C. Amazing Africa   960

Stearns, Precious McKenzie

Manatees   599.5

Whooping cranes   598

STEEL

See also Iron; Metalwork

STEEL CONSTRUCTION

See also Building; Structural engineering

STEEL CONSTRUCTION -- FICTION

Kirk, C. A. Sky dancers   E

STEEL DRUM (MUSICAL INSTRUMENT) -- FICTION

Bootman, C. Steel pan man of Harlem   E

STEEL DRUM (MUSICAL INSTRUMENT)

Greenwood, M. Drummer boy of John John   786.9

STEEL INDUSTRY -- FICTION

Winter, J. Steel Town   E

STEEL INDUSTRY -- TECHNOLOGICAL INNOVATIONS

See also Technological innovations

Steel pan man of Harlem. Bootman, C.   E

Steel Town. Winter, J.   E

Steele, Christy

See also Dance

Step fourth, Mallory! Friedman, L. B.   **Fic**

Step   gently   out.

Step into reading [series]

  Boelts, M. Dogerella   **E**

  Bruchac, J. The Trail of Tears   **970.004**

  Chicks!   **E**

  Corey, S. Monster parade   **E**

  Ghigna, C. Barn storm   **E**

  Harrison, D. L. A monster is coming!   **E**

  Hayes, G. A poor excuse for a dragon   **E**

  Hays, A. J. Smarty Sara   **E**

  Kohuth, J. Ducks go vroom   **E**

  Milton, J. Dinosaur days   **E**

  Redmond Tentacles!   **594**

Step into science [series]

  Burns, K. What's going on?   **507.8**

  Challen, P. C. What just happened?   **507.8**

  Challen, P. C. What's going to happen?   **507.8**

  Hyde, N. What's the plan?   **507.8**

  Johnson, R. R. What do we know now?   **507.8**

STEP into storytime. Ghoting, S. N.   **027.62**

Step-by-step science experiments in astronomy. VanCleave, J. P.   **520**

Step-by-step science experiments in biology. VanCleave, J. P.   **570**

Step-by-step science experiments in earth science. VanCleave, J. P.   **550.78**

Step-by-step science experiments in ecology. VanCleave, J. P.   **577.078**

Step-by-step science experiments in energy. VanCleave, J. P.   **531**

STEPCHILDREN

  See also Children; Parent-child relationship

STEPCHILDREN -- FICTION

  Hahn, M. D. Wait till Helen comes   **Fic**

STEPFAMILIES

  See also Family

STEPFAMILIES -- FICTION

  Clifton, L. Freaky Fast Frankie Joe   **Fic**

  Cohn, R. Two steps forward   **Fic**

  Deriso, C. H. The Right-Under Club   **Fic**

  Grimes, N. Oh, brother!   **E**

  Hicks, B. Out of order   **Fic**

  Jackson, A. Eggs over Evie   **Fic**

  Kilworth, G. Attica   **Fic**

  Manley, C. Skeeter's dream   **Fic**

  Sheinmel, C. All the things you are   **Fic**

  Zimmer, T. V. Sketches from a spy tree   **Fic**

STEPFATHERS

  Freeman, M. The trouble with cats   **Fic**

STEPFATHERS

  See also Fathers; Stepparents

STEPFATHERS -- FICTION

  Bennett, K. Dad and Pop   **E**

  Freeman, M. The trouble with cats   **Fic**

Hunt, L. M. One for the Murphys   **Fic**

  When Otis courted Mama   **E**

Stephen Hawking. Venezia, M.   **92**

Stephens, Claire Gatrell

  (jt. auth) Franklin, P. School library collection development   **025.2**

  Library 101   **027.8**

Stephens, Helen

  The big adventure of the Smalls   **E**

  How to hide a lion   **E**

Stephens, Jay

  Heroes!   **743**

  Monsters!   **743**

  Robots!   **743**

Stephens, John

  The black reckoning   **Fic**

  The emerald atlas   **Fic**

  The fire chronicle   **Fic**

Stephens, Pat

  (il) Hodge, D. Desert animals   **591.7**

  (il) Hodge, D. Forest animals   **591.7**

  (il) Hodge, D. Polar animals   **591.7**

  (il) Hodge, D. Rain forest animals   **591.7**

  (il) Hodge, D. Savanna animals   **591.7**

  (il) Hodge, D. Wetland animals   **591.7**

Stephenson, Kristina

  (il) Bauer, M. D. Thank you for me!   **E**

STEPMOTHERS

  Bunting, E. The memory string   **E**

STEPMOTHERS -- FICTION

  Bodeen, S. A. Shipwreck Island   **Fic**

Stepping stone book [series]

  Kimmel, E. C. Balto and the great race   **636.73**

STEPSISTERS -- FICTION

  Barden, S. Cinderella Smith   **Fic**

Steptoe, Javaka

  (il) Cotten, C. Rain play   **E**

  (il) English, K. Hot day on Abbott Avenue   **E**

  (il) Evans, K. What's special about me, Mama?   **E**

  (il) Golio, G. Jimi: sounds like a rainbow: a story of young Jimi Hendrix

  (il) In daddy's arms I am tall   **811**

  (il) Pearsall, S. All of the above   **Fic**

Steptoe, John

  Mufaro's beautiful daughters   **398.2**

  The story of Jumping Mouse   **398.2**

STEREOPHONIC SOUND SYSTEMS *See* Sound -- Recording and reproducing

Sterling biographies [series]

  Blackaby, S. Cleopatra   **92**

Stern, Steven L.

  Building greenscrapers   **720**

Sternberg, Julie

  Like pickle juice on a cookie   **Fic**

  The top-secret diary of Celie Valentine   **Fic**

Steroids. Schaefer, A.   **362.29**

Martin, B. Baby Bear, Baby Bear, what do you see? E

Martin, B. Barn dance! E

Martin, B. A beasty story E

Martin, B. Brown bear, brown bear what do you see? E

Martin, B. Chicka chicka 1, 2, 3 E

Martin, B. Chicka chicka boom boom E

Martin, B. Kitty cat, kitty cat, are you going to sleep? E

Martin, B. Kitty Cat, Kitty Cat, are you waking up? E

Martin, B. Panda bear, panda bear, what do you see? E

Martin, B. Polar bear, polar bear, what do you hear? 813

Martin, D. Peep and Ducky E

Martin, E. W. Dream animals E

Martin, S. The alphabet from A to Y with bonus letter, Z! E

Marzollo, J. Ten little Christmas presents E

Mazer, N. F. Has anyone seen my Emily Greene? E

McEvoy, A. Betsy B. Little E

McGhee, A. Only a witch can fly E

McGrath, B. B. Teddy bear counting E

McNaughton, C. Not last night but the night before E

McPhail, D. M. Pigs aplenty, pigs galore! 813

Meadows, M. Hibernation station E

Meadows, M. Piggies in the kitchen E

Meister, C. My pony Jack E

Melmed, L. K. Hurry! Hurry! Have you heard? E

Meltzer, L. The construction crew E

Metaxas, E. It's time to sleep, my love (a lullabye) E

Meyers, S. Bear in the air E

Milgrim, D. Time to get up, time to go E

Millen, C. M. The ink garden of brother Theophane E

Minor, F. If you were a panda bear E

Minor, W. My farm friends E

Miranda, A. To market, to market E

Miss Lina's ballerinas E

Modarressi, M. Taking care of Mama E

The monsterator E

Montes, M. Los gatos black on Halloween E

Moonlight E

Mora, P. Uno, dos, tres: one, two, three E

Morales, M. Jam & honey E

Morrow, B. O. Mr. Mosquito put on his tuxedo E

Mortiz, D. Hush little beachcomber E

Moss, L. Zin! zin! zin! a violin E

Muir, L. The little bitty bakery E

Munro, R. Circus E

Murphy, S. J. Leaping lizards E

Murray, A. One two that's my shoe! E

Murray, M. D. Halloween night E

Neitzel, S. The jacket I wear in the snow 646

Nelson, K. Nelson Mandela 968.06

Neubecker, R. What little boys are made of E

Nevius, C. Building with Dad E

Nevius, C. Karate hour E

Nevius, C. Soccer hour E

Newbery, L. Posy! E

Newman, J. Hand book E

Newman, L. Donovan's big day E

Niemann, C. Subway E

Norman, K. Ten on the sled E

Novak, M. A wish for you E

Numeroff, L. J. When sheep sleep E

Nutt, R. Amy's light E

O'Connor, J. Ready, set, skip! E

Odanaka, B. Crazy day at the Critter Cafe E

O'Hair, M. My kitten E

O'Hair, M. My pup E

Olson-Brown, E. Ooh la la polka dot boots E

One starry night E

Orangutanka E

Ormerod, J. If you're happy and you know it! E

Owen, K. I could be, you could be E

Pamintuan, M. Twelve haunted rooms of Halloween E

Panahi, H. L. Bebop Express E

Parenteau, S. Bears on chairs E

Park, L. S. Bee-bim bop! E

Patricelli, L. Be quiet, Mike! E

Paul, A. W. If animals kissed good night-- E

Peet, B. Huge Harold E

Penn, A. A bedtime kiss for Chester Raccoon E

Perrin, M. Look who's there! E

Perry, A. The Bicklebys' birdbath E

The pet project E

Peters, L. W. Cold little duck, duck, duck E

Piggies in pajamas E

Pirateria E

Plourde, L. Dino pets go to school E

Plourde, L. Grandpappy snippy snappies E

Polacco, P. G is for goat E

Preller, J. Mighty Casey E

Pym, T. Have you ever seen a sneep? E

Raczka, B. Snowy, blowy winter E

Raczka, B. Summer wonders E

Raczka, B. Who loves the fall? E

Raschka, C. Farmy farm E

Raschka, C. Five for a little one E

Raschka, C. Little black crow E

Ravishankar, A. Elephants never forget E

Ravishankar, A. Tiger on a tree E

Red is a dragon E

Reidy, J. Too purpley! E

Reiser, L. My baby and me E

Rex, M. Goodnight goon E

Taxali, G. This is silly! E
Ten little caterpillars E
Ten moonstruck piglets E
This day in June E
Thomas, P. Red sled E
Thompson, L. How many cats? E
Thompson, L. Leap back home to me E
Thomson, S. L. Pirates, ho! E
Thong, R. One is a drummer E
Thong, R. Round is a mooncake E
Tillman, N. On the night you were born E
Tillman, N. The spirit of Christmas E
Trapani, I. Haunted party E
Tucker, L. Porkelia E
Tudor, T. 1 is one E
Two little monkeys E
Van Dusen, C. The circus ship E
Van Dusen, C. King Hugo's huge ego E
Van Dusen, C. Learning to ski with Mr. Magee E
Van Laan, N. Nit-pickin' E
Van Laan, N. When winter comes E
Varela, B. Gizmo E
Vestergaard, H. Potty animals E
The voyage of Turtle Rex E
Walker, A. I love Christmas E
Walker, R. D. Mama says E
Walsh, J. The biggest kiss E
Walters, V. Are we there yet, Daddy? E
Ward, J. The busy tree E
Wargin Moose on the loose E
Warnes, T. Daddy hug E
Wax, W. City witch, country switch E
Weeks, S. Drip, drop E
Weeks, S. Mac and Cheese E
Weeks, S. Woof E
Wells, R. Love waves E
Wells, R. Noisy Nora E
Wells, R. Read to your bunny E
Wells, R. Shy Charles E
Wheeler, L. Boogie knights E
Wheeler, L. Bubble gum, bubble gum E
Wheeler, L. Castaway cats E
Whitman, C. Lines that wiggle E
Whybrow, I. The noisy way to bed E
Wild, M. Itsy-bitsy babies E
Williams, S. Let's go visiting E
Willis, J. Susan laughs E
Wilson, K. Bear snores on E
Wilson, K. Bear's loose tooth E
Wilson, K. The cow loves cookies E
Wilson, K. A frog in the bog E
Wilson, K. How to bake an American pie E
Wilson, K. Mama, why? E
Wilson, K. Whopper cake E
Winthrop, E. Shoes E
Witte, A. The parrot Tico Tango E

The wizard E
Wolf, S. Truck stuck E
Wood, A. Piggy Pie Po E
Wright, M. Sleep, Big Bear, sleep! E
Wright, M. Sneeze, Big Bear, sneeze! E
Wright, M. Jake goes peanuts E
Wright, R. The geezer in the freezer E
Yankovic, A. When I grow up E
Yee, W. H. Summer days and nights E
Yee, W. H. Tracks in the snow E
Yolen, J. Baby Bear's books E
Yolen, J. Come to the fairies' ball E
Yolen, J. Creepy monsters, sleepy monsters E
Yolen, J. How do dinosaurs say goodnight? E
Yolen, J. How do dinosaurs say happy birthday? E
Yolen, J. My father knows the names of things E
Yolen, J. Not all princesses dress in pink E
Yolen, J. Off we go! E
Yolen, J. Pretty princess pig E
Yolen, J. Sleep, black bear, sleep E
Zoom, rocket, zoom! E
ZooZical E
Zuravicky, O. C is for city E
The **stories** Julian tells. Cameron, A. **Fic**
The **stories** of the Mona Lisa. Barsony, P. **759.06**
Stories on stage. Shepard, A. **812**
Stories to solve. Shannon, G. **398.2**

STORIES WITHOUT WORDS

Andreasen, D. The treasure bath E
Anno, M. Anno's counting book E
Armstrong, J. Once upon a banana E
Aruego, J. The last laugh E
Baker, J. Home E
Baker, J. Mirror E
Baker, J. Window E
Banyai, I. The other side E
Banyai, I. Zoom **152.14**
Barba, C. Yam: bite-size chunks **741.5**
Bartlett, T. C. Tuba lessons E
Becker, A. Journey E
Boisrobert, A. Popville E
The boy & the book E
The boy, the bear, the baron, the bard E
Boyd, L. Flashlight E
Briant, E. If you lived here you'd be home by now E
Briggs, R. The snowman E
Carle, E. Do you want to be my friend? E
Crews, D. Truck E
Desrosiers, S. Hocus Pocus E
Donovan, J. M. Small, medium & large E
Faller, R. The adventures of Polo E
The farmer and the clown E
Fleischman, P. Sidewalk circus E
Franson, S. E. Un-brella E
Frazier, C. Bee & Bird E

See also Ecology; Freshwater ecology

Streams to the river, river to the sea. O'Dell, S. **Fic**

Streatfeild, Noel

Ballet shoes **Fic**

STREET ART

See also Art

STREET CHILDREN -- FICTION

Pyron, B. The dogs of winter **Fic**

STREET CLEANING

See also Cleaning; Municipal engineering; Public health; Roads; Sanitary engineering; Streets

STREET GANGS *See* Gangs

STREET LIFE

See also City and town life

STREET PEOPLE *See* Homeless persons

STREET RAILROADS

See also Local transit; Railroads

A **street** through time. Millard, A. **936**

STREET TRAFFIC *See* City traffic; Traffic engineering

Street, Pat

Leedy, L. There's a frog in my throat **428**

Streetball crew [series]

Stealing the game **Fic**

STREETS

See also Cities and towns; Civil engineering; Transportation

Strega Nona does it again. **E**

Strega Nona: an old tale. DePaola, T. **E**

Streiffert, Kristi

Kott, J. Nicaragua **972.85**

Streissguth, Thomas

Mexico **972**

STRENGTH OF MATERIALS

Oxlade, C. Changing materials **530.4**

Strep throat. Glaser, J. **616.9**

Strep throat. Landau, E. **616.9**

STREP THROAT

Glaser, J. Strep throat **616.9**

Landau, E. Strep throat **616.9**

STRESS (PHYSIOLOGY)

See also Adaptation (Biology); Physiology

STRESS (PSYCHOLOGY)

Donovan, S. Keep your cool! **616.85**

STRESS (PSYCHOLOGY)

See also Mental health; Psychology

STRESS MANAGEMENT

See also Health

STRETCHING EXERCISES

See also Exercise

Strevens-Marzo, Bridget

(il) Dempsey, K. Mini racer **E**

(il) Wild, M. Kiss kiss! **E**

Strickland, Brad

The sign of the sinister sorcerer **Fic**

Strickland, Shadra

(il) Bandy, M. S. White water **E**

(il) Elliott, Z. Bird **E**

(il) Watson, R. A place where hurricanes happen **E**

Strider. Cleary, B. **Fic**

Strike a pose. Birkemoe, K. **613.7**

Strike three, you're dead. Berk, J. **Fic**

STRIKES

Bartoletti, S. C. Kids on strike! **331.892**

Brill, M. T. Annie Shapiro and the clothing workers' strike **331.8**

STRIKES -- FICTION

Hermes, P. Emma Dilemma and the soccer nanny **Fic**

McCully, E. A. The bobbin girl **E**

Paterson, K. Bread and roses, too **Fic**

STRIKES -- UNITED STATES -- HISTORY

Markel, M. Brave girl **331.892**

STRIKES AND LOCKOUTS *See* Strikes

STRING FIGURES

See also Amusements

STRING FIGURES -- FICTION

Wondriska, W. A long piece of string **E**

A **string** in the harp. Bond, N. **Fic**

A **string** of hearts. Elliott, L. **E**

Stringbean's trip to the shining sea. Williams, V. B. **E**

Stringed instruments. Ganeri, A. **787**

STRINGED INSTRUMENTS

Ganeri, A. Stringed instruments **787**

STRINGED INSTRUMENTS

See also Musical instruments

Stringer, Helen

Spellbinder **Fic**

Stringer, Lauren

(il) Ray, M. L. Deer dancer **E**

When Stravinsky met Nijinsky **781.5**

(il) Ashman, L. Castles, caves, and honeycombs **E**

(il) Orr, W. The princess and her panther **E**

(il) Rylant, C. Snow **E**

Winter is the warmest season **E**

STRIPES

Stockdale, S. Stripes of all types **591.47**

Stripes of all types. Stockdale, S. **591.47**

STROKE -- FICTION

Butler, D. H. My grandpa had a stroke **E**

DePaola, T. Now one foot, now the other **E**

Stroll and walk, babble and talk. Cleary, B. P. **428**

Strom, Kellie

Sadie the air mail pilot **E**

STRONG MEN

Rubinstein, R. E. Zishe the strongman **92**

A **strong** right arm: the story of Mamie Peanut Johnson. Green, M. Y. **92**

Strong stuff. Harris, J. **398.2**

Strong to the hoop. Coy, J. **E**

SULPHUR

Beatty, R. Sulfur   **546**

SULPHUR

    See also Chemical elements

Summer. Schnur, S.   **793.73**

Summer. Smith, S.   **508.2**

SUMMER

    See also Seasons

Gillman, C. The kids' summer fun book   **790.1**

Hesse, K. Come on, rain!   **E**

The other side   **E**

Pfeffer, W. The longest day   **394.26**

Schnur, S. Summer   **793.73**

Schuette, S. L. Let's look at summer   **508.2**

Smith, S. Summer   **508.2**

SUMMER -- FICTION

Fort   **Fic**

Greenwald, L. Dog Beach   **Fic**

Hurwitz, M. W. The summer I saved the world-- in 65 days   **Fic**

St. Antoine, S. Three bird summer   **Fic**

Tan, S. Rules of summer   **E**

The bathing costume, or, The worst vacation of my life   **E**

The great good summer   **Fic**

Perret, D. The Big Bad Wolf Goes on Vacation   **E**

Yee, W. H. Summer days and nights   **E**

Summer according to Humphrey. Birney, B. G. **Fic**

Summer and Bird. Catmull, K.   **Fic**

Summer birds: the butterflies of Maria Merian. Engle, M.   **92**

Summer days and nights. Yee, W. H.   **E**

SUMMER EMPLOYMENT -- FICTION

Paulsen, G. Lawn Boy   **Fic**

The **summer** I learned to fly. Reinhardt, D.   **Fic**

The **summer** I saved the world-- in 65 days. Hurwitz, M. W.   **Fic**

Summer Jackson: grown up.   **E**

The **summer** of the gypsy moths. Pennypacker, S.   **Fic**

SUMMER RESORTS -- FICTION

St. Antoine, S. Three bird summer   **Fic**

SUMMER SCHOOLS

    See also Public schools; Schools

SUMMER SOLSTICE

Pfeffer, W. The longest day   **394.26**

SUMMER SOLSTICE -- FICTION

Hakala, M. Mermaid dance   **E**

SUMMER THEATER

    See also Theater

A **summer** to die. Lowry, L.   **Fic**

The **summer** visitors. Hayes, K.   **E**

Summer wonders. Raczka, B.   **E**

Summer's bloodiest days. Weber, J. L.   **973.7**

Summerland. Chabon, M.   **Fic**

Summers, Susan

The greatest gift   **Fic**

Summiting Everest. Berne, E. C.   **796.522**

Sumner, William

Halls, K. M. Saving the Baghdad Zoo   **636.088**

The **sun.** Capaccio, G.   **523.7**

The **sun.** Landau, E.   **523.7**

SUN

    See also Astronomy; Solar system

Beneath the sun   **591.5**

Branley, F. M. The sun, our nearest star   **523.7**

Capaccio, G. The sun   **523.7**

Carson, M. K. Far-out guide to the sun   **523.7**

Gibbons, G. Sun up, sun down   **523.7**

Landau, E. The sun   **523.7**

Why do elephants need the sun?   **523.7**

Sun & Spoon. Henkes, K.   **Fic**

SUN -- FICTION

Secrets of the seasons   **E**

SUN -- FOLKLORE

Dayrell, E. Why the Sun and the Moon live in the sky   **398.2**

SUN -- RISING AND SETTING -- FICTION

The night world   **E**

Sun and rain. Feeney, S.   **996.9**

The **sun** is my favorite star. Asch, F.   **E**

The **sun** is so quiet. Giovanni, N.   **811**

Sun Ra 1914-1933

About

Raschka, C. The Cosmobiography of sun ra **781.65**

Sun up, sun down. Gibbons, G.   **523.7**

Sun up, sun down. Bailey, J.   **525**

SUN WORSHIP

    See also Religion

The **sun's** daughter. Sherman, P.   **398.2**

The **sun,** our nearest star. Branley, F. M.   **523.7**

Sunantha Phusomsai

Hawker, F. Buddhism in Thailand   **294.3**

The **sundae** scoop. Murphy, S. J.   **511**

SUNDARBANS (BANGLADESH AND INDIA) -- FICTION

Tiger boy   **813.6**

Sunday is for God. McGowan, M.   **E**

SUNDIALS

    See also Clocks and watches; Garden ornaments and furniture; Time

Sundiata. Wisniewski, D.   **398.209**

The **sundown** rule. Townsend, W.   **Fic**

Suneby, Liz

(jt. auth) Heiman, D. It's a-- it's a-- it's a mitzvah!   **296.1**

The **sunflower** sword.   **E**

A **sunflower's** life. Dickmann, N.   **583**

SUNFLOWERS

Dickmann, N. A sunflower's life   **583**

SUNFLOWERS -- FICTION

Schaefer, L. M. This is the sunflower   **E**

Farrey, B. The Grimjinx rebellion **Fic**

Farrey, B. The Vengekeep prophecies **Fic**

SWINE *See* Pigs

SWINE INFLUENZA

Chilman-Blair, K. Medikidz explain swine flu **616.2**

Swine Lake. Marshall, J. **E**

Swing around the sun. Esbensen, B. J. **811**

Swing Cafe. Norac, C. **E**

Swing! Seder, R. B. **E**

Swinney, Geoff

Fish facts **597**

Swirl by swirl. Sidman, J. **811**

Swish. Stewart, M. **796.323**

The Swiss family Robinson. Wyss, J. D. **Fic**

The switch. Horowitz, A. **Fic**

Switch on, switch off. Berger, M. **537**

Switched at birthday. Standiford, N. **Fic**

Switching on the moon. **811**

Switzer, Bob, 1914-1997

About

Barton, C. The Day-Glo brothers **535.6**

Switzer, Joe, d. 1973

About

Barton, C. The Day-Glo brothers **535.6**

SWITZERLAND

Harris, P. K. Welcome to Switzerland **949.4**

SWITZERLAND -- FICTION

Chatterton, M. The Brain full of holes **Fic**

Creech, S. Bloomability **Fic**

Creech, S. The unfinished angel **Fic**

Spyri, J. Heidi **Fic**

SWITZERLAND -- HISTORY -- 20TH CENTURY -- FICTION

Haddix, M. P. Caught **Fic**

Swope, Sam

Gotta go! Gotta go! **E**

The sword in the grotto. Sage, A. **Fic**

The sword in the stone. White, T. H. **Fic**

The Sword of Darrow. Malchow, A. **Fic**

SWORDS

See also Weapons

Sybile, 1977-

(il) Hardy, A. Dancers of the World **E**

Sydor, Colleen

Timmerman was here **E**

Sykes, Judith A.

Conducting action research to evaluate your school library **027.8**

SYLO. MacHale, D. J. **Fic**

Sylvada, Peter

(il) Frank, J. How to catch a fish **E**

(il) Schuch, S. A symphony of whales **E**

Sylver, Adrienne

Hot diggity dog **641.3**

Sylvester and the magic pebble. Steig, W. **E**

Sylvester, Kelvin

(jt. auth) Hlinka, M. Follow Your Money **330**

Splinters **E**

Sylvia and Aki. Conkling, W. **Fic**

Sylvia Jean, scout supreme. Ernst, L. C. **E**

Sylvia Long's Mother Goose. Long, S. **398.8**

Sylvia Long's Thumbelina. Long, S. **E**

Sylvie. Sattler, J. **E**

Sylvie & True. McPhail, D. M. **E**

Sylvie and the songman. Binding, T. **Fic**

SYMBIOSIS

Jenkins, S. How to clean a hippopotamus **591.7**

Rustad, M. E. H. Ants and aphids work together **595.7**

Rustad, M. E. H. Clown fish and sea anemones work together **597**

Rustad, M. E. H. Moray eels and cleaner shrimp work together **597**

Rustad, M. E. H. Zebras and oxpeckers work together **599.66**

SYMBIOSIS

See also Biology; Ecology

SYMBOLIC LOGIC

See also Logic; Mathematics

SYMBOLISM

See also Art; Mythology

SYMBOLISM IN LITERATURE

See also Literature; Symbolism

SYMBOLS *See* Signs and symbols

Symbols of American freedom [series]

Staton, H. Ellis Island **325**

Staton, H. Independence Hall **974.8**

Thomas, W. Mount Rushmore **978.3**

Symes, R. F.

Rocks & minerals **552**

Symes, Ruth

Harriet dancing **E**

SYMMETRY

Kalman, B. What is symmetry in nature? **570**

Leedy, L. Seeing symmetry **516**

Murphy, S. J. Let's fly a kite **516**

SYMPATHY

See also Conduct of life; Emotions

Symphony city. Martin, A. **E**

A symphony of whales. Schuch, S. **E**

SYNAGOGUES

Podwal, M. H. Built by angels **296.4**

SYNAGOGUES

See also Buildings; Religious institutions; Temples

SYNCHRONIZED SWIMMING

See also Swimming

SYNESTHESIA -- FICTION

Parkinson, S. Blue like Friday **Fic**

Synonyms and antonyms. Heinrichs, A. **428**

A **tale** of two daddies. Oelschlager, V. **E**

Tale of two Seders. Portnoy, M. A. **E**

The **talent** show. Hodgkinson, J. **E**

TALENT SHOWS -- FICTION

And two boys booed **E**

Cazet, D. Minnie and Moo, hooves of fire **Fic**

The **talent** thief. Williams, A. **Fic**

TALES See Fables; Fairy tales; Folklore; Legends

TALES -- MEXICO

Endredy, J. The journey of Tunuri and the Blue
Deer' **398.2**

Goldman, J. Whiskers, tails, and wings **398.2**

Tales for very picky eaters. Schneider, J. **Fic**

Tales from Deckawoo Drive [series]

Dicamillo, K. Leroy Ninker saddles up **Fic**

Tales from India. Gavin, J. **398.2**

Tales from old Ireland. Doyle, M. **398.209**

Tales from the Brothers Grimm. **398.2**

Tales from the hood. Buckley, M. **Fic**

Tales from the top of the world. Athans, S. K. **796.52**

Tales of a fourth grade nothing. Blume, J. **Fic**

Tales of a lost kingdom. L'Homme, E. **398.2**

The **tales** of Beedle the Bard. Rowling, J. K. **S**

Tales of Bunjitsu Bunny. Himmelman, J. **Fic**

Tales of Famous Animals. **590.92**

Tales of famous heroes. Roop, P. **920**

Tales of invention [series]

Spilsbury, R. The telephone **621.385**

Tales of terror from the Black Ship. Priestley, C. **Fic**

Tales of the cryptids. Halls, K. M. **001.9**

Tales of the world [series]

Whelan, G. Waiting for the owl's call **E**

Whelan, G. Yuki and the one thousand carriers **E**

The **tales** of Uncle Remus. Lester, J. **398.2**

Tales of young Americans [series]

Scillian, D. Pappy's handkerchief **E**

Swain, G. Riding to Washington **E**

Young, J. Minnow and Rose **Fic**

Tales our abuelitas told. Campoy, F. I. **398.2**

Tales to tickle your funny bone. Livo, N. J. **398.2**

Tales told in tents. Clayton, S. P. **398.2**

Talia and the rude vegetables. Marshall, L. E. **E**

Taliesin

About

Bond, N. A string in the harp **Fic**

TALISMANS -- FICTION

Gibson, J. M. Copper magic **Fic**

TALK SHOW HOSTS

Weatherford, C. B. Oprah **92**

TALK SHOWS

See also Interviewing; Radio programs; Television programs

Talk talk squawk. Davies, N. **591.59**

Talkin' about Bessie: the story of aviator Elizabeth
Coleman. Grimes, N. **92**

TALKING See Conversation

Talking about your weight. Edwards, H. **613.2**

TALKING BOOKS See Audiobooks

Talking Eagle and the Lady of Roses. **232.91**

The **talking** eggs. San Souci, R. **398.2**

Talking tails. Love, A. **636**

Talking walls. Knight, M. B. **721**

Talking with Mother Earth. Argueta, J. **811**

Tall. Alborough, J. **E**

Tall tale [series]

Powell, M. The tall tale of Paul Bunyan: the graphic novel **741.5**

The **tall** tale of Paul Bunyan: the graphic novel.
Powell, M. **741.5**

TALL TALES

Bertrand, L. Granite baby **E**

Casanova, M. The day Dirk Yeller came to town **E**

Fleischman, S. Here comes McBroom! **Fic**

Fleischman, S. McBroom's wonderful one-acre
farm **Fic**

Flora, J. The day the cow sneezed **E**

Gribnau, J. Kick the cowboy **E**

Holt, K. W. The adventures of Granny Clearwater
& Little Critter **E**

Hopkinson, D. Apples to Oregon **E**

Isaacs, A. Dust Devil **E**

Isaacs, A. Swamp Angel **E**

Jackson, A. Desert Rose and her highfalutin hog **E**

Janisch, H. Fantastic adventures of Baron
Munchausen **Fic**

Jean Laffite and the big ol' whale **E**

Johnston, T. Levi Strauss gets a bright idea or **E**

Kellogg, S. Mike Fink **398.22**

Kellogg, S. Paul Bunyan **398.2**

Kellogg, S. Pecos Bill **398.2**

Kellogg, S. Sally Ann Thunder Ann Whirlwind
Crockett **398.2**

Krensky, S. Paul Bunyan **398.2**

Krensky, S. Pecos Bill **398.2**

Langdo, B. Tornado Slim and the magic cowboy
hat **E**

Lorbiecki, M. Paul Bunyan's sweetheart **E**

Miller, B. Davy Crockett gets hitched **398.2**

Mora, P. Dona Flor **E**

Myers, C. Lies and other tall tales **398.2**

Nolen, J. Harvey Potter's balloon farm **E**

Nolen, J. Thunder Rose **E**

Osborne, M. P. American tall tales **398.2**

Pinkney, A. D. Peggony-Po **E**

Powell, M. The tall tale of Paul Bunyan: the graphic novel **741.5**

Root, P. Paula Bunyan **E**

San Souci, R. Cut from the same cloth **398.2**

Schur, M. Gullible Gus **Fic**

Shelby, A. The man who lived in a hollow tree **E**

Willey, M. Clever Beatrice **398.2**

Williams, S. Library Lil **E**

TEACHERS -- UNITED STATES -- HAND-BOOKS, MANUALS, ETC

Crews, K. D. Copyright law for librarians and educators **346.04**

Teachers at work. Kenney, K. L. **371.1**

TEACHERS OF THE BLIND

Adler, D. A. A picture book of Louis Braille **686.2**

Alexander, S. H. She touched the world: Laura Bridgman, deaf-blind pioneer **92**

Freedman, R. Out of darkness: the story of Louis Braille **92**

TEACHERS OF THE DEAF

Amoroso, C. Helen Keller **92**

Delano, M. F. Helen's eyes **92**

Garmon, A. Alexander Graham Bell invents **92**

McCully, E. A. My heart glow: Alice Cogswell, Thomas Gallaudet and the birth of American sign language **92**

Wyckoff, E. B. Sign language man: Thomas H. Gallaudet and his incredible work **92**

TEACHERS' WORKSHOPS

See also Teachers -- Training

TEACHING

Hauser, P. C. How deaf children learn **371.91**

McKeown, R. Into the classroom **370.71**

TEACHING -- AIDS AND DEVICES

Richardson, W. Blogs, wikis, podcasts, and other powerful Web tools for classrooms **371.3**

TEACHING -- DATA PROCESSING *See* Computer-assisted instruction

Teaching banned books. Scales, P. R. **098**

TEACHING TEAMS

Bacon, P. S. 100+ literacy lifesavers **428**

Harada, V. H. Inquiry learning through librarian-teacher partnerships **371.1**

TEACHING TEAMS

See also Teaching

Teaching with the tools kids really use. Brooks-Young, S. **372**

Teague, David

Saving Lucas Biggs **Fic**

Teague, Mark

How do dinosaurs stay safe? **E**

(il) Yolen, J. How do dinosaurs act when they're mad? **E**

(il) Isaacs, A. Pancakes for supper! **E**

(il) Rylant, C. Poppleton **E**

Dear Mrs. LaRue **E**

The doom machine **Fic**

Funny Farm **E**

Pigsty **E**

(il) Yolen, J. How do dinosaurs say goodnight? **E**

(il) Yolen, J. How do dinosaurs say happy birthday? **E**

Team moon. Thimmesh, C. **629.45**

TEAM TEACHING *See* Teaching teams

Teammates. **796.357**

TEASING

Allen, D. Dancing in the wings **E**

D'Amico, C. Ella the Elegant Elephant **E**

TEASING

See also Aggressiveness (Psychology); Interpersonal relations

TEASING -- FICTION

Greene, S. Princess Posey and the first grade boys **E**

Say, A. The favorite daughter **E**

Troto and the trucks **E**

Tebbetts, Chris

Middle school, the worst years of my life **Fic**

The tech-savvy booktalker. Keane, N. J. **021.7**

TECHNICAL EDUCATION

See also Education; Higher education; Technology

TECHNICAL WRITING

See also Authorship; Technology -- Language

Technically, it's not my fault. Grandits, J. **811**

TECHNOLOGICAL CHANGE *See* Technological innovations

TECHNOLOGICAL INNOVATIONS

Lee, D. Biomimicry **608**

TECHNOLOGICAL INNOVATIONS

See also Inventions; Technology

TECHNOLOGICAL INNOVATIONS -- HISTORY

Heinrichs, A. The Aztecs **972**

TECHNOLOGICAL LITERACY

See also Literacy

TECHNOLOGICAL LITERACY -- STUDY AND TEACHING -- CASE STUDIES

Growing schools **370.71**

TECHNOLOGY

Fridell, R. Sports technology **688.7**

Gates, P. Nature got there first **508**

Macaulay, D. The new way things work **600**

Murphy, G. Why is snot green **500**

Piddock, C. Future tech **600**

Robinson, J. Inventions **609**

Woodford, C. Cool Stuff 2.0 and how it works **600**

Zuckerman, A. 2030 **600**

TECHNOLOGY -- COMIC BOOKS, STRIPS, ETC.

Batman science **600**

TECHNOLOGY -- DICTIONARIES

See also Encyclopedias and dictionaries

TECHNOLOGY -- ENCYCLOPEDIAS

Everything you need to know **503**

TECHNOLOGY -- HISTORY

Jedicke, P. Great inventions of the 20th century **609**

Robinson, J. Inventions **609**

Ye The Chinese thought of it **609**

TECHNOLOGY AND CIVILIZATION

TERROR TALES *See* Ghost stories; Horror fiction

TERRORISM

Brown, D. America is under attack **973.931**

Burgan, M. George W. Bush **973.931**

Horowitz, A. Stormbreaker **Fic**

TERRORISM -- FICTION

Diamand, E. Flood and fire **Fic**

Horowitz, A. Ark angel **Fic**

Horowitz, A. Scorpia **Fic**

Horowitz, A. Scorpia rising **Fic**

Horowitz, A. Stormbreaker **Fic**

Hulme, J. The split second **Fic**

Lunis, N. The takedown of Osama bin Laden **958.104**

Smith, R. I, Q.: book one, Independence Hall **Fic**

Smith, R. I. Q.: book two, The White House **Fic**

Stanley, D. Saving Sky **Fic**

TERRORISM -- UNITED STATES

Benoit, P. September 11 we will never forget **973.931**

TERRORIST ACTS *See* Terrorism

TERRORIST ATTACKS, SEPTEMBER 11, 2001
See September 11 terrorist attacks, 2001

TERRORIST BOMBINGS *See* Bombings

TERRORISTS -- BIOGRAPHY

Lunis, N. The takedown of Osama bin Laden **958.104**

Terry, Michael Bad Hand

Daily life in a Plains Indian village, 1868 **970.004**

Terry, Will

(il) Bateman, T. The Frog with the Big Mouth **398.2**

(il) Corey, S. Monster parade **E**

(il) Holub, J. Spring is here! **E**

(il) Ketteman, H. The three little gators **E**

(il) Kimmelman, L. The three bully goats **E**

(il) MacDonald, M. R. Little Rooster's diamond button **398.2**

Tesla's attic. Elfman, E. **Fic**

Tesla, Nikola, 1856-1943

About

Elfman, E. Tesla's attic **Fic**

Watson, G. Edison's gold **Fic**

Tess's tree. Brallier, J. M. **E**

TEST BIAS

See also Discrimination in education; Educational tests and measurements

TEST PILOTS *See* Air pilots; Airplanes -- Testing

TEST PREPARATION GUIDES *See* Examinations -- Study guides

Testa, Fulvio

(il) Waters, F. Aesop's fables **398.2**

Testa, Maria

Almost forever **Fic**

Testing the ice: a true story about Jackie Robinson. **92**

TESTS *See* Educational tests and measurements; Examinations

TETON INDIANS

Cunningham, K. The Sioux **970.004**

TETON INDIANS -- FICTION

Sneve, V. D. H. Lana's Lakota moons **Fic**

TETON INDIANS -- FOLKLORE

Tatanka and the Lakota people **398.2**

TEUTONIC PEOPLES

Helget, N. Barbarians **940.1**

TEUTONIC RACE *See* Teutonic peoples

Tex. Lawson, D. M. **E**

Texas. Altman, L. J. **976.4**

TEXAS

Altman, L. J. Texas **976.4**

Holt, K. W. Dancing in Cadillac light **Fic**

Holt, K. W. When Zachary Beaver came to town **Fic**

Melmed, L. K. Heart of Texas **976.4**

Nagle, J. Texas **976.4**

Somervill, B. A. Texas **976.4**

Winter, J. Born and bred in the Great Depression **976.4**

Texas. Nagle, J. **976.4**

Texas. Somervill, B. A. **976.4**

TEXAS -- BIOGRAPHY

Henrietta King, la patrona **976.4**

TEXAS -- FICTION

Harrington, K. Courage for beginners **Fic**

Meanwhile, back at the ranch **E**

TEXAS -- HISTORY

Chemerka, W. R. Juan Seguin **976.4**

TEXAS -- HISTORY -- 1865-1950 -- FICTION

Johnson, A. All different now **E**

TEXAS -- HISTORY -- REPUBLIC, 1836-1846

Chemerka, W. R. Juan Seguin **976.4**

Texas Rangers. Spradlin, M. P. **976.4**

TEXAS RANGERS

Alter, J. John Barclay Armstrong **92**

Spradlin, M. P. Texas Rangers **976.4**

Texas, 1527-1836. Teitelbaum, M. **976.4**

TEXTBOOKS
See also Books

TEXTILE CHEMISTRY
See also Industrial chemistry; Textile industry

TEXTILE DESIGN
See also Commercial art; Decoration and ornament; Design

TEXTILE INDUSTRY

Hopkinson, D. Up before daybreak **331.7**

TEXTILE INDUSTRY -- HISTORY

Hopkinson, D. Up before daybreak **331.7**

TEXTILE PAINTING
See also Painting; Textile design

TEXTILE PRINTING
See also Printing; Textile industry

The whispering trees — Emerson, Emma, 1950– **Fic**

Thielbar, Melinda
The further Tale of Peter Rabbit

The ancient formula — Simpson, Clare **741.5**

THIEVES
Schroeder, A. Robbers! **364.15**
Thompson, K. Highway robbery **Fic**

THIEVES -- FICTION
Docherty, H. The Snatchabook **E**
Farrey, B. The Shadowhand Covenant **Fic**
Grounded **Fic**
Lane, A. J. B. Stop thief! **E**
Patron, S. Behind the masks **Fic**

Thimmesh, Catherine
Girls think of everything **920**
Lucy long ago **599.93**
Scaly spotted feathered frilled **567.9**
Team moon **629.45**
True Stories of Extraordinary Friendship **591.5**

The **thing** about Georgie. Graff, L. **Fic**
The **thing** about luck. Kadohata, C. **Fic**
The **thingamabob.** Na, I. S. **E**
Things that float and things that don't. Adler, D. A. **532**
Things that go. Gifford, C. **629.2**
Things that go. Ganeri, A. **629**
Think for yourself. MacGregor, C. **170**
Think green, take action. Kriesberg, D. A. **333.72**
Think like a scientist in the gym. Taylor-Butler, C. **530**
Think of an eel. Wallace, K. **597**
The **third** gift. **E**

THIRD PARTIES (UNITED STATES POLITICS)
See also Political parties; United States -- Politics and government

The **third** wheel. Kinney, J. **Fic**
Thirsty Thursday. Root, P. **E**
Thirteen moons on a turtle's back. Bruchac, J. **398.2**
The **thirteenth** princess. Zahler, D. **Fic**
This baby. Banks, K. **E**
This book is not good for you. Bosch, P. **Fic**
This child, every child. **305.23**
This day in June. **E**
This is a moose. **E**
This is just to say. Sidman, J. **811**
This is my family a first look at same sex parents. **306.874**
This is not my hat. Klassen, J. **E**
This is our house. Hyewon Yum **E**
This is rocket science. Skurzynski, G. **629.4**
This is silly! Taxali, G. **E**
This is the baby. Fleming, C. **E**
This is the dream. Shore, D. Z. **811**
This is the farmer. Tafuri, N. **E**
This is the game. Shore, D. Z. **811**
This is the house that Jack built. Taback, S. **398.8**
This is the mountain. **577.5**

This is the stable. Cotten, C. **E**
This is the sunflower. Schaefer, L. M. **E**
This is your life cycle. Miller, H. **595.7**
This isn't what it looks like. Bosch, P. **Fic**
This Jazz man. Ehrhardt, K. **E**
This journal belongs to Ratchet. Cavanaugh, N. J. **Fic**
This little light of mine. **782.25**
This little piggy. **398.8**
This means war! Wittlinger, E. **Fic**
This moose belongs to me. Jeffers, O. **E**
This next New Year. Wong, J. S. **E**
This place is wet. Cobb, V. **574.5**
This plus that. **E**
This school year will be the best! Winters, K. **E**
This strange wilderness. **92**
This time, Tempe Wick? Gauch, P. L. **Fic**
This tree counts! Formento, A. **E**

Thisdale, Francois
Forler, N. Bird child **E**
Pinsker, M. In the days of sand and stars **296.1**
Thisdale, F. Nini **E**

Thomas and the dragon queen. Crum, S. **Fic**
Thomas Edison. Venezia, M. **92**
Thomas Edison. Kesselring, S. **92**
Thomas Edison for kids. Carlson, L. M. **92**
Thomas Jefferson. Kalman, M. **92**
Thomas Jefferson for kids. Miller, B. M. **92**

Thomas, Bill
(il) Cole, J. Asking about sex & growing up **613.9**

Thomas, Cassia
(il) Bergman, M. Lively Elizabeth! what happens when you push **E**

Thomas, Eric
(il) Brown, L. The Children's illustrated Jewish Bible **220.9**

Thomas, Isabel
Why do I burp? **612.3**

Thomas, Jan
(il) Fox, M. Let's count goats! **E**
Can you make a scary face? **E**
The doghouse **E**
Is everyone ready for fun? **E**
Pumpkin trouble **E**
Rhyming dust bunnies **E**
What will Fat Cat sit on? **E**

Thomas, Joyce Carol
The blacker the berry **811**
Brown honey in broomwheat tea **811**

Thomas, Keltie
Animals that changed the world **590**
How basketball works **796.323**
How figure skating works **796.91**
How football works **796.332**

Thomas, Middy
(il) Lowry, L. Gooney Bird and all her charms **FIC**

Lowry, L. Gooney Bird Greene   **Fic**

(il) Lowry, L. Gooney Bird and the room mother   **Fic**

(il) Lowry, L. Gooney Bird is so absurd   **Fic**

(il) Lowry, L. Gooney the fabulous   **Fic**

Thomas, Pat

Don't call me fat a first look at being overweight   **618.92**

I see things differently a first look at autism **616.85**

This is my family a first look at same sex parents   **306.874**

Do I have to go to the dentist?   **617.6**

I think I am going to sneeze   **616.97**

Thomas, Patricia

Nature's paintbox   **811**

Red sled   **E**

Thomas, Peggy

For the birds: the life of Roger Tory Peterson   **92**

Thomas, Rebecca L.

East, K. Across cultures   **011.6**

Popular series fiction for K-6 readers   **016**

Thomas, Shelley Moore

A Good Knight's rest   **E**

Good night, Good Knight   **E**

Thomas, Valerie

About

Thimmesh, C. Girls think of everything   **920**

Thomas, Wes

(il) Bullard, L. Go easy on energy   **333.79**

(il) Bullard, L. Power up to fight pollution   **363.7**

Thomas, William

Mount Rushmore   **978.3**

Thomas, William David

Marine biologist   **578.7**

What are citizens' basic rights?   **323**

What is a constitution?   **342**

Thomason, Mark

Moonrunner   **Fic**

Thomassie, Tynia

Feliciana Feyra LeRoux   **E**

Thompson, Betsy

(il) Halfmann, J. Eggs 1 2 3   **591.4**

Thompson, Carol

I like you the best   **E**

(il) Butler, D. H. My mom's having a baby! **612.6**

(il) Crum, S. Thunder-Boomer!   **E**

(il) Forward, T. What did you do today?   **E**

(il) Hamm, M. Winners never quit!   **E**

(il) Newman, L. Daddy, papa, and me   **E**

(il) Newman, L. Mommy, mama, and me   **E**

(il) Ormerod, J. Molly and her dad   **E**

Thompson, Colin

Good neighbors   **Fic**

Thompson, Colin W.

(il) Silverman, B. Can an old dog learn new tricks?   **590**

Thompson, Emma, 1959-

The Further Tale of Peter Rabbit   **E**

Thompson, Gare

Riding with the mail   **383**

Roald Amundsen and Robert Scott race to the South Pole   **998**

Thompson, Helen

Cookies or carrots?   **613.2**

Thompson, J. E.

The girl from Felony Bay   **Fic**

Thompson, Jill

Gaiman, N. The graveyard book graphic novel Volume 1   **741.5**

Magic Trixie   **741.5**

Scary Godmother   **741.5**

Thompson, Kate

Highway robbery   **Fic**

Most wanted   **Fic**

Thompson, Kay

Kay Thompson's Eloise   **E**

Thompson, Lauren

Polar bear morning   **E**

One starry night   **E**

The apple pie that Papa baked   **E**

Ballerina dreams   **792.8**

The Christmas magic   **E**

How many cats?   **E**

Leap back home to me   **E**

Little Quack   **E**

Little Quack's bedtime   **E**

Polar bear night   **E**

Wee little bunny   **E**

Wee little chick   **E**

Wee little lamb   **E**

Thompson, Laurie Ann

Emmanuel's dream   **92**

Thompson, Margot

(il) Strauss, R. Tree of life   **578**

Thompson, Paul B.

The devil's door   **Fic**

Thomson, Bill

(il) Nevius, C. Baseball hour   **796.357**

(il) Nevius, C. Building with Dad   **E**

(il) Nevius, C. Karate hour   **E**

(il) Nevius, C. Soccer hour   **E**

Chalk   **E**

Thomson, Melissa

Keena Ford and the second-grade mixup   **Fic**

Thomson, Neil

Thomson, R. Toys and models   **745.592**

Thomson, Ruth

The life cycle of an owl   **598**

Portraits   **757**

Terezin   **940.53**

Toys and models   **745.592**

Thomson, Sarah L.

(il) Cleary, B. Ramona forever **Fic**

(il) Cleary, B. Ramona Quimby, age 8 **Fic**

(il) Cleary, B. Ramona's world **Fic**

(il) Cole, J. Why did the chicken cross the road? and other riddles, old and new **793.73**

(il) The Eentsy, weentsy spider: fingerplays and action rhymes **796.1**

(il) Miss Mary Mack and other children's street rhymes **796.1**

Tierney, Fiona

Lion's lunch? **E**

Tierney, Jim

(il) Oppel, K. The Boundless **Fic**

Tierra del Fuego. Lourie, P. **982**

TIERRA DEL FUEGO (ARGENTINA AND CHILE)

Lourie, P. Tierra del Fuego **982**

TIGER -- FICTION

Tiger boy **813.6**

Tiger and turtle. Rumford, J. **E**

Tiger boy. **813.6**

TIGER CUBS

Antle, B. The tiger cubs and the chimp **599.88**

The **tiger** cubs and the chimp. Antle, B. **599.88**

Tiger in my soup. **E**

Tiger math. Nagda, A. W. **511**

Tiger of the snows. Burleigh, R. **92**

Tiger on a tree. Ravishankar, A. **E**

Tiger talk. All about me [series]

Read, L. Keeping well **613**

Read, L. My senses **612.8**

Tiger, tiger. Lillegard, D. **E**

Tigers. Hanel, R. **599.75**

Tigers. Schafer, S. **599.75**

TIGERS

Antle, B. The tiger cubs and the chimp **599.88**

Firestone, M. Top 50 reasons to care about tigers **599.75**

Hanel, R. Tigers **599.75**

Jenkins, M. Can we save the tiger? **591.68**

Nagda, A. W. Tiger math **511**

Ravishankar, A. Tiger on a tree **E**

Schafer, S. Tigers **599.75**

TIGERS -- FICTION

Brown, P. Mr. Tiger goes wild **E**

Logue, M. Sleep like a tiger **E**

Schmid, P. Petunia goes wild **E**

Tiger boy **813.6**

TIGERS -- FOLKLORE

Blia Xiong Nine-in-one, Grr! Grr! **398.2**

Han, S. C. The rabbit's tail **398.2**

TIGHTROPE WALKING

Gerstein, M. The man who walked between the towers **791**

TIGHTROPE WALKING -- FICTION

McCully, E. A. Mirette on the high wire **E**

Tigua. Kissock, H. **970.004**

TIGUA INDIANS

Kissock, H. Tigua **970.004**

Tikal. Mann, E. **972.81**

Tikki Tikki Tembo. Mosel, A. **398.2**

Tilde

(il) Kim, S. How does a seed grow? **581.4**

Tildes, Phyllis Limbacher

(il) Farmer, J. Apples **634**

(il) Goodman, E. Plant secrets **580**

Calico's cousins **636.8**

Will you be mine? **398.8**

TILES

See also Building materials; Ceramics

Till death do us bark. Klise, K. **Fic**

Tillage, Leon, 1936-

About

Tillage, L. Leon's story **92**

Tilley, Debbie

(il) Danzig, D. Babies don't eat pizza **649**

(il) Gordon, J. M. The Gallaudet children's dictionary of American Sign Language **419**

(il) Jukes, M. Growing up: it's a girl thing **612.6**

(il) Weaver, T. Frederick Finch, loudmouth **E**

Tillie lays an egg. Golson, T. **E**

Tillie the terrible Swede. **92**

Tillman, Nancy

(il) Metaxas, E. It's time to sleep, my love (a lullabye) **E**

On the night you were born **E**

The spirit of Christmas **E**

Tillotson, Katherine

(il) Lyon, G. E. All the water in the world **551.48**

(il) McDonald, M. Shoe dog **E**

(il) McDonald, M. It's picture day today! **E**

Tim Duncan. Thornley, S. **796.323**

TIMBER *See* Forests and forestry; Lumber and lumbering; Trees; Wood

Timberlake, Amy

One came home **Fic**

The dirty cowboy **E**

Timblin, Stephen

Swimming **797.2**

Time. Rand, C. **530.1**

TIME

Adamson, T. K. How do you measure time? **529**

Adler, D. A. Time zones **389**

Appelt, K. Bats around the clock **E**

Bernhard, D. While you are sleeping **389**

Danziger, P. It's Justin Time, Amber Brown **E**

Gleick, B. Time is when **529**

Hutchins, H. J. A second is a hiccup **529**

Jenkins, S. Just a second **529**

Koscielniak, B. About time **529**

Maestro, B. The story of clocks and calendars **529**

Murphy, S. J. It's about time! **529**

Today and today. Kobayashi, I. **895.6**

Today I will fly! Willems, M. **E**

Today is Monday. Carle, E. **782.421**

Today is the birthday of the world. Heller, L. **E**

Today on election day. **E**

Today, maybe. Demers, D. **E**

Todd's TV. Proimos, J. **E**

Todd, Mark

Harris, J. My monster notebook **398.2**

Todd, Mary Ellen, 1843-1924

About

Van Leeuwen, J. Bound for Oregon **Fic**

Toddler storytimes II. Briggs, D. **372.6**

TODDLERS -- FICTION

Isadora, R. Jake at gymnastics **E**

Toddy, Irving

(il) Bunting, E. Cheyenne again **E**

Todras, Ellen H.

Explorers, trappers, and pioneers **911**

Wagon trains and settlers **973.8**

Toft, Di

Wolven **Fic**

Toft, Lis

(il) Cameron, A. Gloria's way **Fic**

Tofu quilt. Russell, C. Y. **Fic**

Togo. Blake, R. J. **798.8**

Toilet. Macaulay, D. **644.6**

TOILET TRAINING -- FICTION

Kel Gilligan's daredevil stunt show **E**

TOILET TRAINING -- SONGS

Katz, A. On top of the potty and other get-up-and-go songs **782.42**

TOILETRIES

See also Personal grooming

TOILETS

Albee, S. Poop happened! **363.7**

Macaulay, D. Toilet **644.6**

Raum, E. The story behind toilets **696**

Toklas, Alice B.

About

Yolleck, J. Paris in the spring with Picasso **E**

Toksvig, Sandi

Hitler's canary **Fic**

Tokunbo, Dimitrea

(il) Saint-Lot, K. N. Amadi's snowman **E**

The sound of Kwanzaa **394.26**

TOKYO (JAPAN)

Takabayashi, M. I live in Tokyo **952**

Tolan, Stephanie S.

Surviving the Applewhites **Fic**

Wishworks, Inc. **Fic**

Tolerance. Pryor, K. J. **177**

TOLERANCE *See* Toleration

TOLERATION

Burstein, J. Can we get along? **179**

Pryor, K. J. Tolerance **177**

Wahl, J. Candy shop **E**

TOLERATION

See also Interpersonal relations

TOLERATION -- FICTION

Dumont The chickens build a wall **E**

Kerrin, J. S. Martin Bridge: onwards and upwards! **Fic**

Loizeaux, W. Clarence Cochran, a human boy **Fic**

Rania The sandwich swap **E**

Simmons, J. Beryl **Fic**

Wahl, J. Candy shop **E**

Tolkien, J. R. R. (John Ronald Reuel), 1892-1973

The hobbit **Fic**

About

Ellis, S. From reader to writer **372.62**

Tollins. Iggulden, C. **Fic**

Tolman, Marije

The island **398.209**

The tree house **E**

Tolman, Ronald

(jt. auth) Tolman, M. The island **398.209**

Tolman, M. The tree house **E**

Tom Brady. Wilner, B. **92**

Tom the tamer. Veldkamp, T. **E**

Tom's midnight garden. Pearce, P. **Fic**

Tom's tweet. Esbaum, J. **E**

Tomas and the library lady. Mora, P. **E**

Tomas, Xose

(il) The big book of pirates **S**

TOMATOES

Malam, J. Grow your own sandwich **635**

TOMATOES -- FICTION

Helmore, J. Oh no, monster tomato! **E**

Tomb explorers. Barber, N. **930.1**

Tomb of shadows. Lerangis, P. **Fic**

TOMBS

At home in her tomb **931**

Barber, N. Tomb explorers **930.1**

TOMBS

See also Archeology; Architecture; Burial; Monuments; Shrines

Tomecek, Steve

Art & architecture **701**

Everything rocks and minerals **552**

Moon **523.3**

Music **781.2**

Rocks & minerals **552**

Tools and machines **621.9**

Tomes, Margot

(il) De Regniers, B. S. Little sister and the month brothers **398.2**

(il) Fritz, J. And then what happened, Paul Revere? **92**

(il) Fritz, J. Homesick: my own story **92**

(il) Fritz, J. What's the big idea, Ben Franklin? **92**

(il) Fritz, J. Where was Patrick Henry on the 29th

Top 50 reasons to care about great apes. Barker, D. **599.8**

Top 50 reasons to care about marine turtles. Christopherson, S. C. **597.92**

Top 50 reasons to care about polar bears. Hirsch, R. E. **599.78**

Top 50 reasons to care about rhinos. Firestone, M. **599.66**

Top 50 reasons to care about tigers. Firestone, M. **599.75**

Top 50 reasons to care about whales and dolphins. Christopherson, S. C. **599.5**

Top cat. Ehlert, L. **E**

The **top** job. Kimmel, E. C. **E**

Top of the order. Coy, J. **Fic**

The **top** of the world. Jenkins, S. **796.52**

Top pets for kids with American Humane [series]
Gaines, A. Top 10 dogs for kids **636.7**
Gaines, A. Top 10 reptiles and amphibians for kids **639.3**
Gaines, A. Top 10 small mammals for kids **636.9**
Mead, W. Top 10 birds for kids **636.6**
Rau, D. M. Top 10 cats for kids **636.8**
Rau, D. M. Top 10 fish for kids **639.34**

Top score math [series]
Woods, M. Ace! **796.342**
Woods, M. Goal! **796.334**
Woods, M. Xtreme! Extreme sports facts and stats **796**

Top technology. Gilbert, A. **621.389**

The **top-secret** diary of Celie Valentine. Sternberg, J. **Fic**

The top-secret diary of celie valentine [series]
Sternberg, J. The top-secret diary of Celie Valentine **Fic**

TOPOGRAPHICAL DRAWING
See also Drawing; Surveying

TOPOLOGY
See also Geometry; Set theory

Tops and bottoms. Stevens, J. **398.2**

Topsy-turvy bedtime. Gannij, J. **E**

Topsy-Turvy Town. Melanson, L. **E**

TORAH SCROLLS -- FICTION
Ofanansky, A. The patchwork Torah **E**

Torinos. Portman, M. **629.222**

Torn. Haddix, M. P. **Fic**

Tornado. **Fic**

Tornado Slim and the magic cowboy hat. Langdo, B. **E**

Tornado! Fradin, D. B. **551.55**

Tornadoes. Schuh, M. C. **551.55**

Tornadoes. Silverstein, A. **551.55**

Tornadoes. Simon, S. **551.55**

TORNADOES
Fradin, D. B. Tornado! **551.55**
Gibbons, G. Tornadoes! **551.55**

Rudolph, J. Erased by a tornado! **551.55**
Schuh, M. C. Tornadoes **551.55**
Shores, L. How to build a tornado in a bottle **551.55**
Silverstein, A. Tornadoes **551.55**
Simon, S. Tornadoes **551.55**
Spilsbury, L. Terrifying tornadoes **551.55**

TORNADOES
See also Meteorology; Storms; Winds

TORNADOES -- FICTION
Clements, A. About average **Fic**
Ghigna, C. Barn storm **E**
Long, L. Otis and the tornado **E**
Tornado **Fic**
Tornadoes! Gibbons, G. **551.55**

Tornqvist, Marit
Lindgren, A. Goran's great escape **E**

TORONTO (ONT.) -- FICTION
Croza, L. From there to here **E**

Torque: The unexplained [series]
Doft, T. Nostradamus **133.3**
Erickson, J. Alien abductions **001.9**
Helstrom, K. Crop circles **001.9**
Michels, T. Atlantis **001.9**

Torres, J.
Into the woods **741.5**
The Sound of Thunder **741.5**
The unkindness of ravens **741.5**

Torres, Laura
Rock your party **745.54**
Rock your school stuff **745.5**
Rock your wardrobe **646.4**

Torrey, Rich
Almost **E**
Because **E**
Why? **E**

Torseter, Øyvind
(il) My father's arms are a boat **E**

Torsiello, David P.
Michael Phelps **92**

Tortilla sun. Cervantes, J. **Fic**

Tortillas and lullabies. Tortillas y cancioncitas. Reiser, L. **E**

Tortillitas para mama and other nursery rhymes. **398.8**

The **tortoise** & the hare. **E**

TORTOISES *See* Turtles

TORTURE
Everett, J. H. Haunted histories **133.1**

Toscano, Charles
Papa's pastries **E**

TOTALITARIANISM
See also Political science

The **totally** awesome epic quest of the brave boy knight. Naujokaitis, P. T. **741.5**

Totally human. **612**

Totally Joe. Howe, J. **Fic**

Tyrannosuarus dad. Rosenberg, L.   E
Tz¿u-hsi, Empress dowager of China, 1835-1908
       About
   Krull, K. Lives of extraordinary women   920

U

U'Ren, Andrea
   (il) DeFelice, C. C. One potato, two potato   E
   (il) Kimmel, E. A. Stormy's hat   E
   (il) Moss, M. The bravest woman in America   92
   (il) Schubert, L. Feeding the sheep   E
**U.S. FISH AND WILDLIFE SERVICE -- FO-
     RENSICS LABORATORY**
   Jackson, D. M. The wildlife detectives   363.2
Ubiquitous.   811
Uchida, Yoshiko
   The bracelet   E
   A jar of dreams   Fic
   Journey to Topaz   Fic
Udry, Janice May
   The moon jumpers   E
   A tree is nice   E
Uegaki, Chieri
   Rosie and Buttercup   E
   Suki's kimono   E
Uff, Caroline
   (il) Doyle, M. Get happy   E
UFOS *See* Unidentified flying objects
Uganda. Barlas, R.   967.61
UGANDA
   Barlas, R. Uganda   967.61
   Shoveller, H. Ryan and Jimmy   361.7
Ugliano, Natascia
   (il) Gellman, E. B. Netta and her plant   E
   (il) Jules, J. Abraham's search for God   222
   (il) Jules, J. Benjamin and the silver goblet   222
   (il) Jules, J. Miriam in the desert   222
   (il) Jules, J. Sarah laughs   222
The **uglified** ducky. Claflin, W.   E
The **ugly** dinosaur. Bardoe, C.   E
The **ugly** duckling. Andersen, H. C.   E
The **ugly** duckling. Watts, B.   E
The **ugly** duckling. Braun, S.   E
The **ugly** duckling. Mitchell, S.   E
The **ugly** duckling. Isadora, R.   E
The **ugly** duckling. Pinkney, J.   E
Ugly Pie. Wheeler, L.   E
Uh-oh Cleo [series]
   Harper, J. Underpants on my head   Fic
Uh-oh Max. Scieszka, J.   E
Uh-oh! DePalma, M. N.   E
Uh-oh! Isadora, R.   E
Uh-oh, Cleo. Harper, J.   Fic
Uh-oh, dodo! Sattler, J.   E
Uhlberg, Myron
   Dad, Jackie, and me   E

   A storm called Katrina   E
Uhlich, Gerald R.
   Hatkoff, J. Knut   599.78
Uhlman, Tom
   (il) Carson, M. K. The park scientists   333.78
   (il) Carson, M. K. The bat scientists   599.4
   (il) Carson, M. K. Emi and the rhino scientist   599.66
   (il) Rusch, E. Eruption!   363.34
UIGHUR (TURKIC PEOPLE) -- FICTION
   La Valley, J. The Vine basket   Fic
Ukraine. Bassis, V.   947.7
UKRAINE
   Bassis, V. Ukraine   947.7
UKULELE -- FICTION
   Cox, J. Ukulele Hayley   Fic
Ukulele Hayley. Cox, J.   Fic
Ulmer, Wendy K.
   A isn't for fox   E
Ulrich, George
   (il) Murphy, S. J. Divide and ride   513
The ultimate 10. Natural disasters [series]
   Stewart, M. Blizzards and winter storms   551.55
The **ultimate** dinopedia. Lessem, D.   567.9
Ultimate fighting. Wiseman, B.   796.8
**ULTIMATE FIGHTING CHAMPIONSHIP (OR-
     GANIZATION)**
   Wiseman, B. Ultimate fighting   796.8
Ultimate guide to baseball. Buckley, J.   796.357
Ultimate guide to football. Buckley, J.   796.332
The **ultimate** guide to grandmas and grandpas. Jones, S. L.   E
The **ultimate** guide to your microscope. Levine, S.   502.8
The **ultimate** indoor games book. Gunter, V. A.   793
Ultimate trains. McMahon, P.   385
ULTRASONIC WAVES
   See also Sound waves; Ultrasonics
ULTRASONICS
   See also Sound
Uluru, Australia's Aboriginal heart. Arnold, C.   994
**ULURU-KATA TJUTA NATIONAL PARK (AUS-
     TRALIA)**
   Arnold, C. Uluru, Australia's Aboriginal heart   994
Ulysses Moore [series]
   Baccalario, P. The long-lost map   Fic
Uman, Jennifer
   (il) Jemmy button   E
Umansky, Kaye
   Clover Twig and the magical cottage   Fic
   Solomon Snow and the stolen jewel   Fic
The **umbrella.** Schubert, I.   E
Umbrella. Iwamatsu, A. J.   E
The **Umbrella** Queen. Bridges, S. Y.   E
Umbrella summer. Graff, L.   Fic
UMBRELLAS AND PARASOLS

Up, up, and away. Wadsworth, G. **595.4**

Updale, Eleanor
Johnny Swanson **Fic**

Updike, John, 1932-2009
A child's calendar **811**

UPHOLSTERY
See also Interior design

Upitis, Alvis
(il) Peterson, C. Extra cheese, please! **637**

Upjohn, Rebecca
The secret of the village fool **Fic**

UPPER ATMOSPHERE
See also Atmosphere
The **upside** down boy. Herrera, J. F. **92**

UPSIDE-DOWN BOOKS
Viva, F. A long way away **E**
Upstairs Mouse, downstairs Mole. Yee, W. H. **E**
The **upstairs** room. Reiss, J. **92**
Uptown. Collier, B. **E**

URANIUM
See also Chemical elements
Uranus. Landau, E. **523.4**
Uranus. Sherman, J. **523.4**

URANUS (PLANET)
Carson, M. K. Far-out guide to Uranus **523.4**
Landau, E. Uranus **523.4**
Sherman, J. Uranus **523.4**
Sparrow, G. Destination Uranus, Neptune, and Pluto **523.4**

URANUS (PLANET)
See also Planets

URBAN AGRICULTURE
Hodge, D. Watch me grow! **630**
Martin, J. B. Farmer Will Allen and the growing table **92**

URBAN AGRICULTURE
See also Agriculture
Urban animals. Hill, I. (. T. **729**

URBAN AREAS *See* Cities and towns; Metropolitan areas

URBAN ECOLOGY
Cities **307.76**
Ernst, L. C. How things work in the yard **578.7**
Kaner, E. Earth-friendly buildings, bridges, and more **720**

URBAN ECOLOGY
See also Cities and towns; Ecology
Downer, A. Wild animal neighbors **591.75**

URBAN ENVIRONMENT *See* Urban ecology
URBAN FARMING *See* Urban agriculture

URBAN FOLKLORE
See also Folklore

URBAN FORESTRY
See also Forests and forestry

URBAN LIFE *See* City and town life
Urban outlaws. Black, P. J. **Fic**

URBAN POLICY
See also City and town life; Economic policy; Social policy; Urban sociology
Urban roosts: where birds nest in the city. Bash, B. **598**

URBAN SCHOOLS
See also Schools

URBAN TRAFFIC *See* City traffic

Urban, Linda
Little Red Henry **E**
The center of everything **Fic**
A crooked kind of perfect **Fic**
Hound dog true **Fic**
Mouse was mad **E**

URBANIZATION
See also Cities and towns; Rural sociology; Social change; Social conditions; Urban sociology

Urbanovic, Jackie
(il) Beaumont, K. No sleep for the sheep! **E**
(il) Prelutsky, J. I've lost my hippopotamus **811**
(il) Kimmel, E. C. Glamsters **E**
(il) Sayre, A. P. If you're hoppy **E**
Duck at the door **E**
Sitting duck **E**

Urberuaga, Emilio
(il) Lindo, E. Manolito Four-Eyes **Fic**
(il) Lindo, E. Manolito Four-Eyes: the 2nd volume of the great encyclopedia of my life **Fic**
(il) Lindo, E. Manolito Four-Eyes: the 3rd volume of the great encyclopedia of my life **Fic**

Urbigkit, Cat
Brave dogs, gentle dogs **636.7**
The guardian team **636.7**
Path of the pronghorn **599.65**
The shepherd's trail **636.3**
A young shepherd **636.3**

Urdahl, Catherine
Polka-dot fixes kindergarten **E**
Urgency emergecy! Itsy bitsy spider. **E**

Urgency emergency! [series]
Archer, D. Big Bad Wolf **E**

URINARY ORGANS
Gold, S. D. Learning about the digestive and excretory systems **612.3**

URINE
The Scoop on Poop **E**

Urrutia, María Cristina
Who will save my planet? **304.2**

URSA MAJOR
Branley, F. M. The Big Dipper **523.8**

Ursell, Martin
(il) Lister, A. The Ice Age tracker's guide **569**

Ursu, Anne
Breadcrumbs **Fic**
The Real Boy **Fic**

Uruguay. Jermyn, L.   **989.5**

URUGUAY

  Jermyn, L. Uruguay   **989.5**

The **US** Civil War and Reconstruction. Howell, B.   **973.8**

Use your words, Sophie.   **E**

USED MERCHANDISE *See* Secondhand trade

USEFUL INSECTS *See* Beneficial insects

Usher, Mark David

  The golden ass of Lucius Apuleius   **Fic**

Using alternative energies. Farrell, C.   **333.79**

Using digital images. Rabbat, S.   **775**

Using Earth's underground heat. White, N.   **333.8**

Using energy. Hewitt, S.   **333.79**

Using picture books to teach [series]

  Hall, S. Using picture storybooks to teach literary devices   **016**

Using picture storybooks to teach literary devices. Hall, S.   **016**

Using poetry across the curriculum. Chatton, B.   **372.6**

Using your research. Ollhoff, J.   **929**

Utah. Stefoff, R.   **979.2**

Utah. Kent, D.   **979.2**

UTAH

  Ching, J. Utah   **979.2**

  Kent, D. Utah   **979.2**

  Stefoff, R. Utah   **979.2**

  Utah. Ching, J.   **979.2**

UTAH -- FICTION

  Fitzgerald, J. D. The Great Brain   **Fic**

  Fitzgerald, J. D. The Great Brain is back   **Fic**

UTE INDIANS -- FICTION

  Wyss, T. H. Bear dancer   **Fic**

UTE INDIANS -- FOLKLORE

  Stevens, J. Coyote steals the blanket   **398.2**

UTENSILS, KITCHEN *See* Kitchen utensils

UTILITARIANISM

    See also Ethics

UTILITIES, PUBLIC *See* Public utilities

UTILIZATION OF WASTE *See* Salvage

UTOPIAN FICTION

    See also Fantasy fiction; Science fiction

UTOPIAS

    See also Political science; Socialism

Utterly me, Clarice Bean. Child, L.   **Fic**

Utterly otterly day. Casanova, M.   **E**

Uttley, Colin

  Magnesium   **546**

V

Valmiki

        About

  Arni, S. Sita's Ramayana   **741.5**

Vacation. Harrison, D. L.   **811**

A **vacation** for Pooch. Cocca-Leffler, M.   **E**

VACATION HOMES

    See also Houses

VACATIONS

    See also Recreation

VACATIONS -- FICTION

  Gordon, D. M. Archie's vacation   **E**

  Charlie Joe Jackson's guide to summer vacation **Fic**

  Cocca-Leffler, M. A vacation for Pooch   **E**

  Lulu and the dog from the sea   **Fic**

  Where my wellies take me   **821**

  Yoon, S. Penguin on vacation   **E**

VACATIONS -- POETRY

  Broach, E. The miniature world of Marvin & James   **Fic**

VACCINATION

    See also Immunization; Preventive medicine; Public health

Vail, Rachel

  Justin Case   **Fic**

  Sometimes I'm Bombaloo   **E**

Vainio, Pirkko

  (il) Andersen, H. C. The nightingale   **E**

  (il) Andersen, H. C. The ugly duckling   **E**

  Who hid the Easter eggs?   **E**

Valat, Pierre-Marie

  (il) Inside the body   **611**

Valdivia, Paloma

  Up above and down below   **E**

Valencia, Esau Andrade

  (il) Hayes, J. Don't say a word, mamá = No digas nada, mamá   **E**

Valente, Catherynne M.

  The boy who lost Fairyland   **Fic**

  The girl who circumnavigated Fairyland in a ship of her own making   **Fic**

  The girl who fell beneath Fairyland and led the revels there   **Fic**

  The Girl Who Soared over Fairyland and Cut the Moon in Two   **Fic**

Valentine be mine.   **E**

VALENTINE DECORATIONS

  Owen, R. Valentine's Day origami   **736**

Valentine surprise. Demas, C.   **E**

VALENTINE'S DAY

  McGee, R. Paper crafts for Valentine's Day **745.594**

  Owen, R. Valentine's Day origami   **736**

  Valentine be mine   **E**

  Otto, C. Celebrate Valentine's Day   **394.26**

  The yuckiest, stinkiest, best Valentine ever   **E**

VALENTINE'S DAY

    See also Holidays

VALENTINE'S DAY -- FICTION

  Adler, D. A. Cam Jansen and the Valentine baby mystery   **Fic**

  Carlson, N. L. Henry and the Valentine surprise **E**

  Choldenko, G. A giant crush   **E**

Demas, C. Valentine surprise   E
Elliott, L. A string of hearts   E
Friedman, L. B. Heart-to-heart with Mallory   Fic
Knudson, M. Raymond and Graham, dancing
   dudes   Fic
Parish, H. Amelia Bedelia's first Valentine   E
Petersen, D. Snowy Valentine   E
Scieszka, J. Melvin's valentine   E
Yee, W. H. Mouse and Mole, secret valentine   E
The yuckiest, stinkiest, best Valentine ever   E

VALENTINE'S DAY -- POETRY
Prelutsky, J. It's Valentine's Day   811
Valentine's Day origami. Owen, R.   736

Valentine, Madeline
Little Red Henry   E

Valentine, Saint
About
Sabuda, R. Saint Valentine   270.1

VALENTINES
The ballad of Valentine   E

Valenzuela, Fernando, 1960-
About
Stout, G. Baseball heroes   796.357

Valerio, Geraldo
MacDonald, M. R. Conejito   398.2
MacDonald, M. R. Go to sleep, Gecko!   398.2
MacDonald, M. R. Surf war!   398.2
Spinelli, E. Do you have a cat?   E
Spinelli, E. Do you have a dog?   E
Spinelli, E. When you are happy   E

VALHALLA -- FICTION
Marr, M. Odin's ravens   Fic

Valiant, Kristi
(il) Lazo Gilmore, D. K. Cora cooks pancit   E
(il) Matthies, J. The Goodbye Cancer garden   E

VALLEY FORGE (PA.) -- HISTORY
Allen, T. B. Remember Valley Forge   973.3
Freedman, R. Washington at Valley Forge   973.3

Vallverdu, Josep
Aladdin and the magic lamp   398.2

VALUES
   See also Aesthetics; Ethics; Psychology
Values [series]
Pryor, K. J. Cooperation   177
Pryor, K. J. Courage   179
Pryor, K. J. Honesty   177
Pryor, K. J. Kindness   177
Pryor, K. J. Respect   177
Pryor, K. J. Tolerance   177

Vamos, Samantha R.
The cazuela that the farm maiden stirred   E

Vampire boy's good night. Brown, L.   E

VAMPIRE FILMS
   See also Horror films; Motion pictures

VAMPIRES
Gee, J. Encyclopedia horrifica   001.9

VAMPIRES
   See also Folklore

VAMPIRES -- FICTION
Pace, A. M. Vampirina ballerina   E
Spooky friends   E

VAMPIRES -- GRAPHIC NOVELS
Little Vampire   741.5
Vampirina ballerina. Pace, A. M.   E

Van Allsburg, Chris
(il) The chronicles of Harris Burdick   S
Van Allsburg, C. Queen of the Falls   92
Ben's dream   E
The garden of Abdul Gasazi   E
Just a dream   E
The mysteries of Harris Burdick   E
The Polar Express   E
The stranger   E
The sweetest fig   E
The widow's broom   E
The Z was zapped   411
Zathura   E
The wretched stone   E
(il) Jumanji   E
The wreck of the Zephyr   E

Van Camp, Katie
Cookiebot!   E
Harry and Horsie   E

Van Camp, Richard, 1971-
Little you   E

Van Cleve, Kathleen
Drizzle   Fic

Van der Sterre, Johanna
(il) Bradford, W. Why do I have to make my
   bed?   E
(il) Hyde, H. S. Feivel's flying horses   E

Van Doninck, Sebastiaan
(il) Moser, L. Cowboy Boyd and Mighty Calliope   E

Van Draanen, Wendelin, 1965-
Flipped   Fic
Sammy Keyes and the art of deception   Fic
Sammy Keyes and the cold hard cash   Fic
Sammy Keyes and the curse of Moustache Mary Fic
Sammy Keyes and the dead giveaway   Fic
Sammy Keyes and the Hollywood mummy   Fic
Sammy Keyes and the hotel thief   Fic
Sammy Keyes and the killer cruise   Fic
Sammy Keyes and the night of skulls   Fic
Sammy Keyes and the psycho Kitty Queen   Fic
Sammy Keyes and the runaway elf   Fic
Sammy Keyes and the search for Snake Eyes   Fic
Sammy Keyes and the showdown in Sin City   Fic
Sammy Keyes and the Sisters of Mercy   Fic
Sammy Keyes and the skeleton man   Fic
Sammy Keyes and the wedding crasher   Fic
Sammy Keyes and the wild things   Fic

Island's end **Fic**

Vennema, Peter

Stanley, D. Bard of Avon: the story of William Shakespeare **822.3**

Stanley, D. Cleopatra **932**

Stanley, D. Good Queen Bess: the story of Elizabeth I of England **92**

Venom, poison, and electricity. Pryor, K. J. **591.6**

Venter, Liezl

Van Niekerk, C. Understanding Sam and Asperger Syndrome **616.85**

Venti, Anthony Bacon

(il) Fritz, J. Around the world in a hundred years **910.92**

VENTILATION

See also Air; Home economics; Household sanitation; Hygiene; Sanitation

VENTRILOQUISM

See also Amusements; Voice

Venus. Landau, E. **523.4**

Venus. Bjorklund, R. **523.4**

VENUS (PLANET)

Bjorklund, R. Venus **523.4**

Carson, M. K. Far-out guide to Venus **523.4**

Landau, E. Venus **523.4**

VENUS (PLANET)

See also Planets

Venuti, Kristin Clark

Leaving the Bellweathers **Fic**

Vera's first day of school. Rosenberry, V. **E**

VERBAL LEARNING

See also Language and languages; Psychology of learning

Verbs. Heinrichs, A. **428**

Verburg, Bonnie

The kiss box **E**

Verde, Susan

The museum **E**

Verdi, Giuseppe, 1813-1901

About

Krull, K. Lives of the musicians **920**

Verdick, Elizabeth

The survival guide for kids with autism spectrum disorders (and their parents) **618.92**

Crist, J. J. Siblings **306.8**

Don't behave like you live in a cave **395**

Mealtime **E**

Words are not for hurting **177**

Verdu, Jean-Yves

Niepold, M. Oooh! Picasso **730.9**

Vere, Ed

Banana! **E**

Veregin, Howard

(ed) Rand McNally Goodes World Atlas **912**

Veres, Laszlo

(il) The Kid's Guide to Exploring Nature **508**

Verhoeven, Rian

Rol, R. v. d. Anne Frank, beyond the diary **940.53**

The **Vermeer** interviews. Raczka, B. **759.9**

Vermeer, Johannes, 1632-1675

About

Balliett, B. Chasing Vermeer **Fic**

Raczka, B. The Vermeer interviews **759.9**

VERMIN See Household pests; Pests

Vermont. Sommers, M. **974.3**

Vermont. Heinrichs, A. **974.3**

VERMONT

Anderson, M. T. The Game of Sunken Places **Fic**

Heinrichs, A. Vermont **974.3**

Hesse, K. Witness **Fic**

Sommers, M. Vermont **974.3**

Wilson, N. H. Mountain pose **Fic**

VERMONT -- FICTION

Blakemore, M. F. The spy catchers of Maple Hill **Fic**

VERMONT -- HISTORY -- 20TH CENTURY -- FICTION

Blakemore, M. F. The spy catchers of Maple Hill **Fic**

Kinsey-Warnock, N. True colors **Fic**

Vermont Folklife Center children's book series

Walter, M. P. Alec's primer **E**

VERNAL EQUINOX

Pfeffer, W. A new beginning **394.26**

VERNAL POOL ECOLOGY

The secret pool **577.63**

Wechsler, D. Frog heaven **577.6**

VERNAL POOLS

The secret pool **577.63**

Verne, Jules

20,000 leagues under the sea **Fic**

Vernick, Audrey

Brothers at bat **796.357**

She loved baseball: the Effa Manley story **92**

Is your buffalo ready for kindergarten? **E**

Teach your buffalo to play drums **E**

Water balloon **Fic**

Vernick, Shirley Reva

The blood lie **Fic**

Vernon, Ursula

Castle Hangnail **Fic**

Dragonbreath: attack of the ninja frogs **Fic**

Dragonbreath: curse of the were-wiener **Fic**

Verplancke, Klaas

Applesauce **E**

Verroken, Sarah

(il) Derom, D. Pigeon and Pigeonette **E**

VERSIFICATION

See also Authorship; Poetics; Rhythm

Verstraete, Larry

Surviving the Hindenburg **363.12**

VERTEBRATES

Patent, D. H. Saving Audie   636.7

VICTIMS OF CRIMES

    See also Crime

Victoria, Queen of Great Britain, 1819-1901

    About

  Deedy, C. A. The Cheshire Cheese cat   **Fic**

  Krull, K. Lives of extraordinary women   **920**

  The mouse with the question mark tail   **Fic**

  Queen Victoria's Bathing Machine   **E**

Victory. Cooper, S.   **Fic**

Vidal, Beatriz

  (il) Aardema, V. Bringing the rain to Kapiti Plain   **398.2**

  (il) Alvarez, J. A gift of gracias   **E**

Vidal, Oriol

  (il) Dahl, M. Nap time for Kitty   **E**

Vidali, Valerio

  (il) Jemmy button   **E**

VIDEO ART

    See also Art; Television; Video recording

VIDEO BLOGS

    See also Weblogs

VIDEO GAME DESIGN

    See also Video games

Video game developer. Jozefowicz, C.   **794.8**

VIDEO GAMES

  Egan, J. How video game designers use math   **794.8**

  Gallaway, B. Game on!   **025.2**

  Jozefowicz, C. Video game developer   **794.8**

  Oxlade, C. Gaming technology   **794.8**

VIDEO GAMES

    See also Electronic toys; Games

VIDEO GAMES AND CHILDREN

  Gallaway, B. Game on!   **025.2**

VIDEO GAMES AND TEENAGERS

  Gallaway, B. Game on!   **025.2**

VIDEO RECORDINGS -- PRODUCTION AND DIRECTION -- FICTION

  Farrant, N. After Iris   **Fic**

VIDEO TELEPHONE

    See also Data transmission systems; Telephone; Television

Viegas, Jennifer

  Beethoven's world   **92**

VIENNA (AUSTRIA) -- FICTION

  Glatstein, J. Emil and Karl   **Fic**

  Ibbotson, E. The star of Kazan   **Fic**

  A gift for Mama   **Fic**

Vietnam. Green, J.   **959.7**

VIETNAM

  Green, J. Vietnam   **959.7**

  Guile, M. Culture in Vietnam   **959.7**

VIETNAM -- FICTION

  Listen, Slowly   **Fic**

  In a village by the sea   **E**

VIETNAM VETERANS MEMORIAL (WASHINGTON, D.C.) -- FICTION

  Bunting, E. The Wall   **E**

VIETNAM WAR, 1961-1975

  Collins, S. Year of the jungle   **E**

  Skrypuch, M. F. Last airlift   **959.704**

VIETNAM WAR, 1961-1975 -- FICTION

  Dogs of war   **741.5**

  Dowell, F. O. Shooting the moon   **Fic**

  Kadohata, C. Cracker!   **Fic**

  Myers, W. D. Patrol   **E**

  Partridge, E. Dogtag summer   **Fic**

  Sherlock, P. Letters from Wolfie   **Fic**

  Testa, M. Almost forever   **Fic**

VIETNAM WAR, 1961-1975 -- MISSING IN ACTION -- FICTION

  Listen, Slowly   **Fic**

VIETNAM WAR, 1961-1975 -- VETERANS

  Poulsen, D. A. Old Man   **Fic**

VIETNAMESE -- FICTION

  Starke, R. Noodle pie   **Fic**

VIETNAMESE AMERICANS -- FICTION

  Dionne, E. Ollie and the science of treasure hunting   **Fic**

  Jules, J. Duck for Turkey Day   **E**

  Lai, T. Inside out and back again   **Fic**

  Partridge, E. Dogtag summer   **Fic**

  Paterson, K. Park's quest   **Fic**

VIETNAMESE CONFLICT, 1961-1975 *See* Vietnam War, 1961-1975

VIETNAMESE NEW YEAR

  Jeffrey, L. S. Celebrate Tet   **394.26**

VIETNAMESE REFUGEES

    See also Refugees

VIETNAMESE WAR, 1961-1975 *See* Vietnam War, 1961-1975

The **view** from Saturday. Konigsburg, E. L.   **Fic**

The **view** from the cherry tree. Roberts, W. D.   **Fic**

The **vigilante** poets of Selwyn Academy. Hattemer, K.   **Fic**

Vigilante, Danette

  Trouble with half a moon   **Fic**

VIGILANTES

    See also Crime; Criminal law

Viking easy-to-read [series]

  Adler, D. A. Young Cam Jansen and the 100th day of school mystery   **E**

  Adler, D. A. Young Cam Jansen and the dinosaur game   **E**

  Chaconas, D. Cork & Fuzz   **E**

  Holub, J. The garden that we grew   **E**

  Meister, C. My pony Jack   **E**

  Meister, C. Tiny's bath   **E**

  Spohn, K. Turtle and Snake's day at the beach   **E**

  Ziefert, H. Little Red Riding Hood   **398.2**

The **Vikings.** Malam, J.   **948**

(il) Yep, L.   When the circus came to town   **Fic**
Wang Xiaohong
One year in Beijing   **E**
Wang, Jen, 1984-
Angleberger, T. Fake mustache   **Fic**
Wang, Lin
(il) Yoo, P. Shining star: the Anna May Wong story   **92**
Wangari's trees of peace. Winter, J.   **92**
Wanted: the perfect pet. Roberton, F.   **E**
WAR
Walker, N. Why do we fight?   **303.6**
War & peace. Walter, V. A.   **016**
WAR -- BIBLIOGRAPHY
Crew, H. S. Women engaged in war in literature for youth   **016**
Walter, V. A. War & peace   **016**
WAR -- FICTION
DiTerlizzi, T. The battle for WondLa   **Fic**
Lynch, C. The right fight   **Fic**
WAR -- GRAPHIC NOVELS
Dogs of war   **741.5**
WAR -- RELIGIOUS ASPECTS
See also Religion; War
WAR AND CHILDREN *See* Children and war
WAR AND CIVILIZATION
See also Civilization; War
WAR AND EMERGENCY POWERS
See also Constitutional law; Executive power; Legislative bodies; War
WAR CASUALTIES
See also War
War comes to Willy Freeman. Collier, J. L.   **Fic**
WAR CRIMES
See also Crimes against humanity; International law; War
War dogs. Selbert, K.   **E**
WAR FILMS
See also Historical drama; Motion pictures
War games. Couloumbis, A.   **Fic**
WAR GAMES
See also Military art and science; Military maneuvers; Simulation games; Tactics
War horse. Morpurgo, M.   **Fic**
War in Afghanistan and Iraq. Souter, J.   **355**
WAR IN ART
Chapman, C. Battles & weapons: exploring history through art   **355**
Serres, A. And Picasso painted Guernica   **759**
WAR OF 1812
Brown, D. Dolley Madison saves George Washington   **92**
WAR OF 1812 -- FICTION
Frost, H. Salt   **Fic**
WAR OF THE AMERICAN REVOLUTION *See*
United States -- History -- 1775-1783, Revolution

WAR OF THE WORLDS (RADIO PROGRAM)
McCarthy, M. Aliens are coming!   **791.44**
WAR ON TERRORISM
Brown, D. America is under attack   **973.931**
Fradin, D. B. September 11, 2001   **973.931**
WAR PHOTOGRAPHY
See also Photography; Photojournalism
WAR POETRY
America at war   **811**
Greenfield, E. When the horses ride by   **811**
Walker, A. Why war is never a good idea   **811**
WAR POETRY
See also Poetry
WAR SONGS
See also National songs; Songs
WAR STORIES
Bondoux A time of miracles   **Fic**
Buckley, M. The Everafter War   **Fic**
Cali, D. The enemy   **E**
Erskine, K. The badger knight   **Fic**
Flanagan, J. Erak's ransom   **Fic**
Flanagan, J. The kings of Clonmel   **Fic**
Flanagan, J. The siege of Macindaw   **Fic**
Frost, H. Salt   **Fic**
Hardy, J. Blue fire   **Fic**
Hardy, J. The shifter   **Fic**
Hof, M. Against the odds   **Fic**
Lisle, H. The silver door   **Fic**
McPhail, D. M. No!   **E**
Pratchett, T. Only you can save mankind   **Fic**
Tallec, O. Waterloo & trafalgar   **E**
Williams, M. Brothers in hope   **Fic**
Wolf-Morgenlander, K. Ragtag   **Fic**
WAR STORIES
See also Fiction; Historical fiction
WAR TELEVISION PROGRAMS
See also Television programs
The **war** that saved my life.   **Fic**
WAR USE OF DOGS *See* Dogs -- War use
WAR VETERANS *See* Veterans
Warburton, Tom
1000 times no   **E**
Ward, April
(il) Fletcher, R. A writing kind of day   **811**
(il) Garza, X. Juan and the Chupacabras   **E**
Ward, David
Between two ends   **Fic**
Ward, David J.
Materials science   **620.1**
Ward, Elaine M.
Old Testament women   **221.9**
Ward, Helen, 1962-
The town mouse and the country mouse   **E**
Ward, Jennifer
What will hatch?   **E**
The busy tree   **E**

Ferris, J. C. Noah Webster and his words **423**

Webster, Sheryl

Noodle's knitting **E**

Wechsler, Doug

Frog heaven **577.6**

Marvels in the muck **578.7**

Weddell seal. Markovics, J. L. **599.79**

WEDDINGS -- FICTION

Coville, B. Amber Brown is tickled pink **Fic**

English, K. Nikki & Deja **FIC**

Violet Mackerel's personal space **Fic**

Wells, R. Max and Ruby at the Warthogs' wedding **E**

WEDDINGS -- FOLKLORE

Miller, B. One fine trade **398.2**

Wedekind, Annie

A horse of her own **Fic**

Wild Blue **Fic**

Wedges. Tomljanovic, T. **621.8**

WEDGES

See also Simple machines

Thales, S. Wedges to the rescue **621.8**

Tomljanovic, T. Wedges **621.8**

Walker, S. M. Put wedges to the test **621.8**

Wedges to the rescue. Thales, S. **621.8**

The **Wednesday** surprise. Bunting, E. **E**

The **Wednesday** wars. Schmidt, G. D. **Fic**

The **wee** Christmas cabin. Hodges, M. **E**

Wee little bunny. Thompson, L. **E**

Wee little chick. Thompson, L. **E**

Wee little lamb. Thompson, L. **E**

Wee Winnie Witch's Skinny. Hamilton, V. **E**

Weedflower. Kadohata, C. **Fic**

WEEDS

See also Agricultural pests; Economic botany; Gardening; Plants

Weeds find a way **E**

Weeds find a way. **E**

WEEK

See also Calendars; Chronology

WEEK -- FICTION

Alko, S. Every-day dress-up **E**

Darbyshire, K. Put it on the list **E**

Downing, J. No hugs till Saturday **E**

Glenn, S. M. Just what Mama needs **E**

Hanson, W. It's Monday, Mrs. Jolly Bones **E**

Levine, A. A. Monday is one day **E**

Rosenstiehl, A. Silly Lilly in what will I be today? **741.5**

Weeks, Marcus

Mozart **92**

Weeks, Sarah

As simple as it seems **Fic**

Drip, drop **E**

Ella, of course! **E**

Jumping the scratch **Fic**

Mac and Cheese **E**

Oggie Cooder **Fic**

Oggie Cooder, party animal **Fic**

Pie **Fic**

So B. it **Fic**

Sophie Peterman tells the truth! **E**

Two eggs, please **E**

Woof **E**

Weezer changes the world. McPhail, D. M. **E**

Wegener, Alfred Lothar, 1880-1930

About

Saunders, C. What is the theory of plate tectonics? **551.1**

Wehrman, Richard

(il) Han, S. C. The rabbit's tail **398.2**

Wehrman, Vicki

(il) Lehman-Wilzig, T. Hanukkah around the world **296.4**

Weigel, Jeff

Thunder from the sea **741.5**

Weight. Sullivan, N. **530**

WEIGHT

See also Physics

WEIGHT CONTROL *See* Weight loss

WEIGHT LIFTING

See also Athletics; Exercise

WEIGHT LOSS

Edwards, H. Talking about your weight **613.2**

Hunt, J. The truth about diets **613.2**

Simons, R. I eat when I'm sad **616.85**

Zahensky, B. A. Diet fads **613.2**

WEIGHT LOSS -- FICTION

Bunting, E. My dog Jack is fat **E**

The **Weight** of Water. Crossan, S. **Fic**

WEIGHTS AND MEASURES

Adamson, T. K. How do you measure weight? **530.8**

Adler, D. A. Perimeter, area, and volume **516**

Cleary, B. P. On the scale **530.8**

Gardner, R. Ace your math and measuring science project **530.8**

Murphy, S. J. Mighty Maddie **389**

Parker, V. How big is big? **530.8**

Parker, V. How heavy is heavy? **530.8**

Parker, V. How small is small? **591.4**

Parker, V. How tall is tall? **720**

Robbins, K. For good measure **530.8**

Schwartz, D. M. Millions to measure **530.8**

Somervill, B. A. Mass and weight **530.8**

Sullivan, N. Weight **530**

WEIGHTS AND MEASURES

See also Physics

Weihs, Erika

(il) Chaikin, M. Menorahs, mezuzas, and other Jewish symbols **296.4**

Weihs, Jean

(ed) Cataloging correctly for kids **025.3**

Social policy; State, The

WELFARE WORK *See* Charities; Social work

WELFARE, PUBLIC *See* Public welfare

The **well.** Taylor, M. D.   **Fic**

The **well** between the worlds. Llewellyn, S.   **Fic**

WELL BORING *See* Drilling and boring (Earth and rocks)

Weller, Frances Ward

  The day the animals came   **E**

Wellington, Monica

  Apple farmer Annie   **E**

  Mr. Cookie Baker   **E**

  Pizza at Sally's   **E**

  Riki's birdhouse   **E**

  Truck driver Tom   **E**

WELLS

  Shoveller, H. Ryan and Jimmy   **361.7**

The **Wells** Bequest. Shulman, P.   **Fic**

Wells, Ken

  Rascal   **Fic**

Wells, Kitty

  Paw power   **Fic**

Wells, Robert E.

  (il) Can we share the world with tigers?   **599.75**

  Did a dinosaur drink this water?   **551.48**

  Polar bear, why is your world melting?   **363.7**

  What's so special about planet Earth?   **525**

  (il) Why do elephants need the sun?   **523.7**

Wells, Rosemary

  (il) Hands off, Harry!   **E**

  Ivy takes care   **Fic**

  (il) Stella's starliner   **E**

  Use your words, Sophie   **E**

  Max & Ruby's treasure hunt   **E**

  Max and Ruby at the Warthogs' wedding   **E**

  Time-out for Sophie   **E**

  A Visit to Dr. Duck   **E**

  Yoko learns to read   **E**

  Opie, I. A. Here comes Mother Goose   **398.8**

  Opie, I. A. Mother Goose's little treasures   **398.8**

  Opie, I. A. My very first Mother Goose   **398.8**

  Tallchief, M. Tallchief   **92**

  Emily's first 100 days of school   **E**

  Lincoln and his boys   **Fic**

  Love waves   **E**

  Mary on horseback   **92**

  Max & Ruby's bedtime book   **E**

  Morris's disappearing bag   **E**

  My Havana   **Fic**

  My shining star   **649**

  Noisy Nora   **E**

  On the Blue Comet   **Fic**

  Otto runs for President   **E**

  Read to your bunny   **E**

  Ruby's beauty shop   **E**

  Shy Charles   **E**

Yoko   **E**

Yoko's show and tell   **E**

Wells-Barnett, Ida B., 1862-1931

               About

  Dray, P. Yours for justice, Ida B. Wells   **92**

  Let it shine   **920**

  Myers, W. D. Ida B. Wells   **92**

  Wishinsky, F. Freedom heroines   **920**

Wells-Cole, Catherine

  Charles Dickens   **823**

Welply, Michael

  Osborne, M. P. The Random House book of Bible stories   **220.9**

Welsbacher, Anne

  Earth-friendly design   **745.2**

  Protecting Earth's rain forests   **577.34**

Welsh, M. L.

  Heart of stone   **Fic**

  Mistress of the Storm   **Fic**

Welton, Jude

  Henri Matisse   **92**

Wemberly worried. Henkes, K.   **E**

Wendland, Paula Zinngrabe

  (il) Poetry speaks to children   **811**

Wendorff, Anne

  Gymnastics   **796.44**

  Soccer   **796.334**

  Swimming   **797.2**

  Tennis   **796.342**

Wensell, Ulises

  (il) Ada, A. F. Ten little puppies   **398.8**

  (il) Lopez, S. The best family in the world   **E**

Wentworth, Marjory

  Shackles   **E**

Wenzel, Angela

  13 art mysteries children should know   **759.2**

  13 artists children should know   **709**

  13 paintings children should know   **750**

  13 sculptures children should know   **731**

Wenzel, Brendan

  (il) DiTerlizzi, A. Some bugs   **E**

Wenzel, David

  (il) Murphy, S. J. More or less   **513**

  (il) Murphy, S. J. Rodeo time   **529**

Wenzel, David T.

  (il) Lepp, B. The King of Little Things   **E**

The **werewolf.** Hirschmann, K.   **398.24**

WEREWOLVES

  Hirschmann, K. The werewolf   **398.24**

WEREWOLVES

    See also Folklore

WEREWOLVES -- FICTION

  Jobling, C. The rise of the wolf   **Fic**

  Mould, C. The wooden mile   **Fic**

  Stewart, P. The curse of the night wolf   **Fic**

  Toft, D. Wolven   **Fic**

Wereworld [series]
 Jobling, C. The rise of the wolf **Fic**

Werner, Miriam
 (ed) Weiner, M. Shakespeare's Seasons **822.3**

Werner, Sharon
 (jt. auth) Forss, S. Alphasaurs and other prehistoric types **567.9**
 Alphabeasties and other amazing types **411**
 Bugs by the numbers **595.7**

Wertz, Michael
 (il) Cerullo, M. M. The truth about great white sharks **597**
 (il) Franco, B. A curious collection of cats **811**

Weslandia. Fleischman, P. **E**

Wesson, Andrea
 Knudsen, M. Argus **E**
 Young, J. D. A pet for Miss Wright **E**

Wesson, Lindsey Patrick
 Green reads **016**

WEST (U.S.)
 Scott, A. H. Cowboy country **978**

WEST (U.S.) -- BIOGRAPHY
 Green, C. R. Buffalo Bill Cody **978**
 Green, C. R. Calamity Jane **978**
 Green, C. R. Zebulon Pike **978**

WEST (U.S.) -- EXPLORATION
 Adler, D. A. A picture book of Sacagawea **978**
 Bodden, V. Through the American West **917.804**
 Green, C. R. Zebulon Pike **978**
 Perritano, J. The Lewis and Clark Expedition **978**
 Perritano, J. The transcontinental railroad **385**
 Pringle, L. P. American slave, American hero **92**
 Ray, D. K. Down the Colorado **92**
 Schanzer, R. How we crossed the West **917**
 Waldman, S. The last river **978**

WEST (U.S.) -- EXPLORATION
 See also United States -- Exploration

WEST (U.S.) -- FICTION
 Burell, S. Diamond Jim Dandy and the sheriff **E**
 Byars, B. C. The Golly sisters go West **E**
 Casanova, M. The day Dirk Yeller came to town **E**
 Davis, D. Fandango stew **E**
 Fleming, D. Buster goes to Cowboy Camp **E**
 Garland, S. The buffalo soldier **E**
 Hemphill, H. The adventurous deeds of Deadwood Jones **Fic**
 Holt, K. W. The adventures of Granny Clearwater & Little Critter **E**
 Langdo, B. Tornado Slim and the magic cowboy hat **E**
 Moser, L. Kisses on the wind **E**
 Naylor, P. R. Emily's fortune **Fic**
 Nolen, J. Thunder Rose **E**
 Parish, H. Go west, Amelia Bedelia! **E**
 Paulsen, G. The legend of Bass Reeves **Fic**
 Puttock, S. Little lost cowboy **E**

 Sharmat, M. W. Gila monsters meet you at the airport **E**
 Shea, B. Kid sheriff and the terrible Toads **E**
 Stanley, D. Saving Sweetness **E**
 Stein, D. E. Cowboy Ned and Andy **E**
 Williams, V. B. Stringbean's trip to the shining sea **E**

WEST (U.S.) -- HISTORY
 Explore the wild west! **978**

WEST (U.S.) -- HISTORY
 See also United States -- History

WEST (U.S.) -- HISTORY -- 1860-1890 -- FICTION
 Pierpoint, E. The last ride of Caleb O'Toole **Fic**

WEST (U.S.) -- HISTORY -- TO 1848
 Green, C. R. Zebulon Pike **978**

WEST (U.S.) -- SOCIAL LIFE AND CUSTOMS
 King, D. C. Pioneer days **978**

WEST (U.S.) IN ART
 Judge, L. Yellowstone Moran **92**

WEST BANK -- FICTION
 Abdel-Fattah, R. Where the streets had a name **Fic**

West from home. Wilder, L. I. **92**

WEST INDIAN LITERATURE (FRENCH)
 See also Literature

West of the moon. Preus, M. **Fic**

West Virginia. Hoffman, N. **975.4**

West Virginia. Byers, A. **975.4**

WEST VIRGINIA
 Byers, A. West Virginia **975.4**
 Hoffman, N. West Virginia **975.4**

WEST VIRGINIA -- FICTION
 Bauer, J. Close to famous **Fic**
 Bolden, T. Finding family **Fic**
 Hahn, M. D. Witch catcher **Fic**
 Kennedy, M. The dog days of Charlotte Hayes **Fic**
 Naylor, P. R. Shiloh **Fic**
 Porter, T. Billy Creekmore **Fic**
 Rylant, C. Missing May **Fic**
 White, R. Way Down Deep **Fic**
 Yolen, J. Snow in Summer **Fic**

WEST VIRGINIA -- HISTORY -- 1951- -- FICTION
 White, R. The treasure of Way Down Deep **Fic**

West, Benjamin, 1738-1820
    About
 Brenner, B. The boy who loved to draw: Benjamin West **92**

West, Jacqueline
 Still life **Fic**

West, Krista
 Bromine **546**

Westcott, Nadine Bernard
 (il) Harris, R. H. What's in there? **612.6**
 (il) Harris, R. H. What's so yummy? **613.2**
 (il) Ashman, L. To the beach! **E**

You'll like it here (everybody does) **Fic**

White, T. H.
The sword in the stone **Fic**

White, Vicky
(il) Jenkins, M. Ape **599.8**
(il) Jenkins, M. Can we save the tiger? **591.68**

Whiteblack the penguin sees the world. Rey, M. **E**

Whitehead, Jenny
(il) Bruno, E. K. A punctuation celebration! **428**

Whitehead, Kathy
Art from her heart: folk artist Clementine Hunter **92**

Whitehead, Sarah
How to speak cat **636.8**

Whitfield, Simon
Simon says gold: Simon Whitfield's pursuit of athletic excellence **92**

About
Whitfield, S. Simon says gold: Simon Whitfield's pursuit of athletic excellence **92**

Whitfield, Susan
Afghanistan **958.1**

Whitford, Rebecca
Little yoga **613.7**

Whiting, Jim
Space and time **530.11**
The role of religion in the early Islamic world **297.09**
LeVert, S. Steroids **362.29**
Threat to ancient Egyptian treasures **932**
W.E.B. Du Bois **92**

Whiting, Sue
The firefighters **E**

Whitman, Candace
Lines that wiggle **E**

Whitman, Narcissa Prentiss, 1808-1847
About
Harness, C. The tragic tale of Narcissa Whitman and a faithful history of the Oregon Trail **92**

Whitman, Sylvia
Under the Ramadan moon **297.3**

Whitman, Walt, 1819-1892
When I heard the learn'd astronomer **E**
About
Kerley, B. Walt Whitman **92**

Whitt, Kelly Kizer
Solar system forecast **551.5**

Whitt, Shannon
(il) Weiner, M. Shakespeare's Seasons **822.3**

Whittemore, Jo
Odd girl in **Fic**

Whittenberg, Allison
Sweet Thang **Fic**

Whittington. Armstrong, A. **Fic**

Whittington, Richard, d. 1423
About
Hodges, M. Dick Whittington and his cat **398.2**

Whitty, Hannah

(il) Platt, C. A little bit of love **E**
The **Whizz** Pop Chocolate Shop. Saunders, K. **Fic**
Who ate all the cookie dough? Beaumont, K. **E**
Who can swim? Braun, S. **E**
Who could that be at this hour? **Fic**
Who discovered America? Wyatt, V. **970.01**
Who do I see? Yoon, S. **E**
Who do you think you are? Waddell, D. **929**
Who eats what? Lauber, P. **577**
Who feels scared? Graves, S. **152.4**
Who has these feet? **591.4**
Who has what? Harris, R. H. **612.6**
Who hid the Easter eggs? Vainio, P. **E**
Who invented the automobile? Williams, B. **629.222**
Who is baseball's greatest pitcher? Kisseloff, J. **796.357**
Who is stealing the 12 days of Christmas? Freeman, M. **Fic**
Who likes rain? Yee, W. H. **E**
Who likes the rain? Kaner, E. **551.57**
Who likes the snow? Kaner, E. **551.57**
Who likes the wind? Kaner, E. **551.51**
Who lives here? **E**
Who lives here? [series]
Hodge, D. Desert animals **591.7**
Hodge, D. Forest animals **591.7**
Hodge, D. Polar animals **591.7**
Hodge, D. Rain forest animals **591.7**
Hodge, D. Savanna animals **591.7**
Hodge, D. Wetland animals **591.7**
Who lives in a colorful coral reef? Lynette, R. **591.7**
Who lives in a deep, dark cave? Lynette, R. **591.7**
Who lives in a wet, wild rain forest? Lynette, R. **591.7**
Who lives in an alligator hole? Rockwell, A. F. **597.98**
Who lives on a towering mountain? Lynette, R. **591.7**
Who lives on the icy, cold tundra. Lynette, R. **591.7**
Who loves the fall? Raczka, B. **E**
Who loves the little lamb? Evans, L. **E**
Who made this cake? Nakagawa, C. **E**
Who on earth is Dian Fossey? Kushner, J. M. **92**
Who on earth is Rachel Carson? Scherer, G. **92**
Who on earth is Sylvia Earle? Reichard, S. E. **92**
Who said coo? Ruddell, D. **E**
Who says women can't be doctors? **E**
Who stole Grandma's million-dollar pumpkin pie? Freeman, M. **Fic**
Who stole Halloween? Freeman, M. **Fic**
Who stole Mona Lisa? Knapp, R. **E**
Who stole New Year's Eve? **Fic**
Who stole Uncle Sam? Freeman, M. **Fic**
Who took the farmer's [hat]? Lexau, J. M. **E**
Who wants a cheap rhinoceros? **E**
Who wants pizza? Thornhill, J. **641.3**

Who will I be, Lord? Nelson, V. M.　**E**

Who will plant a tree? Pallotta, J.　**582.16**

Who will save my planet? Urrutia, M. C.　**304.2**

Who would like a Christmas tree? Obed, E. B.　**E**

Who wrote that? [series]

Abrams, D. Gary Soto　**92**

Who's afraid of the dark? Bonsall, C. N.　**E**

Who's at the seashore? Himmelman, J.　**591.7**

Who's awake in springtime? Gershator, P.　**E**

Who's been here? Hodgkins, F.　**E**

Who's buying? Who's selling? Larson, J. S.　**381**

Who's hiding? Onishi, S.　**E**

Who's in charge?　**320.3**

Who's in Rabbit's house? Aardema, V.　**398.2**

Who's in the forest? Gershator, P.　**E**

Who's like me?　**590**

Who's that knocking on Christmas Eve. Brett, J.　**398.2**

Who's that stepping on Plymouth Rock? Fritz, J.　**974.4**

WHODUNITS *See* Mystery and detective plays; Mystery fiction; Mystery films; Mystery radio programs; Mystery television programs

WHOLE LANGUAGE

See also Education -- Experimental methods; Language arts

A **whole** nother story. Soup, C.　**Fic**

Whoo goes there?　**E**

Whooo's that? Winters, K.　**E**

Whooping cranes. Stearns, P. M.　**598**

Whoops-a-daisy world [series]

Lloyd, S. Doctor Meow's big emergency　**E**

Whopper cake. Wilson, K.　**E**

Whose chick are you? Tafuri, N.　**E**

Whose mouse are you? Kraus, R.　**E**

Whose nest is this? Roemer, H. B.　**591.56**

Whose shoes? Swinburne, S. R.　**E**

Why are the ice caps melting? Rockwell, A. F.　**363.7**

Why are you picking on me? Burstein, J.　**302.3**

Why are you so scared? Andrews, B.　**616.85**

Why did the chicken cross the road? Agee, J.　**E**

Why did the chicken cross the road? and other riddles, old and new. Cole, J.　**793.73**

Why do birds sing? Holub, J.　**598**

Why do cats have whiskers? MacLeod, E.　**636.8**

Why do cats meow? Holub, J.　**636.8**

Why do dogs have wet noses? Coren, S.　**636.7**

Why do elephants need the sun?　**523.7**

Why do horses have manes? MacLeod, E.　**636.1**

Why do I brush my teeth? Royston, A.　**617.6**

Why do I burp? Thomas, I.　**612.3**

Why do I have to make my bed? Bradford, W.　**E**

Why do I run? Royston, A.　**613.7**

Why do I sleep? Royston, A.　**612.8**

Why do I wash my hands? Royston, A.　**613**

Why do leaves change color? Hicks, T. A.　**575**

Why do leaves change color? Maestro, B.　**582.16**

Why do snakes hiss? Holub, J.　**597.96**

Why do we fight? Walker, N.　**303.6**

Why does it thunder and lightning? Bailer, D.　**551.55**

Why don't you get a horse, Sam Adams? Fritz, J.　**92**

Why I sneeze, shiver, hiccup, and yawn. Berger, M.　**612.7**

Why Is Milk White? Coelho, A.　**540**

Why is snot green. Murphy, G.　**500**

Why is there life on Earth? Solway, A.　**576.8**

Why it works [series]

Claybourne, A. Electricity　**537**

Claybourne, A. Light and dark　**535**

Claybourne, A. Materials　**620.1**

Claybourne, A. Pushes and pulls　**531**

Why mosquitoes buzz in people's ears. Aardema, V.　**398.2**

Why not, Lafayette? Fritz, J.　**973.3**

Why pi. Ball, J.　**530.8**

Why the chicken crossed the road. Macaulay, D.　**E**

Why the sky is far away. Gerson　**398.2**

Why the Sun and the Moon live in the sky. Dayrell, E.　**398.2**

Why war is never a good idea. Walker, A.　**811**

Why? Torrey, R.　**E**

Why? DePaola, T.　**92**

Whybrow, Ian

The noisy way to bed　**E**

Wiacek, Bob

(il) Tocci, S. More simple science fair projects, grades 3-5　**507.8**

WICCA

See also Paganism

Wichman, David

(jt. auth) Evans, M. The adventures of Medical Man　**616**

Wichman, Emily T.

Librarian's guide to passive programming　**025.5**

Wick, Walter

(il) Marzollo, J. I spy a Christmas tree　**793.73**

(il) Marzollo, J. I spy an egg in a nest　**793.73**

(il) Marzollo, J. I spy school days　**793.73**

Can you see what I see?　**793.73**

Can you see what I see? Cool collections　**793.73**

Can you see what I see? Dream machine　**793.73**

Can you see what I see? On a scary, scary night　**793.73**

Can you see what I see? Seymour and the juice box boat　**793.73**

Can you see what I see? toyland express　**793.73**

Can you see what I see?: once upon a time　**793.73**

Can you see what I see?: Treasure ship　**793.73**

A drop of water　**553.7**

I spy　**793.73**

I spy extreme challenger!　**793.73**

I spy fantasy　**793.73**

WILDLIFE SANCTUARIES *See* Wildlife refuges

Wilds, Kazumi Inose
 Moore, W. All about Japan   **952**

Wildsmith, Brian
 (il) Stevenson, R. L. A child's garden of verses **821**
 Brian Wildsmith's ABC   **E**
 Brian Wildsmith's Amazing animal alphabet   **E**
 Jesus   **232.9**
 Jungle party   **E**

Wildwood.   **Fic**

Wildwood chronicles [series]
 Wildwood imperium   **Fic**

Wildwood imperium.   **Fic**

Wilensky, Alexander
 (il) Schwartz, B. A. The splendid spotted snake **E**

Wiles, Deborah
 Revolution   **Fic**
 The Aurora County All-Stars   **Fic**
 Countdown   **Fic**
 Freedom Summer   **E**
 Love, Ruby Lavender   **Fic**

Wilhelm, Hans
 (il) Harrison, D. L. A monster is coming!   **E**

Wilkes, Angela
 My world of discovery   **031**

Wilkes, Sybella
 Out of Iraq   **956.7**

Wilkin, Binnie Tate
 African and African American images in Newbery Award winning titles   **810**

Wilkinson, Philip
 Gandhi   **92**

Wilkinson, Steve
 Knudson, M. Raymond and Graham rule the school   **Fic**

Will at the Battle of Gettysburg, 1863. Calkhoven, L.   **Fic**

Will I have a friend? Cohen, M.   **E**

Will it be a baby brother? Bunting, E.   **E**

Will Moses Mother Goose. Moses, W.   **398.8**

Will puberty last my whole life?   **613**

Will Sparrow's road. Cushman, K.   **Fic**

Will you be mine? Tildes, P. L.   **398.8**

Will you read to me? Cazet, D.   **E**

Will you sign here, John Hancock? Fritz, J.   **92**

Will you still love me? Roth, C.   **E**

Will's mammoth. Martin, R.   **E**

Willard, Nancy
 A visit to William Blake's inn   **811**

Willem, Mo
 City Dog, Country Frog   **E**
 (il) The duckling gets a cookie!?   **E**
 (il) Hooray for Amanda & her alligator!   **E**
 (il) Leonardo, the terrible monster   **E**
 (il) The pigeon needs a bath!   **E**
 Waiting is not easy!   **E**

A big guy took my ball!   **E**
 Don't let the pigeon drive the bus!   **E**
 Edwina, the dinosaur who didn't know she was extinct   **E**
 Goldilocks and the three dinosaurs   **E**
 Happy Pig Day!   **E**
 I broke my trunk!   **E**
 Let's go for a drive!   **E**
 That is not a good idea!   **E**
 (il) Hooray for Amanda & her alligator!   **E**
 (il) Leonardo, the terrible monster   **E**
 Can I play too?   **E**
 Cat the Cat, who is that?   **E**
 Don't let the pigeon drive the bus!   **E**
 Edwina, the dinosaur who didn't know she was extinct   **E**
 Knuffle Bunny   **E**
 Knuffle Bunny free   **E**
 Naked Mole Rat gets dressed   **E**
 Should I share my ice cream?   **E**
 There is a bird on your head!   **E**
 Today I will fly!   **E**

Willett, Mindy
 Andre We feel good out here   **970.004**
 (jt. auth) Enzoe, P. The caribou feed our soul   **970.004**
 McLeod, T. The Delta is my home   **970.004**
 Proud to be Inuvialuit   **970.004**
 Zoe, T. Living stories   **970.004**

Willey, Bee
 (il) Gavin, J. School for princes   **398.209**

Willey, Margaret
 The 3 bears and Goldilocks   **398.2**
 Clever Beatrice   **398.2**
 A Clever Beatrice Christmas   **E**

William Harvey. Yount, L.   **92**

William S. and the great escape. Snyder, Z. K.   **Fic**

William Shakespeare. Nettleton, P. H.   **822.3**

William Shakespeare & the Globe. Aliki   **792.09**

William Shakespeare's A midsummer night's dream. Coville, B.   **822.3**

William Shakespeare's Twelfth night. Coville, B.   **822.3**

William's doll. Zolotow, C.   **E**

William's midsummer dreams. Snyder, Z. K.   **Fic**

Williams Ruggi, Gilda
 Renshaw, A. The art book for children   **701**

Williams, Alex
 The talent thief   **Fic**

Williams, Amanda
 Cerny, R. Outstanding library service to children   **027.62**

Williams, Anthony
 (il) Hama, L. The battle of Iwo Jima   **940.54**

Williams, Barbara
 Albert's impossible toothache   **E**

Friedman, L. B. Mallory on the move **Fic**
Thong, R. Wish **398**
Yep, L. The magic paintbrush **Fic**

WISHES -- FICTION
Garland, M. Fish had a wish **E**
Mobley, J. Katerina's wish **Fic**
Urban, L. The center of everything **Fic**

WISHES -- SONGS
When you wish upon a star **782.42**

Wishes and wings. Duey, K. **Fic**

The **Wishing** Club. Napoli, D. J. **E**

Wishing for tomorrow. McKay, H. **Fic**

Wishinsky, Frieda
Freedom heroines **920**
Weaver, J. It's your room **747**
Maggie can't wait **E**
Please, Louise! **E**
You're mean, Lily Jean! **E**

Wishworks, Inc. Tolan, S. S. **Fic**

Wisnewski, Andrea
(il) Millen, C. M. The ink garden of brother Theophane **E**

Wisniewski, David
(il) Clements, A. Workshop **621.9**
Golem **398.21**
Rain player **398.2**
Sundiata **398.209**

Wissinger, Tamera Will
Gone fishing **Fic**

WIT AND HUMOR
Brewer, P. The Beatles were fab (and they were funny) **782.421**
Brewer, P. Lincoln tells a joke **92**
Brewer, P. You must be joking, two! **817**
Funny business **920**
Gordon, D. M. Archie's vacation **E**
Ling & Ting **E**
Livo, N. J. Tales to tickle your funny bone **398.2**
Lutz, L. How to negotiate everything **302.3**
My first ghost **E**
Reid, A. Ounce, dice, trice **428**
Rosenthal, A. K. The wonder book **817**
Schwartz, A. There is a carrot in my ear, and other noodle tales **398.2**
Take away the A **428.1**

WIT AND HUMOR
See also Literature
Funny business **920**
Rosenthal, A. K. The wonder book **817**
What Body Part Is That? **818.602**
Reid, R. What's black and white and Reid all over? **027.62**

Witch Baby and me. Gliori, D. **Fic**
Witch Baby and me after dark. Gliori, D. **Fic**
Witch Baby and me on stage. Gliori, D. **Fic**
Witch catcher. Hahn, M. D. **Fic**

The **witch** of Blackbird Pond. Speare, E. G. **Fic**
The **witch's** boy. Barnhill, K. R. **Fic**
The **witch's** child. Yorinks, A. **E**
The **witch's** walking stick. Meddaugh, S. **E**

WITCHCRAFT
Hill, D. Witches & magic-makers **133.4**
Jackson, S. The witchcraft of Salem Village **133.4**
Roach, M. K. In the days of the Salem witchcraft trials **133.4**

WITCHCRAFT
See also Folklore; Occultism

WITCHCRAFT -- FICTION
Bellairs, J. The house with a clock in its walls **Fic**
DeKeyser, S. The Brixen Witch **Fic**
Konigsburg, E. L. Jennifer, Hecate, Macbeth, William McKinley, and me, Elizabeth **Fic**
Magaziner, L. The only thing worse than witches **Fic**
Norton, M. Bed-knob and broomstick **Fic**
Odyssey, S. T. The Wizard of Dark Street **Fic**
Snyder, Z. K. The witches of Worm **Fic**
Speare, E. G. The witch of Blackbird Pond **Fic**
Thompson, P. B. The devil's door **Fic**
Van Allsburg, C. The widow's broom **E**
The **witchcraft** of Salem Village. Jackson, S. **133.4**
Witches. Christian, C. **E**

WITCHES
See also Witchcraft

WITCHES
Howard, A. Hoodwinked **E**
Kerns, A. Wizards and witches **133.4**
Norton, M. Bed-knob and broomstick **Fic**
Witches & magic-makers. Hill, D. **133.4**

WITCHES -- FICTION
Battle of the beasts **Fic**
Castle Hangnail **Fic**
DeKeyser, S. The Brixen Witch **Fic**
Magaziner, L. The only thing worse than witches **Fic**
Muncaster, H. I am a witch's cat **E**
The Thickety **Fic**
Under my hat **S**
A very witchy spelling bee **E**
Welsh, M. L. Heart of stone **Fic**

WITCHES -- FOLKLORE
Hirsh, M. The rabbi and the twenty-nine witches **398.2**

WITCHES -- GRAPHIC NOVELS
Fuji, M. The big adventures of Majoko, volume 1 **741.5**
The **witches** of Dredmoore Hollow. Waite, M. P. **Fic**
The **witches** of Worm. Snyder, Z. K. **Fic**
With a mighty hand. Ehrlich, A. **220.95**
With a name like Love. Hilmo, T. **Fic**
With love, Little Red Hen. **E**
With the might of angels. Pinkney, A. D. **Fic**

The story blanket **E**

Wolfgang Amadeus Mozart. Riggs, K. **92**

Wolfie the bunny. **E**

Wolfram

Paterson, K. Parzival **398.2**

Wolfsgruber, Linda

(il) Lottridge, C. B. Stories from the life of Jesus **232.9**

Wolfsnail. Campbell, S. C. **594**

Wolfson, Jill

Home, and other big, fat lies **Fic**

What I call life **Fic**

Wolfson, Ron

Hoffman, L. A. What you will see inside a synagogue **296.4**

Wolitzer, Meg

The fingertips of Duncan Dorfman **Fic**

Wolk-Stanley, Jessica

(il) Cobb, V. How to really fool yourself **152.1**

Wolny, Philip

Delaware **975.1**

Waterfowl **799.2**

WOLOF (AFRICAN PEOPLE)

One plastic bag **363.728**

Wolven. Toft, D. **Fic**

WOLVERINES

Jacques, B. Rakkety Tam **Fic**

Wolves. Riggs, K. **599.77**

Wolves. Gravett, E. **E**

WOLVES

Bidner, J. Is my dog a wolf? **636.7**

Brandenburg, J. Face to face with wolves **599.77**

Cohn, S. One wolf howls **599.77**

George, J. C. The wolves are back **599.77**

Gibbons, G. Wolves **599.74**

Goldish, M. Red wolves **599.77**

Markle, S. Wolves **599.77**

Marshall, J. Swine Lake **E**

McAllister, I. The sea wolves **599.77**

Patent, D. H. When the wolves returned **599.77**

Read, T. C. Exploring the world of wolves **599.77**

Riggs, K. Wolves **599.77**

Rutherford, C. A dog is a dog **636.7**

Slade, S. What if there were no gray wolves? **577.3**

Whatley, B. Wait! No paint! **E**

Wolves. Markle, S. **599.77**

Wolves. Gibbons, G. **599.74**

WOLVES -- FICTION

Archer, D. Big Bad Wolf **E**

Gliori, D. What's the time, Mr. Wolf? **E**

Gravett, E. Wolf won't bite! **E**

Little Red Riding Hood **E**

Stiefvater, M. Hunted **Fic**

The unseen guest **Fic**

Virginia Wolf **Fic**

Wolfie the bunny **E**

WOLVES -- FOLKLORE

Ernst, L. C. Little Red Riding Hood: a newfangled prairie tale **398.2**

Galdone, P. The three little pigs **398.2**

Grimm, J. Little Red Riding Hood **398.2**

Grimm, J. The story of Little Red Riding Hood **398.2**

Hennessy, B. G. The boy who cried wolf **398.2**

Hyman, T. S. Little Red Riding Hood **398.2**

Kellogg, S. The three little pigs **398.24**

Marshall, J. Red Riding Hood **398.2**

Marshall, J. The three little pigs **398.2**

Pinkney, J. Little Red Riding Hood **398.2**

Spirin, G. Little Red Riding Hood **398.2**

Young, E. Lon Po Po **398.2**

Zemach, M. The three little pigs **398.2**

Ziefert, H. Little Red Riding Hood **398.2**

WOLVES -- FOLKLORE -- GRAPHIC NOVELS

Alley, Z. B. There's a wolf at the door **398.2**

WOLVES -- SONGS

Rueda, C. Let's play in the forest while the wolf is not around **782.42**

The **wolves** are back. George, J. C. **599.77**

The **wolves** in the walls. **E**

The **wolves** of Willoughby Chase. Aiken, J. **Fic**

WOMAN *See* Women

A **woman** for president. Krull, K. **92**

The **woman** who lived with wolves, & other stories from the tipi. Goble, P. **398.2**

The **woman** who married a bear. James, E. **398.2**

The **woman** who outshone the sun. Cruz, A. **398.21**

A **woman's** place in early America. Gelletly, L. **305.4**

Wombat walkabout. Shields, C. D. **E**

A **wombat's** world. Arnold, C. **599.2**

WOMBATS

Arnold, C. A wombat's world **599.2**

WOMBATS -- FICTION

French, J. Christmas wombat **E**

French, J. Diary of a baby wombat **E**

French, J. Diary of a wombat **E**

Shields, C. D. Wombat walkabout **E**

WOMEN

Branzei, S. Adventurers **920.72**

Green, M. Y. A strong right arm: the story of Mamie Peanut Johnson **92**

Thimmesh, C. Girls think of everything **920**

Yolen, J. Not one damsel in distress **398.22**

WOMEN -- BIBLIOGRAPHY

Crew, H. S. Women engaged in war in literature for youth **016**

WOMEN -- BIOGRAPHY

Hartland, J. Bon appetit! **641.509**

McCann, M. R. Girls who rocked the world **920.72**

Branzei, S. Adventurers **920.72**

Cummins, J. Women daredevils **920**

WORLD WAR, 1939-1945 -- AFRICAN AMERICANS

See also African Americans

WORLD WAR, 1939-1945 -- ART AND THE WAR

See also Art

WORLD WAR, 1939-1945 -- ATROCITIES

Samuels, C. Life under occupation   **940.53**

WORLD WAR, 1939-1945 -- BIOGRAPHY

See also Biography

WORLD WAR, 1939-1945 -- CAMPAIGNS

Seiple, S. Ghosts in the fog   **940.54**

WORLD WAR, 1939-1945 -- CAMPAIGNS -- AFRICA, NORTH -- FICTION

Lynch, C. The right fight   **Fic**

WORLD WAR, 1939-1945 -- CAMPAIGNS -- FRANCE

Drez, R. J. Remember D-day   **940.54**

WORLD WAR, 1939-1945 -- CARTOONS AND CARICATURES

See also Cartoons and caricatures

WORLD WAR, 1939-1945 -- CENSORSHIP

See also Censorship

WORLD WAR, 1939-1945 -- CHILDREN

Hodge, D. Rescuing the children   **940.53**

WORLD WAR, 1939-1945 -- CHILDREN

See also Children and war

WORLD WAR, 1939-1945 -- CHILDREN -- FICTION

The secret of the village fool   **Fic**

Stone, P. Romeo blue   **Fic**

WORLD WAR, 1939-1945 -- CHILDREN -- GREAT BRITAIN -- FICTION

Hartnett, S. The children of the King   **Fic**

WORLD WAR, 1939-1945 -- CIVILIAN RELIEF

See also Charities; Food relief; Foreign aid; Reconstruction (1939-1951); World War, 1939-1945 -- War work

WORLD WAR, 1939-1945 -- COMMANDO OPERATIONS -- NORWAY -- VEMORK

Sheinkin, S. Bomb   **623.4**

WORLD WAR, 1939-1945 -- CRYPTOGRAPHY

Samuels, C. Spying and security   **940.54**

WORLD WAR, 1939-1945 -- DIPLOMATIC HISTORY

Franklin and Winston   **940.53**

WORLD WAR, 1939-1945 -- DISPLACED PERSONS *See* World War, 1939-1945 -- Refugees

WORLD WAR, 1939-1945 -- ECONOMIC ASPECTS

Samuels, C. Home front   **940.53**

WORLD WAR, 1939-1945 -- ETHICAL ASPECTS

See also Ethics

WORLD WAR, 1939-1945 -- EUROPE

Samuels, C. Life under occupation   **940.53**

WORLD WAR, 1939-1945 -- EVACUATION OF CIVILIANS

See also Civil defense; World War, 1939-1945 -- Refugees

WORLD WAR, 1939-1945 -- EVACUATION OF CIVILIANS -- ENGLAND -- FICTION

Hartnett, S. The children of the King   **Fic**

Stone, P. Romeo blue   **Fic**

The war that saved my life   **Fic**

WORLD WAR, 1939-1945 -- EVACUATION OF CIVILIANS -- GREAT BRITAIN -- FICTION

Stone, P. Romeo blue   **Fic**

WORLD WAR, 1939-1945 -- FICTION

Hughes, S. Hero on a bicycle   **Fic**

Number the Stars   **Fic**

WORLD WAR, 1939-1945 -- FOOD SUPPLY

See also Food relief

WORLD WAR, 1939-1945 -- FRANCE

Ruelle, K. G. The grand mosque of Paris   **940.53**

Spielman, G. Marcel Marceau   **92**

WORLD WAR, 1939-1945 -- GERMANY

Rubin, S. G. The flag with fifty-six stars   **940.53**

WORLD WAR, 1939-1945 -- GRAPHIC NOVELS

City of spies   **741.5**

Hama, L. The battle of Iwo Jima   **940.54**

WORLD WAR, 1939-1945 -- GREAT BRITAIN -- FICTION

Hartnett, S. The children of the King   **Fic**

WORLD WAR, 1939-1945 -- GREAT BRITAIN

Selbert, K. War dogs   **E**

WORLD WAR, 1939-1945 -- HUMOR

See also Wit and humor

WORLD WAR, 1939-1945 -- ITALY -- FICTION

Russo, M. I will come back for you   **E**

WORLD WAR, 1939-1945 -- JAPAN

Lawton, C. Hiroshima   **940.54**

WORLD WAR, 1939-1945 -- JEWS

Frank, A. The diary of a young girl: the definitive edition   **92**

Hiding from the Nazis   **940.53**

Hurwitz, J. Anne Frank: life in hiding   **940.53**

Metselaar, M. Anne Frank: her life in words and pictures   **92**

Reiss, J. The upstairs room   **92**

Rol, R. v. d. Anne Frank, beyond the diary   **940.53**

The secret of the village fool   **Fic**

WORLD WAR, 1939-1945 -- JEWS

See also Jews

WORLD WAR, 1939-1945 -- JEWS -- RESCUE

Irena Sendler and the children of the Warsaw Ghetto   **92**

Irena's jars of secrets   **92**

Meltzer, M. Rescue: the story of how Gentiles saved Jews in the Holocaust   **940.53**

Mochizuki, K. Passage to freedom   **940.53**

Ruelle, K. G. The grand mosque of Paris   **940.53**

World's greatest lion. Helfer, R.   **E**
The **world's** oceans. Green, J.   **551.46**
WORLD'S RECORDS *See* World records
Worlds beyond [series]
  Miller, R. Earth and the moon   **525**
Worley, Rob M.
  Scratch 9   **Fic**
The **worm** whisperer.   **Fic**
Wormell, Christopher
  (il) Moore, C. C. 'Twas the night before Christmas   **811**
  George and the dragon   **E**
  Mice, morals, & monkey business   **398.2**
Worms. Trueit, T. S.   **592**
WORMS
  Dixon, N. Lowdown on earthworms   **592**
  Pfeffer, W. Wiggling worms at work   **592**
  Trueit, T. S. Worms   **592**
WORMS
     See also Animals
WORMS -- FICTION
  Donaldson, J. Superworm   **E**
  Messner, K. Marty McGuire digs worms!   **Fic**
Worms for lunch? Gore, L.   **E**
WORRY
  Crist, J. J. What to do when you're scared & worried   **158**
  Graves, S. But what if?   **152.4**
  Henkes, K. Wemberly worried   **E**
WORRY
     See also Emotions
WORRY -- FICTION
  Violet Mackerel's possible friend   **Fic**
WORSHIP
     See also Religion; Theology
The **worst** of friends. Jurmain, S.   **973.4**
The **Worst** wildfires of all time. Garbe, S.   **363.34**
Wortche, Allison
  Rosie Sprout's time to shine   **E**
Worth. LaFaye, A.   **Fic**
Worth, Richard
  Johnny Appleseed   **92**
  Louisiana, 1682-1803   **976.3**
  New France, 1534-1763   **971.01**
Worth, Valerie
  Animal poems   **811**
  All the small poems and fourteen more   **811**
  Pug and other animal poems   **811**
Wouk, Henry
  Kung fu   **796.8**
Would I trade my parents? Numeroff, L. J.   **E**
Wounded brains. Markle, S.   **617**
Wounded Knee: an Indian history of the American West. Ehrlich, A.   **970.004**
WOUNDS AND INJURIES
  Cobb, V. Your body battles a skinned knee   **617.1**

Evans, M. The adventures of Medical Man   **616**
Fromer, L. My achy body   **612**
Landau, E. Bumps, bruises, and scrapes   **617.1**
Landau, E. Sprains and strains   **617.1**
Lew, K. Clot & scab   **617.1**
Ouch!   **616**
Royston, A. Cuts, bruises, and breaks   **617.1**
WOUNDS AND INJURIES -- FICTION
  Harper, J. Uh-oh, Cleo   **Fic**
  Urgency emergecy! Itsy bitsy spider   **E**
Wow! America! Neubecker, R.   **E**
Wow! city! Neubecker, R.   **E**
Wow! Ocean! Neubecker, R.   **E**
Wow! said the owl. Hopgood, T.   **E**
Wow! school! Neubecker, R.   **E**
Wozniak, Stephen, 1950-
     About
  Venezia, M. Steve Jobs & Steve Wozniak   **92**
WRATH *See* Anger
Wrath of the Bloodeye. Delaney, J.   **Fic**
The **wreck** of the Zephyr.   **E**
The **wreckers.** Lawrence, I.   **Fic**
Wrede, Patricia C.
  Dealing with dragons   **Fic**
  Searching for dragons   **Fic**
Wrestling. Ditchfield, C.   **796.8**
WRESTLING
  Ditchfield, C. Wrestling   **796.8**
  Ellis, C. Wrestling   **796.8**
  Jones, P. The main event   **796.812**
WRESTLING
     See also Athletics
Wrestling. Ellis, C.   **796.8**
WRESTLING -- FICTION
  Garza, X. Lucha libre: the Man in the Silver Mask   **Fic**
  Garza, X. Maximilian and the mystery of the Guardian Angel   **Fic**
  Morales, Y. Niño wrestles the world   **E**
WRESTLING -- HISTORY
  Jones, P. The main event   **796.812**
The **wretched** stone.   **E**
The **Wright** 3. Balliett, B.   **Fic**
The **Wright** brothers. Venezia, M.   **92**
The **Wright** brothers fly. O'Sullivan, R.   **92**
The **Wright** Brothers for kids. Carson, M. K.   **629.13**
The **Wright** brothers: how they invented the airplane. Freedman, R.   **92**
Wright, Amy Bartlett
  Latimer, J. P. Caterpillars   **595.7**
Wright, Annabel
  (il) Davies, N. The Lion who stole my arm   **Fic**
Wright, Barbara
  Crow   **Fic**
Wright, Betty Ren
  Princess for a week   **Fic**

Mouse and Mole, a winter wonderland E

Tracks in the snow E

Upstairs Mouse, downstairs Mole E

Who likes rain? E

Mouse and Mole, secret valentine E

Summer days and nights E

Yeh-Shen. Louie 398.2

Yelchin, Eugene

(il) Gerber, C. Seeds, bees, butterflies, and more! E

(il) Beaumont, K. Who ate all the cookie dough? E

(il) Farooqi, M. The cobbler's holiday, or, why ants don't have shoes E

(il) Fleming, C. Seven hungry babies E

(il) Hodgman, A. The house of a million pets 92

(il) Wardlaw, L. Won Ton E

Breaking Stalin's nose Fic

YELLOW FEVER

Murphy, J. An American plague 614.5

YELLOW FEVER -- FICTION

Anderson, L. H. Fever, 1793 Fic

Yellow square. Carter, D. A. E

The **yellow** star. Deedy, C. A. Fic

Yellow star. Roy, J. Fic

Yellow umbrella. Liu, J. S. E

Yellow umbrella books for early readers [series]

Rubin, A. How many fish? 513

Yellowstone Moran. Judge, L. 92

YELLOWSTONE NATIONAL PARK

George, J. C. The wolves are back 599.77

Judge, L. Yellowstone Moran 92

Patent, D. H. When the wolves returned 599.77

YELLOWSTONE NATIONAL PARK -- FIC-TION

Markle, S. Family pack E

Yemen. Hestler, A. 953.3

YEMEN (REPUBLIC)

Hestler, A. Yemen 953.3

O'Neal, C. We visit Yemen 953.3

Yeoman, John

The wild washerwomen E

Yep, Kathleen S.

Yep, L. The dragon's child Fic

Yep, Laurence, 1948-

Auntie Tiger E

City of fire Fic

The dragon's child Fic

A dragon's guide to the care and feeding of humans Fic

The lost garden 979.4

The magic paintbrush Fic

The star maker Fic

The traitor Fic

When the circus came to town Fic

Yertle the turtle and other stories. Seuss E

Yes Day! Rosenthal, A. K. E

Yes she can! Stout, G. 920

Yes, let's. Longstreth, G. G. E

Yesterday I had the blues. Frame, J. A. E

YETI

See also Monsters; Mythical animals

Alien encounter Fic

Edmundson, C. Yeti, turn out the light! E

Magoon, S. The boy who cried Bigfoot! E

Yeti, turn out the light! Edmundson, C. E

Yezerski, Thomas

(il) Cutler, J. Rose and Riley E

Meadowlands 577.690

YIDDISH LANGUAGE

Sussman, J. K. My first Yiddish word book 439

YIDDISH LANGUAGE

See also Language and languages

YIDDISH LANGUAGE -- VOCABULARY

Pinkwater, D. M. Beautiful Yetta E

Yikes-lice! Caffey, D. 616.5

Yin

Coolies E

Ying-Hwa Hu

(il) Baby Flo 782.421

Ylvisaker, Anne

The luck of the Buttons Fic

Yo! Yes? Raschka, C. E

Yockteng, Rafael

(il) Jimmy the greatest! E

(il) Messengers of rain and other poems from Latin America 861

YOGA

Birkemoe, K. Strike a pose 613.7

Spilling, M. Yoga step-by-step 613.7

Whitford, R. Little yoga 613.7

YOGA

See also Hindu philosophy; Hinduism; Theosophy

YOGA -- POETRY

Wong, J. S. Twist 811

Yoga step-by-step. Spilling, M. 613.7

Yohalem, Eve

Escape under the forever sky Fic

Yoko. Wells, R. E

Yoko learns to read. Wells, R. E

Yoko's show and tell. Wells, R. E

Yokota, Junko

Temple, C. A. Children's books in children's hands 028.5

Yolen, Jane

Birds of a feather 811

Bug off! 811

The day Tiger Rose said goodbye E

The Emily sonnets 811

How do dinosaurs stay safe? E

Jewish fairy tale feasts 641.5

(jt. auth) Lewis, J. P. Last laughs 818

How do dinosaurs act when they're mad? E

APPENDIX

APPENDIX

The following charts list Caldecott and Newbery medalists in the collection and their locations in the Classified Collection. Caldecott titles with both an author and illustrator are listed under the illustrator's name with a reference to the author's name, under which the book's entry can be found.

Caldecott Medal titles

Author/Illustrator	Title	Dewey Location
Azarian, Mary See Martin, J. B.	*Snowflake Bentley (biography of Wilson Alwyn Bentley)*	92
Brown, Marcia	*Once a mouse*	398.2
Brown, Marcia	*Stone soup*	398.2
Brown, Marcia See Cendrars, B.	*Shadow*	841
Brown, Marcia See Perrault, C.	*Cinderella*	398.2
Burton, Virginia Lee	*The little house*	E
Cooney, Barbara	*Chanticleer and the fox*	E
Cooney, Barbara See Hall, D.	*Ox-cart man*	E
Diaz, David See Bunting, E.	*Smoky night*	E
Dillon, L. and Dillon D. See Musgrove, M.	*Ashanti to Zulu: African traditions*	960
Dillon, Leo See Aardema, V.	*Why mosquitos buzz in people's ears*	398.2
Duvoisin, Roger See Tresselt, A. R.	*White snow, bright snow*	E
Egielski, Richard See Yorinks, A.	*Hey, Al*	E
Emberley, Ed See Emberley B.	*Drummer Hoff*	398.8
Floca, Brian	*Locomotive*	385
Gammell, Stephen See Ackerman, K.	*Song and dance man*	E
Gerstein, Mordicai	*The man who walked between the towers*	E
Goble, Paul	*The girl who loved wild horses*	398.2
Hader, Berta	*The big snow*	E
Haley, Gail E.	*A story, a story*	398.2
Henkes, Kevin	*Kitten's first full moon*	E
Hogrogian, Nonny	*One fine day*	398.2
Hogrogian, Nonny See Leodhas, S. N.	*Always room for one more*	782.42
Hyman, Trina Schart See Hodges, M.	*Saint George and the dragon*	398.2
Jones, Elizabeth Orton See Field, R.	*Prayer for a child*	242
Keats, Ezra Jack	*The snowy day*	E
Klassen, Jon	*This is not my hat*	E
Lathrop, Dorothy P. See Fish, H. D.	*Animals of the Bible*	220.8
Lent, Blair See Mosel, A.	*The funny little woman*	398.2
Lobel, Arnold	*Fables*	Fic
Macaulay, David	*Black and white*	E
McCloskey, Robert	*Make way for ducklings*	E
McCloskey, Robert	*Time of wonder*	E
McCully, Emily A.	*Mirette on the high wire*	E
McDermott, Gerald	*Arrow to the sun*	398.2
Monresor, Beni See De Regniers, B. S.	*May I bring a friend?*	E

Ness, Evaline	*Sam, Bangs & Moonshine*	E
Pinkney, Jerry	*The lion and the mouse*	E
Politi, Leo	*Song of the swallows*	E
Provensen, A. and Provensen M. See Provensen, A.	*The glorious flight: across the Channel with Louis Blériot, July 25, 1909*	92
Raschka, Christopher See Juster, N.	*The hello, goodbye window*	E
Raschka, Christopher	*A ball for Daisy*	E
Rathmann, Peggy	*Officer Buckle and Gloria*	E
Rohmann, Eric	*My friend Rabbit*	E
Rojankovsky, Feodor See Langstaff, J. M.	*Frog went a-courtin'*	782.42
Santat, Dan	*The adventures of Beekle*	E
Say, Allen	*Grandfather's journey*	E
Selznick, Brian	*The invention of Hugo Cabret*	Fic
Sendak, Maurice	*Where the wild things are*	E
Sidjakov, Nicolas See Robbins, R.	*Baboushka and the three kings*	398.2
Simont, Marc See Udry, J. M.	*A tree is nice*	E
Slobodkin, Louis See Thurber, J.	*Many moons (illustrated by Louis Slobodkin)*	E
Small, David See St. George, J.	*So you want to be president?*	973
Spier, Peter	*Noah's ark*	222
Stead, Erin E See Stead, P. C.	*A sick day for Amos McGee*	E
Steig, William	*Sylvester and the magic pebble*	E
Taback, Simms	*Joseph had a little overcoat*	E
Van Allsburg, Chris	*Jumanji*	E
Van Allsburg, Chris	*The Polar Express*	E
Ward, Lyn Kendall	*The biggest bear*	E
Weisgard, L. See Brown, M. W.	*The little island*	E
Wiesner, David	*Flotsam*	E
Wisniewski, David	*Golem*	398.2
Young, Ed	*Lon Po Po*	398.2
Zelinsky, Paul O.	*Rapunzel*	398.2

Newbery Medal titles

Author/Illustrator	Title	Dewey Location
Alexander, K.	*The crossover*	Fic
Applegate, K.	*The one and only Ivan*	Fic
Armstrong, W. H.	*Sounder*	Fic
Avi.	*Crispin: the cross of lead*	Fic
Blos, J. W.	*A gathering of days: a New England girl's journal, 1830-32*	Fic
Brink, C. R.	*Caddie Woodlawn*	Fic
Byars, B. C.	*The summer of the swans*	Fic
Cleary, B.	*Dear Mr. Henshaw*	Fic
Coatsworth, E. J.	*The cat who went to heaven*	Fic
Cooper, S.	*The grey king*	Fic
Creech, S.	*Walk two moons*	Fic
Curtis, C. P.	*Bud, not Buddy*	Fic
Cushman, K.	*The midwife's apprentice*	Fic
De Angeli, M. L.	*The door in the wall*	Fic
DeJong, M.	*The wheel on the school*	Fic
DiCamillo, K.	*Flora and Ulysses*	Fic
DiCamillo, K.	*The tale of Despereaux*	Fic
Du Bois, W. P.	*The twenty-one balloons*	Fic
Estes, E.	*Ginger Pye*	Fic
Field, R.	*Hitty: her first hundred years*	Fic
Fleischman, P.	*Joyful noise: poems for two voices*	811
Fleischman, S.	*The whipping boy*	Fic
Freedman, R.	*Lincoln: a photobiography*	92
Gaiman, N.	*The graveyard book*	Fic
Gantos, J.	*Dead end in Norvelt*	Fic
George, J. C.	*Julie of the wolves*	Fic
Hamilton, V.	*M.C. Higgins, the great*	Fic
Henry, M.	*King of the wind*	Fic
Hesse, K.	*Out of the dust*	Fic
Kadohata, C.	*Kira-Kira*	Fic
Keith, H.	*Rifles for Watie*	Fic
Konigsburg, E. L.	*From the mixed-up files of Mrs. Basil E. Frankweiler*	Fic
Konigsburg, E. L.	*The view from Saturday*	Fic
Krumgold, J.	*Onion John*	Fic
Lawson, R.	*Rabbit Hill*	Fic
L'Engle, M.	*A wrinkle in time*	Fic
Lowry, L.	*The giver*	Fic
Lowry, L.	*Number the stars*	Fic
MacLachlan, P.	*Sarah, plain and tall*	Fic
Naylor, P. R.	*Shiloh*	Fic
Neville, E. C.	*It's like this, Cat*	Fic

O'Brien, R. C.	Mrs. Frisby and the rats of NIMH	Fic
O'Dell, S.	Island of the Blue Dolphins	Fic
Park, L. S.	A single shard	Fic
Paterson, K.	Bridge to Terabithia	Fic
Patron, S.	The higher power of Lucky	Fic
Peck, R.	A year down yonder	Fic
Perkins, L. R.	Criss cross	Fic
Raskin, E.	The Westing game	Fic
Rylant, C.	Missing May	Fic
Sachar, L.	Holes	Fic
Sawyer, R.	Roller skates	Fic
Schlitz, L. A.	Good masters! Sweet ladies!	940.1
Seredy, K.	The white stag	Fic
Speare, E. G.	The bronze bow	Fic
Speare, E. G.	The witch of Blackbird Pond	Fic
Sperry, A.	Call it courage	Fic
Spinelli, J.	Maniac Magee	Fic
Stead, R.	When you reach me	Fic
Taylor, M. D.	Roll of thunder, hear my cry	Fic
Treviño, E. B. d.	I, Juan de Pareja	Fic
Vanderpool, C.	Moon over Manifest	Fic
Vining, E. G.	Adam of the road	Fic
Voigt, C.	Dicey's song	Fic
Willard, N.	A visit to William Blake's inn	811
Wojciechowska, M.	Shadow of a bull	Fic
Yates, E.	Amos Fortune, free man	92